GENERAL BIOCHEMISTRY

GENERAL

SECOND EDITION

NEW YORK · JOHN WILEY & SONS, INC.

London

BIOCHEMISTRY

JOSEPH S. FRUTON

Eugene Higgins Professor of Biochemistry
Chairman, Department of Biochemistry
Yale University

SOFIA SIMMONDS

Associate Professor
of Biochemistry and Microbiology
Yale University

FOURTH PRINTING, OCTOBER, 1961

Library of Congress Catalog Card Number: 58–6072

Printed in the United States of America

The second edition
of this book is
Dedicated to the Memory
of

GERTY THERESA CORI
1896–1957

The first edition
was
Dedicated to the Memory
of

MAX BERGMANN
1886–1944

LEONOR MICHAELIS
1875–1949

RUDOLF SCHOENHEIMER
1898–1941

Preface to the Second Edition

During the five years since the preparation of the first edition, the rapid development of many areas of biochemistry rendered much of what had been written obsolete, and made necessary an extensive revision of the text. Nearly every chapter has undergone considerable change, in most instances to include new knowledge (for example, about protein structure, dehydrogenases, oxidative phosphorylation, photosynthesis, metabolism of carbohydrates, fatty acids, and amino acids, biosynthesis of proteins, vitamins). Several sections (e.g., metabolism of steroids and of nucleic acids) have been reworked completely, and a new chapter on alternative pathways of carbohydrate metabolism has been added. Some chapters (e.g., on thermodynamics, enzyme kinetics, oxidation-reduction) have been revised in an effort to improve the discussion.

Although the text and illustrations have been altered extensively, the structure of the book is unchanged. Also, the general objective remains the same: to offer a coherent introduction to present-day biochemistry for students who wish to examine the subject for its own sake, and to provide a background to the applications of biochemistry in fundamental and applied biology. In particular, the importance of modern biochemistry in clinical medicine is increasingly evident; in the years ahead, the serious medical student will need a searching discussion of general biochemical principles for an adequate understanding of many problems of human physiology and pathology.

A further word of explanation seems desirable for the large number of bibliographic references and the manner in which they are cited. This book cannot convey to the reader more than an outline of each of the topics treated; for the serious student, the text will not be sufficient, and he should have the opportunity of examining original papers and thoughtful reviews that give a more detailed picture. It is impossible, however, to cite all important papers in a textbook, and it is assumed that the references given will be used as sources of further bibliographic information. In the footnote references, we have listed, at the most, the names of two authors. This is made necessary by the numerous publications involving multiple authorship; in recent years, papers bearing the names of five to ten authors have not been uncommon. Although the practice adopted in this book occasionally requires that the name of a senior investigator be omitted, it should be remembered that the prime purpose of the bibliography is to serve as a working guide to the literature. Where necessary, an effort has been made to acquaint the student with the names of leading biochemists who are currently making important contributions.

In the preparation of this revision, we have profited greatly from the kind suggestions of many colleagues and students who drew our attention to errors in the first edition. Several of our friends at Yale have been especially helpful, and we wish to record our gratitude for the generous advice given us by Professors C. E. Carter, H. A. Harbury, D. I. Hitchcock, C. N. H. Long, M. V. Simpson, and J. M. Sturtevant. We are grateful to many authors and publishers for their kind permission to reproduce illustrative material added to the second edition.

JOSEPH S. FRUTON
SOFIA SIMMONDS

New Haven, Connecticut
January 1958

Preface to the First Edition

This book is largely based on a course in general biochemistry offered at Yale University. Intended primarily for candidates for the Ph.D. in the biological sciences and in chemistry, the course has also been attended by qualified college seniors, by students of medicine, and by postdoctoral research students in the medical sciences. The response to the lectures has strengthened our view that the teaching of biochemistry for its own sake, quite apart from its applications to medicine or agriculture, is an essential component in the scientific education of the biologist or the chemist. This book is offered, therefore, in the hope that it may prove useful to students who wish to examine the structure of modern biochemistry from a general point of view.

In some respects, the organization of the contents departs from the practice followed in the many admirable textbooks of biochemistry that have appeared in recent years. We can make no claim for a peculiar excellence in our arrangement of the subject matter, or in the selection of topics for emphasis. In beginning the book with an extensive discussion of protein chemistry, we have attempted to stress the central place of the proteins in the chemical activity of living matter. Also, these first chapters provide a review of several topics in elementary physical chemistry important for biochemists. The chapters on proteins are followed by a discussion of the general properties of enzymes, and of equilibria and rates in enzyme-catalyzed reactions. These sections of the book are intended to focus attention on the important role of the catalytic proteins in metabolism, and to sketch, for the student who lacks an adequate background in physical chemistry, the elementary principles of thermodynamics and kinetics as applied to biochemistry. The major portion of the book is devoted to a consideration of the problems of biochemical dynamics, with especial reference to biological oxidation and to the intermediate metabolism of carbohydrates, lipids, and proteins. The chapters on the chemical structure of carbohydrates and lipids are brief, since this material is usually well treated in courses in organic chemistry; the discussion offered here is intended to provide the minimum of structural biochemistry required for an understanding of the changes these substances undergo in biological systems. In the sections on intermediate metabolism, emphasis has been placed, whenever possible, on the individual enzymes and on the coupled enzyme-catalyzed reactions that are involved. Many biochemical processes cannot be discussed in these terms at present; we have attempted to indicate this wherever appropriate, and, in three of the final four chapters, reference is made to efforts to relate the metabolic role of inorganic ions, of hormones, and of vitamins to known enzyme-catalyzed reactions.

The inclusion of a relatively large number of bibliographic references is, in our opinion, essential in the presentation of subjects whose experimental basis is in rapid flux. This book will have served its purpose if it encourages the inquiring student to broaden his view of the subject through diligent study of the articles and books cited in the text. We hope that he will examine critically some of the original data, and not be content with the generalizations drawn from them. To emphasize the data alone would challenge only the student's memory; the generalizations are essential to capture his imagination, although, without the supporting experimental facts, emphasis on hypothesis invites superficiality. Within the limitations imposed by the requirement that this be a book of reasonable size, we have attempted, whenever possible, to balance facts against hypothesis. For several topics, we have found it expedient to do this by describing their historical development. Apart from its pedagogic advantages, the historical approach should give the student a sense of the dynamic in the growth of biochemistry. We believe it to be our duty to trace the background of present knowledge, since the successes and failures of the past emphasize the transitory nature of views now current and indicate the promise of the future.

In the preparation of this book we were fortunate in having the generous advice and encouragement of many kind friends. To mention all of them by name would make this preface unduly lengthy, but we must record our especial debt to Dr. A. Bendich, Prof. W. M. Clark, Prof. D. I. Hitchcock, Prof. C. N. H. Long, Prof. J. P. Peters, Prof. E. Racker, Prof. S. Ratner, and Dr. H. B. Vickery. In expressing to these individuals, and to others, our gratitude for their help, we do not wish to transfer to them any responsibility for the shortcomings that will be apparent to the critical reader; for any errors of omission or commission, we are alone accountable. We appreciate the courtesy of many authors and publishers in giving us permission to quote or reproduce copyrighted material. We reserve our final though no less heartfelt thanks for the devoted assistance of Miss R. V. Brown, who typed the manuscript and checked the bibliography.

JOSEPH S. FRUTON
SOFIA SIMMONDS

New Haven, February 1953

Contents

1 • Scope and History of Biochemistry   1

2 • General Properties of Proteins   14

3 • Amino Acids as Structural Units of Proteins   45

4 • Amino Acids and Proteins as Electrolytes   85

5 • Structure of Proteins   113

6 • Metalloporphyrin Proteins   162

7 • Nucleoproteins   184

8 • General Chemistry of Enzymes   209

9 • Equilibria and Free-Energy Changes in Biochemical Reactions   223

10 • Kinetics of Enzyme Action   244

11 • Oxidation and Reduction   284

12 • Pyridine Nucleotides and Dehydrogenases   307

13 • Flavin Nucleotides and Flavoproteins   330

14 • Metal-Containing Oxidases   347

15 • Coupled Enzyme-Catalyzed Reactions   370

16 • Methods for the Study of Intermediate Metabolism   387

17 • Chemistry of the Carbohydrates   402

18 • Enzymic Cleavage and Synthesis of Glycosidic Bonds   430

19 • Fermentation and Glycolysis   456

20 • Aerobic Breakdown of Carbohydrates   501

21 • Alternative Pathways of Carbohydrate Metabolism   525

22 • Photosynthesis   545

23 • Chemistry of Fats and Phospholipids   557

24 • General Metabolism of Fats and Phospholipids   574

25 • Intermediate Metabolism of Fatty Acids   590

26 • Chemistry and Metabolism of Steroids   619

27 • Chemistry and Metabolism of Carotenoids, Anthocyanins, and
     Related Compounds   652

28 • Metabolic Utilization of Inorganic Nitrogen Compounds   673

29 • Enzymic Cleavage and Synthesis of Peptide Bonds   684

30 • Metabolic Breakdown and Synthesis of Proteins   723

31 • General Metabolism of Protein Amino Acids   750

32 • Special Aspects of Amino Acid Metabolism   771

33 • End Products of Amino Acid Metabolism   847

34 • Metabolism of Porphyrins   864

35 • Metabolism of Nucleic Acids   877

36 • Role of Inorganic Ions in Metabolism   907

37 • Heat Changes in Metabolism   928

38 • The Hormonal Control of Metabolism   939

39 • Vitamins and Growth Factors   976

     Index   1015

1 · Scope and History of Biochemistry

The discipline called "biochemistry" deals with the study of (1) the nature of the chemical constituents of living matter and of chemical substances produced by living things, (2) the functions and transformations of these chemical entities in biological systems, and (3) the chemical and energetic changes associated with these transformations in the course of the activity of living matter. The ultimate goal of biochemistry is to describe the phenomena that distinguish the "living" from the "nonliving" in the language of chemistry and physics.

It will be seen at once that the first part of our definition falls within the scope of organic chemistry. Indeed, in its original meaning, the term "organic chemistry" referred to the chemistry of "organized," or living, matter. A clear statement of this may be found in the *Lectures in Animal Chemistry,* first published in 1806, by the great Swedish chemist Jöns Jacob Berzelius (1779–1848):

> The part of physiology which describes the composition of living bodies, and the chemical processes which occur in them, is termed organic chemistry.

Implicit in this definition was the thought that the chemical substances produced by living things were fundamentally different from the "inorganic" materials found in inanimate matter; many distinguished chemists of the period held the view that organic compounds were the result of the operation of "vital forces" and could not be synthesized artificially from inorganic substances. This view had to be abandoned, however, in the face of the successes of Friedrich Wöhler (1800–1882) in the artificial synthesis of urea (1828), of Hermann Kolbe (1818–1884) who first synthesized acetic acid in 1845, and especially of Marcellin Berthelot (1827–1907), from whose work synthetic organic chemistry received tremendous impetus during the middle of the last century. A major consequence of this development was a change in the definition of the scope of organic chemistry. Thus, August Kekulé (1829–1896) wrote in his famous textbook of organic chemistry, published in 1859–1860:

We have come to the conviction that . . . no difference exists between organic and inorganic compounds. . . . We define organic chemistry therefore as the chemistry of the carbon compounds. . . . It must be emphasized that organic chemistry does not deal with the study of the chemical processes in the organs of plants or animals. This study forms the basis of physiological chemistry.

Increasing specialization of this kind is inevitable in the face of rapidly expanding knowledge; it must be stressed, however, that arbitrary divisions of science do not abolish the intimate interrelationships among the component disciplines—they can only obscure the essential unity of science. No student of biochemistry can enter upon this subject without adequate grounding in the methods and concepts of modern organic chemistry. Also, the student will do well to remember that organic chemistry is undergoing constant extension, revision, and refinement, and that these advances will influence the methods and concepts of biochemistry. A modern textbook of organic chemistry is therefore a valuable adjunct to the study of biochemistry. The treatises of Fieser and Fieser[1] and of Royals[2] are recommended for this purpose.

The second and third parts of our definition of the scope of biochemistry refer to the chemical dynamics of living matter, and here the tie to physiology, the study of the functions of living things, is obvious. In a very real sense, the problems that the biochemist seeks to solve are the problems of physiology, and many of the important discoveries that now fall within the scope of biochemistry were the outcome of the study of biological phenomena whose chemical aspects were only appreciated much later. Of particular importance were the accurate observations of skilled clinicians who studied the physiological dysfunctions of man. It must be added at once that the term "physiology," as used here, refers to the bodily or cellular functions not only of man, or other animals, but of plants and of microorganisms as well. Such a view of the field of physiology has frequently been denoted by the term "general physiology."[3] Though many men have contributed to the development of general physiology, the work and writings of Claude Bernard (1813–1878)[4] and of Louis Pasteur (1822–1895)[5] were pre-eminent in their influence. Perhaps the most important concept to emerge from the researches of Bernard, Pasteur, and their contemporaries was that, on the biochemical level, there is unity among the manifold forms of living

---

[1] L. Fieser and M. Fieser, *Organic Chemistry*, 3rd Ed., Reinhold Publishing Corp., New York, 1950.

[2] E. E. Royals, *Advanced Organic Chemistry*, Prentice-Hall, Englewood Cliffs, N. J., 1954.

[3] H. Davson, *Textbook of General Physiology*, J. and A. Churchill Ltd., London, 1951.

[4] J. M. D. Olmstead, *Claude Bernard*, Harper and Brothers, New York, 1938.

[5] R. J. Dubos, *Louis Pasteur*, Little, Brown and Co., Boston, 1950.

matter. In the face of the fragmentary chemical knowledge of their time, this concept could only be dimly perceived; with the rise of modern biochemistry, during the past half-century, it has received extensive documentation. It is now clear that a chemical process studied in a yeast culture may illumine a comparable series of reactions in mammalian muscle; or the study of the respiratory pigments of invertebrates may provide basic data for the elucidation of a general mechanism of biological oxidation. Although there is much diversity in the chemical activities of different biological forms, it is becoming ever clearer that many fundamental biochemical reactions underlying cellular function exhibit a striking uniformity from the lowest to the most highly organized forms of life. In its subsequent historical development, therefore, a major section of "general physiology" has been transformed into "general biochemistry."

In the study of the functions of living things, one is confronted by physical phenomena (e.g., motion, electric conductance, absorption or emission of light, production of heat). It has long been the task of one area of general physiology, now called "biophysics," to study such phenomena. The growth of biochemistry has permitted, in many instances, the correlation of physical events in biological systems with chemical processes. The biochemist, therefore, must consider a physiological process not only in terms of the chemical nature of the substances that are involved in it, but also in terms of the physical relations among these substances, and of these substances to the environment. To do this adequately, he must call into play the body of knowledge known as "physical chemistry." In order to understand the energy relations in biological systems, an acquaintance with thermodynamics is essential, and no approach to the chemical dynamics of living things can be made without a knowledge of the kinetics of chemical reactions. Much of modern biochemistry has its foundations in the work of Josiah Willard Gibbs (1839–1903)[6] on chemical thermodynamics, of Jacobus Henricus van't Hoff (1852–1911) on chemical kinetics, and of Svante Arrhenius (1859–1927) on electrolytic dissociation. Among the many excellent textbooks of physical chemistry are those of Glasstone[7] and of Daniels and Alberty;[8] valuable books on this subject, as applied to biochemical problems, are those of Clark[9] and of Bull.[10]

[6] L. P. Wheeler, *Josiah Willard Gibbs,* Yale University Press, New Haven, 1951.

[7] S. Glasstone, *Textbook of Physical Chemistry,* Van Nostrand Co., Princeton, N. J., 1940.

[8] F. Daniels and R. A. Alberty, *Physical Chemistry,* John Wiley & Sons, New York, 1955.

[9] W. M. Clark, *Topics in Physical Chemistry,* 2nd Ed., Williams and Wilkins Co., Baltimore, 1952.

[10] H. B. Bull, *Physical Biochemistry,* 2nd Ed., John Wiley & Sons, New York, 1951.

From the foregoing discussion of the scope of biochemistry, it will be clear that this field resists classification as a biological or a physical science. Not only does biochemistry cut across the artificial boundaries set up within chemistry and within biology—it also serves to link the physical with the animal and plant sciences. Many separate streams of knowledge thus nourish the growth of biochemistry, and its rapid development in recent decades is the direct consequence of the fruitful blending of many broad lines of experimental endeavor. For example, the newer knowledge of atomic structure and the resultant discovery of isotopes have provided the most powerful method yet devised for the study of chemical changes in intact animals, plants, or microorganisms. In the same way, purely biological studies on genetics and the artificial production of mutations also have led to the study of biochemical reactions from new points of view. These are but two recent examples of the cumulation of knowledge from different disciplines brought to bear on biochemical problems. The earlier history of biochemistry is replete with other examples.

Because of its successes in gaining a clearer understanding of the chemical activity of all forms of living matter, biochemistry has had many important applications in medicine and agriculture, and thus has contributed materially to human welfare. It is well to remember, however, that, though these practical benefits of biochemistry have been great, and promise to be greater, they are the result of studies largely undertaken for their own sake, rather than as conscious attempts to cure a disease or to increase a crop. The student of applied biochemistry (e.g., nutrition, chemical pharmacology) cannot go far in his field without a clear appreciation of the fundamental facts and principles of biochemistry, and, what is perhaps more important, of the gaps in biochemical knowledge that still remain to be filled.

Some Historical Aspects of Biochemistry

The origins of biochemistry may be traced to the writings of that turbulent upsetter of the *status quo*, Theophrastus Bombastus von Hohenheim (1493–1541), who gave himself the name Paracelsus. Paracelsus began his education in the mining region of Carinthia, and there he acquired a knowledge of the chemistry of his time. When he entered the field of medicine, he brought his chemistry with him. The union of chemistry with medicine animated the work of many who followed Paracelsus, and who called their field "medical chemistry" (iatrochemistry). Of these men, Jan Baptist van Helmont (1577–1644) was perhaps the most important. During the seventeenth century, the groundwork of scientific chemistry was laid by Johann Rudolph Glauber (1604–1670), Robert

Boyle (1627–1691), and others.[11] They paved the way for the "revolution in chemistry" during the latter half of the eighteenth century, when the scientific basis of biochemistry emerged from the studies of men like Karl Wilhelm Scheele (1742–1786) and Antoine Lavoisier (1743–1794).[12]

Scheele, a Swedish pharmacist, was interested in the chemical composition of vegetable drugs, and of plant and animal materials in general. During his lifetime, he isolated a large number of new substances; among them were citric acid from lime juice, lactic acid from sour milk, tartaric acid from wine, malic acid from apples, and uric acid from urine. Also, by heating plant and animal fats with alkali, Scheele discovered glycerol. The substances that Scheele isolated from living matter and the many others obtained by his contemporaries had to remain the objects of curiosity until two important steps had been taken in the establishment of chemistry as a science. The first of these was the development of the concept of oxidation, by Lavoisier, and the second, the enunciation, in 1804, of the atomic theory by John Dalton (1766–1844). These, in turn, led to the development of the techniques of quantitative elementary analysis by Berzelius and by Justus von Liebig (1803–1873).[13] The analysis of the many products that had been isolated from plants and animals by 1850 showed them to contain carbon. The study of the structure of these compounds became the task of organic chemistry, and, by the end of the nineteenth century, synthetic organic chemists had made in the laboratory many of the compounds originally found in biological materials. At first only simple substances such as urea were synthesized, but, by 1885, nature had been successfully imitated in the synthesis of two plant dyes of complex structure—indigo and alizarin.

The experimental contributions of Liebig played an important part in the early development of biochemistry, and several of his books profoundly influenced subsequent efforts in this field. Of special significance was his *Organic Chemistry in its Application to Physiology and Pathology*, published in 1842. The fragmentary data available to him at that time did not deter Liebig from extensive speculation as to the chemical basis of biological processes. For this reason, his book elicited from Berzelius the following comment, which has meaning even today:

This easy kind of physiological chemistry is created at the writing desk and is the more dangerous, the more genius goes into its execution.

[11] L. T. More, *The Life and Works of the Honourable Robert Boyle,* Oxford University Press, London, 1944.

[12] D. McKie, *Antoine Lavoisier,* Constable, London, 1952.

[13] W. A. Shenstone, *Justus von Liebig,* The Macmillan Co., New York, 1895.

The high point in the development of structural biochemistry came in the work of Emil Fischer (1852–1919),[14] who, in the course of his scientific career, completely altered the direction of research on the chemistry of the principal organic components of living matter—the sugars, the fats, and the proteins. The decisive factor in Fischer's success was his skillful use of the techniques of organic chemistry to obtain from complex materials of unknown structure simpler chemical substances whose structure could be established, first by degradation, and then by synthesis. Much inconclusive work had been done by Fischer's predecessors on the chemistry of complex biochemical substances; his genius set descriptive biochemistry upon the fruitful path it still follows.

Just as the roots of descriptive biochemistry lie in the researches of Scheele, the basis of dynamic biochemistry may clearly be found in the work of Lavoisier. In replacing the phlogiston theory of combustion by the concept of oxidation, Lavoisier also clarified the nature of animal respiration and the relation of this physiological phenomenon to the production of body heat. There are few sentences in the literature of biochemistry more dramatic in their impact than the following, taken from Lavoisier's memoir on heat, published in 1780:

Respiration is therefore a combustion, slow it is true, but otherwise perfectly similar to that of charcoal.

The study of heat, during the first part of the nineteenth century, led to the formulation, in 1842, by Julius Robert Mayer (1814–1878), of the law of conservation of energy, which he explicitly applied to both living and nonliving things. The work of Mayer, of Hermann von Helmholtz (1821–1894), and of those who followed, led to the establishment of the science of thermodynamics, essential to the understanding of energy relations in biological systems.

Although Lavoisier, in common with most of his contemporaries, thought that the combustion of foodstuffs occurred in the lungs, and Liebig later said that it took place in the blood, subsequent work, principally by Eduard Pflüger (1829–1910), showed clearly that the tissues were the site of this process. Much of the research in modern biochemistry has been concerned therefore with the mechanisms whereby the cells of tissues oxidize chemical substances derived from the food.

In addition to the process of respiration, another physiological phenomenon, that of digestion, occupied the attention of the pioneers of biochemistry. The initial advances in this field came from the work of van Helmont, who sponsored a chemical theory of the digestion of food by animals. The decisive experimental evidence for this view came from the researches of Réné de Réaumur (1683–1757) and of Lazzaro

[14] M. O. Forster, *Trans. Chem. Soc.*, **117**, 1 (1920).

Spallanzani (1729–1799). These investigations led to the study of the digestive enzymes by Theodor Schwann (1810–1882), Willy Kühne (1837–1900), and others.

The nineteenth century also witnessed the refinement of experimental surgery as a technique for the study of animal physiology. Through the efforts of François Magendie (1783–1855), Claude Bernard, Karl Ludwig (1816–1895), and their students, a firm groundwork was laid for the study of many physiological processes, and in the course of these efforts some of the chemical aspects of these processes became evident. By the end of the century, experimental surgery had reached a high point of development in the hands of Ivan Petrovich Pavlov (1849–1936). Many of the problems that the nineteenth-century physiologists sought to solve came from clinical medicine and, in particular, from the study of the etiology of metabolic diseases. The production of experimental diabetes by the extirpation of the pancreas, described in 1889, is but one evidence of this close historical relation between physiology and medicine. Other clinical studies which profoundly influenced the development of physiology and of biochemistry dealt with goiter and Addison's disease. However, many dysfunctions of man, such as the deficiency diseases, still resisted fruitful experimental study during the last century. These had to await the further rise of biochemistry and the discovery of the vitamins.

Another biological process whose study had a decisive impact on the development of biochemistry was that of fermentation. In embarking, in 1857, upon the study of the chemical activities of microorganisms, Pasteur founded the science of microbiology and began a line of research that is actively pursued to this day. During the period 1900–1950 the close tie between microbiology and biochemistry was further strengthened through the work and influence of the Russian microbiologist Winogradsky,[15] of the Dutch investigators led by Beijerinck and Kluyver,[16] and by Stephenson[17] in England, among others. Some of the most convincing evidences of the biochemical unity of living matter have come from microbiological studies.

All the investigators who concerned themselves with the chemical activities of living organisms were aware of the contrast between the manifold chemical capacities of biological systems and the much more limited methods of the chemical laboratory. It was natural that in the early days of scientific chemistry this should have been taken as the expression of some vital force not observed in nonliving matter. Here

---

[15] S. A. Waksman, *Sergei N. Winogradsky,* Rutgers University Press, New Brunswick, 1953.

[16] C. B. van Niel, *Bact. Revs.,* **13,** 161 (1949).

[17] D. D. Woods, *J. Gen. Microbiol.,* **9,** 151 (1953)

biochemistry impinges upon philosophy, for the question "What is Life?" has been a compelling one throughout the history of human thought. With the discovery of the phenomenon of catalysis, during the first part of the nineteenth century, the assumption of a peculiarly biological chemical force became unnecessary, and Berzelius could write, in 1836:

> We have justifiable reason to suppose that, in living plants and animals, thousands of catalytic processes take place between the tissues and the fluids and result in the formation of the great number of dissimilar chemical compounds, for whose formation out of the common raw material, plant juice or blood, no probable cause could be assigned. The cause will perhaps in the future be discovered in the catalytic power of the organic tissues of which the organs of the living body consist.

The work of the past hundred years has shown that this "catalytic power" resides in a group of proteins which direct and control chemical reactions in biological systems—the enzymes. Some of the greatest successes of biochemistry have come from studies of the enzyme-catalyzed reactions involved in the degradation and formation of important chemical constituents of living matter, and it has become clear that enzyme chemistry is linked directly with every aspect of the biochemical dynamics of living cells.

Currently, the only comprehensive work on the history of biochemistry is that of Lieben.[18] A valuable account of the early development of biochemistry in the United States may be found in the book by Chittenden.[19] Other important books on the history of biochemistry are those of Browne[20] and of Bayliss.[21]

Some Comments on the Terms "Living" and "Nonliving"

In defining the scope of biochemistry its aim was stated to be the description, in the language of chemistry and physics, of the physiological phenomena observed in living matter. It appears desirable, in this introductory chapter, to examine briefly the meaning of the term "living" as distinguished from "nonliving." For a stimulating discussion of this question, see the article by Pirie.[22]

[18] F. Lieben, *Geschichte der physiologischen Chemie,* Franz Deuticke, Leipzig and Vienna, 1935.

[19] R. H. Chittenden, *The Development of Physiological Chemistry in the United States,* Chemical Catalog Co., New York, 1930.

[20] C. A. Browne, *A Source Book of Agricultural Chemistry,* Chronica Botanica Co., Waltham, 1944.

[21] W. M. Bayliss, *Principles of General Physiology,* 4th Ed., Longmans, Green and Co., London, 1924.

[22] N. W. Pirie, in J. Needham and D. E. Green, *Perspectives in Biochemistry,* Cambridge University Press, Cambridge, 1937.

Since the middle of the nineteenth century, the phenomenon of "life" has been directly associated with morphological units termed "cells." The recognition of the cellular basis of living matter may be attributed to Matthias Jacob Schleiden (1804–1881) and to Theodor Schwann, although the experimental origins of the theory which they enunciated in 1838 may be traced to the work of the first microscopists (Hooke, Malpighi, Grew) in the seventeenth century. The concept of the cell as the structural unit of biological systems led to the famous dicta of Rudolf Virchow (1821–1902)—*Omnis cellula e cellula* (Every cell from a cell)— and of Pasteur—*Omne vivum e vivo* (Every living thing from a living thing). The studies of many cytologists (cf. Wilson,[23] Bourne[24]) have given experimental evidence of the transmission, from one biological organism to another, of structural units which enable the progeny to maintain a characteristic form and function.

It is customary to refer to the material of the cell as a jelly-like "protoplasm," but this is a vague term which includes numerous distinct morphological units such as the cell nucleus (diameter, 50–100 μ), mitochondria (length, 1–3 μ), and microsomes (diameter, 0.06–0.15 μ). Techniques are available for the physical separation of some of these cellular components, after rupture of the cell membrane, and they have been shown to be quite different in their chemical properties.[25] A living cell, therefore, is not an undifferentiated mass of protoplasm, but is rather an integrated multicomponent whole; many biological functions of the living cell depend on the maintenance of the integrity of this intracellular organization. It is this integration of structure that may be considered to serve as a basis for the differentiation of "living" from "nonliving" systems. However, as pointed out by Pirie,[22] the line of demarcation between the two is not a sharp one, and it is not possible at present to establish a completely satisfactory criterion for their differentiation.

Living cells may vary considerably in size and discernible complexity of intracellular structure, and these properties cannot be taken as criteria for their characteristic biological nature. Nor can adaptation, irritability, or motility be considered general properties of living systems, since there are many biological forms which, under certain conditions, do not exhibit the capacity to adapt to changes in their environment, to react to external stimuli, or to move. A more general biological property is that of growth, i.e., the assimilation of nutrients and their con-

23 E. B. Wilson, *The Cell in Development and Heredity,* The Macmillan Co., New York, 1928.

24 G. H. Bourne, *Cytology and Cell Physiology,* 2nd Ed., Oxford University Press, London, 1951.

25 W. C. Schneider and G. H. Hogeboom, *Cancer Research,* **11,** 1 (1951); E. L. Kuff et al., *J. Biophys. and Biochem. Cytol.,* **2,** 33 (1956).

version into more "protoplasm," but it must be recalled that nonliving systems also exhibit the capacity to "grow." Perhaps the most striking evidence of this is the increase in the size of a crystal when placed in a supersaturated solution of the corresponding substance; here the presence of the seed leads to an organization of molecules or ions into a growing crystal lattice. Closely related to the biological phenomenon of growth is that of reproduction, which involves the formation of new cells and organisms, but, here again, "self-reproducing" nonliving systems may be cited. For example, Jacques Loeb showed that it was possible to cause oil droplets to grow to a certain size and then to divide. Also, living cells may be able to divide under one set of environmental conditions but are unable to do so under other circumstances.

All the above criteria for the differentiation of the "living" from the "nonliving" are related to another general property of biological systems, that of metabolism, which may be defined as the totality of the chemical changes undergone by the constituents of living matter. The occurrence of chemical change cannot, in itself, be a valid criterion of life, since many component reactions of cells have been made to proceed under the influence of enzymes obtained from cells or of particulate components (e.g., mitochondria) separated from broken cells.

Although no one of the properties usually associated with living matter is exclusively the attribute of biological systems, taken together they are an expression of a complexity of function which must be assumed to be the consequence of a remarkable structural organization of the working parts of each living cell. In metazoa, the individual cells are interdependent in form and function, and the products of the metabolic activity of one group of cells may affect the activity of other cells in the same organ, or may be transported by the fluids of the organism to the cells of another organ. At the multicellular level, therefore, account must be taken not only of the structural organization of the working parts of the individual cells but also of the integration of the activity of these cells.

In considering the chemical properties of biological systems, therefore, the biochemist studies the individual working parts of an extremely complex multicomponent structure. A large number and variety of chemical substances have been isolated from organs, or cells, or parts of cells. Certain compounds, or groups of compounds, are ubiquitous constituents of living cells. The most important of these components is water, which may represent between 70 and 90 per cent of the weight of a tissue. The cellular fluids contain a variety of inorganic ions; Na^+, K^+, Ca^{2+}, Mg^{2+}, Cl^-, HPO_4^{2-}, HCO_3^-, and SO_4^{2-} are the most abundant. The variety of organic chemicals obtained from living cells is extremely great. The most important of these are the proteins and substances chemically related to the proteins, the carbohydrates and related substances, and the lipids.   In addition, there are numerous organic constituents of biological systems which cannot be fitted readily into one of these three categories.   It is the purpose of this book to consider in turn the various chemical components isolated from living systems and to examine some of the available information concerning their metabolic interrelationships.   As will be seen from the pages to follow, the chemical structure of many of the working parts of cells has been established by the methods of organic chemistry, but the study of the manner in which these substances interact in the intact cell is a task of much greater difficulty.   The principal objective of biochemistry is therefore to bridge the wide gap that still remains between the highly integrated activity of the living cell and the properties of its individual chemical components.   In the words of Frederick Gowland Hopkins (1861–1947) :[26]

The task of the biochemist wishing to get to the heart of his problem is exceptional in that he must study systems in which the organization of chemical events counts for more, and is carried far beyond, such simpler coordinations as may be found in non-living systems. He would be over-bold were he to claim at present that such high organization can depend alone upon adjusted concentrations and ordered structural distribution among specialized colloidal catalysts, but he is justified, I think, in feeling sure that such factors contribute to that organization in a significant sense. The biochemist, when he aims at describing living systems in his own language, comes in contact with philosophical thought.   Current philosophy is busy in emphasizing the truism that the properties of the whole do not merely summarize but emerge from the properties of its parts, and some exponents hold a priori that biochemical data can throw no real light on the nature of an organism which, in its very essence, is a unit. The biologist has long studied living organisms as wholes and will continue to do so with ever-increasing interest. But these studies can tell us nothing of the nature of the "physical basis of life," which no form of philosophy can ignore. It is for chemistry and physics to replace the vague concept "protoplasm"—a pure abstraction—by something more real and descriptive. I know of nothing which has shown that current efforts to this end do not deal with realities. It is only necessary for the biochemist to remember that his data gain their full significance only when he can relate them with the activities of the organism as a whole. He should be bold in experiment but cautious in his claims. His may not be the last word in the description of life, but without his help the last word will never be said.[27]

The Literature of Biochemistry

Since biochemistry is a large subject that is developing rapidly, the student cannot depend entirely upon a single printed work for his infor-

[26] J. Needham and E. Baldwin (eds.), Hopkins and Biochemistry, Heffer and Son Ltd., Cambridge, 1949.

[27] F. G. Hopkins, Problems of Specificity in Biochemical Catalysis, Oxford University Press, London, 1931.

mation. It is to be anticipated that much of what will be found in the succeeding pages of this book will have undergone extension or revision during the time required for the printing of the text. For this reason, auxiliary reading, both to obtain further information about older work mentioned in these pages and to learn of new developments, is essential. Among the more useful sources of such information are the volumes of several serial publications, listed below. The abbreviations that follow the titles will be used throughout this book.

Review Publications

Advances in Carbohydrate Chemistry   (Advances in Carbohydrate Chem.)
Advances in Enzymology   (Advances in Enzymol.)
Advances in Protein Chemistry   (Advances in Protein Chem.)
American Scientist   (Am. Scientist)
Annals of the New York Academy of   (Ann. N. Y. Acad. Sci.)
    Sciences
Annual Reports of the Chemical Society   (Ann. Reps.)
Annual Review of Biochemistry   (Ann. Rev. Biochem.)
Annual Review of Microbiology   (Ann. Rev. Microbiol.)
Annual Review of Physiology   (Ann. Rev. Physiol.)
Annual Review of Plant Physiology   (Ann. Rev. Plant Physiol.)
Bacteriological Reviews   (Bact. Revs.)
Biochemical Society Symposia   (Biochem. Soc. Symposia)
Biological Reviews   (Biol. Revs.)
British Medical Bulletin   (Brit. Med. Bull.)
Chemical Reviews   (Chem. Revs.)
Cold Spring Harbor Symposia on Quan-   (Cold Spring Harbor Symposia Quant.
    titative Biology   Biol.)
Harvey Lectures   (Harvey Lectures)
Physiological Reviews   (Physiol. Revs.)
Quarterly Review of Biology   (Quart. Rev. Biol.)
Quarterly Reviews of the Chemical So-   (Quart. Revs.)
    ciety
Vitamins and Hormones   (Vitamins and Hormones)

Research Publications

Acta Chemica Scandinavica   (Acta Chem. Scand.)
American Journal of Physiology   (Am. J. Physiol.)
Archives of Biochemistry and Biophysics   (Arch. Biochem. and Biophys.)
    (until 1951, Archives of Biochemistry)   (until 1951, Arch. Biochem.)
Berichte der deutschen chemischen Ge-   (Ber. chem. Ges.)
    sellschaft
Biochemical Journal   (Biochem. J.)
Biochemische Zeitschrift   (Biochem. Z.)
Biochimica et Biophysica Acta   (Biochim. et Biophys. Acta)
Bulletin de la société chimie biologique   (Bull. soc. chim. biol.)

Canadian Journal of Biochemistry and Physiology   (Canad. J. Biochem. Physiol.)

Endocrinology   (Endocrinology)

Enzymologia   (Enzymologia)

Federation Proceedings   (Federation Proc.)

Helvetica Chimica Acta   (Helv. Chim. Acta)

(Hoppe-Seyler's) Zeitschrift für physiologische Chemie   (Z. physiol. Chem.)

Journal of the American Chemical Society   (J. Am. Chem. Soc.)

Journal of Bacteriology   (J. Bact.)

Journal of Biological Chemistry   (J. Biol. Chem.)

Journal of Biophysical and Biochemical Cytology   (J. Biophys. and Biochem. Cytol.)

Journal of Cellular and Comparative Physiology   (J. Cellular Comp. Physiol.)

Journal of the Chemical Society   (J. Chem. Soc.)

Journal of Clinical Investigation   (J. Clin. Invest.)

Journal of Endocrinology   (J. Endocrinol.)

Journal of Experimental Medicine   (J. Exptl. Med.)

Journal of General Microbiology   (J. Gen. Microbiol.)

Journal of General Physiology   (J. Gen. Physiol.)

Journal of Immunology   (J. Immunol.)

Journal of Neurochemistry   (J. Neurochem.)

Journal of Nutrition   (J. Nutrition)

Journal of Organic Chemistry   (J. Org. Chem.)

Journal of Pharmacology and Experimental Therapeutics   (J. Pharmacol. Exptl. Therap.)

Journal of Physical & Colloid Chemistry   (J. Phys. & Colloid Chem.)

Journal of Physiology   (J. Physiol.)

(Liebig's) Annalen der Chemie   (Ann. Chem.)

Nature   (Nature)

Naturwissenschaften   (Naturwissenschaften)

Plant Physiology   (Plant Physiol.)

Proceedings of the National Academy of Sciences   (Proc. Natl. Acad. Sci.)

Proceedings of the Royal Society   (Proc. Roy. Soc.)

Proceedings of the Society for Experimental Biology and Medicine   (Proc. Soc. Exptl. Biol. Med.)

Science   (Science)

Yale Journal of Biology and Medicine   (Yale J. Biol. and Med.)

Zeitschrift für Naturforschung   (Z. Naturforsch.)

2 ·

General Properties of Proteins

It is proper to begin the study of biochemistry with a discussion of the proteins because this group of chemical substances occupies a central place in both the structural and the dynamic aspects of living matter. From a biochemical point of view, life is uniquely characterized by its association with proteins; the only system now known for the synthesis of proteins is the living cell. It will become clearer as one proceeds through successive topics in biochemistry that proteins play a part in all activities of living matter. Among the proteins are the enzymes, which selectively catalyze most of the chemical reactions essential for normal cellular function; some of the hormones, which are key regulators of metabolic processes; antibodies elaborated by an organism to counteract agents harmful to it; some of the bacterial toxins; contractile proteins such as the myosin of the muscle; respiratory proteins such as hemoglobin. This list of proteins, though fragmentary, will suffice to indicate the manifold variety of physiological function exhibited by these substances.

An important reference work on proteins has been edited by Neurath and Bailey.[1] Another valuable book in this field is that of Cohn and Edsall.[2]

Early History of Protein Chemistry

The appreciation of the importance of proteins in biochemical phenomena came early in the history of scientific biochemistry, during the first half of the nineteenth century. The starting point of these investigations was the empirical knowledge gained about materials such as egg white, blood serum, and milk curd. It had been noted by many workers

[1] H. Neurath and K. Bailey, *The Proteins*, Academic Press, New York, 1953–1954.
[2] E. J. Cohn and J. T. Edsall, *Proteins, Amino Acids and Peptides*, Reinhold Publishing Corp., New York, 1943.

that these materials had certain properties in common, as for example their coagulability by heat or by treatment with strong acids and alkalies. With the rise of scientific chemistry, it was realized that these materials all contained nitrogen, and this came to be considered a distinctive property of the proteins. The first systematic investigation of these nitrogen-containing materials was begun during the 1830's by the Dutch chemist Gerardus Johannes Mulder (1802–1880), who applied the then new methods of elementary analysis to the examination of materials such as silk, blood fibrin, egg white, and gelatin. It may be of interest to quote from Mulder's *General Physiological Chemistry*, published in 1844–1851:

> There is present in plants as well as animals a substance which . . . performs an important function in both. It is one of the very complex substances, which under various circumstances may alter their composition, and serves . . . for the regulation of chemical metabolism. . . . It is without doubt the most important of the known components of living matter, and it would appear that, without it, life would not be possible. This substance has been named protein.

Recent historical research has revealed that this name, which has come to occupy such an important place in the language of biochemistry, was suggested to Mulder by Berzelius in a letter dated July 10, 1838, and apparently received by Mulder while he was writing the scientific papers in which "protein" (Greek *proteios,* of the first rank) made its first public appearance.[3]

The study of proteins was next taken up by Liebig,[4] who extended Mulder's analytical studies. At first it was believed that the various materials that Mulder, Liebig, and others had examined all contained the same fundamental radical and that there was only one kind of "protein." As Liebig put it in a letter to Wöhler in 1841,

> . . . we have plant albumin, plant fibrin, and plant casein all identical with each other and with the animal proteins that bear the same name.

A few years later, in 1845, Liebig changed his views on the identity of the "protein" radical in these natural substances, and during the succeeding half-century a variety of terms was in use to describe them. In the German literature there may be found the names *Eiweisskörper, Proteinkörper, Proteinstoffe,* and *Proteinsubstanz,* and these appeared in English scientific papers as "protein bodies," "albuminoids," or "proteids." At the beginning of the present century, however, Mulder's term, originally proposed to designate a radical, began to be adopted in place of these varied general names, and in what follows "proteins" will refer to a class of substances.

[3] H. B. Vickery, *Yale J. Biol. and Med.,* **22,** 387 (1950).
[4] H. B. Vickery, *J. Chem. Education,* **19,** 73 (1942).

Classification of Proteins

The work of the latter half of the nineteenth century showed that proteins are complex nitrogenous substances of high molecular weight, and that, on decomposition by acids, alkalies, or enzymes, they yield a mixture of simpler compounds termed amino acids. Proteins were found in plant and animal cells, tissues, and exudates, and it became abundantly clear that there were many kinds of proteins in nature. There then arose the problem of how to classify them. It was obvious from the work of Mulder and Liebig that elementary analysis could not be used for this purpose (p. 27). Instead, an attempt was made to differentiate the proteins from one another on the basis of their solubility properties.

At this point it may be well to emphasize that the biochemist, in order to study the properties of chemical components of living matter, must separate these components from the other substances with which they are associated. In other words, he must disintegrate the tissue, thus destroying the intracellular organization characteristic of many phenomena of life, and must isolate from the resulting mixture the substance he wishes to examine. As a consequence of such efforts to isolate and to characterize proteins, much was learned about their solubility properties, and perhaps the most significant early contributions were those of investigators who studied the proteins of plant tissues—Heinrich Ritthausen (1826–1912) and, more importantly, Thomas Burr Osborne (1859–1929).[5] In the course of their work, these two men developed methods that came to be used widely for the isolation of proteins from all tissues, both plant and animal. More recently the systematic studies performed by Edwin J. Cohn (1892–1953) and his associates on the fractionation of the proteins of human blood plasma have provided new methods of wide applicability.

The classification of proteins generally used today is based on the proposals of committees of the British Physiological Society and of the American Physiological Society in 1907 and 1908, respectively. Accordingly one speaks of:

1. Albumins: Soluble in water and salt solutions.
2. Globulins: Sparingly soluble in water but soluble in salt solutions.
3. Prolamines: Soluble in 70–80 per cent ethanol but insoluble in water and in absolute ethanol.
4. Glutelins: Insoluble in all of the above solvents but soluble in acid or alkali.
5. Scleroproteins: Insoluble in aqueous solvents.

[5] H. B. Vickery, *Physiol. Revs.,* **25,** 347 (1945); *J. Nutrition,* **59,** 3 (1956).

Examples of the first four groups are found in plant material, but few if any proteins obtained from animal tissues exhibit the solubility properties ascribed to prolamines and glutelins. In addition to these five groups, numerous others were listed in the proposals of 1907–1908, but they have questionable validity as a basis for general classification. As will be seen from the later discussion, several groups of proteins were assigned names descriptive of one or another chemical attribute. For example, the principal proteins of sperm cells, called protamines, are strongly basic substances, and they were distinguished from the somewhat less basic histones found in a variety of animal cells. Then again, proteins found to have an unusually high phosphorus content such as casein of milk or vitellin of egg yolk were termed phosphoproteins.

The groups of proteins just mentioned were referred to as "simple proteins," not to indicate that their chemical structure is simple, which it is not, but because it was believed that, on decomposition with acids, the only organic products formed were amino acids. The "simple proteins" were thus distinguished from the so-called "conjugated proteins" which liberate, on decomposition, an organic chemical component (a "prosthetic group") distinct from proteins or amino acids. Among these conjugated proteins are the nucleoproteins (prosthetic group—nucleic acid), glycoproteins (prosthetic group—carbohydrate), chromoproteins (prosthetic group—a pigment), lipoproteins (prosthetic group—a lipid).

With the growth of knowledge about proteins, the lines of demarcation established in this classification have proved to be extremely fluid. A sharp distinction between the globulins and albumins on the basis of solubility in water and in salt solutions cannot be made. Thus, it has been necessary to refer to pseudoglobulins, which are soluble in water, and to euglobulins, which do not dissolve in salt-free water. Again, many proteins previously thought to belong to the class of "simple proteins" have been found to be invariably associated with nonprotein material, as for instance egg albumin, which has been shown to contain a carbohydrate component. Despite the unsatisfactory state of protein classification, the student must be familiar with the terms that it has brought into the biochemical literature; it is unlikely that, in the immediate future, efforts will be made to revise it appreciably, since much still remains to be learned about the chemistry of proteins.

Isolation of Proteins [6]

As was indicated before, the decisive first step in the chemical study of a protein is its isolation from the cellular mass or the biological fluid

[6] J. F. Taylor, in H. Neurath and K. Bailey, *The Proteins*, Vol. IA, Chapter 1, Academic Press, New York, 1953.

in which it is found. The isolation of proteins is frequently attended by great difficulties, primarily because of their extreme instability. This instability is reflected in altered solubility properties and may be caused by heat, strong acid or alkali, or a variety of chemical reagents. The process of conversion of the "native" protein to a product with altered properties is frequently termed "denaturation," and the product is a "denatured" protein. (The subject of denaturation of proteins will be discussed more fully on pp. 153 f.)

Another source of difficulty in the isolation of proteins arises from their ability to interact with other organic substances—lipids, carbohydrates, nucleic acids, etc.—that are constituents of the mixture present in a biological fluid or obtained by disintegration of a tissue or of a mass of microbial cells. For example, the association of many cellular proteins with water-insoluble lipids often prevents the extraction of the desired protein with aqueous solvents. However, preliminary treatment of a ground tissue suspension with an organic solvent (e.g., butanol) disrupts this association, and frequently permits the extraction of an apparently "insoluble" protein with water or salt solutions.[7]

The careful studies of a number of investigators have provided a body of experience which has served well as a guide for the isolation of many proteins. Of special importance are the following procedures and precautions:

1. The temperature should be maintained as low as possible. However, in some instances, the desired protein is found to be much more stable to heat than many of the accompanying proteins. Under these circumstances, it may be advantageous to subject a crude tissue extract to a brief heat treatment, thus causing the denaturation and precipitation of much of the undesired protein. Occasionally it may be desirable to take advantage of the influence of temperature on the solubility. In general, however, experience has shown that it is best to work at temperatures near the freezing point of the solvent in use.

2. The acidity or alkalinity must be carefully controlled, and kept as near that of the native protein as possible. It will be recalled that water dissociates according to the equation $H_2O \rightleftharpoons H^+ + OH^-$ and that the equilibrium in this reaction is far to the left. At 25° C, the "ion product constant" of water, $K_w' = [H^+][OH^-] = 1 \times 10^{-14}$ M. When $[H^+] = [OH^-]$, the hydrogen ion concentration $[H^+] = 1 \times 10^{-7}$ M. In dealing with solutions of such low concentration of hydrogen ions, it is more convenient to refer to the pH, defined as the negative logarithm (to the base 10) of the hydrogen ion "activity," which may be considered

[7] R. K. Morton, in S. P. Colowick and N. O. Kaplan, *Methods in Enzymology,* Vol. I, p. 25, Academic Press, New York, 1955.

to approximate the molar concentration of hydrogen ions in extremely dilute solutions. For convenience, therefore, $pH = -\log_{10}[H^+] = \log_{10} 1/[H^+]$. The pH of aqueous solutions may be measured accurately either by means of a "hydrogen electrode" (p. 296) or by means of a glass electrode assembly.[8]

The solubility of proteins varies greatly with the pH of the solution, and for each protein there is a pH value at which it is least soluble (p. 101). As with temperature, the variations in pH that can be withstood without resultant denaturation differ greatly from protein to protein, and advantage may sometimes be taken of this fact to aid in the elimination of undesired proteins.

3. The concentration of protein should be kept as high as possible since dilution, in many cases, favors denaturation.

4. In order to isolate a protein from an aqueous solution, a widely used procedure has been to effect precipitation by the addition of a sufficient amount of an inorganic salt. Among the salts that have proved useful for this purpose, ammonium sulfate is outstanding because of its high solubility in water (760 grams per liter at 20° C) and its relatively low temperature coefficient of solubility. An excellent example of the fractionation of a mixture of proteins by means of ammonium sulfate is provided by the separation of the albumins and globulins of horse serum,[9] for which data are given in Table 1; the designation of the

Table I. **Fractionation of Serum Protein with Ammonium Sulfate** [9]

Concentration of Ammonium Sulfate		Type of Protein Precipitated	Per Cent of Total Protein
Moles per Liter	Per Cent of Saturation		
1.39	34	Largely γ-globulins	20
1.64	40	α-, β-, and γ-globulins	15
2.05	50	α- and β-globulins	14
2.57	62	Largely crystalline albumin	32
2.80	68	Crystalline albumin, etc.	14
		Total	95

several types of serum globulin as α-, β-, or γ-globulins refers to the differences in their behavior when they move in an electric field (p. 106).

Other sulfates, such as magnesium sulfate or sodium sulfate, though less soluble than ammonium sulfate, have the advantage that the solutions may be analyzed directly for nitrogen to gain an estimate of the

[8] R. G. Bates, *Electrometric pH Determinations*, John Wiley & Sons, New York, 1954; V. Gold, *pH Measurement*, Methuen and Co., London, 1956.

[9] E. J. Cohn et al., *J. Am. Chem. Soc.*, **62**, 3386 (1940).

protein content. A fortunate property of neutral salts is that they tend to stabilize proteins in solution, and thus to counteract the harmful effect of unfavorable temperature or acidity.

5. Organic solvents such as ethanol, methanol, or acetone have also been used for the precipitation of proteins from aqueous solution. In general, the use of such precipitants has been successful only at extremely low temperatures (near $-10°$ C).

In considering these isolation procedures, it must be noted in advance (cf. pp. 98 f.) that proteins are large molecules with many positively and negatively charged groups, such as $-NH_3{}^+$ and $-COO^-$. These groups can interact electrostatically with each other, or with small ions of opposite charge in the solvent; they can also react with water; i.e., they are hydrophilic. It will be recalled from elementary physics that the force of electrostatic attraction (F) between two oppositely charged particles is given by the equation $F = e^+e^-/Dr^2$, where e^+ and e^- are the charges, r is the distance between them, and D is the dielectric constant of the medium. D is a measure of the influence of the medium on the attraction; it is defined as the ratio of the potential between the charges when they are separated by a vacuum to the potential in the medium. Water has a relatively high dielectric constant (78.54 at $25°$ C), and, in aqueous solution, the interaction between the charged groups of separate protein molecules tends to be repressed, and the interaction of these groups with water molecules correspondingly enhanced, thus favoring solubility. Albumins and pseudoglobulins are soluble in salt-free water because the protein-solvent interaction is stronger than the protein-protein interaction. On the other hand, euglobulins are insoluble in salt-free water because the protein-protein interaction is the stronger.

If a neutral salt such as ammonium sulfate is added to water, the solubility of a protein in the salt solution not only is a function of the concentration of the salt, but also depends on the charges of the inorganic ions. For this reason, the conditions of a fractionation of proteins by means of neutral salts are best described in terms of the "ionic strength" of the solution. The molar ionic strength $\Gamma/2$ is given by the equation

$$\frac{\Gamma}{2} = \frac{\sum C_n Z_n{}^2}{2}$$

To calculate the ionic strength of a solution, one multiplies the molar concentration (C) of each ion (n) by the square of the number of electric charges (Z) on that ion, adds all the products, and divides the sum by 2. Thus, a 2 M solution of ammonium sulfate has an ionic strength of

$$\frac{(4 \times 1) + (2 \times 4)}{2} = 6$$

At low salt concentrations, the charged groups of a protein interact with the inorganic ions; the euglobulins are brought into solution and the solubility of the albumins is increased. The proteins are said to be "salted in." As the ionic strength is increased further, the effective concentration ("activity") of water is decreased, until a point is reached where the protein-protein interaction begins to exceed the protein-water interaction. The protein is now being "salted out."

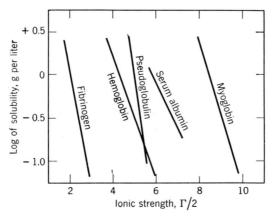

Fig. 1. Effect of ionic strength on the solubility of proteins in ammonium sulfate solutions. (From E. J. Cohn and J. T. Edsall.[2])

In concentrated salt solutions, there is a straight-line relationship between the solubility of a protein and the ionic strength of the solution:

$$\log S = \beta' - K_s' \frac{\Gamma}{2}$$

where S is the solubility (in grams per liter), β' is the logarithm of the hypothetical solubility, S', at zero ionic strength, and K_s' is the "salting out" constant. β' is the extrapolated intercept (for zero ionic strength), on the ordinate axis, of the lines drawn in Fig. 1, and K_s' is the slope of the line. The values of K_s' for proteins are relatively high, and small changes in ionic strength cause an appreciable effect on the solubility. Although K_s' is independent of temperature and pH, β' is markedly influenced by these factors.

If an organic solvent such as ethanol is added to an aqueous solution of a protein, the dielectric constant of the medium is lowered and the activity of water is decreased, thus favoring protein-protein interaction and precipitation. At 20° C, the dielectric constant of ethanol is 25.0; the corresponding values for methanol and acetone are 32.4 and 19.6 respectively.

From the above discussion it is clear that, in any fractionation procedure based on the use of neutral salts and organic solvents as precipitants, the following variables must be controlled carefully: temperature, pH, protein concentration, ionic strength, and the dielectric constant.

A striking demonstration of the successful application of these principles is provided by the work of Cohn and his associates on the fractionation of the proteins present in human plasma.[10] A summary of one of their procedures may be cited. To a plasma adjusted to pH 7.2 and at a low ionic strength, ethanol was added at $-3°$ C until the alcohol concentration reached 10 per cent; this precipitated mainly the fibrinogen (fraction I). By increasing the ethanol concentration to 25 per cent at $-5°$ C, fractions II and III, consisting mainly of β- and γ-globulins, were obtained. Further addition of alcohol (to 40 per cent ethanol) at pH 5.2 gave a precipitate of fraction IV (largely α-globulins), and adjustment of the pH of the supernatant solution to 4.8 precipitated most of the serum albumin (fraction V).

In later work, this procedure was extended and improved by the addition of extremely small concentrations of divalent cations such as zinc or barium,[11] which interact specifically with chemical groups on the protein molecule (p. 108). Under these conditions, lower concentrations of alcohol are required, and the possibility of denaturation correspondingly lessened.

It has been found that, under optimal conditions of temperature and pH, individual proteins may be precipitated by neutral salts or by organic solvents within a relatively narrow concentration range of the precipitants. In the isolation of proteins, therefore, advantage is taken of the wide differences among them with regard to the concentration of precipitant required to throw them out of solution, and what is done is to perform a fractional precipitation which effects separation of the protein components of the mixture. In many instances, such fractional precipitation procedures, when combined with favorable changes in acidity and temperature, lead to the separation of the protein in the form of crystals. One of the early successes in the crystallization of a protein by means of salt fractionation was that of Franz Hofmeister (1850–1922), who in 1889 described the preparation of crystalline egg albumin from egg whites. Since that time, many proteins have been obtained in crystalline form; some of these crystals are shown in Fig. 2.

Although the procedures listed above represent the most widely applied methods for the isolation and purification of proteins, there are a number of auxiliary techniques which also have proved useful. One of the oldest of these is the selective adsorption of proteins on agents such

[10] J. T. Edsall, *Advances in Protein Chem.*, **3**, 383 (1947).

[11] E. J. Cohn et al., *J. Am. Chem. Soc.*, **72**, 465 (1950).

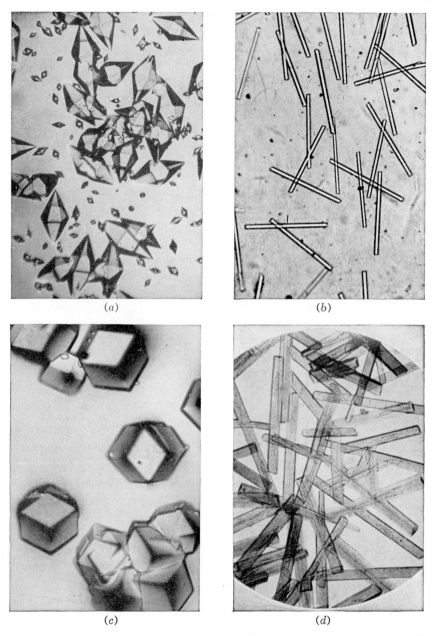

Fig. 2. Crystalline protein preparations. (*a*) Pepsin (an enzyme crystallized by J. H. Northrop from swine gastric juice). (*b*) Phosphorylase (an enzyme crystallized by A. A. Green and G. T. Cori from extracts of rabbit muscle). (*c*) Bushy stunt virus (crystallized by W. M. Stanley from virus-infected tomato plants). (*d*) Oxyhemoglobin (crystallized from horse blood by E. T. Reichert and A. P. Brown).

as kaolin (a hydrated aluminum silicate), aluminum hydroxide, ferric hydroxide, or lead phosphate. Adsorption techniques may be useful for the removal of unwanted proteins from a crude mixture, and the proteins remaining in solution may then be separated more easily by means of fractional precipitation. On the other hand, the desired protein may be preferentially adsorbed by the agent used, and thus is removed from the bulk of other protein material in the mixture; the adsorbed protein may frequently be brought back into solution ("eluted") by washing the adsorbent at a pH different from that used for the adsorption. In many instances, however, proteins are denatured upon adsorption.[12] Some success in the fractionation of proteins has been achieved by the use of columns filled with a suitable adsorbent, and passage of a solution containing a protein mixture down the column. Since under a given set of conditions different proteins may be adsorbed to a different extent by the same adsorbent, an appreciable fractionation may be effected. Advantage has been taken of this fact for the "chromatographic" separation (cf. p. 115) of mixtures of proteins. Recent examples of the application of chromatographic techniques to the separation of mixtures of proteins may be found in the work of Porter[13] and of Boardman and Partridge.[14]

Since proteins are usually more stable in dry form than in solution, it is customary to subject a protein preparation to the process of lyophilization whereby the water is removed by evaporation at extremely low temperatures and in a high vacuum.[15] In this manner, the proteins in crude tissue extracts as well as in highly purified preparations may be preserved in the native state for long periods of time.

The impression may have been gained from the above that the isolation and purification of a protein is an empirical operation. This is only partly true, since the careful studies of numerous biochemists, notably Cohn and his associates, have given the subject a much sounder experimental and theoretical basis. As will be seen from the subsequent discussion of the behavior of proteins as electrolytes (Chapter 4), the clearer understanding of the interactions of proteins with one another and with inorganic ions has made possible a more rational approach to the problem of the separation of proteins.

Homogeneity of Protein Preparations

The crystallization of a protein has served as the starting point for many fruitful investigations of its chemical and physical properties and

[12] C. A. Zittle, *Advances in Enzymol.*, **14**, 319 (1953).

[13] R. R. Porter, *Biochem. J.*, **59**, 405 (1955).

[14] N. K. Boardman and S. M. Partridge, *Biochem. J.*, **59**, 543 (1955).

[15] E. W. Flosdorf and S. Mudd, *J. Immunol.*, **29**, 389 (1935).

its biological activity. It would be incorrect, however, to conclude, from the fact that a protein has been crystallized, that it has been obtained as a single pure chemical substance in the same sense that one is accustomed to think of a sample of crystalline benzoic acid. It will be evident from the subsequent discussion of the chemistry of proteins that they are extremely complex in structure, and the definition of their purity is an experimental problem of the greatest difficulty. Much of the work of protein chemists during the period 1940–1955 underlines the need for the most cautious and conservative attitude on the question of the purity of proteins. Many crystalline proteins have been found to be mixtures of several chemical components, and even where such heterogeneity has not been demonstrated it must be suspected. For example, the crystalline protein β-lactoglobulin (from cow's milk) was long considered one of the most homogeneous proteins known; however, it is now recognized[16] that the crystalline material contains several distinct protein components. The application of chromatographic techniques for the separation of proteins has also shown that crystalline preparations of ribonuclease or of lysozyme represent mixtures of protein components.[17]

Several methods are available for the examination of the homogeneity of a purified protein (cf. pp. 40, 106). Of the various known criteria for the purity of a chemical substance, that which depends on the application of Gibbs' phase rule has the greatest theoretical validity. The phase rule states that, for a system in equilibrium, the following relationship holds: $P + F = C + 2$, where P is defined as the number of phases, i.e., the number of homogeneous, physically distinct, and mechanically separable portions; C is defined as the number of components, i.e., those constituents that undergo independent variation in the different phases; and F is defined as the number of degrees of freedom, i.e., the number of variable factors such as temperature, pressure, and concentration of components. These components must be fixed arbitrarily in order to define the system.

In the application of Gibbs' phase rule to the study of the solubility of proteins, P equals either 1 or 2; there is either complete solution or solution plus solid. C will be determined by the number of kinds of molecules present in the system; if one considers the solvent as one of the components, the other components will be the number of kinds of proteins present. As for F, the temperature and pressure may be kept

[16] O. Smithies, *Biochem. J.,* **58,** 31 (1954); A. G. Ogston et al., *ibid.,* **59,** 644 (1955); **66,** 399 (1957).

[17] A. J. P. Martin and R. R. Porter, *Biochem. J.,* **49,** 215 (1951); C. H. W. Hirs et al., *J. Am. Chem. Soc.,* **73,** 1893 (1951); H. H. Tallan and W. H. Stein, *ibid.,* **73,** 2976 (1951).

constant, while the concentration of the components may be varied at will. If one now considers an experiment in which increasing amounts of a single protein (expressed as milligrams of nitrogen) are added to a solvent, at first the protein will dissolve completely. Under these circumstances there are one phase (the solution) and two components (the solvent and the dissolved protein). The solvent mixture may contain salts, but if the salt content of this mixture remains constant the entire solvent mixture may be considered as a single component. Under these circumstances, $1 + F = 2 + 2$, or $F = 3$. There are therefore three

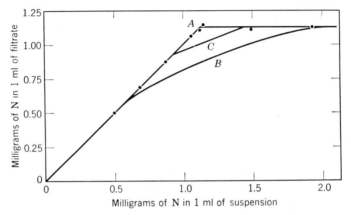

Fig. 3. Solubility curves of proteins. The experimental points corresponding to curve A refer to the solubility behavior of the protein chymotrypsinogen at pH 5 in 0.19 saturated $MgSO_4$ (from J. A. V. Butler[18]). Curve B describes the solubility behavior of a solid solution of two or more proteins. Curve C describes the behavior of a mixture of two protein components.

degrees of freedom, two of which are fixed, and the third, the concentration of protein, is a variable. When the amount of protein is so great that a solid phase is in equilibrium with the solution $(P = 2)$, $2 + F = 2 + 2$, there are only two degrees of freedom. Thus, since the temperature and pressure are held fixed, the number of phases is equal to the number of components. This is illustrated by the diagram in Fig. 3. In practice, the important criterion of purity is whether the inflection point of the curve is a sharp one. If the protein preparation is a solid solution of two or more proteins, a saturated solution may be attained, but the sharp inflection point (A) will be replaced by a curve, indicated (B) in the diagram. If a protein preparation contains two components which do not form a solid solution, two breaks in the curve (C) may be noted.[18] Though theoretically sound, the solubility

18 J. A. V. Butler, *J. Gen. Physiol.,* **24,** 189 (1940).

measurement of proteins is difficult to perform with the required accuracy to establish completely a sharp inflection point. A few proteins appear to satisfy the phase rule criteria adequately, but the published data for most of the other proteins claimed as "pure" by solubility criteria are decidedly ambiguous in the region of the inflection point.

In what follows, frequent reference will be made to individual proteins as though single substances were involved; it is important to emphasize that this is done for convenience only. Therefore, when one speaks of a protein such as egg albumin or horse hemoglobin, one is referring, in essence, to a method of preparation, and one assumes, as a first approximation, that the product is composed entirely, or at least predominantly, of a single molecular species. Penetrating discussions of the problems involved in the determination of the "purity" of proteins may be found in the articles by Pirie,[19] by Shedlovsky,[20] and by Colvin et al.[21]

Elementary Composition of Proteins

In the study of the chemical structure of an organic compound, the first step is usually the analysis of the compound to determine the proportion of the various elements it contains. This is what Mulder did in initiating the systematic study of proteins, and since that time the elementary composition of many proteins has been determined. Protein preparations usually contain some inorganic matter, as well as bound water; it is customary to express the analytical data on a protein in terms of the percentage composition of a carefully dried sample, and a correction is applied for any ash that may have been found in it. In their elementary composition, proteins may be said to contain 50 to 55 per cent of carbon, 6 to 7 per cent of hydrogen, 20 to 23 per cent of oxygen (usually determined by difference), and 12 to 19 per cent of nitrogen. It is this last element that is most characteristic of the proteins, and the nitrogen analysis of a tissue or a food is frequently used to gain an estimate of its protein content. It has become a widespread practice to assume that proteins contain about 16 per cent nitrogen, and the protein content of the plant or animal material under analysis is sometimes estimated by multiplying the nitrogen content (in per cent) by the factor 6.25 (100/16). Since the nitrogen content of different purified proteins varies between 12 and 19 per cent, and since not all of the nitrogen in a tissue or a food sample is necessarily protein in nature, the use of the factor 6.25 is, at best, a rough approximation.

In the quantitative determination of the nitrogen content of a protein,

[19] N. W. Pirie, *Biol. Revs.*, **15**, 377 (1940).
[20] T. Shedlovsky, *Ann. N. Y. Acad. Sci.*, **43**, 259 (1943).
[21] J. R. Colvin et al., *Chem. Revs.*, **54**, 687 (1954).

the most reliable results are given by the Kjeldahl method. This procedure depends on the conversion of the bound nitrogen into ammonium ions by digestion of the protein with concentrated sulfuric acid in the presence of a suitable catalyst (e.g., mercuric sulfate, copper sulfate, selenium oxychloride). The digestion mixture is then made alkaline, and the ammonia is steam-distilled into an excess of standard acid and determined quantitatively by titration. A widely used micro modification of this general method is that described by Miller and Houghton.[22] A somewhat less accurate but more rapid method involves the determination of ammonia by the estimation of the color formed upon the addition of Nessler reagent, a solution of mercuric potassium iodide in aqueous sodium hydroxide.

In addition to the elements cited above, proteins have been found to contain others in lesser amount. The presence of sulfur (0.2 to 3.0 per cent) and of phosphorus (0 to 6 per cent) in proteins had been recognized by Mulder, but he assumed that these were combined in different proportions with the same radical $C_{40}H_{62}O_{12}N_{10}$. Though this view was quickly abandoned, Mulder's work gave an impetus to analyses of several proteins for their sulfur content. An especially important contribution in this regard was made by Osborne, who conducted a careful analysis of the best preparation of egg albumin available around 1900, and found 1.62 per cent S, in addition to 52.75 per cent C, 7.10 per cent H, and 15.51 per cent N.

The elementary analysis of proteins gave the first quantitative indications of the fact that proteins represent substances of rather large molecular weight. The calculation of a minimal molecular weight of a compound from its elementary analysis is a standard procedure in organic chemistry, and depends on the simple relationship:

Minimal molecular weight =
$$\frac{\text{Atomic weight of element} \times \text{number of atoms} \times 100}{\text{Per cent of element in compound}}$$

For example, the finding of 0.34 per cent of iron in the iron-containing protein hemoglobin made it possible to calculate that the minimal weight that would account for 1 atom of iron per molecule of protein is approximately 16,500. Osborne assumed that each molecule of egg albumin contains 8 sulfur atoms and thus obtained a value of 15,700 for the minimal molecular weight of the protein. Such a calculation is not always practicable, since most proteins do not contain an element such as iron in sufficiently small amount. Consequently, protein analysts occasionally select one or more amino acids which can be determined accurately. For example, if a protein were found to contain 0.29 per

[22] L. Miller and J. A. Houghton, *J. Biol. Chem.*, **159**, 373 (1945).

cent of the amino acid tryptophan (molecular weight 204), the minimal molecular weight of the protein would be approximately 70,000.

Particle Weight of Proteins [23]

The comparatively large molecular size of proteins became evident in 1860 when Thomas Graham (1805–1869) showed that simpler crystalline compounds such as inorganic salts or glucose readily diffused through membranes of parchment, but that the proteins he tested for this property did not. He accordingly applied to the diffusible substances the term crystalloids, and to the nondiffusible materials, which he had in amorphous form, colloids (Greek *colla*, glue).

One important practical consequence of the "colloidal" behavior of proteins is that inorganic salts may largely be removed from a protein solution without loss of the protein by the operation known as "dialysis." The solution is placed in a bag made of a material (e.g., cellophane) which serves as a selective membrane permitting the passage of the inorganic ions but not of the protein, and the bag is suspended in a large volume of water which is replaced at frequent intervals. Many types of apparatus are available for the rapid dialysis of protein solutions.

With membranes of suitable porosity, proteins of moderate size (up to particle weight 45,000) may pass through, and studies of the rate of dialysis can give useful information about the size and shape of proteins.[24]

It was natural to attribute the inability of the colloidal proteins to diffuse through the membrane to the fact that their molecular dimensions were considerably greater than those of the crystalloids. The large molecular weights that had been calculated from the results of elementary analysis were in accord with this conclusion. As was indicated above, these molecular weights represented minimal values; chemical analysis alone could not decide, for example, how many iron atoms there were in a molecule of hemoglobin. Other methods were required to gain an estimate of the actual size of protein molecules.

Osmotic Pressure of Proteins. One of the first techniques employed for the estimation of the size of protein molecules involved the measurement of the osmotic pressure of protein solutions. It will be recalled that the osmotic pressure of a solution is one of the colligative properties of that solution; others are the elevation of the boiling point and the depression of the freezing point. These colligative properties, so called because they are "bound together," depend solely on the number of each type of molecule present in the solution, and not on the nature of

[23] J. T. Edsall, in H. Neurath and K. Bailey, *The Proteins,* Vol. IB, Chapter 7, Academic Press, New York, 1953.
[24] L. C. Craig et al., *J. Am. Chem. Soc.,* **79,** 3729 (1957).

these molecules. In theory, therefore, any one of these colligative properties may be used for the determination of the molecular weight of a solute. If a solute is added to a solvent such as water, the vapor pressure of water is lowered and the boiling point is increased. This is expressed in the form of Raoult's equation:

$$\frac{P_0 - P}{P_0} = \frac{n_2}{n_1 + n_2}$$

where P_0 is the vapor pressure of the solvent, P is the vapor pressure of the solution, n_1 is the number of moles of solvent, and n_2 is the number of moles of solute. The fraction to the right in the equation is termed the mole fraction. Since n is the weight (w) of susbtance divided by the molecular weight (M), one may write the equation

$$\frac{P_0 - P}{P_0} = \frac{w_2/M_2}{w_1/M_1 + w_2/M_2}$$

Clearly, in very dilute solutions, w_2/M_2 is small in comparison with w_1/M_1, and the last equation becomes

$$\frac{P_0 - P}{P_0} = \frac{w_2 M_1}{w_1 M_2}$$

For the determination of the molecular weights of organic substances it is more frequently the practice to determine the effect on the freezing or melting point of a solvent. Here the effect of a solute is to lower the temperature of the melting point of the pure solvent, and the magnitude of this effect is proportional to the mole fraction of the solute. Thus,

$$\Delta t = K \frac{n_2}{n_1 + n_2}$$

Since n_2 is small in comparison with n_1, and n_1 is nearly constant, the freezing point depression may be set equal to $K_f n_2$ or $K_f w_2/M_2$. If K_f is defined as the decrease in freezing point when 1 mole of solute is added to a given amount of solvent (e.g., 1000 grams of water), then the K_f characteristic of a given solvent may be determined with a series of substances of known molecular weight and the value of K_f may be employed for the determination of the molecular weights of other substances. It is obvious that the magnitude of the freezing or melting point depression will increase as K_f becomes larger; for this reason camphor ($K_f = 39.7$) is preferred as a solvent over substances such as water ($K_f = 1.858$), phenol ($K_f = 7.4$), or benzene ($K_f = 5.10$). Cohn and Conant[25] attempted in 1926 to determine the molecular weights of several proteins by measurement of their effect on the depression of the freezing point of phenol but found that the temperature difference

[25] E. J. Cohn and J. B. Conant, Z. *physiol. Chem.*, **159**, 93 (1926).

was too small to permit accurate estimates of the values of M. This was to be expected if the molecular weights were large, as can be seen from the inspection of the formula for the freezing point depression. It is clear therefore that measurement of this colligative property, so useful for the determination of molecular weights of the order of 100 to 500, cannot be used with proteins. Also, the measurement of boiling point elevation is not suitable with proteins, because the high temperatures will inevitably cause extensive protein decomposition. Of the colligative properties mentioned above, therefore, only osmotic pressure remains to be considered.

The first systematic studies of osmotic pressure were performed by the botanists de Vries and Pfeffer during the latter half of the nineteenth century. They were interested in studying the fact that, when plant cells are placed in water, water migrates into the cell. Shortly before, Moritz Traube had prepared artificial membranes, which acted like plant cells when the membranes were used to separate two solutions of different concentration with respect to a solute. What was common to the membrane of the plant cell and to the artificial membrane was that they were permeable to the solvent, in this case water, but impermeable to the solute. In this situation, the solvent will migrate by osmosis from the more dilute solution, where its vapor pressure is higher, into the more concentrated solution, where the vapor pressure of the solvent is lower.

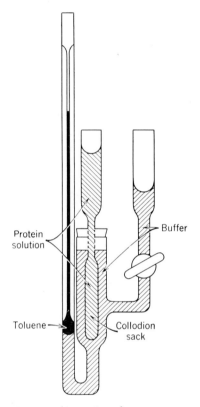

Fig. 4. Apparatus for measurement of osmotic pressure. (From H. B. Bull, *Physical Biochemistry,* 2nd Ed., John Wiley & Sons, New York, 1951.)

Such diffusion may be counteracted by imposing a pressure on the more concentrated solution, in order to maintain equilibrium. This pressure is referred to as the osmotic pressure, and an instrument to measure it is termed an osmometer (Fig. 4).

In sufficiently dilute solution, and at equilibrium with the pure solvent outside the membrane, the osmotic pressure Π is approximately equal to mRT, where m is the concentration of solute in moles per liter, R is the gas constant, and T is the absolute temperature. This is van't Hoff's law, which may be stated in more general terms as

$$\lim_{m \to 0} \frac{\Pi}{m} = RT \qquad m = \frac{c}{M}$$

If the protein concentration (c) is given in grams per cubic centimeter of aqueous solvent, and M is the molecular weight of the solute,

$$\lim_{c \to 0} \frac{\Pi}{cRT} = \frac{1}{M}$$

Consequently, if one plots experimentally determined values of Π/cRT against c, as in Fig. 5, the intercept on the Π/cRT ordinate gives the reciprocal of the molecular weight. If Π is given in atmospheres, R is 82.057 cc-atmosphere per mole per degree (1 atmosphere is equivalent to 760 mm Hg or to 10,300 mm H_2O). The slope of the curve near the intercept is a measure of the "interaction constant" B in the following equation, and describes the departure of the system from ideal behavior.

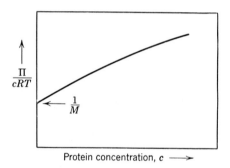

Fig. 5. Determination of molecular weight by osmotic pressure measurements.

$$\frac{\Pi}{cRT} = \frac{1}{M} + Bc$$

An indication of the value of the osmotic pressure method for the determination of the molecular weight of proteins is provided by the following calculation. A protein of molecular weight 50,000, if it is present in aqueous solution in a concentration of 1 per cent at $0°$ C ($273°$ K), and if it obeys van't Hoff's law, gives an osmotic pressure of 46 mm H_2O, a value that can be measured. This may be contrasted with the fact that a solution of the same molarity ($2 \times 10^{-4}M$) would lower the freezing point of water by only about $0.0004°$ C.

It must be emphasized that the van't Hoff equation applies to nonelectrolytes, and that proteins conform to this equation best at pH values at which they possess no net electric charge. The reasons for this will become more apparent from the discussion of the Gibbs-Donnan equilibrium on p. 111.

If a solution contains several proteins of different mass, osmotic pressure measurements will give an average value of the molecular weight; this average is denoted the "number-average" molecular weight, assigned the symbol $\overline{M}_n$, and defined by the equation

$$\overline{M}_n = \frac{\sum c_i}{\sum (c_i/M_i)}$$

where c_i is the concentration of the ith species in grams per cubic centimeter, and M_i is the molecular weight of that species. For equal concentrations, the smallest molecules to which the membrane is impermeable make a greater contribution to the osmotic pressure than do the larger molecules in the mixture.

Although the principle of the determination of the molecular weights of proteins by osmotic pressure measurements is simple, in practice such measurements are rather difficult to perform because of the long periods of time required for equilibrium to be attained, with attendant denaturation of the proteins, and because of the important effects of Gibbs-Donnan equilibria (p. 111). Nevertheless, careful determinations have been made and have yielded values that compare favorably with the results obtained by other methods. The outstanding early work on the osmotic pressure of proteins was done in 1917 by Sørensen, who reported that egg albumin had a molecular weight of 34,000. Somewhat later, Adair reinvestigated the osmotic pressure of hemoglobin and found that the molecular weight of this protein was near 67,000. It will be seen that Sørensen's value for egg albumin is roughly twice the minimal molecular weight calculated by Osborne from elementary analysis, and Adair's value for hemoglobin is four times the minimal molecular weight calculated from its iron content. Since these determinations on egg albumin and hemoglobin, this method has been applied to a number of other proteins. An example of more recent studies may be found in a valuable paper by Scatchard et al.,[26] on the osmotic pressure of solutions of bovine serum albumin.

Scattering of Light by Protein Solutions. Another method for the study of the size of proteins depends on the long-known phenomenon of the scattering of light by colloidal solutions (Tyndall effect). As the number and size of the particles in the solution increase, the proportion of the incident light scattered also increases. The fractional decrease in the intensity of the transmitted light is given by the equation

$$\tau l = \ln \frac{I_0}{I}$$

where I_0 is the intensity of the incident light, I is the intensity of the transmitted light, τ is the "turbidity," and l is the length of the path through the scattering system. The function τ is related to the molecular

---

[26] G. Scatchard et al., *J. Am. Chem. Soc.,* **68**, 2320 (1946).

weight of the particles by the equation $\tau = HcM$, where H is a proportionality constant, c is the concentration in grams per cubic centimeter, and M is the molecular weight. As in the case of the van't Hoff equation for osmotic pressure, this relationship applies to ideal systems, and is approximated more and more closely as c approaches zero. Hence, for a particular system, a plot of Hc/τ against c gives a curve whose intercept is $1/M$. The value of H for any system is given by the equation

$$H = \frac{32\pi^3 n_0^2}{3N\lambda^4} \left(\frac{n - n_0}{c}\right)^2$$

where λ is the wave length of the incident light, N is Avogadro's number, and n_0 and n are the indices of refraction of the solvent and of the solution respectively.

If, instead of measuring the decrease in intensity of the transmitted light, one determines the intensity of the scattered light, the quantity measured is the "reduced intensity," $R_\theta = i_\theta r^2/I_0$, where i_θ is the intensity of the scattered beam at the angle θ per unit volume of medium, and r is the distance from the region of scattering. The reduced intensity at 90° is related to the molecular weight of the solute by the following equation.

$$R_{90} = \left[\frac{2\pi^2 n_0^2 \left(\dfrac{n - n_0}{c}\right)^2}{\lambda^4 N}\right] cM = KcM$$

It will be seen that $\tau = 16\pi R_{90}/3$. A general statement of the relationships used in the determination of molecular weight by light-scattering measurements may be given as follows:

$$\frac{Hc}{\tau} = \frac{Kc}{R_{90}} = \frac{1}{M} + 2Bc$$

where B is an interaction constant describing the departure from ideal behavior.

With protein solutions containing several species of different mass, the turbidity observed will reflect a "weight-average" molecular weight. This average is denoted by the symbol $\bar{M}_w$ and is equal to $\sum c_i M_i/\sum c_i$ (cf. p. 33). Comparison of this relationship with that for the average obtained from osmotic pressure determinations shows that the two methods will give different values for a mixture of proteins of widely different molecular weight. Consequently, if the values for $\bar{M}_n$ and $\bar{M}_w$ are nearly the same for a given protein solution, the probability is increased that the solution contains particles of uniform weight.

The application of this "light-scattering" method has provided many data on the molecular weights of proteins, and the values are, in general, in good agreement with those obtained by other methods. The newer procedure has an important advantage in that it permits the direct observation of rapid changes in the size of protein molecules. A more detailed discussion of the light-scattering method may be found in a valuable review by Doty and Edsall.[27]

Electron Microscopy of Crystalline Proteins. The molecular weight of some proteins may be determined by means of the electron microscope, which permits magnifications up to about 100,000 diameters. If the protein particles oriented in crystals are assumed to be approximately spherical, a calculation may be made of the volume of the protein molecule from the measurement of the diameter of a particle. The molecular weight may then be estimated from the volume and density of the material under examination. In this manner, Hall[28] has found a value of approximately 300,000 for crystalline edestin, in excellent agreement with that reported (310,000) on the basis of ultracentrifugal data.

Sedimentation of Proteins in a Centrifugal Field. When it became clear that proteins are large molecules (macromolecules), the possibility arose that their molecular weights could be determined by subjecting a protein solution to a strong centrifugal field, and by observing the rate of movement of the protein outward from the center of rotation. This method was developed by Svedberg, who, in 1925, invented the instrument called the ultracentrifuge.[29-31] The speeds that can be attained in this centrifuge, or in modifications that have been developed since Svedberg's first model (Fig. 6), are as high as 60,000 revolutions per minute (rpm).[32] At these high speeds, centrifugal fields of the order of 500,000 times gravity may readily be attained. The intensity of a centrifugal field is usually expressed in terms of the magnitude of the relative centrifugal force (RCF) which is related to the speed of rotation by the equation

$$\text{RCF} = 1.118 \times 10^{-5} \times r \times (\text{rpm})^2$$

Here RCF is expressed as the gravitational force acting on a 1-gram mass at a distance r (in centimeters) from the axis of rotation. A convenient graphical method for the calculation of RCF has been reported by Dole and Cotzias.[33]

In using the ultracentrifuge for molecular weight determinations, two

[27] P. Doty and J. T. Edsall, *Advances in Protein Chem.*, **6**, 35 (1951).

[28] C. E. Hall, *J. Biol. Chem.*, **185**, 45 (1950).

[29] J. W. Beams, *Ann. N. Y. Acad. Sci.*, **43**, 177 (1942).

[30] E. G. Pickels, *Chem. Revs.*, **30**, 341 (1942).

[31] T. Svedberg and K. O. Pedersen, *The Ultracentrifuge*, The Clarendon Press, Oxford, 1940.

[32] C. Skarstrom and J. W. Beams, *Rev. Sci. Instr.*, **11**, 398 (1940).

[33] V. P. Dole and G. C. Cotzias, *Science*, **113**, 552 (1951).

lines of approach are possible. In the first, the method of sedimentation equilibrium, a relatively low centrifugal force is applied to a protein solution until the distribution of protein throughout the column of

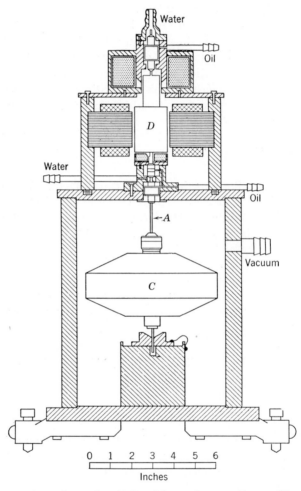

Fig. 6. Cross section of an electrically driven ultracentrifuge. The rotor (*C*) is suspended from a motor armature (*D*) by means of the flexible shaft (*A*), and is spun in an evacuated chamber to reduce friction. (From C. Skarstrom and J. W. Beams.[32])

liquid in the centrifuge tube has reached a steady state. In actual practice, one measures the competition between sedimentation and diffusion by centrifuging until no further movement of the protein is observed.

The molecular weight M may then be calculated by means of the formula

$$M = \frac{2RT \ln (c_2/c_1)}{\omega^2 (1 - V\rho)(x_2{}^2 - x_1{}^2)}$$

where c_1 and c_2 are the concentrations of protein at distances x_1 and x_2 from the axis of rotation, ω is the angular velocity of the centrifuge, V is the partial specific volume (the increment in volume when 1 gram of dry protein is added to a large amount of solvent), and ρ is the density of the solution. The method of sedimentation equilibrium, though theoretically well defined, suffers from the disadvantage that long time periods are required for the attainment of equilibrium. However, by measurement of the rate at which equilibrium is approached, the molecular weight of proteins may be determined after relatively brief centrifugation.[34]

The second procedure, termed the sedimentation velocity method, is the one most widely used for the determination of the molecular weights of proteins. This method involves the measurement of the rate at which proteins move in centrifugal fields of such high intensity that the process of sedimentation is much more rapid than that of free diffusion. The protein molecules, which move outward from the center of rotation, are more dense than the solvent, and a fairly sharp boundary is formed between the pure solvent and the protein solution (Fig. 7). In the measurement of sedimentation rates, advantage is taken of the fact that the refractive index of the liquid in the sedimentation cell changes markedly at such a boundary. In earlier work, the sedimentation of proteins was followed by photographing the cell with ultraviolet light; as will be seen on p. 74, proteins exhibit selective light absorption in the region of 280 mμ.

A number of ingenious optical methods have been devised for the observation of changes in the refractive index of a protein solution in the region of a boundary formed by the movement of a protein in a centrifugal field; several of these methods also have been used to observe the migration of a protein in an electric field ("electrophoresis"; p. 102). For the photographic registration of the boundary, use is made of optical techniques based on the fact that an incident light beam will be bent the most as it passes through the solution in the region of the boundary, where the gradient of protein concentration is greatest. One of these techniques is the "schlieren-scanning method" (cf. Fig. 8) devised by Longsworth[35] in connection with the study of the electrophoresis of proteins; another "schlieren" method involves the use of a diagonal

[34] A. Ginsburg et al., *Arch. Biochem. and Biophys.*, **65**, 545 (1956).
[35] L. G. Longsworth, *Ann. N. Y. Acad. Sci.*, **39**, 187 (1939).

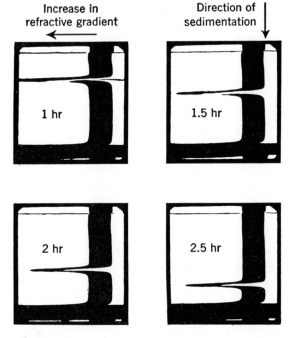

Increase in refractive gradient

Direction of sedimentation

1 hr

1.5 hr

2 hr

2.5 hr

Fig. 7. Sedimentation of hemocyanin. The set of four photographs on the left was recorded by the refractive index method; the series of photographs below was taken by the ultraviolet absorption method. Speed, 18,000 rpm. (From E. G. Pickels.[30])

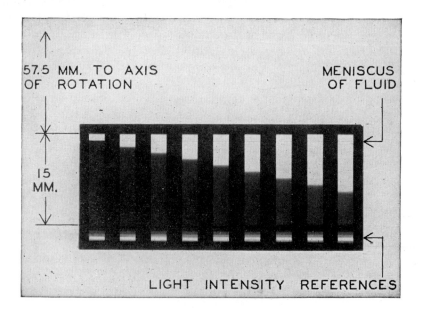

57.5 MM. TO AXIS OF ROTATION

MENISCUS OF FLUID

15 MM.

LIGHT INTENSITY REFERENCES

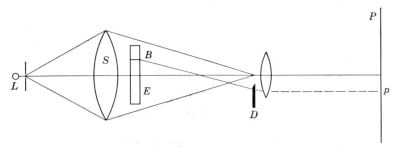

Fig. 8. Diagram of Longsworth's "schlieren scanning" method. *L,* lamp; *S,* schlieren lens; *E,* electrophoresis cell; *D,* schlieren diaphragm, which is moved upward at a constant rate, thus cutting off the light deflected downward by the protein boundary (*B*), and producing a schlieren band (German, *Schliere,* streak, shadow) at *p* on the photographic plate (*P*).

slit and a cylindrical lens, as shown in Fig. 9. The latter optical method is widely employed in measurements of the sedimentation velocity of proteins, as well as in electrophoretic studies. Such methods permit not

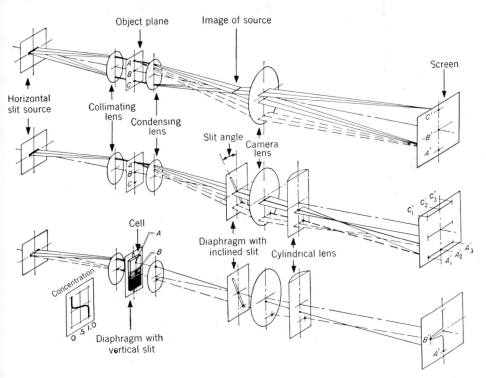

Fig. 9. Diagram of optical assembly for the observation of the rate of change of refractive index gradient during sedimentation of a protein solution. (From E. G. Pickels.[30])

only a measure of the position of a protein boundary in the solution, but also an estimate of the concentration of the protein in question. In the photographs of the sedimentation cell, made by the refractive index method, the boundary appears as the top of a sharp peak, as shown in Fig. 7. The area under the peak is a measure of the concentration of the protein in question. (The diagrams are usually turned through 90° for the purpose of representation in printed articles and books.)

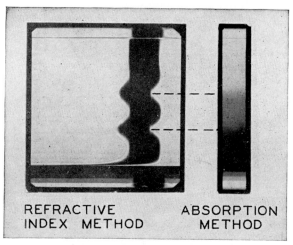

Fig. 10. Sedimentation photographs, taken by the refractive index and absorption methods, of a mixture of two proteins having different sedimentation velocities. The lower peak in the left-hand photograph corresponds to the heavier (more rapidly sedimenting) protein component of the mixture. (From E. G. Pickels.[30])

Only a single boundary will be formed on centrifugation of a solution in which all the protein molecules have the same molecular weight, and only one peak attributable to protein material will be observed in the diagram. However, if two kinds of protein molecules of significantly different molecular weights are present, two boundaries will result, and two peaks will be noted in the diagram (cf. Fig. 10). The observation of the behavior of a protein preparation in an intense centrifugal field thus provides information about its homogeneity. The appearance of a single boundary may be taken as evidence that all the protein molecules are of the same size. It would not be justifiable, however, to call the protein "pure," since highly purified proteins have been found to be "monodisperse" in the ultracentrifuge under a given set of conditions but to behave as mixtures of several molecular species under other experimental conditions or when studied by other methods.

The rate of sedimentation is usually expressed in terms of the sedimentation constant s, which is the velocity for unit centrifugal field of force, and which has the dimensions of time. From the observation of the rate of movement of the protein boundary, s may be calculated by means of the formula

$$s = \frac{dx/dt}{\omega^2 x}$$

where x = distance from the axis of rotation and ω is the angular velocity in radians per second. For the proteins studied hitherto, s lies between 1 and 200×10^{-13} sec. For convenience, it has been agreed to refer to a sedimentation constant of 1×10^{-13} as 1 Svedberg unit (S), and all sedimentation constants are then given in Svedberg units. Data on sedimentation constants are uniformly presented for water as the solvent and for a temperature of 20° C.

In order to use the sedimentation constant for a calculation of the molecular weight (M) of a protein, the found value of s is inserted in the equation

$$M = \frac{RTs}{D(1 - V\rho)}$$

where R is the gas constant, T is the absolute temperature, D is the diffusion coefficient (or constant), ρ is the density, and V is the partial specific volume (p. 37). The partial specific volume of most proteins[36] is in the range 0.70 to 0.75; it is determined by measurements of the density of the solution as a function of the concentration of anhydrous protein. The above equation for the molecular weight is an approximate relationship which becomes more exact as the concentration of protein approaches zero. The sedimentation constant should therefore be determined as a function of concentration, and the value of s extrapolated to zero concentration.

It follows, therefore, that in order to determine M one must have not only a value for s, but also an independent measurement of the diffusion constant D, which may be defined as the quantity of material that diffuses per second across a surface 1 cm² in area when the concentration gradient is 1. To measure diffusion, use is made of a refractometric method similar to that mentioned earlier in connection with the observation of the moving boundary in the sedimentation of a protein. Here no centrifugal field is applied, and one starts with a sharp boundary between the protein solution and the solvent and observes the spreading of the boundary as the protein diffuses into the solvent layer.[37] The diffusion of proteins will be discussed further on pp. 149 f.

[36] T. L. McMeekin and K. Marshall, *Science*, **116**, 142 (1952).
[37] L. G. Longsworth, *Ann. N. Y. Acad. Sci.*, **46**, 211 (1945).

With the data on the sedimentation constant and diffusion constant of a given protein in hand, the molecular weight of a protein may be calculated from the equation given on p. 41. In Table 2 will be found

Table 2. Approximate Particle Weight of Some Purified Proteins as Determined by Various Methods

Protein	Osmotic Pressure	Light Scattering	Sedimentation Equilibrium	Sedimentation Velocity-Diffusion
Ribonuclease (beef pancreas)			14,000	12,700
Cytochrome c (horse heart)				13,200
Myoglobin (horse muscle)			17,500	16,900
Lysozyme (egg white)	17,500	14,800		14,000–17,000
Chymotrypsinogen (beef pancreas)		26,000		24,200
β-Lactoglobulin (milk)	38,000	35,700	38,500	41,500
Egg albumin (egg white)	44,000	45,700	40,500	44,000
Serum albumin (horse serum)	73,000	76,600	68,000	70,000
Hemoglobin (horse erythrocytes)	67,000		68,000	68,000
Hexokinase (yeast)				97,000
Catalase (horse liver)				225,000
Excelsin (Brazil nuts)	214,000	276,000		295,000
Edestin (hemp seed)		335,000		310,000
Fibrinogen (beef plasma)		340,000		330,000
Hemocyanin (*Helix pomatia*)		(6,340,000)†	(6,700,000)†	(8,910,000)†
Bushy stunt virus (tomato)		9,000,000	7,600,000	10,600,000

† Dissociates into smaller components with changes in pH or concentration (cf. p. 43).

several of the values determined by the sedimentation velocity-diffusion method; the results obtained by other methods are included for comparison.

Svedberg suggested that the molecular weights of the proteins that he studied fell into groups, each of which represented multiples of 17,600. Further studies have shown, however, that this is an oversimplification since many proteins have been found to have molecular weights that cannot be fitted readily into such groups. Examples of such proteins are ribonuclease (molecular weight 14,000) and egg albumin (molecular weight 44,000).

Dissociation and Association of Proteins. In considering the numerical values for the molecular weights of proteins in solution, whether obtained by sedimentation-diffusion, osmotic pressure, or light scattering, careful attention must be paid to the effect of changes in the protein concentration and in the composition of the solvent. It has become abundantly clear that, under a given set of conditions, some proteins may behave as single components, but that, if the pH of the solution is changed slightly, or if the protein concentration is decreased, new components of lower molecular weight may be observed. This was first noted with the large hemocyanin molecules[38] and has more recently been studied carefully with the protein hormone insulin. Thus, in neutral solutions containing about 1 per cent of insulin, the sedimentation constant s_{20} is about 3.7S, corresponding to a molecular weight of 36,000; at acid pH values, the value for s_{20} is markedly less (ca. 2.0S). The latter sedimentation constant corresponds to a molecular weight of about 12,000. Similar effects are caused by progressive dilution of the protein solution, and, if one extrapolates to "infinite dilution," the rate of sedimentation again corresponds to particles of 12,000 instead of 36,000. The value of 12,000 is twice the minimal molecular weight calculated from amino acid analysis (cf. p. 146), and osmotic pressure or sedimentation velocity measurements give a value of about 6000 for insulin dissolved in dimethylformamide or in dioxane-water.[39] It would seem, therefore, that in aqueous solution, and at suitable pH values and protein concentration, insulin units of molecular weight 6000 may aggregate reversibly to form particles of higher weight. Another protein known to dissociate into smaller units is the enzyme chymotrypsin which can exist, in solution, in a monomeric form (molecular weight 21,500) and a dimeric form (43,000).[40] Also, horse hemoglobin undergoes dissociation to one-half molecules (molecular weight, ca. 34,000) in 4M urea solutions,[41] upon dilution, or at slightly acid pH values.[42]

These observations raise the question whether one may apply the term "molecular weight" to describe the results obtained on proteins by means of physical methods such as sedimentation-diffusion. In dealing with substances of such large dimensions, relative to the substances familiar to the student of organic chemistry, it may perhaps be more accurate to speak of particle weight than of molecular weight. Although it is customary to use the latter term, it must be remembered that most of

[38] K. O. Pedersen, *Cold Spring Harbor Symposia Quant. Biol.*, **14**, 140 (1949).

[39] E. D. Rees and S. J. Singer, *Nature*, **176**, 1072 (1955); E. Fredericq, *J. Am. Chem. Soc.*, **79**, 599 (1957).

[40] G. W. Schwert and S. Kaufman, *J. Biol. Chem.*, **190**, 807 (1951).

[41] J. Steinhardt, *J. Biol. Chem.*, **123**, 543 (1938).

[42] E. O. Field and J. R. P. O'Brien, *Biochem. J.*, **60**, 656 (1955).

the data have been obtained by techniques designed to measure the behavior of particles in solution; these particles in some instances, represent aggregates of a number of units that may be considered to represent "molecules" of the protein in question. Apart from the intrinsic importance of this question for protein chemistry, it may have implications for the behavior of proteins in living cells. If the molecular sizes of physiologically active proteins turn out to be much smaller than the particle sizes found upon study of the isolated proteins, it may be less difficult to understand how such proteins can traverse cell membranes and thus exert their characteristic biological effects.

3 ·

Amino Acids as Structural Units of Proteins

In the preceding chapter it was seen that the proteins represent organic substances of large molecular size. Thus, each molecule of a protein is composed of very many atoms; for example, an elementary analysis of the milk protein β-lactoglobulin (molecular weight 42,000) has shown it to have an approximate formula of $C_{1864}H_{3012}O_{576}N_{468}S_{21}$. It is obviously impossible to use the results of elementary analysis, which have been so important for the study of simpler organic molecules, in the establishment of the structure of a protein. For this reason, the protein chemist has centered his attention on a variety of relatively small molecules, the amino acids, that are obtained when a protein is subjected to hydrolysis.

The structure of the amino acids formed upon the hydrolysis of proteins has been established both by degradation and by synthesis in the course of extensive work during the period 1850–1950. The simplest amino acid, glycine (NH_2CH_2COOH) was also the first to be recognized as a product of protein hydrolysis; it was isolated by Braconnot in 1820 from a hydrolysate of gelatin. Since that date, about 25 amino acids have been generally accepted to be products of protein breakdown; a list of the amino acids known to be derived from proteins is given in Table 1. An excellent account of the history of this subject up to 1930 may be found in the article by Vickery and Schmidt.[1]

All the amino acids listed in Table 1 do not appear as products of hydrolysis of every protein, and the proportion of a given amino acid varies greatly from protein to protein. It would be rash to predict that no new protein amino acids will be discovered in the future; one may safely say, however, that such new amino acids, if found, will not be present in appreciable amount in the hydrolysates of proteins such as β-lactoglobulin or serum albumin, since it has already been possible to

[1] H. B. Vickery and C. L. A. Schmidt, *Chem. Revs.*, **9**, 169 (1931).

Table I.   Amino Acids Derived from Proteins

I. Aliphatic amino acids
  A. Monoaminomonocarboxylic
     acids
     1. Glycine
     2. Alanine
     3. Valine
     4. Leucine
     5. Isoleucine
     6. Serine
     7. Threonine
  B. Sulfur-containing amino acids
     8. Cysteine
     9. Cystine
     10. Methionine
  C. Monoaminodicarboxylic   acids
     (and their amides)
     11. Aspartic acid
     12. Asparagine
     13. Glutamic acid
     14. Glutamine

I. Aliphatic amino acids (continued)
  D. Basic amino acids
     15. Lysine
     16. Hydroxylysine
     17. Arginine
     18. Histidine†
II. Aromatic amino acids
     19. Phenylalanine
     20. Tyrosine
     21. Diiodotyrosine
     22. Dibromotyrosine
     23. Thyroxine
III. Heterocyclic amino acids
     24. Tryptophan
     25. Proline
     26. Hydroxyproline

† May also be classified as a heterocyclic amino acid.

account for all the nitrogen of these proteins in terms of known amino acids. The possibility does exist that small amounts of new amino acids may be discovered as constituents of the enzymes or protein hormones which exhibit characteristic biological functions.

Hydrolysis of Proteins

For the isolation of glycine from a hydrolysate of gelatin, Braconnot heated the protein with acid; this method of acid hydrolysis still is, in principle, the most useful procedure for the conversion of a protein into its constituent amino acids. The work of Bopp, in 1849, and of Hlasewitz and Habermann, in 1873, led to the use of hydrochloric acid in place of the sulfuric acid employed by Braconnot. When hydrochloric acid is the hydrolytic agent, the protein usually is treated with 5 to 10 times its weight of strong acid (6 to 12 N) at 100° to 110° for 6 to 20 hr. The excess hydrochloric acid is then removed by repeated concentration of the solution (the "hydrolysate") under reduced pressure. The individual amino acids are present in the hydrolysate in the form of their hydrochlorides, and most of them may be isolated by taking advantage of their characteristic differences in chemical properties; this will be discussed in connection with the chemical structure and properties of the individual amino acids. If the experimenter wishes to obtain an acid hydrolysate completely free of the inorganic anion of the acid used for hydrolysis, sulfuric acid is preferable to hydrochloric acid, since the sulfate ion may be removed by the addition of barium hydroxide or calcium hydroxide. Certain of the amino acids are destroyed upon acid hydrolysis of a protein; this is especially true of the amino acid tryptophan, and, to a lesser extent, of the amino acids serine and threonine. When carbohydrates are present in a protein preparation that is subjected to acid hydrolysis, the appearance of black material (humin) is observed. This may be diminished by conducting the hydrolysis in the presence of metallic tin.

A more recent addition to the reagents available for the acid hydrolysis of proteins is a polysulfonic acid resin[2] made by sulfonating polystyrene that has been cross-linked by copolymerization with divinylbenzene (see accompanying formula).

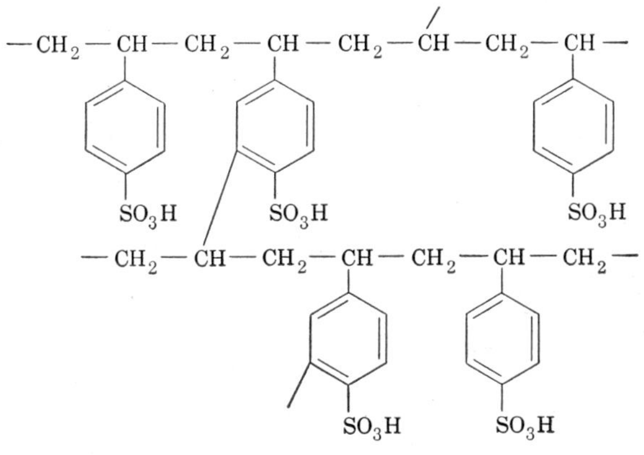

Section of cross-linked sulfonated polystyrene

Proteins also may be hydrolyzed to amino acids by being treated with alkalies; boiling with $2\ N$ sodium hydroxide is effective in this respect. However, the disadvantages of this procedure are so numerous that it is now used very rarely, if at all. Alkaline hydrolysis leads to the destruction of the amino acids arginine, cystine, cysteine, serine, and threonine, and also causes the "racemization" (loss of optical activity) of the protein amino acids.

In the digestion of proteins in the gastrointestinal tract of the higher animals, proteins are hydrolyzed to amino acids under relatively mild conditions of temperature and acidity by the proteolytic enzymes (pepsin, trypsin, etc.) whose properties will be discussed more fully in Chapter **29**.

[2] J. R. Whitaker and F. E. Deatherage, *J. Am. Chem. Soc.*, **77**, 3360 (1955).

It will suffice to note that enzymic hydrolysis of proteins is a third general method for the conversion of proteins to amino acids. The disadvantages from a preparative point of view are many; the most important of these is that the hydrolysis usually requires prolonged incubation and is incomplete. It is only in the isolation of tryptophan, which is destroyed on acid hydrolysis, that the use of proteolytic enzymes has proved of significant value as a preparative method.

As indicated before, the hydrolysis of a protein leads to the formation of a variety of amino acids. With two exceptions, all the known amino acids derived from well-defined proteins have the general formula

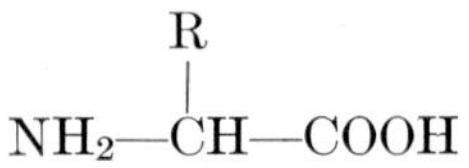

$$\underset{\text{NH}_2-\text{CH}-\text{COOH}}{\overset{\text{R}}{|}}$$

in which the symbol R denotes the characteristic "side chain" of the amino acid in question. The two exceptions are the amino acids proline and hydroxyproline. The compounds having the general formula shown

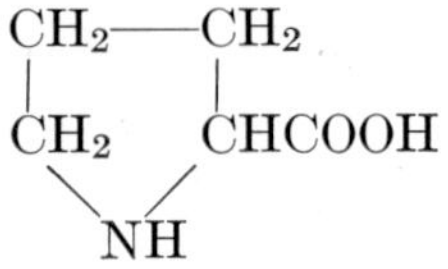

$$\begin{array}{cc}
\text{CH}_2-\text{CH}_2 & \text{HOCH}-\text{CH}_2 \\
| \quad\quad | & | \quad\quad | \\
\text{CH}_2 \quad \text{CHCOOH} & \text{CH}_2 \quad \text{CHCOOH} \\
\diagdown \diagup & \diagdown \diagup \\
\text{NH} & \text{NH} \\
\textit{Proline} & \textit{Hydroxyproline}
\end{array}$$

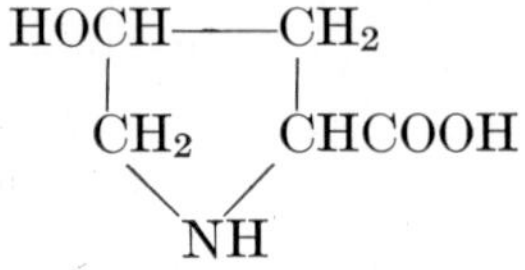

are termed α-amino acids, whereas proline and hydroxyproline are more correctly designated α-imino acids; for convenience, however, these two cyclic compounds are also called amino acids.

General Reactions of Amino Acids

The chemical reactions selected for mention in what follows illustrate properties that will be of importance in the subsequent discussion of the chemistry of proteins or that have proved valuable in biochemical studies as a basis for the analytical determination of the amino acids and their derivatives. A fuller discussion of these and other chemical reactions may be found in the articles on amino acids by Clarke[3] and by Desnuelle.[4]

Reactions of the Amino Group. Like all amino groups, the α-amino groups of amino acids can accept a hydrogen ion (a proton, H^+) to form positively charged ions (p. 92). These may be neutralized by negatively charged ions (e.g., Cl^-, RSO_3^-) to form salts.

$$-\text{NH}_2 + \text{H}^+ + \text{Cl}^- \rightarrow -\text{NH}_3^+\text{Cl}^-$$

[3] H. T. Clarke, in H. Gilman, *Organic Chemistry*, 2nd Ed., Vol. II, Chapter 14, John Wiley & Sons, New York, 1943.

[4] P. Desnuelle, in H. Neurath and K. Bailey, *The Proteins*, Vol. IA, Chapter 2, Academic Press, New York, 1953.

Some of the salts of amino acids are sparingly soluble in water; this has proved to be of value in the isolation of amino acids from protein hydrolysates (p. 64).

In following the course of hydrolysis of a protein, and to determine when the hydrolysis has reached completion, advantage may be taken of the fact that under proper conditions α-amino acids react quantitatively with nitrous acid as follows:

$$\underset{\text{NH}_2}{\overset{\text{R}}{|}}\text{—CH—COOH} + \text{HNO}_2 \rightarrow \overset{\text{R}}{\underset{|}{\text{HO—CH}}}\text{—COOH} + \text{N}_2 + \text{H}_2\text{O}$$

The reaction is conducted in acid solution, and the $\text{RNH}_3{}^+$ group is converted by nitrous acid to an intermediate diazonium ion ($\text{RN}_2{}^+$) which decomposes to form N_2. This reaction, characteristic of aliphatic primary amines, was used in 1912 by Van Slyke as the basis of his "nitrous acid" method for the estimation of amino acids by measurement of the volume of nitrogen liberated. Subsequently, Van Slyke devised a manometric apparatus to determine the amount of nitrogen formed by measurement of the pressure of the gas at constant volume; this apparatus has also been extremely useful in many other analytical procedures.[5]

As the hydrolysis of a protein proceeds, the proportion of the total nitrogen that is found by the nitrous acid method to be α-amino nitrogen (α-NH_2—N) gradually increases until the hydrolysis is complete, and the ratio of α-NH_2—N to total N reaches a maximum. Several of the protein amino acids contain nitrogen which does not react with nitrous acid to give nitrogen gas, and this ratio usually will be less than unity. Thus proline and hydroxyproline are not primary amines, and some of the protein amino acids (arginine, histidine, tryptophan) contain, in their side-chain groups, bound nitrogen which is not liberated by treatment with nitrous acid. If a protein yields appreciable quantities of one or more of these amino acids on hydrolysis, the final ratio of α-amino N to total N may be expected to be much less than unity.

The amino groups of all amino acids (and the imino groups of proline and hydroxyproline) react with a variety of acylating agents. Among these agents are acid chlorides such as acetyl chloride (CH_3COCl), benzoyl chloride ($\text{C}_6\text{H}_5\text{COCl}$), benzenesulfonyl chloride ($\text{C}_6\text{H}_5\text{SO}_2\text{Cl}$) and carbobenzoxy chloride (benzyloxycarbonyl chloride, $\text{C}_6\text{H}_5\text{CH}_2\text{OCOCl}$). These compounds all react with the amino group of an amino acid (in alkaline solution) according to the reaction

[5] J. P. Peters and D. D. Van Slyke, *Quantitative Clinical Chemistry*, Vol. II, Williams and Wilkins Co., Baltimore, 1932.

shown for acetyl chloride:

$$CH_3CO—Cl + NH_2— \quad \rightarrow \quad CH_3CO—NH— + HCl$$

Other acylating agents are acetic anhydride, which causes the formation of acetylamino acids, and phthalic anhydride, by means of which phthaloylamino acids may be prepared.

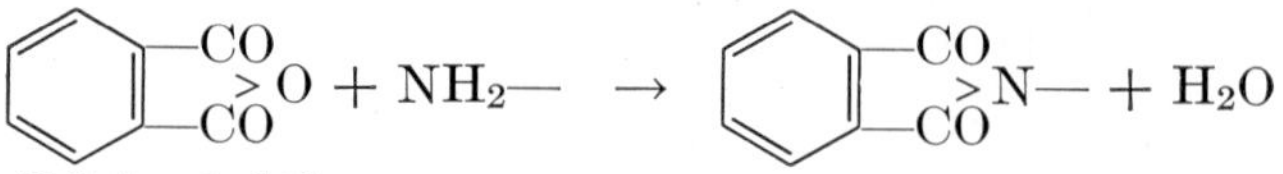

$$\underset{\text{Phthalic anhydride}}{\overset{\text{—CO}}{\underset{\text{—CO}}{\bigcirc}}\!\!>\!O} + NH_2— \quad \rightarrow \quad \overset{\text{—CO}}{\underset{\text{—CO}}{\bigcirc}}\!\!>\!N— + H_2O$$

Another important reaction of the amino groups of amino acids is that with an isocyanate (e.g., phenylisocyanate, C_6H_5NCO) to form hydantoic acids which, in turn, can be converted to hydantoins. An

$$\underset{\text{Phenylhydantoic acid}}{C_6H_5NCO + NH_2\overset{R}{\overset{|}{C}}HCOOH \rightarrow C_6H_5NHCO—NH\overset{R}{\overset{|}{C}}HCOOH} \rightarrow$$

$$\underset{\text{Phenylhydantoin}}{C_6H_5NCO—NH\overset{R}{\overset{|}{C}}HCO}$$

analogous reaction with phenylisothiocyanate (C_6H_5NCS), yielding phenylthiohydantoic acids and phenylthiohydantoins, has proved useful in studies of protein structure (p. 143).

Treatment of α-amino acids with phosgene ($COCl_2$) or with carbon disulfide (CS_2) leads to the formation of N-carboxyanhydrides (oxazolidone diones) or of 2-thio-5-thiazolidones respectively.

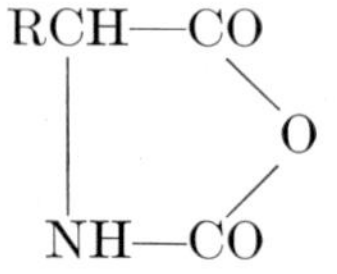

$$\underset{\text{N-Carboxyanhydride}}{\begin{array}{c} RCH—CO \\ | \quad\quad \diagdown \\ \quad\quad\quad O \\ | \quad\quad \diagup \\ NH—CO \end{array}} \quad\quad \underset{\text{2-Thio-5-thiazolidone}}{\begin{array}{c} RCH—CO \\ | \quad\quad \diagdown \\ \quad\quad\quad S \\ | \quad\quad \diagup \\ NH—CS \end{array}}$$

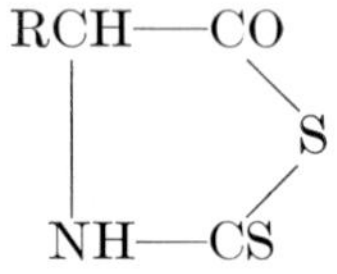

A reaction that has proved extremely valuable for studies of protein structure is the formation of 2,4-dinitrophenyl compounds (cf. pp. 142 f.) upon treatment of amino acids and their derivatives with 1-fluoro-2,4-dinitrobenzene.[6]   Other reactions of the amino group include the

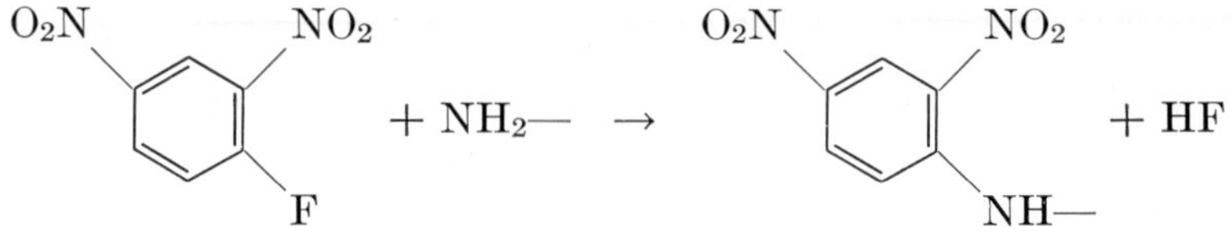

$$\underset{F}{\overset{O_2N \quad\quad NO_2}{\bigcirc}} + NH_2— \quad \rightarrow \quad \underset{NH—}{\overset{O_2N \quad\quad NO_2}{\bigcirc}} + HF$$

[6] R. R. Porter and F. Sanger, *Biochem. J.*, **42**, 287 (1948).

formation of carbamino acids (stable only in the form of their salts, $-NHCOO^-Na^+$) when CO_2 reacts with amino acids and proteins, and the formation of various condensation products with aldehydes. With aromatic aldehydes (e.g., benzaldehyde, C_6H_5CHO), the products are Schiff bases (e.g., $C_6H_5CH=N-$). With aliphatic aldehydes, Schiff bases do not appear to an appreciable extent, and instead methylol (or hydroxymethyl) derivatives are formed. The methylol compounds may

$$-NH_2 + HCHO \rightarrow -NHCH_2OH$$

$$-NH_2 + 2HCHO \rightarrow -N(CH_2OH)_2$$

undergo further reactions. For example, the reaction of glycine with formaldehyde leads to the formation of the cyclic tricarboxymethyl trimethylene triamine. With other amino acids, such as serine, cysteine, asparagine, histidine, intramolecular cyclization occurs.

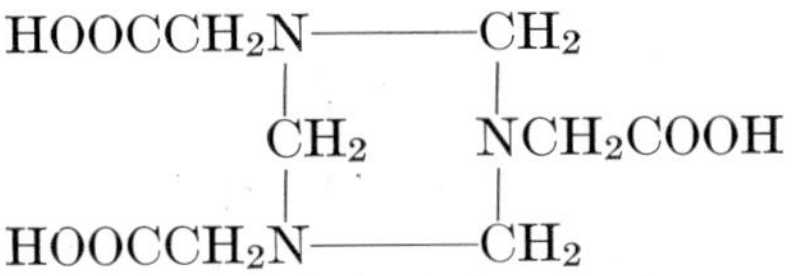

$$HOOCCH_2N \underline{\hspace{1cm}} CH_2$$
$$CH_2 \quad NCH_2COOH$$
$$HOOCCH_2N \underline{\hspace{1cm}} CH_2$$

Tricarboxymethyl trimethylene triamine

Of special importance in the analytical chemistry of amino acids is the reaction of amino groups with the reagent ninhydrin (triketohydrindene hydrate). When treated with ninhydrin, most amino acids are oxidatively deaminated. The resulting ammonia reacts with ninhydrin and its reduction product (hydrindantin) to give a blue substance; methods have been devised for the colorimetric analysis of amino acids by measurement of the intensity of the color formed.[7] This reaction

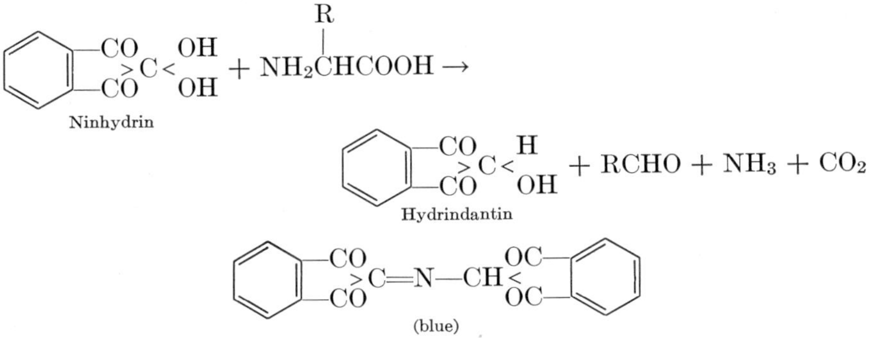

Ninhydrin

Hydrindantin

(blue)

has been used by Van Slyke as a basis for a quantitative method for the estimation of amino acids; here the CO_2 produced may be measured manometrically.[8] Since the formation of CO_2 depends upon the presence

[7] S. Moore and W. H. Stein, *J. Biol. Chem.*, **176**, 367 (1948); **211**, 907 (1954).

[8] D. D. Van Slyke et al., *J. Biol. Chem.* **141**, 627 (1941).

of a free α-carboxyl group as well as of a free α-amino group, the mano-metric ninhydrin method is fairly specific for α-amino acids. It is more specific than the nitrous acid method, mentioned earlier, since the latter procedure will determine primary amino groups in amino acid derivatives where the α-carboxyl group is substituted.

Another colorimetric reaction involving the α-amino group of amino acids (and of amino acid derivatives containing a free amino group) is that with β-naphthoquinone, or one of its derivatives.

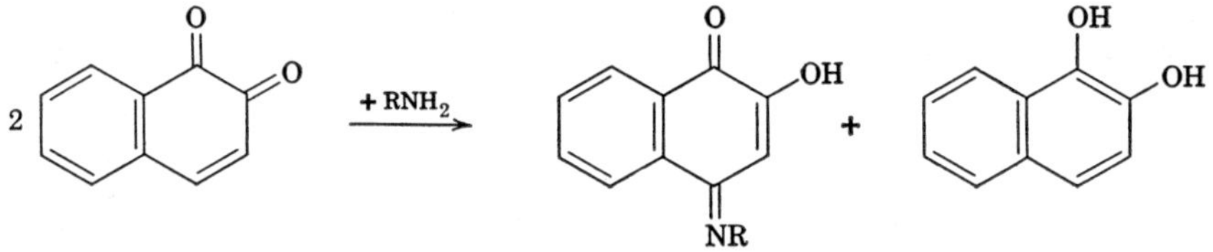

β–Naphthoquinone   (red)

Reactions of the Carboxyl Group. The carboxyl groups of amino acids can release a hydrogen ion, with the formation of negatively charged carboxylate ions; these may be neutralized by cations (e.g., Na^+, Ca^{2+}) to form salts, some of which are sparingly soluble in water, or dilute alcohol.

$$RCOOH + Na^+ + OH^- \rightarrow RCOO^-Na^+ + H_2O$$

Like carboxyl groups in general, the α-carboxyls of amino acids may be esterified by means of alcohols (e.g., CH_3OH) to give the correspond-ing esters (e.g., $RCOOCH_3$). This reaction was used by Emil Fischer and others for the isolation of amino acids. A reaction that has been valuable for studies of protein structure involves reduction of the ester group to the corresponding carbinol (RCH_2OH) by means of lithium aluminum hydride ($LiAlH_4$) or of lithium borohydride ($LiBH_4$); an application of this type of reaction is discussed on p. 131.

It will be recalled that amides are also general derivatives of carboxylic acids; the formation of an amide may be designated schematically as follows:

$$RCOOH + R'NH_2 \rightarrow RCO\text{---}NHR' + H_2O$$

As will be seen from the discussion on pp. 129 f., the individual amino acids within an intact protein are linked by amide bonds, and the cleav-age of a protein by acid hydrolysis involves the hydrolysis of CO—NH bonds, i.e., the reversal of the reaction shown immediately above. The amide bond between two amino acids is usually termed a "peptide bond" or a "peptide linkage."

The Special Chemistry of Amino Acids Formed on Protein Hydrolysis

It will be profitable to consider, in sequence, the various amino acids found in protein hydrolysates, and to discuss those aspects of their chemistry that will have importance for the later sections on protein structure and protein metabolism.

Glycine (aminoacetic acid, NH_2CH_2COOH). Glycine is the simplest of the amino acids; as noted before, it was discovered by Braconnot in 1820. Braconnot knew that wood, on acid hydrolysis, gave sugar; when he treated gelatin in the same way, he obtained crystals which were sweet to the taste, and he therefore called the new substance sugar of gelatin. Subsequent investigators termed it "glycocoll," and in 1848 Berzelius gave glycine its present name.

Glycine is formed from many proteins on hydrolysis, and appears in especially large proportions upon the cleavage of the scleroproteins (skeletal proteins) such as collagen (from hide and tendons) or elastin (from ligaments). Gelatin, a protein preparation derived from collagen, on hydrolysis yields about 25 grams of glycine per 100 grams of protein. The fibrous protein silk fibroin, elaborated by the silkworm, is even richer in its glycine content (about 40 per cent).

A number of substitution products of glycine are of considerable importance in biochemistry. One of the first of these to be discovered was the substance hippuric acid (C_6H_5CO—$NHCH_2COOH$, benzoylglycine), which was isolated from the urine of horses and of other herbivores. Hippuric acid is synthesized in the liver of mammals, and its formation is one of many examples of the "detoxication" of substances harmful to biological systems. An important substitution product of glycine is the monomethyl derivative sarcosine (N-methylglycine); it has been reported that this amino acid is present in an acid hydrolysate of a mixture of arachin and conarachin (peanut proteins). Sarcosine has been shown to be a constituent of the antibacterial agent actinomycin.

On treatment with cyanamide, sarcosine is converted to creatine (methylguanidinoacetic acid), a constituent of mammalian muscle. In acid solution, creatine undergoes ring closure, with the formation of the internal anhydride creatinine.

$$NH_2CN$$

$$+$$

$$CH_3NHCH_2COOH$$
Sarcosine

$$-.$$

$$\underset{\text{Creatine}}{\overset{\displaystyle NH_2}{\underset{\displaystyle CH_3NCH_2COOH}{\overset{\displaystyle |}{\underset{\displaystyle |}{C=NH}}}}}$$

$$\rightarrow$$

$$\underset{\text{Creatinine}}{\overset{\displaystyle NH-}{\underset{\displaystyle CH_3NCH_2CO}{\overset{\displaystyle |}{\underset{\displaystyle |}{C=NH}}}}}$$

On exhaustive methylation, glycine is transformed to the trimethyl derivative betaine, $(CH_3)_3N^+CH_2COO^-$, which is a natural constituent of plant and animal tissues. The betaine content of some plant tissues is appreciable, and beet leaves may contain as much as 3 per cent of the compound. The betaine content of animal tissues is very small.

Alanine (α-aminopropionic acid). This amino acid, like glycine, is widely distributed among the proteins; it was first isolated from a protein in 1888 when Weyl obtained it from silk. Silk fibroin is an especially rich source of this amino acid; nearly 30 grams of alanine may be obtained after the hydrolysis of 100 grams of this protein.

The isomeric compound β-alanine ($NH_2CH_2CH_2COOH$) has not been found to be a constituent of proteins, but it occurs in nature as such (in plant tissues) and as a component of the muscle substances carnosine and anserine (p. 137) and of the important intracellular agent coenzyme A (p. 205). The homologous γ-amino-n-butyric acid ($NH_2CH_2CH_2CH_2COOH$), and its isomer α-amino-n-butyric acid, also are found as such in some plant tissues, but they are not protein amino acids.

Most of the other amino acids isolated from proteins may be considered to be derivatives of alanine, in which the α-methyl group has been altered in various ways by substitution.

$$
\begin{array}{cc}
 & CH_3 \quad CH_3 \\
 & \diagdown \diagup \\
CH_3 & CH \\
| & | \\
NH_2CHCOOH & NH_2CHCOOH \\
\text{Alanine} & \text{Valine}
\end{array}
$$

Valine (α-aminoisovaleric acid). Valine was first isolated in 1856 by Gorup-Besanez, from extracts of pancreas. Its isolation from a protein (casein) hydrolysate was first achieved by Fischer in 1901. In its chemical reactions valine is similar to alanine. However, it differs from alanine in metabolism, since certain animals (e.g., the growing rat) cannot make valine at a rate sufficient to meet the needs of the organism for growth; for this reason it is classified as an "indispensable amino acid" for the immature rat, and must be present in the diet to permit optimum growth of the animal (see Chapter 30).

Although widely distributed among the proteins, valine is not present in any of them in large amounts. Its isolation from protein hydrolysates is not a feasible preparative method, and for this reason valine usually is made synthetically. For the available methods for the laboratory synthesis of this, and the other amino acids, see the article by Clarke[3] and the review by Block.[9]

Leucine (α-aminoisocaproic acid). Leucine is a higher homolog of

[9] R. J. Block, *Chem. Revs.,* **38,** 501 (1946).

valine and is very similar to it in chemical properties. It was isolated, probably in contaminated form, from cheese by Proust in 1819 and from wool (the principal protein of which is the scleroprotein keratin) by Braconnot in 1820. It is widely distributed among the proteins and is classified as an indispensable amino acid for the growing rat.

For a time it was believed that protein hydrolysates contained α-amino-n-caproic acid (norleucine), but more recent work has shown this view to be incorrect.[10]

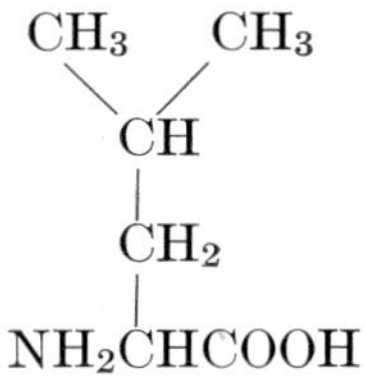

$$CH_3 \quad CH_3$$
$$\diagdown \diagup$$
$$CH$$
$$|$$
$$CH_2$$
$$|$$
$$NH_2CHCOOH$$

Leucine

$$CH_3$$
$$|$$
$$CH_2$$
$$|$$
$$CHCH_3$$
$$|$$
$$NH_2CHCOOH$$

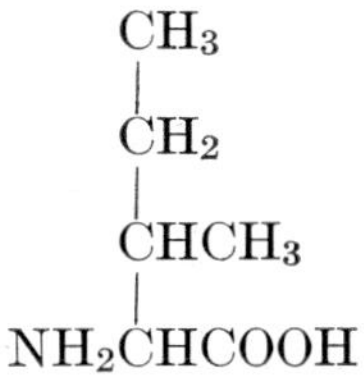

Isoleucine

Isoleucine (α-amino-β-methylvaleric acid). As its name implies, isoleucine is a structural isomer of leucine, and was first isolated from beet sugar molasses by Felix Ehrlich in 1903. Like valine it is widely distributed among the proteins, but only in small proportions, and it is also essential in the diet of the growing rat.

If one considers the α-methyl group of alanine as the "side-chain" group of this amino acid, one may say that the four amino acids alanine, valine, leucine, and isoleucine have hydrocarbon side chains. From a chemical points of view, the reactions of all of these amino acids are similar, but in metabolism the three amino acids with branched side chains have a distinctive importance since valine, leucine, and isoleucine are all indispensable amino acids for higher animals.

Serine (α-amino-β-hydroxypropionic acid). Serine is a substitution product of alanine in which the side-chain methyl group has been converted to an aliphatic alcoholic group. This amino acid was first isolated

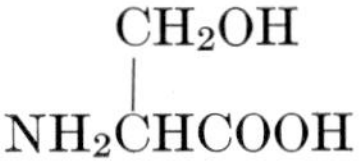

$$CH_2OH$$
$$|$$
$$NH_2CHCOOH$$

Serine

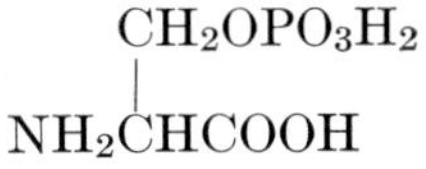

$$CH_2OPO_3H_2$$
$$|$$
$$NH_2CHCOOH$$

O-Phosphoserine

$$O$$
$$\|$$
$$CH_2O-P-OCH_2CH_2NH_2$$
$$| \qquad |$$
$$\quad OH$$
$$NH_2CHCOOH$$

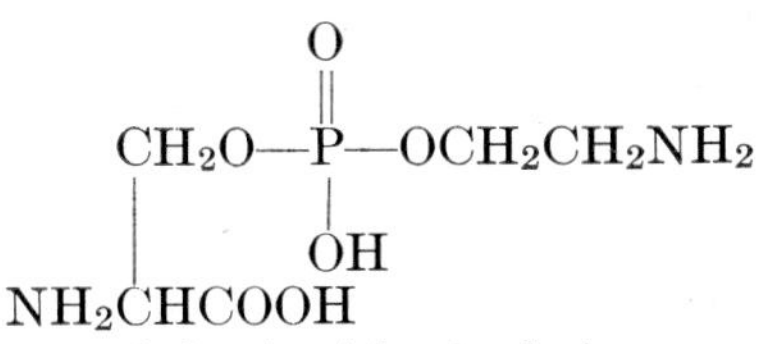

Aminoethanolphosphorylserine

by Cramer in 1856 from the protein sericin (a gelatin-like protein associated with silk fibroin in silk). Silk fibroin also contains appreciable amounts (ca. 14 per cent) of serine, and an excellent method is available for its isolation from silk fibroin hydrolysates. The phosphopro-

[10] R. Consden et al., *Biochem. J.*, **39**, 251 (1945).

teins casein (from milk) and vitellin (from egg yolk) also have a high serine content, and it has been shown that most of the phosphorus in these proteins is linked to serine by ester linkage in the form of phosphoserine.[11] A phosphoprotein (phosvitin) has been isolated from the vitellin fraction of egg yolk, where it represents about 7 per cent of the protein. Its high phosphorus content (10 per cent) is in approximate stoichiometric equivalence with its serine content (32 per cent).[12] A phosphodiester of serine and aminoethanol has been identified in turtle muscle.[13]

As indicated on p. 47, acid hydrolysis of proteins causes some decomposition of serine, while alkaline hydrolysis leads to complete destruction of the amino acid. In alkali, serine is deaminated to yield pyruvic acid.

$$\underset{\text{Serine}}{\underset{|}{\overset{\text{CH}_2\text{OH}}{\underset{\text{NH}_2\text{CHCOOH}}{}}}} \rightarrow \underset{\text{Pyruvic acid}}{\underset{|}{\overset{\text{CH}_3}{\text{O}{=}\text{C}{-}\text{COOH}}}} + \text{NH}_3$$

A valuable analytical method for the determination of serine is based on its reaction with periodate. This reagent causes the cleavage of carbon-carbon linkages if both carbons bear hydroxyl groups, or if a hydroxyl group and an amino group are on adjacent carbons. On treatment with periodate, serine yields glyoxylic acid, formaldehyde, and ammonia, while the periodate is reduced to iodate. In the quantitative

$$\underset{\text{NH}_2\text{CHCOOH}}{\overset{\text{CH}_2\text{OH}}{|}} + \text{HIO}_4 \rightarrow \underset{\text{COOH}}{\overset{\text{CHO}}{|}} + \text{HCHO} + \text{NH}_3 + \text{HIO}_3$$

estimation of serine, either formaldehyde or ammonia is collected and determined.

O-Acyl and N-acyl derivatives of serine exhibit the interesting property of "acyl migration," with the formation of an intermediate oxazoline derivative. This behavior is related to the fact that, upon hydrolysis of proteins with concentrated acid, the α-amino group of serine is among the first to be liberated.[14]

$$\underset{\text{RCO}-\text{NHCHCO}-}{\overset{\text{HOCH}_2}{|}} \rightleftharpoons \text{RC} \underset{\text{NH}-\text{CHCO}-}{\overset{\text{O}-\!-\!-\text{CH}_2}{|}} \rightleftharpoons \underset{{}^+\text{NH}_3\text{CHCO}-}{\overset{\text{RCO}-\text{OCH}_2}{|}}$$

N-Acyl derivative   Oxazoline derivative   O-Acyl derivative

[11] G. Agren et al., *Acta Chem. Scand.*, **5**, 324 (1951).

[12] D. K. Mecham and H. S. Olcott, *J. Am. Chem. Soc.*, **71**, 3670 (1949).

[13] E. Roberts and I. P. Lowe, *J. Biol. Chem.*, **211**, 1 (1954); E. E. Jones and D. Lipkin, *J. Am. Chem. Soc.*, **78**, 2408 (1956).

[14] P. Desnuelle and A. Casal, *Biochim. et Biophys. Acta*, **2**, 64 (1948); D. F. Elliott, *Biochem. J.*, **50**, 542 (1952).

Serine has been found to be a constituent of two interesting growth-inhibitory substances produced by certain molds. One of these is O-diazo-acetylserine (azaserine),[15] and the other is 4-amino-3-isoxazolidone (cycloserine, oxamycin).[16]

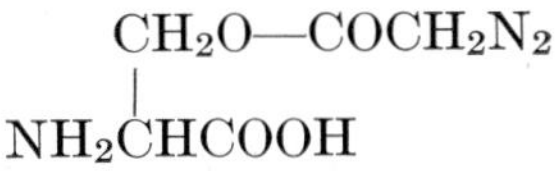

$$CH_2O—COCH_2N_2$$
$$|$$
$$NH_2CHCOOH$$

O-Diazoacetylserine

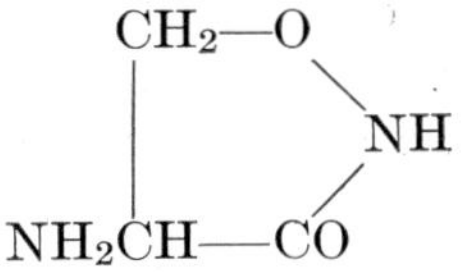

$$CH_2—O$$
$$|~~~~~~~~~\backslash$$
$$|~~~~~~~~~~~NH$$
$$|~~~~~~~~~/$$
$$NH_2CH—CO$$

4-Amino-3-isoxazolidone

Threonine (α-amino-β-hydroxybutyric acid). Threonine is a higher homolog of serine, and shares many of its chemical properties. With periodate, threonine gives acetaldehyde in place of formaldehyde. Threonine is widely distributed among the proteins, but it usually represents

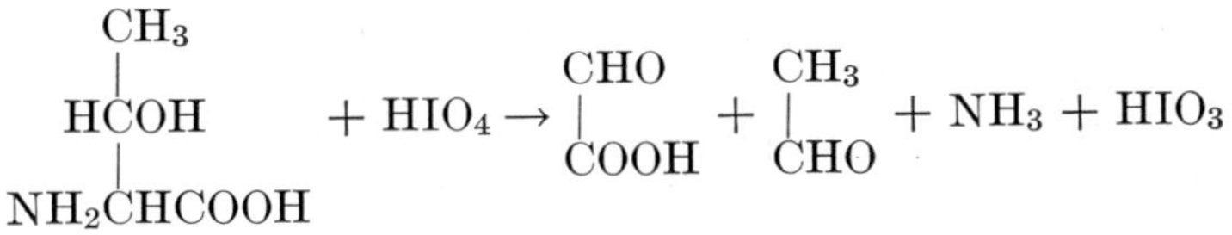

$$CH_3$$
$$|$$
$$HCOH$$
$$|$$
$$NH_2CHCOOH$$

Threonine

$$+ HIO_4 \rightarrow \begin{matrix} CHO \\ | \\ COOH \end{matrix} + \begin{matrix} CH_3 \\ | \\ CHO \end{matrix} + NH_3 + HIO_3$$

a small fraction of the amino acids formed on hydrolysis. Like serine, threonine is unstable in alkali. The discovery of threonine came in 1935 when Rose isolated it from hydrolysates of fibrin (a protein formed when the fibrinogen of blood plasma is allowed to clot). Rose was led to the discovery of this amino acid by the fact that protein hydrolysates caused better growth of immature rats than did a mixture of all the amino acids known at that time to be essential for the organism. By careful and laborious fractionation of the fibrin hydrolysate, and parallel testing of the fractions for their growth-promoting activity, it was possible to isolate the new indispensable amino acid; its structure was then established by degradation and by synthesis.

Cysteine (α-amino-β-mercaptopropionic acid). This sulfur-containing amino acid is closely related structurally to serine. Although it is fairly certain that cysteine is present in many proteins, the cysteine cannot be isolated as such after hydrolysis in the usual manner. There appears instead an oxidation product of cysteine, the amino acid cystine.

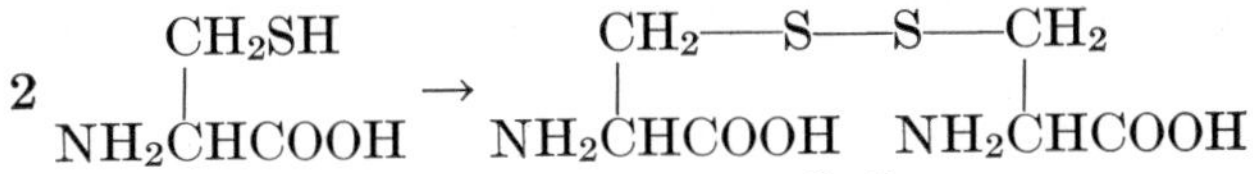

$$2 \begin{matrix} CH_2SH \\ | \\ NH_2CHCOOH \end{matrix} \rightarrow \begin{matrix} CH_2—S—S—CH_2 \\ |~~~~~~~~~~~~~~~~~| \\ NH_2CHCOOH~~NH_2CHCOOH \end{matrix}$$

Cysteine   Cystine

Despite the difficulty in the isolation of the cysteine from protein

[15] C. C. Stock et al., *Nature,* **173**, 71 (1954).
[16] F. A. Kuehl, Jr., et al., *J. Am. Chem. Soc.,* **77**, 2344 (1955); P. H. Hidy et al., *ibid.,* **77**, 2345 (1955).

hydrolysates, it is clear that the SH (sulfhydryl) group of this amino acid is present in intact proteins. Many proteins which yield cystine on acid hydrolysis show a distinctive red color with sodium nitroprusside, $Na_2Fe(CN)_5NO$, a sensitive reagent for sulfhydryl groups.

Cystine is of exceptional importance in the history of the protein amino acids. In 1810 Wollaston isolated cystine from urinary calculi (Latin *calculus*, pebble); it was not until 1899, however, that cystine was obtained by Mörner from a protein hydrolysate. The proteins Mörner used, the scleroproteins such as keratin of the hair, are especially rich sources of cystine (ca. 12 per cent in human hair). Cystine is easy to isolate because of its low solubility in neutral solution; thus the amino acid will precipitate when an acid hydrolysate of keratin is neutralized with alkali. Evidence is at hand to show that the cystine found in keratin hydrolysates did not arise secondarily from cysteine in the course of the hydrolysis. Cystine must be numbered, therefore, among the protein amino acids. Insulin is another protein that is unusually rich in cystine, and the integrity of the disulfide linkage of cystine in this hormone is essential for its biological activity.

The oxidation of the sulfhydryl group of cysteine to the disulfide group of cystine is readily effected by atmospheric oxygen if traces of metal ions (e.g., cupric ion) are present. The oxidation of cysteine to cystine is also effected by iodine in acetic acid, by ferricyanide, and by *o*-iodosobenzoic acid. On treatment of cysteine with bromine water, the oxidation goes beyond the disulfide stage, and the sulfhydryl group is converted to a sulfonic acid group, with the formation of cysteic acid. Cysteic acid may be formed from cystine by treatment with peracids such as peracetic acid (CH_3COOOH). On decarboxylation, cysteic acid gives taurine, a substance found in mammalian bile in the form of a condensation product with a steroid, cholic acid (p. 632). Intermediate stages in the

$$
\begin{array}{ccccc}
CH_2SH & & CH_2SO_3H & & CH_2SO_3H \\
| & \rightarrow & | & \rightarrow & | \\
NH_2CHCOOH & & NH_2CHCOOH & & CH_2NH_2 \\
\text{Cysteine} & & \text{Cysteic acid} & & \text{Taurine}
\end{array}
$$

oxidation of cysteine to cysteic acid are cysteine sulfenic acid (R—SOH) and cysteine sulfinic acid (R—SO_2H).

In analogy with the behavior of serine in alkaline solution, both cystine and cysteine are readily decomposed under these conditions, with the formation of pyruvic acid, ammonia, hydrogen sulfide, and sulfur.

In aqueous solution, a disulfide may undergo reversible cleavage to a sulfenic acid and a sulfhydryl compound ($RSSR + H_2O \rightarrow RSOH + RSH$). If two disulfides ($RSSR$ and $R'SSR'$) are present in a mixture, acid treatment can lead to the formation of a new disulfide ($RSSR'$) by "disulfide interchange."

On treatment with organic halogen compounds, cysteine is converted to S-alkyl or S-aryl compounds, depending on the nature of the reagent.

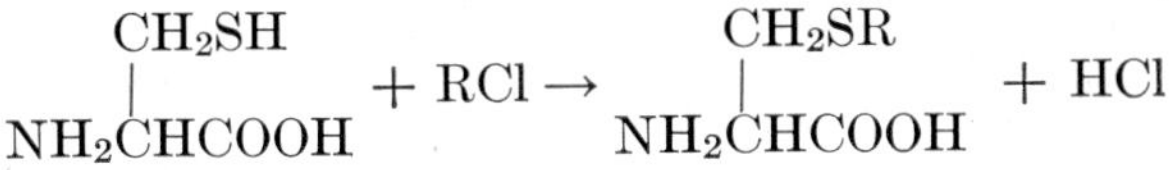

$$
\begin{array}{c}
\text{CH}_2\text{SH} \\
| \\
\text{NH}_2\text{CHCOOH}
\end{array}
+ \text{RCl} \rightarrow
\begin{array}{c}
\text{CH}_2\text{SR} \\
| \\
\text{NH}_2\text{CHCOOH}
\end{array}
+ \text{HCl}
$$

It is of interest that when substances such as bromobenzene are given by mouth to a dog they appear in the urine as S-aryl derivatives of cysteine, in which the α-amino group has been acetylated. Compounds of this type are termed mercapturic acids, and the product obtained after bromobenzene administration is p-bromophenylmercapturic acid. The formation of mercapturic acids may be considered another example of metabolic detoxication.

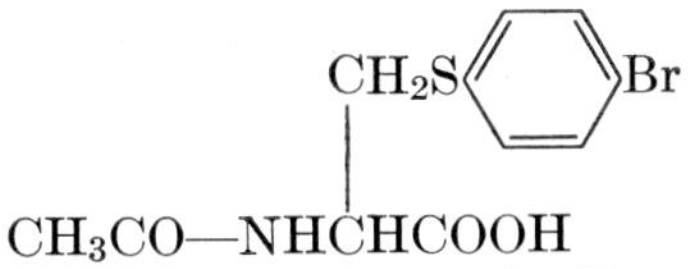

CH₃CO—NHCHCOOH
p-Bromophenylmercapturic acid

Two valuable reagents for cysteine and other sulfhydryl compounds are p-chloromercuribenzoic acid and N-ethylmaleimide.

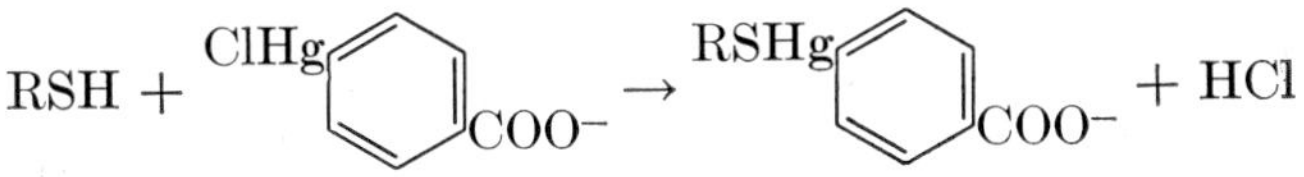

p-Chloromercuribenzoate

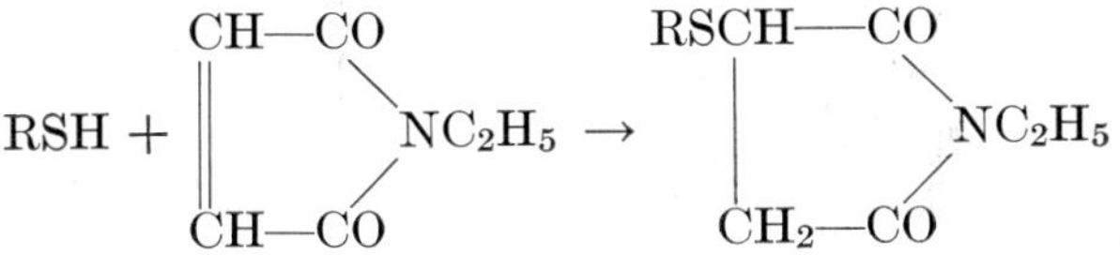

N-Ethylmaleimide

The sulfhydryl group of cysteine and of its derivatives may be acylated to form thiol esters (RS—COR′). Thiol esters are readily hydrolyzed by alkali and are reactive acylating agents; they occupy an important place in metabolism in relation to the action of coenzyme A (p. 205), of lipoic acid (p. 306), and of some enzymes (Chapter 12).

When cysteine reacts with formaldehyde, thiazolidine carboxylic acid is formed; many other aldehydes react with cysteine in a similar manner.

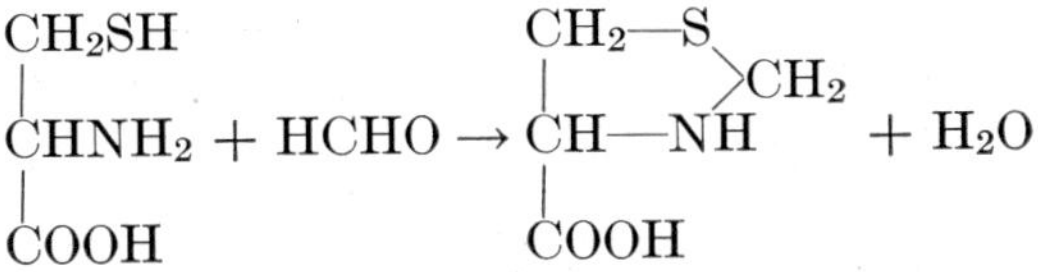

Thiazolidine carboxylic
acid

The reaction of cysteine with aldehydes assumed greater importance when it was found that the products formed, the thiazolidines, are closely related to the important antibacterial agents grouped under the term penicillin. The penicillins contain the β,β'-dimethyl derivative of cysteine (penicillamine), which is present as part of a thiazolidine ring, as shown for penicillin G. In other penicillins, the benzyl group is replaced by other groups.

$$\begin{array}{cc}
CH_3 \quad CH_3 \\
\diagdown \diagup \\
C-SH \\
\big| \\
NH_2CHCOOH \\
\text{Penicillamine}
\end{array}$$

$$\begin{array}{c}
\qquad\qquad\qquad\qquad S \\
\qquad\qquad\qquad\qquad \diagup \diagdown \quad CH_3 \\
C_6H_5CH_2CONHCH-CH \quad C\diagdown \\
\qquad\qquad\qquad |\qquad | \qquad\quad | \; CH_3 \\
\qquad\qquad\qquad OC-N-CH \\
\qquad\qquad\qquad\qquad\qquad\qquad | \\
\qquad\qquad\qquad\qquad\qquad\quad COOH \\
\text{Penicillin G}
\end{array}$$

Interesting cysteine derivatives found in higher plants are S-methylcysteine sulfoxide[17] and S-allylcysteine sulfoxide (alliin).[18]

$$\begin{array}{cc}
O \quad\; NH_2 \\
\| \qquad | \\
CH_3SCH_2CHCOOH \\
\text{S-Methylcysteine} \\
\text{sulfoxide}
\end{array}
\qquad\qquad
\begin{array}{c}
O \quad\; NH_2 \\
\| \qquad | \\
CH_2{=}CHCH_2SCH_2CHCOOH \\
\text{Alliin}
\end{array}$$

A naturally occurring S-alkyl derivative of cysteine is djenkolic acid, present in the Djenkol bean. Another closely related cysteine derivative is formed by the treatment of wool with a solution of sodium carbonate; this amino acid (lanthionine) is not present in the intact protein

$$\begin{array}{c}
CH_2S-CH_2-SCH_2 \\
| \qquad\qquad\qquad | \\
NH_2CHCOOH \quad NH_2CHCOOH \\
\text{Djenkolic acid}
\end{array}
\qquad
\begin{array}{c}
CH_2-S-CH_2 \\
| \qquad\qquad\quad | \\
NH_2CHCOOH \quad NH_2CHCOOH \\
\text{Lanthionine}
\end{array}$$

but is produced in the course of the alkaline hydrolysis.[19] Lanthionine has been found in nature as a constituent of the antibacterial agent subtilin. An S-alkyl derivative of cysteine has been isolated from cat urine, and named felinine; its structure is $HOCH_2CH_2C(CH_3)_2-SCH_2CH(NH_2)COOH$.

Methionine (α-amino-γ-methylthiobutyric acid). Methionine was discovered in 1921 by Mueller in the course of studies on the factors necessary for the rapid growth of certain microorganisms. This work led to the isolation of the amino acid from casein hydrolysates, and several years later Barger established the correct structure by synthesis. In contrast to the sulfur of cystine, that of methionine is stable to alkali, and for this reason the total sulfur of a protein containing methionine

[17] C. J. Morris and J. F. Thompson, *J. Am. Chem. Soc.*, **78**, 1605 (1956); R. L. M. Synge and J. C. Wood, *Biochem. J.*, **64**, 252 (1956).

[18] A. Stoll and E. Seebeck, *Advances in Enzymol.*, **11**, 377 (1951).

[19] A. Schöberl and A. Wagner, *Z. physiol. Chem.*, **304**, 97 (1956).

and cystine is greater than the alkali-labile sulfur. Although methionine is widely distributed among proteins, it represents a very small proportion of the total amino acids formed on hydrolysis.

On treatment with an alkyl halide, methionine is converted to a sulfonium salt; the methyl sulfonium compound has been isolated from cabbage juice. The oxidation of methionine by means of hydrogen peroxide leads to the formation of the corresponding sulfoxide and the

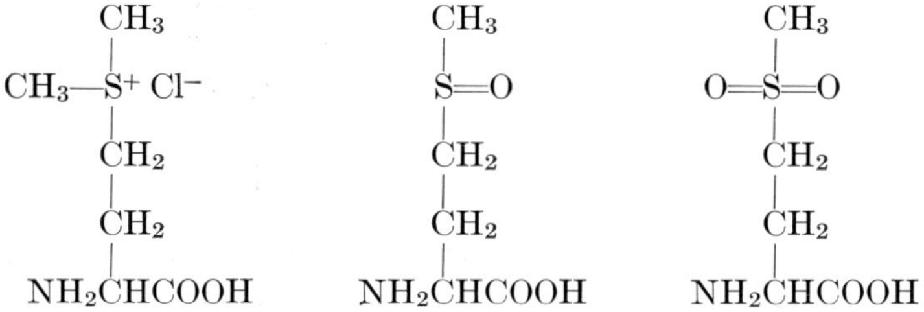

$$
\begin{array}{ccc}
CH_3 & CH_3 & CH_3 \\
| & | & | \\
CH_3\text{—}S^+\ Cl^- & S\text{=}O & O\text{=}S\text{=}O \\
| & | & | \\
CH_2 & CH_2 & CH_2 \\
| & | & | \\
CH_2 & CH_2 & CH_2 \\
| & | & | \\
NH_2CHCOOH & NH_2CHCOOH & NH_2CHCOOH
\end{array}
$$

Methionine methyl sulfonium chloride   Methionine sulfoxide   Methionine sulfone

sulfone. When methionine-containing proteins are treated with nitrogen trichloride ("agene"), and the "agenized" proteins are hydrolyzed, a toxic substance (methionine sulfoximine) related chemically to methionine sulfone is produced.[20] In the sulfoximine, one of the oxygen atoms of the sulfone group has been replaced by an NH group.

Like other thioethers, methionine is decomposed by hydriodic acid; the products are CH_3I and the thiolactone of an amino acid named homocysteine, the next higher homolog of cysteine. The thiolactone is converted to homocysteine when the reaction mixture is made alkaline with ammonium hydroxide.

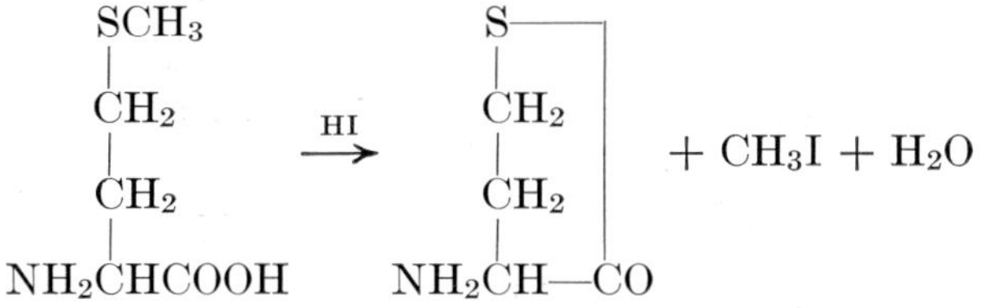

$$
\begin{array}{ccc}
SCH_3 & & S\text{———} \\
| & & | \quad\ | \\
CH_2 & \xrightarrow{HI} & CH_2 \quad\ \\
| & & | \quad\ | \\
CH_2 & & CH_2 \quad\ \\
| & & | \quad\ \\
NH_2CHCOOH & & NH_2CH\text{—}CO
\end{array}
\quad + CH_3I + H_2O
$$

Methionine   Homocysteine thiolactone

The oxidation of homocysteine leads to the formation of the corresponding disulfide compound homocystine. Although homocysteine and

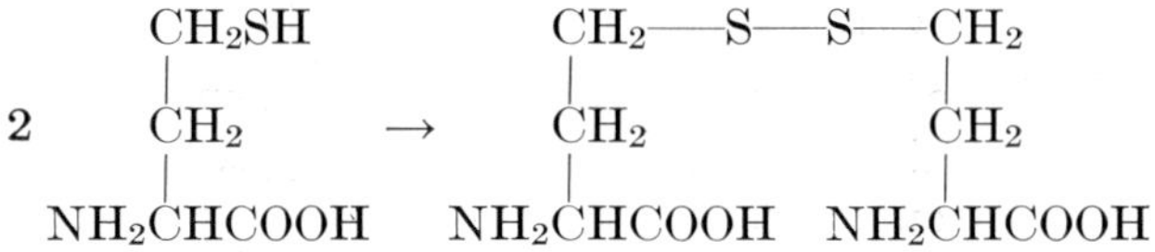

$$
\begin{array}{ccc}
CH_2SH & CH_2\text{—}S\text{—}S\text{—}CH_2 \\
| & | \qquad\qquad | \\
2\quad CH_2 & \rightarrow \quad CH_2 \qquad\qquad CH_2 \\
| & | \qquad\qquad | \\
NH_2CHCOOH & NH_2CHCOOH \quad NH_2CHCOOH
\end{array}
$$

Homocysteine   Homocystine

[20] P. N. Campbell et al., *Biochem. J.*, **48**, 106 (1951).

homocystine are not constituents of proteins, homocysteine has been shown to be an important participant in metabolic reactions involving methionine, which is an indispensable amino acid for the growing rat.

Aspartic Acid (aminosuccinic acid). This acid was first isolated from a protein hydrolysate by Ritthausen in 1868; he showed that the proteins of plants yielded relatively large amounts of aspartic acid on hydrolysis. Aspartic acid had been known for a long time previously, however, since its β-amide, asparagine, had been isolated from asparagus juice by Vauquelin and Robiquet in 1806 and the free acid had been prepared by Plisson in 1826. The monoamide may readily be converted to the parent compound by acid hydrolysis.

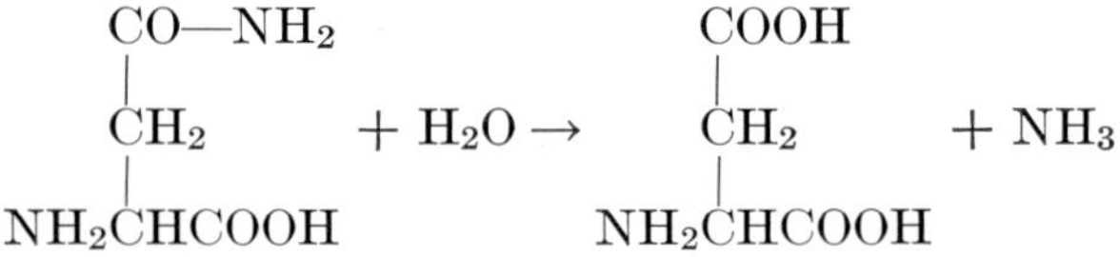

$$
\begin{array}{c}
\text{CO—NH}_2 \\
|\\
\text{CH}_2 \\
|\\
\text{NH}_2\text{CHCOOH} \\
\text{Asparagine}
\end{array}
\quad + \text{H}_2\text{O} \rightarrow \quad
\begin{array}{c}
\text{COOH} \\
|\\
\text{CH}_2 \\
|\\
\text{NH}_2\text{CHCOOH} \\
\text{Aspartic acid}
\end{array}
\quad + \text{NH}_3
$$

Asparagine not only exists as such in plants, where it appears to serve as an important reserve of nitrogen, but has also been isolated after the hydrolysis of a seed protein (edestin) by proteolytic enzymes.

Glutamic Acid (α-aminoglutaric acid). Glutamic acid is the next higher homolog of aspartic acid and, like it, is present in large amounts in the hydrolysates of plant proteins. It was discovered by Ritthausen in 1866. Some of the seed proteins, especially the prolamines, yield 20 to 45 per cent of glutamic acid on hydrolysis. Glutamic acid may be isolated from acid hydrolysates of proteins as the hydrochloride, which is sparingly soluble in hydrochloric acid.

In the variety of its known metabolic functions, glutamic acid is outstanding among the protein amino acids; this substance participates in many important chemical processes in plants, animals, and microorganisms.

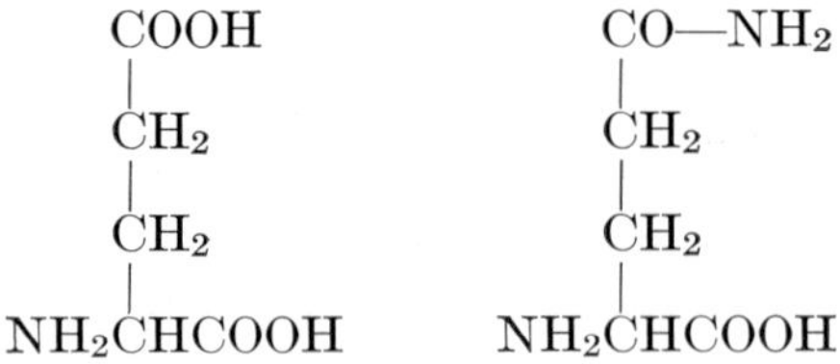

$$
\begin{array}{c}
\text{COOH} \\
|\\
\text{CH}_2 \\
|\\
\text{CH}_2 \\
|\\
\text{NH}_2\text{CHCOOH} \\
\text{Glutamic acid}
\end{array}
\qquad
\begin{array}{c}
\text{CO—NH}_2 \\
|\\
\text{CH}_2 \\
|\\
\text{CH}_2 \\
|\\
\text{NH}_2\text{CHCOOH} \\
\text{Glutamine}
\end{array}
$$

Of particular importance in metabolism is the γ-monoamide of glutamic acid, glutamine. This compound is present in appreciable quantities in plants and is commonly isolated as such from extracts of beet roots. It has also been obtained after the enzymic hydrolysis of plant proteins. Furthermore, glutamine has been identified as an important constituent of the blood and tissues of animals. A valuable summary of the literature on glutamine up to 1945 may be found in the review by Archibald.[21]

An important difference in the chemical behavior of glutamine and asparagine is observed when the two are heated in aqueous solution. Glutamine is readily transformed into pyrrolidone carboxylic acid, whereas asparagine is not affected by this treatment. The deamidation

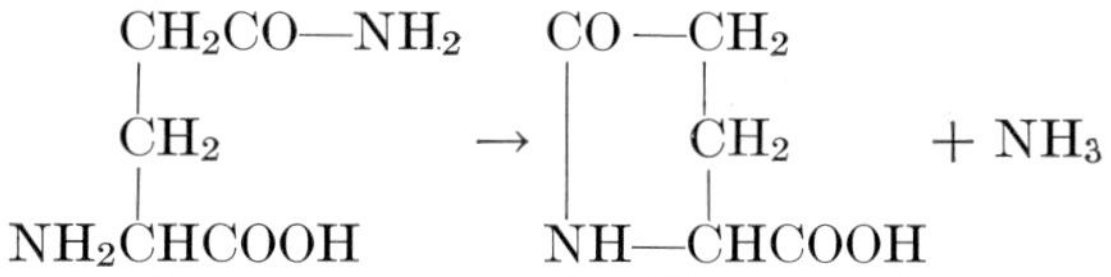

$$\begin{array}{ccc} \mathrm{CH_2CO-NH_2} & \mathrm{CO-CH_2} & \\ | & | & \\ \mathrm{CH_2} & \rightarrow & \mathrm{CH_2} & +\mathrm{NH_3} \\ | & | & \\ \mathrm{NH_2CHCOOH} & \mathrm{NH-CHCOOH} & \\ \text{Glutamine} & \text{Pyrrolidone carboxylic} \\ & \text{acid} \end{array}$$

of glutamine (or of asparagine) may readily be followed by one of the several modifications of the Conway micro-diffusion technique; NH_3 is liberated from the amide in the outer well of a "Conway vessel" and is absorbed by standard acid in the center well of the vessel.[22]

A number of interesting derivatives of glutamic acid have been found in nature. Several types of plant tissue are known to contain γ-methyleneglutamic acid, as well as its γ-amide.[23] Also, a substance which is present in seeds of the sweet pea (*Lathyrus odoratus*), and which produces skeletal abnormalities in rats (lathyrism), has been shown to be β-(γ-glutamyl)aminopropionitrile.[24]

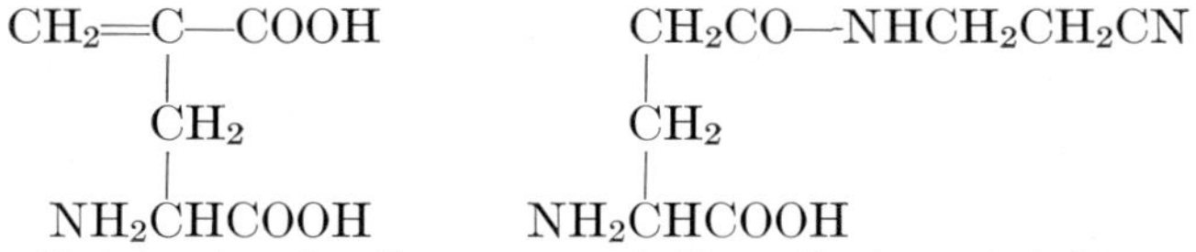

$$\begin{array}{cc} \mathrm{CH_2{=}C-COOH} & \mathrm{CH_2CO-NHCH_2CH_2CN} \\ | & | \\ \mathrm{CH_2} & \mathrm{CH_2} \\ | & | \\ \mathrm{NH_2CHCOOH} & \mathrm{NH_2CHCOOH} \\ \text{γ-Methyleneglutamic acid} & \text{β-(γ-Glutamyl)aminopropionitrile} \end{array}$$

For a time is was believed that β-hydroxyglutamic acid was a protein amino acid, but this view has been abandoned in the light of recent work.[25]

Lysine (α,ε-diaminocaproic acid). Lysine was first isolated in 1889 from a casein hydrolysate by Drechsel. It is a widely distributed amino acid and occurs in the hydrolysates of some proteins (e.g., gelatin, hemoglobin) in moderately high proportions. On the other hand, proteins are known (e.g., zein) that yield no measurable quantities of lysine. In the isolation of lysine from protein hydrolysates, advantage may be

[21] R. M. Archibald, *Chem. Revs.*, **37**, 161 (1945).

[22] E. J. Conway, *Micro-Diffusion Analysis and Volumetric Error*, D. Van Nostrand Co., Princeton, N. J., 1940.

[23] J. Done and L. Fowden, *Biochem. J.*, **51**, 451 (1952).

[24] E. D. Schilling and F. M. Strong, *J. Am. Chem. Soc.*, **76**, 2848 (1954).

[25] C. E. Dent and D. I. Fowler, *Biochem. J.*, **56**, 54 (1954).

taken of the low solubility of its salt with picric acid (2,4,6-trinitro-phenol).

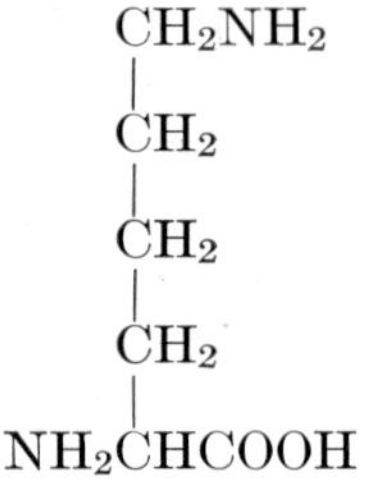

$$
\begin{array}{cc}
\text{CH}_2\text{NH}_2 & \text{CH}_2\text{NH}_2 \\
| & | \\
\text{CH}_2 & \text{CHOH} \\
| & | \\
\text{CH}_2 & \text{CH}_2 \\
| & | \\
\text{CH}_2 & \text{CH}_2 \\
| & | \\
\text{NH}_2\text{CHCOOH} & \text{NH}_2\text{CHCOOH} \\
\text{Lysine} & \text{Hydroxylysine}
\end{array}
$$

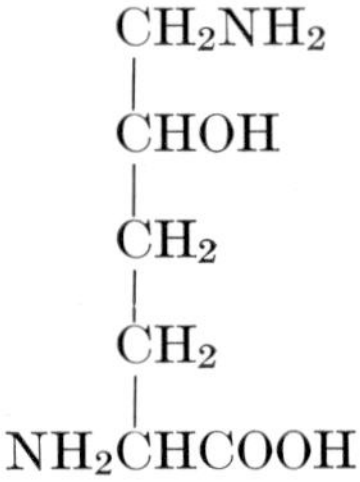

Hydroxylysine (α,ϵ-diamino-δ-hydroxycaproic acid). Hydroxylysine is a recent addition to the list of protein amino acids, having been demonstrated in gelatin by Van Slyke in 1938. Its identification came from the application of the periodate oxidation method (discussed previously in connection with serine and threonine). Hydroxylysine has been found only in hydrolysates of collagen and gelatin (the hydroxylysine content of these proteins is about 1 per cent), and it would appear, therefore, that this amino acid has an extremely restricted distribution.[26]

Arginine (α-amino-δ-guanidinovaleric acid). Arginine was first isolated by Schulze in 1886 from lupin seedlings, and ten years later Kossel showed that the basic proteins of cell nuclei (protamines and histones) yield large amounts of this amino acid on hydrolysis. Certain protamines (e.g., clupein, the basic protein from herring sperm), upon hydrolysis, yield as much as 80 to 90 per cent of their amino acids in the form of arginine, and most other proteins also contain considerable quantities of this amino acid.

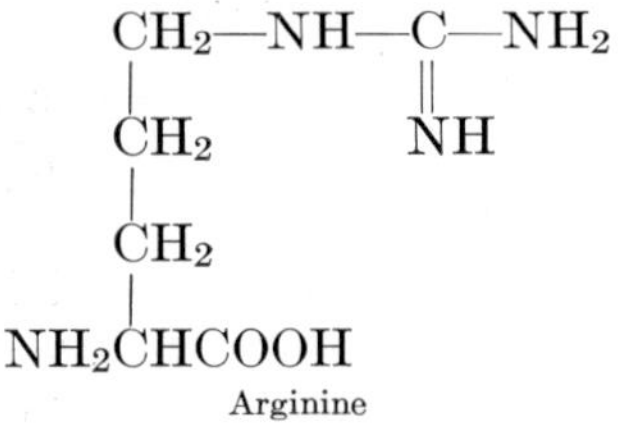

Arginine 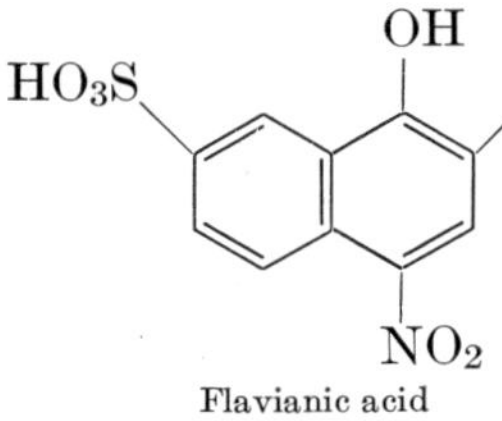   Flavianic acid

Arginine forms sparingly soluble salts with a variety of aromatic sulfonic acids, and one of these, flavianic acid (2,4-dinitro-1-naphthol-7-sulfonic acid) is especially useful for the precipitation of arginine from protein hydrolysates. It may be added that the ability of sulfonic acids to precipitate amino acids is not limited to the instance cited above. The work of Bergmann, Stein, and their associates has shown that all the known protein amino acids form sparingly soluble salts with some but

[26] P. B. Hamilton and R. A. Anderson, *J. Biol. Chem.*, **213**, 249 (1955).

not all aromatic sulfonic acids tested. Thus leucine gives a precipitate with β-naphthalenesulfonic acid, and serine may be obtained in the form of a sparingly soluble salt of p-hydroxyazobenzenesulfonic acid. By taking advantage of the differences in the solubility of the salts of a given sulfonic acid with the amino acids present in a protein hydrolysate, individual amino acids may be isolated from the hydrolysate in a high state of purity.

On treatment with an excess of boiling alkali [e.g., $Ba(OH)_2$], arginine is converted to urea and α,δ-diaminovaleric acid (ornithine), the next lower homolog of lysine. Ornithine is not found in acid hydrolysates of proteins unless the protein has been treated beforehand with alkali; its occurrence in alkaline hydrolysates is due to the decomposition of the preformed arginine. When arginine is treated with an equimolar quantity of aqueous alkali, the amino acid citrulline is formed. Citrulline does not appear to be a constituent of proteins but has been isolated as such from watermelon juice. The preparation of ornithine and citrulline has been described by Hamilton and Anderson.[27]

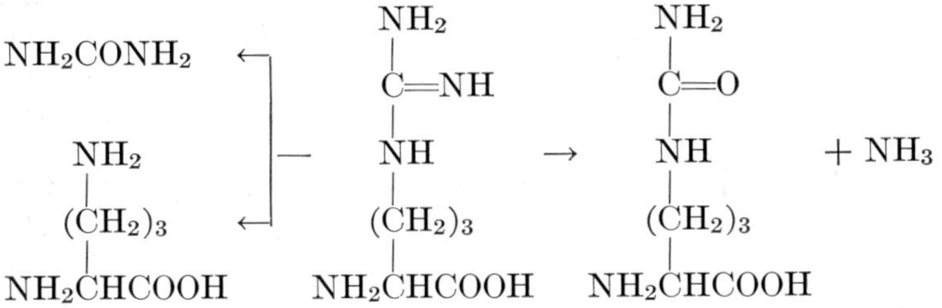

$$
\begin{array}{ccc}
\text{NH}_2\text{CONH}_2 & \xleftarrow{} & \underset{\substack{|\\ \text{C}=\text{NH}\\ |\\ \text{NH}\\ |\\ (\text{CH}_2)_3\\ |\\ \text{NH}_2\text{CHCOOH}}}{\text{NH}_2} & \rightarrow & \underset{\substack{|\\ \text{C}=\text{O}\\ |\\ \text{NH}\\ |\\ (\text{CH}_2)_3\\ |\\ \text{NH}_2\text{CHCOOH}}}{\text{NH}_2} & +\ \text{NH}_3 \\
\end{array}
$$

Ornithine   Arginine   Citrulline

Arginine solutions give a red color upon treatment with α-naphthol and sodium hypochlorite (NaOCl). This reaction, usually termed the Sakaguchi reaction, is due to the presence of the guanidino group; since arginine is the only protein amino acid known to contain this group, the Sakaguchi reaction has been used to estimate the amount of arginine present in protein hydrolysates.

Arginine is found in the muscles of some invertebrates in the form of its phosphoric acid derivative, arginine phosphate (or phosphoarginine).

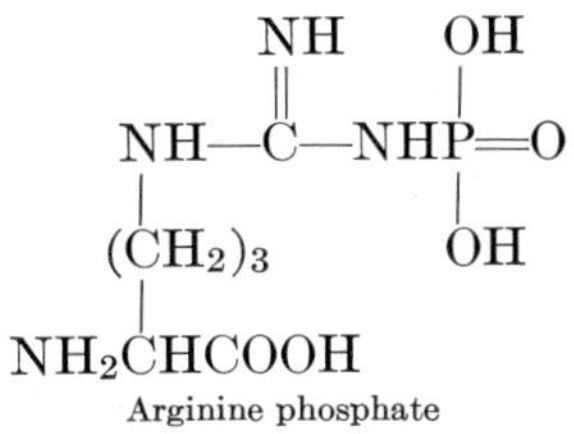

Arginine phosphate 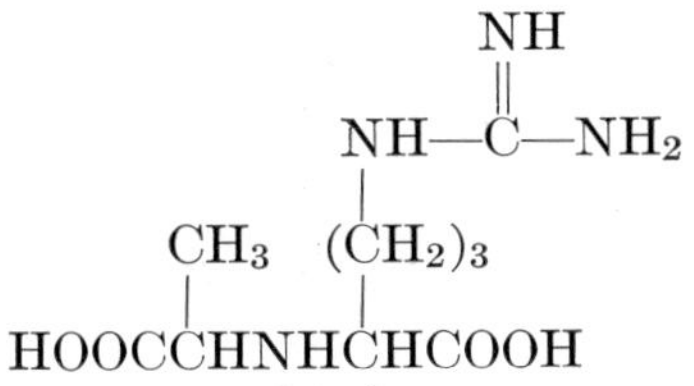   Octopine

[27] P. B. Hamilton and R. A. Anderson, *Biochem. Preparations*, **3**, 96, 100 (1953).

An interesting derivative of arginine, found in the muscles of scallops and other marine invertebrates, is octopine. It will be noted that in octopine a molecule of arginine and a molecule of alanine share a nitrogen atom.

Another naturally occurring substance related to arginine is the hydroxyguanidine derivative canavanine, found in jack beans.[28] The guanidino group of canavanine may be cleaved with the formation of urea and the amino acid canaline.

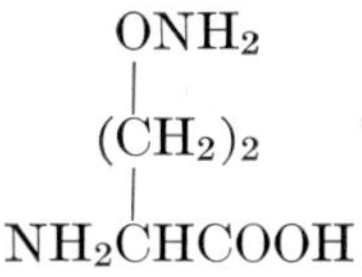

$$
\begin{array}{cc}
\text{ONH}_2 & \overset{\displaystyle \text{NH}}{\underset{\|}{}} \\
| & \text{O—NH—C—NH}_2 \\
(\text{CH}_2)_2 & | \\
| & (\text{CH}_2)_2 \\
\text{NH}_2\text{CHCOOH} & | \\
\text{Canaline} & \text{NH}_2\text{CHCOOH} \\
& \text{Canavanine}
\end{array}
$$

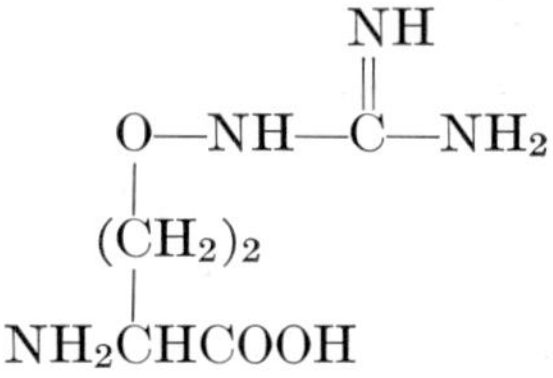

Among the other polyamino compounds found in nature are the substances spermine and spermidine, which occur in various animal tissues, but are especially abundant in human spermatozoa (0.26 g of spermine per 100 g of spermatozoa).

$$\text{NH}_2(\text{CH}_2)_3\text{NH}(\text{CH}_2)_4\text{NH}(\text{CH}_2)_3\text{NH}_2 \qquad \text{NH}_2(\text{CH}_2)_3\text{NH}(\text{CH}_2)_4\text{NH}_2$$

Spermine Spermidine

Histidine (α-amino-β-imidazolylpropionic acid). Histidine was first isolated in 1896 by Kossel from sturin (the protamine from sturgeon sperm) and by Hedin from the hydrolysates of several proteins. It is a widely distributed amino acid, is present in comparatively large amounts in acid hydrolysates of hemoglobin, and may readily be isolated by precipitation with either mercuric chloride or 3,4-dichlorobenzenesulfonic acid. The presence of the imidazole nucleus permits the use of diazobenzenesulfonic acid, which gives a red substitution product with imidazoles, for the colorimetric estimation of histidine. This reaction was first applied by Pauly in 1904 and is usually referred to as the Pauly reaction.

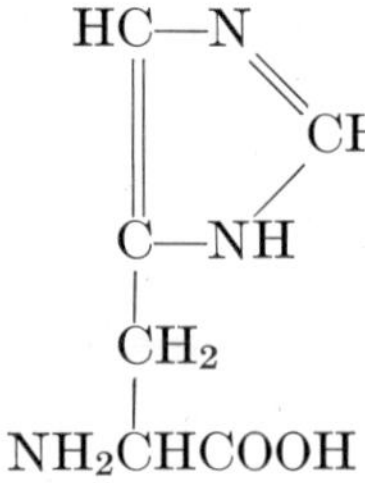

$$
\begin{array}{cc}
\text{HC—N} & \text{HC—N} \\
\| \quad\quad \text{CH} & \| \quad\quad \text{CH} \\
\text{C—NH} & \text{C—NH} \\
| & | \\
\text{CH}_2 & \text{CH}_2 \\
| & | \\
\text{NH}_2\text{CHCOOH} & \text{NH}_2\text{CH}_2 \\
\text{Histidine} & \text{Histamine}
\end{array}
$$

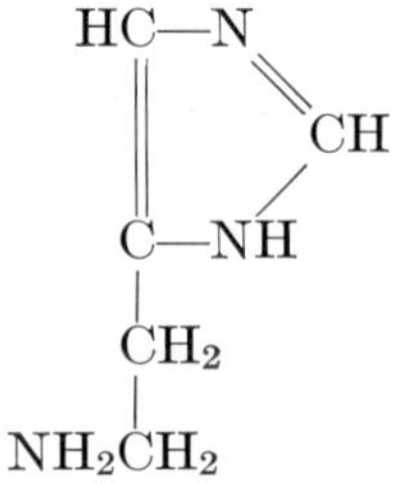

On decarboxylation, histidine gives rise to histamine, a powerful vaso-

[28] W. R. Fearon and E. A. Bell, *Biochem. J.*, **59**, 221 (1955).

dilator, which is present in many animal tissues (lung, muscle, etc.) and in blood.

On treatment with formaldehyde, histidine is converted to a stable compound in which the added methylene group links the α-amino group and one of the CH groups of the imidazole ring, as shown. The imidazole NH group may be acylated to yield a monoacyl derivative; compounds

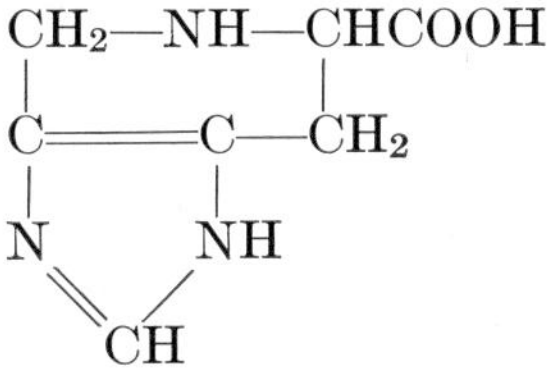

$$CH_2-NH-CHCOOH$$

Product of histidine-
formaldehyde reaction

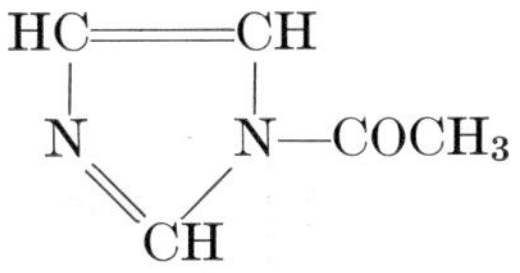

Acetylimidazole

of this type (e.g., acetylimidazole) are readily hydrolyzed by water and are reactive acylating agents.[29]

1-Methylhistidine is a constituent of the muscle substance anserine (p. 137); this methylated amino acid and the isomeric 3-methylhistidine have been identified in human urine.[30]

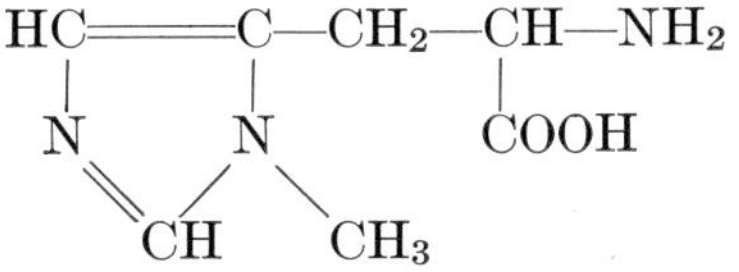

1-Methylhistidine

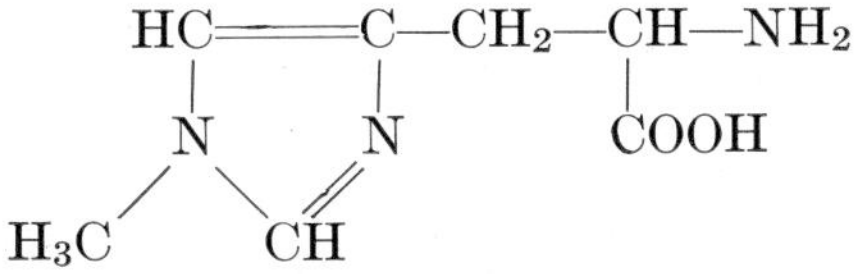

3-Methylhistidine

An interesting derivative of histidine, found in ergot and in mammalian blood, is ergothioneine, the trimethylbetaine of thiolhistidine. Ergothioneine has been discovered in relatively large amounts (about 75 mg per 100 g) in seminal fluid.

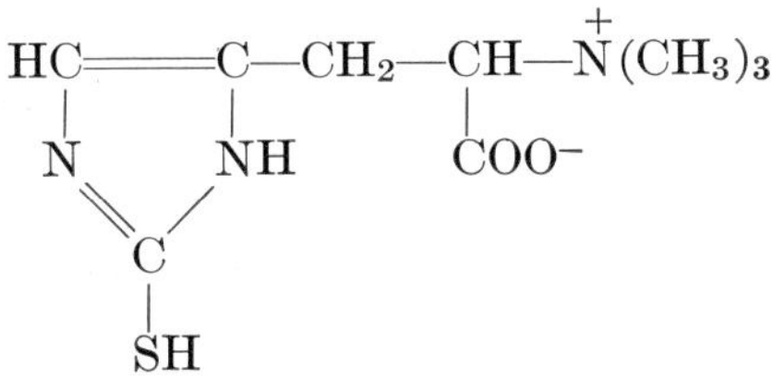

Ergothioneine

Phenylalanine (α-amino-β-phenylpropionic acid). Phenylalanine is a representative of the protein amino acids which contain an aromatic ring as part of their structure. It was first isolated from natural sources (lupin

[29] M. Bergmann and L. Zervas, *Z. physiol. Chem.*, **175**, 145 (1928); E. R. Stadtman, in W. D. McElroy and B. Glass, *Symposium on the Mechanism of Enzyme Action*, p. 581, Johns Hopkins Press, Baltimore, 1954.
[30] H. H. Tallan et al., *J. Biol. Chem.*, **206**, 825 (1954).

seedlings) by Schulze in 1879, and has since been shown to be present in the hydrolysates of proteins, although not in large proportions. The work of Rose has shown phenylalanine to be an indispensable component of the diet of immature rats.

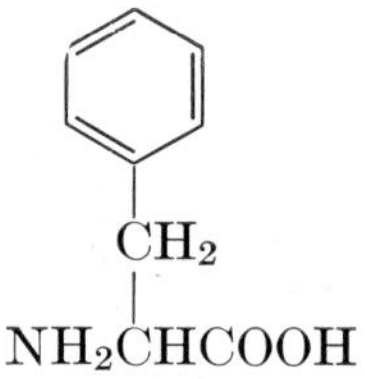

Phenylalanine 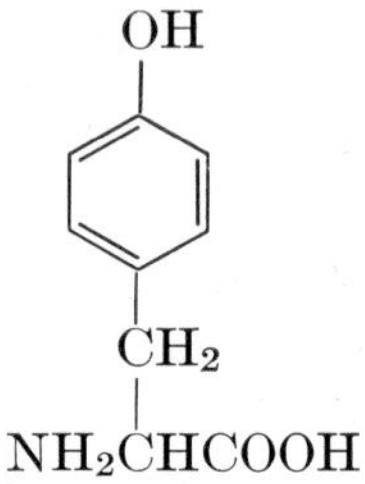   Tyrosine

Tyrosine [α-amino-β-(p-hydroxyphenyl)propionic acid].   Tyrosine was discovered by Liebig in 1846, in the course of a study of the alkaline degradation of casein. This amino acid is widely distributed among the proteins and may readily be isolated because of its low solubility in neutral solutions.

The presence of tyrosine in a solution may be recognized by means of several color reactions. When an acid solution of tyrosine is treated with concentrated nitric acid, a white precipitate appears which, on being heated, becomes yellow; the addition of alkali deepens the color appreciably. This test, known as the xanthoproteic reaction (Greek *xanthos*, yellow), involves the nitration of the benzene ring and the formation of derivatives of nitrophenol. On treatment of tyrosine with a mixture of mercurous nitrate and mercuric nitrate in nitric acid, a white precipitate is formed which turns red when the mixture is heated. This is known as the Millon reaction and is due to the formation of red mercury complexes of nitrophenol derivatives. The Millon reaction is not specific for tyrosine, but is given by phenols generally.

An oxidation product of tyrosine of metabolic interest is 3,4-dihydroxyphenylalanine (sometimes termed "dopa").

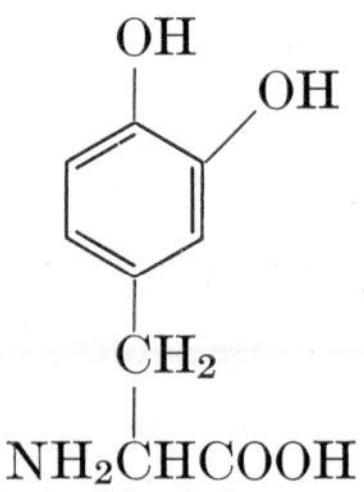

3,4-Dihydroxyphenylalanine 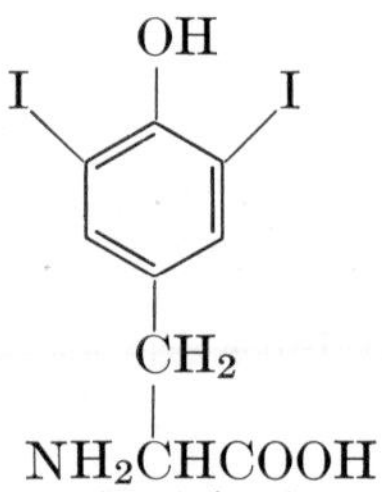   3,5-Diiodotyrosine 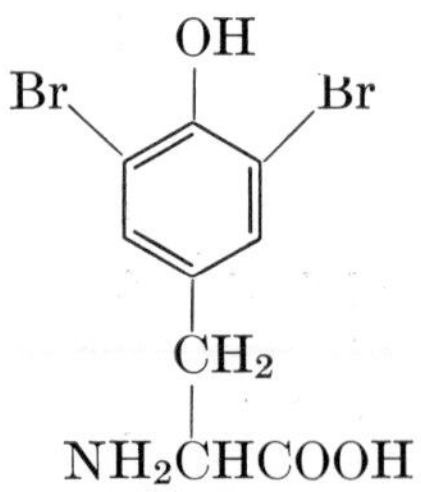   3,5-Dibromotyrosine

Treatment of tyrosine with iodine in alkaline solution gives rise to the formation of 3,5-diiodotyrosine. This iodinated amino acid was found by Drechsel in 1896 as a product of the alkaline hydrolysis of the horny skeleton of the coral *Gorgonia cavolinii*, and the name iodogorgoic acid was assigned to it. This amino acid is, however, widely distributed in marine organisms, and for this reason, among others, the term diiodotyrosine is to be preferred. In some corals, diiodotyrosine is accompanied by the corresponding dibromotyrosine.

Diiodotyrosine also occurs in the mammalian thyroid gland, where it is found in association with the important hormone thyroxine (a constituent of the protein thyroglobulin) and with monoiodotyrosine (3-iodotyrosine). A triiodo derivative of thyroxine has been discovered in thyroid tissue; this compound (3,5,3'-triiodothyronine) appears to be more active biologically than is thyroxine itself. The noniodinated amino acid derived from thyroxine is termed thyronine. The hormonal properties of thyroxine will be discussed in Chapter 38.

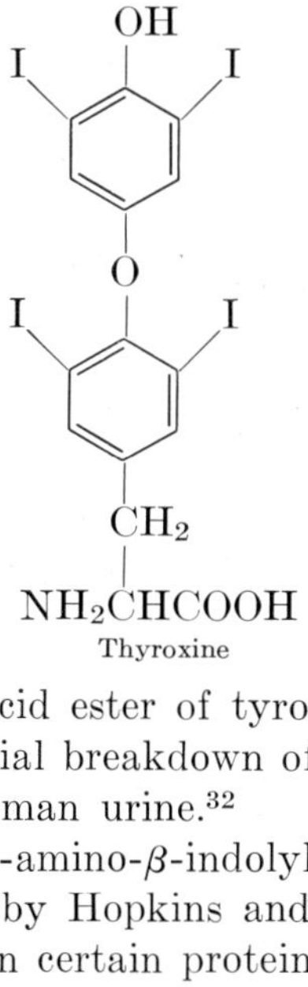

Thyroxine

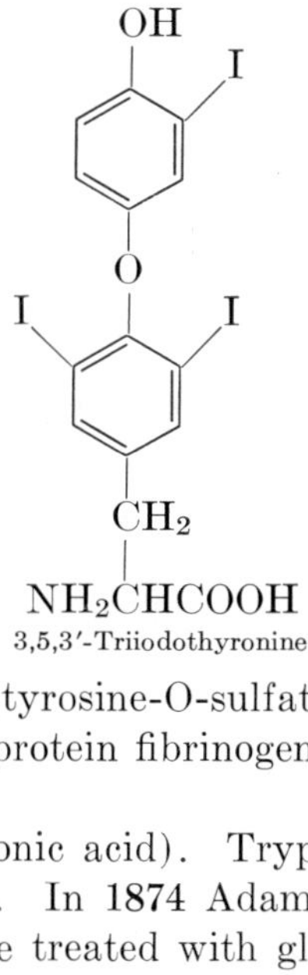

3,5,3'-Triiodothyronine

The sulfuric acid ester of tyrosine (tyrosine-O-sulfate) has been obtained upon partial breakdown of the protein fibrinogen,[31] and has been isolated from human urine.[32]

Tryptophan (α-amino-β-indolylpropionic acid). Tryptophan was discovered in 1901 by Hopkins and Cole. In 1874 Adamkiewicz had observed that, when certain proteins were treated with glacial acetic acid followed by concentrated sulfuric acid, a violet color resulted. Hopkins and Cole showed that the reaction was due to glyoxylic acid present as an impurity in the acetic acid, and proceeded to fractionate protein hydrolysates in order to isolate the material responsible for the color reaction, now frequently termed the Hopkins-Cole reaction. As mentioned previously, tryptophan is destroyed on acid hydrolysis; Hopkins and Cole prepared their protein hydrolysate by subjecting casein to pro-

---

[31] F. R. Bettelheim, *J. Am. Chem. Soc.,* **76,** 2838 (1954).
[32] H. H. Tallan et al., *J. Biol. Chem.,* **217,** 703 (1955).

longed action of the mixture of pancreatic enzymes then called "trypsin." The new amino acid was precipitated from the enzymic hydrolysate by the addition of mercuric sulfate. The name "tryptophane" had been assigned in 1890 by Neumeister to an unidentified substance that was present in tryptic hydrolysates of proteins and gave a red color with chlorine water (a color reaction that had been found by Kühne to be given by indole). Since the material obtained by Hopkins and Cole also gave a red color with chlorine water, they retained the name proposed by Neumeister; more recently, it has been generally agreed to drop the final "e." Although tryptophan is a general protein constituent, it is not present in any protein in appreciable amounts.

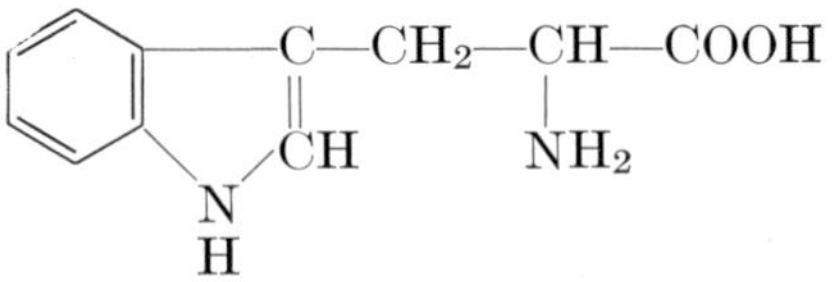

Tryptophan 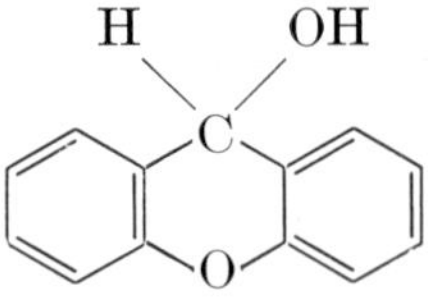   Xanthydrol

Another colorimetric test for tryptophan involves its reaction with xanthydrol to form a colored derivative whose structure has not been established.[33]

Proline (pyrrolidine-2-carboxylic acid). Proline was first isolated from a protein hydrolysate (casein) by Emil Fischer in 1901. It is a widely distributed amino acid and is present in especially large proportions in gliadin, zein, and gelatin. Proline is the only one of the protein amino acids that is soluble in alcohol. An excellent method for the isola-

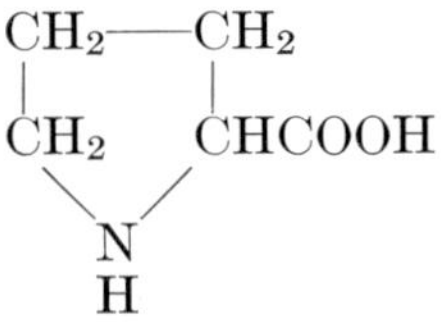

Proline 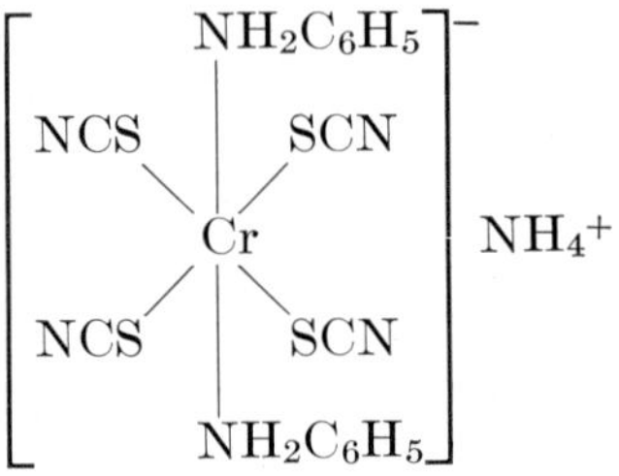   Ammonium rhodanilate

tion of proline from acid hydrolysates of gelatin has been described by Bergmann, who developed the reagent ammonium rhodanilate for this purpose. This reagent belongs to the group of chemical substances some-

[33] S. R. Dickman and A. L. Crockett, *J. Biol. Chem.*, **220,** 957 (1956).

times referred to as "Werner complexes" since they were first studied systematically by the chemist Alfred Werner during the period 1900–1920. The rhodanilate ion forms a sparingly soluble salt with proline in acid solution, and the proline rhodanilate may therefore be obtained in good yield.

As indicated earlier, proline does not react with nitrous acid to liberate nitrogen gas; instead, an N-nitroso derivative is formed which is soluble in organic solvents. This reaction has been used for the determination of the proline content of protein hydrolysates.[34]

Pipecolic acid (piperidine-2-carboxylic acid), 5-hydroxypipecolic acid, and baikain (Δ^4-dehydropipecolic acid), all closely related to proline in structure, have been isolated from plant tissues.[35] Another cyclic amino acid found in plants is azetidine-2-carboxylic acid;[36] it is of interest that, when asparagine is heated to 100° C at pH 6.7, it is converted to the related compound 4-carboxy-2-azetidinone.[37]

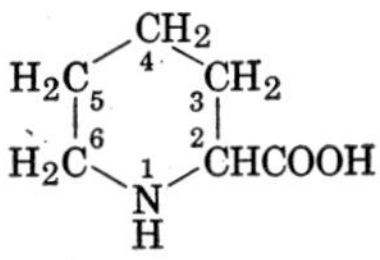

Pipecolic acid

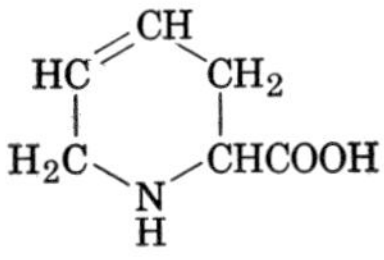

Baikain

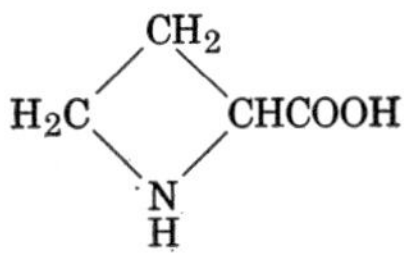

Azetidine-2-carboxylic
acid

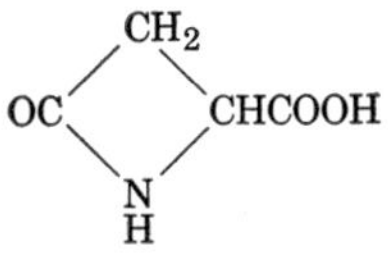

4-Carboxy-2-azetidinone
(4-Oxyazetidine-2-
carboxylic acid)

Hydroxyproline (4-hydroxypyrrolidine-2-carboxylic acid). Hydroxyproline was first isolated from a gelatin hydrolysate by Fischer in 1902. This amino acid has a limited distribution among the proteins, but is found in relatively large amounts in gelatin (ca. 14 per cent). Its isolation from protein hydrolysates is difficult, but Bergmann found that, after removal of proline as the rhodanilate, hydroxyproline could be precipitated as a sparingly soluble salt of another Werner complex, termed ammonium Reineckate.

[34] P. B. Hamilton and P. J. Ortiz, *J. Biol. Chem.*, **184**, 607 (1950).
[35] R. I. Morrison, *Biochem. J.*, **53**, 474 (1953); F. E. King et al., *J. Chem. Soc.*, **1950**, 3590; N. Grobbelaar et al., *Nature*, **175**, 703 (1955).
[36] L. Fowden, *Biochem. J.*, **64**, 323 (1956).
[37] E. A. Talley et al., *J. Am. Chem. Soc.*, **78**, 5836 (1956).

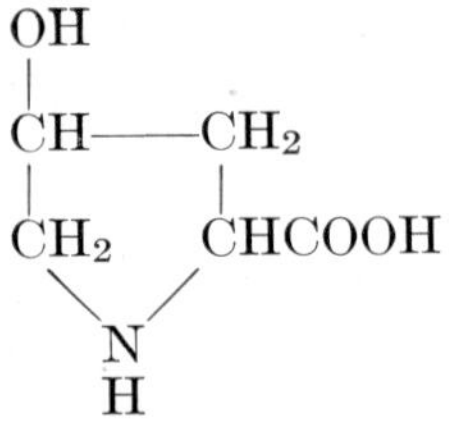

OH
|
CH——CH₂
| \
CH₂   CHCOOH
  \   /
   N
   H

Hydroxyproline

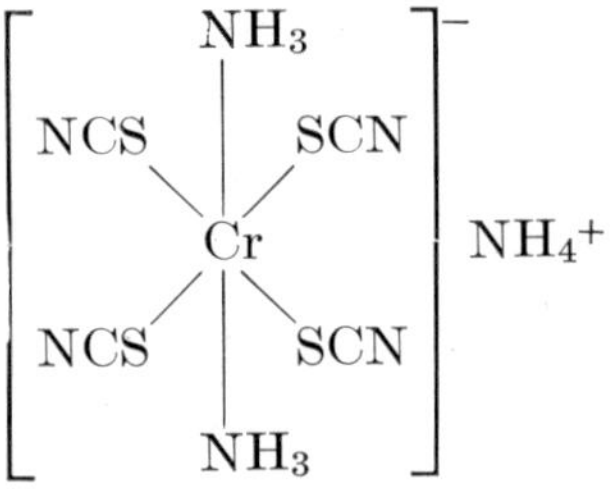

$$\left[\begin{array}{ccc} & NH_3 & \\ NCS & & SCN \\ & Cr & \\ NCS & & SCN \\ & NH_3 & \end{array} \right]^{-} NH_4^{+}$$

Ammonium Reineckate

Some Applications of Amino Acid Chemistry to Protein Analysis

In the course of the preceding discussion, reference has been made to a number of color tests which are characteristic of the side chains of various amino acids. These are the nitroprusside test (sulfhydryl groups), the Sakaguchi reaction (guanidino group), the Pauly reaction (imidazole ring), the xanthoproteic reaction (phenols), and the Millon reaction (phenols). Most of these reactions are also given by proteins which yield the appropriate amino acids on hydrolysis.[38] This may be taken to indicate that, in the unhydrolyzed protein, the side chains of these amino acids are not so substituted as to make them unavailable for chemical reaction with these reagents. These color reactions have been used in qualitative tests for proteins in natural materials. Some of the reactions have also been used to good advantage in attempts to study proteins in intact cells. Of special interest in such cytochemical studies is the use of ultraviolet absorption spectroscopy for the determination of protein concentration in cells and tissues. In view of the importance of spectrophotometric measurements in biochemical studies, a brief discussion of the principles involved is desirable.

The absorption of monochromatic light by a solution may be described by Beer's law, which states that the absorbance, A, or absorbancy, A_s (formerly termed optical density, d), of the solution is given by the expression $\log (I_0/I)$, where I_0 is the intensity of the incident light, and I is the intensity of the emergent light. The specific absorbance, k, or absorbancy index, a_s (formerly termed absorption coefficient or extinction coefficient, E), is defined as A/cl, where c is the concentration of the absorbing material in grams per liter, and l is the distance (in centimeters) traveled by the light through the solution. If one wishes to express the light absorption in terms of the molar concentration of the absorbing material, the molar absorbance, ε, or molar absorbancy index, a_M (formerly termed molecular extinction coefficient, E_{mol}), is given by the equation

[38] R. M. Herriott, *Advances in Protein Chem.*, **3**, 169 (1947); H. S. Olcott and H. Fraenkel-Conrat, *Chem. Revs.*, **41**, 151 (1947).

$\varepsilon = kM$, where M is the molecular weight.[39] If the value of k or of ε at various wave lengths of light is plotted as the ordinate against the wave length as the abscissa, a curve results which gives the absorption spectrum of the absorbing material in the solution. Most modern instruments designed for this purpose permit the accurate estimation of the optical density of a solution at narrowly spaced intervals from about 200 mμ (2000 A) to about 650 mμ (6500 A).[40] [1 m$\mu = 10$ A (angstrom units) $= 10^{-7}$ cm.] Visible light is composed of light rays having wave lengths from about 400 mμ (violet) to about 650 mμ (red), and the region below 400 mμ is termed the ultraviolet region of the spectrum.

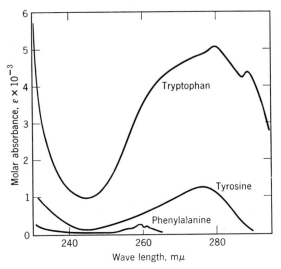

Fig. 1. Ultraviolet absorption spectra of aromatic amino acids derived from proteins (pH 8).

Most organic substances absorb light of wave lengths below 250 mμ; the absorption of light of longer wave lengths is usually associated with the presence, in the molecule, of unsaturated linkages. In general, an increase in the number of unsaturated linkages and their presence in conjugated systems contribute to light absorption at longer wave lengths. Of the widely distributed protein amino acids, only phenylalanine, tyrosine, and tryptophan exhibit extensive light absorption at wave lengths longer than 250 mμ; this may be attributed to their aromatic nature. The absorption spectra of these amino acids are given in Fig. 1, and it

39 W. R. Brode, *Am. Scientist*, **43**, 259 (1955).

40 J. H. Harley and S. E. Wiberley, *Instrumental Analysis*, John Wiley & Sons, New York, 1954

will be seen that phenylalanine exhibits maximal absorption at about 260 mμ, whereas tyrosine and tryptophan have their absorption maxima at about 275 mμ and 280 mμ respectively. If a protein contains one or more of these amino acids, therefore, an aqueous solution of the protein will absorb light in the region 260 to 290 mμ, and this property may be used to measure its concentration. Since the relative proportions and absolute content of the three amino acids vary widely from one protein to another, each protein will, in general, exhibit a different value for the wave length of maximal absorption and the specific absorbance. Thus, a 1 per cent solution of human serum albumin exhibits maximal absorption at 280 mμ, where the value of k is 0.53; on the other hand, a 1 per cent solution of beef insulin absorbs maximally at 277 mμ, and the value for k is 1.13. Clearly, the use of such values is justified only when one is dealing with solutions in which no other substances absorb light appreciably near 280 mμ. In the purification of proteins, it is frequently convenient to determine the protein concentration of crude preparations spectrophotometrically, and a correction is made for the interference by nucleic acids, which absorb maximally near 260 mμ (p. 193). An approximate estimate may be obtained by means of the formula: $1.45A_{280} - 0.74A_{260} =$ mg protein per ml. This procedure, though rapid, is less reliable than the Kjeldahl method (p. 28) or the biuret method (p. 130).

Optical Activity of Amino Acids

The property of amino acids, when in solution, that enables them to rotate the plane of polarized light is termed optical activity. A brief outline of the basic concepts involved in this phenomenon is given in what follows; a more complete discussion may be found in the treatise by Lowry.[41]

In 1669 it was found that when an object is viewed through a crystal of Iceland spar (a transparent variety of calcite, $CaCO_3$) a double image results. This was explained in 1690 by the physicist Huygens, who showed that when a ray of light impinges on the crystal two rays are formed. One of these, called the "ordinary" ray, was refracted (bent) in accord with Snell's law of refraction; the other, termed the "extraordinary" ray, was refracted in a manner that depended upon the angle that the incident ray formed with the crystal (Fig. 2). The phenomenon of "double refraction" was shown to involve a polarization of the two rays, so that one of the rays vibrates in a plane at right angles to the plane of vibration of the other; i.e., the two rays are plane-polarized. In 1828 Nicol described a prism which is made of two pieces of

[41] T. M. Lowry, *Optical Rotatory Power,* Longmans, Green and Co., London, 1935.

Iceland spar cut from a single crystal along a certain plane and then cemented together with Canada balsam. When unpolarized light passes through this prism at the proper angle to the "optic axis," only the

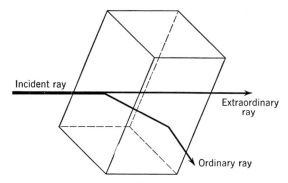

Fig. 2. Double refraction of light by a crystal of Iceland spar.

extraordinary ray is transmitted, while the ordinary ray is absorbed in the darkened lateral faces of the prism. If the emergent extraordinary ray is allowed to fall upon another "Nicol prism," the ray will pass through if the orientation of the prisms is the same (Fig. 3). If the second prism is rotated through an angle of 90°, the plane-polarized

Fig. 3. Two Nicol prisms in parallel.

light will be absorbed in the same way in which the ordinary ray had been absorbed in the first prism. When the extraordinary ray is seen through both prisms they are said to be "parallel"; when the ray is not seen the prisms are said to be "crossed."

During the early part of the nineteenth century, the French physicist Biot found that quartz crystals had the remarkable property of rotating the plane of the polarized light. Following up this discovery, he observed, in 1815, that fluids such as oil of turpentine or an alcoholic solution of camphor also had this property. A few years later he described the rotatory power of aqueous solutions of sucrose, and by 1832 he had shown that a great variety of organic compounds when in solution were "optically active." Among these compounds was tartaric acid, and the subsequent investigation of the optical activity of this substance by Pasteur marked a high point in the history of organic chemistry.

The development of the Nicol prism made it possible, in 1844, to construct an instrument, named the polarimeter, which allows one to measure the angle through which a plane-polarized ray is rotated in passing through a solution of an optically active substance. In the polarimeter, unpolarized light passes into one Nicol prism (the polarizer) in the manner described above, and the emergent polarized ray is allowed to go through the solution containing an optically active substance. If the light is now passed into a second Nicol prism, it will be found that the angle through which this prism must be turned to achieve extinction will not be 90°, as before, but will differ from 90° by the extent to which the optically active substance has rotated the plane of polarized light. If a substance rotates the plane so that the second prism (the analyzer) must be turned clockwise, the substance is said to be dextrorotatory [a plus (+) rotation]; if the analyzer must be turned counterclockwise, the substance is levorotatory [a minus (−) rotation]. Modern polarimeters are so constructed as to permit an accurate measurement in degrees (within 0.001°) of the angle of rotation of the analyzer. An excellent discussion of polarimetry will be found in the book by Bates.[42] At different wave lengths polarized light is rotated to a different extent by an optically active substance; it is necessary therefore that the incident unpolarized light be monochromatic, i.e., of a single wave length. In practice, the D line of the sodium flame ($\lambda = 589$ mμ or 5890 A) or, less frequently, the green line of a mercury discharge lamp ($\lambda = 546$ mμ) is employed.

Since the observed extent of optical rotation (designated α) is dependent on the concentration of the substance in the solution and on the length of the tube containing the solution, it is the custom to report data on the optical activity of organic compounds in terms of their "specific rotations," with an indication of the light source employed, the temperature, the concentration of the solute, and the nature of the solvent. The specific rotation ($[\alpha]$) is given by the formula

$$[\alpha] = \frac{\text{Observed rotation in degrees}}{\text{Length of tube (dm)} \times \text{concentration (g/cc)}}$$

Thus the specific rotation of the proline isolated from protein hydrolysates is $[\alpha]_D^{23} = -85.0°$ (1.0 per cent in water). Reference will be found in the literature to values for the "molar rotation" of substances. This is designated by the symbol $[M]$ and is equal to the product of $[\alpha]$ and the molecular weight, divided by 100.

The first clear appreciation of the relation between optical activity and chemical structure came from the work of Pasteur, who in 1848 discovered that two different crystal forms of the sodium ammonium

---

[42] F. J. Bates et al., *Polarimetry, Saccharimetry and the Sugars,* U. S. Government Printing Office, Washington, 1942.

salts of tartaric acid could be obtained by mechanical separation of the crystals of the salts of an optically inactive form (named racemic acid) of this acid. When the two crystal forms had been separated, Pasteur dissolved each in water and showed that one solution rotated plane-polarized light to the right while the other was levorotatory. An excellent description of this momentous discovery may be found in the biography of Pasteur by Dubos (p. 2).

The *dextro-* and *levo*-tartaric acid salts that Pasteur obtained from the salt of racemic acid could be converted into the free acids, which were found to be identical in melting point, solubility, and other physical properties but to differ in the sign of the optical rotation. What is especially important, the numerical value of the rotation of the two tartaric acids, was the same. Pairs of substances that bear this relationship to each other are termed enantiomorphs (Greek *enantio*, opposite), and they may be designated as the *d*-enantiomorph and the *l*-enantiomorph, where *d* and *l* denote the sign of optical rotation under a given set of conditions. A mixture of equal amounts of the two enantiomorphs forms an optically inactive racemate, which represents the *dl*-form of the compound. In mechanically separating the *d*- and *l*-forms of the tartaric acid salt, Pasteur effected the "resolution" of the racemate. However, this method of resolution is applicable only in exceptional instances, since it is a common phenomenon that racemic compounds crystallize in such a way that each crystal contains equal proportions of the enantiomorphs and no mechanical separation is possible. Indeed, racemic sodium ammonium tartrate, studied by Pasteur, forms such *dl*-crystals above 28° C; it is only below this temperature that the enantiomorphs crystallize separately. In this, as in the later successes he achieved, may be found proof of Pasteur's dictum that "In the field of experimentation, chance favors only the prepared mind."

To the evidence of his experimental skill in the resolution of the salts of racemic acid, Pasteur added one of the outstanding instances of brilliant intuition when he proposed that the two enantiomorphic tartaric acids are asymmetric structures which are related to each other in the same way as an asymmetric object is related to its nonsuperposable mirror image. In 1860 he wrote:

Are the atoms of the dextro acid arranged along the spirals of a right handed helix, or situated at the corners of an irregular tetrahedron . . . ? We cannot answer these questions. But what cannot be doubted is that there is a grouping of the atoms in an asymmetric arrangement which has a non-superposable image. What is not less certain, is that the atoms of the levo acid have precisely the inverse asymmetric arrangement.

With the development of structural formulae in organic chemistry, it became possible for van't Hoff and LeBel, in 1874, to provide a more precise formulation of Pasteur's hypothesis. The theory proposed by these two investigators, who developed it independently but almost simultaneously, was that the optical activity of organic substances is a consequence of the presence in the molecule of an asymmetric carbon atom, i.e., a carbon atom to which are attached 4 different atoms or groups of atoms. This theory was supported by a wealth of experimental evidence, and it forms the basis for the subsequent discussion of the optical activity of amino acids. For a more extensive treatment of the general problem of asymmetry in organic compounds, see Wheland.[43]

If one examines the formula of alanine, it will be seen that it contains an asymmetric carbon atom. One should therefore expect two enantiomorphic forms of the amino acid, which may be represented as shown. The representation of the tetrahedral arrangement of groups

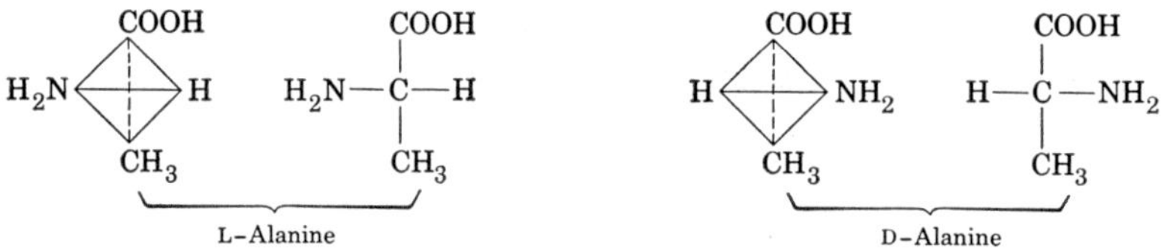

L–Alanine   D–Alanine

about an asymmetric carbon atom follows a convention introduced by Emil Fischer. In the tetrahedron corresponding to L-alanine, if the H atom is selected as the apex, and if one looks down at the other three groups, these groups will be found in the clockwise order: methyl, amino, carboxyl. It has been demonstrated recently that the Fischer convention for the designation of configuration actually corresponds to the "absolute configuration" of optically active molecules.[44]

The form of alanine obtained from acid hydrolysates of proteins is dextrorotatory; $[\alpha]_D^{25} = +14.5°$ (10 per cent in 6 N HCl) or $+2.4°$ (10 per cent in water). Examination of the other protein amino acids shows all of them to be optically active, with the exception of glycine, which has no asymmetric carbon atom. In Table 2 are listed the optical rotations of most of the protein amino acids; it will be noted that in aqueous solution some of the amino acids are dextrorotatory while others are levorotatory. As will be seen later (p. 97), the magnitude and direction of the specific rotation of amino acids depends on pH.

The question then arises about the configuration of the amino acids derived from proteins. For example, isoleucine is dextrorotatory in water and phenylalanine is levorotatory; this does not mean, however, that the relative positions of the corresponding groups about the asym-

[43] G. W. Wheland, *Advanced Organic Chemistry*, Chapter 6, John Wiley & Sons, New York, 1949.

[44] J. M. Bijvoet, *Endeavour*, **14**, 71 (1955).

Table 2. Optical Rotation of Protein Amino Acids

	Temperature, °C	Solvent	Concentration, g per 100 ml of Solution	$[\alpha]_D$
L-Alanine	25	6 N HCl	10.0	+ 14.5
	25	H_2O	10.0	+ 2.4
L-Arginine	23	6 N HCl	1.65	+ 27.6
	20	H_2O	3.5	+ 12.5
L-Aspartic acid	24	6 N HCl	2.0	+ 24.6
	18	H_2O	1.3	+ 4.7
L-Asparagine	20	3.4 N HCl	2.2	+ 34.3
	20	H_2O	1.4	− 5.3
L-Cysteine	26	N HCl	12.1	+ 7.6
L-Cystine	24	N HCl	1.0	− 214.4
Diiodo-L-tyrosine	20	N HCl	5.1	+ 2.9
L-Glutamic acid	25	1.7 N HCl	7.0	+ 31.7
L-Glutamine	23	H_2O	3.6	+ 6.0
L-Histidine	25	6 N HCl	1.0	+ 13.3
	25	H_2O	0.75	− 39.0
Hydroxy-L-lysine	25	6 N HCl	2.0	+ 14.5
Hydroxy-L-proline	20	N HCl	1.3	− 47.3
	22.5	H_2O	1.0	− 75.2
L-Isoleucine	25	6 N HCl	3.2	+ 40.7
	25	H_2O	3.2	+ 12.2
L-Leucine	25	6 N HCl	2.0	+ 15.1
	25	H_2O	2.0	− 10.7
L-Lysine	23	6 N HCl	2.0	+ 25.9
	20	H_2O	6.5	+ 14.6
L-Methionine	20	3 N HCl	5.0	+ 23.4
L-Phenylalanine	25	N HCl	4.0	− 7.7
	25	H_2O	1.6	− 35.2
L-Proline	20	0.5 N HCl	0.6	− 52.6
	23	H_2O	1.0	− 85.0
L-Serine	25	N HCl	9.3	+ 15.0
	20	H_2O	10.4	− 6.8
L-Threonine	26	H_2O	1.1	− 28.3
L-Tryptophan	20	0.5 N HCl	1.0	+ 2.4
	25	H_2O	2.1	− 32.2
L-Tyrosine	20	6.3 N HCl	4.4	− 8.6
L-Valine	20	6 N HCl	3.4	+ 28.8
	20	H_2O	4.0	+ 6.3

metric carbon atom must be mirror images of one another. In fact, extensive experimental work during the period 1920–1950 has shown that all the protein amino acids are configurationally the same with respect to the arrangement of the groups about the α-carbon atom. Also, *dextro*-alanine has a configuration analogous to that arbitrarily defined for levorotatory glyceraldehyde, if the substituents on the asymmetric carbon atoms are equated as shown.

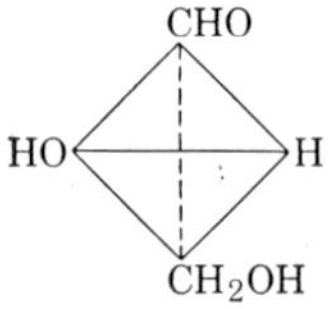

L(−)-Glyceraldehyde

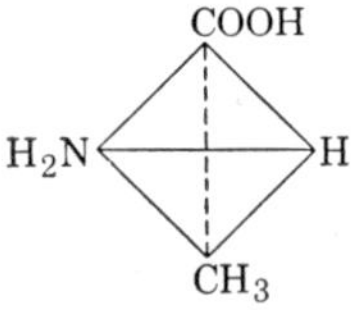

L(+)-Alanine

It is a generally accepted convention to designate the configuration about an asymmetric carbon atom by means of a small capital L or D, where the configuration has been shown experimentally to correspond to that in *levo*-glyceraldehyde (arbitrarily defined as L-glyceraldehyde) or to that in *dextro*-glyceraldehyde (arbitrarily defined as D-glyceraldehyde). The small capitals are reserved for the designation of configuration; they should not be used interchangeably with *d* and *l*, which denote the direction of optical rotation. The sign of rotation is occasionally included in parentheses after the capital letter denoting configuration; however, this is not necessary since the symbol L or D is unambiguous.

The establishment of configurational relationships among a large series of substances is a task of great difficulty, since one must develop chemical methods of transforming one substance into another without destroying the optical activity (racemization) or inverting the spatial arrangement of the substituents about the asymmetric carbon atom (Walden inversion). An excellent account of the work that led to the establishment of the configurational relationships among the amino acids may be found in the article by Neuberger.[45] A key relationship is the assignment of the same configuration to *dextro*-lactic acid and to *dextro*-alanine. The configurational relationship between D-glyceraldehyde and D-lactic acid has been demonstrated by the reaction sequence shown.

D(+)-Glyceraldehyde — D(−)-Glyceric acid — D(+)-β-Bromolactic acid — D(−)-Lactic acid

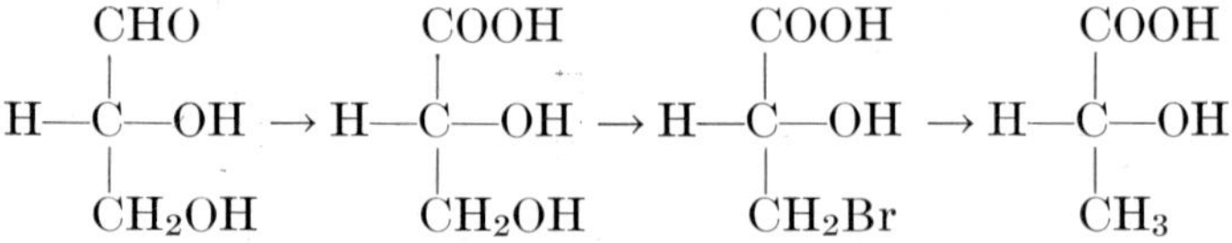

The fact that the amino acids obtained upon hydrolysis of proteins under conditions that avoid racemization all have the L-configuration, regardless of their rotation, does not mean that the enantiomorphic D-amino acids do not occur in nature. D-Amino acids have been found in some substances elaborated by plants and microorganisms. For example, several of the antibiotics produced by bacteria yield D-amino

[45] A. Neuberger, *Advances in Protein Chem.*, **4**, 297 (1948).

acids when they are hydrolyzed. These antibiotics are not proteins but smaller aggregates of amino acids bound in peptide linkage (pp. 137 f.). Thus the gramicidins, elaborated by *Bacillus brevis*, yield D-leucine; this D-amino acid is also obtained on hydrolysis of the polymyxins, formed by *Bacillus polymyxa*. The penicillamine found in the penicillins also has the D-configuration, and the capsular substance of the anthrax bacillus, on hydrolysis, yields D-glutamic acid. It will be clear from the foregoing, therefore, that the occasional designation of the D-amino acids as "unnatural" is contrary to fact, and is to be avoided.

When protein amino acids other than glycine are made in the laboratory by the usual methods of organic synthesis, the products are DL-amino acids. Such DL-compounds are termed racemates, because of their relation to the optically inactive tartaric acid first resolved by Pasteur. If the optically active enantiomorphs are desired, the racemic compound must be resolved. It was noted before that the method used by Pasteur in his classical work of 1848 was not generally applicable; this was realized by Pasteur, and he proceeded to develop a number of methods which in principle are still in use today.

A widely applicable procedure is to add to a solution of the racemate an optically active acid or base which will form sparingly soluble salts with the two enantiomorphs. Examples of suitable optically active bases are *l*-quinine, which Pasteur employed, or *l*-brucine. If a DL-acid is to be resolved, the addition of *l*-brucine will lead to the formation of two salts in the solution: the *l*-brucine salt of the L-acid and the *l*-brucine salt of the D-acid. These two salts not only have different numerical values of rotation, but also differ in their solubility behavior and in other respects as well. The difference in solubility makes it possible to separate the two salts by fractional crystallization and to obtain from each the desired optically active acid. In the application of this method to the resolution of DL-amino acids, the amino group is usually acylated to yield a benzoyl or formyl derivative. After resolution of the enantiomorphs, the protecting group may be removed by hydrolysis.

The characteristic feature of the brucine salts of the D- and L-acids is that they contain more than one center of asymmetry and that they differ in the configuration about only one of these centers. Such compounds, which are not mirror images of each other, are defined as diastereoisomers (Greek *dia,* apart). The work of Pasteur thus showed that resolution of DL-compounds could be effected by converting them into a mixture of diastereoisomeric salts by the addition of a suitable optically active acid or base.

Among the protein amino acids are several that have, in addition to the α-carbon, a second asymmetric carbon. These are threonine, isoleucine, hydroxyproline, and hydroxylysine. If one considers threonine, it will be seen that four stereoisomers are possible, since the number of such isomers is equal to 2^n, where n is the number of asymmetric carbons. The amino acid isolated from proteins has the configuration to which the name L-threonine is assigned; the mirror image gives the configuration of D-threonine. The other two possible isomers are clearly diastereoisomers of the threonines, and they are designated L-allothreonine and D-allothreonine (Greek *allos*, other). Similar considerations apply to

$$\begin{array}{cccc}
\text{COOH} & \text{COOH} & \text{COOH} & \text{COOH} \\
| & | & | & | \\
\text{H}_2\text{N}-\text{C}-\text{H} & \text{H}-\text{C}-\text{NH}_2 & \text{H}_2\text{N}-\text{C}-\text{H} & \text{H}-\text{C}-\text{NH}_2 \\
| & | & | & | \\
\text{H}-\text{C}-\text{OH} & \text{HO}-\text{C}-\text{H} & \text{HO}-\text{C}-\text{H} & \text{H}-\text{C}-\text{OH} \\
| & | & | & | \\
\text{CH}_3 & \text{CH}_3 & \text{CH}_3 & \text{CH}_3 \\
\text{L-Threonine} & \text{D-Threonine} & \text{L-Allothreonine} & \text{D-Allothreonine}
\end{array}$$

the other protein amino acids with two asymmetric carbons. By convention the amino acid obtained from proteins is designated the L-amino acid; this is based solely on the configuration about the α-carbon atom.[46] The enantiomorph of the L-amino acid is the D-amino acid. For the diastereoisomeric amino acids, the prefix "allo" is placed before the commonly accepted name of the protein amino acid. This nomenclature suffers from the disadvantage that the configuration about the second center of asymmetry, though known for threonine, isoleucine, and hydroxyproline, is not specified in the name. Thus the configuration of the L-isoleucine derived from proteins appears to be that given in the accompanying formula;[47] the diastereoisomeric L-amino acid is termed L-alloisoleucine. The hydroxy-L-proline from protein hydrolysates has a configuration in which the OH and COOH groups are in *trans* position. The corresponding diastereoisomeric *cis* form is allohydroxy-L-proline.

$$\begin{array}{cc}
\text{COOH} & \\
| & \\
\text{H}_2\text{N}-\text{C}-\text{H} & \\
| & \\
\text{H}_3\text{C}-\text{C}-\text{H} & \\
| & \\
\text{CH}_2\text{CH}_3 & \\
\text{L-Isoleucine} & \text{Hydroxy-L-proline}
\end{array}$$

When one of the amino acids having two centers of asymmetry is prepared synthetically, two DL-forms may be expected (e.g., DL-threonine and DL-allothreonine).

A special case of compounds having two centers of asymmetry includes substances in which the groups about the two centers are iden-

[46] H. B. Vickery, *J. Biol. Chem.*, **169**, 237 (1947).

[47] M. Winitz et al., *J. Am. Chem. Soc.*, **77**, 3106 (1955).

tical but the configuration about one of the two centers is a mirror image of the other. Compounds of this type are "internally compensated" and hence are optically inactive. They are termed *meso* compounds. Among the amino acids an example is *meso*cystine. Another

$$
\begin{array}{cc}
\text{COOH} & \text{COOH} \\
| & | \\
\text{H}_2\text{N—C—H} \quad \text{H—C—NH}_2 \\
| & | \\
\text{CH}_2\text{—S—S—CH}_2
\end{array}
\qquad
\begin{array}{cc}
\text{COOH} & \text{COOH} \\
| & | \\
\text{H}_2\text{N—C—H} \; \text{H}_2\text{N—C—H} \\
| & | \\
\text{CH}_2\text{—S—S—CH}_2
\end{array}
$$

Mesocystine   L-Cystine

amino acid in which internal compensation is possible is α, ϵ-diaminopimelic acid, found in bacteria;[48] the material isolated from some organisms is optically inactive and apparently is the *meso* form. A similar conclusion has been drawn in regard to the lanthionine obtained from

$$
\begin{array}{cc}
\text{COOH} & \text{COOH} \\
| & | \\
\text{H}_2\text{N—C—H} \quad \text{H—C—NH}_2 \\
| & | \\
\text{CH}_2\text{——CH}_2\text{——CH}_2
\end{array}
\qquad
\begin{array}{cc}
\text{COOH} & \text{COOH} \\
| & | \\
\text{H}_2\text{N—C—H} \quad \text{H—C—NH}_2 \\
| & | \\
\text{CH}_2\text{——S——CH}_2
\end{array}
$$

Meso-α,ϵ-diaminopimelic acid   *Mesolanthionine*

subtilin (cf. p. 60). A naturally occurring derivative of α, ϵ-diaminopimelic acid is tabtoxinine, which is present in *Pseudomonas tabaci*, and which has three centers of asymmetry;[49] the stereochemical configuration of the natural compound has not been elucidated.

$$
\begin{array}{ccc}
\text{NH}_2 & \text{OH} & \text{NH}_2 \\
| & | & | \\
\text{HOOC—CH—CH—CH}_2\text{—CH}_2\text{—CH—COOH}
\end{array}
$$

Tabtoxinine

The optical activity of amino acids is a consequence of their asymmetric structure, and, since the amino acids are constituents of proteins, the intimate structure of proteins is also characterized by molecular asymmetry. In addition to the asymmetry introduced by the presence of the residues of optically active amino acids, other structural factors (cf. p. 160) also contribute to the optical activity shown by aqueous solutions of proteins. As will be seen from later sections of this book, the chemical reactions in living systems involve a selectivity in the way in which stereoisomeric forms are treated in metabolism. Since the enzymic catalysts which mediate these reactions are protein in nature, it becomes more readily understandable why asymmetry in the intimate structure of proteins is of considerable importance in the physiological phenomena observed in living matter.

The ability of living systems to discriminate between stereoisomeric

[48] D. S. Hoare and E. Work, *Biochem. J.*, **61**, 562 (1955); **65**, 441 (1957).

[49] J. M. Stewart and D. W. Woolley, *J. Am. Chem. Soc.*, **78**, 5236 (1956).

forms of a chemical substance also was discovered by Pasteur. In 1857 he found that, when a mold grew in the solution of a salt of the racemic tartaric acid, only the dextrorotatory form was used by the organism, and, when this form had disappeared, as judged by the optical rotation, the levorotatory enantiomorph could be isolated from the solution. It is known today that this selectivity of action is a consequence of the action of enzymes, and there are many methods in the biochemical literature for the resolution of racemic compounds, and especially DL-amino acids, by means of enzymes.[50]

[50] J. P. Greenstein, *Advances in Protein Chem.*, **9,** 121 (1954).

4 ·   Amino Acids and Proteins as Electrolytes

An important property of all amino acids, which arises from the fact that they contain carboxylic (COOH) or amino (NH_2) groups, is their behavior as electrolytes. It is customary to refer to COOH groups as acidic in nature and to NH_2 groups as basic in character. For the purposes of the present discussion, however, it will be useful to redefine acids and bases in the more general terms developed by Brønsted and Lowry. According to this definition, an acid is a substance that can give off protons (hydrogen ions, H^+); a base is a substance that can take up protons.[1] An acid HA, on liberating a hydrogen ion, is transformed into its "conjugate base" A^- and HA is related to A^- as follows.

$$HA \rightleftharpoons H^+ + A^-$$

Thus, in the equilibrium between acetic acid and acetate ion,

$$CH_3COOH \rightleftharpoons H^+ + CH_3COO^-$$

CH_3COOH is the acid, and CH_3COO^- is the base. Similarly, in the equilibrium between methylamine and the methylammonium ion,

$$CH_3NH_3^+ \rightleftharpoons H^+ + CH_3NH_2$$

the methylammonium ion is the acid, and the free amine is the base.

All the dissociation phenomena that will be considered here are assumed to occur in water; under these conditions, the hydrogen ion does not exist in solution as such, but in the form of the hydronium ion, H_3O^+ ($H^+ + H_2O \rightleftharpoons H_3O^+$). For convenience, however, the hydrogen ion formed upon the electrolytic dissociation of an acid may be designated H^+; this is permissible since water does not figure in the equilibrium, although it is essential for the ionization to occur.

In extremely dilute solutions, the concentration (in moles per liter)

[1] R. P. Bell, *Acids and Bases*, Methuen and Co., London, 1952.

of hydrogen ions, and of other substances, may be considered to approximate their "activity." The molar concentration of an ion $[A^-]$ is related to its activity (A^-) by the equation $[A^-]f_{A^-} = (A^-)$, where f_{A^-} is the "activity coefficient" of the ion. In the subsequent discussion, when reference is made to the activity of a substance, the appropriate symbol for that substance will be enclosed in parentheses; when the molar concentration is meant, the symbol will be enclosed in brackets. Thus, hydrogen ion activity will be denoted (H^+) and hydrogen ion concentration will be denoted $[H^+]$. The determination of the pH of a solution gives an approximate measure of the (H^+) of a solution (cf. pp. 18, 296).

Numerical values of activity coefficients for ions in dilute solutions of electrolytes (about 0.01 N or less) may be calculated by means of the limiting law deduced by Debye and Hückel:

$$- \log f_i = 0.5z_i{}^2\sqrt{\Gamma/2}$$

This states that the negative logarithm of the activity coefficient of an ion (i) is directly related to the square of the number of charges on that ion (z_i) and the square root of the molar ionic strength of the solution ($\Gamma/2$) (p. 20). The basic assumption in the formulation of the Debye-Hückel theory is that the ions in a solution do not behave as independent entities, but interact with one another; thus, an ion bearing a positive charge is surrounded by a cloud of ions of opposite charge, and vice versa. The extent of this interaction is determined by the charge on the ion in question and the concentrations and charges of all the ions in the solution.

It will be recalled that some acids (e.g., hydrochloric acid, nitric acid) are completely dissociated in aqueous solution and are referred to as strong acids. In what follows, the discussion will concern primarily the dissociation of weak acids such as acetic acid, which do not dissociate completely in aqueous solution.

If one titrates 30 ml of a solution of N acetic acid with N sodium hydroxide and plots pH (as the ordinate) against the milliliters of alkali added, one obtains a curve (designated A in Fig. 1) which has an inflection at the point at which 15 ml of N NaOH had been added; at this point, the pH of the solution is 4.7. In an analogous titration of 30 ml of N hydrochloric acid, the resulting curve (B in Fig. 1) shows that, instead of the gradual increase in pH observed with acetic acid, the pH of the hydrochloric acid solution does not change appreciably until the neutralization is nearly complete; then the further addition of a small quantity of alkali causes a marked change in pH. In both titrations the addition of OH^- ions causes the removal of H^+ ions from the solution. With acetic acid, which is only slightly dissociated to CH_3COO^- and H^+ at the start of the titration, the addition of OH^- shifts the equilibrium $CH_3COOH \rightleftharpoons CH_3COO^- + H^+$ to the right. The apparent dissociation contant

$$K_a' = \frac{[CH_3COO^-](H^+)}{[CH_3COOH]}$$

becomes equal to (H^+) when $[CH_3COO^-] = [CH_3COOH]$. This is the situation at the inflection point in the titration curve of acetic acid, and the pH corresponding to this point is termed the pK_a' of acetic acid.

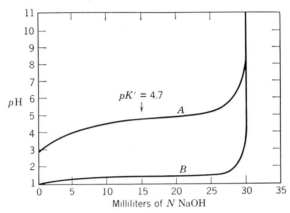

Fig. 1. Titration curves of acetic acid and of hydrochloric acid (cf. text).

Thus the pK_a' of a weak acid is the negative logarithm (to the base 10) of the (H^+) at which the concentrations of the acid and the conjugate base are equal. For acetic acid in a solution of 0.1 ionic strength, $pK_a' = 4.65$; this corresponds to $(H^+) = 2.24 \times 10^{-5}$.

As acetic acid is titrated, it resists changes in the pH of the system. It thus forms what is termed a "buffer." All weak acids, in the presence of their conjugate bases, form buffer solutions. A convenient method for the calculation of the approximate pH of a buffer mixture, given the pK_a' of the acid, is provided by the Henderson-Hasselbalch equation. From the formula for K_a',

$$(H^+) = K_a' \frac{[acid]}{[conjugate\ base]} = K_a' \frac{[acid]}{[salt]}$$

The concentration of the conjugate base (e.g., acetate ion) may be set equal to the concentration of the salt (e.g., sodium acetate) because the latter is almost completely dissociated in solution. Taking the negative logarithms of the terms in the above equation, one obtains

$$- \log (H^+) = - \log K_a' - \log \frac{[acid]}{[salt]}$$

$$pH = pK_a' + \log \frac{[salt]}{[acid]} = pK_a' + \log \frac{[A^-]}{[HA]}$$

The latter equation is the Henderson-Hasselbalch equation and is applicable to buffer systems derived from any weak acid HA which dissociates to $H^+ + A^-$.

In calculating the pH of buffer solutions, it is important to recognize that K_a' usually differs from K_a, the true or limiting value of the dissociation constant. Since

$$K_a' = \frac{(H^+)[A^-]}{[HA]} \quad \text{and} \quad K_a = \frac{(H^+)(A^-)}{(HA)} = \frac{(H^+)[A^-]f_{A^-}}{[HA]f_{HA}}$$

it follows that

$$K_a = K_a' \frac{f_{A^-}}{f_{HA}} \quad \text{or} \quad pK_a' = pK_a + \log \frac{f_{A^-}}{f_{HA}}$$

For salt solutions of moderate concentration, the ratio f_{A^-}/f_{HA} is less than unity, and pK_a' is less than pK_a. The difference is about 0.1 for buffers of 0.1 ionic strength containing only univalent ions, but is as much as 0.4 for $M/15$ phosphate buffers ($pK_a = 7.2$, $pK_a' = 6.8$). For any one buffer the value of pK_a' remains constant as the pH is varied, provided that the total ionic strength of the solution is unchanged.

An important feature of the maintenance of the constancy of the internal environment of living organisms is the operation of buffer systems to control the pH of aqueous fluids within relatively narrow limits. Thus, in mammalian blood, where the pH is maintained near 7.35, a number of inorganic buffer systems (carbonic acid-bicarbonate, primary phosphate-secondary phosphate) contribute to this pH control (Chapter 36). As will be seen later, the proteins of the blood also play an important part in the buffering capacity of this biological fluid.

Among the buffer systems are to be included those pairs of acids and conjugate bases in which the proton donor has a color different from that of the proton acceptor. Buffer systems of this kind may be used as indicators of the pH of a solution and for following a titration. Here we are dealing with an equilibrium

$$\text{H indicator} \rightleftharpoons H^+ + \text{indicator}$$
(color A)   (color B)

For example, the acid form of phenolphthalein is colorless, whereas the conjugate base is red; the pK_a' is 9.7. Hence, this indicator is suitable for use in acid-base titrations in which the stoichiometric end point occurs in the region 8.5 to 10.0. Another indicator is bromphenol blue ($pK_a' = 4.0$), which is yellow at pH 3.1 and blue at pH 4.7. Other pH indicators have widely different pK' values (Table 1) and may therefore be used to good advantage in titrations when the stoichiometric end point falls within the range of greatest color change of the indicator.

The results of a titration in which N hydrochloric acid is added to

Table I. Properties of pH Indicators

Indicator	pK'	Colors and pH Range
Thymol blue (acid range)	1.7	Red-yellow (1.2–2.8)
Methyl orange	3.5	Red-yellow (3.1–4.4)
Bromphenol blue	4.0	Yellow-blue (3.1–4.7)
Bromcresol green	4.7	Yellow-blue (3.8–5.4)
Methyl red	5.0	Red-yellow (4.2–6.3)
Chlorphenol red	6.0	Yellow-red (5.1–6.7)
Bromcresol purple	6.2	Yellow-purple (5.4–7.0)
Bromthymol blue	7.0	Yellow-blue (6.0–7.6)
Phenol red	7.8	Yellow-red (7.0–8.6)
Cresol red	8.3	Yellow-red (7.4–9.0)
Thymol blue (alkaline range)	8.9	Yellow-blue (8.0–9.6)
Phenolphthalein	9.7	Colorless-red (8.3–10.0)

30 ml of N methylamine are shown in Fig. 2. It will be seen that a characteristic inflection is observed at pH 10.6, corresponding to the

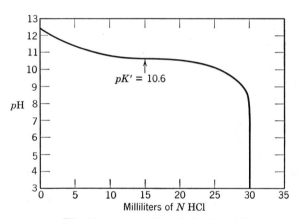

Fig. 2. Titration curve of methylamine (cf. text).

addition of 15 ml of acid. In this titration the amine, which is the conjugate base of the methylammonium ion, is accepting protons, and the equilibrium constant for the dissociation of the acid $CH_3NH_3{}^+$ is

$$K_a' = \frac{[CH_3NH_2](H^+)}{[CH_3NH_3{}^+]}$$

The inflection point in the curve corresponds to a pK_a' of 10.6, or a K_a' of 2.4×10^{-11}.

Similarly, the ammonium ion and ammonia are related to one another by the equation $NH_3 + H^+ \rightleftharpoons NH_4{}^+$; therefore

$$K_a' = \frac{[NH_3](H^+)}{[NH_4{}^+]}$$

At one time it was the practice to refer to NH_4OH as the base, and to write its dissociation in the form

$$K_b' = \frac{[NH_4^+][OH^-]}{[NH_4OH]}$$

Thus $K_b' = [OH^-]$ when the ratio $[NH_4^+]/[NH_4OH] = 1$. K_a' and K_b' are related to one another by the equation $K_a'K_b' = K_w' = 1 \times 10^{-14}$. Consequently, $pK_a' + pK_b' = 14$.

Amino Acids as Dipolar Ions

The reason why it is preferable to use the Brønsted-Lowry definition of acids and to speak only of the K_a' values will become apparent from a consideration of the titration behavior of amino acids. The representation of an amino acid such as glycine by the formula NH_2CH_2COOH suggests that one is dealing with a substance in which the NH_2 group

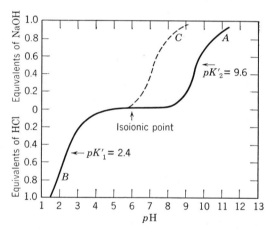

fig. 3. Titration curves of glycine. Curves A and B in aqueous solution; curve C in M formaldehyde.

acts as a conjugate base and the COOH group as an acid. It has been found, however, that this formulation is not a correct representation of the ionic state of an amino acid in aqueous solution.

If one dissolves glycine in water, the pH is about 6. As will be seen from Fig. 3, the addition of sodium hydroxide to this solution gives a curve (A) with an inflection at pH 9.6. In the titration of acetic acid with alkali it was obvious that the carboxyl group was serving as the proton donor. The question arises whether it is the carboxyl group of glycine that has a pK' of 9.6 when the amino acid is titrated with alkali. Certainly, the discrepancy between the value of 9.6 and the pK' of 4.7

for acetic acid is too great to be accounted for simply on the basis of the difference in the structures of glycine and acetic acid. Furthermore, when one titrates a solution of glycine with hydrochloric acid, a curve (B) is obtained with an inflection point at pH 2.4, and this value is far removed from the pK' of the methylammonium ion (10.6) found upon titration of methylamine with hydrochloric acid.

The answer to these discrepancies is provided by the effect of formaldehyde on the titration of glycine. As noted on p. 51, formaldehyde readily combines with the amino group of amino acids to give methylol derivatives; it does not react with NH_3^+ groups. Titration of glycine with hydrochloric acid, in the presence of M formaldehyde, causes no appreciable change in curve B; however, the result of the titration of glycine with sodium hydroxide in the presence of formaldehyde is markedly different from A and may be described by curve C (Fig. 3). What this means is that the group with a pK' at 9.6 is the positively charged NH_3^+ group of glycine, and the group with a pK' of 2.4 is the uncharged COOH group of the amino acid.

The cause of the marked shift in the titration curve in the presence of formaldehyde lies in the fact that the reaction of $NH_2CH_2COO^-$ with HCHO pulls the equilibrium $^+NH_3CH_2COO^- \rightleftharpoons NH_2CH_2COO^- + H^+$ to the right. In the presence of excess HCHO, therefore, the apparent value of pK' is lowered in the equation

$$pH = pK' + \log\frac{[RNH_2]}{[RNH_3^+]}$$

For a more extensive discussion of the reaction of formaldehyde with glycine and with other amino acids, see the article by French and Edsall.[2]

As shown in Fig. 3, the end point of a titration of glycine with alkali is near pH 12 when formaldehyde is absent, but this end point shifts to about pH 9 in the presence of M formaldehyde. This shift brings the stoichiometric end point of the alkalimetric titration within the range of the color change of phenolphthalein ($pK' = 9.7$) and serves as the basis of the Sørensen "formol" titration method for the estimation of amino acids.

From the preceding discussion it is clear that glycine, in common with other amino acids, has two pK' values. By convention it has become the practice to denote the pK' values in the order of increasing pH, with numerical subscripts to indicate the order of these values. Thus, for glycine, $pK_1' = 2.4$; $pK_2' = 9.6$ (at $25°$ C). When amino acids are dissolved in 85 to 90 per cent alcohol or acetone, the dissociation of α-carboxyl groups is repressed, and pK_1' values are raised by 2 to 3 pH units, without any appreciable change in pK_2'. Also, the pK' values of

[2] D. French and J. T. Edsall, *Advances in Protein Chem.*, **2**, 278 (1945).

indicators such as phenolphthalein are increased so that they are 2.5 to 3 pH units more alkaline than that of the α-ammonium group. This permits the alkalimetric titration of α-ammonium groups of amino acids or peptides by procedures such as those devised by Foreman (85 per cent ethanol, phenolphthalein) and by Willstätter and Waldschmidt-Leitz (90 per cent ethanol, phenolphthalein).

When glycine is present in aqueous solution at pH 6, the ionic species that predominates is the doubly charged ion $^+NH_3CH_2COO^-$. The term applied to such ions is "dipolar ion"; this designation is preferable to the earlier German term *Zwitterion* (hybrid ion). Since a dipolar ion can behave either as an acid or as a base, it has been referred to as an "amphoteric electrolyte" or "ampholyte." As alkali is added, the dipolar ion loses a proton; with the addition of acid, it accepts a proton. The predominant ionic species that may be found as one goes from a solution of glycine at low pH (ca. 1) to high pH (ca. 11) are as follows:

$$^+NH_3CH_2COOH \underset{+H^+}{\overset{-H^+}{\rightleftharpoons}} \; ^+NH_3CH_2COO^- \underset{+H^+}{\overset{-H^+}{\rightleftharpoons}} NH_2CH_2COO^-$$
$$\text{pH 1} \qquad\qquad \text{pH 6} \qquad\qquad \text{pH 11}$$

It will be noted that the presence of the NH_3^+ group tends to make the COOH group of glycine a stronger acid (lower pK' value) compared with acetic acid. This may be considered an electrostatic effect of a strong positive charge within a molecule in increasing the tendency of a dissociating group to release protons.

When the α-amino group of an amino acid is acylated, the pK' of the carboxyl group is raised; for example, $CH_3CO—NHCH_2COOH$ (acetyl-glycine) has a pK' of 3.7. Similarly, when the α-carboxyl group of an amino acid is converted to an amide, the pK' of the α-ammonium group is shifted to a lower pH, as with glycinamide ($NH_2CH_2CO—NH_2$), which has a pK' of 7.9. These shifts in pK' values following substitution are additional indications of the mutual electrostatic effect of the charged groups of amino acids.

Further evidence for the dipolar nature of amino acids in aqueous solution is provided by measurements of the dielectric constants of such solutions. The dielectric constant of a solution is given by the equation $D = D_0 + \delta C$, where D_0 is the dielectric constant of the solvent, δ is the "dielectric increment," and C is the concentration of the solute in moles per liter. For amino acids, the value of the dielectric increment is large and a positive number; this indicates that amino acid molecules have a large dipole moment due to the separation of discrete electric charges.

The fact that amino acids are doubly charged molecules in the solid state is indicated by their high melting points; in this regard they resemble inorganic salts (e.g., NaCl) which, in crystalline form, represent oriented arrays of oppositely charged ions.

As might be expected from their structure, the amino acids with paraffin side chains (e.g., alanine, valine, leucine) have pK_1' and pK_2' values close to those of glycine. With aspartic acid, however, there should be two pK' values corresponding to the dissociation of the two carboxyl

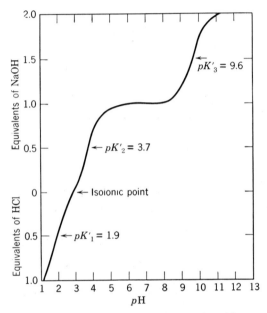

Fig. 4. Titration curve of aspartic acid.

groups, and the titration curve for this amino acid (at 25° C) has the form shown in Fig. 4. Here $pK_1' = 1.9$ (α-COOH); $pK_2' = 3.7$ (β-COOH); $pK_3' = 9.6$ (NH_3^+). Similarly, with glutamic acid (cf. Fig. 5), $pK_1' = 2.2$ (α-COOH); $pK_2' = 4.3$ (γ-COOH); $pK_3' = 9.7$ (NH_3^+). When the diaminomonocarboxylic acid lysine (cf. Fig. 5) is titrated, the following apparent dissociation constants are found: $pK_1' = 2.2$ (COOH); $pK_2' = 8.95$ (α-NH_3^+); $pK_3' = 10.5$ (ϵ-NH_3^+).

It will be recalled that, in addition to amino and carboxyl groups, protein amino acids may contain, as part of their side chains, the guanidino group (arginine), the phenolic group (tyrosine), the imidazolyl group (histidine), or the sulfhydryl group (cysteine). The titration curve of histidine is given in Fig. 5. These groups can participate in the reactions shown; the corresponding pK' values at 25° C are also indicated. The value of pK' for the sulfhydryl group of cysteine has

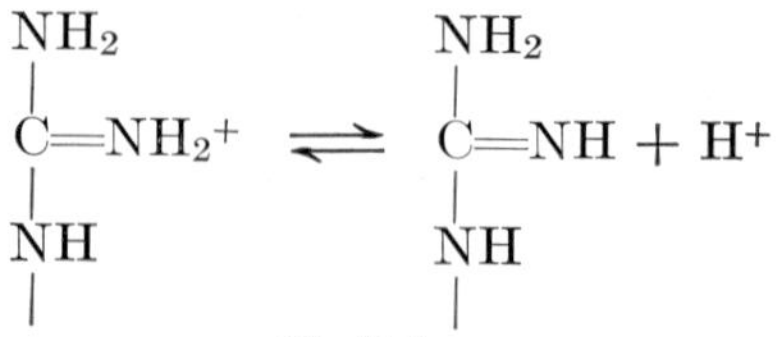

$$\begin{array}{c} NH_2 \\ | \\ C{=}NH_2^+ \\ | \\ NH \\ | \end{array} \rightleftharpoons \begin{array}{c} NH_2 \\ | \\ C{=}NH + H^+ \\ | \\ NH \\ | \end{array}$$

$pK' = 12.5$

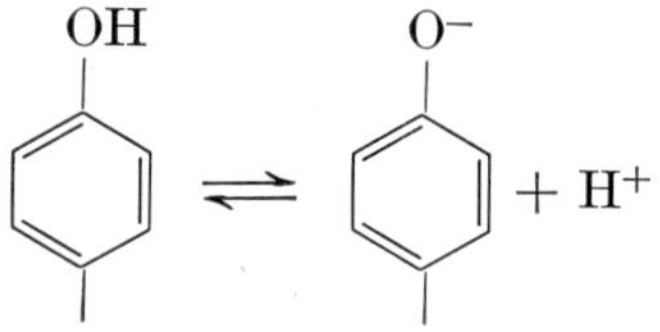

$pK' = 10.1$

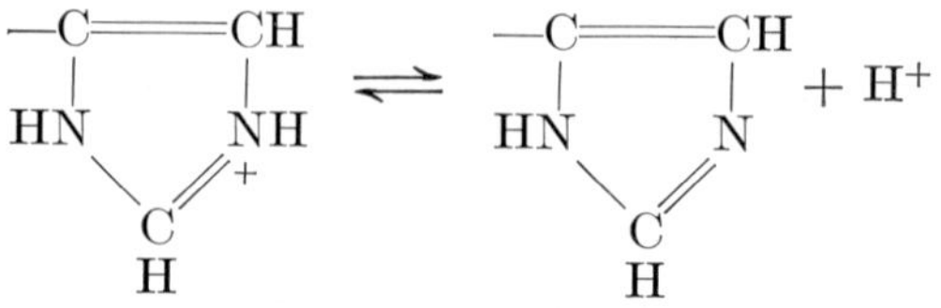

$pK' = 6.0$

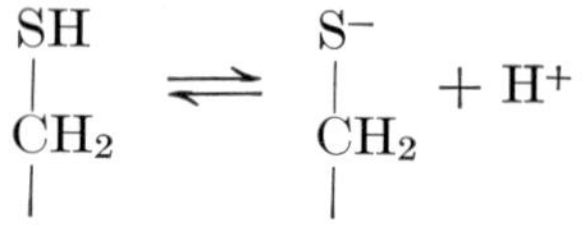

$pK' = ca.9$

been the subject of extensive discussion, and must be considered provisional.[3]

The term "isoionic point," used in Figs. 4 and 5, may be defined as the pH at which the number of protons combined with the basic groups of an ampholyte is equal to the number of protons dissociated from the acidic groups. At the isoionic point, the average net electric charge of the amino acid molecule is zero. Some authors term this pH the "isoelectric point" of the amino acid (however, cf. p. 101). For an amino acid such as glycine, which has one amino and one carboxyl group, the isoionic point $pI = (pK_1' + pK_2')/2 = (2.4 + 9.6)/2 = 6.0$. With an amino acid having three dissociating groups, it is feasible to consider only the two predominant pK' values for the calculation of pI. Thus, for lysine, $pI = (8.95 + 10.5)/2 = 9.7$.

In speaking of amino acids in solution, it is important to specify the pH of the solution because the proportion of the various possible ionic species of an amino acid will vary with changes in pH. The different ionic species will have different properties; in particular, the solubility of an amino acid will vary markedly with pH. A striking example of this is cystine, which is sparingly soluble in neutral solution; this property facilitates its isolation from protein hydrolysates (cf. p. 58). This amino acid has a low solubility over the pH range 2 to 9 where the predominant ionic species is that given in the structural formula. As acid is added, the COO^- groups are converted to COOH; upon the

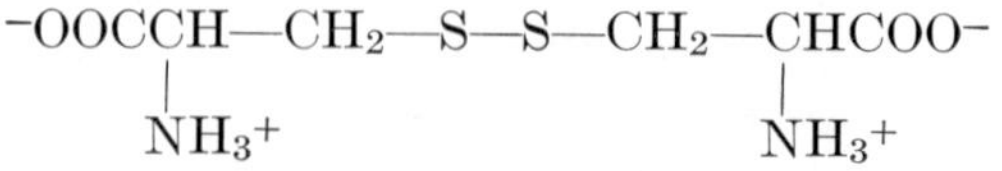

$$\begin{array}{ccc} ^-OOCCH{-}CH_2{-}S{-}S{-}CH_2{-}CHCOO^- \\ | & \qquad\qquad | \\ NH_3^+ & \qquad\qquad NH_3^+ \end{array}$$

[3] M. A. Grafius and J. B. Neilands, *J. Am. Chem. Soc.*, **77**, 3389 (1955); R. E. Benesch and R. Benesch, *ibid.*, **77**, 5877 (1955).

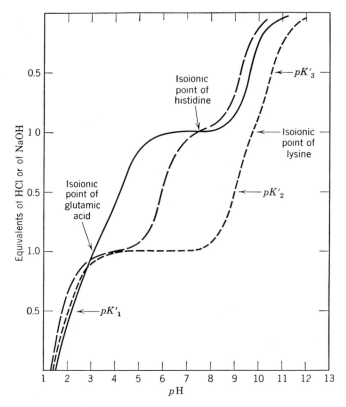

Fig. 5. Titration curves of glutamic acid, histidine, and lysine.

addition of alkali, the $NH_3{}^+$ groups are converted to NH_2. Either of these effects favors the formation of an ionic species which is more soluble than the dipolar ion is. Similar considerations apply to tyrosine, which is sparingly soluble in the pH range 3 to 8 (Fig. 6).

The value of pH is not the only important factor that may influence the solubility of an amino acid. As stated earlier, in the discussion of the activity coefficient, ions in a real solution cannot be considered to act independently of one another in exerting their chemical effects. The interaction among the ions has a profound effect on solubility; this may readily be seen from the study of the solubility of an amino acid as a function of the ionic strength of a solution. For example, if one plots the log of the solubility of L-cystine at a constant pH against the ionic strength, one finds that, as the ionic strength is raised, at first the solubility of the amino acid is increased (Fig. 7). This increase in ionic strength may be achieved by the addition of inorganic salts such as sodium sulfate or ammonium sulfate. One may say then that the amino acid is "salted in." Upon further addition of salt, and consequent further increase in ionic strength, the solubility of the amino acid decreases; i.e., the amino acid is "salted out." These effects of pH and ionic

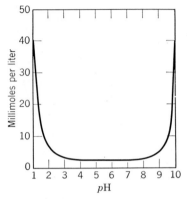

Fig. 6. Effect of pH on the solubility of L-tyrosine. [From D. I. Hitchcock, *J. Gen. Physiol.*, **6**, 747 (1924).]

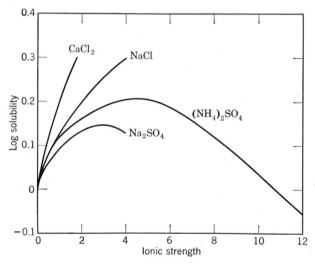

Fig. 7. Solubility of L-cystine in salt solutions. (From E. J. Cohn and J. T. Edsall, *Proteins, Amino Acids and Peptides,* Reinhold Publishing Corp., New York, 1943.)

strength on solubility apply not only to the amino acids, but also, with even greater force, to the proteins. Attention was drawn on p. 21 to the equation $\log S = \beta' - K_s'(\Gamma/2)$ which describes the relationship between the solubility of a protein and the ionic strength in concentrated salt solutions. The values for K_s' for amino acids are small relative to those found for proteins.

The ionic character of an amino acid has a profound effect, not only on its solubility, but on other physical properties as well. Of special interest is the effect of pH on the optical activity of amino acids in aqueous solution. If an L-amino acid is dissolved in water, and the pH is gradually decreased by the addition of acid, the solution becomes more dextrorotatory (or less levorotatory).[4] Thus L-histidine is levoro-

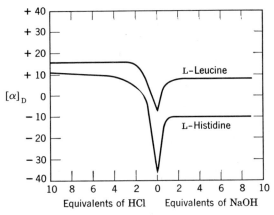

Fig. 8. Effect of acidity or alkalinity on the optical activity of L-leucine and of L-histidine.

tatory in water and becomes dextrorotatory in acid solution, as shown in Fig. 8. With amino acids of the D-configuration, the curves relating the magnitude of rotation to the pH of the solution are the mirror images of those for the corresponding L-forms. This difference in the effect of acid on the sign and magnitude of the rotation of L- and D-amino acids has proved to be of value in the establishment of the configurational relationships of the protein amino acids.

Another physical property that is influenced by pH is the light absorption in the near ultraviolet region of the spectrum. In protein chemistry this is primarily important in the behavior of tyrosine; this amino acid has a maximum absorption at 275 mμ at acid and neutral pH values, but at pH values more alkaline than 10 the position of the maximum shifts to a longer wave length (290 mμ). The shift is clearly associated with the dissociation of the phenolic hydroxyl group of the amino acid to form a phenolate ion.

[4] O. Lutz and B. Jirgensons, *Ber. Chem. Ges.,* **63B,** 448 (1930); **64B,** 1221 (1931); **65B,** 784 (1932); M. Winitz et al., *J. Am. Chem. Soc.,* **77,** 716 (1955).

Proteins as Multivalent Electrolytes[5]

Before considering the acid-base relationships of proteins, it is necessary to anticipate to some extent certain aspects of protein structure which will be discussed more fully in Chapter 5. In general, proteins contain relatively few free α-amino or α-carboxyl groups, since these groups are involved in the amide (peptide) bonds by which the individual amino acids are linked to one another. It follows, therefore, that the principal contribution to the behavior of a protein as an electrolyte will come from the ionizable groups in the amino acid side chains. Thus egg albumin, which on hydrolysis may yield about 300 equivalents of amino acids per weight of 45,000, has been found to contain only about 20 amino groups, largely represented by the ϵ-amino groups of lysine. Pepsin appears to have only 5 amino groups per weight of 35,000. Similarly, hemoglobin (molecular weight, 68,000) has about 87 free carboxyl groups, which include the β-carboxyl of aspartic acid and the γ-carboxyl of glutamic acid. In addition to the ϵ-amino group of lysine, and the β- and γ-carboxyls of aspartic and glutamic acid respectively, consideration must be given to the guanidino group of arginine, the phenolic group of tyrosine, the imidazolyl group of histidine, and the sulfhydryl group of cysteine. A titration curve of a protein with acid or alkali will therefore be determined largely by the number of each of these ionizable side-chain groups and their individual pK' values.

In Fig. 9 titration curves of β-lactoglobulin, as determined by Cannan et al.,[6] are shown. The ordinate gives the number of equivalents (h) of hydrogen ion bound per mole of protein, assuming a molecular weight of 40,000. It will be seen that the protein solution exhibits powerful buffering action. From what has been said before, it is obvious that many different ionizable groups are contributing to this titration curve, and the task of estimating the quantitative contribution of each type of side-chain group is a matter of some difficulty. However, with the aid of additional experimental data such as the effect of formaldehyde (Fig. 9), or of temperature, on the titration curve, and by means of approximate theoretical relationships (cf. Alberty[5]), it is possible to divide the complex titration curve into several regions with different pK' values and to estimate the number of ionizable side-chain groups of each type. For example, Cannan et al.[6] showed that β-lactoglobulin titrates as though it has 58 carboxyl groups per mole. It was later found, by analysis of the amounts of glutamic and aspartic acid formed on

[5] R. A. Alberty, in H. Neurath and K. Bailey, *The Proteins*, Vol. IA, Chapter 6, Academic Press, New York, 1953; J. Steinhardt and E. M. Zaiser, *Advances in Protein Chem.*, **10**, 151 (1955).

[6] R. K. Cannan et al., *J. Biol. Chem.*, **142**, 803 (1942).

hydrolysis, that β-lactoglobulin contains, per mole of protein, about 24 glutamic acid units and 36 aspartic acid units having free γ- and β-carboxyl groups respectively. This would correspond to 60 side-chain carboxyl groups, in excellent agreement with the titration data. The

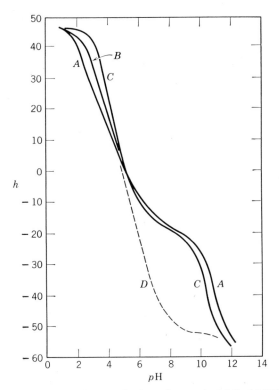

Fig. 9. Titration curves of β-lactoglobulin. Curve A, 0.019 M KCl, 0.5 per cent protein; curve B, 0.135 M KCl, 0.5 per cent protein; curve C, 0.67 M KCl, 0.5 per cent protein; curve D, M formaldehyde, 2 per cent protein. [From R. K. Cannan, *Chem. Revs.*, **30**, 395 (1942).]

titration of insulin (assumed molecular weight, 12,000) has given the following results,[7] in good agreement with the available analytical data (cf. p. 146): 12.5 carboxyl groups, 4 imidazolyl groups, 4 α-amino groups, 10 ϵ-amino plus phenolic groups, and 2 guanidino groups. The interpretation of the titration curves of other proteins, such as bovine serum albumin, lysozyme, and ribonuclease, has been discussed in valuable papers by Tanford.[8]

[7] C. Tanford and J. Epstein, *J. Am. Chem. Soc.*, **76**, 2163, 2170 (1954).

[8] C. Tanford, *J. Am. Chem. Soc.*, **72**, 441 (1950); **77**, 1912 (1955); C. Tanford and J. D. Hauenstein, *ibid.*, **78**, 5287 (1956).

In the previous discussion of the ionization of amino acids, the term isoionic point was defined as that pH at which the number of protons dissociated from proton donors equals the number of protons combined with the proton acceptors. This definition also applies to the isoionic point of proteins and is indicated in the titration curve for β-lactoglobulin (Fig. 9) by the pH at which h equals zero. It must be emphasized that the isoionic point of a protein is not the point of minimum electric charge; on the contrary, there may be more charged groups on a protein molecule at the isoionic point than at acid or alkaline pH values. However, at the isoionic point, the *net* charge on the protein is zero. Operationally, the isoionic point of a protein is the pH of a salt-free solution, and is approached by exhaustive dialysis of the protein solution against water. In general, when a neutral salt such as NaCl is present, the isoionic point as determined by titration will be shifted; for example, the isoionic point of bovine serum albumin is 4.9 in salt-free water and 5.4 in 0.15 M NaCl because the protein binds Cl^- more strongly than Na^+. The value of the isoionic point of a protein is usually different from that of its isoelectric point, which is the pH at which the protein does not migrate in an electric field (cf. p. 101).

It is clear from the foregoing discussion that, by virtue of their large molecular weight and the considerable number of dissociating side-chain groups of their amino acid units, the proteins are multivalent electrolytes with great buffering capacity. This is of decisive importance in biological systems and has been studied especially carefully in relation to the buffers of mammalian blood whose pH is controlled within narrow limits. In human blood the normal range is pH 7.3 to 7.5; as the blood pH approaches 7.0, acidosis, with resultant coma, may ensue, whereas at pH values of about 7.8 the condition of alkalosis may lead to tetany. As noted earlier, mammalian blood contains two principal buffer systems involving inorganic ions: (1) $H_2CO_3 \rightleftharpoons HCO_3^- + H^+$ $(pK' = 6.1)$, and (2) $H_2PO_4^- \rightleftharpoons HPO_4^{2-} + H^+$ $(pK' = 6.8)$. The most important protein of mammalian blood is hemoglobin, present in the erythrocytes; this protein exhibits considerable buffering capacity near pH 7, a behavior that is closely associated with its high histidine content (ca. 8 per cent). The side-chain imidazolyl groups of the protein make a significant contribution to the titration curve of hemoglobin. Approximately 60 per cent of the buffering capacity of whole blood is due to hemoglobin, and about 20 per cent may be attributed to the plasma proteins (chiefly serum albumin and globulins). In addition to their important role as biological buffer systems, the behavior of proteins as polyelectrolytes is significant for their stability and their chemical interactions, and for the action of enzymes. As will be seen from subsequent sections of this book, all properties of proteins are functions of their condition of electric charge, and depend on the pH of the protein solution.

Migration of Proteins in an Electric Field

When a solution containing a substance bearing an electric charge is placed between two electrodes connected to a source of direct current, the substance will migrate to the electrode of opposite charge. Thus, positively charged ions migrate to the cathode and are therefore termed cations, and negatively charged ions migrate to the anode and are termed anions. In the light of the previous discussion on the behavior of proteins as dipolar ions, it is obvious that they should migrate in an electric field. This was first studied systematically in 1899 by Hardy, who showed that particles of denatured egg albumin moved toward the cathode in acid solutions, and toward the anode in alkaline solutions. It was clear that there had to be a pH value at which a given protein would not move toward either electrode. This was defined in 1910 by Michaelis as the isoelectric point of a protein, and he, as well as many other investigators, made measurements of the isoelectric points of numerous proteins.

As indicated on p. 100, the isoelectric point of a protein is usually not identical with its isoionic point. The migration of a protein as a function of pH must be studied in solutions of appreciable ionic strength, and it is therefore necessary to introduce buffer systems such as acetic acid-sodium acetate and also neutral salts such as sodium chloride. Under these circumstances, some of the ionic charges of the protein may be neutralized by the foreign ions which migrate with the protein molecule, and thus cause a difference to be observed between the value for the isoelectric point and that for the isoionic point. As the ionic strength of the protein solution is changed, the behavior of the protein in the electric field also will change; for this reason it is necessary, in describing the migration of a protein in an electric field, to define not only the pH of the solution but the ionic strength and composition of the buffer mixture as well. The isoelectric points of several purified proteins are given in Table 2.

Knowledge of the isoelectric points of individual proteins is of value not only in their characterization, but also as an aid to their isolation and purification (cf. p. 19). It is a general phenomenon that at the isoelectric point a protein has minimum solubility, other factors being kept constant. This is illustrated for egg albumin in Fig. 10. Exceptions to this rule have been reported. For example, chymotrypsinogen does not precipitate at its isoelectric point (9.1) but rather near pH 5.4. In the crystallization of many proteins, the decisive step has been to establish

Table 2.   Isoelectric Points of Some Purified Proteins

Protein	Buffer	$\Gamma/2$	Isoelectric point (pI)
Pepsin	HCl, 0.1 N		<1.1
Egg albumin	Na acetate	0.1	4.6
Serum albumin	Na acetate	0.1	4.7
β-Lactoglobulin	Na acetate	0.1	5.1
Hemoglobin	Na_2HPO_4-NaH_2PO_4	0.1	6.7
α-Chymotrypsin	Na glycinate	0.1	8.3
α-Chymotrypsinogen	Na glycinate	0.1	9.1
Ribonuclease	Na veronal-Na glycinate	0.1	9.45
Cytochrome c	Na glycinate-Na_2HPO_4	0.1	10.65
Lysozyme	Na glycinate	0.01	11.0

a relatively high ionic strength in the protein solution at a pH somewhat removed from the isoelectric point, and then to add acid or alkali so as to approach the isoelectric pH value.

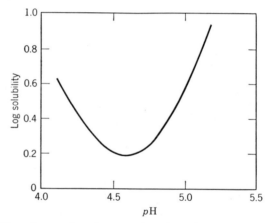

Fig. 10.   Solubility of egg albumin as a function of pH.   [Plotted from data of A. A. Green, *J. Biol. Chem.*, **93**, 517 (1931).]

The modern technique (termed "electrophoresis") for studying the migration of proteins in an electric field involves the use of an apparatus invented by Arne Tiselius in 1933.   Only a brief account of the method can be given here; for further details see Longsworth and MacInnes[9] or Alberty.[5]

The protein solution is placed in a U-shaped rectangular cell divided into three sections so constructed that flow through the cell may be

[9] L. G. Longsworth and D. A. MacInnes, *Chem. Revs.*, **24**, 271 (1939); **30**, 323 (1942).

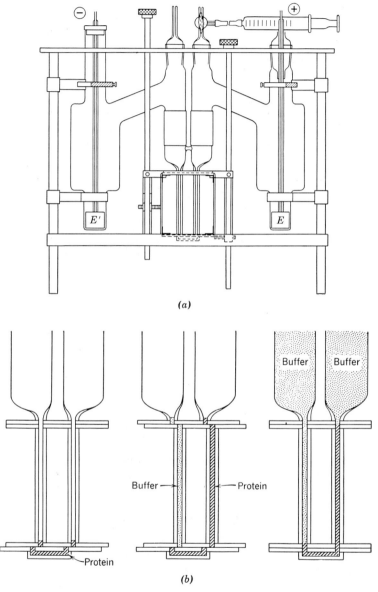

(a)

(b)

Fig. 11. Diagrams of Tiselius electrophoresis apparatus. (a) The electrophoresis cell, electrode vessels and support. (b) Initial formation of boundaries in the electrophoresis cell. [From L. G. Longsworth, *Chem. Revs.*, **30**, 323 (1942).]

interrupted by lateral displacement of the central section (Fig. 11). After introduction of the protein solution, the center section is moved so that the channel is closed, and the residual protein solution in the upper section is removed and replaced by a buffer solution, against which the protein had previously been dialyzed. The center section is then moved to re-establish the channel, thus creating a sharp boundary be-

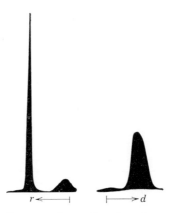

Fig. 12. Electrophoretic diagrams of egg albumin, taken at pH 3.93 by the schlieren scanning method. The sharp peak in the ascending boundary (r) corresponds to the protein; the descending protein boundary is less sharp. [From L. G. Longsworth, *J. Phys. & Colloid Chem.*, **51**, 171 (1947).]

tween buffer and protein, and a direct current is applied. The temperature is controlled near 4° C (since this is the temperature at which the density of water is maximal), thereby reducing the influence of convection currents. The migration of the boundary is observed by measurement of changes in the refractive index in the electrophoresis cell. To accomplish this, use is made of the optical technique known as the "schlieren method" (p. 37), discussed previously in connection with the measurement of the rate of sedimentation of proteins. Various modifications of this optical method have been used in electrophoretic studies.[10]

If the solution contains a single protein which migrates to the cathode under the conditions employed, the photograph of the schlieren diagram after a given time interval will show that the boundary has moved upward into the left channel (ascending boundary) and has moved downward in the right channel (descending boundary). As will be noted from Fig. 12, the electrophoretic diagrams are usually turned through an angle of 90° for graphic representation. The rate of electrophoretic movement ("mobility") is expressed in terms of distance per time in a unit electric field (potential gradient, 1 volt per cm) and is characteristic

[10] L. G. Longsworth, *Anal. Chem.*, **23**, 346 (1951).

of the protein under the specified conditions of pH and ionic strength. The mobility u equals cm per sec/volt per cm, and is given in units of $cm^2sec^{-1}volt^{-1}$. By convention, u is given a plus sign if the protein moves toward the cathode, and a minus sign if the protein migrates toward the anode. In Fig. 13 is shown the mobility of β-lactoglobulin as a function of pH.

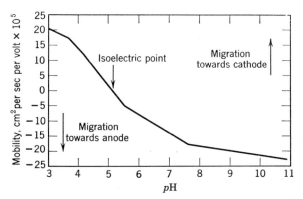

Fig. 13. Electrophoretic mobility of β-lactoglobulin as a function of pH. [From K. O. Pedersen, *Biochem. J.*, **30**, 961 (1936).]

If a solution contains 2 proteins of qualitatively similar (e.g., positive) charge but of different electric mobility at a given pH, the 2 proteins will advance toward the cathode at different rates, and the schlieren diagram will show two peaks. The application of electrophoresis to the study of mixtures of proteins has been especially fruitful in the examination of mammalian plasma. As will be seen from Fig. 14, at least 6 protein peaks are noted when plasma from normal human subjects is subjected to electrophoresis.

Electrophoretic separation of the protein components of a mixture can frequently be performed on a large amount of material in an appropriate apparatus. Such instruments are described in the article by Svensson.[11]

Even when a protein is purified to the point where an electrophoretic analysis at a given pH shows only one peak in the schlieren diagram, one is still not justified in stating that the protein is pure. The result merely indicates that, under the particular conditions employed, all the protein material in the solution behaves as though a single electrical species is present. Often it is found that a protein preparation which gives only one peak at a certain pH exhibits more than one peak if the experiment is conducted at another pH value, and it has become general practice, therefore, to examine the electrophoretic behavior of purified proteins

[11] H. Svensson, *Advances in Protein Chem.*, **4**, 251 (1948).

at several, widely separated pH values at which the protein is known to be stable. If a single boundary is observed under all these conditions, the investigator is justified in claiming that his preparation is electrophoretically homogeneous. He would be overbold were he to claim that the protein is "pure," i.e., that the preparation is composed of a single molecular species.

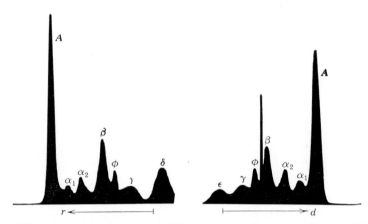

Fig. 14. Electrophoretic patterns of diluted human plasma at pH 8.6. The most rapidly moving component is the albumin (A), followed by the α_1- and α_2-globulins, β-globulin, fibrinogen (ϕ), and γ-globulin. [From L. G. Longsworth, *Chem. Revs.*, **30**, 323 (1942).]

A valuable test for the homogeneity of a protein migrating as a single electrophoretic component is the observation of the boundary on reversal of the current ("reversible boundary-spreading test"). If the boundary is due to a species with a single mobility, the schlieren diagram will not be sharpened when the current is reversed. If the boundary is sharpened appreciably, the protein component may be considered heterogeneous.

An important recent modification of the electrophoretic technique involves the migration of proteins (and of other charged molecules) in an electric field passing through a solution supported by material such as filter paper strips, silica gel, starch gel, or glass powder. A diagram of the type of apparatus usually employed is shown in Fig. 15. This method, frequently termed "zone electrophoresis" or "ionophoresis," permits the ready separation of components of different mobility into zones that can be identified and from which the individual components can be extracted. Zone electrophoresis has proved useful for the study of serum proteins,[12] and for the separation of partial cleavage products of proteins (p. 145) and of nucleic acids (p. 199).

[12] A. Tiselius and P. Flodin, *Advances in Protein Chem.*, **8**, 461 (1953); O. Smithies, *Biochem. J.*, **61**, 629 (1955).

Another method for the separation of proteins is that of electrophoresis-convection,[13] which involves a combination of horizontal electric transport and vertical convective transport. The construction of the

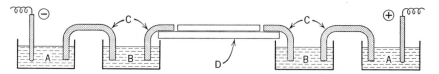

Fig. 15. Diagram of apparatus for zone electrophoresis. *A*, concentrated salt solution; *B*, buffer solution; *C*, filter paper soaked in buffer solution; *D*, filter paper, silica gel, or starch gel suitably supported by means of glass plates or of a tray.

apparatus (Fig. 16) employed in this method is such that the individual proteins distribute themselves in a horizontal electric field. The protein molecules set up a horizontal density gradient which leads to convection,

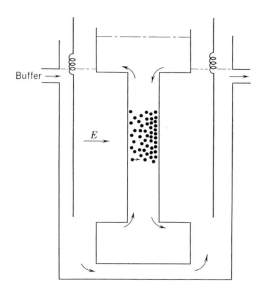

Fig. 16. Schematic representation of electrophoresis-convection apparatus. (Courtesy of J. G. Kirkwood.)

and the proteins with a higher mobility then move down into the vertical channel, where they descend under the force of gravity, and are collected in the lower horizontal chamber.

[13] J. R. Cann and J. G. Kirkwood, *Cold Spring Harbor Symposia Quant. Biol.*, **14**, 9 (1949).

Interaction of Proteins with Ions [14]

In what has gone before, primary attention was given to proteins as acids and bases, i.e., to reactions in which hydrogen ions are released or taken up. It is obvious, however, that inorganic cations (e.g., Ca^{2+}, K^+) can combine with basic groups in the same manner as does H^+. The binding of such inorganic ions by proteins is of considerable physiological importance; thus, approximately 30 to 50 per cent of the inorganic calcium in mammalian blood is bound to plasma proteins. In general, it may be assumed that the inorganic cations are bound by the carboxylate ions of proteins, and, in the case of the phosphoproteins, also by the phosphoryl groups attached to serine hydroxyls.

To the interaction of cations with the carboxylate ions of amino acids and proteins must be added the ability of several heavy metal ions (Cu^{2+}, Co^{2+}, Mn^{2+}, etc.) to form "chelated" (Greek *chela*, claw) coordination complexes with amino acids. Thus, the glycinate ion ($NH_2CH_2COO^-$) forms a complex with cupric ion. Histidine is of special interest in this connection, since it forms an extremely stable chelated complex with the cobaltous ion (Co^{2+}); the imidazolyl group of histidine also binds Zn^{2+} ions readily.

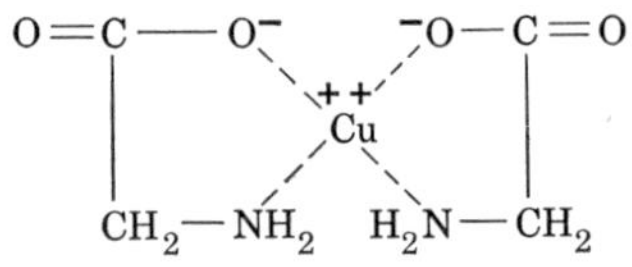

Copper diglycinate

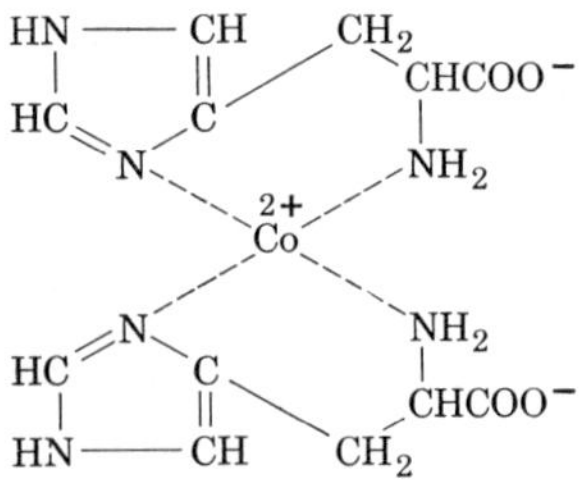

Cobalto–histidine complex

Inorganic anions such as phosphate and thiocyanate combine with positively charged groups on protein molecules. Thus the number of equivalents of metaphosphoric acid (HPO_3) bound by egg albumin agrees with the number of positively charged groups on the protein. It has long been known that proteins also combine with the anions derived from organic acids. Thus picric acid, sulfosalicylic acid, and trichloroacetic acid all combine with proteins to form insoluble precipitates. The last of these reagents is widely used as a means of deproteinizing a biological fluid. In the study of the interaction of proteins with organic anions, use has been made of organic dyes such as methyl orange, whose

[14] I. M. Klotz, in H. Neurath and K. Bailey, *The Proteins*, Vol. IB, Chapter 8, Academic Press, New York, 1953; F. R. N. Gurd and P. E. Wilcox, *Advances in Protein Chem.*, **11**, 311 (1956).

sulfonate ion is bound principally to the guanidino groups of the arginine and to the ϵ-amino groups of the lysine in proteins. Other organic anions that have been shown to combine with proteins are those of the long-chain alkylsulfonic acids such as dodecylsulfuric acid ($C_{12}H_{25}OSO_3H$), an anionic detergent, or of long-chain fatty acids such as caprylic acid ($C_7H_{15}COOH$).

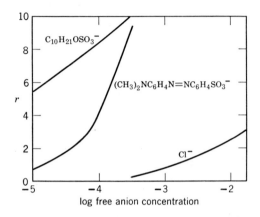

Fig. 17. Binding of anions (decyl sulfate, methyl orange, chloride) by bovine serum albumin. The ordinate (r) denotes the number of moles of bound anion per mole of total protein. (From I. M. Klotz.[14])

Proteins vary greatly in their ability to bind ions. For example, per mole of serum albumin, which binds anions readily, the following number of moles of anion is bound at 5° C (at the anion concentration given): Cl^- (0.1 M), 7; SCN^- (0.1 M), 20; methyl orange anion (0.0004 M), 4. On the other hand, β-lactoglobulin binds these anions to a much lesser extent, and the methyl orange anion is not bound detectably by egg albumin, insulin, or several other proteins.

Many data on the interaction of proteins with small ions have been obtained by the method of equilibrium dialysis (cf. Klotz[14]) and are expressed in terms of the moles of ion bound per mole of protein as a function of the concentration of the small ion. Data of this kind are given in Fig. 17. The method of equilibrium dialysis involves equilibration of a protein solution inside a cellophane sac with a solution of the diffusible ion initially outside the sac. The concentration of the ion outside the sac is determined, and this value is compared with that obtained when a protein-free solution is present in the sac. Since the volumes and initial concentrations are known, the extent of binding can readily be calculated. To estimate the total number of binding sites, it is assumed that the interaction of an ion A with successive binding sites follows the mass action law, and it can be shown that

$$\frac{[PA_i]}{[PA_{i-1}][A]} = k_i = \frac{n - (i + 1)}{i} k$$

where k_i is the association constant for any one of the successive reactions $PA_{i-1} + A \rightleftharpoons PA_i$, n is the total number of binding sites (assumed to be equivalent), and k is an intrinsic constant which is assumed to be the same for any site combining with 1 molecule of A. If r is defined as the number of moles of bound A per mole of total protein, it can be shown that $r/[A] = kn - kr$. Hence a plot of $r/[A]$ against r should be a straight line with an intercept on the r axis $(r/[A] = 0)$ equal to n (cf. Fig. 18). This relationship has permitted the determination of n for several ion-protein interactions; for example, the binding of the methyl orange anion by serum albumin gave a value of $n = 22$. In some cases, as in the binding of Cl^- by serum albumin, account must be taken of the electrostatic interaction between bound and unbound ions.

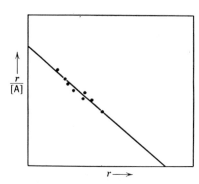

Fig. 18. Extrapolation to determine the maximum number of small ions bound by a protein (for definition of coordinates, see text).

It is of interest that binding of ions by proteins occurs at pH values at which the net charge of the protein is of the same sign as that of the bound ion. This must be attributed to the interaction of an ion with a single oppositely charged group of the protein. Also, in addition to purely electrostatic forces acting between oppositely charged ions, there are interactions that may be attributed to nonpolar groups of proteins (e.g., the side chains of leucine, phenylalanine, serine). Numerous instances are known of the binding of neutral molecules such as decanol, cholesterol, and other steroids by serum albumin.[15] These "van der Waals interactions" are probably of importance in the transport by the plasma proteins of water-insoluble compounds.

Reference has already been made to protein-protein interactions in the isolation of proteins (p. 21) and in the determination of their molecular weight (p. 43). Although the nature of the bonds that are formed and broken in these interactions is not known, it is probable that the electrostatic interaction of oppositely charged ions is involved, in addition to more specific forces based on molecular structure. Such specific protein-protein interactions are of importance in antibody-antigen reactions (Chapter 30) and in other processes such as the combination of the en-

---

[15] J. A. Schellman et al., *J. Am. Chem. Soc.*, **76**, 2808 (1954).

zyme trypsin with a specific inhibitory protein (Chapter 29). Perhaps the clearest evidence of the specificity of interactions involving protein molecules is found in the combination of enzyme proteins with their substrates (Chapter 10).

The Gibbs-Donnan Effect

Another property of proteins that is influenced by their net electric charge is their effect in causing an unequal distribution of diffusible ions on either side of a membrane through which proteins cannot pass. As an example, one may picture a model system in which on one side of a membrane there are protein molecules (concentration c_1) of net negative charge (P^-) and an equivalent concentration of c_1 of diffusible cations (e.g., Na^+), while on the other side of the membrane there are the diffusible ions Na^+ and Cl^- (concentration of each ion c_2), which penetrate the membrane in pairs. Since there is a concentration gradient of Cl^-, this ion will diffuse into the protein solution; in order to maintain electric neutrality, an equivalent quantity of Na^+ must also pass into the protein solution. However, this will tend to establish a concentration gradient of Na^+ and to promote the diffusion of Na^+ from the protein solution. A steady state will be attained at which the concentration gradient of Cl^- toward the protein solution is balanced by the concentration gradient of Na^+ outward from the protein solution. This steady state is usually termed the "Gibbs-Donnan equilibrium," because it is based on Gibbs' theory of equilibria and was studied experimentally by Donnan.

A	B
$Na^+(c_1)$	$Na^+(c_2)$
$P^-(c_1)$	$Cl^-(c_2)$

Initial state

A	B
$Na^+(c_1 + x)$	$Na^+(c_2 - x)$
$P^-(c_1)$	$Cl^-(c_2 - x)$
$Cl^-(x)$	

Final state

If one assumes that volumes A and B are equal, and do not change, then at equilibrium the following equation must apply:

$$(c_1 + x)x = (c_2 - x)^2 \qquad \text{or} \qquad x = \frac{c_2{}^2}{c_1 + 2c_2}$$

This value of x may be inserted in the equation for the ratio of NaCl concentrations in solutions B and A.

$$\frac{[NaCl]_B}{[NaCl]_A} = \frac{[Cl^-]_B}{[Cl^-]_A} = \frac{c_2 - x}{x} = 1 + \frac{c_1}{c_2}$$

This equation states that the ratio of concentration of NaCl on either side of the membrane is equal to unity plus the ratio of concentration (in equivalents) of protein in A and the initial concentration of salt in B. The greater the equivalent concentration of protein, the more uneven will be the final distribution of the diffusible ions. It follows also that, the greater the disparity in the total concentration of ions on either side of the membrane, the greater will be the osmotic pressure at the steady state. The Gibbs-Donnan effect always increases the osmotic pressure, and the magnitude of the effect is decreased by raising the salt/protein ratio. For this reason, the determination of molecular weight by osmotic pressure measurements (cf. p. 32) is best conducted in the presence of relatively high salt concentrations.

If instead of Na^+ one considers H^+ as the diffusible cation, the Gibbs-Donnan effect will lead to the establishment of a pH difference on either side of the membrane; solution B will be more alkaline than solution A. On the other hand, at a pH at which the net charge on the protein is positive (P^+) and solution A contains an equivalent concentration of Cl^- at the initial state, the Gibbs-Donnan effect will be to make solution B more acid. At the isoelectric point of the protein, the Gibbs-Donnan effect will be at its minimum.

In biological systems, concentration gradients of diffusible ions are frequently observed to be of importance in the maintenance of normal physiological function. Although it is probable that the Gibbs-Donnan effect may play a role in some systems (e.g., in mammalian blood), it should be stressed that living cells represent dynamic systems in which the energy for the maintenance of a concentration gradient is derived from intracellular chemical reactions (see Chapter 36).

5 ·

Structure
of Proteins

Amino Acid Analysis of Proteins

In a consideration of the structure of proteins, it is essential to know the proportion of each of the various amino acids formed upon hydrolysis. This information can then be used to calculate the number of units of each kind of amino acid constituting the protein molecule, provided the method of hydrolysis is one that does not involve the destruction of any of the amino acids. As noted previously (p. 47), acid hydrolysis causes complete destruction of tryptophan and partial destruction of the hydroxyamino acids. Also, it is frequently observed that amino acids such as isoleucine and valine are released more slowly than others. For these reasons, it is advisable to analyze hydrolysates obtained after different periods (e.g., 12 hr, 24 hr) of acid treatment at 100° C, to permit correction for the destruction of some amino acids, and for the slow release of others. In addition, a separate determination of tryptophan must be made on an alkaline hydrolysate of the protein under study.

The problem involved in the amino acid analysis of a protein hydrolysate is that of estimating quantitatively each of as many as 20 different amino acids in a mixture. There are few aspects of protein chemistry that have been the object of more intensive study. Nearly all the great names of protein chemistry, Osborne, Fischer, Kossel, Bergmann, Van Slyke, to mention but a few, were associated with research in this field during the period 1900–1940. Among the older analytical methods are that of Emil Fischer, involving conversion of the amino acids into their ethyl esters, which may be subjected to fractional distillation; Kossel's separation of the basic amino acids by precipitation with silver ions followed by phosphotungstic acid; and Van Slyke's method for the partition of the nitrogen in a protein hydrolysate. These procedures, and some of their modifications, are well described in Gortner's textbook.[1] Though extremely important in the historical development of protein chemistry, these methods provided reliable analytical procedures for only a few of the protein amino acids; they did not achieve the objective of accounting for all of the nitrogen of a protein in terms of the individual amino acids formed upon hydrolysis. Nevertheless, during the period prior to 1940, a number of techniques were devised which are still useful today.

It will be recalled that some amino acids, such as cystine and tyrosine, are sparingly soluble at neutral pH values, and the early investigators were able to gain a rough estimate of the amount of these amino acids in some proteins by taking advantage of this property. The fact that certain amino acids form sparingly soluble salts provided the basis for the estimation of glutamic acid (as the hydrochloride), arginine (as the flavianate), lysine (as the picrate), and histidine (as the silver salt). The selective precipitation of amino acids from a protein hydrolysate reached a high point in the work of Max Bergmann during the period 1940–1942, when he and his associates described an extensive series of aromatic sulfonic acids that could be used for the selective precipitation of amino acids.[2] Out of these efforts there was developed the so-called "solubility product method," which may be described briefly as follows. If to a sample of a hydrolysate one adds a known quantity of the L-leucine salt of a sulfonic acid (β-naphthalenesulfonic acid), a certain amount of the salt will dissolve; this amount may be designated S_1. According to the solubility product law, $S_1 (A + S_1) = K_1$, where A is the amount of L-leucine in the hydrolysate, and K_1 is a constant characteristic of L-leucine naphthalenesulfonate under the particular conditions employed. Now, if to a second sample of the hydrolysate one adds an amount R of the sulfonic acid, insufficient to cause precipitation, and again adds a known quantity of the salt, a given amount of the salt (S_2) will dissolve. Under these circumstances, the equation $(R + S_2)(A + S_2) = K_2$ will apply. If the solubility product law is obeyed, K_1 should equal K_2, and $S_1 (A + S_1) = (R + S_2)(A + S_2)$. Since in the last equation all the terms are known except A, the quantity of leucine in the hydrolysate, this can be calculated readily. Unfortunately, this ingenious method suffers from a number of disadvantages which limit its applicability. In the first place, K_1 does not, in general, equal K_2, and, second, the method is fairly laborious. For these reasons, and especially in view of the later development of better procedures, the solubility product method has not been used widely. It is important to stress, however, that a by-

[1] R. A. Gortner, *Outlines of Biochemistry*, 3rd Ed., Chapter 13, John Wiley & Sons, New York, 1949.

[2] W. H. Stein and S. Moore, *Ann. N. Y. Acad. Sci.*, **47**, 95 (1946).

product of the research on this method was the description of valuable sulfonic acid reagents for the isolation of a number of amino acids from protein hydrolysates.

Chromatographic Analysis of Protein Hydrolysates. A decisive advance in amino acid analysis came in 1941 when Martin and Synge introduced the techniques of chromatography[3] into this field. Although chromatography was first studied by Schoenbein in 1861, its development as a systematic method came from the work of the Russian botanist Michael Tswett, in 1906.[4] Tswett was interested in separating the leaf pigments, which include the chlorophylls. He reported:

> If a petroleum ether solution of chlorophyll is filtered through a column of an adsorbent (I use mainly calcium carbonate which is stamped firmly into a narrow glass tube), then the pigments, according to their absorption sequence, are resolved from top to bottom into various colored zones, since the more strongly adsorbed pigments displace the more weakly adsorbed ones and force them farther downwards. This separation becomes practically complete if, after the pigment solution has flowed through, one passes a stream of solvent through the adsorbent column. Like light rays in the spectrum, so the different components of a pigment mixture are resolved on the calcium carbonate column according to a law and can be estimated on it qualitatively and also quantitatively. Such a preparation I term chromatogram and the corresponding method, the chromatographic method.
>
> It is self-evident that the adsorption phenomena described are not restricted to the chlorophyll pigments, and one must assume that all kinds of colored and colorless chemical compounds are subject to the same laws.

From this description, it will be clear that the method devised by Tswett depends on the establishment of an equilibrium between a solid (calcium carbonate) and liquid (petroleum ether) phase (cf. Fig. 1). The rate of movement of the zones depends on the relative extent to which the components of the mixture are adsorbed by the solid; this type of chromatography is usually denoted "adsorption chromatography."

The first of the methods introduced by Martin and Synge involved the establishment of an equilibrium between two liquid phases, one of which is immobilized by being held in the form of a gel. Thus chloroform was employed as the mobile liquid phase, and water bound to silica gel formed the stationary liquid phase. Since the free amino acids are insoluble in chloroform, they were converted to the acetylamino acids, which are soluble in the organic solvent. The relative rates of movement of the acetylamino acids were found to depend on their partition coefficients, i.e., the equilibrium ratio of the concentration (in grams per liter) of a solute in water to that in the organic solvent, when

---

[3] E. Lederer and M. Lederer, *Chromatography,* 2nd Ed., Elsevier Publishing Co., Amsterdam, 1957.

[4] L. Zechmeister, *Ann. N. Y. Acad. Sci.,* **49**, 145 (1948).

an aqueous solution of the solute is shaken with the organic solvent. The method first introduced by Martin and Synge permitted the separation, in 80 to 100 per cent yields, of the acetyl derivatives of proline, valine, phenylalanine, isoleucine, and norleucine. However, the necessity for the acetylation of the amino acids in a protein hydrolysate introduced a factor that would make the analytical data uncertain, since one could not be sure that the acetylation had been quantitative.

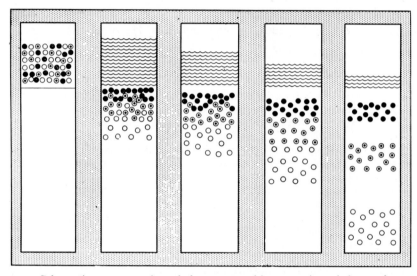

Fig. 1. Schematic representation of chromatographic separation of three substances on a column of adsorbent. The successive diagrams indicate the separation of the substances as solvent is passed through the column. (From W. H. Stein and S. Moore, *Sci. American,* March 1951.)

Obviously, it was desirable to devise a method that would permit the chromatographic separation of the free amino acids. This was achieved in 1944, when Martin and his associates described a technique involving the use of strips or sheets of filter paper to support the stationary water phase and employing a wide variety of solvents as the mobile organic phase.[5] Among the solvents used by Martin and subsequent investigators are collidine, *n*-butanol, *n*-propanol, phenol, acetic acid, and isobutyric acid. This procedure is termed "paper chromatography" and is usually conducted in the following manner. A pencil line is drawn about 5 cm from one end of a long strip of filter paper (20 to 50 cm), and about 0.005 ml of an amino acid solution (containing about 0.01 mg of amino acid) is applied to a spot at the pencil line. The paper strip is suspended

[5] A. J. P. Martin, *Ann. N. Y. Acad. Sci.,* **49,** 249 (1948); R. Consden, *Brit. Med. Bull.,* **10,** 177 (1954).

in a cylinder (or some other suitable glass container) which contains a small amount of the organic solvent saturated with water. The end of the paper nearest the pencil line is inserted into this solvent-water mixture in the bottom of the cylinder, the paper being so arranged that it hangs freely in the cylinder without touching the sides of the chamber. Thus the solvent will ascend into the paper; this procedure is termed "ascending paper chromatography." An alternative arrangement is to

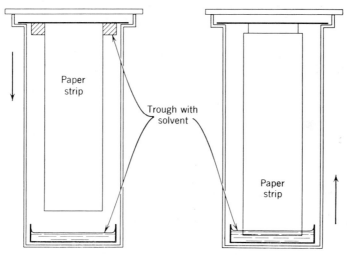

Fig. 2. Cross section of apparatus for descending paper chromatography (left-hand diagram) and for ascending paper chromatography (right-hand diagram).

insert the end of the paper strip into the solvent mixture placed in a narrow trough mounted near the top of the cylinder; here the solvent descends into the paper ("descending paper chromatography"). The assembly commonly employed for paper chromatography is shown diagrammatically in Fig. 2. In either method the chromatography proceeds in an atmosphere saturated with both water vapor and the vapor of the organic solvent. In the course of a number of hours the advance of the solvent front over the filter paper may readily be seen. When the solvent front has progressed a suitable distance (about 40 cm in 24 hr), the paper strip is removed from the cylinder, and the distance of the solvent front from the pencil line is measured. The paper is then dried, and sprayed with a dilute solution of ninhydrin in *n*-butanol. It will be recalled that this reagent gives colored products with amino acids; the colors vary from purple to orange with different amino acids. Thus, wherever an amino acid is adsorbed on the dried filter paper, the ninhydrin treatment will give a colored spot. The ratio of the distance traveled by the amino acid responsible for the colored spot to the distance of the solvent front from the pencil line is characteristic of a given amino acid under a given set of experimental conditions. It is termed the R_F value for that amino acid under the conditions employed. For a discussion of the theoretical basis of R_F, see Martin.[5] As the organic solvent, or the nature of the filter paper, or the temperature is varied, a given amino acid may be expected to give different R_F values (Table 1).

Table I. Approximate R_F Values of Amino Acids
(WHATMAN No. 1 PAPER)

Amino Acid	Phenol-Water	Collidine-Water	Butanol-Acetic Acid-Water	Isobutyric Acid-Water
Glycine	0.36	0.26	0.26	0.34
Alanine	0.55	0.32	0.38	0.42
Valine	0.72	0.43	0.60	0.63
Leucine	0.80	0.55	0.73	0.77
Isoleucine	0.83	0.53	0.72	0.74
Serine	0.30	0.30	0.27	0.32
Threonine	0.43	0.32	0.35	0.41
Cystine	0.24	0.11	0.08	0.14
Methionine	0.74	0.53	0.55	0.63
Proline†	0.88	0.34	0.43	0.55
Aspartic acid	0.22	0.23	0.24	0.27
Glutamic acid	0.23	0.27	0.30	0.33
Phenylalanine	0.83	0.54	0.68	0.70
Tyrosine	0.55	0.59	0.45	0.47
Tryptophan	0.71	0.59	0.50	0.63
Histidine	0.62	0.30	0.20	
Arginine	0.54	0.17	0.20	
Lysine	0.41	0.11	0.14	

† Gives yellow spot with ninhydrin.

If in place of a strip of filter paper a sheet is used, the solution containing an amino acid mixture is placed at one corner of the sheet; the components of the mixture may then be separated chromatographically along one edge of the sheet by means of one pair of solvents (e.g., phenol-water). The paper is then dried and turned through 90°, and chromatography is effected with a different pair of solvents (e.g., collidine-water), in a direction perpendicular to that used first. Upon treatment of the dried sheet with ninhydrin, a "two-dimensional" chromatogram (Fig. 3) is obtained in which there is considerable separation of the spots corresponding to the individual amino acids. Both one-dimensional and two-dimensional paper chromatography have been of great value not only in amino acid chemistry but also for the separation of a large variety of closely related substances of biochemical interest. Paper chromatography is widely used for the identification of substances by comparison of their R_F values in several solvents with those of authentic samples of known compounds. Although the identity of such R_F values

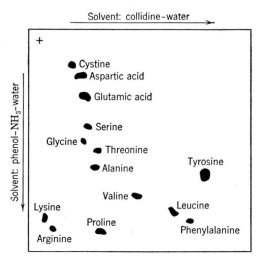

Fig. 3. Two-dimensional paper chromatography of a mixture of amino acids. For description of procedure, see text.

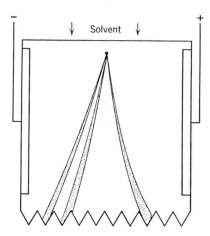

Fig. 4. Diagram of apparatus for combined paper chromatography and electro-phoresis.

may be taken as evidence in favor of identity of structure, dependence on paper chromatography alone occasionally may be misleading. If sufficient material is available, other criteria of identity (e.g., mixed melting point, infrared spectra, derivatives) are desirable.

An interesting combination of vertical paper chromatography and horizontal electrophoresis has been developed. In this method,[6] a solution containing the mixture is placed at the top of a paper sheet; as the components separate vertically by chromatography, the charged molecules migrate laterally in the electric field, as shown in Fig. 4.

Paper chromatography is a simple technique for the qualitative identification of amino acids, and it has been used as a semiquantitative procedure as well. It is not ideally suited, however, to the quantitative estimation of the amino acids in a protein hydrolysate. This was achieved by Stein and Moore,[7] who used partition chromatography on starch, instead of paper, to support the stationary aqueous phase. In this method, a column of starch is first equilibrated with a solvent such as butanol-water, and then a sample of the protein hydrolysate dissolved in aqueous butanol is added at the top of the column (Fig. 5). The equivalent of about 3 mg of protein is sufficient. After the introduction of the hydrolysate, more of the solvent is passed through the column, as in Tswett's procedure. The individual amino acids are adsorbed on the surface of the starch particles and slowly move through the column at rates that depend largely on their chemical nature and on the solvent system used. Under favorable circumstances, these differences in rate may be so great that each of the amino acids emerges from the column separately. An important aspect of the method is the use of an apparatus invented by Stein and Moore for the automatic collection of small aliquots of the effluent solution. These aliquots are then analyzed for their amino acid content by a quantitative colorimetric method, with ninhydrin as the reagent. In this way the successive appearance of the separate amino acids in the effluent solution may be followed accurately. In Fig. 6 is shown the result of the chromatographic fractionation of a hydrolysate of about 2.5 mg of bovine serum albumin. It will be seen that most of the amino acids emerge from the column separately; in those instances where two or three amino acids move together in the column, that fraction may be rechromatographed with a different solvent mixture known to separate the constituent amino acids. The area under each peak in Fig. 6 corresponds to the quantity of the amino acid in the sample of the protein hydrolysate; from this curve, therefore, one may calculate the concentrations of the amino acids in the hydrolysate.

Chromatographic separation on silica gel, paper strips or sheets, or starch columns is usually considered to be due to partition effects. However, the behavior of many substances on these materials, especially

[6] E. L. Durrum, *J. Am. Chem. Soc.*, **73**, 4875 (1951); W. Grassmann et al., *Z. physiol. Chem.*, **299**, 258 (1955).

[7] W. H. Stein and S. Moore, *Cold Spring Harbor Symposia Quant. Biol.*, **14**, 179 (1949); *J. Biol. Chem.*, **176**, 337 (1948); **178**, 79 (1949).

Fig. 5. Apparatus of Stein and Moore for automatic collection of aliquots of the effluent solution in chromatography. (From W. H. Stein and S. Moore, *Sci. American,* March 1951.)

paper or starch, suggests that adsorption phenomena also play a role. Adsorption probably also contributes to the effectiveness of zone electrophoresis on paper or starch (cf. p. 106).

In addition to adsorption chromatography and partition chromatography, a third general method, in which ion-exchange resins are used, has proved extremely useful for the separation of amino acids and of other substances of biochemical interest. Two types of polymeric exchange resins are available: (1) cation exchangers, which are either

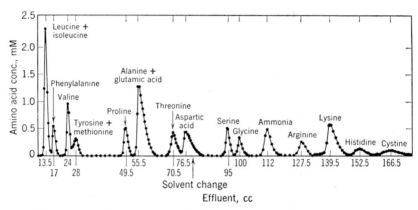

Fig. 6. Chromatographic fractionation on a starch column of a hydrolysate of bovine serum albumin. Solvents, 1:2:1 *n*-butanol-*n*-propanol-0.1 *N* HCl, and 2:1 *n*-propanol-0.5 *N* HCl. (From W. H. Stein and S. Moore.[7])

polysulfonic resins (Dowex 50, Amberlite IR-100, etc.) or polycarboxylic resins (Amberlite IRC-50, Zeo-Karb 216, etc.), and (2) anion exchangers, which are polyamine resins (Dowex 2, Amberlite IR-410, etc.). The action of a cation exchanger in exchanging one ion (e.g., Na^+) for another $(NH_3{}^+R)$ is

$$Resin-SO_3{}^- Na^+ + NH_3{}^+R \rightleftharpoons Resin-SO_3{}^- NH_3{}^+R + Na^+$$

Similarly, the action of an anion exchanger may be shown as

$$Resin-NR_3{}^+ OH^- + R'COO^- \rightleftharpoons Resin-NR_3{}^+ R'COO^- + OH^-$$

Although the use of starch columns solved, in principle, the problem of the complete amino acid analysis of proteins by means of a single procedure, this method has given way to ion-exchange chromatography of protein hydrolysates with polysulfonic resins such as Dowex 50 (p. 47), also developed by Moore and Stein.[8] The resin is first equilibrated with a suitable buffer, and a sample of the protein hydrolysate (from ca. 2.5 mg protein) is introduced. The chromatogram is developed

[8] S. Moore and W. H. Stein, *J. Biol. Chem.*, **192**, 663 (1951); **211**, 893 (1954).

by the continuous addition of more buffer, and by changes in the temperature of the column, and in the ionic strength and pH of the buffer (cf. Fig. 7). The procedure has been improved further by effecting continuous variation of the buffer solution ("gradient elution"). The analytical data for an acid hydrolysate of pancreatic ribonuclease[9] are given in Table 2. It will be noted that the sum of the grams of amino

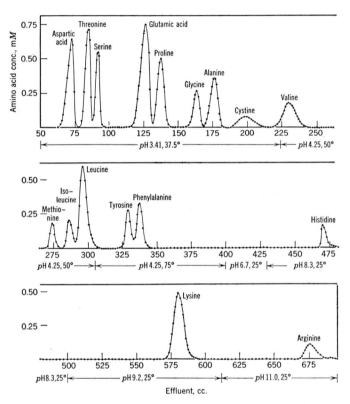

Fig. 7. Separation of a mixture of amino acids on a column (diameter, 0.9 cm; length, 100 cm) of the Na^+ form of Dowex 50. (From S. Moore and W. H. Stein.[8])

acid obtained from 100 grams of protein is greater than 100, since the elements of water enter into the amino acids in the course of hydrolysis of the protein. For this reason, it may be preferred to give the composition of the protein in terms of molar equivalents of amino acid or of the amount of nitrogen corresponding to each of the amino acids per 100 grams of protein nitrogen. The latter may be expressed as per cent of protein N, and the analytical data permit one to account for nearly

[9] C. H. W. Hirs et al., *J. Biol. Chem.*, **211**, 941 (1954); **219**, 623 (1956).

Table 2.   Amino Acid Composition of Pancreatic Ribonuclease[9]

Constituent	Grams per 100 g of Protein	Grams of Amino Acid Residue per 100 g of Protein	N as Per Cent of Protein N	Calculated Number of Residues[†]
Aspartic acid	15.0	13.0	8.9	15
Glutamic acid	12.4	10.9	6.6	12
Glycine	1.6	1.25	1.7	3
Alanine	7.7	6.1	6.8	12
Valine	7.5	6.3	5.0	9
Leucine	2.0	1.7	1.2	2
Isoleucine	2.7	2.3	1.6	3
Serine	11.4	9.4	8.5	15
Threonine	8.9	7.6	5.9	10
Cystine/2	7.0	5.95	4.6	8
Methionine	4.0	3.5	2.1	4
Proline	3.9	3.3	2.7	4
Phenylalanine	3.5	3.1	1.7	3
Tyrosine	7.6	6.8	3.3	6
Histidine	4.2	3.7	6.4	4
Lysine	10.5	9.2	11.3	10
Arginine	4.9	4.4	8.9	4
Amide NH_3	2.1		9.6	17[‡]
Total	116.9	98.8	96.8	124

[†] Number of residues for a unit of molecular weight 13,700; calculated from analytical data and rounded off to the nearest integer.
[‡] Not included in the total.

all of the nitrogen of ribonuclease, within the precision of the experimental method. The data may be used for a calculation of the number of residues of a given amino acid per molecule of protein. For the calculations of the figures in the last column of Table 2, the molecular weight was assumed to be about 13,700. This value is the minimal molecular weight (p. 28), and is in fair agreement with molecular weight determined by the sedimentation velocity-diffusion method (cf. p. 42).

In ion-exchange chromatography of protein hydrolysates, the competition between the ionizable groups of the amino acids (depending on their pK' values) and the buffer ions, as well as adsorption effects, determines the relative retention of the individual amino acids by the resin. It will be seen from Figs. 6 and 7 that the sequence of emergence of the amino acids is different in the two types of chromatography employed. Because of its many advantages over the starch column method, the newer method of Moore and Stein represents the best general procedure now available for the analysis of protein hydrolysates; it has been applied in many laboratories to the study of a large variety of proteins (Table 3).

Table 3. Approximate Amino Acid Composition of Some Proteins

(The values are given in grams of free amino acid per 100 g of protein.)

	Gelatin	Collagen	Hemoglobin (human)	Hemoglobin (horse)	Insulin (beef)	β-Lactoglobulin	Egg Albumin	Carboxypeptidase	Papain	Edestin	Salmine
Glycine	27.5	25.3	4.3	5.6	5.2	1.5	3.1	3.9	6.4	4.3	3.0
Alanine	11.0	10.5	9.8	7.4	4.7	6.6	6.7	4.1	4.5	6.5	0.9
Valine	2.6	2.7	11.0	9.1	10.2	5.7	7.1	4.7	7.1	7.5	3.7
Leucine	3.3	3.9	14.9	15.4	13.7	15.5	9.2	8.1	5.3	4.7	
Isoleucine	1.7	1.7			2.3	5.9	7.0	6.6	5.2	6.3	1.3
Serine	4.2	4.2	5.1	5.8	5.5	4.1	8.2	8.4	4.9	4.0	7.3
Threonine	2.2	2.5	6.0	4.4	2.1	5.8	4.0	7.8	3.3	1.4	
Cystine			0.9	0.9	12.6	3.4	1.0	0.7	3.9		
Cysteine				0.6		1.1	1.4				
Methionine	0.9	0.8	1.2	1.0		3.2	5.2	0.4		2.4	
Aspartic acid	6.7	7.1	10.0	10.6	7.0	11.2	9.3	10.1	9.8	12.8	
Glutamic acid	11.4	11.9	7.4	8.5	18.0	21.5	16.5	9.4	10.9	20.7	
(Amide NH_3)	0.1	0.6	1.1	0.9	1.8	1.3	1.2	1.0	1.5	1.8	
Lysine	4.5	4.1	10.6	8.5	2.6	11.2	6.3	6.9	5.0	2.4	
Hydroxylysine	1.0	1.1									
Arginine	8.8	9.2	3.5	3.7	3.0	2.8	5.7	4.5	7.0	16.7	86.4
Histidine	0.8	1.0	8.5	8.7	5.4	1.6	2.4	3.1	0.8	2.9	
Phenylalanine	2.2	2.9	9.6	7.7	8.6	3.8	7.7	6.4	2.8	5.7	
Tyrosine	0.3	0.6	2.9	3.0	12.6	3.8	3.7	9.3	13.3	4.4	
Tryptophan			2.0	1.7		1.9	1.2	3.3	4.3	1.5	
Proline	16.4	14.7	5.0	3.9	2.0	5.2	3.6	3.1	4.3	4.6	6.9
Hydroxyproline	14.1	14.1									

The ion-exchange resins also have been used for the separation of relatively large quantities of single amino acids from protein hydrolysates.[10] Polycarboxylic resins such as Amberlite IRC-50 have been used to good advantage for the separation of proteins.[11] It will be seen in Chapter 7 that ion-exchange chromatography has been valuable for the study of nucleic acids. In general, the introduction of chromatographic methods involving the use of ion-exchange resins has influenced profoundly many areas of biochemical research.

Other Methods of Analysis of Protein Hydrolysates. Another technique for the amino acid analysis of proteins involves the use of microorganisms as biological indicators of the concentration of an amino acid in a protein hydrolysate. The organisms that have been used most extensively for this purpose are the so-called "lactic acid bacteria," first studied by Pasteur in 1857, and extensively investigated by Orla-Jensen and others during the period 1900–1930. Out of these researches came the recognition that *Lactobacilli* exhibit extremely fastidious nutritional requirements and that amino acids are included among the many organic substances that must be supplied in the medium in order to permit bacterial growth. Each of the lactic acid bacteria requires the presence of several of the protein amino acids, but different strains have nutritional requirements for different groups of amino acids. After careful study of the nutritional requirements of a number of lactic acid bacteria, it has been possible to select a few organisms that permit the microbiological assay of nearly all of the amino acids found in protein hydrolysates. Since, in the course of their metabolism, these bacteria liberate acid into the medium, the amount of acid formed in a given period of time is a measure of their metabolic activity. Consequently, if the culture medium for a given organism meets all the nutritional requirements, with the exception of a particular amino acid, one may study the extent of acid production as a function of increasing amounts of that amino acid. One thus obtains a curve which may then be used as a standard for the assay of unknown solutions for that amino acid (Fig. 8). Although many organisms are classified as "lactic acid bacteria," four strains have proved to be especially useful for amino acid analysis. They are *Lactobacillus arabinosus* 17-5, *Lactobacillus casei*, *Streptococcus faecalis* R, and *Lactobacillus mesenteroides* P-60.[12] In addition, "mutant" strains (or "auxotrophs") of less fastidious organisms (e.g., *Escherichia coli*) may be produced (Chapter 16); many of these strains require individual

[10] S. M. Partridge, *Brit. Med. Bull.,* **10,** 241 (1954).

[11] N. K. Boardman and S. M. Partridge, *Biochem. J.,* **59,** 543 (1955); S. Moore and W. H. Stein, *Advances in Protein Chem.,* **11,** 191 (1956).

[12] M. S. Dunn, *Physiol. Revs.,* **29,** 219 (1949); E. E. Snell, *Advances in Protein Chem.,* **2,** 85 (1945).

amino acids for growth, and may therefore be used for amino acid analysis. When carefully controlled, the microbiological assay of amino acids in a protein hydrolysate has given data in fair accord with the results obtained by other methods. It cannot, however, be assigned a high accuracy.

On p. 72, attention was drawn to a number of colorimetric methods for the qualitative identification of the characteristic side chains of certain of the amino acids. Several of these colorimetric methods have been improved by Brand,[13] who has combined a variety of techniques,

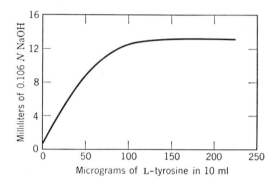

Fig. 8. Microbiological assay of L-tyrosine by means of *Leuconostoc mesenteroides*. The acid production was measured after an incubation period of 72 hr. [From M. S. Dunn et al., *J. Biol. Chem.*, **156**, 703 (1944).]

involving colorimetric, gravimetric, titrimetric, and microbiological procedures, to effect a complete analysis of hydrolysates of β-lactoglobulin and of several other proteins.

An analytical approach that is theoretically the soundest of all the available procedures for protein analysis is the "isotope dilution" method devised by Foster and Rittenberg.[14] In this method, the nitrogen isotope of mass 15 (N^{15}) is used, and a sample of the appropriate amino acid (e.g., L-glutamic acid) is synthesized in such a manner that it is enriched with respect to its N^{15} content. If one now adds a known quantity (A) of this amino acid (N^{15} concentration, C_0) to a sample of the protein hydrolysate and then proceeds to isolate a pure sample of that amino acid (or a suitable derivative), it will be found that the isolated amino acid (after recrystallization to constant isotope concentration) will have an N^{15} concentration C. The amount of amino acid

[13] E. Brand, *Ann. N. Y. Acad. Sci.*, **47**, 187 (1946).

[14] D. Rittenberg and G. L. Foster, *J. Biol. Chem.*, **133**, 737 (1940); D. Shemin and G. L. Foster, *Ann. N. Y. Acad. Sci.*, **47**, 119 (1946); C. C. Baker et al., *J. Chem. Soc.*, **1952**, 1574.

originally present in the protein hydrolysate (B) is then given by the equation $B = A[(C_0/C) - 1]$. This method has the great advantage that only a fraction of the amino acid need be isolated, but suffers from a number of disadvantages which have limited its general utility. Since the principal biochemical application of isotopes has been for the study of pathways of intermediate metabolism, the properties of isotopes and the methods used for their determination will be discussed later, in Chapter 16.

Another isotopic method for the amino acid analysis of proteins involves treatment of the hydrolysate with an acylating agent, p-iodo-phenylsulfonyl chloride ("pipsyl chloride"), in which the iodine is partially present as the radioactive isotope of mass 131. Under the conditions of this method,[15] the pipsyl chloride reacts nearly quantitatively with the free amino groups of the amino acids in the protein hydrolysate to give the corresponding pipsylamino acids. After this reaction has been carried out, a relatively large amount of a single non-

SO$_2$Cl   SO$_2$—NHR

+ NH$_2$R →   + HCl

I   I

p-Iodophenylsulfonyl chloride   Pipsylamino acid
(pipsyl chloride)

isotopic pipsylamino acid is introduced as a "carrier." The great excess of a single pipsylamino acid in the "pipsylated" hydrolysate makes it possible to isolate a pure sample of this amino acid derivative by chromatographic separation or by repeated extraction with organic solvents. In this way one effects the separation of the pipsylamino acid added as carrier, together with the much smaller quantity of the same pipsylamino acid bearing the isotopic label. Because of the extreme sensitivity of the methods for the measurement of radioactivity, the dilution of the isotope can be much greater than in experiments in which stable isotopes such as N^{15} are employed. Since the amount of added nonisotopic carrier is known, the amount of radioactivity indicates the dilution of the radioactive pipsylamino acid derived from the protein. From the dilution the amount of amino acid originally present in the hydrolysate may be calculated. Data obtained by this method on the analysis of several proteins for a number of amino acids are in satisfactory accord with those obtained by other reliable procedures. It should be mentioned, however, that the use of radioactive isotopes has one major disadvantage. The methods for the determination of radioactivity are so sensitive that contamination of the desired product with minute traces of radioactive im-

[15] A. S. Keston and S. Udenfriend, *Cold Spring Harbor Symposia Quant. Biol.*, **14**, 92 (1949); S. F. Velick and S. Udenfriend, *J. Biol. Chem.*, **190**, 721 (1951).

purities can lead to erroneous analytical data. Special care must be taken, therefore, in the purification of the isolated material prior to isotope analysis. In the application of the "pipsyl method," the possibility of such error has been reduced by the simultaneous use of two types of isotopic labels; pipsyl chloride containing I^{131} is employed in the treatment of the protein hydrolysate, and the carrier is the appropriate pipsylamino acid labeled with radioactive sulfur (S^{35}).

As will be seen from the above, the development of reliable and convenient methods for the amino acid analysis of proteins has called into play the skill and ingenuity of many brilliant investigators. It is not to detract from these achievements to say that the solution of the problem of amino acid analysis has not solved the problem of protein structure. What it has done is to place the study of proteins at the historical stage reached for simpler organic molecules around 1850, when it became possible to calculate the relative proportions of the atoms constituting these simpler compounds. From this, organic chemists could proceed to the determination of the arrangement of the atoms in an organic compound. In the same way protein chemists have proceeded with greater confidence to the consideration of the spatial arrangement of the amino acids constituting a protein molecule.

The Peptide Bond

In 1902 Emil Fischer and Franz Hofmeister independently advanced the hypothesis that in proteins the α-amino group of one amino acid and the α-carboxyl group of another amino acid are joined, with the elimination of a molecule of water, to form an amide linkage. The product of such a condensation reaction is a "peptide," and an amide linkage joining two amino acids is a "peptide bond" or "peptide linkage."

$$\underset{\text{Amino acid}}{\overset{\overset{\displaystyle R}{|}}{NH_2CHCOOH}} + \underset{\text{Amino acid}}{\overset{\overset{\displaystyle R'}{|}}{NH_2CHCOOH}} \xrightarrow{-H_2O} \underset{\text{Peptide}}{\overset{\overset{\displaystyle R}{|}}{NH_2CHCO}-\overset{\overset{\displaystyle R'}{|}}{NHCHCOOH}}$$

Each amino acid unit of the peptide chain is usually termed an amino acid "residue," and it is customary to name peptides as acylated derivatives of the amino acid bearing the free α-carboxyl group as shown.

$$\overset{\overset{\displaystyle CH(CH_3)_2}{|}}{NH_2CHCO}-NHCH_2COOH$$
Valylglycine

$$\overset{\overset{\displaystyle CH_3}{|}}{NH_2CHCO}-\overset{\overset{\displaystyle CH_2OH}{|}}{NHCHCO}-\overset{\overset{\displaystyle CH_2COOH}{|}}{NHCHCOOH}$$
Alanylserylaspartic acid

Since the proposal of the Fischer-Hofmeister hypothesis, a considerable body of evidence has been accumulated in its support; this evidence may be listed under four categories:

1. As noted on p. 98, most proteins contain relatively few titratable amino or carboxyl groups compared to the number liberated upon total hydrolysis of a protein. During hydrolysis these groups appear in equal number, as would be expected during the hydrolysis of amide linkages.

2. If a protein is subjected to acid hydrolysis, and the reaction is interrupted before the protein is completely broken down to amino acids, one may isolate compounds in which two amino acids are joined by a peptide bond. One of the earliest examples was the isolation of L-prolyl-L-phenylalanine from a partial hydrolysate of gliadin (Osborne and Clapp, 1907). Much of the early literature on this subject has been reviewed by Synge.[16] With the introduction of chromatographic techniques into protein chemistry, many peptides have been identified in partial hydrolysates of proteins.

In the older biochemical literature, reference will be found to other products of the partial hydrolysis of proteins, termed albumoses (or proteoses) and peptones. The albumoses are considered cleavage products of appreciable molecular size, since they can be precipitated by means of ammonium sulfate. The peptones are thought to be smaller in molecular size, since they are not salted out by ammonium sulfate. However, these terms are unsatisfactory from a chemical point of view because the materials to which they refer probably represent mixtures of peptides of widely varying size and chemical structure.

3. Compounds containing peptide bonds give a characteristic purple color when treated, in alkaline solution, with copper sulfate. This is termed the "biuret reaction" because it is given by the substance biuret, $NH_2CONHCONH_2$. The color deepens as the number of peptide bonds in a series of synthetic peptides is increased, and proteins produce an especially deep blue-violet color. The biuret reaction has provided the basis for useful methods for the determination of protein concentration in a solution.[17] Another reaction for the detection of peptides makes use of the chlorine-starch-iodide reagent.[18]

4. Enzymes known to catalyze the breakdown of proteins to amino acids, and therefore termed "proteinases" (e.g., pepsin, trypsin), also hydrolyze peptide bonds in simple synthetic compounds of suitable structure. The mode of the action of the proteinases will be discussed in Chapter 29.

[16] R. L. M. Synge, *Chem. Revs.*, **32**, 135 (1943).

[17] J. W. Mehl, *J. Biol. Chem.*, **157**, 173 (1944); O. H. Lowry et al., *ibid.*, **193**, 265 (1951).

[18] H. N. Rydon and P. W. Smith, *Nature*, **169**, 922 (1952).

If one grants the validity of the peptide bond hypothesis, it may next be asked how amino acids such as lysine, glutamic acid, and aspartic acid are linked in proteins. Are they solely linked through their α-amino or α-carboxyl groups, or are the ϵ-amino groups of lysine or the side-chain carboxyl groups of glutamic acid and aspartic acid also involved in peptide linkage to other amino acids? The available evidence indicates that, in most proteins, the ϵ-amino group of lysine, the guanidino group of arginine, and the imidazolyl group of histidine do not participate in amide linkage with other amino acids. This conclusion is based in part on the results of titration experiments and in part on the finding that these groups are available for reactions that would not be observed if the groups were substituted.[19] Thus treatment of a protein with benzenesulfonyl chloride gives a product that may be hydrolyzed without appreciable cleavage of the linkage between the benzenesulfonyl group and the free amino groups of the protein. In this way, it has been possible to show that the amount of ϵ-benzenesulfonyl-L-lysine obtained corresponds to the lysine content of the protein. Such results do not exclude the possibility that one of several lysine ϵ-amino groups participates in an amide bond; indeed, chromatographic evidence indicates the presence of small amounts of an ϵ-lysyl peptide in a partial acid hydrolysate of collagen.

The side-chain carboxyls of aspartic acid and of glutamic acid appear to be either free or solely bound in amide linkage with ammonia (as asparagine or glutamine residues). Chibnall and Rees[20] esterified insulin and treated the product with lithium borohydride ($LiBH_4$), a reagent that reduces esters (e.g., $-COOCH_3$) to the corresponding alcohols ($-CH_2OH$) but is without effect on amides. Acid hydrolysis of the reduced insulin gave an amino acid mixture which contained the β- and γ-carbinols corresponding to the aspartyl and glutamyl residues of the original protein, as well as aspartic acid and glutamic acid derived from the asparagine and glutamine residues of insulin.

The assumption that the covalent bonds between the amino acid units of proteins involve solely α-amino or α-carboxyl groups is still a working hypothesis that has not been completely proved. In this connection, the possibility must be considered that the side-chain hydroxyl groups of serine or threonine may be bound to carboxyl groups of other amino acids to form ester linkages which would be susceptible to hydrolysis by acids, alkalies, and enzymes. This possibility, first suggested by Emil Fischer in 1906, requires experimental examination before any conclusion

[19] F. W. Putnam, in H. Neurath and K. Bailey, *The Proteins,* Vol. IB, Chapter 10, Academic Press, New York, 1953.

[20] A. C. Chibnall and M. W. Rees, in G. E. W. Wolstenholme, *The Chemical Structure of Proteins,* J. and A. Churchill, London, 1953.

can be drawn about its validity. Still another type of linkage would be present if the SH group of cysteine were linked to the COOH group of another amino acid to form a thiol ester bond.

Clearly, where a protein amino acid contains two α-amino and two α-carboxyl groups, as in cystine, this amino acid can act as a bridge between two peptide chains or to link different parts of the same peptide chain to form a cyclic structure. The evidence is very strong that the SS bond of cystine is indeed an important mode of linkage in some proteins. For example, the insoluble scleroprotein wool keratin, on treatment with sulfhydryl compounds such as thioglycolic acid ($HSCH_2COOH$), is converted to a soluble product termed "keratein." In this reaction, the disulfide bonds within the protein are reduced to sulfhydryl groups.

$$RSSR + 2HSCH_2COOH \rightarrow 2RSH + [-SCH_2COOH]_2$$

In the protein hormone insulin, the disulfide bonds of cystine serve both to cross-link separate chains and to connect parts of the same chain (cf. p. 146).

Synthesis of Peptides

With increasing support for the peptide bond hypothesis of protein structure, it became clear that peptides are structural intermediates between the complex proteins and the simple amino acids. As a result, much attention has been devoted to the development of methods for the synthesis of peptides derived from the protein amino acids.[21]

The current procedures for the synthesis of peptides depend, in the first place, on the conversion of the α-carboxyl group of an amino acid into a form that will permit the carbon atom of the carbonyl group to react with the α-amino group of a second amino acid. Such derivatives are the acyl halides (—CO—Cl), the azides (—CO—N_3), or the anhydrides (—CO—O—COR). Since the time of Emil Fischer's first studies on peptide synthesis in 1899, one of the salient problems has been to develop methods for the protection of the α-amino group of an amino acid during the conversion of the α-carboxyl to a more reactive derivative and during the reaction of this derivative with the second amino acid. An essential attribute of the substituent on the α-amino group, which was to be unsubstituted in the final peptide, was that the substituent should be removable under conditions that would not cleave the peptide bonds.

Fischer circumvented part of the difficulty by introducing the free α-amino group of the peptide after the peptide bond had been made. For example, to make L-alanyl-L-tyrosine by the Fischer method, one

---

[21] J. S. Fruton, *Advances in Protein Chem.*, **5**, 1 (1949); M. Goodman and G. W. Kenner, *ibid.*, **12**, 465 (1957).

treats L-tyrosine with optically active α-bromopropionyl bromide, and the resulting bromopropionyl-L-tyrosine is treated with ammonia to give the desired peptide. By conducting a series of reactions, in which

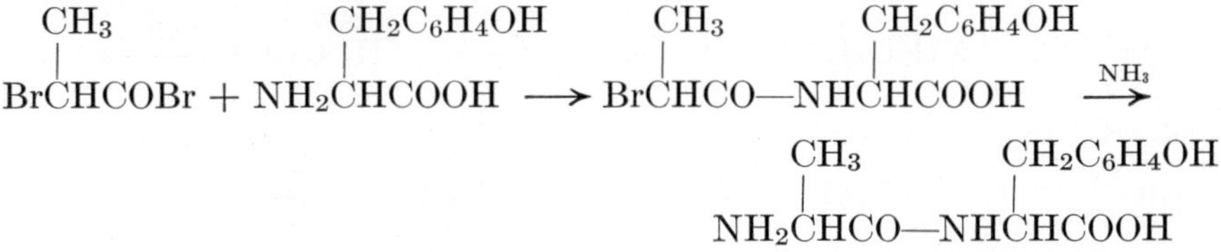

$$
\underset{\substack{|\\ BrCHCOBr}}{\overset{CH_3}{|}} + \underset{\substack{|\\ NH_2CHCOOH}}{\overset{CH_2C_6H_4OH}{|}} \longrightarrow \underset{\substack{|\\ BrCHCO—NHCHCOOH}}{\overset{CH_3\qquad CH_2C_6H_4OH}{|\qquad\qquad|}} \xrightarrow{\ NH_3\ }
$$

$$
\underset{\substack{|\qquad\qquad\ |\\ NH_2CHCO—NHCHCOOH}}{\overset{CH_3\qquad\qquad CH_2C_6H_4OH}{|\qquad\qquad\qquad|}}
$$

L-Alanyl-L-tyrosine

the peptide formed in one series of reactions (such as that shown) was used in a subsequent series of reactions, Fischer made many peptides containing three or more amino acid residues. The crowning achievement in this work was the synthesis, in 1907, of the octadecapeptide L-leucyl(triglycyl)-L-leucyl(triglycyl)-L-leucyl(octaglycyl)glycine.

One of the principal disadvantages of the Fischer method is the difficulty in the preparation of the optically active halogen acyl halides needed for the synthesis of peptides in which protein amino acids other than glycine constitute the acyl group. If in place of the optically active α-bromopropionyl bromide one used the racemic form in the above reaction with L-tyrosine, the peptide preparation obtained upon amination would be a mixture of the diastereoisomeric compounds L-alanyl-L-tyrosine and D-alanyl-L-tyrosine. Since compounds of this type have different physical properties, and occasionally may be separated because of the difference in their solubility, one would not be justified in naming the product of the reaction DL-alanyl-L-tyrosine.

The disadvantages and limitations of the halogen acyl halide method led to many efforts to find more generally applicable methods of peptide synthesis. The most important of the newer procedures is that developed by Bergmann and Zervas in 1932. They solved the problem of the choice of substituent on the α-amino group by taking advantage of the fact that the benzyloxycarbonyl ($C_6H_5CH_2OCO—$) derivatives of amino acids may be cleaved by catalytic hydrogenolysis under very mild conditions.

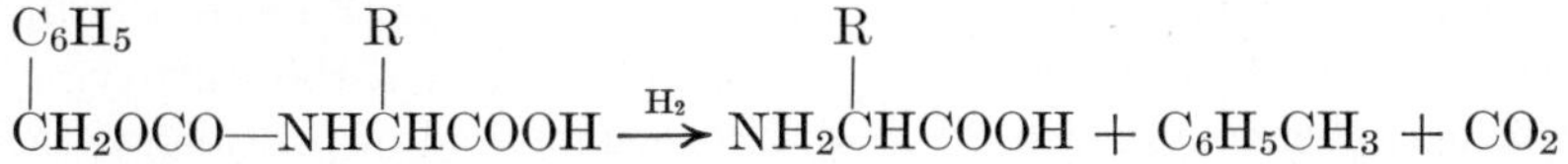

$$
\underset{\substack{|\qquad\qquad\ |\\ CH_2OCO—NHCHCOOH}}{\overset{C_6H_5\qquad\qquad R}{|\qquad\qquad\ |}} \xrightarrow{\ H_2\ } \underset{\substack{|\\ NH_2CHCOOH}}{\overset{R}{|}} + C_6H_5CH_3 + CO_2
$$

If an amino acid is treated with benzyloxycarbonyl chloride (Bergmann and Zervas named this reagent carbobenzoxy chloride), the resulting carbobenzoxyamino acid may be converted to the corresponding azide or acid chloride, which then may be used for reaction with the amino group of an amino acid or a peptide. This sequence of reactions is illustrated by the synthesis of L-alanyl-L-tyrosine by the carbobenzoxy method; in this synthesis the initial step is a reaction between carbo-

benzoxy chloride and L-alanine methyl ester (the carbobenzoxy group
of the amino acid derivatives is abbreviated Cbzo).

$$\underset{\underset{\displaystyle CH_2OCOCl}{|}}{C_6H_5} + \underset{\underset{\displaystyle NH_2CHCOOCH_3}{|}}{CH_3} \longrightarrow Cbzo\text{---}\underset{\underset{\displaystyle NHCHCOOCH_3}{|}}{CH_3} \xrightarrow{NH_2NH_2}$$

$$Cbzo\text{---}\underset{\underset{\displaystyle NHCHCONHNH_2}{|}}{CH_3} \xrightarrow{HNO_2} Cbzo\text{---}\underset{\underset{\displaystyle NHCHCON_3}{|}}{CH_3} \xrightarrow[\text{ethyl ester}]{\text{L-tyrosine}}$$

$$Cbzo\text{---}\underset{\underset{\displaystyle NHCHCO}{|}}{CH_3}\text{---}\underset{\underset{\displaystyle NHCHCOOC_2H_5}{|}}{CH_2C_6H_4OH} \xrightarrow{NaOH}$$

$$Cbzo\text{---}\underset{\underset{\displaystyle NHCHCO}{|}}{CH_3}\text{---}\underset{\underset{\displaystyle NHCHCOOH}{|}}{CH_2C_6H_4OH} \xrightarrow{H_2} \underset{\underset{\displaystyle NH_2CHCO}{|}}{CH_3}\text{---}\underset{\underset{\displaystyle NHCHCOOH}{|}}{CH_2C_6H_4OH}$$

Subsequent work showed that the carbobenzoxy group may be removed,
without scission of peptide bonds, by treatment with sodium in liquid
ammonia or with HBr-acetic acid. Another important modification of
the Bergmann-Zervas method is the use of mixed anhydrides, formed by
the reaction of carbobenzoxyamino acids with acyl halides such as isovaleryl chloride or ethyl chlorocarbonate. The mixed anhydrides react
smoothly with esters of amino acids or peptides as follows:

$$Cbzo\text{---}\underset{\underset{\displaystyle NHCHCO}{|}}{R}\text{---}O\text{---}OCR' + NH_2R'' \rightarrow$$

$$Cbzo\text{---}\underset{\underset{\displaystyle NHCHCO}{|}}{R}\text{---}NHR'' + R'COOH$$

Various modifications of this method have been described by Wieland,
Boissonas, and Vaughan (cf. Vaughan and Osato[22]).

Another recent addition is the use of phosphorus compounds
such as diethylchlorophosphite, $(C_2H_5O)_2PCl$, ethyldichlorophosphite,
$C_2H_5OPCl_2$, or tetraethylpyrophosphite, $(C_2H_5O)_2P\text{---}P(OC_2H_5)_2$,
which react with the NH_2 group of amino acid or peptide esters to form
reactive intermediates that may be coupled with a carbobenzoxyamino
acid or carbobenzoxypeptide.[23] Still another method of peptide synthesis

$$RCOOH + (C_2H_5O)_2P\text{---}NHR' \rightarrow RCO\text{---}NHR' + (C_2H_5O)_2P\text{---}OH$$

involves the reaction of a carbobenzoxyamino acid with an amine in the
presence of dicyclohexylcarbodiimide ($C_6H_{11}N\text{=}C\text{=}NC_6H_{11}$), which

[22] J. Vaughan and R. L. Osato, J. Am. Chem. Soc., **73**, 5553 (1951).

[23] G. W. Anderson et al., J. Am. Chem. Soc., **74**, 5309 (1952); R. W. Young et al.,
ibid., **78**, 2126 (1956).

is converted to dicyclohexylurea.[24]

$$RCOOH + NH_2R' + C_6H_{11}N=C=NC_6H_{11} \rightarrow$$
$$RCO—NHR' + C_6H_{11}NHCONHC_6H_{11}$$

The carbobenzoxy method has been applied with considerable success to the synthesis of peptides of such amino acids as serine, methionine, tryptophan, arginine, histidine, lysine, proline, cystine, and tyrosine, as well as the amino acids containing paraffin side chains. An important advantage over the Fischer halogen acyl halide procedure is that, in the carbobenzoxy method, no reaction at an asymmetric carbon atom is involved at any stage of the procedure. Also, the optically active carbobenzoxyamino acids are not racemized easily, in contrast to the behavior of the corresponding benzoyl or acetyl derivatives. The broadening of the scope of peptide synthesis by the introduction of the carbobenzoxy method has had a profound influence on the development of protein chemistry; this method has made it possible to synthesize model compounds containing the various protein amino acids and to relate the properties of these model substances to the behavior of proteins.

In addition to the carbobenzoxy group, other substituents are available for the protection of the amino group during peptide synthesis. These include the p-toluenesulfonyl group (which may be removed by means of sodium in liquid ammonia or of HI-phosphonium iodide), the formyl group (removed by treatment with dilute acid in alcohol), the triphenylmethyl group (removed by mild acid hydrolysis), and the phthaloyl group (removed by treatment at 25° C with hydrazine, as shown).

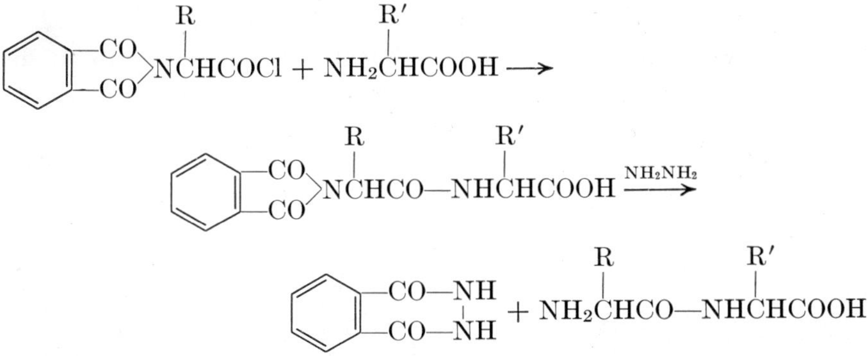

Several heterocyclic derivatives of amino acids also have been used as acylating agents in peptide synthesis. Among these are the oxazolones, 2-thio-5-thiazolidones (p. 50), and N-carboxy anhydrides. The N-carboxy anhydrides have been useful for the preparation of polymeric

24 J. C. Sheehan et al., J. Am. Chem. Soc., 78, 1367 (1956).

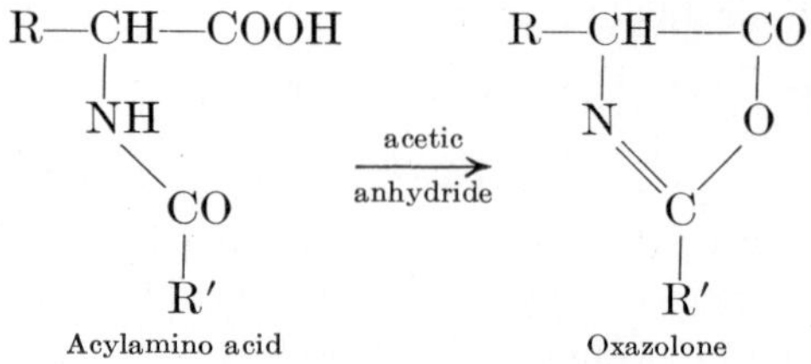

$$\text{R}-\text{CH}-\text{COOH} \qquad\qquad \text{R}-\text{CH}-\text{CO}$$

$$\underset{\text{Acylamino acid}}{\overset{\displaystyle\text{NH}}{\underset{\displaystyle\text{CO}}{\underset{\displaystyle\text{R}'}{|}}}} \xrightarrow[\text{anhydride}]{\text{acetic}} \underset{\text{Oxazolone}}{\overset{\displaystyle\text{N}\quad\text{O}}{\overset{\displaystyle\text{C}}{\underset{\displaystyle\text{R}'}{}}}}$$

peptides containing as many as 100 to 200 amino acid residues per chain.[25]

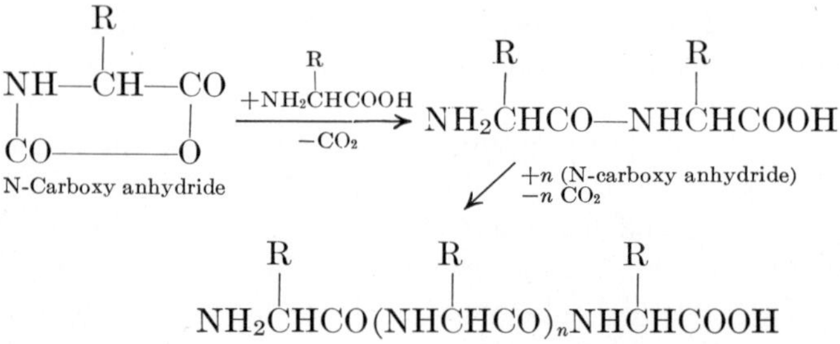

$$\underset{\text{N-Carboxy anhydride}}{\overset{\displaystyle\text{R}}{\underset{\displaystyle\text{CO}\,\text{—O}}{\overset{\displaystyle\text{NH}-\text{CH}-\text{CO}}{|}}}} \xrightarrow[-CO_2]{\overset{\displaystyle\text{R}}{+NH_2CHCOOH}} \overset{\displaystyle\text{R}\qquad\quad\text{R}}{NH_2CHCO\text{—}NHCHCOOH}$$

$$\xRightarrow[-n\ CO_2]{+n\ (\text{N-carboxy anhydride})}$$

$$\overset{\displaystyle\text{R}\qquad\quad\text{R}\qquad\quad\text{R}}{NH_2CHCO(NHCHCO)_nNHCHCOOH}$$

Naturally Occurring Peptides[26]

Interest in the development of new methods of peptide synthesis received considerable impetus during the period 1940–1955, when a large number of peptides were found in nature. Before that time only a few peptides of known structure had been established as constituents of living systems. In 1921 Hopkins isolated from yeast glutathione, later found to be widely distributed in animal and plant cells, and shown to be the tripeptide γ-L-glutamyl-L-cysteinyl-glycine. A closely related peptide (ophthalmic acid, γ-L-glutamyl-L-α-amino-n-butyrylglycine) occurs in calf lens.[27]

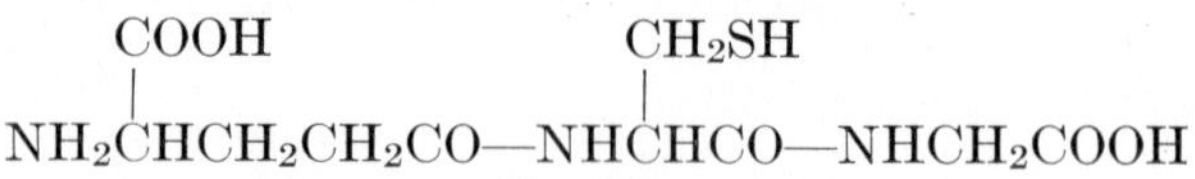

$$\overset{\displaystyle\text{COOH}\qquad\qquad\qquad\text{CH}_2\text{SH}}{NH_2CHCH_2CH_2CO\text{—}NHCHCO\text{—}NHCH_2COOH}$$
Glutathione

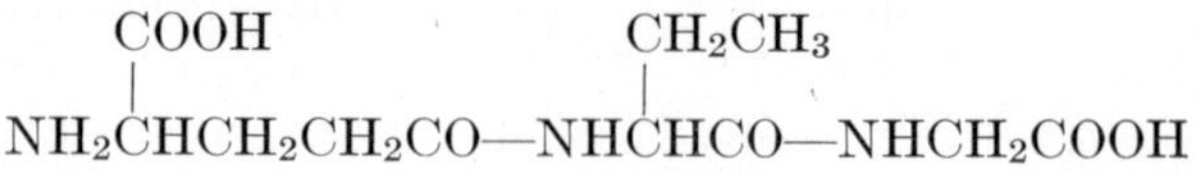

$$\overset{\displaystyle\text{COOH}\qquad\qquad\qquad\text{CH}_2\text{CH}_3}{NH_2CHCH_2CH_2CO\text{—}NHCHCO\text{—}NHCH_2COOH}$$
Ophthalmic acid

[25] E. Katchalski, *Advances in Protein Chem.*, **6**, 123 (1951); C. H. Bamford et al., *Synthetic Polypeptides*, Academic Press, New York, 1956.

[26] R. L. M. Synge, *Quart. Revs.*, **3**, 245 (1949); E. Bricas and C. Fromageot, *Advances in Protein Chem.*, **8**, 1 (1953).

[27] S. G. Waley, *Biochem. J.*, **64**, 715 (1956); **67**, 172 (1957); **68**, 189 (1958).

Another peptide found in nature is carnosine; it was discovered in 1900 by Gulewitch. Carnosine (β-alanyl-L-histidine) is a constituent of aqueous extracts of muscle of vertebrates, and is accompanied by its N-methyl derivative anserine (β-alanyl-1-methyl-L-histidine). Although carnosine and anserine may be considered dipeptides, one of the amino acid residues, that of β-alanine, is not found in proteins. Snake muscle contains a dipeptide ("ophidine") shown to be a derivative of carnosine in which the carbon atom between the 2 nitrogens of the imidazolyl ring bears a methyl group.[28]

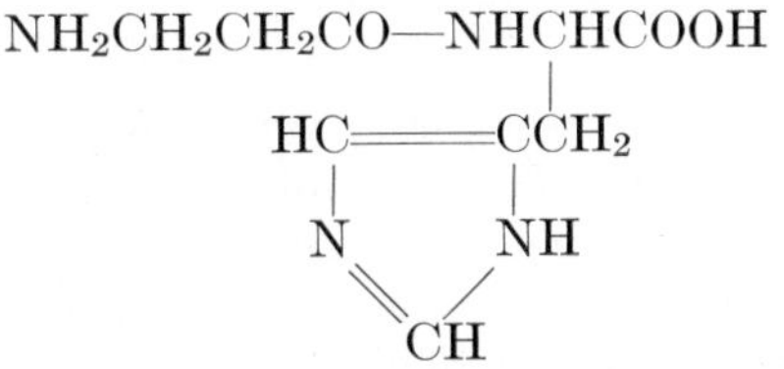

$$NH_2CH_2CH_2CO\text{---}NHCHCOOH$$

HC====CCH$_2$

N   NH

CH

Carnosine

$$NH_2CH_2CH_2CO\text{---}NHCHCOOH$$

HC====CCH$_2$

N   N---CH$_3$

CH

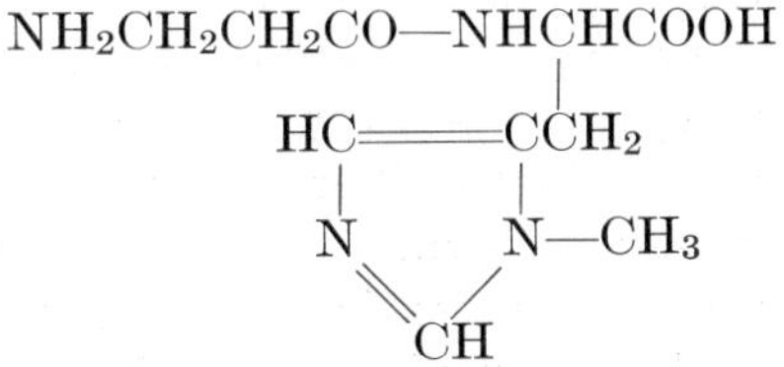

Anserine

One factor in the rise of interest in peptides was the discovery that various strains of microorganisms elaborate peptides that have antibacterial activity toward other microorganisms. Among the first of these was a material named "gramicidin," obtained from *Bacillus brevis* by Dubos and Hotchkiss. Although this preparation was obtained in crystalline form, Craig showed that it was not a homogeneous peptide. As a result, the principal component is named gramicidin A, and the minor components are termed gramicidin B, C, etc. Upon hydrolysis, "gramicidin" yields L-tryptophan and D-leucine as the main products, together with smaller quantities of D-valine, L-valine, L-alanine, glycine, and 2-aminoethanol (ethanolamine). Since no free amino or carboxyl groups can be demonstrated in the intact material, it has been concluded that "gramicidin" has a cyclic structure; molecular weight determinations suggest that the average molecular weight of the gramicidins is near 4000.

With the gramicidins are elaborated a group of basic peptides, named tyrocidines, which on hydrolysis yield a number of amino acids including L-ornithine and D-phenylalanine. The simplest known member of this group of peptides was obtained by the Russian investigator Gause, and misnamed by him "gramicidin S" (Soviet gramicidin). On hydrolysis, gramicidin S yields equimolar amounts of L-ornithine, L-valine, L-leucine, L-proline, and D-phenylalanine.[29] Since only the δ-amino group of ornithine appears to be free, it has been concluded that gramicidin S also is a cyclopeptide, probably containing 10 amino acid residues. The closely related tyrocidine A and tyrocidine B have been shown to be

[28] T. Ono and R. Hirohata, *Z. physiol. Chem.*, **304**, 77 (1956).
[29] R. L. M. Synge, *Biochem. J.*, **39**, 363 (1945).

cyclic decapeptides;[30] tyrocidine B differs from tyrocidine A in having an L-tryptophyl residue in place of the L-phenylalanyl residue of tyrocidine A.

L-valyl-L-ornithyl-L-leucyl-D-phenylalanyl-L-prolyl
   | |
L-tyrosyl-L-glutamyl-L-aspartyl-D-phenylalanyl-L-phenylalanyl

Tyrocidine A

Among the numerous other peptides known to be elaborated by microorganisms are the polymyxins[31] (from *Bacillus polymyxa*), the bacitracins[32] (from *Bacillus licheniformis*), and the actinomycins[33] (from *Actinomycetes*). One of the polymyxins (polymyxin A) yields, on hydrolysis, L-threonine, D-leucine, and α,γ-diaminobutyric acid; actinomycin C_2 has been shown to contain L-threonine, sarcosine, L-proline, D-valine, N-methyl-L-valine, and D-alloisoleucine. These microbial peptides are antibacterial agents ("antibiotics"), among which are included the penicillins (p. 60) which contain D-penicillamine. The penicillins (elaborated by fungi of the *Penicillium* family), may be considered derivatives of the dipeptide α-formylglycyl-D-penicillamine. It will be

$$\text{CHO} \quad \text{HS—C(CH}_3)_2$$
$$\quad|\qquad\qquad\quad|$$
$$\text{NH}_2\text{CHCO—NHCHCOOH}$$

α-Formylglycyl-D-penicillamine

noted that a characteristic feature of the above antibacterial agents is the presence of amino acids that are either stereoisomers of protein amino acids or are nonprotein amino acids.[34]

Other fungi also produce interesting peptides. For example, the poisonous mushroom *Amanita phalloides* contains a peptide, named "phalloidine," which, on hydrolysis, yields cystine, alanine, and allohydroxy-L-proline (cf. p. 82).[35] Peptide-like structures have been shown to be components of the ergot alkaloids (Chapter 33) and of the tomato-wilt factor (lycomarasmin) of the fungus *Fusarium lycopersici*.

Of special interest was the finding, in 1937, by Ivanovics and Bruckner that the capsular substance of *Bacillus anthracis* and of related species is completely converted, on hydrolysis, to D-glutamic acid. Later work has suggested that the capsular material has a high molecular weight (about 50,000), but that this large molecule breaks down readily to

[30] A. Paladini and L. C. Craig, *J. Am. Chem. Soc.,* **76,** 688 (1954); T. P. King and L. C. Craig, *ibid.,* **77,** 6627 (1955).

[31] P. H. Long et al., *Ann. N. Y. Acad. Sci.,* **51,** 853 (1949).

[32] J. R. Weisiger et al., *J. Am. Chem. Soc.,* **77,** 3123 (1955); I. M. Lockhart and E. P. Abraham, *Biochem. J.,* **58,** 633 (1954).

[33] H. Brockmann, *Angew. Chem.,* **66,** 1 (1954).

[34] T. S. Work, *Biochem. Soc. Symposia,* **1,** 61 (1948).

[35] T. Wieland et al., *Ann. Chem.,* **577,** 215 (1952).

particles having a molecular weight of only a few thousand. Also, evidence has been presented for the presence, in this substance, of CO—NH bonds involving the γ-carboxyl group of glutamic acid.[36]

It was noted above that a decisive contribution to the study of the chemistry of the gramicidins was made by Craig, who was able to separate a number of peptides from one another. Craig's method has proved to be of considerable value for the fractionation of mixtures of closely related substances, and it depends on the same general principles underlying the familiar laboratory procedures for the extraction of a

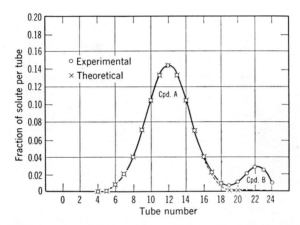

Fig. 9. Separation of two compounds (A and B) by countercurrent distribution involving 24 transfers. [From B. Williamson and L. C. Craig, *J. Biol. Chem.*, **168**, 687 (1947).]

chemical substance from one solvent, such as water, by another solvent, such as chloroform. Its theoretical basis is similar to that of partition chromatography (cf. p. 115). Craig's method is termed "countercurrent distribution," and involves the use of an ingenious apparatus which permits one to perform as many as 100 or more successive extractions in a single operation, and to determine the distribution of the components of a mixture.[37] In Fig. 9 is shown the separation of a mixture of 90 per cent of substance A (partition coefficient = 1) and 10 per cent of substance B (partition coefficient = 10). The countercurrent distribution method has been applied with signal success to the purification of oxytocin,[38] a peptide hormone of the posterior pituitary gland (Chapter 38).

[36] S. G. Waley, *J. Chem. Soc.*, **1955**, 517.

[37] L. C. Craig et al., *Cold Spring Harbor Symposia Quant. Biol.*, **14**, 24 (1949); P. Von Tavel and R. Signer, *Advances in Protein Chem.*, **11**, 237 (1956).

[38] J. G. Pierce et al., *J. Biol. Chem.*, **199**, 929 (1952).

In a brilliant series of investigations, du Vigneaud and his associates have established the chemical structure of oxytocin by amino acid analysis, by systematic degradation, and by chemical synthesis.[39] In the posterior pituitary, oxytocin is accompanied by vasopressin, a different but structurally related peptide hormone. The structure of oxytocin

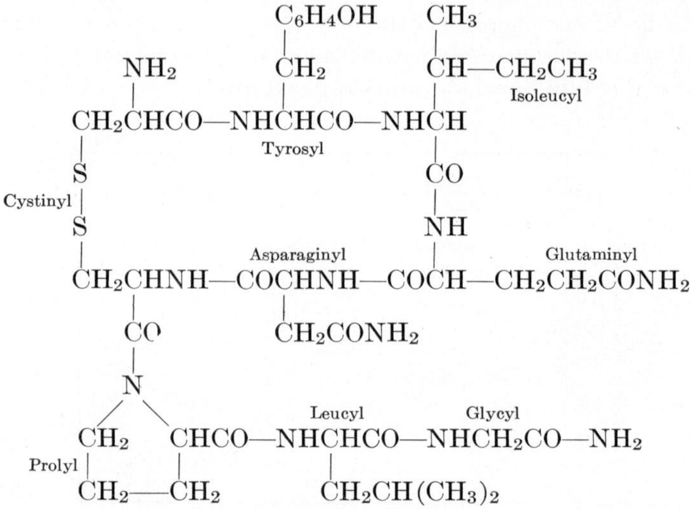

Structure of oxytocin

(from beef and swine) is shown; in beef vasopressin, the isoleucyl and leucyl residues are replaced by phenylalanyl and arginyl residues respectively, whereas in swine vasopressin they are replaced by phenylalanyl and lysyl residues.[40] All the amino acid residues of these hormones have the L-configuration. A distinctive structural feature is the presence of a macrocyclic ring involving the disulfide bond of cystine; a similar cyclic structure forms a part of the insulin molecule (cf. p. 146).

The use of countercurrent distribution and chromatographic techniques has also been decisive in the elucidation of the structure of peptides obtained from the anterior pituitary, and which stimulate the secretion of adrenal cortical hormones (Chapter 38). Other peptide-like substances of physiological importance are secretin and hypertensin (or angiotonin); the latter substance is formed by the kidney when the blood supply of this organ has been curtailed, and promotes a rise in blood pressure. A purified preparation of a hypertensin has been obtained by partition chromatography, and found to have the following amino acid

[39] V. du Vigneaud et al., *J. Am. Chem. Soc.*, **75**, 4879 (1953); **76**, 3115 (1954); V. du Vigneaud, *Harvey Lectures*, **50**, 1 (1956).

[40] V. du Vigneaud et al., *J. Am. Chem. Soc.*, **75**, 4880 (1953); **76**, 4751 (1954); **79**, 5572 (1957).

sequence:[41]

> Aspartyl-arginyl-valyl-tyrosyl-valyl-histidyl-
> prolyl-phenylalanyl-histidyl-leucine

Finally, mention may be made of the occurrence of peptides of L-glutamic acid in nature. Of special importance are the glutamyl peptides linked to a pteroyl residue (p. 207) in the group of vitamins termed folic acid (Chapter 39). A peptide isolated from yeast, and related structurally to folic acid, yields, on hydrolysis, 10 to 11 units of L-glutamic acid. Another peptide of L-glutamic acid, found in nature, is the derivative of tri-L-glutamine which was obtained from extracts of the brown marine alga *Pelvetia fastigiata;* the substance may be named "fastigiatin."[42]

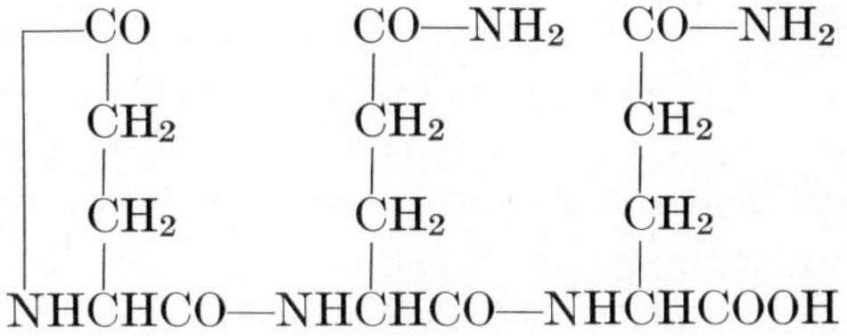

Fastigiatin

At the beginning of this chapter, several items of experimental evidence were presented in favor of the Fischer-Hofmeister hypothesis of the structure of proteins. The widespread occurrence in living systems of peptides may be taken as additional indirect evidence of the fact that the peptide bond is the principal mode of linkage between the amino acid components of many natural products, including the proteins.

Sequence of Amino Acid Residues in Proteins

The picture of protein structure that will have emerged from the discussion thus far shows the amino acids to be joined to one another in chain-like aggregates by means of peptide bonds involving the α-amino and α-carboxyl groups, with occasional cross-links between separate peptide chains and between parts of the same chain. If this is assumed as a basis for further work, and one knows the proportion of amino acids released on complete hydrolysis of a protein, an approach may be made to the determination of the sequence of the individual residues in the peptide chain of that protein. In recent years, decisive progress has been made in the development of methods for such studies.[43] Procedures

[41] W. S. Peart, *Biochem. J.,* **62,** 520 (1956); D. F. Elliott and W. S. Peart, *ibid.,* **65,** 246 (1957).

[42] C. A. Dekker et al., *J. Biol. Chem.,* **181,** 719 (1949).

[43] F. Sanger, *Advances in Protein Chem.,* **7,** 1 (1952); H. G. Khorana. *Quart. Revs.,* **6,** 340 (1952).

are available for the identification of the amino acid residue bearing the free α-amino group of the peptide chain ("N-terminal residue"), the one bearing the free α-carboxyl group ("C-terminal residue"), and also for the determination of the amino acid sequences of segments of the peptide chain. In Sanger's brilliant work on insulin, to be discussed in what follows, the information obtained by these methods permitted him to formulate the complete amino acid sequence of this protein hormone. It is likely that further developments in this field will lead to the elucidation of the complete sequences in other proteins.

Determination of N-Terminal Amino Acid Residues. In 1945, Sanger introduced the use of 2,4-dinitrofluorobenzene (DNFB) as a general reagent in protein chemistry.[44] DNFB reacts with the free amino groups of peptide chains to give dinitrophenyl (DNP) peptides (cf. p. 50). The choice of the DNP group was based on the finding that its linkage with an amino group is more stable to hydrolysis than the peptide linkages of the protein. In addition, the presence of the DNP group confers upon its derivatives a yellow color that is useful in following the fractionation of a mixture of DNP compounds. When insulin was treated with DNFB, and the DNP-insulin was hydrolyzed with acid to break all its peptide bonds, those amino acids which, in the intact protein, had a free amino group were present in the hydrolysate as yellow dinitrophenyl derivatives. Clearly, if lysine is present in the interior of the peptide chain, the free ϵ-amino group will also react to form an ϵ-DNP-lysyl derivative. DNFB reacts with the phenolic hydroxyl of tyrosine and the imidazolyl group of histidine but yields colorless DNP compounds.

Sanger separated the colored DNP derivatives by chromatography on silica gel, and identified them by comparison with authentic samples of DNP-amino acids. Since DNP-glycine and DNP-phenylalanine were the only α-substituted amino acids obtained from DNP-insulin, Sanger concluded that glycine and L-phenylalanine represent the N-terminal residues of the peptide chains of insulin. For a time it was thought that the molecular weight of insulin is 12,000, and the results of the end group studies were interpreted to indicate the presence in the protein of 4 peptide chains (2 glycyl chains and 2 phenylalanyl chains), but with the recognition that the molecular weight may be about 6000 (cf. p. 43), only 1 glycyl and 1 phenylalanyl chain need to be considered.

The DNP technique of end group analysis has been applied to many proteins (Table 4). In the use of this method, and other methods for the same purpose, it is important to bear in mind the assumption that a reagent such as DNFB reacts with all the N-terminal groups of a protein molecule. If a terminal amino acid is not accessible to the

[44] F. Sanger, *Cold Spring Harbor Symposia Quant. Biol.,* **14,** 153 (1949).

Table 4. N-Terminal and C-Terminal Residues of Some Proteins

Protein	Assumed Molecular Weight	N-Terminal	C-Terminal
Insulin (beef, swine, sheep)	6,000	1 glycyl 1 phenylalanyl	1 asparagine 1 alanine
Lysozyme (egg white)	14,700	1 lysyl	1 leucine
Ribonuclease (beef pancreas)	14,000	1 lysyl	1 valine
Papain	20,300	1 isoleucyl	
Trypsin (beef pancreas)	23,500	1 isoleucyl	
β-Lactoglobulin	40,000	3 leucyl	1 isoleucine 1 histidine
Egg albumin	45,000		1 proline
Serum albumin (human, horse, beef)	69,000	1 aspartyl	
Hemoglobin (beef, sheep, goat)	66,000	2 valyl 2 methionyl	
Hemoglobin (adult human)	66,000	4 valyl	
Myoglobin (horse)	17,000	1 glycyl	
Myoglobin (whale)	17,000	1 valyl	
Aldolase (rabbit muscle)	140,000	2 prolyl	
Tobacco mosaic virus protein	17,000		1 threonine

reagent, possibly because of folding of the long peptide chain (cf. p. 154), it may not be substituted. For example, p-iodophenylsulfonyl chloride does not appear to react with as many amino groups of a protein as does DNFB.[45] Some proteins, such as myosin or egg albumin, do not give any α-DNP derivatives of amino acids by the Sanger method, and the question arises whether the protein is composed of cyclic peptides lacking N-terminal groups, or whether such groups are present but not accessible to the reagent.[46] In any end group method, it is essential that the yield of the terminal amino acid (or its derivative) bear a stoichiometric relation to amount of protein used. Any contamination by detectable amounts of free amino acids or peptides will lead to erroneous results, since these substances will also react with DNFB or a similar reagent.

Other useful chemical methods for the determination of N-terminal residues include the phenylthiocarbamyl method of Edman[47] and the thiocarbamate method of Levy.[48] In the Edman method, the protein or peptide is treated with phenylisothiocyanate to form a phenylthiocarbamyl (PTC) peptide, which is then cleaved by anhydrous HCl in an

[45] S. Udenfriend and S. F. Velick, *J. Biol. Chem.*, **190**, 733 (1951).

[46] K. Bailey, *Biochem. J.*, **49**, 23 (1951)

[47] P. Edman, *Acta Chem. Scand.*, **4**, 283 (1950); **10**, 761 (1956); H. Fraenkel-Conrat and J. I. Harris, *J. Am. Chem. Soc.*, **76**, 6058 (1954).

[48] A. L. Levy, *J. Chem. Soc.*, **1950**, 404.

organic solvent (nitromethane) to give the phenylthiohydantoin of the N-terminal amino acid (cf. p. 50). The phenylthiohydantoin is soluble in the organic solvent, and may be identified by chromatography, whereas the rest of the peptide chain is insoluble. The recovery of the insoluble peptide (minus the original N-terminal residue) permits one to repeat the Edman procedure on this material, and to identify the second amino acid from the α-amino end of the peptide chain. In favorable cases, this procedure has been repeated several times to determine the sequence of amino acids in the N-terminal segment of a long peptide chain. In the Levy method, CS_2 is allowed to react with the peptide in alkali to form the thiocarbamate ($-NHCSS^-$); at pH 3 to 4, this product undergoes ring closure to give the 2-thio-5-thiazolidone (p. 50) of the N-terminal amino acid. An additional method which offers promise for the determination of terminal α-amino groups involves the treatment of proteins or peptides with bromoacetate ($BrCH_2COO^-$) to form N-carboxymethyl derivatives ($-NHCH_2COO^-$).[49]

In addition to the end group methods based on chemical substitution of the N-terminal residue, use has been made of the enzyme aminopeptidase (Chapter 29). This enzyme specifically hydrolyzes peptide bonds adjacent to free α-amino groups, and the liberated amino acids may be identified chromatographically.[50]

Determination of C-Terminal Amino Acid Residues. One of the available procedures is to treat a protein with lithium borohydride ($LiBH_4$), which reduces the free terminal carboxyl groups to carbinol (CH_2OH) groups (cf. p. 131). The terminal amino acid residue thus is converted to the corresponding amino alcohol. The reduced protein is then hydrolyzed, and the amino alcohol is identified by chromatography. Another chemical method involves treatment of the protein with hydrazine (NH_2NH_2) at $100°$ C; this cleaves all the peptide bonds and converts all amino acid residues except the C-terminal residue to hydrazides ($-CONHNH_2$). The liberated C-terminal amino acid then may be determined chromatographically.[51]

A valuable enzymic method is the use of carboxypeptidase (Chapter 29), which specifically hydrolyzes peptide bonds adjacent to free α-carboxyl groups. The liberated amino acids are identified chromatographically. Despite several limitations, this method appears to be the best one now available for the determination of the C-terminal residues of peptide chains, and it has been used successfully with several proteins (cf. Table 4).

[49] S. Korman and H. T. Clarke, *J. Biol. Chem.*, **221**, 113, 133 (1956).
[50] R. L. Hill and E. L. Smith, *J. Biol. Chem.*, **228**, 577 (1957).
[51] C. Niu and H. Fraenkel-Conrat, *J. Am. Chem. Soc.*, **77**, 5832 (1955); J. H. Bradbury, *Biochem. J.*, **68**, 475, 482 (1958).

The Structure of Insulin.[52]   The work of Sanger on insulin represents one of the greatest achievements in protein chemistry because it was the first to provide the complete amino acid sequence of a well-defined protein.   As noted before, the insulin molecule was found to be composed of two peptide chains; these are joined by disulfide bonds.   To cleave these bonds, Sanger treated insulin or DNP-insulin with performic acid (HCOOOH), which converts cystine into 2 molecules of cysteic acid (cf. p. 58).   The two peptide chains of oxidized insulin could now be separated from each other, and each was subjected to amino acid analysis and to partial degradation by hydrolysis with acid and with proteinases (cf. Chapter 29).   The glycyl chain of oxidized beef insulin was found to be composed of 21 amino acid residues, and was termed the "A-chain"; the phenylalanyl chain, with 30 residues, was termed the "B-chain."   To establish an unequivocal sequence for each of the two chains, many fragments had to be isolated and identified; for example, in the study of the A-chain, about 35 peptides formed on partial acid hydrolysis were examined to determine their structure by complete amino acid analysis and by end group assay.   The approach may be illustrated by the identification of the N-terminal octapeptide segment of the A-chain; a number of peptides (not all are listed) were separated and identified, thus permitting the formulation of a unique sequence for this segment, as shown in the scheme.

Dipeptides:	Ileu-val Glu-cys
	Val-glu
	Glu-glu
Larger peptides:	Ileu-val-glu Cys-cys-ala
	Gly-ileu-val-glu
	Glu-cys-cys-ala
	Ileu-val-glu-glu
Sequence of segment:	Gly-ileu-val-glu-glu-cys-cys-ala

By combining the information about the amino acid sequences of large segments of each chain, and the relation of the segments to each other, Sanger concluded that the complete amino acid sequence of the A-chain of oxidized beef insulin is

Glycyl-isoleucyl-valyl-glutamyl-glutaminyl-cysteyl-cysteyl-
alanyl-seryl-valyl-cysteyl-seryl-leucyl-tyrosyl-glutaminyl-
leucyl-glutamyl-asparaginyl-tyrosyl-cysteyl-asparagine

and that of the B-chain is

[52] F. Sanger and H. Tuppy, *Biochem. J.*, **49**, 463, 481 (1951); F. Sanger and E. O. P. Thompson, *ibid.*, **53**, 366 (1953); F. Sanger et al., *ibid.*, **60**, 541 (1955).

Phenylalanyl-valyl-asparaginyl-glutaminyl-histidyl-leucyl-cysteyl-glycyl-seryl-histidyl-leucyl-valyl-glutamyl-alanyl-leucyl-tyrosyl-leucyl-valyl-cysteyl-glycyl-glutamyl-arginyl-glycyl-phenylalanyl-phenylalanyl-tyrosyl-threonyl-prolyl-lysyl-alanine.

The examination of peptides formed upon enzymic degradation of insulin made it possible to establish the position of the glutaminyl and asparaginyl residues, and of the disulfide bridges, thus permitting the formulation of the structure of beef insulin shown in Fig. 10. It will be

Glycine (4)	
Alanine (3)	
Valine (5)	
Isoleucine (1)	
Threonine (1)	
Serine (3)	
Asparagine (3)	
Glutamic acid (4)	
Glutamine (3)	
Proline (1)	
Cystine (3)	
Leucine (6)	
Tyrosine (4)	
Phenylalanine (3)	
Histidine (2)	
Lysine (1)	
Arginine (1)	

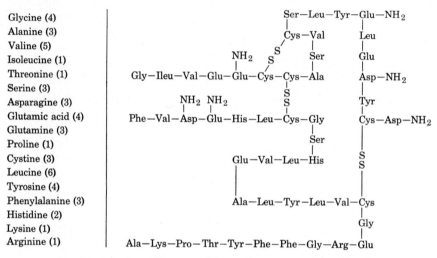

Fig. 10. Amino acid composition and sequence of beef insulin.

seen that the beef insulin molecule is characterized by the presence of a ring involving 3 "half-cystine" residues, alanine, serine, and valine of the A-chain. A similar cyclic structure has been established in the peptide hormones of the posterior pituitary (cf. p. 140).

Insulin preparations from other species have also been examined by Sanger, and have been found to have a structure similar to that of beef insulin, except for the nature of the amino acid residues in the ring mentioned in the previous paragraph. The ala-ser-val sequence of the A-chain of beef insulin is replaced by thr-ser-ileu in swine insulin, by ala-gly-val in sheep insulin, by thr-gly-ileu in horse insulin, and by thr-ser-ileu in whale insulin.[53]

Amino Acid Sequences in Other Proteins. The success achieved by Sanger with insulin led to the study of the amino acid sequences of other proteins, and to the development of new methods for the fractionation of peptides formed by partial degradation. Whereas Sanger's work

[53] H. Brown et al., *Biochem. J.,* **60,** 556 (1955); J. I. Harris et al., *Arch. Biochem. and Biophys.,* **65,** 427 (1956).

largely involved the use of paper chromatography and of ionophoresis (p. 106), other investigators have employed ion-exchange chromatography and countercurrent distribution. In particular, chromatography on ion-exchange resins such as Dowex-50 (p. 122) has proved valuable for the separation of peptides of closely related structure.[54]

Clearly, as the length of a peptide chain increases, the problem of establishing its amino acid sequence becomes more difficult. However, the elucidation of the structure of the adrenocorticotropic peptides (Chapter 38), with 39 amino acid residues, already has shown that the limits imposed by the available methods have not been reached. Furthermore, significant progress is being made toward the formulation of the complete amino acid sequence of ribonuclease, which consists of a single peptide chain of 124 amino acid residues.[55] It may be concluded, therefore, that the study of the amino acid sequence of proteins is now on a secure experimental basis, and likely to advance in the future with the development of improved methods.

In the face of the experimental difficulties encountered in the establishment of the amino acid sequence in the peptide chains of proteins, it is not surprising that assumptions should have been made in an attempt to simplify the problem. One such postulate, which has recurred at intervals in the history of protein chemistry, is that each type of amino acid residue is regularly repeated along a peptide chain. Thus Kossel in 1906 suggested that clupein, the protamine derived from herring sperm, consisted of a regular arrangement of arginine residues (A) and of monoamino acid residues (M) as follows:

$$—A—A—M—A—A—M—A—A—M—$$

More recently, Bergmann and Niemann[56] put forward the hypothesis that any particular amino acid residue is repeated in a peptide chain with a frequency given by the expression $2^m \times 3^n$, where m and n are either zero or positive integers. On the basis of the then available data for the amino acid composition of silk fibroin, for example, they concluded that each glycine residue (G) recurred in the chain with a frequency of 2, the alanine residue (A) had a periodicity of 4, and the tyrosine residue had a periodicity of 16. If the other amino acid residues are denoted by X, a segment of the silk fibroin molecule, according to this view, would have the following structure:

$$–A–G–T–G–A–G–X–G–A–G–X–G–A–G–X–G–A–G–T–G–$$

[54] Y. P. Dowmont and J. S. Fruton, *J. Biol. Chem.*, **197**, 271 (1952).

[55] C. H. W. Hirs et al., *J. Biol. Chem.*, **221**, 151 (1956); R. R. Redfield and C. B. Anfinsen, *ibid.*, **221**, 385 (1956); A. P. Ryle and C. B. Anfinsen, *Biochim. et Biophys. Acta*, **24**, 633 (1957); S. Moore and W. H. Stein, *Harvey Lectures*, **52**, 119 (1958).

[56] M. Bergmann and C. Niemann, *Science*, **86**, 187 (1937).

The periodicity hypothesis of Bergmann and Niemann served as a great stimulus to the development of accurate methods for the determination of the amino acid composition of proteins, and it soon became evident that the hypothesis was untenable in the form in which it had been proposed. Examination of the amino acid sequence of insulin gives no evidence of periodicity. Also, studies on partial hydrolysates of silk fibroin indicate that the chain contains sequences of the type —G—X—A—G—A—G—X—.[57] It is clear that the periodicity hypothesis was an oversimplification, and its history serves to caution against mathematical theories of protein structure insecurely founded on experiment. For a discussion of some of the many hypotheses of protein structure, see the articles by Vickery and Osborne,[58] by Pauling and Niemann,[59] and by Bull.[60]

The Shape of Protein Molecules[61]

The determination of the sequence of amino acids in long peptide chains, and of the location of disulfide bridges, provides a sound basis for the understanding of protein structure, but does not suffice to describe completely the chemical properties of protein molecules. As will be seen from the subsequent discussion, the existence of chemical linkages in addition to peptide and disulfide bonds must be invoked to interpret studies on the shape of protein molecules. Some proteins, such as the scleroproteins keratin and silk fibroin, are normally obtained in the form of fibers, and may be considered to approximate ribbon-like structures of several hundred amino acid residues linked by peptide bonds. The disulfide bonds of keratin help to join the separate chains, and it is assumed that, in the unstretched fibrous protein, "hydrogen bonds" cooperate to confer upon each peptide chain a characteristic coiling (p. 154). The vast majority of known proteins normally do not behave as long fibers, but tend to be rounded in shape; these are termed "globular" or "corpuscular" proteins. The long peptide chains of each of the globular proteins must therefore be held in a coiled structure by chemical forces that confer upon the protein molecule its characteristic physical shape. The changes in several properties of globular proteins (e.g., solubility, enzymic activity) that accompany denaturation (p. 153) are associated with changes in their molecular shape.

[57] E. Slobodian and M. Levy, *J. Biol. Chem.*, **201**, 371 (1953).

[58] H. B. Vickery and T. B. Osborne, *Physiol. Revs.*, **8**, 393 (1928).

[59] L. Pauling and C. Niemann, *J. Am. Chem. Soc.*, **61**, 1860 (1939).

[60] H. B. Bull, *Advances in Enzymol.*, **1**, 1 (1941).

[61] J. T. Edsall, in H. Neurath and K. Bailey, *The Proteins,* Vol. IB, Chapter 7, Academic Press, New York, 1953.

Although there are several experimental techniques for the study of the shape of protein molecules, the data given by these methods do not give the desired information without assumptions of uncertain validity. A widely used procedure involves the measurement of the rate of diffusion of proteins in solution. This is determined by forming a sharp boundary between a protein solution and the solvent, and by observing the change in refractive index gradient, as in electrophoresis. The schlieren optical technique (p. 37) has been used for this purpose, but an interferometric method has been developed that is more precise.[62] As the protein diffuses into the solvent, the peak in the schlieren diagram flattens, and from measurements of the rate of this change one may obtain the diffusion constant (D) of the protein. D has the dimensions cm^2 sec^{-1}, and is 10^{-6} to 10^{-7} for most proteins. It will be recalled that a value of D is needed for the determination of the particle weight of a protein by the sedimentation velocity-diffusion method (cf. p. 41).

The diffusion constant (or coefficient) is given by the equation

$$D = \frac{KT}{f} = \frac{RT}{Nf}$$

where K is the gas constant per molecule $(K = R/N)$, T is the absolute temperature, R is the gas constant per mole, and N is Avogadro's number (6.02×10^{23}). The term f is a constant that is characteristic of the particles and of the medium and may be considered the force that acts per molecule to give it a velocity of 1 cm per sec. If one assumes that the particles are spherical, Stokes' law may be applied, i.e.,

$$f_0 = 6\pi\eta r$$

where η is the viscosity of the medium, and r is the radius of the dissolved particle. Since the radius of a spherical particle is equal to $(3VM/4\pi N)^{1/3}$,

$$f_0 = 6\pi\eta \left(\frac{3VM}{4\pi N}\right)^{1/3}$$

In this equation, M is the molecular weight and V is the partial specific volume. The value of f, obtained from an experimental determination of D, is always greater than that of f_0 calculated from known values of M and V; i.e., the ratio f/f_0 is always greater than unity. This ratio is termed the "frictional ratio" or "dissymmetry constant," and several representative values are given in Table 5.

The ratio f/f_0 is a measure of the extent to which the shape of a protein molecule deviates from that of a perfect sphere. The use of the ratio for the calculation of the shape of the particle is made difficult by the fact that the asymmetry may be a consequence both of the binding of water by the protein ("hydration") and of the intrinsic asymmetry of

[62] L. J. Gosting, *Advances in Protein Chem.*, **11**, 429 (1956).

Table 5. Molar Frictional Ratio of Several Proteins

Protein	f/f_0	Protein	f/f_0
Ribonuclease	1.04	Egg albumin	1.16
Cytochrome c	1.29	Hemoglobin	1.24
Carboxypeptidase	1.16	γ-Globulin (human)	1.49
β-Lactoglobulin	1.26	Fibrinogen (human)	1.98
Insulin	1.13	Tobacco mosaic virus	3.12

the anhydrous protein. It is convenient to express f/f_0 as the product of the two ratios f/f_e and f_e/f_0, where f_e applies to the anhydrous protein. One may then make assumptions about the shape of the anhydrous particle. If it is assumed that proteins are elongated ellipsoids such as shown in Fig. 11, the ratio of the major to the minor axes (a/b) may be

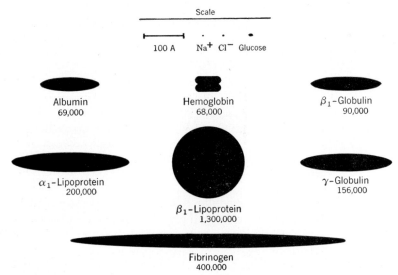

Fig. 11. Relative dimensions of various proteins. (From J. L. Oncley, *Conference on the Preservation of the Cellular and Protein Components of Blood,* American National Red Cross, Washington, 1949.)

calculated from values assigned to f_e/f_0. For a prolate spheroid, if $a/b = 2$, $f_e/f_0 = 1.044$; if $a/b = 5$, $f_e/f_0 = 1.255$. An estimate may be made of f/f_e, the asymmetry due to hydration, if the amount of water bound per gram of protein is known, but it is not possible at present to be certain of the relative contributions of f_e/f_0 and of f/f_e to the observed values of f/f_0. In some calculations of a/b, the factor of hydration has been neglected; with highly asymmetric particles of f/f_0 above 2 this is justified. Because of the assumptions and uncertainties in the calculation of a/b, the "cigar-shaped" protein molecules depicted in Fig. 11 are only rough approximations, and should not be considered to represent the actual shapes of the proteins shown.

The hydration of proteins is an important factor in the evaluation of their physical properties, since the quantity of water bound by a protein may be between 20 and 50 per cent of its dry weight. Most of the bound water can be removed from a protein crystal by drying at 100° C, but some bound water may still be present after such treatment. It should be added that, although the determination of D gives the diffusion constant of the hydrated protein, the value of the particle weight (M) obtained by sedimentation velocity-diffusion refers to the anhydrous protein.

The diffusion method described above measures "translational diffusion." If the molecules in a solution are oriented in a given direction by the imposition of an external electric field, and then the field is cut off, they undergo "rotary diffusion" to establish a random orientation. The "relaxation time" required to reach the random state is related to molecular shape, and may be used for the calculation of axial ratios of assumed elliptical models.

In addition to diffusion methods, the study of the viscosity of protein solutions has given information about the shape of protein molecules. The viscosity of a liquid is measured by determining the time required for a given volume to pass through a capillary tube. The coefficient of viscosity, η, is a measure of the resistance of a liquid to the stress imposed by forcing the molecules to move relative to each other; the unit of viscosity is the poise (gram cm^{-1} sec^{-1}). The relative viscosity η_r of a solution is equal to η/η_0, where η is the viscosity of the solution and η_0 that of the solvent. Einstein showed that a dilute solution of spherical particles should obey the equation $\eta_{sp} = \eta_r - 1 = 2.5\phi$, where η_{sp} is the "specific viscosity" and ϕ is the volume fraction of the solute. Since ϕ refers to the hydrated protein molecules, it is convenient to define an "intrinsic viscosity," $[\eta] = \eta_{sp}/c$, as c (grams of anhydrous protein per cubic centimeter) approaches zero. Protein solutions give values of η_{sp}/ϕ greater than 2.5 as ϕ approaches zero, and the magnitude of this viscosity increment may be used to calculate the ratio of the axes of an assumed ellipsoid. Clearly, elongated or flattened spheroids will increase the viscosity of a solvent to a greater extent than will an equal number of equivalent spherical molecules. As with the frictional ratio, the interpretation of viscosity data is fraught with uncertainty as regards the relative contribution of hydration and of molecular asymmetry. The calculations of the ratio of major to minor axes of assumed spheroids have given values that are in fair agreement with those obtained from diffusion data. For example, for serum albumin, $[\eta] = 6.5$ and $f/f_0 =$

1.25; the axial ratios for elongated spheroids calculated from these data are 5.0 and 5.6 respectively.

Another procedure for the study of the shape of protein molecules is especially useful with asymmetric proteins. If one passes a beam of polarized light into a protein solution at rest, the protein molecules will be randomly oriented, and the light beam will not be affected. On the other hand, if the protein solution is allowed to flow through a narrow tube, the asymmetric molecules will orient themselves with respect to one another, and, the more rapid the flow, the greater will be the parallel orientation. This will cause the phenomenon of "double refraction of flow" or "flow birefringence," and measurement of the extent of the double refraction of flow at different velocities of flow will give a measure of the asymmetry of the protein molecules.[63] This phenomenon has been studied extensively with the muscle protein myosin; if zero hydration is assumed, flow birefringence data suggest that this protein is about 2000 A long for an axial ratio of 100.

Still another method is to subject the protein solution to an alternating-current field. In an electric field of sufficiently low frequency, the charged protein molecules can rotate to follow the alternation of the field. As the frequency is increased, however, the protein molecules are unable to follow the field. The difference in orientation of the protein molecules may be observed by measurement of the dielectric constant (p. 20) of the solution. At low frequencies the protein molecules are completely oriented, and the dielectric constant is high; at high frequencies the molecules are unoriented, and a lower value of the dielectric constant results. From the form of the curves obtained on plotting dielectric constant against frequency, conclusions have been drawn about the ratio of major to minor axes of assumed spheroids corresponding to the proteins studied. This approach involves the assumption that the charge distribution on a protein molecule is fixed; however, Kirkwood has proposed an interpretation of the dielectric behavior of proteins based on the fluctuation of the charge distribution.[64]

A recent procedure developed for the study of the shape of protein molecules depends on the measurement of the polarization of the fluorescence of protein derivatives.[65]

---

[63] J. T. Edsall, *Advances in Colloid Sci.,* **1,** 269 (1942); R. Cerf and H. A. Scheraga, *Chem. Revs.,* **51,** 185 (1952).

[64] J. G. Kirkwood and J. B. Shumaker, *Proc. Natl. Acad. Sci.,* **38,** 855, 863 (1952); S. N. Timasheff et al., *J. Am. Chem. Soc.,* **79,** 782 (1957).

[65] G. Weber, *Advances in Protein Chem.,* **8,** 415 (1953).

Denaturation of Proteins[66]

The problem of the intramolecular forces responsible for the shape of globular proteins is related to the phenomenon of denaturation, mentioned previously in connection with the methods for the isolation of proteins. Denaturation is a term that is difficult to define exactly because it refers merely to changes in the properties of a protein. One of the distinctive consequences of the denaturation of a protein is a decrease in solubility at its isoelectric point. The proteins that exhibit characteristic biological activity as enzymes, hormones, or viruses usually lose these attributes on denaturation. Also, protein denaturation is accompanied by an increased reactivity of several of the side-chain groups such as the sulfhydryl group of cysteine, the disulfide group of cystine, and the phenolic group of tyrosine. On denaturation, new ionizable groups become available for acid-base titration.[67] In addition, there is a change in optical rotation in the direction of increased levorotation (cf. p. 160).[68]

Denaturation may be caused in various ways. Among them are heating, or treatment with acid, alkali, organic solvents, concentrated solutions of urea or guanidine hydrochloride, aromatic anions such as salicylate, or anionic detergents such as dodecyl sulfate. Not all anions are denaturing agents; caprylate and aromatic carboxylate ions actually protect egg albumin from heat denaturation. Ultraviolet irradiation or high pressures also cause denaturation. All these treatments will cause an alteration in the solubility properties of most proteins, but proteins show a wide difference in their sensitivity to any one of these methods of denaturation. For example, the protein enzyme ribonuclease is relatively stable to heat treatment, and the protein enzyme trypsin is stable at acid pH values.

If the treatment is not prolonged unduly, the denaturation may be reversed by restoring the conditions at which the protein is stable. Thus Kunitz and Northrop were able to cause parallel loss of solubility and of enzymic activity of the protein enzyme trypsin by exposing it to a temperature of 80 to 90° C. When the solution was cooled to 37° C, the solubility and activity of the enzyme were regained. One must distinguish therefore between "reversible" and "irreversible" denaturation of proteins. In the conversion of reversibly denatured β-lactoglobulin to the irreversibly denatured form, it appears likely that sulfhydryl groups of the protein are oxidized (by atmospheric oxygen) to disulfide groups.

[66] H. Neurath et al., *Chem. Revs.*, **34**, 158 (1944); F. W. Putnam, in H. Neurath and K. Bailey, *The Proteins*, Vol. IB, Chapter 9, Academic Press, New York, 1953.

[67] J. Steinhardt and E. M. Zaiser, *J. Biol. Chem.*, **190**, 197 (1951); W. F. Harrington, *Biochim. et Biophys. Acta*, **18**, 450 (1955).

[68] R. B. Simpson and W. Kauzmann, *J. Am. Chem. Soc.*, **75**, 5139 (1953).

There is insufficient information at present to state with certainty that all the various means of denaturation cause the same chemical changes in a "native" protein molecule. It is amply clear, however, that the conditions favorable for denaturation are not sufficiently drastic to bring about the cleavage of the peptide bonds. It was suggested by Wu in 1931 that the essential feature of the denaturation process was associated with an unfolding of tightly coiled peptide chains, leading to the disorganization of the internal structure of the protein. This hypothesis has been widely adopted and has received excellent experimental support.

The view that denatured proteins consist of disorganized peptide chains is strengthened by the results of measurements of the effect of denaturation on the characteristic shape of a protein. In general, denaturation causes an increase in asymmetry; i.e., the molecules become more like fibrous proteins. This greater asymmetry has been found for a variety of proteins by viscosity studies, or by determination of the frictional ratio from sedimentation and diffusion data. The effect of denaturing agents such as urea on the titration curves and the optical rotation of proteins is also consistent with the view that denaturation is accompanied by the unfolding of the native protein.[69] The increased reactivity of side-chain groups may reasonably be attributed to the "unmasking" of these groups upon protein denaturation. Since denatured proteins usually are more susceptible to the attack of proteolytic enzymes than native proteins, it has been concluded that the unfolding of the native protein makes the peptide bonds of the protein more accessible to enzymic action.[70]

Other evidence of the disorganization of the internal structure of the native protein by denaturation is the fact that denatured proteins cannot be crystallized, and thus they fail to exhibit the phenomenon most obviously associated with the establishment of an ordered array of molecules in a definite geometrical pattern.

The Hydrogen Bond and Protein Structure

Clearly, knowledge about the nature of the linkages that confer upon proteins their characteristic shape is of great importance for the understanding of the structure of proteins and of the mode of action of substances such as the enzymes, protein hormones, and viruses. Mirsky and Pauling[71] made a significant contribution to the solution of this problem when they suggested that a major factor in conferring upon an extended peptide chain of a protein its characteristic folding is the presence of "hydrogen bonds." The importance of the role of a hydrogen

[69] M. D. Sterman and J. F. Foster, *J. Am. Chem. Soc.*, **78**, 3652, 3656 (1956).
[70] K. Linderstrøm-Lang, *Cold Spring Harbor Symposia Quant. Biol.*, **14**, 117 (1949).
[71] A. E. Mirsky and L. Pauling, *Proc. Natl. Acad. Sci.*, **22**, 439 (1936).

atom in serving as a bridge between 2 atoms (e.g., 2 oxygen atoms, or an oxygen and a nitrogen atom) was demonstrated by Pauling when he showed that formic acid has the dimeric structure given in the formula.

$$
\begin{array}{ccc}
& O\cdots\cdots HO & \\
HC & & CH \\
& OH\cdots\cdots O &
\end{array}
$$

The formation of the two hydrogen bonds may be considered an expression of the tendency of the hydrogen atom to share the electrons of an oxygen atom:

$$
\overset{+\,-}{\underset{}{\ \ \ \ }}\ \ \ \ \ \overset{+\,-}{\underset{}{\ \ \ \ }} \qquad\qquad
$$

$$
{>}C::\ddot{O}:\quad H:\ddot{O}{-} \quad \rightarrow \quad {>}C::\ddot{O}:\ \cdots\ H:\ddot{O}{-}
$$

Although these bonds are very weak individually, if a molecule has many hydrogen bonds, they will reinforce one another and thus produce a stable structure. As applied to proteins, the hydrogen bond hypothesis visualizes the sharing of hydrogen atoms between the nitrogen and the carbonyl oxygen of different peptide bonds to form linkages of the type —NH⋯⋯⋯⋯OC—. Evidence for the existence of such linkages in polypeptides and in proteins has come from infrared spectroscopy.[72]

Numerous studies support the view[73] that the process of protein denaturation involves the cleavage of hydrogen bonds which are responsible for holding parts of the peptide chains in a unique configuration. Reagents such as urea or guanidine are presumed to cause denaturation by the same general mechanism as heat or unfavorable pH, since they are known to participate in hydrogen bond formation, and thus may be expected to break such bonds in native proteins. It is likely that the failure of side-chain groups (e.g., sulfhydryl, phenol) of native proteins to react with appropriate reagents is a consequence of their participation in hydrogen bonding.[74]

Whatever their nature, the bonds that link the parts of peptide chains to one another must be extremely labile. In addition to the evidence of denaturation studies, this lability is indicated by the fact that molecules of globular proteins can form thin films on the surface of water.[75] Such protein films behave as monolayers whose thickness corresponds to the

[72] S. Mizushima, *Advances in Protein Chem.*, **9**, 299 (1954); P. Doty and E. P. Geiduschek, in H. Neurath and K. Bailey, *The Proteins*, Vol. IA, Chapter 5, Academic Press, New York, 1953.

[73] W. Kauzmann, in W. D. McElroy and B. Glass, *The Mechanism of Enzyme Action*, Johns Hopkins Press, Baltimore, 1954.

[74] M. Laskowski and H. A. Scheraga, *J. Am. Chem. Soc.*, **76**, 6305 (1954)

[75] D. F. Cheesman and J. T. Davies, *Advances in Protein Chem.*, **9**, 440 (1954).

dimensions of single peptide chains (cf. p. 159). When the films are fully expanded, they have a thickness of about 5 A; upon compression of the film, the thickness is 10 A. The phenomenon of the "spreading" of protein molecules suggests that the weak bonds holding the peptide chains together are rapidly broken.

X-Ray Analysis of Protein Structure[76]

The study of protein structure by the chemical and physical methods discussed in preceding sections of this chapter has been paralleled by the application of the important technique of X-ray diffraction. X-rays are emitted when high-speed electrons strike atoms, and they have wave lengths of the order of interatomic distances; in much of the work on protein structure, the X-ray beam of 1.542 A, produced by electron

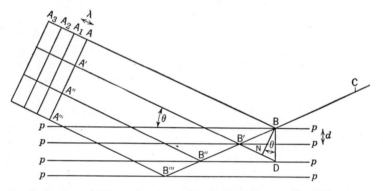

Fig. 12. Reflection of X-rays by successive lattice planes. The difference in path for the wave striking the first plane and that striking the second plane is $A'B'C - ABC = ND = n\lambda = 2d \sin\theta$. (From W. L. Bragg, *The Crystalline State*, Vol. I, G. Bell and Sons, London, 1933; used with permission of The Macmillan Co., New York.)

bombardment of copper, is used. When a narrow parallel beam of monochromatic X-rays strikes a crystal, the rays are "reflected" (diffracted) by the extranuclear electrons of the atoms in the crystal. These atoms are arranged in a regular array in the crystal lattice, and the lattice may be considered as a three-dimensional set of planes with the atoms at the lattice points. Such a lattice will have a repeating "unit cell" composed of a few molecules or atoms. The scattering of

[76] B. Low, in H. Neurath and K. Bailey, *The Proteins*, Vol. IA, Chapter 4, Academic Press, New York, 1953; J. C. Kendrew and M. F. Perutz, in F. J. W. Roughton and J. C. Kendrew, *Hemoglobin*. Butterworths Scientific Publications, London, 1949.

the X-rays from the repeated array of atoms will be reinforced whenever the relationship $n\lambda = 2d \sin \theta$ (the Bragg equation) is satisfied; n is an integer, λ is the wave length, d is the distance between parallel planes of atoms, and θ is the angle of incidence (and of reflection) of the X-ray beam with respect to the planes. Hence reinforcement of a diffracted beam will occur when the difference in path for a monochromatic X-ray wave striking two parallel planes is an integral number (n) of wave lengths (cf. Fig. 12). Such reinforcement will produce points or regions of higher intensity of diffracted X-rays, corresponding to planes of repeating units of high electron density. By photographing the diffracted X-rays, the angle of scattering may be determined, and an estimate may be made of the distance between the repeating planes and of the dimensions of the unit cell. Under favorable circumstances, the relative intensity of the diffraction maxima can be used to determine the arrangement of the atoms within the unit cell. An outstanding instance is that of copper phthalocyanine (p. 170), which lies in one plane with a center of symmetry at the electron dense metal ion. The X-ray analysis of crystals of this substance has permitted an unequivocal mapping of the relative positions of the constituent atoms. For most organic substances, X-ray diffraction does not give such self-consistent data, but the information it provides is frequently decisive in the choice between alternative structures derived from chemical studies. Examples of the value of X-ray data for the determination of structure may be found in the work on penicillin[77] and on vitamin B_{12} (Chapter 39).[78]

Studies of the X-ray diffraction by crystals of amino acids and peptides[79] have permitted estimates to be made of the dimensions of a fully extended peptide chain (cf. Fig. 13). Important features of this structure are the planar arrangement of the atoms of the CO—NH group and the alternate projection of the side-chain groups to either side of the plane of the peptide chain. The bond angles and distances indicated in Fig. 13 have been valuable for the interpretation of the X-ray diffraction patterns obtained with stretched fibers of keratin (β-keratin) and other scleroproteins. Although β-keratin is not a crystalline substance, it gives strong diffractions when a beam of X-rays is allowed to strike the fiber in a direction perpendicular to its axis,[80] and this may be taken as

[77] D. Crowfoot et al., in H. T. Clarke et al., *The Chemistry of Penicillin*, Chapter 11, Princeton University Press, Princeton, 1949.

[78] D. C. Hodgkin et al., *Nature*, **176**, 325 (1955); **178**, 64 (1956).

[79] R. B. Corey, *Advances in Protein Chem.*, **4**, 385 (1948); *Ann. Rev. Biochem.*, **20**, 131 (1951).

[80] R. S. Bear and H. J. Rugo, *Ann. N. Y. Acad. Sci.*, **53**, 627 (1951); J. C. Kendrew, in H. Neurath and K. Bailey, *The Proteins*, Vol. IIB, Chapter 23, Academic Press, New York, 1954.

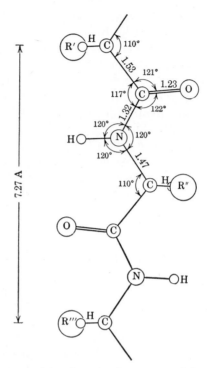

Fig. 13. Bond distances and bond angles in an extended peptide chain. (From L. Pauling et al.[81])

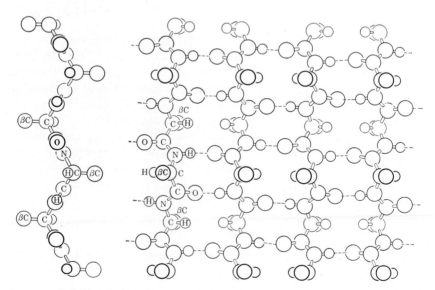

Fig. 14. A "pleated sheet" structure proposed for β-keratin. The structure at the left represents the configuration of a single chain. (From Pauling et al.[81])

evidence of regularity of structure within the fiber. X-ray diagrams of β-keratin show the presence of a 3.3 A spacing, and silk fibroin has a 3.5 A spacing. These figures are near the value to be expected for the —NHCHCO— distance (3.64 A) in Fig. 13. The data for β-keratin also show spacings of 4.65 A, close to the expected distance between the CO group of one peptide chain and the nearest NH group of a neighboring chain (cf. Fig. 14), and of 9.8 A, near the value to be expected for the distance between separate chains in the plane of the side groups (side-chain spacing). The latter figure is only slightly larger than the value calculated for the maximum length of the side chain of a large amino acid such as arginine (8.4 A). It is also close to the thickness of com-pressed monolayer films of proteins (cf. p. 156). The X-ray data for β-keratin and for other proteins indicate a 5.1 A spacing, but a satis-factory explanation of this repeating unit is not available.

A series of molecular models for β-keratin fibers has been proposed by Astbury, Huggins, Pauling, and others. Of these models, the one shown in Fig. 14, and denoted a "pleated sheet" structure,[81] accounts well for most of the X-ray data. It has also been suggested that this structure applies to regions of the silk fibroin fiber.[82] A feature of the model is the hydrogen bonding of CO groups with NH groups of neigh-boring peptide chains.

On stretching, keratin fibers double in length. Hence the formation of β-keratin from the unstretched fiber (α-keratin) suggests the unfolding of coiled peptide chains present in α-keratin. Several hypotheses have been offered about the intramolecular folding in α-keratin; in particular, several helical structures have been proposed. One of these is the "α-helix" with 3.7 amino acid residues per turn (cf. Fig. 15). It has received strong support from X-ray studies by Perutz,[83] who found a 1.5 A spacing for several proteins; this value is the expected distance between planes perpendicular to the axis of the α-helix. It is assumed that intramolecular hydrogen bonding occurs between the terminal NH and CO groups of the coiled sequence —NH[CO—CHR—NH]$_3$CO—, as shown in Fig. 15. In addition, intermolecular hydrogen bonds are involved in the association of separate helices to form the unstretched fiber.

Although there is good evidence in favor of the helical structure of some fibrous proteins such as α-keratin and of long-chain synthetic polypeptides prepared by the N-carboxy anhydride method (p. 136), the situation in regard to the globular proteins is less clear. It has been suggested that the α-helix describes the intramolecular coiling of the individual peptide chains, but the problem of the folding of such helices

[81] L. Pauling et al., *Proc. Natl. Acad. Sci.*, **37**, 205, 235, 729 (1951); **38**, 86 (1952).
[82] R. E. Marsh et al., *Biochim. et Biophys. Acta,* **16**, 1 (1955).
[83] M. F. Perutz, *Nature,* **167**, 1053 (1951).

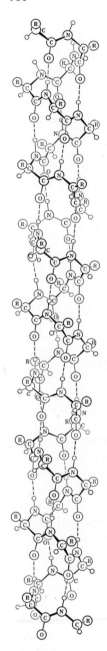

to form spheroidal molecules has proved more difficult. Among the important X-ray studies on this question have been those on hemoglobin and methemoglobin.[84] X-ray analysis of denatured globular proteins has shown the presence of extended peptide chains (as in β-keratin), in agreement with the view that denaturation involves the disorganization of coiled peptide chains (cf. p. 154).

It may be added that the helical structure of long peptide chains has received support from theoretical and experimental studies on the optical activity of polypeptides and of proteins.[85] Long-chain peptides such as polyglycine (made by the N-carboxy anhydride method), in which the individual amino acid residues are not optically active, are dextrorotatory; this optical activity is a consequence of the asymmetry of the coiled structure, which appears to be that of a right-handed helix. Fitts and Kirkwood have derived an equation for the optical rotation to be expected from the coiling of an infinitely long helical polypeptide (—NH—CHR—CO—)$_n$; the calculated values for the expected change in optical rotation upon the disorganization of such a helix are close to those observed experimentally in the denaturation of proteins (cf. p. 153).

Apart from its value for the study of molecular structure, the X-ray method provides a means for the determination of the dimensions of the unit cell of a protein, and hence of the volume of the unit cell. If the density of the crystal is known, the weight of the unit cell is obtained. For several proteins, the unit cell represents one protein molecule, and the molecular weight (M) may be calculated. In general,

Fig. 15. The α-helix with 3.7 amino acid residues per turn (from Pauling et al.[81]). The terminal NH and CO of each sequence —NH[CO—CHR—NH]$_3$CO— (reading upward) are linked by a hydrogen bond. The α-helix shown represents a left-handed screw composed of D-amino acid residues; it is the equivalent of a right-handed helix of L-amino acid residues.

[84] M. F. Perutz, *Proc. Roy. Soc.*, **195A**, 474 (1949); D. W. Green et al., *ibid.*, **225A**, 287 (1954).

[85] D. D. Fitts and J. G. Kirkwood, *Proc. Natl. Acad. Sci.*, **42**, 33 (1956); *J. Am. Chem. Soc.*, **78**, 2650 (1956); J. T. Yang and P. Doty, *ibid.*, **79**, 761 (1957).

$M = VN\omega\rho/n$, where V is the volume of the unit cell (in milliliters), N is Avogadro's number, ω is the proportion by weight of protein in the crystal, ρ is the density of the crystal (in grams per milliliters), and n is the number of molecules per unit cell. The values for M obtained from crystallographic and density data, corrected for hydration, are in good agreement with the results of other methods.[86] If large crystals are available for X-ray examination, the precision of this method for the determination of M is very high.

[86] M. M. Bluhm and J. C. Kendrew, *Biochim. et Biophys. Acta,* **20,** 562 (1956).

6 · Metalloporphyrin Proteins

The capacity of proteins to combine specifically with other substances is one of their most important biochemical properties. Some of the compounds formed by the specific interaction of proteins with nonprotein organic materials are sufficiently stable to be isolated from natural fluids and cell extracts. As noted on p. 17, such compounds are termed "conjugated proteins," and the non-amino acid part of a conjugated protein is denoted the "prosthetic group." It is well to recognize that the conjugated proteins isolated from biological sources represent one extreme of a general phenomenon. At the other extreme are examples of conjugated proteins that readily dissociate into the protein and prosthetic group during isolation. Such instances will be seen in the discussion of enzyme action. The stability of a conjugated protein depends on many factors: the chemical structure of the protein and of the prosthetic group, the nature of the chemical bonds that join them, as well as the pH, ionic strength, and temperature of their environment.

The first stable conjugated proteins to be studied intensively were those in which the prosthetic group is a coordination compound of a porphyrin (Greek *porphyra,* purple) with a metal ion. The best known example of the metalloporphyrin proteins are the iron-containing hemoglobins, whose systematic study was initiated in 1862 by Felix Hoppe-Seyler (1825–1895). Other important iron-porphyrin proteins were identified later, and it is now recognized that this class of conjugated proteins plays a significant role in the physiological activity of nearly all forms of life. For a comprehensive discussion of these substances, see Lemberg and Legge,[1] Wyman,[2] and Theorell.[3]

The hemoglobins from the erythrocytes of most vertebrates have

---

[1] R. Lemberg and J. W. Legge, *Hematin Compounds and Bile Pigments,* Interscience Publishers, New York, 1949.

[2] J. Wyman, Jr., *Advances in Protein Chem.,* **4,** 407 (1948).

[3] H. Theorell, *Advances in Enzymol.,* **7,** 265 (1947).

particle weights near 68,000, and contain 4 iron atoms per unit particle weight. However, a hemoglobin molecule does not consist of 4 identical sub-units, since analysis of several hemoglobins shows that the number of some amino acid residues (per 68,000) is not a multiple of 4. The isoelectric points of the mammalian hemoglobins lie in the range pH 6.7 to 7.1. Thus normal human hemoglobin (hemoglobin A) has an isoelectric point of 6.87, whereas the value is 7.09 for hemoglobin S, found in patients with the hereditary disease sickle cell anemia; the difference in electrophoretic behavior has been attributed to the replacement of a glutamyl residue of hemoglobin A by a valyl residue in hemoglobin S. Other abnormal human hemoglobins that have been identified by electrophoretic studies are hemoglobins C, D, and E.[4] Fetal human hemoglobin (F) also exhibits a distinct electrophoretic mobility. For the normal hemoglobins of different animals, and for the hemoglobins from the fetal and adult forms of the same animal, differences are observed in amino acid composition (cf. p. 125), nature of N-terminal amino acid residues (cf. p. 143), ease of denaturation, solubility, and crystal form.[5] The markedly lower solubility of hemoglobin S, as compared to that of hemoglobin A, appears to be responsible for the abnormal shape of the erythrocytes ("sickle" or "oat" shaped) in the venous blood from patients with sickle cell anemia. Since the same prosthetic group is present in the various vertebrate hemoglobins that have been examined, the differences in the properties of the conjugated proteins must be attributed to differences in the protein portion, termed "globin." Cleavage of a hemoglobin into its prosthetic group and globin is effected by acid.

The physiological function of the vertebrate hemoglobins is to transport oxygen from the lungs to the tissues. These proteins are present in erythrocytes in high concentration; the hemoglobin content of human red cells is about 32 per cent, corresponding to about 14.5 grams per 100 ml of whole blood. This value may be compared with that for serum albumin (ca. 3.5 grams) or for the total serum globulins (ca. 3.1 grams). Their high concentration confers on the hemoglobins an important role as blood buffers (Chapter 36).

Respiratory pigments similar to the vertebrate hemoglobins have been identified in many invertebrates. Among the invertebrate hemoglobins (termed erythrocruorins by some investigators) is the one found in larvae of the horse botfly (Gastrophilus); it has a particle weight of

[4] H. A. Itano, Science, **117**, 89 (1953); L. Pauling, Harvey Lectures, **49**, 216 (1955); V. M. Ingram, Nature, **178**, 792 (1956); **180**, 326 (1957).

[5] E. T. Reichert and A. P. Brown, The Differentiation and Specificity of Corresponding Proteins and Other Vital Substances in Relation to Biological Classification and Organic Evolution. The Crystallography of Hemoglobins, Carnegie Institution, Washington, 1909.

34,000 and contains 2 iron atoms per protein molecule. Some invertebrates, such as the polychaete worms (e.g., *Spirographis*) contain iron-
porphyrin proteins (chlorocruorins) of extremely high molecular weight
(about 3,000,000) and a correspondingly large number of iron atoms
(about 190) per protein unit. Dilute solutions of the chlorocruorins are
green, but concentrated solutions are red.

There are a number of other types of iron-porphyrin proteins that are
chemically related to hemoglobin. Among these are the myoglobins,
present in muscle cells of vertebrates and invertebrates. Like the hemoglobins, these proteins combine reversibly with molecular oxygen. The
myoglobin of horse heart has a molecular weight of about 17,000 and
contains 1 iron atom per molecule. Its isoelectric point is at pH 6.8.

A hemoglobin has been found in the root nodules of leguminous plants.[6]
The formation of this pigment occurs only upon symbiosis between a
nitrogen-fixing bacterium (*Rhizobium*) and the plant root (Chapter 28).
When grown separately, neither biological form makes the pigment.
Hemoglobins have also been identified in molds and in yeast.[7]

The cytochromes are iron-porphyrin proteins found in the cells of all
aerobic organisms. One of the cytochromes (cytochrome c) has been
purified extensively; its molecular weight is ca. 13,000 and it contains 1
atom of iron per molecule. The catalases are iron-porphyrin enzymes
found largely in the tissues of animals and in some bacteria. Several of
the catalases have been obtained in a crystalline state; they have a
particle weight of about 225,000, and contain 4 iron atoms per unit.
Plants, which do not appear to contain appreciable amounts of the
catalases, have iron-porphyrin enzymes named peroxidases. The peroxidase obtained from the horseradish has been crystallized; it has a
molecular weight of 44,000 and contains 1 iron atom per molecule.
Peroxidases are also found in milk (lactoperoxidase) and in leucocytes
(verdoperoxidases). Crystalline lactoperoxidase has 1 iron atom per
unit of 92,000. The biochemical properties of the cytochromes, catalases,
and peroxidases will be discussed in Chapter 14.

In all the conjugated proteins listed above, a characteristic protein is
linked to a prosthetic group which is an iron-porphyrin. Moreover, with
a few exceptions (e.g., the chlorocruorins), the nature of the prosthetic
group is the same for all these conjugated proteins. The differences in
the chemical nature and physiological role of the various iron-porphyrin
proteins are associated with differences in the nature of the protein part
and with the character of the linkages which bind the protein component
to the prosthetic group.

[6] D. Keilin and Y. L. Wang, *Nature*, **155**, 227 (1945).
[7] D. Keilin, *Nature*, **172**, 390, 393 (1953).

Heme and Related Compounds

The iron-porphyrin nucleus of the hemoglobins is the ferrous complex of protoporphyrin IX, and is called heme (or protoheme). Consequently, the conjugated proteins containing this prosthetic group may be termed heme proteins. Protoporphyrin IX is a member of a large group of substances that may be considered derivatives of the cyclic tetrapyrrole nucleus porphin, in which 4 pyrrole rings are linked by means of methene bridges (denoted α, β, γ, δ in the accompanying formula). The elucidation

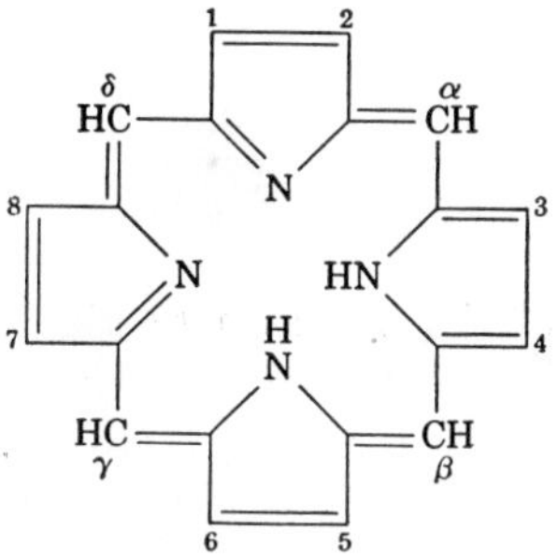

Porphin

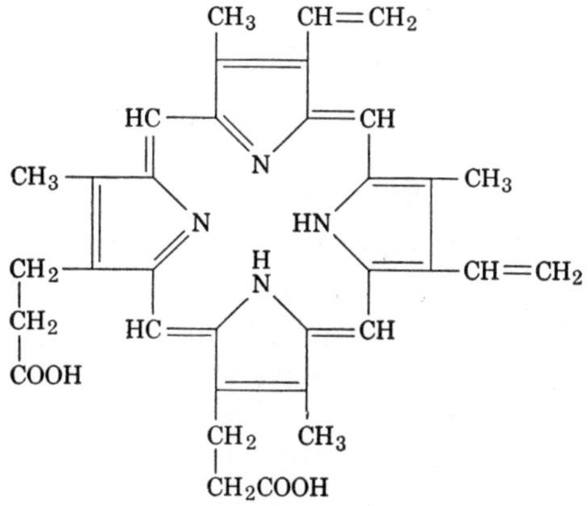

Protoporphyrin IX

of the structure of the porphyrins is largely the result of researches conducted by Küster and by Hans Fischer during the period 1910–1940. By chemical synthesis, Fischer established the constitution not only of protoporphyrin but also of nearly all the other porphyrins that had been found in nature. In addition, he determined the structure of many of the compounds obtained by chemical treatment of naturally occurring porphyrins. An account of Fischer's work may be found in the review by Corwin.[8]

The chemical formulae of the porphyrins are characterized by a large number of alternating double bonds in the porphin nucleus. It must be stressed, however, that the structure of protoporphyrin IX and of other porphyrins cannot be represented accurately by any particular arrangement of the alternating double bonds; the situation resembles that encountered in a simpler form in the case of benzene, for which several alternative structural formulae may be written. As with benzene, the

---

[8] A. H. Corwin, in H. Gilman, *Organic Chemistry*, 2nd Ed., Vol. II, Chapter 16, John Wiley & Sons, New York, 1943.

porphyrins are said to be "resonance hybrids"; a consequence of this property is the uncertainty in the assignment of the 2 hydrogen atoms attached to pyrrole nitrogens. Although an arbitrary assignment is made, it should be remembered that the nitrogen atoms of all 4 pyrrole rings are essentially equivalent in their chemical behavior.

The many porphyrins that have been found in biological systems, or made artificially, differ from protoporphyrin in the nature and arrangement of the side-chain groups attached to carbon atoms 1 to 8 of the porphin nucleus. For convenience, the porphin nucleus may be represented in a simplified form as shown. Protoporphyrin IX is one of 15

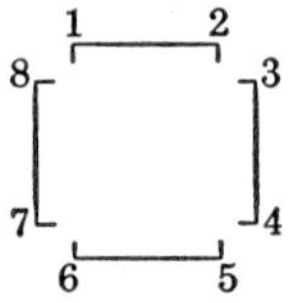

possible isomers that differ in the arrangement of the 8 groups (2 vinyl, 4 methyl, 2 propionic acid) attached to the porphin ring. If the 2 vinyl groups of protoporphyrin IX are hydrogenated to ethyl groups, the product is mesoporphyrin IX, which is also one of 15 possible structural isomers. The simplest of the porphyrins obtained upon chemical modification of protoporphyrin (or mesoporphyrin) is etioporphyrin, which has 4 methyl groups and 4 ethyl groups in positions 1 to 8 of the porphin ring. Four isomeric forms of etioporphyrin are possible, depending on the arrangements of these groups, and the isomer obtained from protoporphyrin IX is etioporphyrin III. Another porphyrin derived from protoporphyrin IX is hematoporphyrin IX, in which the 2 vinyl groups have been converted to hydroxyethyl (—CHOH—CH$_3$) groups.

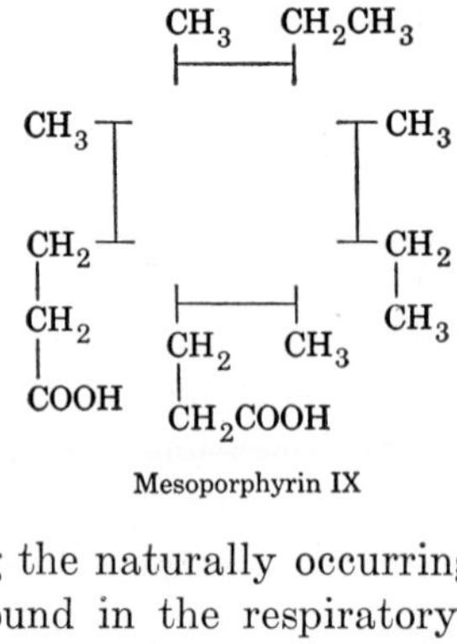

Mesoporphyrin IX 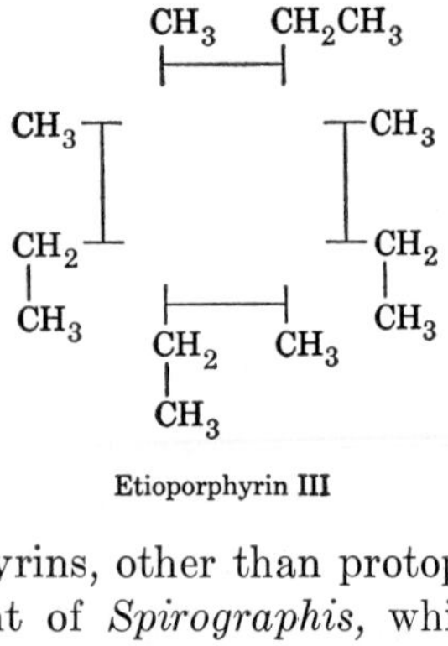   Etioporphyrin III

Among the naturally occurring porphyrins, other than protoporphyrin, is one found in the respiratory pigment of *Spirographis*, which differs from protoporphyrin IX in that the vinyl group in 2 position is replaced by a formyl (—CHO) group. Yeast contains a porphyrin that has 4

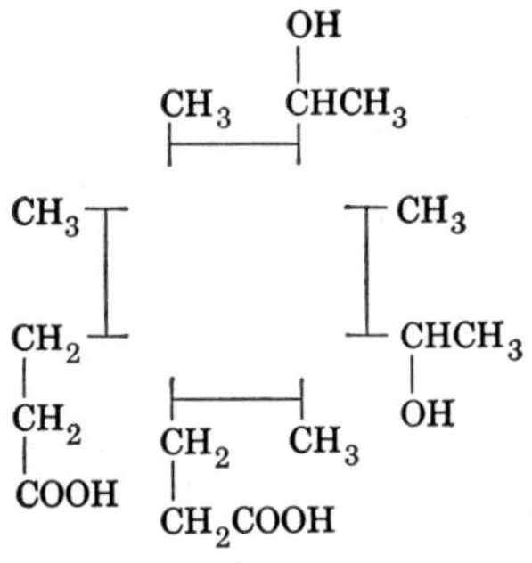

Hematoporphyrin IX

methyl groups and 4 propionic acid groups as side chains, and is named coproporphyrin. Of the four possible isomers of this porphyrin, the one present in yeast is designated coproporphyrin I; it is the chief porphyrin found in human feces (Greek *kopros*, dung). Another naturally occurring porphyrin is that found as a red copper complex (turacin) in the feathers

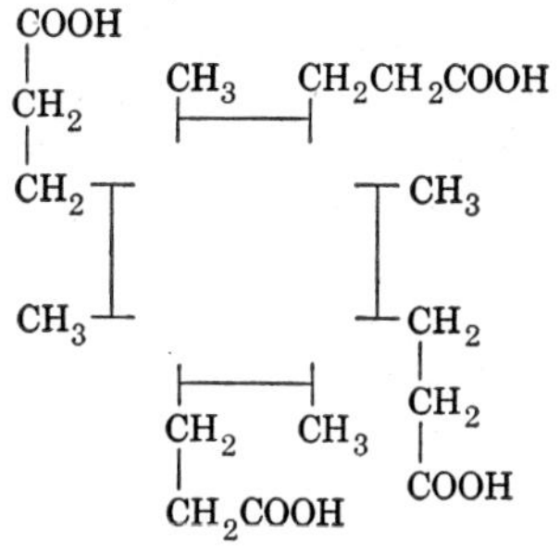

Coproporphyrin I 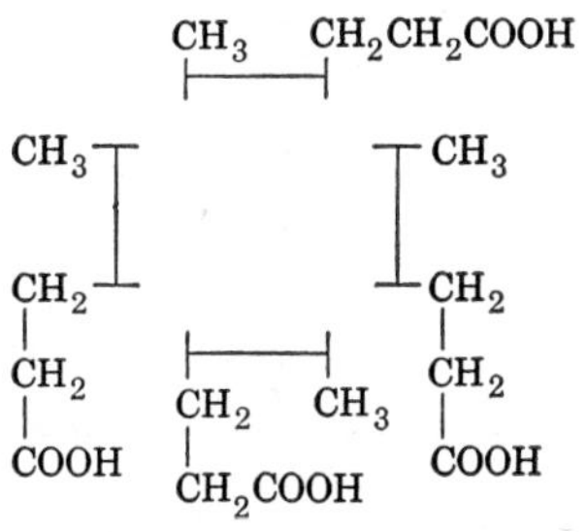   Coproporphyrin III

of certain birds (*Turaco corythaix*); this is uroporphyrin III and has 4 propionic acid and 4 acetic acid (—CH$_2$COOH) side chains in the positions indicated. This porphyrin, together with the isomeric uroporphyrin I, occurs in the urine of patients suffering from a disorder of porphyrin metabolism known as porphyria (Chapter 34). Small amounts of porphyrin also have been identified in normal human urine.[9] Recent work on the separation and identification of porphyrins present in biological materials has been furthered by the use of chromatographic and counter-current distribution techniques.[10]

The porphyrins are closely related structurally to the bile pigments; these substances are linear tetrapyrrole compounds formed in the meta-

[9] A. Comfort et al., *Biochem. J.*, **58**, 177 (1954).
[10] J. E. Falk, *Brit. Med. Bull.*, **10**, 211 (1954); S. Granick and L. Bogorad, *J. Biol. Chem.*, **202**, 781 (1953).

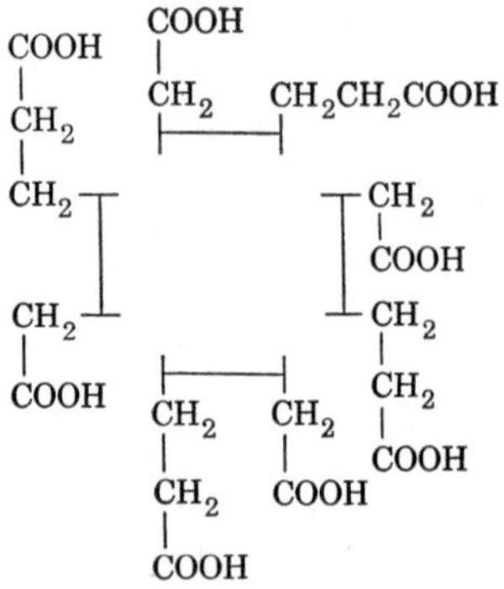

COOH
|
CH₂   CH₂   CH₂CH₂COOH
| | └──────┘
CH₂ |
|
CH₂┐   ┌CH₂
| | | |
   | | COOH
CH₂┘   └CH₂
| |
COOH   ┌───┐   CH₂
       CH₂ CH₂ |
       | | COOH
       CH₂ COOH
       |
       COOH

Uroporphyrin I

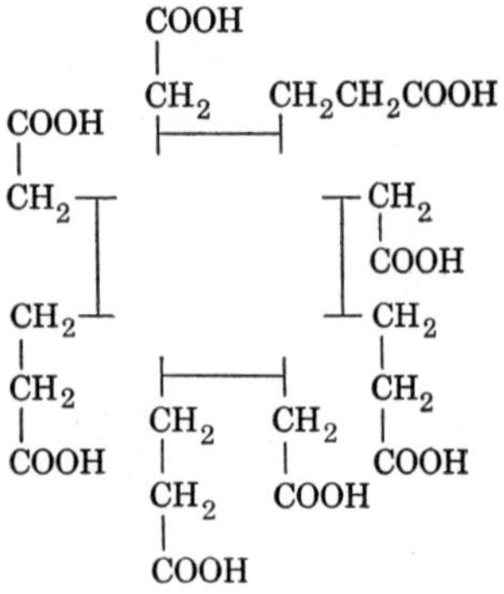

COOH
|
CH₂   CH₂   CH₂CH₂COOH
| | └──────┘
CH₂ |
|
CH₂┐   ┌CH₂
| | | |
   | | COOH
CH₂┘   └CH₂
| |
CH₂   ┌───┐   CH₂
| CH₂ CH₂ |
COOH | | COOH
      CH₂ COOH
      |
      COOH

Uroporphyrin III

bolic degradation of porphyrins by the oxidation of one of the methene bridges, followed by further modification of the tetrapyrrole molecule (Chapter 34). Linear tetrapyrroles related to the bile pigments are linked to a globulin-like protein in the phycobilins. Such metal-free conjugated proteins are found in the red algae, where the red phycoerythrins predominate, and in the blue-green algae, which contain the blue phycocyanins. Some of the phycobilins have been obtained in crystalline form and have particle weights near 275,000.

Vitamin B_{12}, which plays an important role in the control of anemia, has been shown to be a coordination compound of cobalt with a porphyrin derivative (Chapter 39). Another substance structurally related to the porphyrins is the red pigment prodigiosin, produced by *Bacillus prodigiosus* (now termed *Serratia marcescens*).

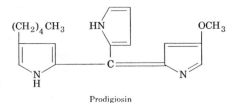

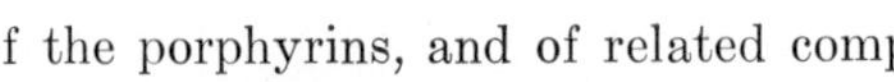

Prodigiosin

In the study of the porphyrins, and of related compounds, advantage is taken of their characteristic absorption spectra. Because of the extensive conjugation of unsaturated linkages, the porphyrins have striking absorption bands in both the visible and the ultraviolet regions of the spectrum. For example, a solution of coproporphyrin in hydrochloric acid gives the absorption curve shown in Fig. 1. It will be seen that there is an absorption band near 400 mμ; this is characteristic of the porphin ring and is noted for all porphyrins, regardless of their side chains. It is usually termed the Soret band. In addition there are two weaker bands, with maxima at 548 and 591 mμ, which may be seen as dark stripes if one looks at a coproporphyrin solution through a visual spectroscope with small dispersion, such as the Hartridge reversion spectroscope.   The positions of the several absorption maxima are, in general, characteristic for each of the porphyrins, and are therefore useful for their identification and for the rapid observation of reactions in which porphyrins may participate.   The absorption bands of heme compounds are sharpened at low temperatures ($-50°$ to $-200°$ C), thus permitting more precise definition of the absorption maxima.[11]

It was noted earlier that a large group of naturally occurring conjugated proteins have an iron-porphyrin nucleus as the prosthetic group.   The great tendency of porphyrins to form complexes with metal ions is one of their most characteristic properties.   The metal ion is bound to the nitrogen atoms of the pyrrole rings, and X-ray analysis of the copper complex of phthalocyanine (closely related to the porphyrins) has shown that the metal ion is located in the center of a planar structure (p. 170). The porphyrin of hemoglobin, protoporphyrin, like other porphyrins,

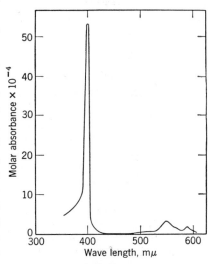

Fig. 1. Absorption spectrum of coproporphyrin I in $0.15\,N$ hydrochloric acid. [From E. M. Jope and J. R. P. O'Brien, *Biochem. J.*, **39**, 239 (1945).]

forms metallic complexes not only with iron, but also with copper, manganese, magnesium, and zinc ions.   The complex formed between protoporphyrin and ferrous ions (Fe^{2+}) is termed heme (sometimes also spelled haem) or protoheme.   When a porphyrin combines with a metal ion, its absorption spectrum in the visible region changes.   Thus protoporphyrin in alkaline solution shows several sharp absorption bands (645, 591, 540 mμ), whereas heme has a broad band with a plateau from 540 to 580 mμ.   Heme may be oxidized to the ferric form (Fe^{3+}); this is discussed on p. 178.

Heme and other ferrous complexes of porphyrins readily react with bases such as primary amines, pyridine, ammonia, imidazole compounds (e.g., histidine), and hydrazine to form hemochromogens (also termed hemochromes).   The hemochromogens are characterized by a typical two-banded spectrum in the visible region, in addition to the Soret band.

---

[11] D. Keilin and E. F. Hartree, *Nature,* **165,** 504 (1950); R. W. Estabrook, *J. Biol. Chem.,* **223,** 781 (1956).

It is customary to designate the band lying at the longer wave length the α-band, and the other the β-band. For example, pyridine ferroprotoporphyrin has its α-band at 558 mμ, and its β-band at 525 mμ. In the formation of a hemochromogen, 2 molecules of a base are bound to the iron of the ferrous porphyrin. No more than 2 molecules of a

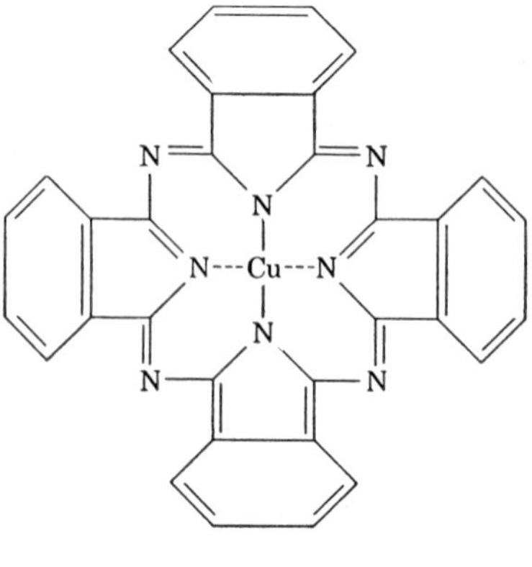

Copper phthalocyanine

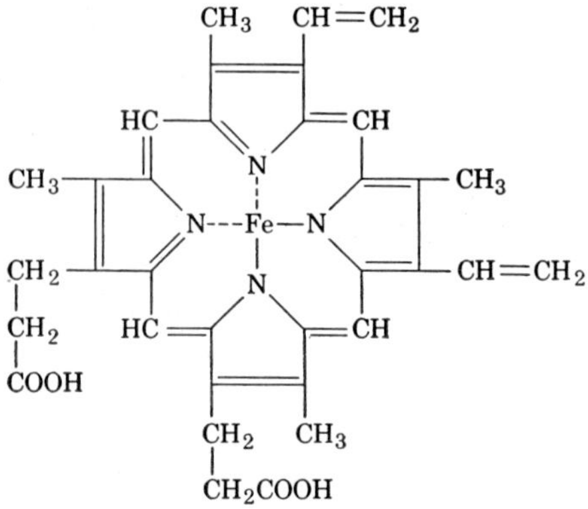

Ferrous protoporphyrin (heme)

nitrogenous base can be accepted since the coordination number of iron is 6, and 4 of the 6 valences are satisfied by the linkages between the ferrous iron and the nitrogen atoms of the pyrrole rings.

The properties of heme and its derivatives are related to the electronic state of the iron atom in these compounds. The ferrous ion has 24 extranuclear electrons, of which 18 form an argon core. The remaining 6 electrons are in the outermost (M) shell, and normally can occupy five 3d orbitals of this shell. No more than 2 electrons can occupy an orbital; when electrons are paired in this manner, their spins are opposed. If an electron is unpaired, its unopposed spin confers a permanent magnetic moment on the molecule, and the molecule is attracted by an external magnetic field, i.e., it is paramagnetic. If all the electrons in a molecule are paired, the substance is said to be diamagnetic, and is repelled by an external magnetic field.[12] The magnetic moment of substances is determined by the measurement of their magnetic susceptibility, defined as the ratio of the intensity of magnetization (I) of the material under study to the intensity of the field (H). The susceptibility per gram mole (χ_m) equals $MI/H\rho$ (M is the molecular weight, ρ is the density), and represents the sum of the diamagnetic susceptibility ($N\alpha$) and of the paramagnetic susceptibility ($N\mu_B{}^2/3kT$), where N is Avogadro's number, μ_B is the magnetic moment (in Bohr magnetons), k is the Boltzmann

[12] P. W. Selwood, *Magnetochemistry*, 2nd Ed., Interscience Publishers, New York, 1956.

constant, and T is the absolute temperature. After correction for the relatively small negative contribution of $N\alpha$, one may estimate the permanent magnetic moment μ_B, which is related to the number of unpaired electrons (n) by the equation $\mu_B = [n(n + 2)]^{1/2}$. The calculated magnetic moment (in Bohr magnetons) for several values of n are as follows: $n = 0$, 0; $n = 1$, 1.73; $n = 2$, 2.83; $n = 3$, 3.88; $n = 4$, 4.90; $n = 5$, 5.92. This approach has given important information about the electronic structure of iron compounds;[13] for example, the hydrated ferrous ion,

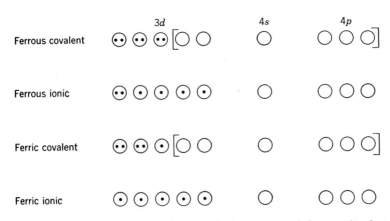

Fig. 2. Orbital distribution of 3d electrons in iron atom of ferrous (6 electrons) and of ferric (5 electrons) compounds. The bracketed orbitals are occupied by 6 pairs of electrons donated by the atoms to which the iron atom is bound by covalent linkage.

$[Fe(H_2O)_6]^{2+}$, has a magnetic moment of 4.90, corresponding to 4 unpaired electrons. This indicates that the six 3d electrons of iron are distributed among the 5 orbitals in such a manner that there is an electron pair in one orbital and 4 unpaired electrons in the other 4 orbitals.

In its chemical reactions, the iron atom may accept electrons into its extranuclear core until a total of 36 electrons (corresponding to krypton) is present. If 12 electrons are added in this way to Fe^{2+}, the six 3d electrons of iron occupy 3 orbitals, and, in addition to the 2 other 3d orbitals, 4 orbitals of the N shell (one 4s, three 4p) are available for the 6 pairs of electrons added (cf. Fig. 2). Such covalent bonding is denoted by the symbol d^2sp^3, and since all the electrons are paired $(n = 0)$, the substance will be diamagnetic. This is the result found for the hemochromogens and for substances such as the ferrocyanide ion, $Fe(CN)_6^{4-}$. On the other hand, if the bonding of the iron atom is not covalent, but ionic, the magnetic moment of Fe^{2+} is retained. This is the result found

[13] L. Pauling and C. D. Coryell, *Proc. Natl. Acad. Sci.*, **22**, 159, 210 (1936).

for heme, which has a magnetic susceptibility corresponding to 4 unpaired electrons. In heme, therefore, the ferrous ion is bound to the pyrrole nitrogens by ionic bonds with the displacement of 2 protons from the porphyrin, as shown. The two negative charges on the porphyrin may be considered to be equally distributed by resonance among the nitrogen atoms of the 4 pyrrole rings. The change in electronic structure that

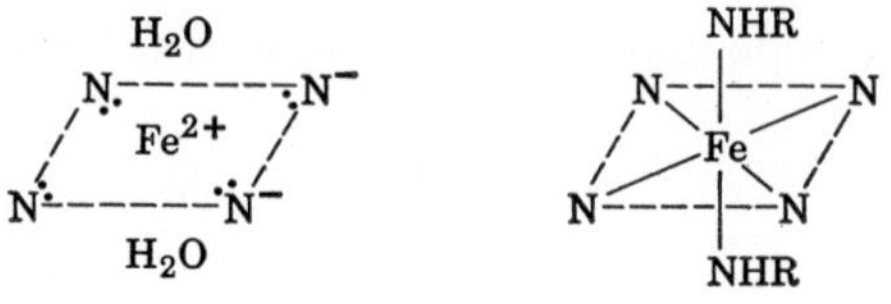

Heme　　　　　　　　　　　　　　Hemochromogen

occurs when heme reacts with 2 molecules of a base to form a hemochromogen is accompanied by an alteration in the absorption spectrum (Table 1). The 2 molecules of base (NHR) in the hemochromogens are symmetrically located on either side of the plane of the 4 pyrrole nitrogens and of the iron atom. In ferrous porphyrins such as heme, 2 similarly located molecules of water are believed to be bound loosely to the iron atom, thus satisfying all 6 coordination valences.

Table I.　Types of Bonding in Heme Derivatives

Bond Type	Example	Color	Absorption Bands	Number of Unpaired Electrons
Ferrous ionic	Heme Hemoglobin	Purplish red	One broad band in green	4
Ferrous covalent	Hemochromogens Oxyhemoglobin CO-hemoglobin	Bright red	Two bands in green	0
Ferric ionic	Methemoglobin	Brownish red	One band in red	3–5
Ferric covalent	Cyanide-met- hemoglobin Ferrihemochro- mogens	Red	One broad or two narrow bands in green	1

Properties of Hemoglobin[14]

The combination of heme with denatured globin leads to the formation of globin hemochromogen with absorption bands at 589 mμ (α-band) and 528 mμ (β-band). On the other hand, native hemoglobins show one broad band with a maximum near 559 mμ. Also, whereas globin

[14] F. J. W. Roughton and J. C. Kendrew, *Haemoglobin*, Butterworths Scientific Publications, London, 1949.

hemochromogen is diamagnetic, the mammalian hemoglobins are paramagnetic and exhibit a magnetic susceptibility of 5.4 Bohr magnetons per gram mole of iron. These differences in properties show that the mode of linkage between heme and protein is not the same in native hemoglobin and in globin hemochromogen. The nature of the amino acid groups in native globin that are involved in its linkage to heme has not been established; however, evidence has been offered in favor of the view that they include imidazolyl groups of histidine side chains.

The physiological importance of hemoglobin lies in its ability to combine reversibly with oxygen, and thus act as a transport agent for this gas from the air to the tissues of animals.[15] This property of combining with O_2 is shared by the myoglobins and the invertebrate hemoglobins; in all these respiratory pigments the iron must be in the ferrous state to combine with O_2, and it remains in the ferrous state in the oxygenated compounds. On a stoichiometric basis, 1 gram of iron may be expected to combine with 400.9 ml of O_2 (at 0° C and 760 mm); the measurements of Peters in 1912 gave values for ox and sheep blood in fair agreement with this figure.

When hemoglobin becomes oxygenated, its spectrum changes, and the broad band with a maximum near 559 mμ is replaced by two bands at 578 mμ and 543 mμ. The product (oxyhemoglobin) is diamagnetic, indicating covalent bonding of the iron atom. Since both hemoglobin

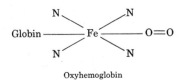

Oxyhemoglobin

and O_2 are paramagnetic substances, their combination to form oxyhemoglobin involves a change in the electronic structure of both. The mode of linkage may be written as shown; the ferrous iron is bound to the globin (possibly through an imidazolyl group of a histidine residue) and to oxygen. On oxygenation, the isoelectric point of hemoglobin is shifted; with horse hemoglobin, the change is from pH 6.81 to 6.70. The increased acidity of oxyhemoglobin is of importance in the regulation of the pH of mammalian blood (Chapter 36).

In considering the equilibrium established in the oxygenation reaction, it may be convenient to examine first the behavior of myoglobin (Mb), which contains 1 iron atom per protein molecule. The product of the oxygenation of myoglobin is termed oxymyoglobin (MbO_2), and the reac-

[15] J. Barcroft, *The Respiratory Function of the Blood,* Part II, Cambridge University Press, London, 1928; A. Redfield, *Quart. Rev. Biol.,* **8,** 31 (1933).

tion may be written

$$Mb + O_2 \rightleftharpoons MbO_2$$

The equilibrium constant of the reaction is

$$K' = \frac{[MbO_2]}{[Mb][O_2]}$$

Since the concentration of O_2 is proportional to the partial pressure of the gas (Henry's law), the term for concentration of O_2 may be replaced by pO_2. Therefore,

$$\frac{[MbO_2]}{[Mb]} = K \times pO_2$$

This final relationship is usually termed Hüfner's equation; if one plots the per cent of the total protein converted to MbO_2 ("per cent saturation") against pO_2, the curve should have the form of a rectangular

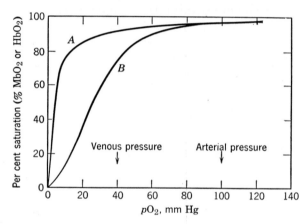

Fig. 3. Oxygen dissociation curves of myoglobin (*A*) and of hemoglobin (*B*).

hyperbola (Fig. 3). Such data may be obtained by equilibration of a solution of myoglobin with a gas phase having a known partial pressure of oxygen, followed by analytical determination of O_2 in the gas and liquid phases. Correction must be made for the dissolved O_2 not bound as MbO_2. Theorell and others have shown that the combination of myoglobin with oxygen does in fact behave in accord with Hüfner's equation.[16] Also, Keilin and Wang have found that the hemoglobin of *Gastrophilus* (which contains 2 hemes per protein molecule) gives oxygenation data that fit this curve.

The oxygenation curves given by the hemoglobins (Hb) from human and other vertebrate blood, however, usually differ from the theoretical

16 G. A. Millikan, *Physiol. Revs.*, **19**, 503 (1939).

mass action curve in that they are approximately sigmoid in shape; these curves may be described by the equation

$$\frac{[HbO_2]}{[Hb]} = K \times (pO_2)^n$$

where the magnitude of n determines the extent to which the hyperbolic curve ($n = 1$) is converted into a sigmoid curve (Fig. 3). When $[HbO_2]$ is expressed as the per cent saturation (y), $[Hb]$ is $100 - y$; then, if x is the pressure of oxygen,

$$\frac{y}{100} = \frac{Kx^n}{1 + Kx^n}$$

The last equation is usually referred to as Hill's equation, and, for the sigmoid curve (for human blood) drawn in Fig. 3, $n = 2.5$. The fact that n is greater than 1 may be taken as evidence that the 4 hemes of hemoglobin are not acting independently of one another in the oxygenation reaction. Indeed, studies of the rates of oxygenation and deoxygenation of mammalian hemoglobins have demonstrated that these processes occur in a stepwise manner.[17] Measurements of the equilibrium constants

$$Hb_4 \underset{-O_2}{\overset{+O_2}{\rightleftarrows}} Hb_4O_2 \underset{-O_2}{\overset{+O_2}{\rightleftarrows}} Hb_4O_4 \underset{-O_2}{\overset{+O_2}{\rightleftarrows}} Hb_4O_6 \underset{-O_2}{\overset{+O_2}{\rightleftarrows}} Hb_4O_8$$

for the individual steps indicate that, whereas in the first three steps deoxygenation is favored, the equilibrium in the last step favors oxygenation. The relative magnitude of these equilibrium constants may be expected to vary with different vertebrate hemoglobins, since hemoglobins of various species differ greatly in their affinity for oxygen (Fig. 4).

It will be noted from Fig. 3 that, at the venous pressure of oxygen, oxymyoglobin is less dissociated than oxyhemoglobin is. This higher affinity of myoglobin for oxygen is of physiological significance, because it facilitates the transfer of oxygen from oxyhemoglobin to the sites of oxidation in the muscle cell.

The rate of the reaction between hemoglobin and oxygen is extremely rapid.[18] At $pO_2 = 75$ mm, dissolved hemoglobin from the adult sheep is 50 per cent converted to HbO_2 in about 0.004 sec. In the intact erythrocyte the corresponding "half-time" is 0.05 sec. The dissociation of HbO_2 is somewhat slower; at pH 6.8 the half-time values are 0.034 sec for dissolved HbO_2, and 0.21 sec for HbO_2 in the sheep erythrocytes.

An important aspect of the dissociation of HbO_2 is that, as the CO_2 tension is increased, with an accompanying decrease in pH, the oxygen-binding capacity of hemoglobin at a given oxygen tension is decreased

[17] F. J. W. Roughton et al., *Proc. Roy. Soc.*, **144B**, 29 (1955).

[18] H. Hartridge and F. J. W. Roughton, *J. Physiol.*, **62**, 232 (1927).

(Fig. 5). Thus, when CO_2 enters oxygenated blood, the release of O_2 is facilitated.

It has long been known that hemoglobin can combine with carbon monoxide (CO). The resulting product, carboxyhemoglobin (or carbon monoxide hemoglobin) has absorption maxima at 570 mμ and 542 mμ

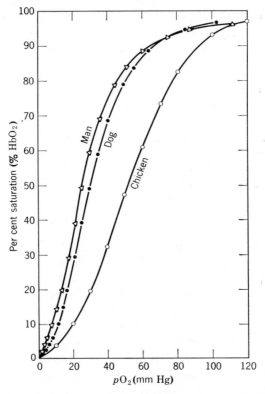

Fig. 4. Oxygen dissociation curves of the hemoglobins of several species. [From V. E. Morgan and D. F. Chichester, *J. Biol. Chem.*, **110**, 285 (1935).]

and is a brighter red than oxyhemoglobin. The affinity of hemoglobin for CO is greater than for O_2, and consequently CO can displace O_2 from oxyhemoglobin. The relative affinities of the two gases for a given heme protein may be expressed by the proportionality factor a, in the equation

$$\frac{[\text{HbCO}]}{[\text{HbO}_2]} = a \frac{p\text{CO}}{p\text{O}_2}$$

The value of the proportionality factor varies for different heme proteins. For various hemoglobins, it lies in the range 120 to 550; for myoglobins, in the range 28 to 51. The ability of CO to compete with O_2 for a heme protein provides the basis for its capacity to act as a respiratory poison. A characteristic property of carboxyhemoglobin, and of other CO-heme compounds, is that the linkage to CO is readily dissociated by light. As will be seen in Chapter 14, this property has been used to advantage in the study of the intracellular respiratory pigments.

CO-hemoglobin is diamagnetic, and the iron is therefore linked by covalent bonds, as in oxyhemoglobin. The interconversion of CO-hemo-

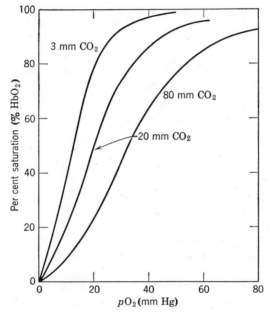

Fig. 5. Effect of CO_2 tension on the oxygen dissociation curve of hemoglobin.

globin and oxyhemoglobin may be pictured as the replacement of O_2 by CO in the formula shown on p. 173; the carbon atom of CO is in covalent linkage to the iron.

Hemoglobin and other heme proteins also combine with cyanide ion, nitric oxide, and ethylisocyanide (C_2H_5NC), to give ferrous compounds analogous to CO-hemoglobin. Until recently it was believed that, among the heme compounds, the dissociation by light was limited to the CO compounds of ferroheme derivatives. It is now known, however, that cyanide complexes of ferromyoglobin and of ferroperoxidase also undergo reversible photodissociation.[19]

[19] D. Keilin and E. F. Hartree, *Biochem. J.*, **61**, 153 (1955).

Methemoglobin and Related Compounds

In all the reactions of the heme proteins considered thus far, the iron was in the ferrous state. Like Fe^{2+} itself, the ferrous iron in hemoglobin may be oxidized to the ferric state (Fe^{3+}) by treatment with agents such as ferricyanide. The resulting product is usually termed methemoglobin; other names assigned to it are hemiglobin and ferrihemoglobin. Methemoglobin is brown in solution and has an absorption band with a maximum at 634 mμ. In normal human blood approximately 2 per cent of the total hemoglobin is methemoglobin, which does not combine with O_2; its appearance in appreciable quantities in human blood (methemoglobinemia) is an indication of disease. A number of drugs (acetophenetidin, sulfonamides) cause methemoglobinemia. Methemoglobin carries a positive charge; therefore, at alkaline pH values, it is converted to the hydroxide. The iron-porphyrin compound which corresponds to methemoglobin is ferric protoporphyrin (ferriheme, hematin), whose chloride is known as hemin. Crystals of hemin are formed upon the

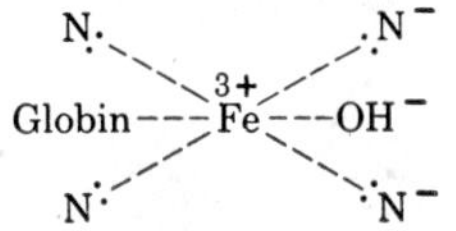

Methemoglobin hydroxide 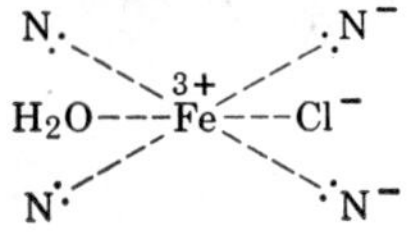   Hemin

treatment of hemoglobin with acetic acid and sodium chloride at an elevated temperature. This reaction was discovered by Teichmann in 1853, and has long served in legal medicine as aid in the identification of blood. Compounds analogous to hemin may be formed from iron-porphyrins other than heme; for example, *Spirographis* hemin has also been obtained as a crystalline substance.

If hemin is dissolved in alkali, a hydroxyl ion replaces the chloride ion in the ferriporphyrin complex, and the product is alkaline hematin (absorption maximum at about 585 mμ in borate buffer, pH 10). On acidification of a solution of alkaline hematin, this substance is changed into a slightly different coordination compound ("acid hematin"), whose structure is not definitely established. Hematin combines with cyanide in alkaline solution, and the CN^- ions replace the OH^- ions in the complex. In an analogous manner, methemoglobin, in alkaline solution, can combine with cyanide ions. Other ions that can combine with methemoglobin are fluoride, sulfide, and azide. Reduction of methemoglobin by $Na_2S_2O_4$ gives hemoglobin. Anson and Mirsky were able to "resynthesize" hemoglobin by combining alkaline hematin with native globin to give methemoglobin, which was then converted to hemoglobin.

In methemoglobin and in hemin, the ferric ion is linked by ionic bonds, as shown by a magnetic moment corresponding to 5 unpaired electrons (cf. p. 171). On oxidation of Fe^{2+} to Fe^{3+}, one of the 6 outer electrons is lost, and the remainder distribute themselves among the five $3d$ orbitals. On the other hand, cyanide methemoglobin has a magnetic moment that is close to the value for one unpaired electron, indicating that two $3d$ orbitals are involved in covalent bond formation. Apparently, in methemoglobin hydroxide, only one $3d$ orbital participates in covalent bonding, since the magnetic moment of this substance corresponds to 3 unpaired electrons.[20] The relationship of the electronic structure of ferriheme derivatives to their color is summarized in Table 1.

As will be seen in Chapter 14, the catalases and peroxidases are ferriheme proteins, in which the prosthetic group is the same as that of methemoglobin, but the specific proteins and the mode of their linkage to ferriheme are different. The ferriheme proteins can undergo further oxidation,[21] and it has been suggested that this oxidation occurs at one of the methene bridges of the porphin ring with the formation of biliverdin (Chapter 34). The oxidation of methemoglobin in this manner gives rise to "choleglobin," in which a bile pigment and iron are linked to globin. The possibility exists that such oxidation of the porphin ring is important in the catalysis of the reactions of hydrogen peroxide by catalases and peroxidases.

The prosthetic group of methemoglobin is also found (in modified form) in ferricytochrome c. The absorption spectrum and other properties of ferrocytochrome c place it among the hemochromogens, and its reversible oxidation to the ferric form is an important reaction in biological oxidation processes (Chapter 14). Like hemoglobin and methemoglobin, the ferrohemochromogens and ferrihemochromogens (also termed hemichromes or parahematins) can be reversibly oxidized and reduced. The principles underlying such oxidation-reduction reactions are discussed in Chapter 11.

From the above, it is possible to make a distinction among three types of physiologically active heme proteins, depending on the valence state of the iron. These types may be listed as follows:

1. Fe remains divalent (hemoglobin, myoglobin).
2. Fe is reversibly oxidized and reduced (cytochrome c).
3. Fe remains trivalent (catalases and peroxidases).

In all three types, the same iron-porphyrin nucleus is involved as the prosthetic group, and the essential biochemical reactions in which these

[20] C. D. Coryell et al., *J. Am. Chem. Soc.*, **59**, 633 (1937).

[21] R. Lemberg et al., *Biochem. J.*, **35**, 328 (1941); P. George and D. H. Irvine, *ibid.*, **58**, 188 (1954).

conjugated proteins function center about the iron atom. Nevertheless, the biological effect exerted by each type of heme protein is different. The distinctive nature of each reaction must be ascribed, therefore, to the specific structure of the protein portion and to the mode of attachment of the protein to the prosthetic group.

Other Metalloproteins

In addition to the iron-porphyrin proteins (hemoglobins, myoglobins, chlorocruorins) that serve as oxygen transport agents, there are two other types of respiratory proteins, the hemocyanins and the hemerythrins, which contain a metal but no porphyrin. The hemocyanins are copper proteins found in solution in the blood of invertebrates classified as cephalopods, mollusks, and crustacea (these include crabs, lobsters, snails, squid, and octopuses).[22] The oxygenated form of the hemocyanins is blue (Greek *kyanas*, a dark-blue substance), whereas the nonoxygenated form is colorless. The dissociation curves of the oxyhemocyanins are similar to those of the hemoglobins. In oxyhemocyanin, 1 molecule of O_2 is present per 2 atoms of copper, and it has been reported that one-half of the copper is in the cuprous (Cu^+) form, and one-half in the cupric (Cu^{2+}) form.[23] The oxygen molecule appears to be reduced by a cuprous ion to form O_2^-, the form probably bound by hemocyanin.

The hemocyanins that have been crystallized and studied with respect to their molecular size are extremely large particles at pH values 5 to 7. In this pH range, for example, the hemocyanin of *Helix pomatia* (a snail) has a sedimentation constant of $s_{20} = 100$ S, corresponding to a particle weight of about 6,000,000 (cf. p. 42). At pH values below 4, however, the $s_{20} = 60$ S, corresponding to half-particles; at pH values above 8, $s_{20} = 20$ S, corresponding to one-eighth the original size. This indicates extensive dissociation of the protein. In addition, dissociation of certain hemocyanins may be effected at pH 5.2 if salt is present.

The manner in which the copper of hemocyanin is bound to the protein is not clear; it has been suggested that the copper is bound to sulfur atoms of the protein. Thus far, no convincing evidence has been provided for the presence of an organic prosthetic group linked by the metal to the protein in the way that iron links protoporphyrin IX to a protein in the heme proteins.

Whatever the mode of linkage of the copper in the hemocyanins, it

---

[22] A. C. Redfield, *Biol. Revs.*, **9**, 175 (1934); C. R. Dawson and M. F. Mallette, *Advances in Protein Chem.*, **2**, 179 (1945).

[23] I. M. Klotz and T. A. Klotz, *Science*, **121**, 477; **122**, 559 (1955).

appears to be less stable than that of iron in the heme proteins. This was shown by Kubowitz, who dialyzed octopus hemocyanin against cyanide at pH 7.4, and found that the copper was removed from the protein. Restoration of the cuprous ion in the absence of air led to the re-formation of a large portion of the copper protein, as indicated by its capacity to accept oxygen.

The other group of nonporphyrin respiratory pigments, the iron-containing hemerythrins, are reddish substances found in the erythrocytes of certain marine worms[24] (e.g., *Phascolosoma, Sipunculus*). Some hemerythrins have been crystallized and found to have a particle weight of about 120,000. Klotz and Klotz[23] have suggested that, on oxygenation, 2 ferrous atoms are oxidized by a molecule of O_2, and that the oxygen is bound in the form of $O_2{}^{2-}$. Neither the hemerythrins nor the hemocyanins combine with CO.

An important iron-containing protein, found in the spleen and liver of various animals, is ferritin. Because of its role as the principal storage form of iron in the animal body, its properties are discussed later (Chapter 36) in relation to the metabolism of iron.

A copper protein (hemocuprein), present in the erythrocytes of several animals (ox, sheep, horse), has been obtained in crystalline form;[25] it has a particle weight of about 35,000 and contains 2 copper atoms. Mann and Keilin also have described another copper protein (hepatocuprein), obtained from ox liver. In both copper proteins, the metal is bound loosely, and is liberated on treatment with trichloroacetic acid; neither copper protein combines with oxygen. Normally, all the copper in mammalian sera is bound to protein in the form of ceruloplasmin,[26] a copper-containing α-globulin of particle weight ca. 150,000. A copper-containing protein (cerebrocuprein) has been isolated from ox brain.[27]

Among the known copper proteins are several enzymes (e.g., polyphenol oxidase, ascorbic acid oxidase) that will be discussed later (Chapter 14). Other metal enzymes are carbonic anhydrase, carboxypeptidase, and some dehydrogenases (all reported to be zinc proteins), arginase and several peptide-splitting enzymes (believed to be manganese proteins), and enolase (believed to be a magnesium protein). The presence of metal ions in these enzymes, and of iron in the catalytic heme proteins, indicates the important role of these ions in metabolic processes.

Chlorophylls. For the maintenance of the life of multicellular organisms, perhaps the most important metal proteins are those containing the magnesium-porphyrin compounds (chlorophylls) that make possible the

---

[24] E. Boeri and A. Ghiretti-Magaldi, *Biochim. et Biophys. Acta*, **23**, 489 (1957).

[25] T. Mann and D. Keilin, *Proc. Roy. Soc.*, **126B**, 303 (1938).

[26] C. G. Holmberg and C. B. Laurell, *Acta Chem. Scand.*, **2**, 550 (1948).

[27] H. Porter and J. Folch, *J. Neurochem.*, **1**, 260 (1957).

utilization of the energy of sunlight for the biosynthesis of carbohydrates (cf. Chapter 22).

The work of Willstätter and Stoll in 1913 showed that the leaf chlorophylls exist in two forms, named chlorophyll a and chlorophyll b, and that both forms are composed of a porphyrin, magnesium, and phytol (a long-chain optically active aliphatic alcohol, $C_{20}H_{39}OH$). The linkage

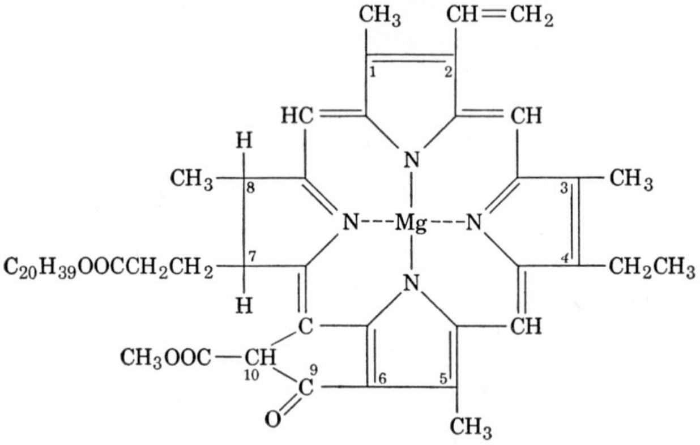

Chlorophyll a

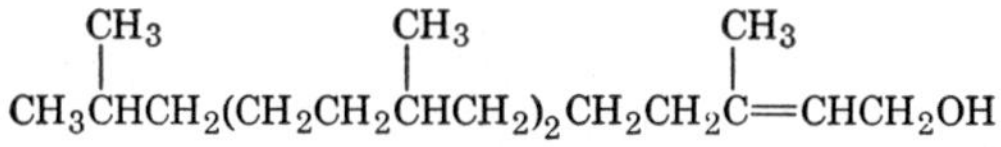

Phytol

between the porphyrin and phytol is an ester bond and may be cleaved by an enzyme termed chlorophyll esterase (or chlorophyllase). The structure of the chlorophylls was definitely established by Hans Fischer. The formula given is that of chlorophyll a; in chlorophyll b, the methyl group in 3 position is replaced by a formyl (—CHO) group. In the green leaves of higher plants, the chlorophyll content is about 0.1 per cent of the fresh weight, and the ratio of chlorophyll a to chlorophyll b is usually about 2.5. In green algae, there appears to be considerable variation in the total chlorophyll content, and in the ratio of chlorophyll a to chlorophyll b. Although there is evidence for the view that, in green leaves, the chlorophylls are bound to protein, it has not been possible thus far to extract from leaf tissue a chlorophyll-protein compound that may be considered with certainty to represent the native conjugated protein.

The magnesium of chlorophyll a may be removed by means of dilute acid, to yield pheophytin a. Treatment of chlorophyll a with stronger acid leads to the removal of the metal and the phytyl group, to form pheophorbide a; with HI, pheophorbide a is dehydrogenated at the 7,8-bond to yield pheoporphyrin a_5.

In addition to chlorophylls a and b, several closely related compounds have been found in nature. Among these are the substances designated chlorophylls c and d; their chemical structure has not been established, and the identification is based largely on differences in absorption spectra.

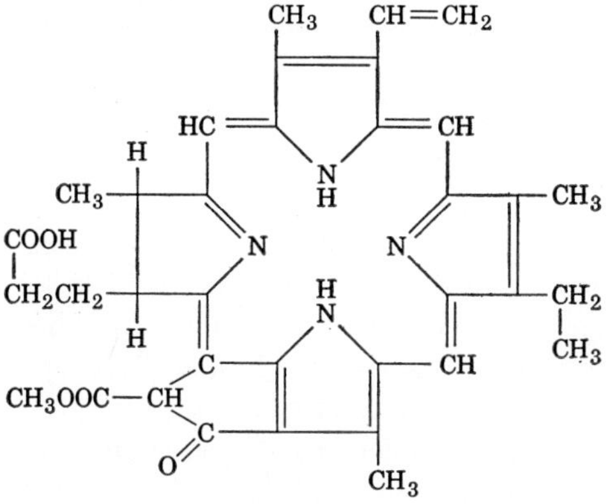

Pheophorbide a

In the brown algae, diatoms, and flagellates, chlorophyll a is accompanied by chlorophyll c; in the red algae, chlorophylls a and d are present. The photosynthetic purple sulfur bacteria contain bacteriochlorophyll, which has been shown to differ from chlorophyll a in the replacement of the vinyl group in 2 position by an acetyl ($-COCH_3$) group and in the hydrogenation of the 3,4-double bond.

7 ·   Nucleoproteins

The nucleoproteins are conjugated proteins in which acidic non-amino acid units named nucleic acids are linked to proteins. The nucleoproteins have attracted much interest because of their association with the chromosomes of cell nuclei, and it is widely believed that these chromosomal nucleoproteins are intimately involved in the transmission of hereditary characters. Nucleoproteins are also present in the extranuclear material of living cells, and are believed to play an important role in the biosynthesis of cytoplasmic proteins.

The initial studies on nucleic acids were those of Friedrich Miescher (1844–1895),[1] who was interested in the chemical constituents of cell nuclei. In 1869 he obtained from pus cells a nonprotein material ("nuclein") which was strongly acidic and contained an appreciable quantity of phosphorus. Miescher then turned his attention to sperm cells, which were known to consist principally of nuclear material; from these he obtained a preparation of "nuclein" and also a basic substance which he termed protamine. The term "nuclein" was replaced by "nucleic acid" in 1889. Subsequent studies led to the conclusion that the nucleic acids were components of conjugated proteins (nucleoproteins) and that the nucleic acids were widely distributed not only in animal cells but also in plants and microorganisms. The first intensive chemical investigations of the nucleic acids were undertaken by Albrecht Kossel (1853–1927), and were followed by the studies of P. A. Levene (1869–1940)[2] and of Walter Jones (1865–1935).[3] A valuable monograph on nucleic acids has been prepared by Davidson.[4] For detailed information about

[1] J. P. Greenstein, *Sci. Monthly,* **57,** 523 (1943).

[2] P. A. Levene and L. W. Bass, *Nucleic Acids,* Chemical Catalog Co., New York, 1931.

[3] W. Jones, *Nucleic Acids,* Longmans, Green and Co., London, 1920.

[4] J. N. Davidson, *The Biochemistry of the Nucleic Acids,* 3rd Ed., Methuen and Co., London, 1957.

the chemistry and metabolism of nucleic acids, the volumes edited by Chargaff and Davidson[5] should be consulted.

The nucleic acid content of microorganisms, and especially of bacteria, is relatively high (as much as 15 per cent of the dry weight). Yeast, which contains about 4 grams of nucleic acid per 100 grams dry weight, has long been a valuable source of nucleic acid preparations used for chemical study. Among mammalian tissues, the thymus gland is particularly rich in nucleic acids (about 3 grams per 100 grams of fresh tissue), and preparations of "thymus nucleic acid" also were studied extensively by the early investigators in this field.

Of special interest among the biological materials that contain nucleic acids are the viruses.[6] The term "virus" is applied to infective agents that act as intracellular parasites and are small enough (diameter 10 to 300 mμ) to pass through filters that retain bacteria. A wide variety of filterable viruses has been recognized; although they differ greatly in complexity of composition, all viruses that have been studied chemically are characterized by the presence of nucleoprotein material. The simplest of the known viruses, such as the purified plant viruses (e.g., tobacco mosaic virus, bushy stunt virus), are nucleoproteins.[7] Other viruses (elementary bodies of vaccine virus, influenza virus) are more complex. Among the viruses are included the intracellular parasites of bacteria; these agents are termed "bacteriophages,"[8] and also are largely composed of nucleoprotein.

It is relatively easy to obtain preparations of nucleic acid; the properties of the isolated material, however, depend greatly on the method employed. For example, the procedure developed by E. Hammersten in 1924 for the isolation of thymus nucleic acid involves extraction of the tissue with neutral salt solutions in the cold. The material obtained in this manner (or by one of the more recent modifications of the Hammersten method) represents the sodium salt of thymus nucleic acid, and has been found to consist of thread-like particles of high particle weight (near 6 million).[9] The asymmetry of the particles is shown by the intense streaming birefringence and viscosity of their solutions. A more drastic method for the preparation of nucleic acids was used by P. A. Levene and others and involves extraction of the nucleic acid with

[5] E. Chargaff and J. N. Davidson, *The Nucleic Acids,* Academic Press, New York, 1955.

[6] S. Luria, *General Virology,* John Wiley & Sons, New York, 1953.

[7] R. Markham and J. D. Smith, in H. Neurath and K. Bailey, *The Proteins,* Vol. IIA, Chapter 12, Academic Press, New York, 1954; G. Schramm, *Advances in Enzymol.,* **15,** 449 (1954); N. W. Pirie, *Advances in Virus Research,* **4,** 159 (1957).

[8] F. W. Putnam, *Advances in Protein Chem.,* **8,** 175 (1953); J. S. K. Boyd, *Biol. Revs.,* **31,** 71 (1956).

[9] P. Doty et al., *J. Am. Chem. Soc.,* **76,** 3047 (1954).

alkali, followed by acidification of the extract. Solutions of such material show a greatly decreased streaming birefringence, and the particles have a much lower apparent molecular weight. Later studies showed that treatment of Hammersten's preparation with alkali led to the breakdown ("depolymerization") of the high-molecular-weight material with the formation of smaller particles of varied size. For example, if tobacco mosaic virus is denatured by heat treatment, and the nucleic acid portion is extracted with a solution of NaCl, the resulting nucleic acid preparation has an apparent particle weight of about 300,000, and the particles exhibit considerable asymmetry; however, on treatment of the saline solution with cold alkali, the mean particle weight of the material is reduced to about 15,000.[10] Nucleic acid preparations of particle weight 900,000 can be obtained from tobacco mosaic virus by means of phenol; such preparations are unstable, and depolymerize to fragments of particle weight 60,000.[11] That the method of preparation of the nucleic acids determines, to a large degree, their physical properties must be borne in mind in evaluating descriptions of their chemical properties.[12] Although the samples of yeast and thymus nucleic acid used in the early chemical studies, and prepared by alkaline extraction, were assumed to represent undegraded materials, it is now known that this assumption was incorrect. Furthermore, all the nucleic acid preparations described thus far, with possibly only a few exceptions, appear to represent mixtures of different but closely related substances.

Products of the Cleavage of Nucleic Acids

Yeast Nucleic Acid. On treatment of yeast nucleic acid with N NaOH, the nucleic acid is hydrolyzed to compounds termed nucleotides, in which three components—a nitrogenous base (a derivative of purine or pyrimidine), the five-carbon sugar D-ribose, and phosphoric acid—are linked to one another. The nucleotides derived from yeast nucleic acid differ from each other in the nature of the purine or pyrimidine derivative, and in the site of attachment of the phosphoric acid group. Alkaline hydrolysis of yeast nucleic acid yields 4 pairs of nucleotides; both members of each pair have the same nitrogenous base, but differ in the position of the phosphoryl group. The 4 pairs are named adenylic acid, guanylic acid, cytidylic acid, and uridylic acid.

Treatment of the nucleotides with hydrochloric acid results in complete hydrolysis with the formation of the purine or pyrimidine, phosphoric

[10] S. S. Cohen and W. M. Stanley, *J. Biol. Chem.*, **144**, 589 (1942).

[11] H. Schuster et al., *Z. Naturforsch.*, **11b**, 339 (1956).

[12] S. Zamenhof and E. Chargaff, *J. Biol. Chem.*, **186**, 207 (1950); A. M. Crestfield et al., *ibid.*, **216**, 185 (1955).

acid, and furfural (a degradation product of ribose). The manner in which the three components of the nucleotides are joined together was elucidated by the results of treatment with dilute acid or alkali. On mild acid hydrolysis of a nucleotide, a nitrogenous base and a sugar phosphate are formed; mild alkaline hydrolysis (e.g., aqueous pyridine) gives phosphoric acid and a compound (a nucleoside) in which the base is still joined to the sugar. The nucleosides corresponding to the nucleotides mentioned above are adenosine, guanosine, cytidine, and uridine respectively. It is clear, therefore, that the arrangement of the three components of the nucleotides is as follows:

Nitrogenous base—ribose—phosphoric acid

In general, the glycosidic bond of the pyrimidine nucleosides is much more stable to acid hydrolysis than that of the purine nucleosides; this treatment usually does not yield a sugar phosphate from a pyrimidine nucleotide, and other methods had to be applied to demonstrate the sequence of the components.

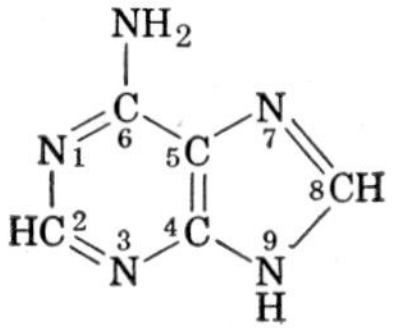

Adenine (6-aminopurine)

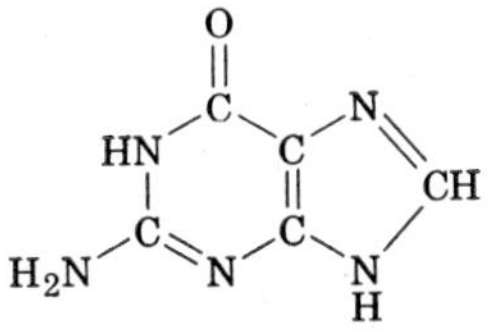

Guanine (2-amino-6-oxypurine)

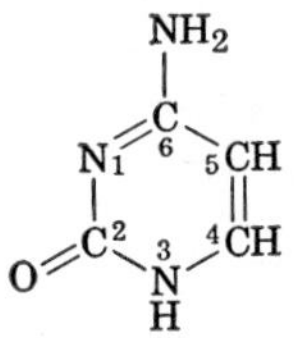

Cytosine (2-oxy-6-aminopyrimidine)

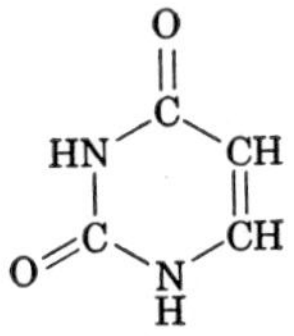

Uracil (2,6-dioxypyrimidine)

The nitrogenous base obtained from each of the 4 pairs of nucleotides is the purine adenine (from adenylic acid), the purine guanine (from guanylic acid), the pyrimidine cytosine (from cytidylic acid), or the pyrimidine uracil (from uridylic acid). Guanine, as its name implies, was first isolated from guano (the excrement of certain sea birds); its discovery dates from 1844. Guanine also has been identified as the principal nitrogenous component of the excrement of some spiders.[13] Adenine was first found in extracts of pancreas by Kossel in 1885. The pyrimidines were first obtained by Kossel from a nucleic acid preparation. In the

---

[13] G. Schmidt et al., *Biochim. et Biophys. Acta,* **16,** 533 (1955).

formulae shown, the numbering of the purine ring and of the pyrimidine ring is given; thus adenine is 6-aminopurine, and cytosine is 2-oxy-6-aminopyrimidine. It should be added, however, that in some recent chemical publications the numbering of the pyrimidine ring begins with the nitrogen atom to which the number 3 is assigned in the formula for cytosine; according to this convention (not used in this book), cytosine is 2-oxy-4-aminopyrimidine. In the above formulae, the NH—CO groups are written in the lactam form, which is in equilibrium with the lactim

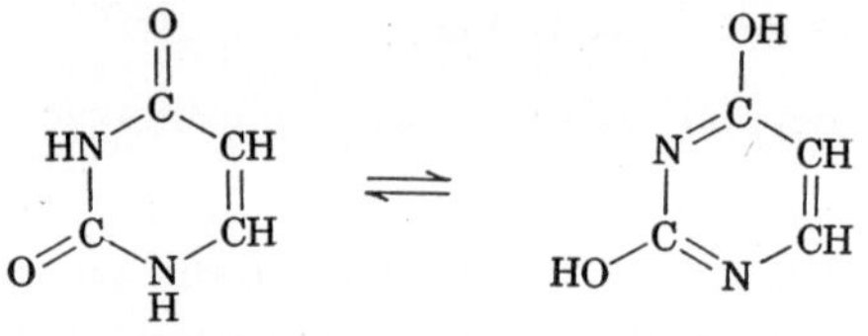

(Lactam)   (Lactim)

form (N=COH), as illustrated for uracil; the lactam form is the predominant tautomer.

Extensive evidence is available for the view that the point of attachment of the ribose to the purine ring is at position 9, and to the pyrimidines at position 3; the sugar is linked to the appropriate nitrogenous base through a glycosidic bond involving its carbon 1 (cf. formula for D-ribose) to form a nucleoside. Thus adenosine is 9-D-ribosyladenine

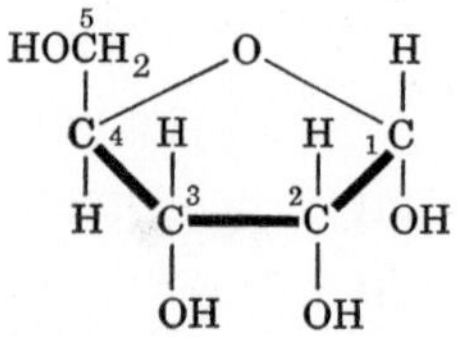

D-Ribose

or adenine-9-D-riboside. Since the ribose molecule is present in the nucleoside in the form of a 5-membered "furanose" ring, and the configuration about carbon 1 of this structure is known and denoted β, adenosine is 9-β-D-ribofuranosyladenine. The structure and isomerism of glycosides are discussed in Chapter 17.

For many years it was believed that, in the nucleotides derived from yeast nucleic acid by treatment with alkali, the phosphoric acid group is linked to the ribose by means of an ester bond at carbon 3 of the sugar. It is now recognized, however, that a pair of adenylic acids is produced on alkaline hydrolysis; the two compounds differ in the position of the phosphoric acid group. The isomeric adenylic acids were first separated by column chromatography,[14] and were named adenylic acid a and adenylic acid b to denote the sequence of their emergence from the column. Subsequent work showed that adenylic acid a is adenosine-2'-phosphate and adenylic acid b is adenosine-3'-phosphate.[15] The structure of adenosine-3'-phosphate is shown. The available evidence indicates that each of the 3 other pairs of nucleotides derived from yeast

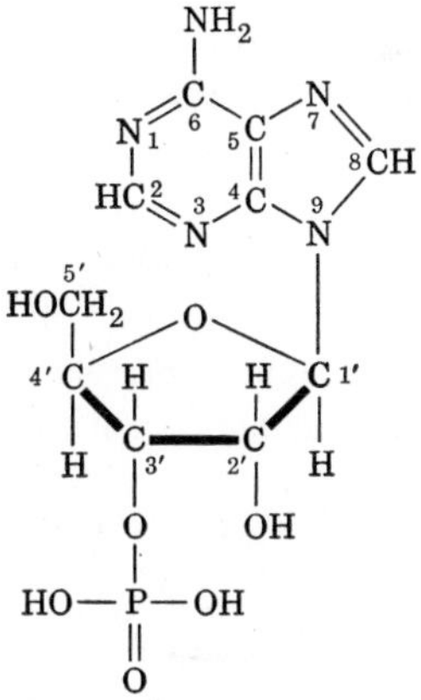

Adenosine-3'-phosphate

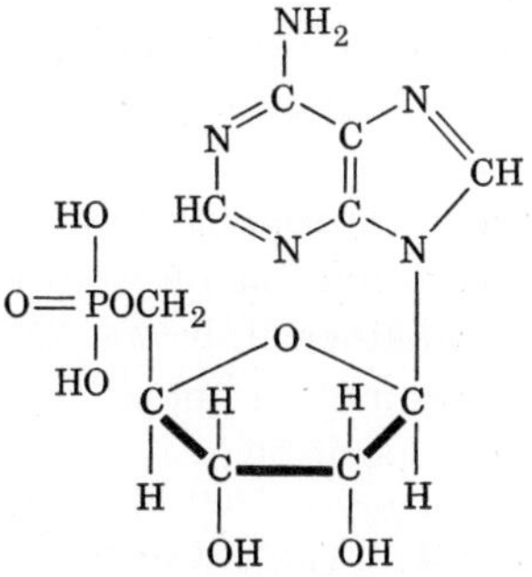

Adenosine-5'-phosphate

nucleic acid by alkaline hydrolysis is a mixture of the isomeric 2'- and 3'-phosphates; they are named guanosine-2'-phosphate and guanosine-3'-phosphate, uridine-2'-phosphate and uridine-3'-phosphate, cytidine-2'-phosphate and cytidine-3'-phosphate.

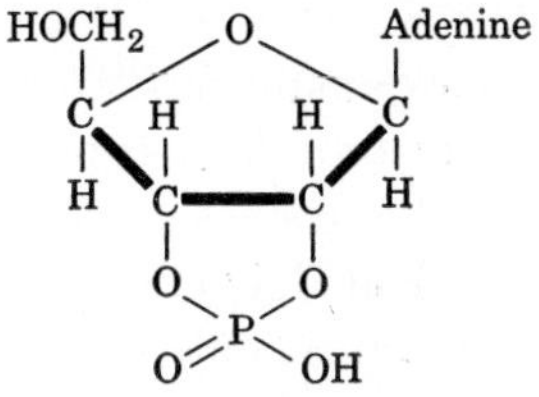

Adenosine-2', 3'-phosphate

The studies of Brown and Todd[16] and of Markham and Smith[17] showed that the occurrence of the isomeric pairs of nucleotides in alkaline hydrolysates of yeast nucleic acid is a consequence of the intermediate formation of cyclic nucleoside-2',3'-phosphates, in which the phosphoryl group is linked to the hydroxyl groups at both the 2' and 3' positions; the

[14] C. E. Carter, *J. Am. Chem. Soc.*, **72**, 1466 (1950).
[15] D. M. Brown et al., *J. Chem. Soc.*, **1954**, 1448; J. X. Khym and W. E. Cohn, *J. Am. Chem. Soc.*, **76**, 1818 (1954).
[16] D. M. Brown et al., *J. Chem. Soc.*, **1952**, 52, 2708; **1953**, 2040.
[17] R. Markham and J. D. Smith, *Biochem. J.*, **52**, 552 (1952).

structure of adenosine-2',3'-phosphate (related to the isomeric adenylic acids) is shown. Such cyclic phosphates have been obtained from yeast nucleic acid by treatment with $BaCO_3$ (pH ca. 9) at 100° C, and have been synthesized from nucleotides in which one of the two remaining acidic functions of phosphoric acid is esterified (cf. formula of benzyl ester of cytidine-3'-phosphate). In strongly alkaline solution (N NaOH), the cyclic phosphates are readily hydrolyzed to yield a mixture of the nucleoside-2'- and 3'-phosphates. It should be noted that adenosine-2'-phosphate and adenosine-3'-phosphate are not interconvertible in the presence of alkali.

The important discovery of the cyclic nucleoside phosphates thus explained the formation of isomeric pairs of nucleotides, but left open the question whether it is the 2'- or the 3'-hydroxyl of ribose that is linked to phosphate in intact yeast nucleic acid. Strong evidence in favor of the 3' position was obtained in experiments with ribonuclease

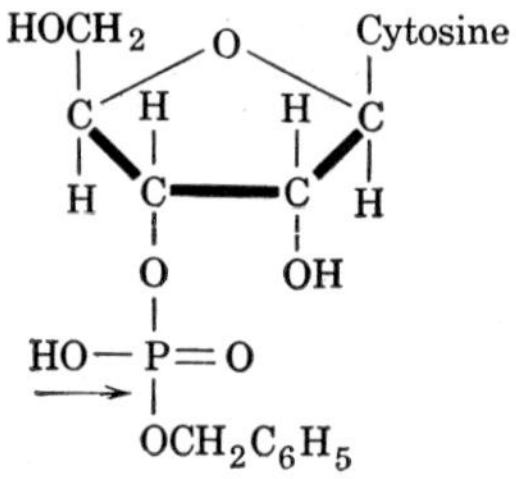

Benzyl ester of cytidine-3'-phosphate   Benzyl ester of cytidine-2'-phosphate
(hydrolyzed by ribonuclease)   (not hydrolyzed by ribonuclease)

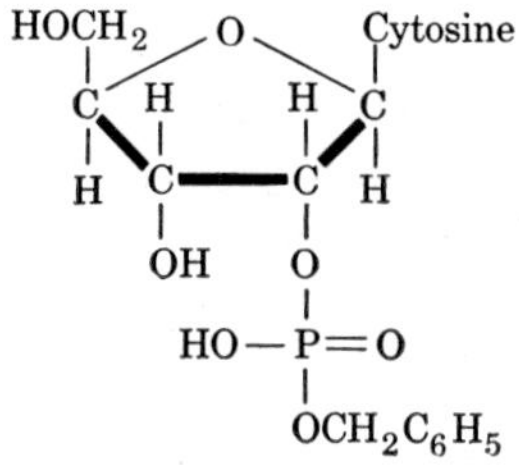

(an enzyme that hydrolyzes yeast nucleic acid, see Chapter 35); this enzyme cleaves synthetic phosphodiesters of cytidine-3'-phosphate (the benzyl ester is shown) or of uridine-3'-phosphate to form the nucleotide, whereas the isomeric 2'-phosphodiesters are not attacked. In the action of ribonuclease on yeast nucleic acid, cyclic 2',3'-phosphates of pyrimidine nucleotides appear as intermediates; only 3'-phosphates are formed when the enzyme is allowed to act on such cyclic compounds.

If yeast nucleic acid is subjected to the action of an enzyme preparation (from snake venom) that attacks phosphodiesters, the principal products are not nucleoside-2'- or 3'-phosphates, but rather nucleoside-5'-phosphates;[18] see structure of adenosine-5'-phosphate on p. 189. Since the two methods of enzymic hydrolysis (ribonuclease and phosphodiesterase) yield 3'- and 5'-phosphates respectively, it has been concluded that, in the intact yeast nucleic acid, the nucleotides are joined to each other by means of phosphoryl groups that link the 3' position of one nucleoside to the 5' position of another nucleoside. Cleavage of one of

[18] W. E. Cohn and E. Volkin, *J. Biol. Chem.*, **203**, 319 (1953).

the phosphoryl bonds will lead to the formation of either 3′- or 5′-nucleotides. It has also been hypothesized that some nucleoside units may be joined by means of phosphoryl groups between the 2′- and 3′-hydroxyl groups of two nucleosides, but the status of this possibility is uncertain at present. The structure of yeast nucleic acid and of related nucleic acids is discussed further on pp. 194 f.

Thymus Nucleic Acid. Early studies of the products formed upon acid hydrolysis of thymus nucleic acid preparations demonstrated that this material, like yeast nucleic acid, contains the purines adenine and guanine and the pyrimidine cytosine, in the form of nucleotides. However, in

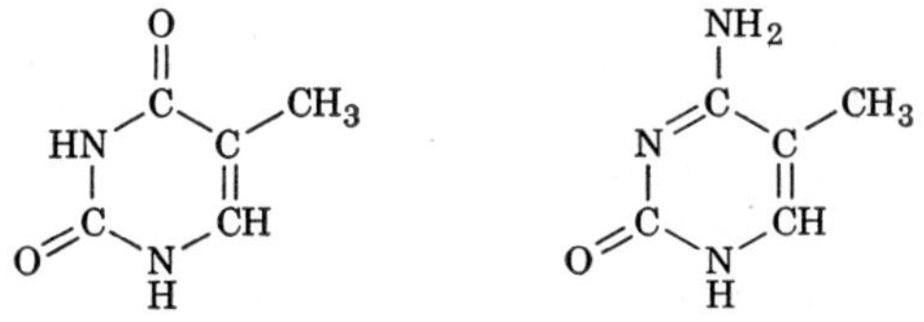

Thymine   5–Methylcytosine

place of uracil, the pyrimidine thymine was found. More recent work has shown that, in addition to adenine, guanine, cytosine, and thymine, hydrolysates of thymus nucleic acid contain small amounts of 5-methylcytosine. As in yeast nucleic acid, the nitrogenous bases of thymus nucleic acid are present in the form of nucleotides, but a distinctive difference between the nucleotides from the two sources is the presence, in thymus nucleic acid, of 2-deoxy-D-ribose instead of D-ribose.[19] The mode and

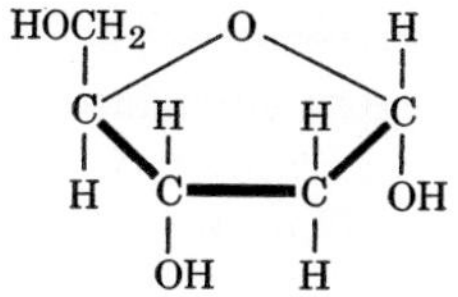

2–Deoxy–D–ribose

place of attachment of the sugar to the nitrogenous base in the deoxyribonucleosides from thymus nucleic acid appears to be the same as in the ribonucleosides from yeast nucleic acid. Thus thymine deoxyriboside (thymidine) is 3-β-2′-deoxy-D-ribofuranosylthymine.[20] The other nucleosides from thymus nucleic acid are termed deoxyadenosine, deoxyguanosine, deoxycytidine, and 5-methyldeoxycytidine. The corresponding nucleotides are thymidylic acid, deoxyadenylic acid, deoxyguanylic acid, deoxycytidylic acid, and 5-methyldeoxycytidylic acid.

In the deoxyribonucleotides isolated after enzymic degradation of

[19] S. G. Laland and W. G. Overend, *Acta Chem. Scand.*, **8**, 192 (1954); I. G. Walker and G. C. Butler, *Canad. J. Chem.*, **34**, 1168 (1956).

[20] A. M. Michelson and A. R. Todd, *J. Chem. Soc.*, **1955**, 816.

thymus nucleic acid, the phosphoryl residue is linked to the 5'-hydroxyl group of deoxyribose.[21]   In the intact nucleic acid, this phosphoryl group is also linked to the 3'-hydroxyl of another deoxyribonucleoside unit, as shown by the isolation of thymidine-3',5'-diphosphate and deoxycytidine-3',5'-diphosphate on degradation of thymus nucleic acid with acid.   The glycosidic linkage of the purine deoxyribonucleotides is very labile under these conditions.

PNA and DNA.   The chemical investigation of nucleic acid preparations from many biological sources has demonstrated that they resemble either yeast nucleic acid and contain a pentose probably identical with D-ribose, or thymus nucleic acid and contain a deoxypentose probably identical with 2-deoxy-D-ribose.   The first of these two general types of nucleic acids is termed pentose nucleic acid (abbreviated PNA) or ribose nucleic acid (RNA); the other type is named deoxypentose nucleic acid (DNA).   Although it was once thought that the pentose nucleic acids were characteristic of plant tissues whereas the deoxypentose nucleic acids were confined to animal cells, this separation is incorrect; both PNA and DNA have been found in nearly all types of cells examined.   There is considerable evidence, however, that the relative proportion of the two types of nucleic acid in a given cell depends on the relative proportion of the nuclear material compared with the cytoplasmic material.   Thus tissues rich in nuclei have a preponderance of DNA; in calf thymus, for example, there is about four times as much DNA as PNA, whereas rat liver has about four times as much PNA as DNA.[22]   In the determination of the DNA and PNA content of animal tissues, advantage is taken of the fact that treatment of tissues with warm alkali causes the breakdown of PNA to the component nucleotides, which are soluble in acid, whereas the DNA is not measurably affected by the alkaline treatment and is precipitated by acid.   This difference in lability to alkali is now readily understandable in terms of the conversion of PNA to cyclic nucleoside-2',3'-phosphates (p. 189); the absence of a 2'-hydroxyl in the sugar unit of DNA prevents this conversion.   In this method, devised by Schmidt and Thannhauser,[23] the estimation of the proportion of the two types of nucleic acid is based on the phosphorus content of the acid-soluble and acid-insoluble fractions.   Another method for the estimation of PNA and DNA is that of Schneider,[24] who treated tissues with hot trichloroacetic acid and estimated the DNA content by means of a colorimetric reaction with diphenylamine,[25] which appears to react with

[21] C. E. Carter, *J. Am. Chem. Soc.*, **73**, 1537 (1951).

[22] J. N. Davidson, *Cold Spring Harbor Symposia Quant. Biol.*, **12**, 50 (1947).

[23] G. Schmidt and S. J. Thannhauser, *J. Biol. Chem.*, **161**, 83 (1945).

[24] W. C. Schneider, *J. Biol. Chem.*, **161**,   293 (1945).

[25] K. Burton, *Biochem. J.*, **62**, 315 (1956).

the purine deoxyribosides and not with the purine ribosides. The two methods outlined above represent valuable contributions to the difficult problem of the separation and estimation of closely related but poorly defined chemical materials; it may be expected that further progress in the quantitative estimation of PNA and DNA will be forthcoming.

A qualitative method for distinguishing the two types of nucleic acid is that of Feulgen, who found that fuchsin sulfurous acid gives a red color with solutions of DNA but not with PNA. This reaction has been applied by cell biologists to the study of the distribution of DNA and PNA in various parts of the cell. For a review of the Feulgen reaction and of other cytochemical techniques for nucleic acids, see Swift (in Chargaff and Davidson[5]).

The fact that most of the Feulgen-positive material is localized in the nuclei has strengthened the view that the nucleus is the repository of DNA, whereas the cytoplasm contains the PNA. However, isolated cell nuclei have been found to contain small amounts of PNA,[26] and it has been reported that most of the DNA in the frog's egg is in the cytoplasm.[27] Stimulating conclusions about the distribution and transformation of nucleic acids (both PNA and DNA) have been drawn by Caspersson[28] from studies of the ultraviolet absorption of parts of cells. This method involves measurement of the extent of light absorption at about 260 mμ, where the spectra of the purine and pyrimidine rings of the nucleic acids show maxima. It has been suggested that the characteristic capacity of certain bacteria (Gram-positive bacteria) to take the Gram stain (crystal violet, followed by I_2) is a reflection of their greater content in a magnesium salt of pentose nucleoprotein.[29]

The nuclei of tissue cells from animals of a single species contain relatively constant amounts of DNA per nucleus; thus a determination of the quantity of DNA in a tissue permits an estimate to be made of the number of cells in that tissue, and provides a useful basis for defining the amount of a given component (e.g., an enzyme) per cell (see Vendrely, in Chargaff and Davidson[5]).

From the foregoing it will be clear that one may speak today of two general types of nucleic acid; both occur in living cells and can be separated more or less satisfactorily from each other. None of the cell nucleic acids has yet been obtained in a state of homogeneity approaching that of the more highly purified proteins. Perhaps the most reproducible preparations obtained thus far are the nucleic acids derived from the

---

[26] E. R. M. Kay, *Biochem. J.*, **62**, 160 (1956).

[27] E. Hoff-Jorgensen and E. Zeuthen, *Nature*, **169**, 245 (1952).

[28] T. Caspersson, *Cold Spring Harbor Symposia Quant. Biol.*, **21**, 1 (1956).

[29] A. S. Jones et al., *Nature*, **166**, 650 (1950); P. Mitchell and J. Moyle, *ibid.*, **166**, 218 (1950).

crystalline plant viruses. The work of Bawden and Pirie and of Stanley has shown these nucleoproteins to contain nucleic acids of the PNA type only.[30] On the other hand, bacteriophages of *Escherichia coli* are of the DNA type. Some insects contain viruses that appear as inclusion bodies in cell nuclei, and contain DNA, whereas in other insects the virus occurs in the cytoplasm and contains PNA.[31] PNA preparations have been obtained from a wide variety of animal tissues (liver, spleen, brain, sea urchin eggs, etc.). In addition to the thymus gland, other animal tissues (e.g., spleen, kidney) have yielded preparations of DNA, as have plant tissues (e.g., wheat germ) and microorganisms (tubercle bacilli, pneumococci, yeast, etc.). It is doubtful whether any of the numerous PNA and DNA preparations described in the literature thus far represent homogeneous chemical substances, no matter how carefully prepared by the available methods. For example, the heterogeneity of thymus DNA preparations has been demonstrated experimentally.[32]

Structure of Nucleic Acids

Composition of Nucleic Acids. The early work of Levene and Jones suggested that yeast nucleic acid (thought to have a molecular weight of about 1500) was composed of equivalent proportions of the four nucleotides formed on treatment with alkali. On the basis of the weights of the products isolated from such degradation reactions, it was concluded that a molecule of yeast nucleic acid was formed by the union of adenylic, guanylic, cytidylic, and uridylic acids, each contributing a molecule to the "tetranucleotide." By analogy, thymus nucleic acid (prepared by extraction with alkali) was believed to be a tetranucleotide composed of equimolar proportions of the deoxypentose nucleotides derived from adenine, guanine, cytosine, and thymine. When it was recognized that the nucleic acids could be obtained in the form of particles of extremely high molecular weight, the tetranucleotide hypothesis had to be modified, and it was suggested that nucleic acids actually represented aggregates of these tetranucleotides. More recent work has disproved the tetranucleotide hypothesis; some of the experimental data that led to the abandonment of this view are considered in what follows.

The development of the methods of chromatography for the amino acid analysis of protein hydrolysates encouraged the application of

[30] C. A. Knight, *Cold Spring Harbor Symposia Quant. Biol.,* **12,** 115 (1947).

[31] G. Bergold and L. Pister, *Z. Naturforsch.,* **3b,** 332, 406 (1948); A. Krieg, *Naturwissenschaften,* **43,** 537 (1956).

[32] A. Bendich et al., *J. Biol. Chem.,* **203,** 305 (1953); E. Chargaff et al., *Nature,* **172,** 289 (1953); A. Bendich et al., *J. Am. Chem. Soc.,* **77,** 3671 (1955).

similar techniques for the quantitative determination of the products formed on cleavage of the nucleic acids. In 1947–1949 it was found by a number of investigators, using various solvents, that the purines and pyrimidines had different R_F values, and that the position of each of these bases on paper strips or in the effluents of a chromatographic column could readily be established either by ultraviolet spectroscopy or by relatively specific chemical reactions. The separation of nucleic acid components by paper chromatography has been reviewed by Wyatt,[5] and Cohn[5] has summarized the work with ion-exchange columns.

Table I. Composition of Pentose Nucleic Acids[33]

Source of Nucleic Acid	Compound	N Accounted for as Per Cent of Nucleic Acid N	Moles of Base per Mole of Nucleic Acid P	Relative Molar Proportions
Yeast	Adenine	30.9	0.261	3.2
	Guanine	30.3	0.256	3.1
	Cytosine	17.3	0.244	3.0
	Uracil	3.9	0.083	1.0
Swine pancreas	Adenine	19.2	0.166	3.6
	Guanine	46.6	0.402	8.8
	Cytosine	14.2	0.205	4.5
	Uracil	2.1	0.046	1.0

A valuable method for the identification of purines and pyrimidines on paper strips involves treatment of the chromatogram with mercuric salts, which combine with the nitrogenous bases to form mercuric complexes, followed by ammonium sulfide. The presence of a purine or pyrimidine is thus made evident by the appearance of a spot of the black mercuric sulfide. When the position of a particular nitrogenous base has been established, the corresponding part of the paper chromatogram not treated with mercury salts is cut out and extracted, and the amount of the base determined by measurement of the extent of light absorption at about 260 mμ. The application of this method to the analysis of PNA preparations from yeast and from swine pancreas has given data[33] such as those shown in Table 1. In these analyses, the recovery of nitrogen was only about 82 per cent of the total present in each nucleic acid preparation. As may be seen from the last column in Table 1, the relative proportions of the four nitrogenous bases rule out the possibility that either of the PNA preparations consisted of tetranucleotides of the type postulated by

[33] E. Vischer and E. Chargaff, *J. Biol. Chem.*, **176**, 715 (1948).

Levene. Chromatographic analyses of nucleic acids from other biological materials likewise gave results which failed to accord with the simple tetranucleotide structure. A comparison of the data for yeast PNA and pancreatic PNA indicates that these two preparations are significantly different in their composition. Some of the difference may be due to the presence in the pancreas of an enzyme (ribonuclease) which degrades PNA. It has been reported[34] that, if the ribonuclease is removed before the isolation of the pancreatic PNA, the composition of the resulting nucleic acid preparation resembles that of yeast PNA more closely.

The development of chromatographic methods has influenced decisively all studies of the composition and structure of nucleic acids. The techniques of paper chromatography have not only permitted the analysis of mixtures of purines and pyrimidines, but also have led to the discovery of new nitrogenous bases as constituents of nucleic acids. Thus 5-methylcytosine (p. 191) was found to be a component of thymus DNA

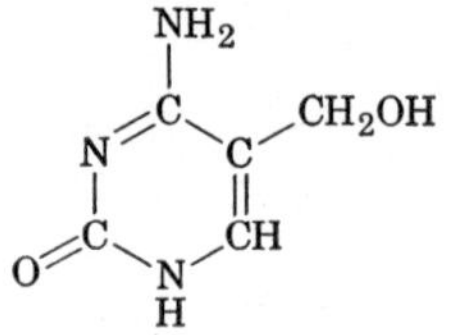

5-Hydroxymethylcytosine 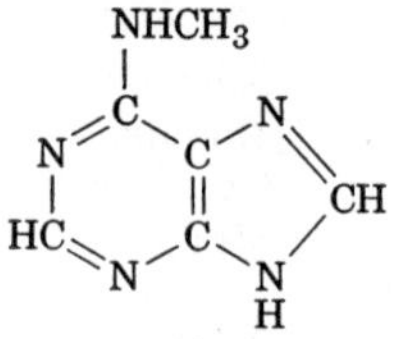   6-Methylaminopurine

preparations, and 5-hydroxymethylcytosine was identified as a constituent of the DNA of several *Escherichia coli* bacteriophages (T_2, T_4, T_6); the 5-hydroxymethyl group of the latter pyrimidine is linked to glucose.[35] Also, 6-methylaminopurine has been shown to be a minor component of the DNA of several bacteria. The use of column chromatography led to the separation of the isomeric pairs of nucleotides formed on alkaline hydrolysis of PNA preparations (p. 189), and both ion exchange and paper chromatography have been valuable for the quantitative analysis of nucleosides and nucleotides present in nucleic acid hydrolysates.

In addition to the chromatographic methods, electrophoresis (usually with paper as a supporting medium; cf. p. 106) has been extremely useful for the separation of nucleic acid components (see J. D. Smith[5]). Examination of the structural formulae of the purines, pyrimidines, and nucleotides given earlier in this chapter will show that they contain ionizable groups; these groups include the enolic hydroxyls of uracil, cytosine, thymine, and guanine (pK' in the range 9 to 12.5), the NH_2 groups of cytosine, adenine, and guanine (pK' in the range 2 to 4.5), and,

[34] J. E. Bacher and F. W. Allen, *J. Biol. Chem.*, **183**, 641 (1950).

[35] G. R. Wyatt and S. S. Cohen, *Biochem. J.*, **55**, 774 (1953); E. Volkin, *J. Am. Chem. Soc.*, **76**, 5892 (1954); R. L. Sinsheimer, *Proc. Natl. Acad. Sci.*, **42**, 502 (1956).

in the case of the nucleotides, the two acidic functions of the phosphoric acid group with pK' values of about 1 for the primary phosphate dissociation and of about 6 for the secondary phosphate dissociation. The differences in net electric charge at a given pH for various nucleic acid components are reflected in different electrophoretic mobilities. This electrophoretic method has been especially valuable for the separation of partial cleavage products of nucleic acids.

Table 2. Nucleotide Composition of Pentose Nucleic Acids[36]

| | Molar Proportions in PNA | | | |
Source	Adenylic Acid	Guanylic Acid	Cytidylic Acid	Uridylic Acid
Yeast (prep. 1)	1.0	0.97	0.61	0.70
Yeast (prep. 4)	1.0	1.05	0.80	1.02
Swine pancreas	1.0	2.25	0.98	0.46
Beef liver	1.0	1.46	1.09	0.66

Perhaps the most significant data on the composition of nucleic acids have come from the application of chromatographic techniques to the quantitative determination of the nucleotides present in a hydrolysate. PNA preparations are usually completely hydrolyzed to nucleotides by means of alkali (e.g., 0.3 N KOH at 37° C for 18 hours); with DNA preparations, the hydrolysis is usually effected by heating to 175° with formic acid for about 1 hr in a sealed tube. The nucleotide analyses obtained with such hydrolysates have accounted more completely for the nucleic acid hydrolyzed than did the analyses for the free purines and pyrimidines, as given in Table 1. Some representative data on the nucleotide composition of PNA preparations are given in Tables 2 and 3.

Table 3. Nucleotide Composition of Virus Nucleic Acids[37]

| | Molar Proportions in PNA | | | |
Plant Virus	Adenylic Acid	Guanylic Acid	Cytidylic Acid	Uridylic Acid
Tobacco mosaic (strain M)	1.0	0.89	0.65	0.88
Tobacco mosaic (strain TMV)	1.0	0.85	0.62	0.88
Cucumber mosaic (strain CVA)	1.0	1.0	0.75	1.15
Tomato bushy stunt (strain BS)	1.0	1.0	0.74	0.89
Turnip yellow mosaic (TY)	1.0	0.76	1.68	0.98

Clearly, the molar proportions of the nucleotides from the PNA preparations do not accord with those to be expected of a simple tetra-

[36] E. Chargaff et al., *J. Biol. Chem.*, **186**, 51 (1950).

[37] R. Markham and J. D. Smith, *Biochem. J.*, **49**, 401 (1951); R. W. Dorner and C. A. Knight. *J. Biol. Chem.*, **205**, 959 (1953).

nucleotide. The same conclusion applies to DNA preparations; the four principal nucleotides formed on hydrolysis in most instances are not present in equimolar ratios, and in addition several DNA preparations contain small amounts of other nucleotides (e.g., 6-methyldeoxyadenylic acid). In the *Escherichia coli* bacteriophages T_2, T_4, and T_6, deoxycytidylic acid appears to be absent, and is replaced by 5-hydroxymethyldeoxycytidylic acid. Of the many data in the literature on the nucleotide composition of DNA preparations, a few are cited in Table 4. In general,

Table 4. Composition of Deoxypentose Nucleic Acids from Various Sources[38]

Molar Proportions in DNA

Source	Adenine	Guanine	Cytosine	Thymine	5-Methyl-cytosine
Calf thymus	1.6	1.3	1.0	1.5	0.06
Beef spleen	1.6	1.3	1.0	1.5	0.06
Human sperm	1.6	1.0	1.0	1.7	
Wheat germ	1.5	1.4	1.0	1.6	0.31
Escherichia coli	0.9	0.8	1.0	1.1	0.00
Bacteriophage T_5					
($E.\ coli$)	3.1	2.0	1.0	3.5	0.00

the DNA preparations from animal tissues and from yeast are characterized by a predominance of adenine and thymine, whereas the preparations from bacteria sometimes exhibit a predominance of guanine and cytosine. It is of interest that, in general, the sum of the purine nucleotides equals the sum of pyrimidine nucleotides, that the molar ratio of adenine to thymine is unity, and that the molar ratio of guanine to cytosine plus 5-methylcytosine also is unity. This apparent "pairing" of the nitrogenous bases of DNA preparations also means that the total number of 6-amino groups (of adenine, cytosine, and 5-methylcytosine) equals the number of 6-keto groups (of guanine and thymine).

Linkage of Nucleotides in Nucleic Acids.[39] The nucleic acids are polynucleotides, in which one of the two acidic groups of the phosphoric acid residue of a mononucleotide is esterified by one of the sugar hydroxyls of another mononucleotide. This conclusion is supported by the results of Gulland and Jordan,[40] who have examined the acid-base

[38] E. Chargaff et al., *J. Biol. Chem.*, **177**, 405 (1949); **192**, 223 (1951); *Nature*, **165**, 756 (1950); J. D. Smith and G. R. Wyatt, *Biochem. J.*, **49**, 144 (1951).

[39] D. M. Brown and A. R. Todd, in E. Chargaff and J. N. Davidson, *The Nucleic Acids*, Vol. I, Chapter 12, Academic Press, New York, 1955.

[40] J. M. Gulland, *Cold Spring Harbor Symposia Quant. Biol.*, **12**, 95 (1947); D. O. Jordan, in E. Chargaff and J. N. Davidson, *The Nucleic Acids*, Vol. I, Chapter 13, Academic Press, New York, 1955.

titration curves of nucleic acids.

$$\underset{\text{Mononucleotide}}{R—O—\overset{\overset{\text{OH}}{|}}{\underset{\underset{O}{\|}}{P}}—OH} + R'OH \rightarrow \underset{\text{Dinucleotide}}{R—O—\overset{\overset{\text{OH}}{|}}{\underset{\underset{O}{\|}}{P}}—O—R'}$$

   In the nucleotides of DNA the only sugar hydroxyl available for the
formation of a phosphoric acid ester is that in the 3′ (or 5′) position of
deoxyribose.   Therefore, the nucleotides must be joined by phosphate
ester linkages involving the 3′ position of one deoxyribose unit and the
5′ position of another.   The ribose moiety of the PNA nucleosides has
unsubstituted hydroxyls at the 2′, 3′, and 5′ positions of the sugar; as
noted earlier (p. 190), the available evidence strongly indicates that the
principal mode of internucleotide linkage is through 3′,5′-phosphodiester
bonds.   Support for this view has come from studies on the partial
degradation of PNA preparations by ribonuclease or by mild acid treatment (e.g., 6 N HCl at 20° for 2.5 min).   By means of electrophoresis on
paper or of ion-exchange chromatography, such partial hydrolysates have
been found to contain products identified as di- and trinucleotides
(substances in which two or three nucleotides are still linked to one
another), and shown to be linked by 3′,5′-phosphodiester bonds.[41]   The
dinucleotides obtained from DNA preparations also have been shown to
be 3′,5′-phosphodiesters.   As mentioned before (cf. p. 191), the possibility

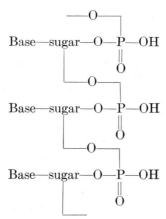

Portion of polynucleotide chain of DNA

exists that 2′,3′-phosphodiester linkages may also be present in PNA

---

[41] R. Markham and J. D. Smith, *Biochem. J.,* **52,** 558 (1952); E. Volkin and W. E. Cohn, *J. Biol. Chem.,* **205,** 767 (1953).

preparations; however, 2′,5′-phosphodiester linkages or phosphotriester bonds appear to be excluded.[42]

Because of the inhomogeneity of nucleic acid preparations, little can be said at present about the sequence of mononucleotide units in a single mononucleotide chain. Partial hydrolysis of yeast PNA has given products (oligonucleotides) in which all of the 16 possible dinucleotide combinations could be identified, but it cannot be stated whether all these dinucleotide sequences apply to a single polynucleotide or to a mixture of chains with different sequences. The heterogeneity of nucleic acid preparations also prevents the fruitful application of available end group methods or of chemical procedures for the stepwise degradation of nucleic acids.[43]

Whatever the arrangement of the nucleotides in the nucleic acids, it is likely that some of the specific biological properties of certain of the nucleic acids have their basis in their intimate chemical structure. For example, Avery isolated a DNA preparation from type III pneumococci and showed that this material specifically promotes the transformation of the uncapsulated (rough) strain type II pneumococci to the capsulated (smooth) form of the type III organism. This transformation, which could not be achieved by the use of DNA preparations from other sources (e.g., calf thymus), is accompanied by the conversion of an avirulent organism to a virulent one.[44] Later work demonstrated other examples of this important phenomenon of the "transformation" of the metabolic activity of bacteria by specific DNA preparations. The biological specificity of nucleic acids also is indicated by studies on the purified plant viruses. Thus PNA preparations obtained from tobacco mosaic virus by treatment with phenol retain a measurable fraction of the infectivity of the original nucleoprotein; this finding has been interpreted to indicate that the characteristic lesion associated with the virus is caused by the PNA portion.[45]

Although much still remains to be done to purify and to characterize individual nucleic acids, stimulating hypotheses have been advanced about the manner in which the polynucleotide chains are arranged in space. The "pairing" of the nitrogenous bases in DNA preparations (p. 198), together with X-ray diffraction data, have provided the basis for an ingenious speculation by Crick and Watson,[46] who have proposed

[42] D. M. Brown et al., *J. Chem. Soc.*, **1955**, 4396.

[43] D. M. Brown et al., *J. Chem. Soc.*, **1955**, 2206; A. S. Jones et al., *ibid.*, **1956**, 2573, 2579, 2584.

[44] M. McCarty, *Bact. Revs.*, **10**, 63 (1946).

[45] A. Gierer and G. Schramm, *Nature*, **177**, 702 (1956); R. C. Williams, *Proc. Natl. Acad. Sci.*, **42**, 811 (1956); A. Gierer, *Nature*, **179**, 1297 (1957).

[46] F. H. C. Crick and J. D. Watson, *Nature*, **171**, 737 (1953); *Proc. Roy. Soc.*, **223A**, 80 (1954).

a helical structure for DNA. It is assumed that two polynucleotides are coiled in such a manner that an adenine of one chain is hydrogen-bonded to a thymine of the other (cf. accompanying diagram), and that a guanine of one chain is bonded to a cytosine of the other. This hydrogen

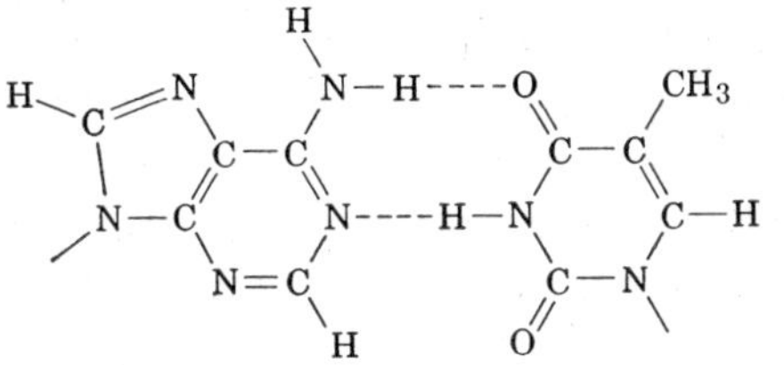

Postulated pairing of adenine and thymine residues of two polynucleotide chains of DNA

bonding is thought to involve the 6-keto and 6-amino groups, and has received experimental support from acid-base titration curves of DNA.[47] As in the case of proteins (cf. p. 153), treatment of DNA with acid or alkali leads to the appearance of new titratable groups; these have pK' values in the range of the 6-keto and 6-amino groups of the nitrogenous bases, in agreement with the assumption that they are hydrogen-bonded in the intact nucleic acid. Studies of the light scattering of DNA solutions have given results consistent with the view that a two-stranded structure is present, and that the two strands are held together by hydrogen bonds.[48] Sedimentation studies have led to the suggestion that the Crick-Watson model be modified to an interrupted two-stranded helical structure, rather than two continuous strands.[49]

The Protein Portion of Nucleoproteins

The protein portion of the nucleoproteins is, in general, rather basic in character. The protamines discovered by Miescher in the sperm cells of various fish are poorly characterized nitrogenous substances of molecular weight 2000 to 5000; on hydrolysis, they are converted to amino acids. For this reason, the protamines are usually classified as proteins, although their small molecular size places them among the larger peptides.[50] Typical protamines are salmine, sturin, and clupein, which are rich in the basic amino acids arginine, histidine, and lysine. The proteins (histones) associated with the nucleic acids of glandular tissues (e.g., thymus, pancreas) also have not been adequately characterized, but they appear to contain relatively large proportions of arginine and lysine.[51]

[47] D. O. Jordan et al., *J. Chem. Soc.*, **1956**, 154, 158.

[48] P. Alexander and K. A. Stacey, *Biochem. J.*, **60**, 194 (1955).

[49] C. A. Dekker and H. K. Schachman, *Proc. Natl. Acad. Sci.*, **40**, 894 (1954).

[50] K. Felix, *Am. Scientist*, **43**, 431 (1955); F. S. Scanes and B. T. Tozer, *Biochem. J.*, **63**, 565 (1956).

[51] C. F. Crampton et al., *J. Biol. Chem.*, **215**, 787 (1955); **225**, 363 (1957).

Reference may be found in the literature to nucleoprotein preparations obtained from cell nuclei; here, apparently, a basic protein (of the histone type) is linked to nucleic acid. Among these is a nucleoprotein preparation obtained by Mirsky and Pollister from thymus, which they considered to be closely related to, if not identical with, the chromosomes of the thymus lymphocytes. In considering the nucleoproteins of this type, it may be appropriate to mention that, if a solution of a nucleic acid is added to a solution of a basic protein (e.g., a protamine or histone) at pH 5, a sparingly soluble precipitate results. When the very basic polylysine (prepared by the N-carboxy anhydride method; p. 136) is mixed with a nucleic acid in solution, similar precipitates are formed.[52] Such products clearly represent protein-nucleate salts; the possibility therefore exists that, in macerating a cell in order to extract a nucleoprotein, acidic nucleic acids and basic proteins may be brought together and may form insoluble salts that are essentially artifacts. For example, the protein avidin has been isolated from egg white in association with a deoxypentose nucleic acid,[53] but it cannot be stated at present whether this is a nucleoprotein preformed in the egg or an artifact of isolation.

In addition to the basic proteins identified as components of nucleoproteins, several instances of the association of nucleic acids with nonbasic proteins have been reported. The protein portion of a nucleoprotein obtained from tubercle bacilli is not basic,[54] and evidence has been presented in favor of the view that chromosomes contain, in addition to a basic histone, a nonbasic protein rich in tryptophan.[55]

Of the known nucleoproteins, the purified plant viruses appear to be best suited for the study of the protein component. For example, analysis of three strains of tomato bushy stunt virus has shown their amino acid composition to be very similar; they all contain about 9 to 10 per cent arginine and 3 per cent lysine, in addition to 16.5 per cent PNA.[56] It has been reported that the separated nucleic acid portion and the protein portion of tobacco mosaic virus can be caused to recombine, with the reconstitution of particles similar in appearance (under the electron microscope) to that of the original virus.[57] However, the interaction of virus protein with virus nucleic acid may not be a specific phenomenon,

---

[52] P. Spitnik et al., *J. Biol. Chem.,* **215,** 765 (1955).

[53] H. Fraenkel-Conrat et al., *J. Am. Chem. Soc.,* **72,** 3826 (1950).

[54] E. Chargaff and H. F. Saidel, *J. Biol. Chem.,* **177,** 417 (1949).

[55] E. Stedman and E. Stedman, *Cold Spring Harbor Symposia Quant. Biol.,* **12,** 224 (1947).

[56] D. de Fremery and C. A. Knight, *J. Biol. Chem.,* **214,** 559 (1955).

[57] H. Fraenkel-Conrat, *J. Am. Chem. Soc.,* **78,** 882 (1956); *Biochim. et Biophys. Acta,* **24,** 540 (1957); B. Commoner et al., *Nature,* **178,** 767 (1956).

since the protein forms noninfective virus-like particles with artificial noninfective polynucleotides.[58]

Naturally Occurring Nucleotides

It was noted previously that enzymic degradation of yeast nucleic acid can yield nucleoside-5′-phosphates, among them adenosine-5′-phosphate (p. 189). This compound was isolated in 1927 from mammalian muscle, and was termed "muscle adenylic acid" to distinguish it from adenosine-3′-phosphate ("yeast adenylic acid"). The first nucleotide to be found in nature is inosinic acid, isolated in 1847 from a meat extract by Liebig. Later work showed that inosinic acid is the deamination product of adenosine-5′-phosphate; the adenine of the latter nucleotide has been converted to the purine hypoxanthine. Hypoxanthine was found by Scherer (1850); its two oxidation products, xanthine and uric acid, have also been isolated from natural sources. Xanthine was discovered by Marcet (1817), and uric acid by Scheele (1776).

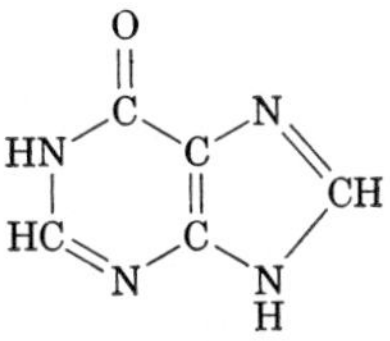

Hypoxanthine
(6-oxypurine)

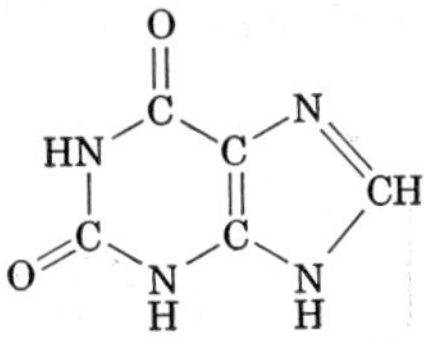

Xanthine
(2,6-dioxypurine)

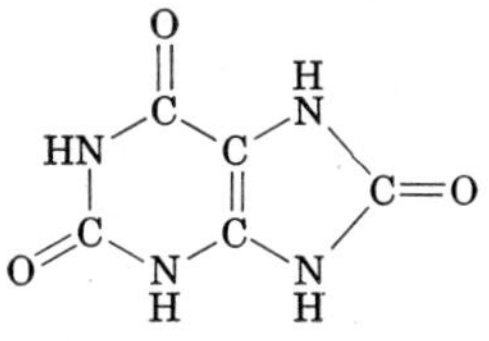

Uric acid
(2,6,8-trioxypurine)

In 1929 an important derivative of adenosine-5′-phosphate was isolated from muscle almost simultaneously by Lohmann in Germany and by Fiske and SubbaRow in the United States. This adenine nucleotide was found to contain 3 phosphoric acid groups, 2 of which proved to be extremely labile upon acid hydrolysis. Subsequent work indicated that it was adenosine-5′-triphosphate (abbreviated ATP); it is also referred to in the literature as adenylpyrophosphate. The structure of ATP has been confirmed by synthesis.[59] Since its discovery, biochemical research on the role of ATP in metabolism has shown this substance to be one of the most important low-molecular-weight materials in living matter. The role of ATP in biochemical dynamics will be discussed in later sections of this book. For the present it may suffice to list it and the closely related adenosine-5′-pyrophosphate or adenosine-5′-diphosphate (ADP) among the substances related structurally to components of the nucleic acids. In ATP the 2 terminal phosphoric acid groups may be split off

[58] R. G. Hart and J. D. Smith, *Nature,* **178,** 739 (1956).
[59] J. Baddiley et al., *Nature,* **161,** 761 (1948); *J. Chem. Soc.,* **1949,** 582.

readily by treatment for a short time (7 to 10 min) with boiling N hydrochloric acid; this treatment also removes the terminal phosphoric acid group of ADP. In both reactions, adenosine-5'-phosphate (adenosine

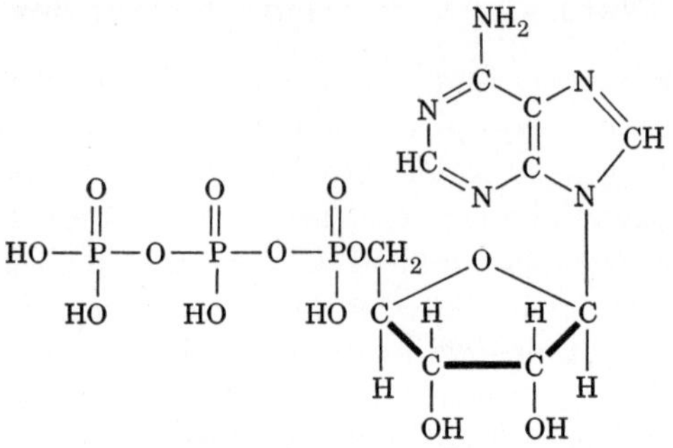

Adenosine–5'–triphosphate (ATP)

monophosphate or AMP) is formed. On treatment of ATP with barium hydroxide, AMP and pyrophosphate are formed; an additional product is a cyclic adenosine-3',5'-phosphate, whose structure is shown.[60]

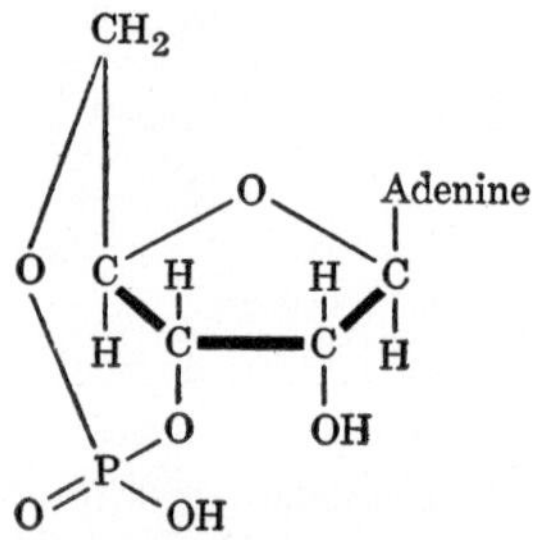

Adenosine–3',5'–phosphate

The introduction of chromatographic methods led to the demonstration that ATP is not the only nucleoside triphosphate present in muscle; guanosine-5'-triphosphate (GTP), cytidine-5'-triphosphate (CTP), and uridine-5'-triphosphate (UTP) also have been found.[61] Moreover, some ATP preparations contain small amounts of adenosine-5'-tetraphosphate.

In addition to ATP and the nucleotides closely related to it, a number of other nucleotide derivatives are essential participants in key metabolic reactions, and will be referred to frequently in later pages. Among these are the electron carriers diphosphopyridine nucleotide (DPN) and triphosphopyridine nucleotide (TPN), in which the 5'-phosphoryl group of

---

[60] W. H. Cook et al., *J. Am. Chem. Soc.*, **79**, 3607 (1957).

[61] R. Bergkvist and A. Deutsch, *Acta Chem. Scand.*, **8**, 1880, 1889 (1954); H. Schmitz et al., *J. Biol. Chem.*, **209**, 41 (1954).

adenosine-5'-phosphate or of adenosine-2',5'-diphosphate is linked by a pyrophosphate bond to nicotinamide ribosyl-5'-phosphate (p. 309). The electron carrier flavin adenine dinucleotide (FAD) also contains an adenosine-5'-phosphate moiety; this is linked by a pyrophosphate bond to riboflavin-5'-phosphate (p. 336).

A group of substances shown to be important in several facets of carbohydrate metabolism are derivatives of uridine-5'-pyrophosphate (more commonly termed uridine-5'-diphosphate, UDP). They include UDP-glucose, in which the phosphoryl groups of glucose-1-phosphate

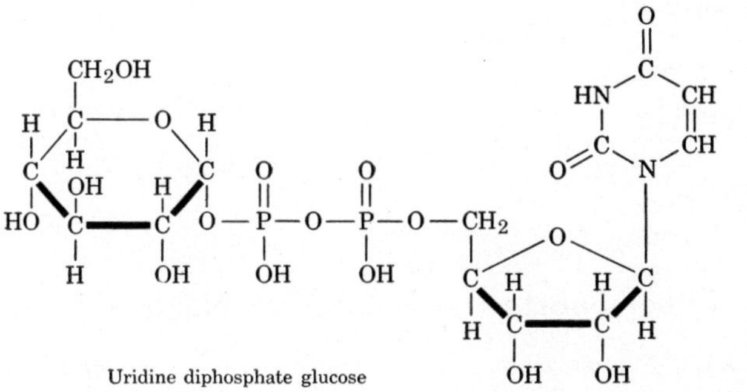

Uridine diphosphate glucose

and of uridine-5'-phosphate (uridine monophosphate, UMP) are joined by a pyrophosphate bond (cf. formula). The structure of UDP-glucose has been established by chemical synthesis.[62] Other naturally occurring UDP derivatives are UDP-glucuronic acid and UDP-acetylgalactosamine (Chapter 19); in addition, a number of UDP-containing compounds accumulate in cells of *Staphylococcus aureus* grown in the presence of penicillin. A series of compounds related to the UDP derivatives contain cytidine; thus, cytidine diphosphate glycerol and cytidine diphosphate ribitol have been isolated from *Lactobacillus arabinosus*.[63] Another substance of similar structure is guanosine diphosphate mannose, found in yeast.

A widely distributed nucleotide derivative that plays a decisive role in many metabolic processes is named coenzyme A (CoA); in this compound, the 5'-phosphoryl group of adenosine-3',5'-diphosphate is linked by a pyrophosphate bond to phosphopantetheine, a derivative of the vitamin pantothenic acid (Chapter 39). The structure of CoA is shown on p. 206; its metabolic functions will be discussed in later chapters.

The important vitamin cyanocobalamin (vitamin B_{12}) contains a nucleotide linked to a tetrapyrrole derivative (Chapter 39).

[62] G. W. Kenner et al., *J. Chem. Soc.*, **1954**, 2843; A. M. Michelson and A. R. Todd, *ibid.*, **1956**, 3459.

[63] J. Baddiley et al., *Biochem. J.*, **64**, 599 (1956).

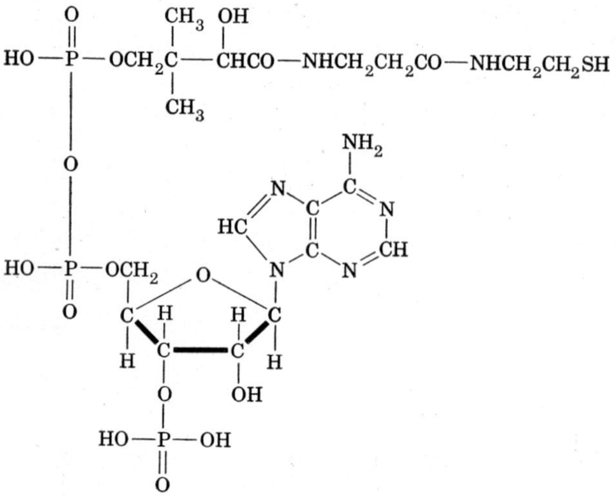

$$\text{HO}-\overset{\overset{\displaystyle O}{\|}}{\underset{\displaystyle O}{P}}-OCH_2\overset{\overset{\displaystyle CH_3}{|}}{\underset{\displaystyle CH_3}{C}}-\overset{\overset{\displaystyle OH}{|}}{CH}CO-NHCH_2CH_2CO-NHCH_2CH_2SH$$

Coenzyme A

Other Substances Related to Nucleic Acids

It was noted earlier that some of the purines identified as constituents of the nucleic acids had been known since the middle of the nineteenth century. In addition to those already mentioned, caffeine (1,3,7-trimethylxanthine) and theobromine (3,7-dimethylxanthine) occur in tea, and many plant extracts contain inosine (hypoxanthine riboside)

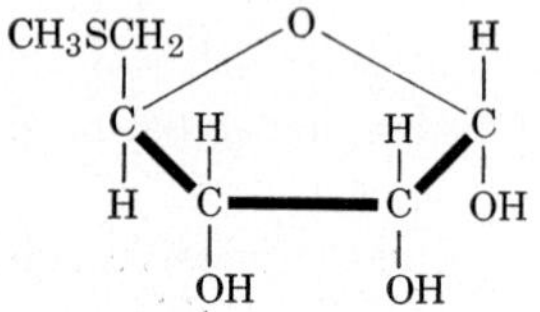

5-Methylthio-D-ribose

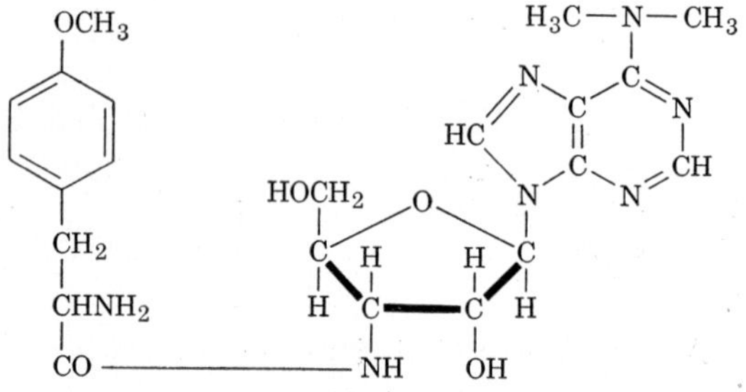

Puromycin

and guanosine. It would appear that nucleosides are widely distributed in nature; for example, 9-β-ribofuranosylpurine (nebularine) has been isolated from mushrooms, uric acid riboside has been found in beef blood, and sponges have been shown to contain spongouridine (3-β-D-arabinofuranosyluracil), spongothymidine (3-β-D-arabinofuranosylthymine), and spongosine (a D-riboside of 2-methoxy-6-aminopurine).[64] A nucleoside isolated from yeast is composed of adenine and 5-methylthio-D-ribose,

[64] W. Bergmann and D. C. Burke, *J. Org. Chem.*, **21**, 226 (1956).

and 6-furfurylaminopurine (kinetin) was found in DNA preparations. The antibiotic puromycin (from *Streptomyces alboniger*) is the nucleoside derivative 6-dimethylamino-9-[3'-deoxy-3'-(p-methoxy-L-phenylalanyl-amino)-β-D-ribofuranosyl]-purine.[65]

A particularly interesting chapter in the history of biochemical studies on purine compounds is that concerned with the attempts to determine the nature of the pigments of butterfly wings. In one of his earliest

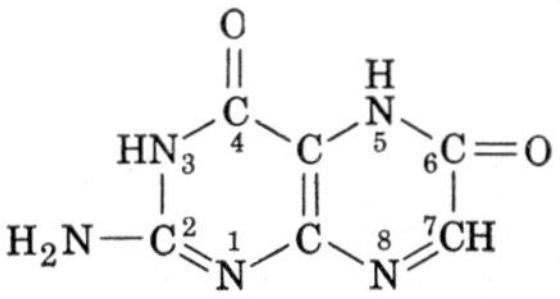

Xanthopterin (2–amino–4,6–dioxypteridine)

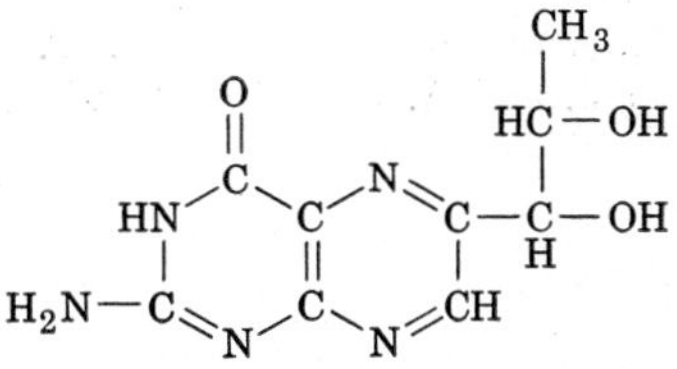

Biopterin

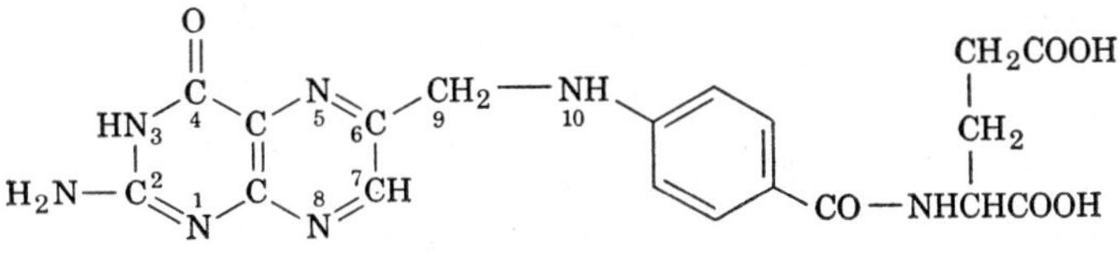

Pteroyl-L-glutamic acid

scientific papers, published in 1889, F. G. Hopkins described a yellow pigment which he obtained from this source; later work (1896) led him to the conclusion that it was a derivative of uric acid. Although butterfly wings do contain uric acid, as well as isoguanine (2-oxy-6-aminopurine), the researches of Wieland and Purrmann some 40 years later showed that the yellow pigment is not a purine, but a member of a new group of related substances (the pterins); it is now termed xanthopterin. The work of Wieland and Purrmann might have remained of academic interest had it not been for the discovery in 1945 that an important vitamin, first found in leaves, but later shown to have a widespread distribution, is a pterin-containing compound. This vitamin is folic acid (Chapter 39), and it occurs in the form of several modifications of the same basic structure known as pteroyl-L-glutamic acid. It will be noted that a pterin (2-amino-4-oxypteridine) is linked to the amino group of p-aminobenzoic acid by means of a methylene bridge; the pterin-amino-benzoic acid compound is termed pteroic acid, and the corresponding acyl group is the pteroyl group. In the formula shown, the pteroyl radical is linked to the α-amino group of L-glutamic acid.

An interesting pterin (biopterin) has been isolated from the fruit fly

[65] B. R. Baker et al., *J. Am. Chem. Soc.*, **77**, 5911 (1955).

Drosophila melanogaster, and also found to be a constituent of normal human urine; its structure is 2-amino-4-oxy-6(1,2-dioxypropyl)-pteridine.[66]

The chemistry of the pterins has been reviewed by Gates and Albert.[67] More recent work in this field is summarized in the book edited by Wolstenholme and Cameron.[68]

[66] E. L. Patterson et al., *J. Am. Chem. Soc.,* **78,** 5868, 5871 (1956).

[67] M. Gates, *Chem. Revs.,* **41,** 63 (1947); A. Albert, *Quart. Revs.,* **6,** 197 (1952).

[68] G. E. Wolstenholme and M. P. Cameron, *The Chemistry and Biology of Pteridines,* J. and A. Churchill, London, 1954.

8 ·

General Chemistry
of Enzymes

The enzymes are proteins whose biological function is the catalysis of chemical reactions in living systems. As indicated in Chapter 1, the initial recognition of the role of enzymes came from studies on the chemical mechanism of digestion and fermentation. Among the first to consider digestion as a chemical process, rather than merely a mechanical "concoction," was van Helmont. In the early part of the seventeenth century, he suggested that digestion involved an actual chemical transformation of foodstuffs through the agency of "ferments" (Latin *fermentare*, to agitate). The choice of this word was suggested by his earlier studies on the fermentation of wine, a process that he also considered chemical in nature.

By the end of the nineteenth century there was much further knowledge of digestion as a chemical process and it was known that, in the digestion of food by man, the initial action by constituents of saliva was followed by the action of juices elaborated by the stomach, pancreas, and intestine. The ability of these juices to decompose food was attributed to ferments which subjected the food to chemical alteration. Perhaps the most convincing of the early experiments was described by Réaumur in 1752. Taking advantage of the fact that birds of prey eject from their stomachs articles of food that they cannot digest, Réaumur fed a kite perforated metal tubes filled with different types of food materials and examined the condition of the food upon ejection of the tubes. His conclusion was that the stomach juice had a distinct solvent power. A decade later, Réaumur's method was taken up by Spallanzani, who not only confirmed Réaumur's work on birds, but extended it to other kinds of animals, including man.

With the birth of scientific chemistry, in the first part of the nineteenth century, a series of chemical phenomena was discovered that provided a key to the understanding of the mode of action of the digestive ferments.

For example, in 1812 Kirchhoff found that starch was converted to glucose by the action of dilute acid, and that the acid itself was unchanged by the process. A little later (1817–1823), it was noted by several investigators (Davy, Döbereiner, Mitscherlich, Thenard) that several chemical reactions (e.g., the decomposition of hydrogen peroxide) were accelerated in the presence of metals, without any appreciable change in the metal used. It is of interest that Thenard noted that "blood fibrin" also accelerated the decomposition of H_2O_2, an effect probably due to methemoglobin. Empirical observations of this kind led to the proposal in 1836 that such reactions involved a special kind of chemical force, which Berzelius termed "catalysis" (Greek *katalysis*, dissolution). To quote his own words: ". . . catalytic power appears to consist essentially in the fact that substances are able to set into activity affinities which are dormant at a particular temperature, and [to do] this, not by their own affinity, but by their presence alone." Among the catalytic phenomena, Berzelius explicitly included the processes of digestion and fermentation, and he made the prophetic statement (quoted on p. 8) which served as a conceptual synthesis in bridging the gap between the chemical capacities of living systems and those of the chemical laboratory.

During the first half of the nineteenth century a series of catalytic activities also was identified in biological materials. Thus Kirchhoff found in 1814 that the conversion of starch to sugar could be effected, not only by dilute acid, but also by an extract of wheat. A ferment of this type (named diastase) was obtained from malt extract by alcohol precipitation (Payen and Persoz, 1833), and diastase activity was also recognized in saliva. In 1830 Robiquet found in bitter almonds what he called an "albuminoid" material which catalyzed the hydrolysis of the plant glucoside amygdalin (formed by the union of 2 molecules of glucose, 1 of benzaldehyde, and 1 of HCN). Liebig and Wöhler in 1837 studied this catalytic agent further and named it emulsin. In 1836 Eberle and Schwann described a constituent of stomach juice (named pepsin) which degraded proteins; twenty years later, Corvisart described trypsin, a protein-splitting component of pancreatic juice. In 1846 Dubrunfaut discovered in yeast a catalytic component which converted sucrose to glucose and fructose; this was later named invertase.

In Berzelius' definition of catalysis there was a vagueness to which some of his contemporaries, notably Liebig, objected violently. Liebig stated that "the assumption of this new force is detrimental to the progress of science, since it appears to satisfy the human spirit, and thus provides a limit to further research." Instead, Liebig suggested that the so-called catalytic agent (whether an inorganic substance or a ferment) is itself unstable and that, in the course of its decomposition, it induces otherwise unreactive substances to undergo chemical change. However, the later work of Dumas forced Liebig to modify his views greatly, and by 1870 he had abandoned his explanation of the mechanism of catalysis.

A more precise understanding of the concept of catalysis required the quantitative measurements of the rates of chemical reactions by van't Hoff and Ostwald, during the latter half of the nineteenth century. These studies led to the currently accepted definition of a catalyst (proposed by Ostwald) as a substance that changes the rate of a chemical reaction without appearing in the over-all reaction; in other words, it does not affect the nature of the final products. It would be incorrect to infer from this definition that the catalyst does not participate in the reaction in question; as will become evident from the discussion in Chapter 10, the catalyst must interact with one of the reactants to be effective. In general, catalysts may be characterized by the following properties:

1. They are effective in small amounts. With enzymes, a useful term to describe the amount of starting material ("substrate") converted in unit time by a given quantity of enzyme is the "turnover number," which is defined as the number of moles of substrate converted by 1 mole of enzyme per minute. The term "substrate" was introduced by Duclaux in 1883 to denote a substance acted upon by an enzyme. As will be seen from the later discussion, the turnover numbers of enzymes vary widely (100 to 3,000,000).

2. They are unchanged in the reaction. This property of ideal catalysts can only be approximated by enzymes that are completely stable under the conditions of an experiment. As proteins, enzymes are susceptible to denaturation.

3. If present in small amount relative to the substrate, an ideal catalyst does not affect the equilibrium of a reversible chemical reaction, and the function of the catalyst is to hasten the process in either direction. Many of the reversible reactions that occur in biochemical systems would proceed at an extremely slow rate if a catalyst were not present to accelerate the approach to equilibrium. The equilibria in enzyme-catalyzed reactions will be considered further in Chapter 9.

4. They exhibit specificity in their ability to accelerate chemical reactions. This means that a given catalyst is limited in its catalytic ability to a more or less restricted type of chemical reaction. From the later discussion, it will be evident that this property of catalysts is exhibited more clearly by enzymes than by nonprotein catalysts, and that enzymes are extremely selective in their action on a group of closely related substrates.

With the rapid development of organic chemistry during the latter half of the nineteenth century, enough information accumulated about the structure of many of the chemical constituents of living matter to permit a more accurate description of the chemical reactions catalyzed by the "ferments" mentioned above, and by the many others discovered in later work. It soon became clear that, from the point of view of the biochemist, one of the most striking aspects of the dynamics of life processes is the multitude of organic chemical reactions demonstrable in living cells and in biological fluids. The importance of organic chemistry for progress in the understanding of enzyme action was clearly stated by Emil Fischer in his Faraday Lecture (1907):

> The ultimate aim of biochemistry is to gain complete insight into the unending series of changes which attend plant and animal metabolism. To accomplish a task of such magnitude, complete knowledge is required of each individual chemical substance occurring in the cycle of changes and of analytical methods which will permit of its recognition under conditions such as exist in the living organism. As a matter of course, it is the office of organic chemistry, especially of synthetic chemistry, to accumulate this absolutely essential material.

Fischer himself offered one of the most eloquent proofs of the correctness of this view through his work on the enzymes which hydrolyze linkages in carbohydrate derivatives (Chapter 18). It is fair to say that modern enzyme chemistry rests on the knowledge of the chemical structure of the substrates and of the products in enzyme-catalyzed reactions; where there is obscurity about the chemical nature of these components, there also is uncertainty about the chemical reactions catalyzed by enzymes that act on these substrates.

However, a knowledge of the initial and final products in a biochemical process, though essential, is not sufficient for a description of the process in terms of the enzymes that are involved as catalysts. In living systems, enzymes do not function alone, but as parts of a complex "multienzyme" (more correctly, polyenzyme) apparatus. If one compares a living cell to a factory, then the individual enzymes might be considered analogous to the machines that cooperate to cause the transformation of a starting material (e.g., steel) into parts of a finished product (e.g., an automobile). These considerations have played an important role in the development of enzyme chemistry, as may be seen from a brief review of the early discussions about the nature of the catalysts of fermentation.

Through the work of Lavoisier (1789) and of Gay-Lussac (1810), it was established that the process of alcoholic fermentation by yeast involves the conversion of 1 mole of glucose to 2 moles of ethyl alcohol and 2 moles of CO_2. Neither of these investigators concerned themselves greatly with the nature of the yeast "ferment" that caused this conversion, the important chemical problem of their time being the elucidation of the quantitative relationships between the initial and final products in chemical reactions. In 1837 Cagniard-Latour, Kützing, and Schwann independently demonstrated that yeast was composed of living cells, and the question then arose whether the ability of yeast to break down glucose depended on the life of the yeast cells or whether yeast contained a ferment, analogous to pepsin or invertase, that could perform this decomposition independently of the life of the cell. This issue was brought to the fore by Pasteur, who claimed that the act of fermentation was indissolubly linked with the life of the yeast cell, since many trials to extract from yeast cells a catalytic agent which would cause alcoholic fermentation in the absence of living cells were unsuccessful. In 1860, Pasteur expressed his point of view in this fashion:

> The chemical act of fermentation is essentially a phenomenon correlative with a vital act, commencing and ceasing with the latter. I believe that alcoholic fermentation never occurs without simultaneous organization, development, and multiplication of cells, or the continued life of cells already formed . . . If I am asked in what consists the chemical act of the decomposition of sugar, and what is its real cause, I admit that I am completely ignorant of it.

As a consequence of this view, there arose a distinction between the so-called organized (or formed) ferments, of which the living yeast cell was an example, and the so-called unorganized (or unformed) ferments such as invertase, diastase, or pepsin, i.e., those which could be extracted from cells. This unfortunate separation was not accepted by all of Pasteur's contemporaries, however. For example, in 1878 M. Traube restated views that he had expressed 20 years earlier, as follows:

> . . . the ferments are not, as Liebig assumed, unstable substances which transmit to usually unreactive materials their chemical vibration but they are chemical substances, related to the proteins, and which . . . like all other substances, possess a definite chemical structure and evoke changes in other substances through the agency of specific chemical affinities . . . The hypothesis proposed by Schwann (and later adopted by Pasteur) that fermentation is to be considered as the expression of the vital activity of lower organisms is unsatisfactory . . . The converse of Schwann's hypothesis is correct. Ferments are the causes of the most important biochemical processes, not only in the lower organisms but in the higher organisms as well.

Although other investigators of that period, notably Berthelot and Bernard, questioned the desirability of the separation of the "formed" and "unformed" ferments, there still remained the failure to prepare a cell-free extract of yeast that would cause fermentation. In order to avoid the confusion engendered by the double use of the word "ferment," Kühne in 1878 introduced the term "enzyme" to describe the so-called unformed ferments. It may be of interest to quote Kühne on this point.

> The latter designations (formed and unformed ferments) have not gained general acceptance, since on the one hand it was objected that chemical bodies, like pepsin etc., could not be called ferments since the name was already given

to yeast cells and other organisms; while, on the other hand, it was said that yeast cells could not be called ferments, because then all organisms, including man, would have to be so designated. Without stopping to enquire further why the name has excited so much opposition, I have taken the opportunity to suggest a new one, and I give the name enzymes to some of the better known substances, called by many unformed ferments. This name is not intended to imply any particular hypothesis, it merely states that *en zyme* (Greek, in yeast) something occurs which exerts this or that activity, which is supposed to belong to the class fermentative. The name is not, however, intended to be limited to the invertin of yeast, but it is intended to imply that more complex organisms, from which the enzymes pepsin, trypsin etc. can be obtained, are not so fundamentally different from the unicellular organisms as some people would have us believe.

In 1897 the basis for a distinction between "organized" and "unorganized" ferments was removed by the success of Buchner in preparing a cell-free yeast extract which would cause the fermentation of glucose to ethanol and CO_2. It then became possible to consider the catalytic components of this extract as enzymes, in the sense of Kühne's definition. However, there still remained the question whether the conversion of glucose to alcohol involved one or many enzymes. The complete elucidation of this question required some 35 years of intensive biochemical research, and it is now known that alcoholic fermentation involves the cooperative catalytic activity of about 12 different enzymes (cf. Chapter 19). To establish the sequence in which these enzymes act it was necessary to isolate and identify intermediate products of the degradation of glucose, to isolate the component enzymes, and to demonstrate the nature of the chemical reaction catalyzed by each of the enzymes. Another example which illustrates the recognition of the multienzyme character of some of the older "ferments" is the trypsin of Corvisart, long thought to be a single enzyme, but later shown to contain at least three separate catalytic agents. Clearly, the discovery of an enzyme-catalyzed chemical reaction in an extract of cells, or a biological fluid, does not permit one to state that the extract or fluid is "the enzyme" that causes the reaction in question. The history of biochemistry is replete with instances in which a chemical reaction first thought to involve a single catalytic entity turned out to involve the successive action of a number of enzymes.

For a great many chemical reactions that occur in living systems it is possible to assign, with reasonable certainty, single enzymes or groups of related enzymes. Consequently, it is occasionally the custom to designate a group of enzymes that have a particular type of substrate by combining the root of the substrate with the suffix -ase; thus an enzyme that acts on proteins is a proteinase, etc. There are so many exceptions to this practice, however, that it cannot be considered a general rule. For example, the traditional names for enzymes such as pepsin and emulsin are still found in the current literature. Also, some enzymes are named according to the type of reaction they catalyze, as phosphorylases or dehydrogenases. Because of the rapid development of enzyme chemistry, there has been considerable confusion in terminology. There are instances in which a single type of enzyme has been given several different names. In addition, there has been a tendency to assign a name before it is established whether or not a single enzyme is involved. An example of the latter is the term "transmethylase" to denote an enzyme that presumably causes the transfer of a methyl group from a compound such as choline to homocysteine. When this name was introduced, the biochemical importance of transmethylation was well established, but no evidence was available to show whether it was catalyzed by a single enzyme or by a series of separate enzymes. It is now known that a multienzyme system is involved in this process.

The number of biochemical reactions to which individual enzymes can be assigned is very great; a selection of the more important types of reaction, and of some of the appropriate groups of enzymes, is given in Table 1. Although the list does not include all the types of enzyme-catalyzed reactions to which reference will be found in later pages of this book, it suffices to indicate the manifold chemical capacities of the enzymic apparatus of biological systems. All living cells do not contain representatives of all the groups of enzymes cited; certain of these groups are found in nearly all cells, whereas other enzymes are more restricted in their distribution.

With few exceptions, enzymic reactions are performed at pH values near neutrality and at temperatures between $20°$ and $40°$ C; in order to imitate these reactions in the organic chemical laboratory, without the mediation of enzymes, more drastic conditions are usually required. In some instances such efforts may be unsuccessful, since the extreme conditions required in the absence of the appropriate enzyme may cause extensive decomposition of the components of the reaction. In general, it may be said that enzyme-catalyzed reactions are performed with a delicacy and precision that cannot be matched by the classical methods of organic chemistry.

It will be noted that most of the reactions in Table 1 are given as reversible processes. In principle, all enzyme-catalyzed reactions are thermodynamically reversible (cf. p. 230); in some instances, however, the equilibrium is so far in one direction as to make it impossible, in practice, to perform the reverse reaction. The function of the appropriate enzyme is to catalyze the attainment of equilibrium from either direction, whenever this is possible.

Table I.   Some Type Reactions Catalyzed by Enzymes

Type Reactions	Enzyme Group
1. Hydrolysis-condensation or replacement	
$RCO\!-\!NHR'+H_2O \rightleftharpoons RCOOH+R'NH_2$ $RCO\!-\!NHR'+R''NH_2 \rightleftharpoons RCO\!-\!NHR''+R'NH_2$	Proteinases, peptidases, and amidases
$RCO\!-\!OR'+H_2O \rightleftharpoons RCOOH+R'OH$ $RCO\!-\!OR'+R''OH \rightleftharpoons RCO\!-\!OR''+R'OH$	Esterases
$RCO\!-\!SR'+H_2O \rightleftharpoons RCOOH+R'SH$ $RCO\!-\!SR'+R''H \rightleftharpoons RCO\!-\!R''+R'SH$	Thiol esterases
$R\!-\!PO_3H_2+H_2O \rightleftharpoons RH+H_3PO_4$ $R\!-\!PO_3H_2+R'OH \rightleftharpoons RH+R'O\!-\!PO_3H_2$ $R\!-\!PO_3H_2+R'NH_2 \rightleftharpoons RH+R'NH\!-\!PO_3H_2$	Phosphatases and transphosphorylases
$R\!-\!CH\!-\!OR'+H_2O \rightleftharpoons RH+HO\!-\!CH\!-\!OR'$	Glycosidases†
$R\!-\!CH\!-\!OR'+R''H \rightleftharpoons RH+R''\!-\!CH\!-\!OR'$	Transglycosidases†
2. Phosphorolysis-condensation	
$R\!-\!CH\!-\!OR'+H_3PO_4 \rightleftharpoons RH+H_2O_3PO\!-\!CH\!-\!OR'$	Phosphorylases†
3. Cleavage or formation of C—C linkages	
$RCOOH \rightleftharpoons RH+CO_2$	Decarboxylases
$\begin{array}{cc} H & H \\ HO\!-\!C\!-\!C\!-\!OH \\ R & R' \end{array} \rightleftharpoons RCH_2OH+R'CHO$	Aldolases
4. Hydration-dehydration and related processes	
$\begin{array}{cc} H & H \\ R_2C\!-\!C\!-\!OH \\ & R \end{array} \rightleftharpoons \begin{array}{c} H \\ R_2C\!=\!C \\ R \end{array} +H_2O$	Hydrases and related enzymes (elements of H_2O or NH_3 may be replaced by those of H_2S)
$\begin{array}{cc} H & H \\ R_2C\!-\!C\!-\!NH_2 \\ & R \end{array} \rightleftharpoons \begin{array}{c} H \\ R_2C\!=\!C \\ R \end{array} +NH_3$	
5. Oxidation-reduction	
$AH_2+B \rightleftharpoons A+BH_2$	Dehydrogenases
$2Fe^{2+}+\tfrac{1}{2}O_2+2H^+ \rightarrow 2Fe^{3+}+H_2O$ $AH_2+O_2 \rightarrow A+H_2O_2$	Oxidases
$AH_2+H_2O_2 \rightarrow A+2H_2O$ $2H_2O_2 \rightarrow 2H_2O+O_2$	Peroxidases and catalases

† The type formula $R\!-\!CH\!-\!OR'$ denotes a glycoside (Chapter 17).

The Protein Nature of Enzymes

At the beginning of this chapter, enzymes were defined as catalytic proteins. Although the protein nature of enzymes is widely acknowledged today and was implicit in the views of Traube and other investigators of the nineteenth century, there was a period (1920–1930) in which it was not accepted. This change in opinion arose from the work of Willstätter, who had purified several enzymes, in particular, yeast invertase, and obtained enzyme solutions which were extremely active catalytically but did not show to any appreciable extent the characteristic color reactions for tryptophan. The prestige attached to Willstätter's views led many to overlook the importance of Sumner's achievement in 1926, when he obtained the enzyme urease (which hydrolyzes urea to CO_2 and NH_3) in the form of protein crystals. Not until later was it demonstrated that the catalytic activity of purified enzymes is so great that an enzyme solution may be too dilute for the protein color tests to be effective but still may be sufficiently concentrated to permit observation of the catalytic activity. Sumner's crystallization of urease was followed in 1930 by the crystallization of pepsin by Northrop, and the succeeding years witnessed the isolation of many enzymes in the form of crystalline proteins. Foremost in this development was the work of Northrop, Kunitz, and their associates.[1] By 1956 about 75 enzymes had been crystallized, and the study of the properties of these highly purified preparations documented the view that the characteristic catalytic activity of an enzyme was indissolubly linked with its protein nature.

A selected list of crystalline enzymes described before 1957 is given in Table 2. The methods for their isolation from cell extracts or from biological fluids are essentially those described in Chapter 2 for the purification of proteins. Clearly, the same doubts must be applied to the consideration of the "purity" of crystalline enzymes as to that of crystalline proteins in general. With the enzymes, however, one may add to the criteria of homogeneity in solubility behavior, sedimentation, and electrophoretic mobility the criterion of maximal enzyme activity and freedom from other enzymic activities. If all four of these criteria are satisfied, the probability that the enzyme is "pure" is increased.

Some indication of the difficulty in defining the "purity" of an enzyme is provided by studies on several of the enzymes found in rabbit muscle. One of the crystalline proteins obtained from this source, named myogen A, contains at least two different enzyme activities, even after repeated recrystallization. These two enzymes, aldolase and L-glycerophosphate

---

[1] J. H. Northrop, M. Kunitz, and R. M. Herriott, *Crystalline Enzymes*, 2nd Ed., Columbia University Press, New York. 1948.

Table 2. Some Crystalline Enzymes

Enzyme	Source	Reference
Alcohol dehydrogenase	Yeast	E. Negelein and H.-J. Wulff, *Biochem. Z.*, **293**, 351 (1937).
	Horse liver	R. K. Bonnichsen, *Acta Chem. Scand.*, **4**, 715 (1950).
Aldolase	Muscle (rabbit, rat)	J. F. Taylor et al., *J. Biol. Chem.*, **173**, 591 (1948).
α-Amylase	Barley	S. Schwimmer and A. K. Balls, *J. Biol. Chem.*, **179**, 1063 (1949).
	Human saliva	K. H. Meyer et al., *Helv. Chim. Acta*, **31**, 2158 (1948).
	Swine pancreas	K. H. Meyer et al., *Helv. Chim. Acta*, **30**, 64 (1947).
β-Amylase	Sweet potato	A. K. Balls et al., *J. Biol. Chem.*, **173**, 9 (1948).
ATP-1,3-diphospho-glyceric acid trans-phosphorylase	Yeast	T. Bücher, *Biochim. et Biophys. Acta*, **1**, 292 (1947).
ATP-phosphopyruvic acid transphospho-rylase	Rat muscle	F. Kubowitz and P. Ott, *Biochem. Z.*, **317**, 193 (1944).
Carbonic anhydrase	Beef erythrocytes	D. A. Scott and A. M. Fisher, *J. Biol. Chem.*, **144**, 371 (1942).
Carboxypeptidase	Beef pancreas	M. L. Anson, *J. Gen. Physiol.*, **20**, 663 (1937).
Catalase	Beef liver	J. B. Sumner and A. L. Dounce, *J. Biol. Chem.*, **121**, 417 (1937).
	Beef erythrocytes	M. Laskowski and J. B. Sumner, *Science*, **94**, 615 (1941).
	Micrococcus lysodeikticus	D. Herbert and A. J. Pinsent, *Biochem. J.*, **43**, 193 (1948).
Chymopapain	*Carica papaya*	E. F. Jansen and A. K. Balls, *J. Biol. Chem.*, **137**, 459 (1941).
α-Chymotrypsin	Beef pancreas	M. Kunitz and J. H. Northrop, *J. Gen. Physiol.*, **18**, 433 (1935).
Crotonase	Beef liver	J. R. Stern et al., *J. Biol. Chem.*, **218**, 971 (1956).
Deoxyribonuclease	Beef pancreas	M. Kunitz, *J. Gen. Physiol.*, **33**, 349 (1950).
Enolase	Yeast	O. Warburg and W. Christian, *Biochem. Z.*, **310**, 384 (1942).
Fumarase	Swine heart	V. Massey, *Biochem. J.*, **51**, 490 (1952).
Glutamic dehydro-genase	Beef liver	J. A. Olsen and C. B. Anfinsen, *J. Biol. Chem.*, **197**, 67 (1952).
Glyceraldehyde phosphate dehydrogenase	Rabbit muscle	G. T. Cori et al., *J. Biol. Chem.*, **173**, 605 (1948).
Hexokinase	Yeast	M. Kunitz and M. R. McDonald, *J. Gen. Physiol.*, **29**, 393 (1946).

Table 2. (*Continued*)

Enzyme	Source	Reference
Lactic dehydrogenase	Beef heart	F. B. Straub, *Biochem. J.*, **34**, 483 (1940).
Lysozyme	Egg white	G. Alderton and H. L. Fevold, *J. Biol. Chem.*, **164**, 1 (1946).
Papain	*Carica papaya*	A. K. Balls and H. Lineweaver, *J. Biol. Chem.*, **130**, 669 (1940).
Penicillinase	*Bacillus cereus*	M. R. Pollock et al., *Biochem.*, *J.* **62**, 387 (1956).
Pepsin	Swine stomach	J. H. Northrop, *J. Gen. Physiol.*, **13**, 739 (1930); **30**, 177 (1946).
	Salmon	E. R. Norris and D. W. Elam, *J. Biol. Chem.*, **134**, 443 (1940).
Peroxidase	Horseradish	H. Theorell, *Enzymologia*, **10**, 250 (1942).
	Milk	H. Theorell and Å. Åkeson, *Arkiv Kemi*, **17B**, no. 7 (1943).
Phosphorylase	Rabbit muscle	A. A. Green and G. T. Cori, *J. Biol. Chem.*, **151**, 21 (1943).
Pyrophosphatase	Yeast	M. Kunitz, *J. Gen. Physiol.*, **35**, 423 (1952).
Rennin	Calf stomach	N. J. Berridge, *Biochem. J.*, **39**, 179 (1945).
Ribonuclease	Beef pancreas	M. Kunitz, *J. Gen. Physiol.*, **24**, 15 (1940).
Transketolase	Yeast	G. de la Haba et al., *J. Biol. Chem.*, **214**, 409 (1955).
Trypsin	Beef pancreas	J. H. Northrop and M. Kunitz, *J. Gen. Physiol.*, **16**, 267 (1932); **19**, 991 (1936).
Urease	Jack bean	J. B. Sumner, *J. Biol. Chem.*, **69** 435 (1926).
Yellow enzyme	Yeast	H. Theorell and Å. Åkeson, *Arch. Biochem. and Biophys.*, **65**, 439 (1956).

dehydrogenase, have been crystallized, and are distinct from myogen A in their physical properties. Nevertheless, the obviously inhomogeneous myogen A behaves as a single component during electrophoresis in the pH range 5.8 to 7.6 and in the ultracentrifuge.[2]

The crystalline enzymes are classed among the proteins for a variety of reasons. In their elementary composition, the enzymes show the usual proportion of C, H, N, and S found in proteins. Some crystalline enzymes contain, in addition, small amounts of P, or metal ions such as Fe, Cu, Mg, and Zn. On hydrolysis by means of strong acids, the crystal-

[2] T. Baranowski and T. R. Niederland, *J. Biol. Chem.*, **180**, 543 (1949).

line enzymes yield amino acids, and chromatographic analysis of the hydrolysates of several enzymes has accounted for all the protein N in the form of amino acids and ammonia. It should be recalled, however, that some enzymes crystallize as conjugated proteins. Thus the "yellow enzyme" is isolated as a conjugated protein in which the non-amino acid portion is riboflavin phosphate (p. 332), and catalase is an iron-porphyrin-containing protein. The presence of the non-amino acid components is essential for the enzymic activity of these conjugated proteins, but, without the protein, the characteristic enzymic behavior is absent. Neuberg and Euler termed the nonprotein part the "coenzyme," the protein portion the "apoenzyme," and the conjugated protein the "holoenzyme." The term "coenzyme" had been introduced by Bertrand in 1897 to designate dialyzable substances essential for enzymic activity.

Additional evidence for the conclusion that enzymes are proteins comes from studies in which enzymes are subjected to the action of those enzymes specifically adapted to the hydrolysis of the peptide bonds of proteins. Since the protein-splitting enzymes have been purified extensively, the hydrolysis of an enzyme preparation in their presence can be attributed to a proteolysis. There are many data in the literature to show that the catalytic activity of enzymes decreases in parallel with their degradation by proteinases. Several examples are cited in Northrop's book[1] and in articles by Cori and Green[3] and by Sumner.[4]

The cleavage of peptide bonds in a crystalline enzyme does not always lead to loss of catalytic activity. For example, Hill and Smith[5] have shown that the peptide chain of crystalline papain may be extensively degraded by means of aminopeptidase (p. 144) with retention of papain activity. This indicates that a sizable portion of the N-terminal sequence of the peptide chain of papain is not essential for catalytic action, and that the "active center" of this enzyme is located in the partially degraded protein. Similar partial proteolysis without the disappearance of catalytic activity has been reported for pepsin (Chapter 29) and for ribonuclease (Chapter 35). Such findings are of great importance in the study of the structural basis for enzyme action; however, they do not invalidate the general conclusion as to the protein nature of the crystalline enzymes isolated from biological systems.

The behavior of solutions of crystalline enzymes in the ultracentrifuge supports the view that enzymes are proteins. The smallest particle weight assigned to a purified enzyme is 13,000 for ribonuclease. Other

[3] G. T. Cori and A. A. Green, *J. Biol. Chem.,* **151,** 31 (1943).

[4] J. B. Sumner et al., *J. Biol. Chem.,* **98,** 543 (1932).

[5] R. L. Hill and E. L. Smith, *Biochim. et Biophys. Acta,* **19,** 376 (1956).

enzymes have particle weights between this figure and about 500,000 (cf. p. 42). The data given on p. 150 also show that the frictional ratio f/f_0 for the enzymes cited is near unity, indicating that these enzymes belong to the group of the so-called globular proteins.

Like other proteins, enzymes behave as amphoteric electrolytes in an electric field, and the isoelectric points of a large number of purified enzymes have been determined (cf. p. 102). When an enzyme has been purified sufficiently so that only one component is observed on electrophoresis, it becomes possible to test whether the enzyme activity migrates together with the protein. In the same way, it may be determined whether, in the sedimentation of an enzyme, the protein boundary and the enzyme activity move together in the centrifugal field.

Like other proteins, enzymes readily undergo denaturation (p. 153). If the crystalline proteinase chymotrypsin is exposed to an unfavorable pH, the per cent of the protein that is found to be denatured at any time is approximately equal to the per cent loss in enzymic activity. Similar effects have been noted upon heat denaturation of enzymes; this inactivation sometimes is reversible if the heat treatment is not too drastic.

Finally, it may be mentioned that highly purified enzymes, on injection into suitable animals, elicit the formation of specific antibodies (Chapter 30). Although this does not prove the protein nature of enzymes, since a number of nonprotein materials have been shown to serve as antigens, the finding is further support for the view that enzymes are proteins. In some instances it has been possible to demonstrate the formation of antibodies that act as specific inhibitors of the enzyme employed as an antigen.[6]

It will be seen from the foregoing, therefore, that there is an impressive body of data to show that enzymes are proteins, and that the understanding of the mechanism whereby enzymes exert their catalytic action depends, in large measure, on the understanding of the details of protein structure. Because of the large gaps that still remain in this area of biochemical knowledge (cf. Chapter 5), many aspects of the mode of action of the enzymes are still obscure. However, the properties of enzymes as catalysts may be studied without immediate regard to the mechanism of their action, and, as will be seen from the succeeding chapters, such studies have provided valuable information on the manner in which enzymes act in biological systems.

A number of general reference books on enzymes may be recommended. Among these are the encyclopedic work edited by Sumner and Myrbäck[7]

---

[6] B. Cinader, *Biochem. Soc. Symposia,* **10**, 16 (1953).

[7] J. B. Sumner and K. Myrbäck, *The Enzymes,* Academic Press, New York, 1950–1952.

and books by Sumner and Somers[8] and by J. B. S. Haldane.[9]   An
extremely valuable reference work on methods in enzymology has been
edited by Colowick and Kaplan.[10]

[8] J. B. Sumner and G. F. Somers, *Chemistry and Methods of Enzymes,* 2nd Ed.,
Academic Press, New York, 1947.

[9] J. B. S. Haldane, *Enzymes,* Longmans, Green and Co., London, 1930.

[10] S. P. Colowick and N. O. Kaplan, *Methods in Enzymology,* Academic Press,
New York, 1955–1956.

9 ·
Equilibria and
Free-Energy Changes
in Biochemical Reactions

In the preceding chapter, it was stated that enzyme-catalyzed chemical reactions are reversible, that the condition of equilibrium for a given reversible reaction may be approached from either direction, and that small amounts of a catalyst do not influence the position of the equilibrium. Since a knowledge of the equilibria in isolated biochemical reactions is useful for the understanding of metabolic processes, a brief review of some of the fundamental principles involved is desirable.

It may be convenient to begin with the reaction

$$CH_3COOH + C_2H_5OH \rightleftharpoons CH_3COOC_2H_5 + H_2O$$

This equation is written as a reversible process to indicate that, in the esterification of acetic acid by means of ethyl alcohol, the reaction will tend to go to the right until a certain proportion of the four components has been attained. In fact, as Berthelot and Pean de St. Giles showed in 1862, if one starts with equimolar proportions of alcohol and acid, the reaction proceeds until about two-thirds of the reactants have been converted into ethyl acetate and water. Likewise, if equimolar proportions of the ester and water are brought together under the same conditions, the reaction proceeds to the left until about one-third of these substances is converted to acid and alcohol. In other words, the reaction is reversible, a condition of equilibrium resulting when the speeds of the two reactions indicated by the upper and lower arrows become equal. In general, a reversible reaction such as that between ethyl alcohol and acetic acid may be written

$$A + B \rightleftharpoons C + D$$

According to the mass law, the speed with which A and B react is proportional to the product of the activities of A and B. Thus the rate of the forward reaction is given by the expression $k_1 (A) (B)$, where k_1 is a constant. The products of the reaction, C and D, in turn react to give

A and B, and the rate of this back reaction is given by k_2 (C) (D). At equilibrium, the rates of the forward and back reactions are equal, and therefore k_1 (A) (B) equals k_2 (C) (D). If the quotient k_1/k_2 is set equal to a constant K, then

$$K = \frac{(C)(D)}{(A)(B)}$$

Here K is the equilibrium constant of the reversible reaction.

An important relationship exists between the equilibrium constant of a reversible chemical reaction and the difference in "free energy" between the end products and the initial reactants. Since there will be frequent occasion to refer to the energy changes in enzyme-catalyzed reactions, it is necessary to define the term "free energy." To do this, a limited exposition of some of the methods of the science of thermodynamics is essential. For more extended and logically more rigorous treatments of this subject, the reader is referred to standard textbooks on physical chemistry or to the treatises on chemical thermodynamics by Klotz,[1] Rossini,[2] and Glasstone.[3]

Chemical Thermodynamics

The science of thermodynamics describes the laws that relate to energy changes in any physical or chemical process. These energy changes may be manifested either in the absorption or liberation of heat or in the performance of work (electrical or mechanical work, a chemical reaction, etc.). The first law of thermodynamics states that, whenever energy is transferred from one place to another, or whenever one kind of energy (e.g., chemical, mechanical, electric, or heat energy) is transformed into another, the total quantity of energy taken over all the systems involved in the process remains constant. For example, if, at the start of a given process, the energy of a system is E_1, and at the end of the process the system has a greater amount of energy, E_2, the increment of energy $(E_2 - E_1 = \Delta E)$ must correspond to the loss of an equivalent amount of energy from the surroundings. More generally, the sum of all the energy changes in all the systems participating in a process equals zero.

If a system receives from the surroundings a quantity of heat energy (Q), and also produces an amount of mechanical energy (W), thus doing work on the surroundings (e.g., as in the expansion of a gas against

[1] I. M. Klotz, *Chemical Thermodynamics*, Prentice-Hall, Englewood Cliffs, N. J., 1950.

[2] F. D. Rossini, *Chemical Thermodynamics*, John Wiley & Sons, New York, 1950.

[3] S. Glasstone, *Thermodynamics for Chemists*, D. Van Nostrand Co., New York, 1947.

atmospheric pressure), the first law of thermodynamics states that

$$\Delta E = Q - W$$

When heat is absorbed, the numerical value assigned to Q is positive; when heat is released, the value of Q is negative. When a system does work upon its surroundings, the numerical value of W is positive; when work is done upon the system, the value of W is negative.

When a system neither absorbs nor evolves heat in a process, i.e., an adiabatic process, as in the expansion of an ideal gas, $Q = 0$, and, by the first law,

$$\Delta E = -W$$

It follows from the first law that, if a system does no work upon its surroundings, the total energy change in the system is equal to the change in heat energy. This situation applies to the occurrence of a chemical reaction at constant volume in a system that can absorb heat from a heat reservoir or provide heat to such a reservoir. Under these circumstances, if heat is absorbed by the system,

$$\Delta E = Q$$

The change in heat energy in the reservoir may be measured by determining the change in its temperature; this is, in essence, the principle of the calorimeter.[4] The capacity of the substance in the calorimeter to increase its energy by an increase in its temperature (from T_1 to T_2) is termed its "heat capacity," which is a proportionality constant assigned the symbol C.

$$Q = C(T_2 - T_1)$$

This relationship provides an experimental basis for the definition of units of heat energy. Historically, the first such unit to be used widely was the calorie (abbreviated cal); it was defined as the quantity of heat required to raise the temperature of 1 gram of water 1 degree centigrade. Since the heat capacity of water varies with temperature, it became necessary to specify the temperature interval employed. Thus, the 15° calorie was defined as the quantity of heat needed to increase the temperature of 1 gram of water from 14.5° to 15.5° C. It is occasionally the practice to refer to large quantities of heat energy in terms of kilocalories (abbreviated kcal); the 15° kilocalorie is the amount of heat required to raise the temperature of 1000 grams of water from 14.5° to 15.5° C. In discussions of heat changes in biological systems (cf. Chapter 37), some biochemists have referred to the kilocalorie as "large calorie" or even "Calorie" (abbreviated Cal).

[4] J. M. Sturtevant, in A. Weissberger, *Physical Methods of Organic Chemistry*, 2nd Ed., Chapter 14, Interscience Publishers, New York, 1949.

The classical studies of Joule (1843) on the mechanical equivalent of heat and the development after 1910 of accurate methods for the measurement of the electrical equivalent of heat have led to the establishment of the absolute joule as a fundamental unit of energy. One 15° calorie is equal to 4.185 joules. Since 1948, the 15° calorie has been replaced by the "absolute calorie" (also termed "defined calorie" or "thermochemical calorie"), which is equal to 4.184 absolute joules. Electric energy is expressed in terms of the absolute volt-faraday, which equals 96,496 absolute joules, or 23,063 absolute calories (cf. p. 293).

In considering the change in the heat energy that accompanies a chemical reaction, it is important to know the value of Q when the pressure is kept constant, since most chemical reactions proceed at constant, i.e., atmospheric, pressure. Under these circumstances, the system that absorbs heat from the reservoir also increases in volume, thus performing work. For an increase in volume of ΔV, at constant pressure P, the work done will be $P \Delta V$. Thus, when the only work done by a system is $P \Delta V$, and the system absorbs the quantity of heat energy Q from the surroundings,

$$Q = \Delta E + P \Delta V$$

This change in heat energy at constant pressure is termed the change in "heat content" or "enthalpy," and is denoted by the symbol ΔH. If heat is evolved, the reaction is said to be exothermic, and ΔH has a negative sign; if heat is absorbed, the reaction is endothermic, and ΔH is positive.

The measurement of ΔH for chemical reactions is performed calorimetrically (cf. Sturtevant[4]). Since the oxidation of organic compounds to carbon dioxide and water, i.e., the combustion of organic compounds, is of importance in biochemistry, such reactions may be selected as illustrative examples. Thus, in the combustion of glucose (solid) to water (liquid) and carbon dioxide (gas),

$$C_6H_{12}O_6 \ (s) + 6O_2 \ (g) \rightarrow 6H_2O \ (l) + 6CO_2 \ (g)$$

the value of ΔH_{293} is $-673,000$ cal per mole of glucose at 20° C and at a pressure of 1 atmosphere. This value is termed the "heat of combustion" of glucose under the stated conditions. The change in enthalpy varies with temperature, and it is customary to denote a particular ΔH value with a subscript that indicates the appropriate absolute temperature on the Kelvin scale (0° C = 273.1° K).

When a fatty acid such as palmitic acid (Chapter 23) is burned with oxygen,

$$C_{16}H_{32}O_2 \ (s) + 23O_2 \ (g) \rightarrow 16CO_2 \ (g) + 16H_2O \ (l)$$

$\Delta H_{293} = -2,380,000$ cal per mole of fatty acid. In the combustion of an amino acid such as cysteine, the bound nitrogen is converted to N_2 and the bound sulfur is oxidized to sulfate.

$$C_3H_7O_2NS\ (s) + 5.25O_2\ (g) \rightarrow$$
$$3CO_2\ (g) + 0.5N_2\ (g) + (H_2SO_4 \cdot 3.5H_2O)\ (l) - H_2O\ (l)$$

In this reaction, $\Delta H_{293} = -532,420$ cal per mole of cysteine burned. The heats of combustion of several organic substances are given in Table 1.

Table I. Heats of Combustion of Several Organic Substances of Biochemical Interest

The values in this table refer to the change in enthalpy in passing from initial to final products at 20° C and at 1 atmosphere. The physical state of each substance is indicated as (s) solid or (l) liquid.

Substance	$-\Delta H$, kcal per mole	Substance	$-\Delta H$, kcal per mole
Glucose (s)	673	Stearic acid (s)	2680
Galactose (s)	670	Oleic acid (l)	2657
Maltose (s)	1350	Glycine (s)	234
Sucrose (s)	1349	Leucine (s)	856
Lactic acid (s)	326	Tyrosine (s)	1070
Glycerol (l)	397	Cysteine (s)	532
Palmitic acid (s)	2380	Urea (s)	152

The enthalpy change in a reversible chemical reaction may be estimated by the determination of the equilibrium constant at different temperatures. Such measurements give a value of $\Delta H°$; this symbol refers to the enthalpy change when the products and reactants are in their standard states (p. 233). In general, ΔH is approximately equal to $\Delta H°$, and for practical purposes it is justifiable to use the numerical values for ΔH and $\Delta H°$ interchangeably. The relationship between the change in equilibrium constant as a function of temperature and the enthalpy change is given by the van't Hoff equation:

$$\frac{d \ln K}{dT} = \frac{\Delta H°}{RT^2}$$

where K is the equilibrium constant, R is the gas constant (1.987 cal per degree per mole), and T is the absolute temperature. If $\Delta H°$ is constant over the temperature range studied, integration of this equation gives $\ln K = -(\Delta H°/RT) + C$, where C is a constant. When $\log K$ is plotted against $1/T$, one obtains a straight line whose slope is $-\Delta H°/2.303R$. Integration between limits of temperature T_1 and T_2, corresponding to equilibrium constants K_1 and K_2, gives the equation

$$\log \frac{K_2}{K_1} = -\frac{\Delta H°}{2.303R} \left(\frac{1}{T_2} - \frac{1}{T_1} \right)$$

It is possible, for example, to calculate the heat of ionization of acids from measurements of their pK values at different temperatures. The ionization of the carboxyl group of glycine at 25° C ($pK_1 = 2.35$) has an enthalpy change of $\Delta H°_{298} = 1156$ cal per mole; for the ionization of the ammonium group of glycine ($pK_2 = 9.78$), $\Delta H°_{298} = 10,806$ cal per mole. These two ionizations are endothermic reactions, since heat is absorbed upon release of H^+.

In the calorimetric measurement of ΔH for chemical reactions, careful attention must be given to the heats of the ionizations that take place. For example, in the hydrolysis of adenosine triphosphate (p. 204) to adenosine diphosphate and phosphate at pH 8 (glycylglycine buffer), the following reaction occurs:

$$ATP^{4-} + H_2O \rightarrow ADP^{3-} + HPO_4{}^{2-} + H^+$$

The ΔH_{293} measured calorimetrically was -16.1 kcal per mole. However, the heat of neutralization by the buffer of the H^+ liberated was -11.5 kcal (the ΔH_{293} of ionization for the pK_2 of glycylglycine is about $+11.5$ kcal). Therefore, the actual ΔH_{293} in the hydrolysis of ATP is about -4.6 kcal per mole.[5]

Free Energy

Experience has shown that certain natural processes can occur spontaneously, e.g., the diffusion of molecules from a region of high concentration to a region of lower concentration, or the separation of a solid from a supersaturated solution, or the running down of a clock, or the descent of an object from a hill to the valley below. These are all spontaneous processes in which a system changes its state in the direction of equilibrium; in order to reverse these processes, work must be introduced by means of an external agency. This body of experience is summarized in the second law of thermodynamics, which states that for any system (under a given set of conditions) there is a state of equilibrium toward which the system may change spontaneously; however, any change of the system away from the equilibrium state can occur only at the expense of the displacement of another system toward equilibrium.

For the study of a reversible chemical reaction, whether it occurs in living things or in inanimate matter, it is important to know the direction in which the reaction can proceed spontaneously under a given set of conditions, and the amount of change that occurs before equilibrium is reached under these conditions. If a chemical reaction proceeds sponta-

[5] R. J. Podolsky and M. F. Morales, *J. Biol. Chem.*, **218**, 945 (1956).

neously in a given direction, and is continuously opposed by a force tending to reverse it, the reaction may be made to do useful work. For example, a reversible electrochemical cell represents a system capable of doing electrical work when a chemical reaction occurs; if the electromotive force of the cell is continuously balanced by an equal and opposite force (so that no current flows), the maximum useful work obtainable from the cell at constant temperature and pressure may be determined. The maximum useful work that can be obtained from a chemical reaction by operating it in a perfectly reversible manner, at constant temperature and pressure, is termed the change in free energy of the reaction. This free energy change is denoted by the symbol ΔF. As will be seen from the discussion to follow, the sign of ΔF indicates whether a reaction can proceed spontaneously under a given set of conditions, and the magnitude of ΔF gives the maximum amount of work that can be obtained from the reaction under these conditions. At one time it was believed that the sign and magnitude of the ΔH associated with a chemical reaction provided valid criteria for a decision about the direction and extent of spontaneous change, but this view has been abandoned.

It will be recalled that, when a system at constant pressure does no work other than $P \Delta V$ work, $\Delta E = Q - P \Delta V$ (cf. p. 226). For any reversible process in which a system absorbs from its surroundings energy other than heat energy and $P \Delta V$ work energy, at constant temperature and pressure,

$$\Delta E = Q_{\text{rev}} - P \Delta V + \Delta F$$

If free energy is released by the system to the surroundings, ΔF will be a negative quantity. Since $\Delta H = \Delta E + P \Delta V$,

$$\Delta F = \Delta H - Q_{\text{rev}}$$

The significance of Q_{rev} for the present discussion lies in its relationship to the property of the system termed the entropy, and denoted by the symbol S. For a reversible process operating at constant temperature, the change in entropy ΔS equals Q_{rev}/T, where T is the absolute temperature. ΔS is expressed in calories per degree per mole (1 entropy unit = 1 cal per degree). From the previous definition of ΔF, it follows that

$$\Delta F = \Delta H - T \Delta S$$

A general property of a spontaneous process operating at constant temperature and pressure is an increase in the entropy of the system undergoing change. This increase in entropy (positive ΔS) as a system approaches equilibrium is related to the transition from a more highly ordered distribution of atoms and molecules to a less ordered state, as in the diffusion of a solute from a concentrated to a dilute solution. At equilibrium, the entropy of the system is at a maximum, and the capacity of the system to do work upon its surroundings (i.e., to displace another system away from equilibrium) is at a minimum. A general criterion of thermodynamic equilibrium in a reversible process is given by the condition that at equilibrium ΔF equals zero.

From the foregoing it follows that the change in free energy (ΔF) is more meaningful than ΔH in the consideration of the capacity of a chemical reaction to do work, since ΔF takes into account the energy $T \Delta S$ that is not measured in the usual enthalpy determinations. There will be frequent occasion, in the consideration of the energy changes in enzyme-catalyzed reactions, to refer to the sign and magnitude of the free-energy changes in these reactions. In general, it can be said that, if, at constant temperature and pressure, ΔF for a reaction is characterized by a negative value, that reaction may take place spontaneously; such a reaction is termed an exergonic reaction. If energy must be put into the system to make the reaction go, and ΔF is a positive number, the reaction is said to be an endergonic reaction. The F function is frequently termed the "Gibbs function," the "Gibbs free energy," or the "Lewis free energy." In some recent books, the symbol ΔG is preferred to avoid confusion with other uses of the letter F.

It is important to emphasize that a large negative value for ΔF does not automatically mean that the reaction considered will take place at a rate sufficiently rapid to be measured. This fact arises from the very nature of thermodynamic data; they only provide information about the difference in the energy content of the final and initial states of the reaction, but make no statement about the speed of the reaction. In many instances, strongly exergonic reactions may be so slow that they cannot be observed; for such reactions to proceed at a measurable rate, a suitable catalyst must be present. For example, in living systems, substances frequently meet without interacting to an appreciable extent, even though it is known from other data that the possible reaction has a large negative value for ΔF; in such instances, the appropriate catalysts may be absent or in an inactive state.

If, in a chemical reaction, the value for ΔF is a large positive number, the reaction will not proceed to a measurable extent in an isolated system even though a suitable catalyst may be present. In order to cause such endergonic reactions to proceed, work must be put into the system. Furthermore, for the forward part of a given reversible reaction, the value for ΔF will be the same, but of opposite sign, as for the back reaction; thus a knowledge of the amount of energy made available by an exergonic reaction gives information about the amount of work required to reverse it.

The use of the term "work" in relation to the ΔF of chemical reactions requires brief comment. It will be recalled that work is equal to force multiplied by displacement; for example, in the isothermal expansion of gas at constant pressure, the product of the pressure P (force per unit area) and the change in volume (ΔV) is the work done ($P \Delta V$) upon the surroundings. The pressure may be defined as the "potential" of the gas, and its magnitude (relative to a standard) is a measure of the capacity of the gas to do work by expansion. The concept of chemical work is less explicit, but here a potential ("chemical potential") is also involved. The term chemical potential may be considered to refer to the potential ability of a substance to pass from one chemical state to another state. The concept of the chemical potential was introduced by Gibbs in 1876 in his classical formulation of the thermodynamic laws governing equilibrium relationships in chemical systems.

The chemical potential of a substance A may be denoted μ_A, and is given by the expression

$$\mu_A = \mu^\circ_A + RT \ln (A) = \mu^\circ_A + RT \ln [A] f_A$$

where R is the gas constant, T is the absolute temperature, (A) is the activity of A, [A] is the molar concentration of A, and f_A is the activity coefficient of A (cf. p. 86). μ°_A is defined by the relationship $\mu_A = \mu^\circ_A$ when (A) equals unity.

For a reversible chemical reaction,

$$aA + bB \rightleftharpoons cC + dD$$

where the capital letters denote the chemical species, and the lower-case letters denote the number of moles, the free-energy change in the reaction is given by the relationship

$$\Delta F = c\mu_C + d\mu_D - a\mu_A - b\mu_B$$

Hence

$$\Delta F = c\mu^\circ_C + d\mu^\circ_D - a\mu^\circ_A - b\mu^\circ_B + RT \ln \frac{(C)^c (D)^d}{(A)^a (B)^b}$$

$$= \Delta F^\circ + RT \ln \frac{(C)^c (D)^d}{(A)^a (B)^b}$$

If the four reacting species are present at equilibrium activities, ΔF equals zero, and

$$\Delta F^\circ = -RT \ln K$$

Therefore

$$\Delta F = -RT \ln K + RT \ln \frac{(C)^c (D)^d}{(A)^a (B)^b}$$

The term K is the equilibrium constant, i.e., the ratio of the product of the activities of C and D to the product of the activities of A and B *at equilibrium*. The last term in the equation includes the reactants (A and B) and the products (C and D) at any activity values. It is a matter of convention to write the products of the reaction in the numerators of the two ratios of activities. An important special case of this equation refers to the conversion of unit activities of A and B to unit activities of C and D; under these circumstances, the last term of the equation becomes equal to zero, and $\Delta F = \Delta F°$. The symbol $\Delta F°$ ("standard free-energy" change) thus describes the maximum useful work that can be obtained upon the conversion of A and B to C and D, all four reactants being at unit activity. It does not denote the free-energy change in the transformation of unit activities of A and B to equilibrium activities of C and D. In the equation relating $\Delta F°$ to the equilibrium constant, R is the gas constant (1.987 cal per degree per mole) and T is the absolute temperature. If the equation is converted to the form in which common logarithms (to the base 10) are used in place of the natural logarithms, it becomes

$$\Delta F° = -4.575T \log K$$

The experimental determination of the equilibrium constant K of a reversible chemical reaction thus provides a measure of the standard free-energy change $\Delta F°$ for that reaction. If K is a very large number (e.g., 1000), $\Delta F°$ has a large negative value; in other words, if the reaction $A + B \rightleftharpoons C + D$ tends to go far to the right, the conversion of $A + B$ to $C + D$ is strongly exergonic. If K is a very small number (e.g., 0.0001), $\Delta F°$ has a large positive value, and the reaction will not proceed far to the right spontaneously.

It will be seen that the definition of chemical potentials, and hence of ΔF and $\Delta F°$, refers to activities rather than molar concentrations (gram molecular weight per liter) or molal concentrations (gram molecular weight per 1000 grams of solvent). As noted earlier (cf. p. 86), the activity of a substance is the concentration of the substance as judged by its chemical effects. In the application of the equation relating free-energy changes to equilibrium constants, it is necessary, therefore, to know the activity coefficients of the substances participating in the reversible reactions. These activity coefficients may be determined by measurement of the colligative properties of the substances concerned or, better still, by measurements in electric cells. For many substances of biochemical interest, however, the activity coefficients are not known, and are frequently assumed to be unity. If concentrations are used instead of activities, the apparent equilibrium constant (sometimes denoted K') will be different from the thermodynamic equilibrium constant. In the discussion of the thermodynamics of reversible biochemical reactions, it has frequently been assumed that $\Delta F°$ is approximately equal to $-RT \ln K'$.

In the above equations for ΔF and $\Delta F°$, these quantities refer to a moles of A, b moles of B, etc.; for this reason, attention must be paid to the concentration units used. If the number of moles of reactants $(a + b)$ equals the number of moles of products $(c + d)$, the measurement of K will give a value of $\Delta F°$ that is independent of the concentration units employed. On the other hand, if the molar quantities are not equal (as in the reaction $A + B \rightleftharpoons C$), the actual value of $\Delta F°$ will depend on the concentration units.

In order to compare and correlate the free-energy changes in chemical reactions, it is necessary to define standard states for the reactants and products, i.e., at which $\mu = \mu°$. By convention, it is customary to define the standard state of a pure substance as the state of the substance at a given temperature (e.g., $25°$ C) and at a pressure of 1 atmosphere. Thus, solid glucose, liquid water, and gaseous oxygen are in their standard states under these conditions. For solutions, the standard state of the solvent may be taken as that at which its activity equals unity, and the standard state of a solute as that at which its concentration is one molal.

Free-Energy Changes in Biochemical Reactions

Reversible Denaturation of Proteins. Before considering the free-energy changes in enzyme-catalyzed reactions, it may be instructive to illustrate the fundamental relationships discussed above as they apply to the reversible denaturation of proteins (p. 153). Anson and Mirsky[6] showed that the protein enzyme trypsin behaves in a manner indicating that there is an equilibrium between enzymically active native trypsin (T_n) and enzymically inactive denatured trypsin (T_d). Thus

$$T_n \rightleftharpoons T_d$$

and

$$K' = \frac{[T_d]}{[T_n]}$$

The value for K' was determined at several temperatures (Table 2), and,

Table 2.   Reversible Denaturation of Trypsin[6]

Temperature, °K	Inactivation, per cent	K'	log K'
315.1	32.8	0.488	−0.3115
317.1	50.0	1.00	0
318.1	57.4	1.35	0.1294
321.1	80.4	4.10	0.6130

[6] M. L. Anson and A. E. Mirsky, *J. Gen. Physiol.*, **17**, 393 (1934).

by use of the van't Hoff equation (p. 227), the value of ΔH° in the reversible denaturation of trypsin was found to be $+67,600$ cal over the temperature range studied. It will be seen in Table 2 that at 317.1° K $(44^\circ$ C), log $K' = 0$. Since $\Delta F^\circ = -RT \ln K'$, it follows that at 44° C the free-energy change in this reaction is zero, and $\Delta H^\circ = T \Delta S^\circ$. It is possible, therefore, to calculate ΔS°, which has a value of $+213$ entropy units per mole. This is an extremely large increase in entropy; most chemical reactions are accompanied by much smaller changes (0 to 60 entropy units). It was mentioned earlier that there is an entropy increase in passing from a highly organized arrangement to a more random arrangement. The increase in entropy which accompanies protein denaturation is thus consistent with the hypothesis that this process involves the disorganization of the complex structure of the native protein. The thermodynamic calculations given above indicate the disruption of the structure of the protein through the cleavage of the specific bonds which hold the peptide chains in a particular mutual orientation. In general, when a chemical bond in a molecule is broken, heat may be released, and, what is more important, the molecule passes from a more oriented structure (in the sense of the mutual relationship of the several groups within the molecule) to a less oriented structural assembly. To restore the original molecule, it will be necessary to do more than just restore the heat liberated (ΔH) when the bond was broken; additional work will have to be done to restore the assembly to its original state or orientation.

Free-Energy Changes in Enzyme-Catalyzed Reactions. To illustrate the application of thermodynamics to the study of enzyme-catalyzed reactions, it will be useful to consider a specific instance in which the equilibrium constant of such a reaction has been determined. Several investigators[7] have carefully studied the reaction between water and fumarate ion to form malate ion; it is catalyzed by the enzyme fumarase, which has been crystallized from swine heart (cf. p. 218). In the absence of the enzyme, the reaction does not proceed to a measurable extent at pH 7 and 25° C. As will be seen from the equation, fumarase belongs to the group of enzymes designated "hydrases" (cf. p. 216).

$$\begin{array}{ccc} {}^-\text{OOC}-\text{CH} & & \text{HO}-\text{CH}-\text{COO}^- \\ \| & + \text{H}_2\text{O} \rightleftharpoons & | \\ \text{HC}-\text{COO}^- & & \text{CH}_2-\text{COO}^- \\ \text{Fumarate}^- & & \text{Malate}^- \end{array}$$

The measurements of Scott and Powell showed that at 25° C $(298^\circ$ K) equilibrium was attained when the concentration ratio of malate to

[7] F. M. Scott and R. Powell, *J. Am. Chem. Soc.,* **70**, 1104 (1948); R. M. Bock and R. A. Alberty, *ibid.,* **75**, 1921 (1953); H. A. Krebs. *Biochem. J.,* **54**, 78 (1953).

fumarate was 4.03:1; thus, if the initial concentration of fumarate was 0.1 M, the reaction ceased when the final concentrations of fumarate and malate were 0.0199 M and 0.0801 M, respectively. The initial activity of water is set at unity by convention and does not change significantly during the reaction. If it is also assumed that the ratio of the activity coefficients of fumarate and malate is unity, the equilibrium constant is

$$K = \frac{[\text{Malate}^=]}{[\text{Fumarate}^=][\text{H}_2\text{O}]} = \frac{(0.0801)}{(0.0199)(1)} = 4.03$$

Thus

$$\Delta F°_{298} = -4.575 \times 298 \times \log 4.03 = -825 \text{ cal}$$

which is a measure of the useful work available from the conversion of fumarate and water to malate at 25° C and at unit activity. This may be written as follows:

$$\text{Fumarate}^=(1\ M) + \text{H}_2\text{O}\ (1\ M) = \text{Malate}^=\ (1\ M)$$

$$\Delta F°_{298} = -825 \text{ cal}$$

The logarithm of the equilibrium constant was found to vary linearly with the reciprocal of the absolute temperature; at 40° C the equilibrium constant is 3.1 and $\Delta F°_{313} = -700$ cal. From the variation of log K with temperature, and by use of the van't Hoff equation (cf. p. 227), Scott and Powell calculated a value of $\Delta H°$ of -3650 cal for the conversion of fumarate and water to malate at unit activity. An independent calorimetric measurement of ΔH gave a value of -3800 cal.[8]

Attention should be called to the convention of assigning to water an activity of unity in the calculation of the equilibrium constant for the reversible conversion of fumarate to malate. This applies to a reaction in pure water at a molar concentration of 55.6 M (1000/18). When the solvent is not pure water, the activity of water must be specified if it is a reactant. If for the reaction A + $\text{H}_2\text{O} \rightleftharpoons$ B + C, the molar concentration of water is less than 55.6 M (e.g., the hydrolysis of A in a glycerol-water solution), the standard free-energy change in the reaction is given by

$$\Delta F° = -4.575T \log \frac{(\text{B})(\text{C})55.6}{(\text{A})(\text{H}_2\text{O})} = -4.575T \log (55.6K)$$

In this equation, the molar concentration of water is given in the denominator of the ratio, and activities are assumed to be equal to concentrations. The value of $\Delta F°$ will be 4.575T log 55.6 more negative when this equation is used instead of $\Delta F° = -RT \ln K$; at 38° C this difference amounts to -2500 cal. Since authors are not always explicit about the convention

[8] P. Ohlmeyer, Z. physiol. Chem., **282**, 37 (1945).

employed, the student is advised to consider this point in comparing values of ΔF° cited in the biochemical literature.

Many reversible biochemical reactions involve hydrogen ions; when such reactions are conducted in a buffer solution, the hydrogen ion concentration is held constant. Thus in the reaction $A + B \rightleftharpoons C + D + H^+$, the equilibrium constant $K = (C)(D)(H^+)/(A)(B)$, and $(C)(D)/(A)(B) = K/(H^+)$. If the free-energy change for the reaction is defined $\Delta F'$ when all reactants except the hydrogen ion are in their standard states,

$$\Delta F' = -RT \ln \frac{(C)(D)}{(A)(B)} = \Delta F^\circ - 2.303RT\ \text{pH}$$

The question may next be raised of the validity of the value for ΔF° obtained by measurement of an equilibrium constant in an enzyme-catalyzed reaction. How can one be certain that the enzyme employed led to the establishment of a thermodynamic equilibrium? One would have more confidence in the value of ΔF° obtained if it could be confirmed by independent means. In fact, the very nature of thermodynamic data permits such confirmation. It will be recalled that the free-energy data refer only to the difference in the energy between the final and the initial states, and it does not matter by what route, or how rapidly, one proceeds from one state to the other. Thus, if there were a way to determine the standard free energy of formation of fumarate, water, and malate from their respective elements, the standard free-energy change in the over-all reaction would be given by the difference between the standard free energy of formation of the final product and the standard free energy of formation of the initial reactants, i.e.,

$$\Delta F^\circ = \Delta F^\circ_f \text{(malate}^=) - \Delta F^\circ_f \text{(fumarate}^=) - \Delta F^\circ_f \text{(H}_2\text{O)}$$

Data on the standard free energy of formation (ΔF°_f) of a large variety of chemical substances have been obtained by determination of ΔH°_f (standard heat of formation) and by experimental measurement of heat capacities as a function of temperature. The latter gives ΔS° (cf. Rossini[2] or Klotz[1]), and ΔF°_f may be calculated by means of the relationship

$$\Delta F^\circ_f = \Delta H^\circ_f - T\,\Delta S^\circ$$

In this manner, one may calculate for the standard free energy of formation of solid glycine (at 25° C and 1 atmosphere)

$$2C(s) + 2.5H_2(g) + O_2(g) + 0.5N_2(g) = C_2H_5O_2N(s)$$

$$\Delta F^\circ_f = -88{,}920 \text{ cal per mole}$$

Values for the standard free energy of formation of other substances of biochemical interest are given in Table 3. Such values may be used for

Table 3. Standard Free Energy of Formation of Some Substances of Biochemical Interest

(Temperature 25° C, 1 atmosphere)

$-\Delta F°_f$, kcal per mole

Substance	Gas	Liquid	Solid	1 Molal Solution (aq.)	Cation (aq.)	Anion (aq.)
Acetic acid	91.2	94.5		96.2		89.7
L-Alanine			88.8	89.1	92.3	75.9
Ammonia	3.9			6.3	19.0	
L-Aspartic acid			175.4	172.9	175.5	155.0†
Carbon dioxide	94.5					
Carbonic acid				148.8		126.4†
L-Cysteine			82.5	81.6	84.0	70.3
L-Cystine			166.6	162.1	166.3‡	137.2
Ethanol	38.7	40.2		41.9		
Fumaric acid			156.7	154.8		144.6
D-Glucose			215.8	217.0		
D-Glutamic acid			174.8	172.5	175.4	154.0†
Glycine			88.9	89.6	92.7	76.4
Hippuric acid			90.4	88.1		82.9
Hydrogen ion				0		
Hydrogen peroxide		28.2				
Hydroxyl ion				37.6		
L-Leucine			83.8	82.8	86.0	69.7
L-Malic acid			211.5	213.6		201.9†
Palmitic acid		78.6	80.0			
Phosphoric acid				270.0		257.3†
Succinic acid			178.8	178.5		165.1†
Sucrose			371.6			
L-Tyrosine			97.6	94.1	97.1	81.6
Urea			47.4	49.0		
Water	54.6	56.7				

† Divalent anion.
‡ Divalent cation.

the calculation of the standard free-energy change at 25° C in the combustion of glucose (cf. p. 226) as follows:

$$C_6H_{12}O_6(s) \rightarrow 6C(s) + 6H_2(g) + 3O_2(g); \Delta F°_1 = +215.8 \text{ kcal}$$

$$6C(s) + 6O_2(g) \rightarrow 6CO_2(g); \Delta F°_2 = 6 \times -94.45 = -566.7 \text{ kcal}$$

$$6H_2(g) + 3O_2(g) \rightarrow 6H_2O(l); \Delta F°_3 = 6 \times -56.7 = -340.2 \text{ kcal}$$

$$\Delta F° \text{ (reaction)} = \Delta F°_1 + \Delta F°_2 + \Delta F°_3 = -691.1 \text{ kcal}$$

The precision of the data given in Table 3 is variable, and some of the $\Delta F°$ values may require revision when better measurements are possible.

A critical discussion of the available free-energy data for several substances of biochemical interest has been presented by Burton and Krebs.[9]

In dealing with reactions that involve ionized organic substances, one must add to the value for the $\Delta F°_f$ of the undissociated solid compound the ΔF for the transfer of the solid compound to a solution at unit activity and the $\Delta F°$ of ionization. For example, in the calculation of $\Delta F°$ for the reaction (at 38° C)[10]

$$C_6H_5COO^- \ (1 \ M) + \ ^+NH_3CH_2COO^- \ (1 \ M) \rightarrow$$
$$C_6H_5CONHCH_2COO^- \ (1 \ M) + H_2O \ (l)$$

the $\Delta F°_f$ of the benzoate ion at unit activity may be calculated from that of solid benzoic acid as follows. The solubility of benzoic acid at 38° is 0.0426 moles per 1000 grams of H_2O and its pK' is 4.20. In transferring benzoic acid from the solid state to a saturated solution, $\Delta F = 0$, since this system is at equilibrium. If it is assumed that activity equals concentration, the molal concentration of C_6H_5COOH in the saturated solution may be calculated to be 0.0409. The ΔF for the transfer of benzoic acid from a saturated solution to a hypothetical 1 molal solution is given by the equation $\Delta F = -RT \ln 0.0409 = 1980$ cal per mole. The free-energy change in the process $C_6H_5COOH \ (1 \ M) \rightarrow C_6H_5COO^-$ $(1 \ M) + H^+ \ (1 \ M)$ is given by the equation $\Delta F° = -RT \ln K' = 2.3RT \ pK' = 5990$ cal per mole. The $\Delta F°$ of formation of solid benzoic acid at 38° C is $-57{,}600$ cal per mole; therefore, for the process

$$7C(s) + 3H_2(g) + O_2(g) \rightarrow C_6H_5COO^- \ (1 \ M) + H^+ \ (1 \ M)$$

the standard free-energy change is

$$\Delta F° = -57{,}600 + 1980 + 5990 = -49{,}630 \text{ cal per mole}$$

In like manner, the $\Delta F°$ of formation of hippurate $(1 \ M) + H^+ \ (1 \ M)$ is calculated to be $-78{,}470$ cal per mole at 38° C. The $\Delta F°_f$ values for the dipolar glycine ion $(1 \ M)$ and for H_2O (l) are $-87{,}685$ and $-56{,}180$ respectively. Hence, for the over-all reaction in the synthesis of hippurate ion (the H^+ cancels out),

$$\Delta F°_{311} = -78{,}470 - 56{,}180 - (-49{,}630) - (-87{,}685)$$
$$= +2665 \text{ cal per mole}$$

Each of the $\Delta F°_f$ values is subject to some uncertainty (about 300 cal), and the use of $\Delta F°_f$ values to calculate the standard free-energy change for a reaction is not as reliable as direct measurement of the equilibrium constant. Also, because of the experimental difficulties involved, there are many substances of biochemical interest for which

[9] K. Burton and H. A. Krebs, *Biochem. J.*, **54**, 94 (1953).
[10] H. Borsook and J. W. Dubnoff, *J. Biol. Chem.*, **132**, 307 (1940).

values of $\Delta S°$ are unavailable; for this reason, several of the values for $\Delta F°_f$ given in Table 2 have been calculated from the results of equilibrium studies. This is the case for the free energy of formation of malic acid, and it has not been possible to make an independent calculation of the free-energy change in the fumarase-catalyzed reaction (cf. p. 235) to check the value obtained from equilibrium data. The best that can be said at present is that it is reasonably certain that the position of the equilibrium in the conversion of fumarate to malate is not affected by the enzyme preparation. The enzyme, in acting as a perfect catalyst, merely hastens the attainment of equilibrium.

Coupled Reactions

In complex biochemical systems, enzyme-catalyzed reactions usually do not proceed alone; frequently the product of one reaction is a reactant in another chemical process, and is thus removed from the equilibrium in the first reaction. To illustrate this, one may consider the process Malate= $\rightarrow$ Fumarate= $+$ H_2O. This is the reversal of the reaction for which a $\Delta F°_{298}$ of -825 cal was found; therefore, in order to convert malate to fumarate and water (all at unit activity), work would have to be put into the system to the extent of $+825$ cal. Under the particular conditions employed by Scott and Powell,[7] the same equilibrium would be attained; i.e., 20 per cent of the malate would have been converted to the products. However, if one now introduces into the system a catalyst that causes removal of fumarate in a reaction with a large negative $\Delta F°$ value, the effective concentration of fumarate would be decreased, and this would tend to drive the reaction to the right until nearly all the malate had disappeared. By disturbing the equilibrium of the fumarase-catalyzed reaction in this way, an exergonic process has been "coupled" to an endergonic one, and work has thus been put into the system. This may be visualized more clearly by considering the relationship

$$\Delta F = \Delta F° + RT \ln \frac{(C)^c(D)^d}{(A)^a(B)^b}$$

In the present instance,

$$\Delta F = +825 + 4.575 \times 298 \times \log \frac{(\text{fumarate}^=)(H_2O)}{(\text{malate}^=)}$$

It follows that any factor that will tend to make the ratio of the activities a smaller number (as by removal of the fumarate) will tend to make the last term in the equation more negative. When the ratio is less than 0.25, the sum of the two terms on the right-hand side of the equation will be a negative number, and the fumarase-catalyzed reaction will lead to the disappearance of more than 20 per cent of the initial malate.

An exergonic process which may be coupled to the endergonic conversion of malate to fumarate is the reaction between fumarate and ammonium ion to form aspartate. This reaction is specifically catalyzed

$$\begin{array}{cc} ^{-}OOC-CH & CH_2COO^- \\ \parallel \qquad + NH_4^+ \;\rightleftharpoons\; & \overset{+}{\underset{|}{}} \;| \\ HC-COO^- & H_3N-CH-COO^- \\ \text{Fumarate}^- & \text{Aspartate}^{\pm} \end{array}$$

by the enzyme aspartase, present in extracts of *Escherichia coli*, and the equilibrium constant (pH 7.4, 37° C) has been reported to be 417.[11] From this value it may be calculated that the free-energy change in the conversion of fumarate and ammonium ion to aspartate (all at unit activity) is $\Delta F^{\circ}_{310} = -3720$ cal. At 37° C, the ΔF°_{310} for the conversion of malate to fumarate and water is $+700$ cal. Therefore, in the coupled reaction, catalyzed by fumarase plus aspartase,

$$\text{Malate}^= + NH_4^+ \rightarrow \text{Aspartate}^{\overset{+}{=}} + H_2O$$
$$\Delta F^{\circ}_{310} = -3720 + (+700) = -3020 \text{ cal}$$

It may be left as an exercise to calculate the equilibrium concentration of malate when the initial activity of this substance is 0.1 M, and that of the ammonium ion is relatively high (activity 1 M). Such a calculation will show that approximately 99 per cent of the initial malate will have been converted to aspartate in the coupled reaction via fumarate.

There will be further occasion to refer to such coupled enzyme-catalyzed reactions in later sections of this book, and especially in Chapter 15. At this point it may be sufficient to emphasize that, in discussions of enzyme-catalyzed reactions in living cells, it cannot be assumed that each individual reaction proceeds in a homogeneous system until it attains thermodynamic equilibrium. Instead, in living systems few if any of the chemical reactions are at such equilibrium positions; one may go further and say that such thermodynamic equilibria are incompatible with life. For example, the process of the conversion of a protein to the constituent amino acids is an exergonic reaction; the maintenance of the integrity of the living cell requires, therefore, that this tendency for protein degradation be counteracted. The living cell achieves this by constantly supplying energy in a suitable form by means of other chemical processes, and, what is especially important, it does this at a rate sufficient to counteract the tendency to attain thermodynamic equilibrium. This chemical work can be made available in a variety of ways; as will be seen later, the breakdown of carbohydrates

[11] J. H. Quastel and B. Woolf, *Biochem. J.*, **20**, 545 (1926); H. Borsook and H. M. Huffman, *J. Biol. Chem.*, **99**, 663 (1933).

and of fats represents the most important of the exergonic reactions used by living systems to provide energy for endergonic processes such as the synthesis of proteins from amino acids. A little reflection will show, however, that other processes also may play important roles in providing energy. A living organism is not a homogeneous system but a polyphase system; it follows that the mechanical removal (e.g., by the circulatory system) of a product of an endergonic process will be a way of putting energy into the system and of making the endergonic reaction proceed to a large extent. Furthermore, each cell is itself a polyphase system with distinct cytological differentiation (nucleus, cytoplasm, mitochondria, etc.).

It cannot be emphasized too strongly that thermodynamic considerations should be applied to living systems with an appreciation of the fact that such systems, even when their chemical composition does not change, are not in a state of thermodynamic equilibrium, but in a "steady state," in which the rates of chemical synthesis and of breakdown are balanced. It is essential, however, for the biochemist to know the individual chemical reactions that proceed in a given biological system, and the free-energy changes associated with them; otherwise it would not be possible to assess the magnitude of the energy required to maintain the components of such reactions in a ratio compatible with life. Unfortunately, the accurate estimation of the free-energy changes in biochemical reactions is a matter of considerable difficulty. In this chapter, mention has been made of two experimental methods for the determination of $\Delta F°$ for a reversible chemical reaction in a homogeneous system at constant temperature and pressure. These methods involve (1) determination of the equilibrium constant, and (2) determination of ΔH and of ΔS by thermal measurements. In Chapter 11 it will be shown that for oxidation-reduction reactions $\Delta F°$ may be calculated from the "normal oxidation-reduction potentials." All these methods are attended by experimental difficulties which biochemists frequently attempt to circumvent by means of simplifying assumptions; for example, it is usually assumed that the concentrations of the reactants and of the reaction products are equal to their respective activities. Also, since determinations of the equilibrium constant (K) are subject to considerable error when the reaction proceeds very far (ca. **99** per cent) in one direction, it has proved advantageous, with reactions of this type, to use isotopic methods, which increase the accuracy of the determination of K. Where a determination of the equilibrium constant is not possible, and ΔH values are available, the latter have occasionally been used for an estimation of $\Delta F°$, even without experimental data on ΔS; here the value of ΔS is assumed to be zero, or some small number.

Because of these uncertainties, most of the $\Delta F°$ values in the biochemical literature must be considered approximations, subject to correction when the results of more accurate experimental studies become available. In reading the chapters to follow, the student is urged to remember the tentative nature of the free-energy data that are given; it is unlikely that more than a few of the figures for the $\Delta F°$ of biochemical reactions have a precision greater than ± 10 per cent.

The assumptions that attend the calculation of the magnitude of free-energy changes in biochemical reactions *in vivo* are even of a more serious character. The fact that biological systems are heterogeneous, polyphase systems has already been mentioned. Moreover, the concentrations (assumed to equal activities) of the reactants and reaction products in a given process are very different from 1 molal, and these concentrations must be determined by analytical methods of varying accuracy applied to complex biological materials (e.g., tissue slices, bacterial extracts). These difficulties are overshadowed, however, by the fact that the chemical constituents of a living organism are in a dynamic state. Under such conditions, the concentration ratio of the reaction products to the reactants in a biochemical process will obviously be determined by the rates at which the reactants are brought together and at which the products are removed. It follows, therefore, that, although the value of $\Delta F°$ for a given biochemical reaction is independent of the rate at which the process is effected, the chemical work that may be derived from that reaction in a particular biological system is determined by kinetic factors operating in the steady-state system.[12] Although little is known about the rates of enzyme-catalyzed chemical reactions *in vivo*, much has been learned about the kinetics of such reactions in homogeneous systems. This aspect of enzyme chemistry will be considered in the next chapter.

Because of the importance to biology of the concept of the steady state, it may be useful to contrast briefly the properties of a steady-state system with those of a system at thermodynamic equilibrium. A steady state is reached in a system if energy or matter and energy flow into the system at a rate equal to that at which energy or matter and energy flow out of the system. Thus, if heat is supplied at a constant rate at one end of a piece of metal, and removed at the same rate from the other end, the temperature at any point of the metal will tend to maintain a constant value. Such a system has been termed an "open system," in contrast to the "closed system" defined for thermodynamic equilibrium, where there is no net flow of matter or energy. The steady state may be the resultant of both reversible processes and irreversible processes, whereas thermodynamic equilibrium refers to reversible processes only.

---

[12] J. Z. Hearon, *Federation Proc.,* **10,** 602 (1951).

In a sense, therefore, thermodynamic equilibrium is a special instance of the more general phenomenon of the steady state.

At thermodynamic equilibrium, a closed system cannot do useful work without internal change (cf. p. 230). However, a steady-state system is capable of doing work on its surroundings or on the components of the system. Furthermore, thermodynamic equilibrium is unstable in the sense that it is shifted to a different state by a single addition of energy to the system, whereas the steady state has stability, and is rapidly re-established (the property of "equifinality"). Of special importance is the fact that the concentrations of the reactants at thermodynamic equilibrium are independent of the concentrations of substances that catalyze the reaction (cf. p. 211), whereas the stationary concentrations of the reactants in a steady-state system are determined by the catalyst concentration. Clearly, a biological system that is apparently constant in chemical composition approximates more closely a steady-state system than one at thermodynamic equilibrium. Matter and energy are continuously taken into the biological system and removed from it. The chemical composition of a biological system is determined by the rates of uptake and release of matter and energy, as well as by the rates of the transformation and translocation of matter and energy within the system. These rates are influenced by the concentration of enzymic catalysts, by agents which determine the catalytic activity of the component enzymes, by variations in irreversible diffusion processes, and by other factors. Within the biological steady-state system, there are gradients of matter and of energy, and the system can do work to maintain such gradients. Energy can be expended (e.g., muscular movement) or received (e.g., absorption of light energy) by the system, and a change in the steady state ensues; when the intake or output of energy ceases, the biological system returns to its former condition.

Because of the complexity of biological systems, the application of the thermodynamic theory developed to describe steady-state systems[13] is difficult, and has been undertaken in only a few special instances. As will be seen later, however, several metabolic mechanisms, such as electron transfer from metabolites to oxygen (Chapter 14), have been studied experimentally as steady-state systems in the living cell.

[13] K. G. Denbigh, *The Thermodynamics of the Steady State,* Methuen and Co., London, 1951.

Kinetics
of Enzyme Action

In 1850, from his studies of the rate of hydrolysis of sucrose by acids, Wilhelmy showed that the rate of a chemical reaction in which one molecular species disappears is proportional at each instant to the amount of that species. This relationship may be expressed mathematically as $-dC/dt = kC$, where C is the concentration of substance undergoing change, t is the time, and k is a proportionality constant. This equation, usually designated as one of "first order," also describes other processes in which the amount of a single component is changing with time, for example, the decay of a radioactive element. The differential term $-dC/dt$ denotes the velocity of the reaction; the change of velocity with increasing time is represented graphically in Fig. 1.

To study the rate of a first-order chemical reaction, one determines the amount of a substance S that has undergone change at increasing intervals of time. If the chemical reaction goes nearly to completion, i.e., if the equilibrium constant is a large number, then one may integrate the differential equation given above between the limits of the concentration C at time $t = 0$ (let this concentration be equal to a) and of the concentration of S at time t [let this concentration be equal to $(a - x)$]. The quantity x is therefore the amount of S that has undergone reaction in time t, and the differential equation may be rewritten $dx/dt = k(a - x)$. Integration between limits gives

$$k = \frac{1}{t} \ln \frac{a}{a - x} = \frac{2.303}{t} \log \frac{a}{a - x}$$

The last equation permits one to calculate, from the measurement of the values for x at various time intervals, the value of the "first-order" velocity constant k. If the reaction is truly first order in nature, the separate values of k obtained in this manner should be the same, within the precision of the experimental measurements.

Since $a/(a - x)$ is a ratio of concentrations, this quotient will be independent of the units employed to express these concentrations, provided the same units are used for the numerator and denominator. In other words, one may resort to quantities such as moles per liter, milliliters of a volumetric reagent, the partial pressure of a gas, the degrees of optical rotation, or per cent conversion. Also, since the logarithm of the ratio $a/(a - x)$ is a pure number, the velocity constant k is expressed in reciprocal time units; if t is given in minutes, then k is given in terms

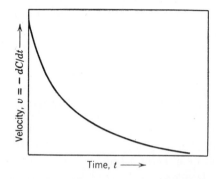

Fig. 1. Change in velocity of a first-order reaction as a function of time.

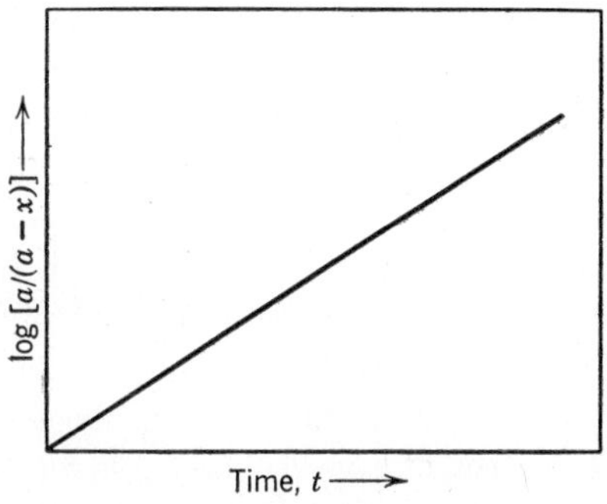

Fig. 2. Plot of log $[a/(a - x)]$ against t for a first-order reaction.

of min^{-1}. Another important consequence of the first-order equation emerges from the calculation of the time required to transform one-half of a; at this time $(t_{1/2})$, $x = a/2$. Substitution of this value of x in the integrated form of the first-order equation gives

$$t_{1/2} = \frac{\ln 2}{k} = \frac{2.303 \log 2}{k} = \frac{0.693}{k}$$

Therefore the time required for the transformation of 50 per cent of S is independent of the initial concentration; in a first-order reaction, the time required to reduce the concentration of S from 1 M to 0.5 M is the same as that required to reduce the concentration from 0.0001 M to 0.00005 M.

It will be seen from the integrated first-order equation that a plot of log $a/(a - x)$ against t gives a straight line with a slope of $k/2.303$ (Fig. 2). This is a simple way to test whether a set of rate measurements accords with first-order kinetics, and it allows a graphic estimation of k.

Later in this chapter it will be shown that, depending on the substrate concentration, the kinetics of an enzyme-catalyzed reaction may be described by the first-order rate equation, or the rate may be independent of substrate concentration. In the latter situation, "zero-order" kinetics is said to apply. If we use the same symbols as before, the differential equation for a zero-order reaction is $dx/dt = k$, which upon integration gives $k = x/t$.

When a catalyst, such as an enzyme, is present, the rate of a reaction depends on the enzyme concentration. If the enzyme is stable during the period of measurement of the reaction rate, its concentration, (E), becomes part of the proportionality constant in the first-order equation $-dC/dt = [k(E)]C$ or in the zero-order equation $-dC/dt = k(E)$. It will be obvious that, when the concentration of the enzyme is doubled, the rate should also be doubled; in general, therefore, the rate of an enzyme-catalyzed reaction is proportional to the enzyme concentration. This has been shown to be true in a large number of studies in which the conditions of temperature and pH were chosen carefully to avoid side reactions that might cause the inactivation of the enzyme during the reaction.

Such proportionality, once established, is useful for the assay of the activity of enzyme preparations obtained in the course of the purification of an enzyme from a tissue extract. It is customary to define arbitrarily a convenient "unit" of enzyme activity, i.e., an amount of enzyme that will cause a given extent of reaction in a given time under carefully specified experimental conditions. Occasionally, when the substrate concentration must be kept low, and first-order kinetics applies (cf. p. 244), one may define a unit of the enzyme as that amount which, under the specified experimental conditions, will cause the first-order constant to have an arbitrarily selected numerical value. However, it is preferable to select an initial substrate concentration that is high enough to give zero-order kinetics (cf. p. 245), and to determine the initial rate of reaction (e.g., the amount of S converted per minute during the first 10 min). This procedure has the additional advantage of minimizing the effect of any inactivation of the enzyme; also, during this initial period, the products of the reaction, which may cause a slowing of the rate, are at a low concentration relative to that of the substrate. An example is provided by the data given in Table 1 for the hydrolysis of urea in the presence of urease according to the reaction:

$$CO(NH_2)_2 + H_2O \rightarrow CO_2 + 2NH_3$$

It will be noted from Table 1 that, under the specified conditions, the initial rate of urea hydrolysis was constant, and the substrate was decomposed at a rate of 1.42 micromoles of urea per milliliter per minute. If one defines a unit of urease activity as the amount of enzyme giving a rate of 10 micromoles of urea per milliliter per minute, the reaction mixture contained 0.142 urease unit per milliliter.

In order to express the "purity" (or, better, "specific activity") of a given enzyme preparation, one may give the units of enzyme per milligram of protein (or of protein N) present in the preparation. Calculation from the data in Table 1 will show that the enzyme preparation contained

76.3 urease units per gram. One of the criteria for the homogeneity of enzyme proteins, in the course of their purification, is the attainment of a maximal value for the number of enzyme units per milligram of protein nitrogen, and the fact that this value does not increase on further recrystallization or other means of protein fractionation.

Table I. Enzymic Hydrolysis of Urea

Initial concentration of urea, 200 μmoles per ml†
Temperature 30°; pH 7.4
Urease concentration, 1.86 mg per ml

Time, min	Amount of Urea Decomposed, μmoles per ml	Hydrolysis, per cent
5	7.3	3.6
10	14.2	7.1
15	21.8	10.9
25	35.2	17.6

† 1 μmole = 1 $\times$ 10^{-3} millimole = 1 $\times$ 10^{-6} mole.

Although many enzyme-catalyzed reactions proceed at rates that accord with the first-order equation, these reactions usually involve the participation of more than one molecular species. For example, an examination of the urease-catalyzed reaction shows that it is a process in which two molecular species, i.e., urea and water, participate; however, the concentration of the water does not change to an appreciable extent and may be considered constant. Therefore, although two reactants are involved in the reaction, the concentration of only one of them is undergoing change. Such reactions are frequently termed "pseudomonomolecular" reactions (or "quasi-unimolecular" reactions).

Where two reactants both undergo change in concentration in the course of their mutual interaction, as in the reaction A + B → products,

$$\frac{-dC_A}{dt} = \frac{-dC_B}{dt} = kC_A C_B$$

If the initial concentration (a) of each of the reactants is the same, and x is the amount of A or B converted after time t, the velocity of the resulting bimolecular reaction is given by the equation

$$\frac{dx}{dt} = k(a - x)^2$$

The integrated form of this second-order equation is

$$k = \frac{1}{t} \times \frac{x}{a(a - x)}$$

If the initial concentrations of the two reactants are a and b respectively, then the rate is given by the equation

$$\frac{dx}{dt} = k(a - x)(b - x)$$

and the integrated form is

$$k = \frac{1}{t(a - b)} \ln \frac{b(a - x)}{a(b - x)}$$

An equation of this type was first deduced by Berthelot in 1862 from his studies of the rate of the bimolecular reaction between ethyl alcohol and acetic acid. The velocity constant of a reaction of the second order has the dimensions of the reciprocal of the product of concentration and time, e.g., liters per mole and per minute (M^{-1} min^{-1}). In a second-order reaction in which $a = b$, $t_{1/2} = 1/ka$, the half-time being inversely proportional to the initial concentration of the reactants. It is thus possible to differentiate simply between the kinetics of a first- and a second-order reaction by examination of the effect of change in the initial concentration on the half-time. In the study of enzyme-catalyzed bimolecular reactions, it is frequently the practice to study the rate of change in the concentration of only one reactant under conditions where the concentration of the other reactant is so large that it may be considered to remain constant during the reaction. This applies not only to the "pseudo-monomolecular" hydrolytic reactions, but to experiments with other enzyme-catalyzed reactions as well (cf. p. 256).

It will be recalled that nearly all types of enzymic reactions are reversible (cf. p. 215). In the form given above, the equations for the rates of first- and second-order reactions refer to situations in which the equilibrium is very far to the right; i.e., the reactions proceed nearly to completion. There are numerous enzyme-catalyzed reactions, however, in which the free-energy change is small; here the equilibrium is characterized by the presence of appreciable concentrations of initial reactants as well as of final products. For example, consider a simple case in which the equilibrium may be described as follows:

$$A \underset{k_2}{\overset{k_1}{\rightleftharpoons}} B$$

where k_1 is the first-order rate constant for the conversion of A to B, and k_2 is the first-order rate constant for the reverse process, the conversion of B to A. If, at the start of the reaction the concentration of A is equal to a and no B is present, then after time t the concentration of A will be $(a - x)$ and that of B will be x. The rate of conversion of A will then be given by the equation

$$\frac{dx}{dt} = k_1(a - x) - k_2 x$$

When the system reaches equilibrium, $dx/dt = 0$, and, if the amount of A converted to B at equilibrium be designated x_e,

$$k_1(a - x_e) = k_2 x_e$$

Substitution for k_2 in the differential equation, followed by integration, gives the equation

$$\frac{k_1 a}{x_e} = \frac{1}{t} \ln \frac{x_e}{x_e - x}$$

However, since $k_1 a/x_e = k_1 + k_2$, one may write the equation

$$k_1 + k_2 = k = \frac{1}{t} \ln \frac{x_e}{x_e - x}$$

It will be evident that a reversible first-order reaction may consequently be treated as if it went nearly to completion, providing the initial concentration (a) is replaced in the first-order equation by the amount of A converted at equilibrium.

The importance of the precise study of the kinetics of enzyme reactions cannot be exaggerated. Measurements of rates are the principal means for the description of such reactions, and thus provide the principal tool in the discovery, purification, and characterization of enzymes. Furthermore, the quantitative study of the kinetics of enzyme action has led to important conclusions about the manner in which enzymes act as catalysts in biochemical reactions. Of particular significance have been studies of the kinetics of enzyme-catalyzed reactions as a function of the initial substrate concentration and of the temperature.

Effect of Substrate Concentration on Rate of Enzyme Action

When the enzyme concentration is kept at a constant value and the initial substrate concentration is varied between wide limits, in a reaction in which one component is undergoing change, the variation in initial reaction velocity $(-d(S)/dt$, expressed as the amount of substrate converted per unit of time) may be described by means of the curve in Fig. 3. It will be seen that the curve at first rises linearly, then slopes off, and finally reaches a constant maximum value. Occasionally, a diminution in velocity may be caused by further increase in the substrate concentration. It will be noted from the graph that, at low substrate concentrations, the first-order equation $-d(S)/dt = k(E)(S)$ applies, and that the initial velocity is directly proportional to the initial substrate concentration (S). However, as the substrate concentration is increased, a maximal reaction velocity is attained that is independent of substrate concentration. Here the relationship $-d(S)/dt = k(E)$ applies; this is the differential equation of a zero-order reaction. The "diphasic" character of the substrate dependence curve of enzyme action was first studied independently by V. Henri and A. J. Brown in 1902; these investigators examined the action of invertase on sucrose, which because of its great solubility in water is especially suitable for experiments of this nature. Henri explained the diphasic character of the curve by the assumption that the enzyme and substrate combine with each other to

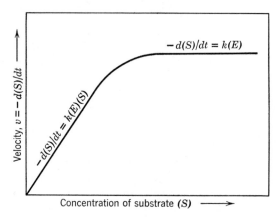

Fig. 3. Effect of increasing substrate concentration on the velocity of an enzyme-catalyzed reaction.

form an enzyme-substrate compound and that the substrate undergoes reaction only after it has combined with the enzyme. This may be written as follows:

Sucrose + invertase → Sucrose-invertase →

Glucose + fructose + invertase

From this assumption it follows that, at low substrate concentrations, some of the enzyme molecules are not combined with the substrate at any given moment, and the incomplete saturation of the enzyme is the cause of the failure of the enzyme to show its maximal catalytic activity. When this maximal activity is attained, all the enzyme molecules are combined with substrate, and a further increase in substrate concentration is without effect on the rate since the enzyme is now completely saturated. An excellent discussion of this concept may be found in the article by Van Slyke.[1]

The theory thus assumes that the enzyme E combines with the substrate S to form a compound ES by a reversible reaction

$$E + S \underset{k_2}{\overset{k_1}{\rightleftharpoons}} ES$$

where k_1 is the rate constant for the formation of ES, and k_2 is the rate

[1] D. D. Van Slyke, *Advances in Enzymol.*, **2**, 33 (1942).

constant for the dissociation of ES to E and S. After combination with the enzyme to form ES, S is converted into the products of the over-all reaction, thus making E available for further combination with more S. The rate of the conversion of ES to the products of the reaction may be indicated by the constant k_3, and the complete process involves a step-wise series of reactions:

$$E + S \underset{k_2}{\overset{k_1}{\rightleftharpoons}} ES \overset{k_3}{\longrightarrow} \text{Products} + E$$

Although the theory of the enzyme-substrate compound in enzymic catalysis has long been in the literature, direct experimental evidence for the existence of such compounds has been difficult to obtain. In 1943, however, Chance described an ingenious new method for the study of rapid enzymic reactions and applied it to measurements of the rate of combination of peroxidase with H_2O_2.[2] This reaction leads to a marked change in the absorption spectrum of the heme protein, and it is therefore possible to demonstrate spectroscopically the existence of the peroxidase-H_2O_2 compound in the solution. There will be further occasion in Chapter 14 to discuss Chance's data in connection with the properties of the heme-containing enzymes; for the present it suffices to cite the above result as one of the most convincing demonstrations of the reality of the enzyme-substrate compound postulated by Henri from the study of the substrate dependence curve of invertase action.

The first satisfactory mathematical analysis of the effect of substrate concentration on the reaction velocity of enzyme-catalyzed reactions was made in 1913 by Michaelis and Menten.[3] Because of the important place their contribution has come to occupy in biochemistry, it is necessary to discuss in some detail the derivation of the equation which they proposed to describe the diphasic character of the substrate dependence curve.

Michaelis and Menten assumed, as did Henri, that the enzyme combines with the substrate, and that the rate of decomposition of the substrate is proportional to the concentration of the intermediate enzyme-substrate complex. In the derivation of their equation, the following symbols will be used:

(E) = total concentration of enzyme E (e.g., invertase)

(S) = total concentration of substrate S (e.g., sucrose), so chosen that (S) is much greater than (E)

(ES) = concentration of enzyme-substrate complex

$(E) - (ES)$ = concentration of free enzyme

[2] B. Chance, *J. Biol. Chem.*, **151**, 553 (1943); *Advances in Enzymol.*, **12**, 153 (1954).

[3] L. Michaelis and M. L. Menten, *Biochem. Z.*, **49**, 333 (1913).

If one assumes that the reaction $E + S \rightleftharpoons ES$ is a reversible process, then one can write for the dissociation constant of ES, defined as K_m,

$$K_m = \frac{[(E) - (ES)](S)}{(ES)}$$

On rearranging the equation so as to solve for (ES),

$$(ES) = \frac{(E)(S)}{K_m + (S)}$$

If the velocity constant for the decomposition of ES is k_3, and the measured velocity is v, then $v = k_3(ES)$, and

$$v = \frac{k_3(E)(S)}{K_m + (S)}$$

The maximal velocity V will be attained when the concentration of ES is maximal, i.e., when all of the enzyme is bound by the substrate, and $(ES) = (E)$. Under these circumstances,

$$V = k_3(ES) = k_3(E)$$

If V is substituted for $k_3(E)$, the Michaelis-Menten equation is obtained.

$$v = \frac{V(S)}{K_m + (S)} \qquad \text{or} \qquad K_m = (S)\left[\frac{V}{v} - 1\right]$$

Since K_m and V are constants, the equation is that of a rectangular hyperbola, which is the form of the diphasic curve found experimentally. When V/v equals 2, i.e., when the measured velocity v is one-half the value of the limiting velocity V, then K_m equals (S). Thus the substrate concentration required for the attainment of half-maximal velocity is a characteristic constant of an enzyme-catalyzed reaction. The constant K_m is termed the Michaelis constant; sometimes it is denoted by the symbol K_s, employed by Michaelis and Menten.[3]

If one plots $-\log(S)$ against v/V, a sigmoid curve is obtained with an inflection point at $v/V = \frac{1}{2}$, and this point corresponds to a value of $-\log(S)$ from which K_m may be calculated (cf. Fig. 4). In this manner Michaelis and Menten found a value of 0.0167 for the invertase preparation they used. The Michaelis constants of a great many enzymes have been determined and have been found to vary from values as low as 1×10^{-8} to values as high as 1.

The method described above for the determination of K_m is somewhat cumbersome, and simpler procedures have been devised.[4] If one takes the reciprocal of the Michaelis-Menten equation, the following equation is obtained:

$$\frac{1}{v} = \frac{K_m + (S)}{V(S)} = \frac{K_m}{V}\left[\frac{1}{(S)}\right] + \frac{1}{V}$$

[4] H. Lineweaver and D. Burk, *J. Am. Chem. Soc.*, **56**, 658 (1934); B. H. J. Hofstee, *Science*, **116**, 329 (1952); G. S. Eadie, *ibid.*, **116**, 688 (1952).

This is known as the Lineweaver-Burk equation, and its great advantage becomes evident if one plots $1/v$ against $1/(S)$, as in Fig. 5. Since the equation is linear in form, there results a straight line with its intercept on the ordinate at $1/V$. The slope of the line is K_m/V, and, since V can be determined from the intercept, K_m may also be calculated. It will be

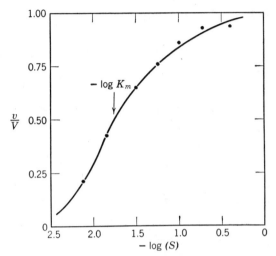

Fig. 4. Plot of v/V against $-\log (S)$ for invertase. (Data of Michaelis and Menten.[3])

noted from Fig. 5 that the straight line intersects the abscissa at a value of $1/(S)$ equal to $-1/K_m$. Another graphical procedure for the calculation of K_m and of V from experimental data on v as a function of (S) involves the multiplication of both sides of the Lineweaver-Burk equation by (S) to give

$$\frac{(S)}{v} = \frac{K_m}{V} + \frac{(S)}{V}$$

If $(S)/v$ is plotted against (S) (cf. Fig. 6), a straight line results; the slope is $1/V$ and the intercept K_m/V. The line intersects the abscissa at a value of (S) equal to $-K_m$. In a third method of linear plotting (proposed by Eadie), the Michaelis-Menten equation has the form

$$v = V - K_m \frac{v}{(S)}$$

If v is plotted against $v/(S)$, the resulting straight line (slope $-K_m$) has an intercept on the ordinate at V and on the abscissa at V/K_m (cf. Fig. 7). For most purposes, the two latter methods are more satisfactory for the determination of V and of K_m.

Although the Michaelis-Menten equation and its various modifications have been of the greatest value in the study of the kinetics of enzyme-catalyzed reactions, the reader must be reminded of the assumption that the experimentally determined value for K_m represents the dissociation constant of ES. Briggs and Haldane[5] pointed out that this assumption is

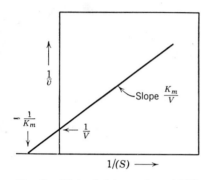

Fig. 5. Plot of $1/v$ against $1/(S)$ according to method of Lineweaver and Burk.

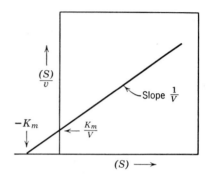

Fig. 6. Plot of $(S)/v$ against (S) according to method of Lineweaver and Burk.

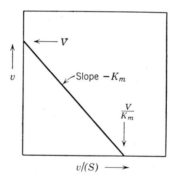

Fig. 7. Plot of v against $v/(S)$ according to the method of Eadie.

valid only if the velocity of the dissociation of ES is much greater than the rate of its conversion to products and E. For example, one may denote the rate of formation of ES by the term $k_1[(E) - (ES)](S)$, and the rate of decomposition of ES by the term $[k_2(ES) + k_3(ES)]$, where k_1, k_2, and k_3 have the same significance as before (cf. p. 251). The over-all rate of change in the concentration of ES is therefore

$$\frac{d(ES)}{dt} = k_1[(E) - (ES)](S) - k_2(ES) - k_3(ES)$$

So long as the rate of the reaction (v) is constant, then (ES) is constant

5 G. E. Briggs and J. B. S. Haldane, *Biochem. J.*, **19**, 338 (1925).

and the term $d(ES)/dt = 0$.   Under these circumstances,

$$(ES) = \frac{k_1(E)(S)}{k_1(S) + k_2 + k_3} = \frac{(E)(S)}{(S) + [(k_2 + k_3)/k_1]}$$

If the quotient $(k_2 + k_3)/k_1$ is set equal to K_m, this expression is the same as that derived by Michaelis.   In other words, the K_m calculated from a set of experimental data may not be the true dissociation constant; it only approaches k_2/k_1 when k_2 is much greater than k_3.   In most enzyme-catalyzed reactions, k_3 is sufficiently large to affect the equilibrium $E + S \rightleftharpoons ES$; consequently, unless it has been shown experimentally that k_2 is much greater than k_3, the reciprocal of K_m is not a measure of the association between E and S (i.e., enzyme-substrate affinity), as originally assumed (cf. p. 250).

The most generally useful statement of the kinetics of an enzyme-catalyzed reaction is the integrated form of the Michaelis-Menten equation which has been developed by a number of investigators (cf. Neurath and Schwert[6]) and may be given as

$$k_3(E)t = 2.303 K_m \log \frac{a}{a - x} + x$$

It will be noted that the right-hand part of this equation has a first-order term, which corresponds to the situation when all of the enzyme is not saturated with substrate, and a zero-order term, which applies to the situation when the maximal velocity has been attained.   When K_m is large, the first-order term will predominate; when K_m is small, the zero-order term will become relatively more important.   The equation also indicates that a plot of x/t against $(1/t) \log [a/(a - x)]$ will give a straight line with a slope of $-2.303 K_m$ and an intercept of $k_3(E)$.   For the determination of the turnover number of an enzyme (p. 211), zero-order kinetics must apply.   Under these circumstances, $V = k_3(ES) = k_3(E)$; all of the enzyme is in the form of the enzyme-substrate complex. The turnover number is therefore $k_3 = V/(E)$; by convention, V is denoted in moles of substrate converted per minute, and (E) in moles of enzyme.

In the above derivation of the Michaelis-Menten equation for the enzymic hydrolysis of sucrose, the participation of water was neglected, since its concentration is much greater than that of the substrate.   For an enzyme-catalyzed reaction $S + A \rightarrow$ products, where the concentrations of both S and A undergo significant change, and the enzyme combines specifically with S, the sequence of events may be written

$$E + S \underset{k_2}{\overset{k_1}{\rightleftharpoons}} ES \qquad ES + A \overset{k_4}{\longrightarrow} E + \text{products}$$

[6] H. Neurath and G. W. Schwert, *Chem. Revs.*, **46**, 69 (1950).

The kinetics of many enzyme-catalyzed oxidation-reduction reactions involves a second-order constant k_4, which is defined by the equation $-d(A)/dt = k_4(ES)(A)$. Under these circumstances, the concentration of S for half-maximal velocity is $K_m = [k_2 + k_4(A)]/k_1$. It will be noted that $k_4(A)$ is equivalent to the term k_3 in the kinetic equations for enzyme-catalyzed hydrolysis, where (A) is considered constant.

Another limitation of the Michaelis-Menten equation, as derived above, is that the enzyme-catalyzed conversion of a substrate may involve several discrete enzyme-substrate compounds of different chemical structure:

$$E + S \rightarrow ES_I \rightarrow ES_{II} \rightarrow ES_{III} \rightarrow E + \text{products}$$

If, under a given set of conditions, the reaction $ES_I \rightarrow ES_{II}$ is rate-determining, then the kinetic data will describe the sequence

$$E + S \rightarrow ES_I \rightarrow E + \text{products}$$

However, under another set of experimental conditions, the reaction $ES_{II} \rightarrow ES_{III}$ may be the slowest step, with ES_{II} as the rate-determining intermediate. In general, therefore, the "Michaelis compound" is the enzyme-substrate intermediate that is rate-determining under a given set of conditions.

In a reversible enzyme-catalyzed reaction $A \rightleftharpoons B$, the forward reaction $A \rightarrow B$ will be characterized by a Michaelis constant $K_m{}^A$ and maximum velocity V_F; the corresponding constants for the reverse reaction $B \rightarrow A$ may be designated $K_m{}^B$ and V_R. For some reversible enzymic reactions (e.g., fumarase; p. 234), these constants are related to the equilibrium constant K by the relationship $K = V_F K_m{}^B / V_R K_m{}^A$.[7]

For further discussion of the assumptions implicit in the Michaelis-Menten equation, and of efforts to provide more generalized treatments, see the articles by Alberty[8] and by Huennekens.[9]

Inhibition of Enzyme Action

An important application of the Michaelis-Menten equation and of the Lineweaver-Burk plotting method is the mathematical analysis of the action of inhibitors. One must distinguish between two general types of inhibition of enzyme action. The first of these, in which the inhibitor competes with the substrate for the enzyme, has been designated competitive inhibition. Here the extent of inhibition depends on the relative concentrations of substrate and inhibitor, and, if the substrate concen-

[7] R. A. Alberty et al., *J. Am. Chem. Soc.*, **76**, 2485 (1954).

[8] R. A. Alberty, *Advances in Enzymol.*, **17**, 1 (1956).

[9] F. M. Huennekens, in S. L. Friess and A. Weissberger, *Investigation of Rates and Mechanisms of Reactions*, Interscience Publishers, New York, 1953.

tration is high enough, the maximal velocity attained is that found in the absence of the inhibitor. Among such competitive inhibitors are frequently found the products of an enzyme-catalyzed reaction; thus glucose is a competitive inhibitor in the action of invertase on sucrose. The second type of inhibition is termed noncompetitive; here the inactivation of the enzyme depends solely on the concentration of the inhibitor, and the maximal velocity attained is less than that found in the absence of the inhibitor. Examples of noncompetitive inhibition are the action of heavy metal ions such as Hg^{2+} or Ag^+ on various enzymes and the action of cyanide on an iron-porphyrin enzyme. In general, inhibitors of this kind combine with some part of the enzyme essential for catalytic action, but the exact mechanism of inhibition differs with individual enzymes.

For the application of the Michaelis-Menten equation to the competitive inhibition of enzymes, one must consider not only the reaction sequence $E + S \rightleftharpoons ES \rightarrow E +$ products, but also the equilibrium $E + I \rightleftharpoons EI$, where I denotes the inhibitor. In the presence of a competitive inhibitor, therefore, the concentration of free enzyme is given by the expression $[(E) - (ES) - (EI)]$, and the dissociation of the enzyme-inhibitor compound is defined

$$K_i = \frac{[(E) - (ES) - (EI)](I)}{(EI)}$$

The over-all rate of formation of ES is

$$\frac{d(ES)}{dt} = k_1[(E) - (ES) - (EI)](S) - k_2(ES) - k_3(ES)$$

At the steady state of the reaction, $d(ES)/dt = 0$ and

$$(ES) = \frac{(S)[(E) - (EI)]}{(S) + K_m}$$

Substituting for (EI) (from above equation for K_i),

$$(ES) = \frac{(E)(S)K_i}{K_m K_i + K_m(I) + K_i(S)}$$

In a manner similar to that used in the derivation of the Michaelis-Menten equation one obtains the expression

$$v = \frac{V(S)K_i}{K_m K_i + K_m(I) + K_i(S)}$$

The modification of this equation by the method of Lineweaver and Burk gives

$$\frac{1}{v} = \frac{1}{V}\left[K_m + \frac{K_m(I)}{K_i}\right]\left[\frac{1}{S}\right] + \frac{1}{V}$$

Now, if $1/v$ is plotted against $1/(S)$, as before, the slope of the resulting straight line is $(K_m/V)[1 + (I)/K_i]$ and the intercept is $1/V$. Since K_m may be determined in the absence of an inhibitor, the value of K_i may then be calculated. It will be noted that the effect of a competitive inhibitor is to increase the slope of the line by the factor $[1 + (I)/K_i]$ without a change in the intercept $1/V$ (cf. Fig. 8). In other words, if the substrate concentration is large enough, the effect of the inhibitor can be overcome.

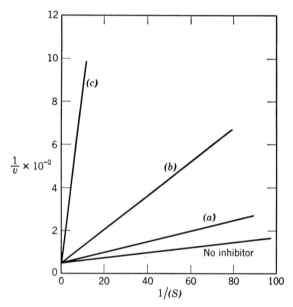

Fig. 8. Competitive inhibition of carboxypeptidase by (a) D-phenylalanine, (b) phenylacetate, (c) hydrocinnamate. [From F. Elkins-Kaufman and H. Neurath, *J. Biol. Chem.*, **178**, 647 (1949).]

The action of an enzyme on one of its substrates may be inhibited competitively by another substrate. For example, trypsin hydrolyzes the ester linkage of benzoyl-L-arginine ethyl ester and the $CO-NH_2$ linkage of benzoyl-L-argininamide (Chapter 29). The amide is a competitive inhibitor in the enzymic hydrolysis of the ester; the value of K_i is approximately equal to that of K_m for the hydrolysis of the amide by trypsin.[10]

In the presence of a competitive inhibitor, the integrated form of the Michaelis-Menten equation may be written as follows:

$$k_3(E)t = 2.303 \left[K_m + \frac{K_m(I)}{K_i} \right] \log \frac{a}{a - x} + x$$

For examples in which this equation has been successfully applied, see

[10] S. A. Bernhard, *J. Am. Chem. Soc.*, **77**, 1973 (1955).

the article by Neurath and Schwert.[6] A similar equation has been employed for the situation in which one of the products of the reaction is a competitive inhibitor, but here (I) increases as the reaction proceeds.[11]

In the presence of a noncompetitive inhibitor, the maximal velocity attained will be less than that found in the absence of the inhibitor. The Lineweaver-Burk equation for this type of inhibition is

$$\frac{1}{v} = \left[1 + \frac{(I)}{K_i}\right]\left[\frac{1}{V} + \left(\frac{K_m}{V}\right)\left(\frac{1}{(S)}\right)\right]$$

As will be seen from Fig. 9, the effect of a noncompetitive inhibitor is to increase both the slope and the intercept of the line by the factor

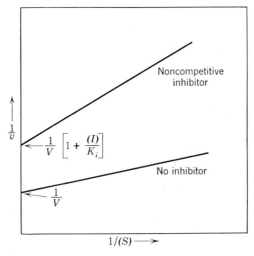

Fig. 9. Noncompetitive inhibition of enzyme action.

$[1 + (I)/K_i]$. The difference in the nature of the Lineweaver-Burk plot for competitive and noncompetitive inhibition thus provides a quantitative means of distinguishing between the two. Several instances have been reported in which the inhibition is of an "uncompetitive" type, where the inhibitor combines with the enzyme-substrate complex but not with the free enzyme. For further discussion of these equations and additional literature citations, the reader is referred to articles by Alberty,[8] Huennekens,[9] Massart,[12] and Friedenwald and Maengtwyn-Davies.[13]

[11] I. D. Frantz, Jr., and M. L. Stephenson, *J. Biol. Chem.*, **169**, 359 (1947).

[12] L. Massart, in J. B. Sumner and K. Myrbäck, *The Enzymes*, Academic Press, New York, 1950.

[13] J. S. Friedenwald and G. D. Maengtwyn-Davies, in W. D. McElroy and B. Glass, *The Mechanism of Enzyme Action*, Johns Hopkins Press, Baltimore, 1954.

It is a striking fact that, in general, substances that exert a competitive inhibitory effect on a given enzyme are closely related in chemical structure to the substrate of that enzyme. One of the classical cases of such inhibition by structural analogs is the inhibition, by malonic acid ($HOOC—CH_2—COOH$) of the enzyme that catalyzes the conversion of succinic acid ($HOOC—CH_2—CH_2—COOH$) to fumaric acid.[14] The concept of competitive inhibition has been invoked to explain the mode of action of certain antibacterial agents, such as sulfanilamide which is thought to interfere competitively in enzyme reactions involving p-aminobenzoic acid (Chapter 39).

$$H_2N—\bigcirc—SO_2NH_2$$

Sulfanilamide

$$H_2N—\bigcirc—COOH$$

p-Aminobenzoic acid

The "Active Center" of Enzymes

The concept of the enzyme-substrate compound is a basic idea in enzyme chemistry and has been buttressed by an impressive body of experimental data. It is natural that there should be speculation about the linkages involved in the union of an enzyme with its substrate. It has been assumed that each enzyme molecule has an active catalytic center of precisely defined chemical structure and that the combination with the substrate occurs at this center. This is a plausible hypothesis, but it is difficult to examine experimentally because such catalytic centers, if they exist, are parts of complex protein molecules. The task is made even more difficult by the fact that the catalytic action of an enzyme protein is usually observed only when the protein is in the native state; treatment that leads to denaturation of the protein also destroys the enzymic activity. In a very real sense, therefore, questions concerning the mode of combination of an enzyme with its substrate and the catalysis of a reaction involving that substrate are intimately connected with more general problems of protein structure which still await solution.

Many experimental efforts have been made with several purified enzymes to identify the structural elements that are responsible for catalytic activity. For example, the proteinases crystallized by Northrop and his associates (cf. Chapter 29) are not present in the appropriate tissue as such, but in the form of enzymically inactive proteins (sometimes termed zymogens) which may be crystallized and characterized. In fact, one of the most homogeneous proteins yet isolated is the pancreatic protein named chymotrypsinogen, which may be converted into a proteinase (chymotrypsin) through the action of catalytic amounts of

[14] J. H. Quastel, *Brit. Med. Bull.*, **9**, 142 (1953).

another proteinase, trypsin. It has been shown that the conversion of chymotrypsinogen to the active proteinase apparently involves the cleavage of a single peptide bond (Chapter 29), and that the catalytic center of chymotrypsin is thus made available for action. The presence of an "active center" in this enzyme is further indicated by experiments[15] which showed that the reagent diisopropylphosphorofluoridate (diisopropylfluorophosphate, DFP) does not react to an appreciable extent with chymotrypsinogen, but that one molecule of chymotrypsin combines with one molecule of DFP with the complete inhibition of the catalytic

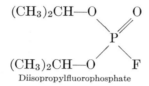

Diisopropylfluorophosphate

activity of the enzyme. Although this inhibition may be caused by the reaction of DFP with the hydroxyl group of a serine residue in chymotrypsin, the nature of the group attacked by DFP has not been established unequivocally.

The enzymes ribonuclease and papain may be subjected to selective hydrolysis of some of their peptide bonds with retention of catalytic activity. This provides further evidence for the view that the entire protein molecule may not be required for enzymic activity, and that the catalysis is effected by a relatively restricted region of the enzyme protein.

Kinetic studies have also been applied to the problem of the active center of enzymes. For example, an examination of the variation of k_3 with pH may be expected to indicate the pK' value of a group that is involved in the enzymic catalysis. Experiments of this kind have led Gutfreund[16] to conclude that the catalytic center of trypsin contains an imidazolyl group, since k_3 is markedly dependent on pH near pH 6, where the imidazolium group has its pK' (cf. p. 94).

The possibility exists that some enzyme proteins have more than one active center, and that each enzyme molecule can combine with more than one substrate molecule at a time. If several active centers are present in a single enzyme, and if they act independently of each other, the observed kinetics may be expected to be the same as for an enzyme with a single catalytic site. However, if the several catalytic sites do not function independently, the kinetic behavior may be more complex. At present, it is difficult to define unequivocally the number of active

[15] A. K. Balls and E. F. Jansen, *Advances in Enzymol.,* **13,** 321 (1952); N. K. Schaffer et al., *J. Biol. Chem.,* **202,** 67 (1953).

[16] H. Gutfreund, *Trans. Faraday Soc.,* **51,** 441 (1955).

centers per enzyme molecule, although there is evidence that in some enzymes (e.g., chymotrypsin), only one active center is present per protein molecule.

Activation of Enzymes

The conversion of chymotrypsinogen to chymotrypsin, in the presence of trypsin as the catalyst, follows the kinetics of a first-order reaction. Other zymogens, such as trypsinogen (the precursor of trypsin), may also be "activated" by catalytic amounts of trypsin. Here, however, the newly formed trypsin serves to accelerate the activation and the form of the rate curve is S-shaped, which is characteristic of an autocatalytic

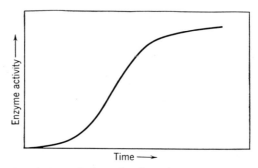

Fig. 10.   Autocatalytic activation of an enzyme precursor.

process (cf. Fig. 10). If trypsinogen is converted to trypsin at a pH value at which trypsin itself has no appreciable catalytic action, the reaction again follows the kinetics of a first-order process. The latter situation was demonstrated in the activation of trypsinogen at pH 4.5 by a proteinase obtained from a mold. Enzymes that convert zymogens to the corresponding active enzyme are frequently termed kinases. A physiologically important kinase is the enterokinase of intestinal mucosa, which catalyzes the conversion of pancreatic trypsinogen to trypsin (Chapter 29).

Frequent reference will be found in the literature to other modes of activation of enzymes. For example, the addition of metal ions to certain peptidases, amidases, and phosphatases greatly increases the catalytic activity of these enzymes.[17] Also, the addition of sulfhydryl compounds such as cysteine favors the action of a number of intracellular proteinases. It is not possible to generalize extensively about the mode of action of these activators, and discussion of this question may be post-

[17] A. L. Lehninger, *Physiol. Revs.*, **30**, 393 (1950).

poned until some of the individual enzymes that exhibit such activation behavior are considered. In some instances, however, it has been demonstrated clearly that activation processes of this kind involve the binding of an inhibitor, as in the combination of cysteine with inhibitory heavy metals. Here the state of homogeneity of the enzyme preparation is clearly of importance, and it is frequently noted that the purification of an enzyme appreciably alters its response to a substance previously thought to be an "activator."

When an activation results from the combination of an added substance (e.g., a metal ion) with an enzyme, it cannot be concluded from kinetic data alone that the substance has become part of the "active center." The possibility must be considered that the activator combines with an enzymic group different from the site at which the substrate is bound, but that this alteration of the enzyme leads to a change in the catalytic properties of the active center. This possibility also applies to the inhibition of enzyme action. Hence, kinetic data on activation and inhibition do not in themselves provide information about the mode of combination of an enzyme with a substrate, an inhibitor, or an activator.[18]

Effect of Temperature on the Rate of Enzymic Action

In general, increase in temperature results in an acceleration of a chemical reaction. If one describes the increase in rate constant for a 10-degree change by the symbol Q_{10} and sets the rate constant of an imaginary reaction equal to unity at 0°, then, if $Q_{10} = 2.5$, the variation of the rate constant with temperature will be found to be

Temperature	0°	10°	50°	100°
Rate constant	1	2.5	97.6	9537

In 1889 Arrhenius examined the available data on the effect of temperature on the rates of chemical reactions and proposed the following equation:

$$\frac{d \ln k}{dT} = \frac{A}{RT^2}$$

where k is the reaction velocity constant, R is the gas constant (1.987 cal per degree per mole), T is the absolute temperature, and A is a constant. Integration of this equation between T_1 and T_2, corresponding to velocity constants k_1 and k_2 respectively, gives the equation

$$\ln \frac{k_2}{k_1} = \frac{A}{R} \left(\frac{1}{T_1} - \frac{1}{T_2} \right)$$

A can be calculated from the slope of the line obtained on plotting log k

[18] A. G. Ogston, *Discussions Faraday Soc.*, **20**, 161 (1956).

against $1/T$ (cf. Fig. 11). The slope is equal to $A/2.303R$ or $A/4.58$. A review by Sizer[19] lists the values of A for a large number of enzyme-catalyzed reactions. On the whole, the values fall within the range 1000 to 25,000 cal. In biological studies, it has been occasionally the practice to substitute for A the term μ. It may be added that values of μ have been determined for a variety of physiological phenomena (see Crozier[20]).

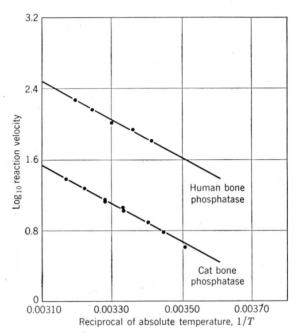

Fig. 11. Arrhenius plot of data on hydrolysis of β-glycerophosphate by bone phosphatases. The value of A (or μ) was calculated from the slope and was found to be 9940 cal over the temperature range studied. [From O. Bodansky, *J. Biol. Chem.*, **129**, 197 (1939).]

Thus the rate of creeping of ants, of the chirping of crickets, and of the flashing of fireflies all appear to have μ values near 12,200 cal. The respiratory rhythms of a number of animal species, and the frequency of heart beat, are characterized by a μ of 16,700. Clearly, these physiological processes involve the integrated activity of a number of chemical reactions; however, the over-all rate was considered by Crozier to be determined by the slowest of these component reactions (the "pacemaker" reaction), and therefore the μ value of the slowest reaction would determine the temperature dependence of the over-all rate.

[19] I. W. Sizer, *Advances in Enzymol.*, **3**, 35 (1943).
[20] W. J. Crozier, *J. Gen. Physiol.*, **7**, 189 (1924)

An alternative form of the integrated Arrhenius equation is

$$\ln k = \frac{-A}{RT} + \ln C \qquad \text{or} \qquad k = Ce^{-A/RT}$$

where C is a constant. The empirical constant A assumed theoretical significance when it was recognized that A denotes the apparent "energy of activation" (E^*) that molecules must acquire before they undergo reaction under a given set of conditions. According to one theory, which assumes that the rate of a chemical reaction depends on the frequency of collision of molecules having enough energy to react,

$$k = PZe^{-E^*/RT}$$

where k is the number of molecules reacting per second per unit volume, Z is the number of molecules colliding per second per unit volume, and P is a steric factor which depends on the relative orientation of the reacting molecules. The exponential term is a measure of the fraction of the molecules having excess energy E^* or more, and E^* is defined as the minimum energy that reacting molecules must acquire before they will react. An alternative statement of the above equation is

$$\log k = \log (PZ) - \frac{E^*}{2.303RT}$$

An extremely important advance in the understanding of the energy of activation was made by Eyring.[21] Instead of limiting himself to the assumption that a successful reaction occurs only when "reactive" molecules, i.e., those having an energy of E^* or more, collide, he pictures the mechanism of a chemical reaction as shown schematically in Fig. 12. Here the ordinate denotes energy, and it is assumed that the reactants, in order to be converted into products, must acquire an increment of energy E_1^*, and pass through a "transition state" in which an activated complex is present. The reverse reaction, products $\rightarrow a + b$, requires an increment of energy E_2^* to form the activated complex. The energy change in the reversible reaction $a + b \rightleftharpoons$ products is therefore $E = E_1^* - E_2^*$. It must be emphasized that the rate of the reaction $a + b \rightarrow$ products depends on the magnitude of E_1^*, and does not bear any necessary relation to the energy change E. Hence a knowledge of ΔH or of ΔF for a given reaction cannot be used for the calculation of the rate of the reaction.

In the transition-state theory it is assumed that the reactants (e.g., a and b) are in equilibrium with the activated complex (ab^*); the equilibrium constant of the reaction $a + b \rightleftharpoons ab^*$ is denoted by the symbol K^*. The rate constant k of the reaction $a + b \rightarrow$ products is approxi-

[21] H. Eyring, *J. Chem. Physics*, **3**, 107 (1935); H. Eyring and A. E. Stearn, *Chem. Revs.*, **24**, 253 (1939).

mately equal to $(RT/Nh)K^*$, where R is the gas constant, T is the absolute temperature, N is Avogadro's number, and h is Planck's constant $(6.62 \times 10^{-27}$ erg sec). The standard free energy, enthalpy, and

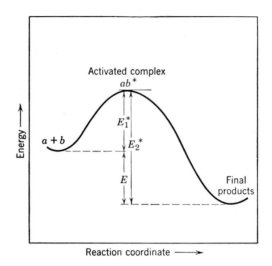

Fig. 12. Schematic formulation of the mechanism of a reaction, according to Eyring.

entropy of activation, i.e., for the reaction $a + b \rightarrow$ products, may be denoted ΔF^*, ΔH^*, and ΔS^* respectively. Since $K^* = e^{-\Delta F^*/RT}$, and $\Delta F^* = \Delta H^* - T\,\Delta S^*$,

$$k = \frac{RT}{Nh}\,e^{-\Delta F^*/RT} = \frac{RT}{Nh}\,e^{\Delta S^*/R}e^{-\Delta H^*/RT}$$

The relationship of this equation to the integrated Arrhenius equation (p. 265) may be seen from the fact that, for solutions, $\Delta H^* = A + RT$; thus, for high activation energies and for low temperatures, the experimentally determined value of A (or μ) is approximately equal to ΔH^*, the standard enthalpy of activation. The term $(RT/Nh)e^{\Delta S^*/R}$ is approximately equal to the term PZ of the equation based on collision theory (p. 265).

When enzyme-catalyzed reactions are considered from the point of view of transition-state theory, at least two activated complexes must be considered, one in the reaction $E + S \rightleftharpoons ES_1{}^* \rightleftharpoons ES$, and another in the reaction $ES \rightleftharpoons ES_2{}^* \rightarrow$ products (cf. Fig. 13). When the substrate concentration is sufficiently high so that all of the enzyme is in the form of ES, it is possible to calculate for the activation of ES (i.e., $ES \rightleftharpoons ES_2{}^*$) th values of ΔF^* (from determinations of k_3), of ΔH^* (from the temperature-dependence of k_3), and of ΔS^* by means of the equations

$$k_3 = \frac{RT}{Nh}\, e^{-\Delta F^*/RT}$$

$$\frac{d \ln k_3}{dT} = \frac{\Delta H^* + RT}{RT^2}$$

$$\Delta S^* = \frac{\Delta H^* - \Delta F^*}{T}$$

For several proteolytic enzymes, ΔF^* for the activation of ES is in the range 13 to 19 kcal per mole; ΔH^* in the range 10 to 16 kcal per mole; and ΔS^* in the range -6 to -23 eu.[6] These values are based on the

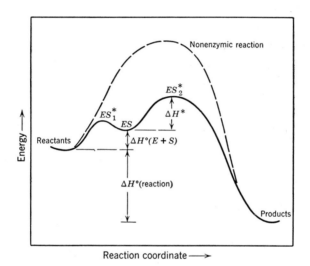

Fig. 13. Enthalpy changes in an enzyme-catalyzed reaction (solid curve), and comparison of heats of activation for enzymic and nonenzymic catalysis.

assumption that 1 enzyme molecule combines with only 1 molecule of substrate.

At low substrate concentrations, the magnitude of K_m is significant in determining the rate of an enzyme-catalyzed reaction (cf. p. 255). It will be recalled that $K_m = (k_2 + k_3)/k_1$. When k_2 is much greater than k_3, K_m may be considered an equilibrium constant, and ΔF°, ΔH°, and ΔS° in the reaction $E + S \rightleftharpoons ES$ may be determined by means of the following equations: (1) $\Delta F^\circ = -RT \ln (1/K_m) = RT \ln K_m$; (2) $d[\ln (1/K_m)]/dt = \Delta H^\circ/RT^2$; (3) $\Delta S^\circ = (\Delta H^\circ - \Delta F^\circ)/T$. However, since usually K_m is not a true equilibrium constant, such values have no true thermodynamic significance unless it has been demonstrated experimentally that k_2 is much greater than k_3. For the special case where

$K_m = k_2/k_1$, the Arrhenius heat of activation at low substrate concentrations corresponds to the sum of ΔH^* and $\Delta H^\circ (E + S)$, as illustrated in Fig. 13.

If the values of μ or of ΔH^* for an enzyme-catalyzed reaction (at high substrate concentration) are compared with values found in the absence of the enzyme or with a nonenzymic catalyst, it is frequently found that the heat of activation of the enzymic reaction is much lower than that for the nonenzymic reaction. Thus, in the decomposition of H_2O_2 by catalase, the value of μ is about 2 kcal; when catalyzed by colloidal platinum, $\mu =$ ca. 12 kcal, and, when no catalyst is added, $\mu =$ ca. 18 kcal. Determination of ΔH^* for the hydrolysis of urea, catalyzed by hydrogen ion and by urease, have given values of about 24.5 and 10 kcal respectively.[22] Such comparisons of values for μ or for ΔH^* are valid if the difference in the corresponding values for ΔS^* is not great. In general, it may be concluded that the role of an enzyme is to cause the formation of an activated complex at a lower energy level than that of the activated complex formed in the absence of enzyme (cf. Fig. 13). It must be surmised that these two activated complexes are somewhat different in chemical nature.

The study of the effect of temperature on the rate of enzyme-catalyzed reactions has led therefore to the important generalization that an enzyme lowers the energy barrier which substrates must overcome before they can be converted into final products. Some idea of the effect this may have on the rate of a chemical reaction may be gained from a consideration of the following relationship between values of μ and the corresponding first-order velocity constants (at 25° C):

μ	k, sec^{-1}	$t_{1/2}$
10,000	7.7×10^5	9×10^{-6} sec
15,000	1.7×10^2	0.004 sec
25,000	8.0×10^{-4}	145 min

It will be noted that a decrease in μ from 25,000 to 15,000 cal increases the rate constant by a factor of about 10^6.

In Fig. 13, the standard enthalpy change in the over-all reaction is denoted ΔH° (reaction). This energy change, as well as the change in free energy (ΔF°) in the reaction, is independent of the path by which the reactants are converted to products; as noted earlier, the function of the enzyme (at low enzyme concentrations) is to speed up the attainment of equilibrium without altering the equilibrium concentrations. It must be reiterated that there is no necessary relation between the free energy of activation ΔF^* or the enthalpy of activation ΔH^* and the standard free-energy change ΔF° or the standard enthalpy change ΔH°

[22] K. J. Laidler and J. P. Hoare, *J. Am. Chem. Soc.*, **72**, 2489 (1950).

in the over-all reaction. In other words, the chemical lability of a substance in a given reversible reaction, as indicated by kinetic data, cannot be inferred from the energy changes in the over-all reaction.

The conclusions discussed above apply under conditions where the enzyme is stable; this limits the experimental investigation of the effect of temperature on the rate of the enzyme-catalyzed reaction to a relatively narrow range. In general, if a wider temperature range is studied,

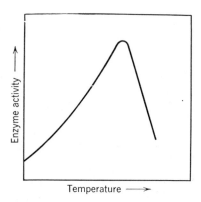

Fig. 14. Effect of temperature on the rate of enzyme action.

it is found that the rate of enzyme action first increases with increasing temperature, and then decreases abruptly, as shown by the curve in Fig. 14. The abrupt decrease in rate is associated with the thermal inactivation of the enzyme by denaturation. In general, the values of μ for protein denaturation lie in the range 40 to 100 kcal.[23] In the reversible denaturation of chymotrypsinogen at pH 2 and 47.2° C, $\Delta H^* = 84.5$ kcal, $\Delta F^* = 20$ kcal, and $\Delta S^* = 202$ eu. From equilibrium measurements, $\Delta H° = 99.6$ kcal, $\Delta F° = -1.4$ kcal, and $\Delta S° = 316$ eu.[24] These data indicate the importance of the entropy changes in protein denaturation (cf. p. 234); the large increase in the entropy of activation suffices to favor denaturation despite the large enthalpy of activation.

The usual procedure in studying the effect of heat on an enzyme preparation is to subject a solution of the enzyme to a certain temperature for a stated period of time, to cool the solution, and to determine the residual enzyme activity. Under these conditions the rate of enzyme inactivation usually follows the kinetics of a first-order reaction. The composite effect of temperature on the rate of an enzyme-catalyzed

[23] H. Neurath et al., *Chem. Revs.*, **34,** 157 (1944); A. E. Stearn, *Advances in Enzymol.*, **9,** 25 (1949).

[24] M. A. Eisenberg and G. W. Schwert, *J. Gen. Physiol.*, **34,** 583 (1951).

reaction may be illustrated by means of data on catalase[25] (cf. Fig. 15).
It will be noted that the plot of $\log k$ against $1/T$ shows a value of
$\mu = 4200$ cal† in the temperature region where the rate of H_2O_2 decomposition is increasing, and a value of $\mu = 51,000$ in the temperature
region where the rate is decreasing. Occasionally, reference will be
found to the "temperature optimum" of an enzyme; under the conditions
of Sizer's experiments this is $53°$ C. Since the temperature optimum is a

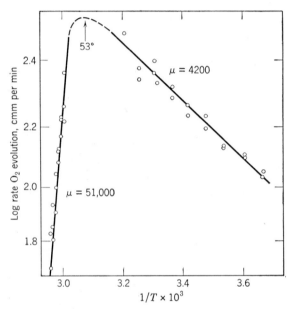

Fig. 15. Effect of temperature on the rate of decomposition of hydrogen peroxide
by catalase. (From I. W. Sizer.[25])

resultant of two effects, both of which are profoundly influenced by the
presence of impurities, the pH of the solution, and other factors, this
temperature value is of dubious significance in the characterization of
an enzyme. For example, crude preparations of myokinase (p. 459) are
relatively stable to heat, but in more highly purified form the enzyme
is extremely heat-labile.[26] Occasionally, enzymes present in a cell extract
may appear to be "activated" by heat treatment, as a consequence of

[25] I. W. Sizer, *J. Biol. Chem.*, **154**, 461 (1944); E. Hultin, *Acta Chem. Scand.*, **9**,
1700 (1955).

† The value of $\mu = 4200$ for catalase is too high, as shown by R. K. Bonnichsen
et al. [*Acta Chem. Scand.*, **1**, 685 (1947)]. Their more careful measurements with
purified catalase were conducted under conditions where the enzyme is not destroyed
in the course of the reaction. The correct value of μ is probably near 1700 cal.

[26] W. J. Bowen and T. D. Kerwin, *Arch. Biochem. and Biophys.*, **64**, 278 (1956)

the denaturation of a heat-labile inhibitor.[27] It may be added that, in general, enzymes are less readily denatured by heat in the presence of their substrates than in their absence; this suggests that the active center of many enzymes may be the region of greatest instability in the thermal denaturation of enzyme proteins.

Effect of pH on the Rate of Enzyme Action[8]

Brief reference has already been made to the importance of the control of pH in enzyme experiments. This was first pointed out by Sørensen in 1909, and many studies have been conducted since that time on the dependence of the rates of enzyme-catalyzed reactions on the pH of

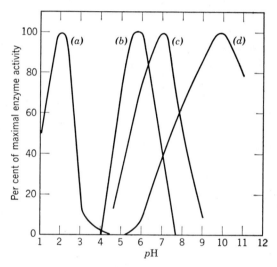

Fig. 16. Dependence of rate of enzyme action on pH. (a) Pepsin, (b) glutamic acid decarboxylase, (c) salivary amylase, (d) arginase.

the solution. The result usually obtained on plotting the rate against pH is shown in Fig. 16, and it will be noted that, at a certain region of pH, the activity of the enzyme appears to be maximal. The pH value (or region) at which such maximal activity is observed is termed the pH optimum. Purified enzymes vary greatly in their pH optima. For example, pepsin acts optimally on proteins at about pH 2, whereas pancreatic carboxypeptidase has its optimum at about pH 8. Some enzymes exhibit relatively sharp pH optima, and here the pH must be controlled very carefully; others have pH optima that extend over several pH units (e.g., catalase). Although the pH optimum of an enzyme is a

[27] M. N. Swartz et al., *Science*, **123**, 50 (1956).

useful datum in its characterization, it must be emphasized that the value found for one substrate may not necessarily apply to all substrates for that enzyme. Also, the control of the pH requires the presence of buffer ions which frequently have an influence on the catalytic activity of enzymes.

In a consideration of the effect of pH on the rate of enzyme-catalyzed reactions, at least three factors must be borne in mind. The first of these is the influence of pH on the stability of the enzyme. As noted before, nearly all enzymes are sensitive to extremes of acidity or alkalinity, and certain enzymes, such as pepsin, are readily inactivated even at neutral pH values. For this reason, in a determination of the pH optimum of an enzyme it is desirable to know the stability of the enzyme over the pH range employed. There are many pH-dependence curves in which the drop in rate on one side of the optimum is due to enzyme inactivation.

A second factor in the relation of pH to the activity of enzymes arises from the fact that enzyme proteins, like other proteins, are multivalent dipolar ions. Their dissociation depends, therefore, on the pH of the medium. Although it is not yet possible to specify precisely the nature of the protein groups involved in the formation of enzyme-substrate compounds, it has been assumed that the steep portions of a pH-dependence curve correspond to the dissociation of ionizing groups on the enzyme. In this manner, estimates have been made of the pK' values of groups thought to be essential for the catalytic activity of trypsin (cf. p. 261), acetylcholine esterase,[28] and fumarase.[29] General treatments of the effect of pH on the kinetic constants of enzyme-catalyzed reactions have been developed by Waley[30] and by Dixon.[31]

The third factor of importance is the dissociation of the substrate. If, for example, a peptide, in order to be hydrolyzed by a peptidase, must combine via its uncharged α-amino group with the enzyme, pH values that favor a relatively high concentration of the conjugate base, as against the charged $-NH_3^+$ form, will also favor more rapid reaction. In general, therefore, the dissociation of the substrate will influence the character of the pH dependence curve and the pH optimum.

Specificity of Enzyme Action

The specificity of a catalyst may be defined operationally by introducing the catalyst into a sufficiently large number of systems, thermodynamically capable of reaction, and observing the selectivity of the

[28] F. Bergmann et al., *Biochem. J.,* **63,** 684 (1956).
[29] R. A. Alberty et al., *J. Am. Chem. Soc.,* **76,** 2485 (1954).
[30] S. G. Waley, *Biochim. et Biophys. Acta,* **10,** 27 (1953).
[31] M. Dixon, *Biochem. J.,* **55,** 161 (1953).

catalyst in its effect on the rates of the reactions examined. Although enzymes are characterized by a high degree of specificity, this property is not limited to enzymes alone. For example, the reaction

$$CH_3COOH + C_6H_5NH_2 \rightarrow CH_3CO\text{—}NHC_6H_5 + H_2O$$

is specifically catalyzed by strong acids such as picric acid, and the rate of the reaction is proportional to the concentration of the catalyst. Here the catalysis is due to the intermediate formation of the aniline salt of picric acid. Another example of nonenzymic catalysis which exhibits specificity is the decarboxylation of α- and β-keto acids in the presence of amines.[32] In all these instances the catalysis depends on the formation of an intermediate compound which leads to an activated complex at a lower energy level than that required in the absence of the catalyst.

The specificity of enzymes differs from the specificity of simpler organic catalysts in that it is much more restricted. The nature of the chemical reaction catalyzed by a given enzyme is, therefore, the most characteristic feature of the enzyme. For this reason enzymes are usually classified on the basis of their specificity. The classification presented on p. 216, and others to be found in various text and reference books on enzyme chemistry, are based mainly on the finding that each of the large number of enzymes identified thus far catalyzes a given type of chemical reaction. One speaks, therefore, of the "absolute specificity" with respect to the type of reaction catalyzed. Consequently one refers to hydrolytic enzymes (hydrolases) which act specifically at glycosidic bonds (glycosidases), at peptide bonds (peptidases), at ester linkages (esterases), and so forth. Although this basis of classification is useful as a rough guide, its rigid application may lead to confusion and misunderstanding. The so-called hydrolytic enzymes catalyze the attainment of equilibrium in reversible reactions, and therefore can also catalyze the condensation reactions which are the reverse of the hydrolytic processes. Furthermore, certain of the hydrolytic enzymes have been shown to catalyze bimolecular reactions in which a substrate reacts, not with water, but with an organic alcohol or amine. Here one is dealing not with a hydrolysis or simple condensation, but with a "replacement" reaction; the example given below is a "transesterification," catalyzed by an esterase:

$$RCO\text{—}OR' + R''OH \rightleftharpoons RCO\text{—}OR'' + R'OH$$

In a similar manner, peptidases catalyze "transpeptidation" reactions. The importance of these replacement reactions in the activity of the so-called hydrolytic enzymes has been appreciated only recently.

Another disadvantage of the currently employed classification schemes is the considerable overlapping of a number of the groups of enzymes.

[32] W. Langenbeck, *Advances in Enzymol.*, **14**, 163 (1953).

For example, certain peptidases are not restricted in their catalytic action
to CO—NH linkages between two amino acid residues, but can also act
at CO—NH$_2$ bonds, in which only the carbonyl group is part of an
amino acid residue; therefore, the peptidases can behave like the so-called
amidases. Furthermore, it has been shown that certain highly purified
peptidases and proteinases can act at ester linkages; consequently, there
is not so sharp a line of demarcation between the peptidases and the
esterases as was first believed.

Perhaps the most serious difficulty in the classification of enzymes is
that most of the known catalytic activities are associated with enzyme
preparations of uncertain homogeneity (cf. p. 217). The difficulty is
greatly increased when the substrates employed in the study of the
specificity of an enzyme preparation are of uncertain or complex chemical
structure. Thus, as long as the complex proteins were the only substrates
available for the study of the specificity of the proteinases (e.g., trypsin,
pepsin), or only the complex nucleic acids were available for the study
of ribonucleases, it was not possible to define unequivocally the specificity
of these enzymes. Although, at the present state of knowledge, a rational
classification of the enzymes on the basis of their specificity is not possible, the list given on p. 216 may be useful as a compendium of the
names assigned to the better-known groups of enzymes.

The truly remarkable features of enzyme specificity emerge more
clearly from a consideration of a group of catalysts that act at similar
linkages. Since the enzymes that act at CO—NH bonds have been
examined most carefully from this point of view, the specificity of the
peptidases and proteinases may be considered first (see also Chapter 29).
Crystalline pancreatic carboxypeptidase hydrolyzes CO—NH bonds in
substrates of the general formula

$$\overset{\displaystyle R'}{\underset{\displaystyle RCO\text{—}NHCHCOOH}{\downarrow}}$$

A structural requisite of substrates of this enzyme is the presence of a
free α-carboxyl group adjacent to the peptide bond to be hydrolyzed.
Carboxypeptidase will not hydrolyze the peptide bond of glycylglycinamide (NH$_2$CH$_2$CO—NHCH$_2$CO—NH$_2$), but this substance will serve
as a substrate for a different type of peptidase (aminopeptidase) which
requires in its substrates a free α-amino group adjacent to the sensitive
peptide bond. For the action of certain of the proteinases, the sensitive peptide bond must involve the participation of particular amino acid
residues. For example, crystalline trypsin acts at the CO—NH linkages
that involve the carbonyl group of a lysine or arginine residue; substitution of either of these by another amino acid prevents enzymic action.
Similarly, crystalline chymotrypsin acts at linkages in which the carbonyl

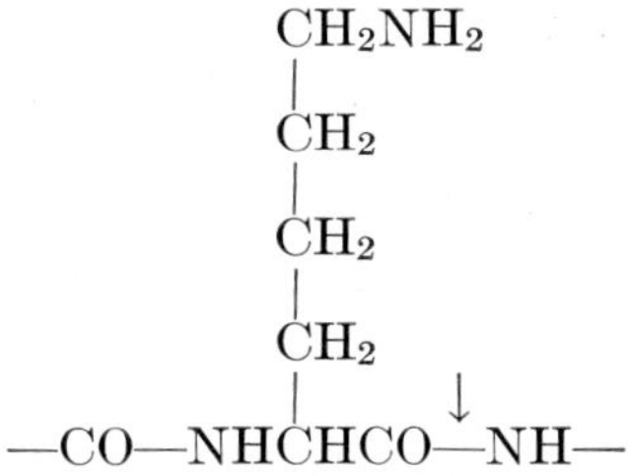

$$CH_2NH_2$$
$$|$$
$$CH_2$$
$$|$$
$$CH_2$$
$$|$$
$$CH_2$$
$$|　　\downarrow$$
$$—CO—NHCHCO—NH—$$

Substrate for trypsin

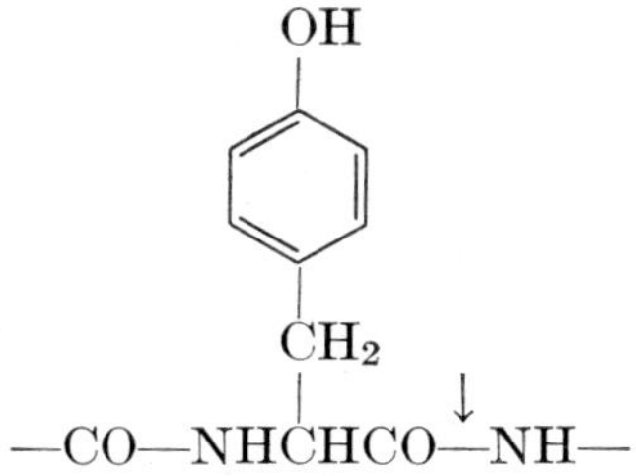

$$OH$$

$$CH_2$$
$$|　　\downarrow$$
$$—CO—NHCHCO—NH—$$

Substrate for chymotrypsin

group of tyrosine, phenylalanine, tryptophan, or, to a lesser extent, methionine is involved. Thus trypsin will not act on the same peptide bonds as chymotrypsin, nor will chymotrypsin attack the linkages broken by trypsin. Unlike carboxypeptidase and aminopeptidase, neither trypsin nor chymotrypsin requires the presence of free α-amino or α-carboxyl groups in its substrates.[33]

For the esterases, the specificity of the individual members of this group is largely determined by the nature of the alcohol that is involved in ester linkage. Liver esterase appears to be specifically adapted to the hydrolysis of simple esters such as methyl butyrate, while the principal ester-splitting enzyme in pancreatic extracts is a lipase that acts preferentially on glycerol esters of fatty acids (Chapter 24). A different group of esterases is specific for the hydrolysis of esters such as acetylcholine in which the nitrogenous alcohol choline is involved; these enzymes are termed acetylcholine esterases.

$$(CH_3)_3\overset{+}{N}CH_2CH_2O—OCCH_3$$

Acetylcholine

These examples can be multiplied, but the discussion of the specificity of individual enzymes may be appropriately postponed until their role in metabolic processes is considered. Some general conclusions about the specificity of enzymes may be drawn at this point, however. For a more extensive discussion, see Helferich.[34]

In the first place, for the study of enzyme specificity, the availability of purified enzymes must be supplemented by substrates of known chemical structure. Only when such substrates are available is it possible to establish unequivocally the nature of the chemical reaction that is being catalyzed, and only then can one modify the structure of the substrates so as to determine the effect of changes in substrate structure on the action of an enzyme. For this reason the methods of synthetic

[33] M. Bergmann and J. S. Fruton, *Advances in Enzymol.,* **1,** 63 (1941).

[34] B. Helferich, in J. B. Sumner and K. Myrbäck, *The Enzymes,* Academic Press, New York, 1950.

organic chemistry are of special importance for progress in the under-standing of the mode of enzyme action.

In the quantitative study of the specificity of an enzyme, it is found occasionally that, of a large number of related compounds, only one can serve as a substrate. A classical example is the enzyme urease, which appears to be specific for urea. Any substitution of the urea molecule thus far attempted renders the bonds resistant to hydrolysis by the enzyme. Here, in addition to an absolute specificity with respect to reaction type, the enzyme exhibits absolute specificity for only one substance, namely, urea. On the other hand, a series of related com-pounds all may serve as substrates for a single purified enzyme, but may be attacked at different rates. This situation is exemplified by carboxy-peptidase, whose action on a series of carbobenzoxyglycylamino acids has been studied.[35] The following relative rates of hydrolysis were found:

Carbobenzoxyglycyl-L-phenylalanine	100
Carbobenzoxyglycyl-L-tyrosine	46
Carbobenzoxyglycyl-L-leucine	20
Carbobenzoxyglycyl-L-isoleucine	4
Carbobenzoxyglycyl-L-alanine	0.3
Carbobenzoxyglycylglycine	0.004

Such marked differences in the action of one enzyme on a series of sub-strates are usually taken as evidence of "relative specificity." Another enzyme whose relative specificity has been studied carefully is β-glucosi-dase (Chapter 18).[36] Helferich showed that variation in the nature of R in

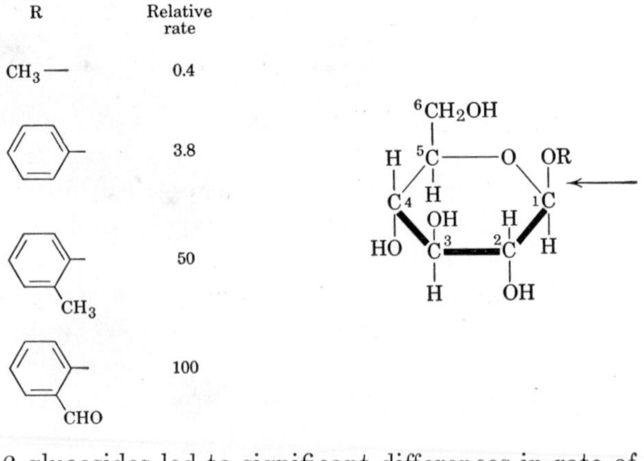

a series of β-glucosides led to significant differences in rate of hydrolysis. When dealing with enzymes of dubious homogeneity, it is sometimes not

[35] M. A. Stahmann et al., *J. Biol. Chem.,* **164,** 753 (1946).

[36] W. W. Pigman, *Advances in Enzymol.,* **4,** 41 (1944); R. L. Nath and H. N. Rydon, *Biochem. J.,* **57,** 1 (1954).

immediately evident whether all the compounds acted upon by a given preparation are substrates for a single enzyme. Occasionally it is possible to demonstrate that partial inactivation of a given enzyme preparation leads to a parallel decrease in the rate of reaction for the series of substrates employed. Though this is not conclusive evidence that only a single enzyme is under study, it strengthens the argument that such is in fact the case.

Perhaps the most striking aspect of the specificity of enzymes is their ability to select between enantiomorphous compounds. This may be termed stereochemical specificity. For example, carboxypeptidase, which catalyzes the hydrolysis of carbobenzoxyglycyl-l-phenylalanine, has no measurable action on carbobenzoxyglycyl-d-phenylalanine. Also, the β-glucosidase, mentioned above, is inactive in promoting the hydrolysis of α-glucosides, which differ from β-glucosides in the configuration about carbon atom 1 of the glucose unit. As will be seen later, the enzymes that catalyze the oxidative deamination of amino acids are sharply differentiated in their action on the l- and d-forms. One speaks, therefore, of l-amino acid oxidases and of d-amino acid oxidases.

These examples of stereochemical specificity involve an absolute discrimination between enantiomorphs. Enzymes may be cited, however, that exhibit what may be termed relative stereochemical specificity (e.g., partially purified esterase preparations attack both the *d*- and *l*-forms of optically active esters, but at different rates). Thus *l*-mandelic acid methyl ester is hydrolyzed by swine liver esterase about twice as rapidly as the *d*-isomer.

Many investigators have proposed theories to account for the remarkable selectivity exhibited by enzymes. All these theories begin with the basic assumption that the enzyme combines with the substrate. In order to explain the ability of an enzyme protein to catalyze a particular chemical reaction, it is further assumed that the combination with the substrate must involve a particular spatial relationship between certain essential groups of the substrate and certain parts of the enzyme molecule. For example, it has been assumed that, in the formation of the enzyme-substrate complex between carboxypeptidase and a specific substrate, the enzyme binds, in a particular way, the terminal α-carboxyl group of the substrate and some part of the CO—NH bond that is broken during the reaction. In addition, it is thought that there must be a specific mutual orientation of the side-chain group of the terminal amino acid residue in the substrate and a group in the enzyme. This theory, which may be illustrated by the diagram on p. 278, has been termed the "polyaffinity" theory of enzyme action.[33] The polyaffinity theory has been successful in explaining the stereochemical specificity of the peptidases and proteinases and has also been invoked to explain the asym-

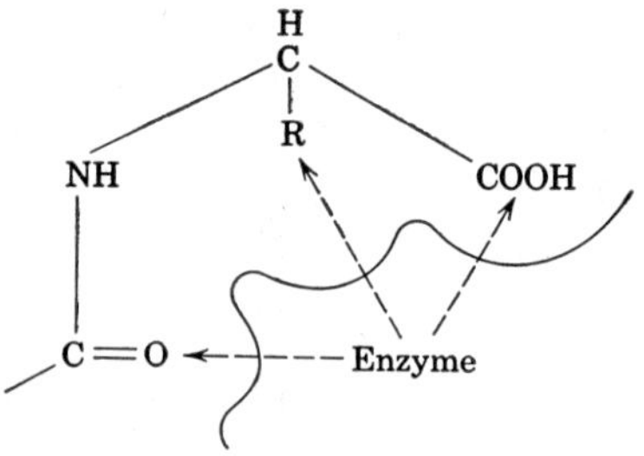

$$H$$
$$C$$
$$|$$
$$R$$
NH   COOH

C=O ←----- Enzyme

metric character of other enzyme-catalyzed reactions.[37] Stated generally, it suggests that, for an enzyme reaction to proceed in an asymmetric manner, the substrate must have a definite spatial relationship to the enzyme, and that there are at least three points of specific interaction between enzyme and substrate.

It is a logical consequence of the "polyaffinity" hypothesis that the active center of an enzyme must have an asymmetric character, and that the stereochemical specificity of enzymes is in part the expression of the asymmetric nature of protein molecules (p. 83). The question may be raised, but cannot now be answered, whether two enzymes that catalyze the same type reaction but differ in their stereochemical specificity have stereochemically opposite catalytic centers.

The consideration of the specific interaction of enzymes and their substrates by "polyaffinity" leads to a clearer picture of the mode of the action of competitive inhibitors. If an inhibitor and a substrate have certain groups in common, and the inhibitor can combine by means of these groups with one or more of the essential groups in the active center of the enzyme so as to prevent the approach of the corresponding groups of the substrate, competitive inhibition may be expected.

It will be obvious that the mere combination of an enzyme with a given substance does not necessarily lead to the catalysis of a chemical reaction involving that substance. Nor does the value of K_m for an enzyme-substrate complex in itself give information on the rate of the chemical reaction; when all of the enzyme is in the form of the enzyme-substrate compound, the value of k_3 describes the rate at which the products of the reaction are formed (p. 255). In some instances, the specificity of an enzyme may be described by a comparison of values of $k_3/2.3K_m$ (denoted C_{max}) for a series of substrates.[6]

The foregoing discussion of the specificity of enzymes has emphasized the exceptional selectivity that they exhibit in the catalysis of thermodynamically possible reactions. It will be seen from the later consideration of the properties of individual enzymes, and of their metabolic role, that this group of catalysts, by virtue of their specificity, can direct

[37] A. G. Ogston, *Nature,* **162,** 963 (1948).

preferentially sequences of chemical reactions in living cells. Enzymes thus serve not only as accelerators of biochemical reactions, but as directors of metabolic pathways as well.

Mechanism of Enzyme Action

The recognition that the selectivity of enzymic catalysis is related to the specific combination of a substrate with an active site of an enzyme protein has led to efforts to elucidate the mechanism of enzyme action through the identification and characterization of enzyme-substrate intermediates. Because of the manifold variety of known enzymes, and the wide differences in the nature of the chemical reactions they catalyze, the intimate mechanisms of the action of individual enzymes are often very different. In later pages of this book, the mechanisms of several enzyme-catalyzed reactions will be discussed, to the extent that they have been elucidated. A few examples may be cited here, however, to indicate some of the experimental approaches that have proved fruitful.

Studies on the mechanism of enzyme action have been profoundly influenced by the knowledge gained from work on the nonenzymic catalysis of organic reactions.[38] In the examination of the mechanism of a reaction catalyzed by a simple substance of known structure, a variety of methods has been used. Among these is the determination of kinetic constants as functions of changes in the composition of the solvent, and of the structure and concentration of the reactants and the catalyst; another technique depends on the use of compounds labeled with isotopes (Chapter 16). Similar general methods have been applied to the study of enzyme-catalyzed reactions, but, since the chemical structure of the active sites of enzymes is largely unknown, the interpretation of the data is more difficult than for the nonenzymic catalysis by substances of known structure. However, where similarities have been observed in the catalysis of a reaction by an enzyme and by a simpler substance whose mechanism of action is known, it has been possible to formulate hypotheses about the mechanism of the enzymic catalysis.

For example, the decarboxylation of β-keto acids such as dimethyloxaloacetic acid is catalyzed by metal ions such as Cu^{2+}; this has been attributed[39] to the formation of a chelated intermediate and to the attraction by the positively charged copper ion of electrons away from the β-carboxyl group, with the liberation of CO_2 (see p. 280). This mechanism may simulate the enzymic decarboxylation of β-keto acids,

---

[38] C. K. Ingold, *Structure and Mechanism in Organic Chemistry*, Cornell University Press, Ithaca, 1953; A. A. Frost and R. G. Pearson, *Kinetics and Mechanism*, John Wiley & Sons, New York, 1953.

[39] R. Steinberger and F. H. Westheimer, *J. Am. Chem. Soc.*, **73**, 429 (1951).

which is known to be dependent on the presence of metal ions. Other examples of experiments with "enzyme models" of known structure will be mentioned later; these simple catalysts share with enzymes the property of changing the mechanism of a chemical reaction to a different mechanism that has a lower energy of activation, although the non-enzymic catalysts do not exhibit the specificity shown by enzymes.

$$
\begin{array}{ccccccc}
\text{COO}^- & & \text{COO}^- & & & & \text{H} \\
| & & | & & & & | \\
\text{C(CH}_3)_2 & \xrightarrow[-2\text{H}_2\text{O}]{+\text{Cu(H}_2\text{O)}_4{}^{2+}} & \text{C(CH}_3)_2 & \xrightarrow{-\text{CO}_2} & \text{C(CH}_3)_2 & & \text{C(CH}_3)_2 \\
| & & | & & \| & & | \\
\text{C}=\text{O} & & \text{C}=\text{O} & & \text{C}-\text{O}^- & \xrightarrow[-\text{Cu(H}_2\text{O)}_4{}^{2+}]{+\text{H}^+ + 2\text{H}_2\text{O}} & \text{C}=\text{O} \\
| & & | \quad \diagdown & & | \quad \diagdown & & | \\
\text{C}-\text{O}^- & & \quad\quad \text{Cu}^{2+} & & \quad\quad \text{Cu}^{2+} & & \text{C}-\text{O}^- \\
\| & & \diagup \text{(H}_2\text{O)}_2 & & \diagup \text{(H}_2\text{O)}_2 & & \| \\
\text{O} & & \text{C}-\text{O}^- & & \text{C}-\text{O}^- & & \text{O} \\
& & \| & & \| & & \\
& & \text{O} & & \text{O} & &
\end{array}
$$

Since enzymes may be expected to have more than one point of interaction with their substrates (cf. p. 277), "polyfunctional" model catalysts are of special interest for enzyme chemistry. Thus 2-hydroxy-pyridine is a more effective catalyst of the mutarotation of tetramethyl-glucose than is an equivalent mixture of phenol and pyridine;[40] presumably, the location of the acidic phenolic group and the basic nitrogen in 2-hydroxypyridine favors a two-pronged concerted attack by the catalyst on the substrate.

2-Hydroxypyridine

For the hydrolysis of esters, catalyzed by hydroxide ion, kinetic and isotope studies[41] indicate that the following mechanism accords best with the data:

$$
\begin{array}{ccccccc}
& \text{O} & & \text{O}^- & & \text{O} & & \text{O} \\
& \| & & | & & \| & & \| \\
\text{HO}^- + & \text{C}-\text{OR}' & \rightleftharpoons \text{HO}-\text{C}-\text{OR}' & \rightleftharpoons & \text{HO}-\text{C} + {}^-\text{OR}' & \rightarrow {}^-\text{O}-\text{C} + \text{HOR}' \\
& | & & | & & | & & | \\
& \text{R} & & \text{R} & & \text{R} & & \text{R}
\end{array}
$$

The hydroxide ion is thought to donate a pair of electrons to the carbonyl carbon atom; the resulting transition-state complex gives rise to an unstable intermediate in which the R and OR′ groups are still attached to the carbon, and which decomposes as shown. It will be noted that

[40] C. G. Swain and J. F. Brown, Jr., J. Am. Chem. Soc., 74, 2538 (1952).

[41] M. L. Bender, J. Am. Chem. Soc., 73, 1626 (1951); M. L. Bender and B. W. Turnquest, ibid., 77, 4271 (1955).

the cleavage of the ester occurs between the carbonyl carbon and the OR′ group ("acyl-oxygen fission"). This was demonstrated experimentally by conducting the hydrolysis in the presence of water enriched with respect to the oxygen isotope of mass 18 (O^{18}), and by finding O^{18} in the carboxylate group of $RCOO^-$ but not in R′OH. An entirely analogous result was obtained for the enzymic hydrolysis of acetylcholine by acetylcholine esterase (p. 275); when the reaction occurred in the presence of H_2O^{18}, the isotope appeared in the carboxylate group of acetate.[42]

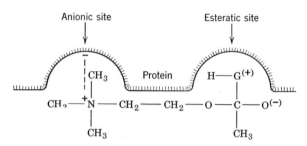

Fig. 17. Postulated interaction between active groups of acetylcholine esterase and its substrate. (From Wilson.[43])

Furthermore, from a study of the kinetics and specific inhibition of acetylcholine esterase, Wilson[43] has concluded that the enzyme-substrate compound may be described as shown in Fig. 17. According to this hypothesis, a basic group G of the "esteratic site" of the enzyme donates an electron pair to the carbonyl carbon atom, with the formation of an unstable intermediate analogous to that postulated for hydroxide ion catalysis. This intermediate is thought to decompose with the elimination of choline (as R′OH) and the formation of an "acyl-enzyme" in which the acetyl group (RCO—) remains bound to G. The acyl-enzyme is hydrolyzed by water to form $RCOO^-$ and to regenerate the basic group G of the enzyme. The assumption of an "anionic site" (cf. Fig. 17) is based on the observed effects of inhibitors, and provides an explanation of the specificity of the enzyme. Here a negatively charged group on the enzyme is thought to combine with the positively charged trimethylammonium group of the substrate.

The hypothesis of the intermediate formation of acyl-enzymes in the enzymic hydrolysis of esters has received support from work with several enzymes other than acetylcholine esterase. With chymotrypsin, which hydrolyzes most effectively esters or amides of aromatic L-amino acids

[42] S. S. Stein and D. E. Koshland, *Arch. Biochem. and Biophys.*, **45**, 467 (1953).

[43] I. B. Wilson, in W. D. McElroy and B. Glass, *Mechanism of Enzyme Action*, Johns Hopkins Press, Baltimore, 1954.

(e.g., L-phenylalanine) in which the α-amino group is acylated (cf. p. 274), it appears probable that an acyl-L-phenylalanyl-enzyme is formed as an intermediate. To account for the specificity of chymo-

$$RCO\text{—}NH\overset{\overset{\textstyle CH_2C_6H_5}{\vert}}{C}HCO\text{—}OR' + \text{chymotrypsin} \rightleftharpoons$$

$$RCO\text{—}NH\overset{\overset{\textstyle CH_2C_6H_5}{\vert}}{C}HCO\text{—chymotrypsin} + R'OH$$

$$\downarrow {\scriptstyle +H_2O}$$

$$RCO\text{—}NH\overset{\overset{\textstyle CH_2C_6H_5}{\vert}}{C}HCOO^- + H^+ + \text{chymotrypsin}$$

trypsin, it is necessary to assume that the enzyme interacts specifically with the acyl-L-phenylalanyl portion of the substrate molecule, not only at the sensitive carbonyl group, but at other points as well. It may be added that the intermediate formation of an acylphenylalanyl-enzyme is indicated by the fact that chymotrypsin catalyzes not only hydrolysis, but also the transfer of the acylphenylalanyl group to amines (Chapter 29). Furthermore, if an acyl-L-phenylalanine is incubated with chymotrypsin in water enriched with respect to H_2O^{18}, the isotope is incorporated into the carboxylate group of the acylamino acid.[44] In the absence of enzyme, no significant incorporation is observed.

Although the nature of the "esteratic site" of acetylcholine esterase or of chymotrypsin is still unknown, kinetic studies of several enzymes that act at ester and amide bonds have suggested that the imidazolyl group of a histidine residue may serve as the basic electron donor, and that the acyl-enzyme may be, in some cases, an acyl-imidazole derivative.

The isotope technique has proved to be an extremely valuable tool for the study of the mechanism of enzymic reactions. In addition to the instances cited above, isotopic compounds have been used to test hypotheses about the nature of enzyme-substrate intermediates in enzyme-catalyzed reactions. For example, if, in the reaction A-B + C $\rightarrow$ B + D, the enzyme E combines with the A portion of A-B to form E-A, which reacts with C to give the products, the reaction sequence is:

(1)   A-B + $E \rightleftharpoons E$-A + B

(2) E-A + C $\rightarrow E$ + D

Thus, if unlabeled A-B and isotopically labeled B (denoted B*) are

[44] D. B. Sprinson and D. Rittenberg, *Nature,* **167,** 484 (1951); F. Vaslow, *Biochim. et Biophys. Acta,* **16,** 601 (1955); M. L. Bender and K. C. Kemp, *J. Am. Chem. Soc.,* **79,** 111, 116 (1957).

incubated in the presence of the enzyme (no C is present), then after a suitable time the substrate A-B will be found to be labeled (A-B*). However, if labeled A is used in place of labeled B, no label will be found in A-B. Such "isotope-exchange" reactions have been used for the study of the mechanism whereby adenosine triphosphate participates in important biochemical processes. In evaluating the data obtained in this manner, however, it is important to consider the homogeneity of the enzyme preparation, and to be certain that the over-all reaction (A-B + C → B + D) and the isotope exchange (A-B + B* ⇌ A-B* + B) are catalyzed by the same enzyme.

The use of isotopes, especially O^{18}, has been valuable for the determination of the site of enzymic cleavage, not only of esters and amides, but also of phosphate compounds and of glycosides. For example, it has been shown that, in the enzymic hydrolysis of adenosine triphosphate to adenosine diphosphate and inorganic phosphate, the cleavage occurs between the oxygen and the terminal phosphorus atom, since in the presence of H_2O^{18} the isotope appears in the inorganic phosphate. As

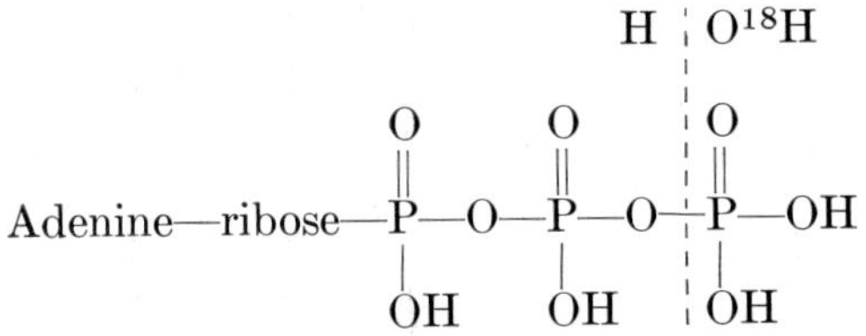

$$\text{Adenine—ribose—P—O—P—O—P—OH}$$

will be seen from the later discussion of phosphorylases (Chapter 18) that act on compounds of the general type $R—OPO_3H_2$, isotope studies have shown the site of cleavage to be at the bond between the R group and the oxygen atom, rather than between the oxygen and the phosphorus atoms.[45]

Other isotopes that have been used with success for studies of the mechanism of enzymic reactions are deuterium (the hydrogen isotope of mass 2) and tritium (the hydrogen isotope of mass 3); these have given significant information about the mode of action of dehydrogenases, of fumarase, and of aldolase. In particular, the use of the hydrogen isotopes has provided striking evidence of the stereochemical specificity of enzyme action even at nonasymmetric carbon atoms. Some enzymic reactions occur at an asymmetric carbon atom with retention of the original configuration; in other reactions there is an inversion of the configuration (Walden inversion).[46] The mechanism of these various reactions may be more profitably considered later, in relation to the properties of the individual enzymes involved.

[45] M. Cohn, *Biochim. et Biophys. Acta*, **20**, 92 (1956).
[46] D. E. Koshland, *Biol. Revs.*, **28**, 416 (1953).

11 · Oxidation and Reduction

In order to permit the enzymic catalysis of endergonic reactions, such as the synthesis of proteins from amino acids, these reactions must be supplied with energy arising from exergonic processes. It is a general biochemical property of living matter that the occurrence of energy-requiring reactions is linked to reactions in which energy is released; the mechanism and rate of the transfer to endergonic processes of energy released in exergonic processes are determined by the nature of the enzyme-catalyzed reactions involved in the coupling. It is therefore important to know something of the enzymes that catalyze biochemical reactions in which energy is released; one may then consider the mechanisms whereby the action of these enzymes is linked to other enzyme-catalyzed reactions that require energy.

The principal energy-yielding reactions in higher forms of living matter are those involving the oxidation of food materials. In animals, the oxidation of carbohydrates and fats is the major source of chemical energy for the maintenance of normal structure and function. The complete oxidation of these foodstuffs involves the conversion of carbon compounds to CO_2 and H_2O with the concomitant release of energy. Many microorganisms are able to obtain chemical energy from processes that do not involve the ultimate participation of molecular oxygen, but many of the exergonic reactions that occur "anaerobically" are closely related to component reactions in the oxidative breakdown of carbohydrates and fats. Even in animals, under conditions of oxygen lack, some tissues call into play energy-yielding reactions that are anaerobic in character. Although the more detailed discussion of these various exergonic processes will be postponed until the appropriate chapters on the intermediate metabolism of carbohydrates and fats, it may be reiterated that, in the unicellular organisms classified as aerobes as well as in multicellular species, the major source of chemical energy is derived from the oxidation of food materials by molecular oxygen.

One of the most important of these nutrients is glucose, or compounds chemically related to it. To maintain life on this planet, it is necessary to have a mechanism for reversing the continual oxidation of glucose by living things. The principal method of achieving this is the utilization, by chlorophyll-bearing plants, of solar energy for the synthesis of glucose from CO_2 and H_2O. This process is termed photosynthesis. It was noted earlier that the standard free-energy change at 25° C in the oxidation of glucose to CO_2 and H_2O is about -690 kcal. The photosynthetic organisms thus use the energy of sunlight to achieve an endergonic process with a $\Delta F°_{298}$ of $+690$ kcal per mole of glucose. In a sense, therefore, these organisms are the truly productive members of the biological population of the earth. In terms of their energy requirements, they are self-supporting ("autotrophic"); moreover, they enable animals and other "heterotrophic" organisms to subsist. It will be clear, therefore, that the process of photosynthesis is the means whereby the continued occurrence of exergonic reactions, involving oxidation of glucose, is made possible. In the succeeding chapters, consideration will be given to the way in which energy derived from the oxidation of glucose and other carbon compounds is made available for useful work. Some of the knowledge about the mechanism of photosynthesis will be summarized in Chapter 22.

The scientific study of the mechanisms of biological oxidations may be said to have begun with the work of Lavoisier, who in 1777 showed that during respiration, animals remove oxygen from the air. He concluded that this uptake of oxygen continues until the animal has absorbed all the available oxygen and has converted it into carbon dioxide. In 1780, in a joint research with Laplace, Lavoisier measured the oxygen intake and CO_2 output of guinea pigs and established the quantitative relations in this respiratory exchange of gases; the ratio of the number of moles of CO_2 produced to the number of moles of O_2 taken up is usually termed the "respiratory quotient"(R.Q.). If it is assumed that the behavior of the two gases approximates that of an ideal gas, Avogadro's law may be applied. Therefore,

$$\text{R.Q.} = \frac{\text{Volume of } CO_2 \text{ produced (at standard temperature and pressure)}}{\text{Volume of } O_2 \text{ taken up (at standard temperature and pressure)}}$$

Lavoisier and Laplace also measured the heat production of an animal and compared the amount of heat produced with the amount released when carbon was burned in the presence of the quantity of oxygen consumed by the animal. Their conclusions were stated as follows:

Since we have found . . . the two quantities of heat to be nearly the same, we can conclude directly and without hypothesis that the production of animal heat in the body is due at least in greater part to the transformation of oxygen to carbon dioxide during the process of respiration.

A few years later, in 1785, Lavoisier recognized that he had been incorrect in supposing that respiration involved only the oxidation of carbon. As a result of more careful quantitative measurement of the respiratory quotient, he realized that a portion of the oxygen was used for some process other than the oxidation of carbon to carbon dioxide, and concluded that some of the oxygen was used for the oxidation of hydrogen to give water. In 1780 he could not have known this, because the latter reaction was not discovered until 1781 by Cavendish.

The century that followed Lavoisier's discoveries witnessed many modifications and extensions of his basic ideas. The sites of the oxidation of metabolites were shown by Pflüger (1875) to be the cells and tissues, as foreshadowed by the studies of Spallanzani (published by Senebier in 1807). With the emergence of enzyme chemistry during the latter half of the nineteenth century, it was recognized that biological oxidations are catalyzed by intracellular enzymes, then termed "oxidases" (Bertrand, 1897); these were believed to be metal compounds that activate molecular oxygen. The work of Battelli and Stern[1] was of special importance in emphasizing the role, in cellular respiration, of the enzymic oxidation of metabolites such as succinic acid. From the subsequent work of Wieland and Thunberg[2] it became clear that biological oxidation involves the loss of hydrogen atoms from a substrate (dehydrogenation). Around 1925, there ensued an active discussion about the relative importance of the enzymic activation of molecular oxygen and of the enzymic activation of bound hydrogen. It will be seen from the succeeding chapters that the oxidations studied by the early investigators are catalyzed by multienzyme systems, involving a sequence of enzyme-catalyzed reactions, and that both "oxygen activation" and "hydrogen activation" are important. Some aspects of the history of this subject have been summarized by Keilin and Slater.[3]

In modern studies on biological oxidations, the manometric apparatus invented by Barcroft and Haldane in 1902 and improved by Warburg in 1923 has been of decisive importance.[4] More recently, the apparatus has undergone further modification to increase its sensitivity.[5] A suitable biological preparation (tissue slices, a tissue extract, or a solution of

[1] F. Battelli and L. Stern, *Ergebn. Physiol.,* **15**, 96 (1912).

[2] T. Thunberg, *Ergebn. Physiol.,* **39**, 76 (1937).

[3] D. Keilin and E. C. Slater, *Brit. Med. Bull.,* **9**, 89 (1953).

[4] W. W. Umbreit et al., *Manometric Techniques and Tissue Metabolism,* 2nd Ed., Burgess Publishing Co., Minneapolis, 1949; M. Dixon, *Manometric Methods,* 3rd Ed., Cambridge University Press, Cambridge, 1951.

[5] D. Burk and G. Hobby, *Science,* **120**, 640 (1954).

purified enzyme) is added to a buffer solution, and (usually) placed in the main vessel of the reaction flask of the manometric assembly (cf. Fig. 1), while the appropriate substrate is introduced into the side arm of the flask. The flask is then attached to the manometer and placed in a constant-temperature bath; after the flask contents have reached the desired temperature, they are mixed, and the oxidation is allowed to proceed. The manometric fluid (Brodie solution) is so selected that a column of 10,000 mm has the same pressure as 760 mm of mercury (1 atmosphere). If gas mixtures other than air are employed (e.g., 95 per cent O_2 and 5 per cent CO_2), the air in the closed portion of the assembly, i.e., in contact with the reaction mixture, must be displaced by the appropriate mixture. If only O_2 is taken up and CO_2 is evolved, the latter is removed by means of alkali in the center well of the reaction flask. As oxygen is absorbed, the level of the manometric fluid in the right-hand limb rises; to determine the amount of gas taken up, the gas volume is restored to that at the start of the experiment. The volume in the closed portion of the assembly is thus kept constant; this causes a fall in pressure and a drop in the level of fluid in the open left-hand limb of the manometer. The extent of this drop thus gives a measure of the change in gas pressure in the reaction flask. The volume of O_2 (in microliters, μl, or cubic millimeters, cmm) absorbed (x) is proportional to the alteration in the reading (in millimeters) on the open limb of the manometer (h); thus $x = -hk$, where k is a proportionality constant characteristic of the volume of the empty flask plus the gas space in the

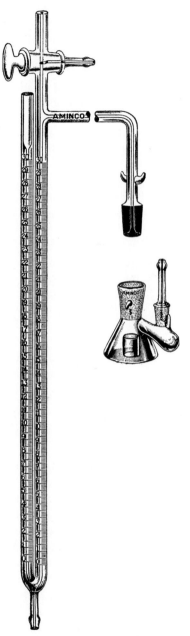

Fig. 1. Warburg manometer and reaction flask. (Courtesy of American Instrument Co.)

right-hand limb, the volume and vapor pressure of the fluid, the solubility of oxygen, and the temperature and atmospheric pressure.

The rate of oxygen uptake by a tissue preparation is usually expressed in terms of Q_{O_2}, which equals the microliters of O_2 (at standard temperature and pressure) taken up per milligram of dry weight of tissue per hour (cf. Table 1). The manometric apparatus may be used, in a manner similar to that described above, for the measurement of the rate of absorption or release of gases other than oxygen. Thus, if CO_2 is evolved, one may speak of Q_{CO_2}, i.e., microliters of CO_2 given off per milligram of dry weight of tissue per hour. For further details about the many modifications of this important technique, see the monograph by Umbreit et al.,[4] cited above.

Table I. Rate of Respiration of Several Tissues and Organisms

	Temperature, °C	$-Q_{O_2}$
Rat kidney slices	37	21
Rat brain slices	37	14
Rat liver slices	37	9
Human spermatozoa	37	1
Azotobacter	28	200–4000
Yeast	28	0.4–0.8
Yeast (in glucose)	28	40–80
Chlorella (in glucose)	25	5
Neurospora (dormant spores)	25	0.25
Neurospora (germinating spores)	25	19.6

Oxidation-Reduction[6,7]

The term oxidation was considered by Lavoisier and his contemporaries to refer to the addition of oxygen atoms to the substance being oxidized. The opposite process, that of reduction, was defined as the removal of oxygen from an oxide. During the nineteenth century numerous reactions were discovered in which hydrogen atoms were lost from organic compounds, and these reactions also were termed oxidations. The addition of hydrogen atoms to a compound thus would represent a reduction. Furthermore, the term oxidation was applied to reactions such as the conversion of a ferrous ion (Fe^{2+}) to a ferric ion (Fe^{3+}); here there is a loss of an electron. The reverse process, the addition of an electron to a ferric ion, was termed a reduction.

[6] D. A. MacInnes, *Principles of Electrochemistry*, Reinhold Publishing Corp., New York, 1939.

[7] W. M. Clark et al., *U. S. Pub. Health Service Hyg. Lab. Bull.*, No. 151 (1928).

A unified theory of oxidation became possible only after the recognition that the essential characteristic of oxidation processes is the removal of electrons from the substance being oxidized. More specifically, oxidation is defined as the withdrawal of electrons from a substance, whether or not there is an accompanying addition of oxygen, and whether or not there is an accompanying loss of hydrogen. The applicability of this definition to the oxidation of ferrous ion to the ferric form is immediately apparent. Here

$$Fe^{2+} \rightarrow Fe^{3+} + e$$

where e denotes the electron released in the oxidation. In a similar manner, the oxidation of a molecule of hydrogen to 2 protons may be represented as

$$H_2 \rightarrow 2H^+ + 2e$$

The reverse of each of these oxidation reactions is a reduction process, and the definition of reduction, as a reaction in which electrons are added to a substance, is obvious. Clearly, a reduction need not involve the accompanying removal of oxygen or the addition of hydrogen. The two reactions written above are reversible reactions, and the pairs of substances involved, i.e., Fe^{2+}-Fe^{3+} or H_2-$2H^+$, are termed "oxidation-reduction systems."

In reactions in which electrons are released, free electrons are not actually present in the solution in appreciable amounts; in order to permit an oxidation to proceed, there must be present in the solution a substance that will take up these electrons. Thus the electron acceptor is an oxidizing agent (oxidant) which is reduced by the reductant.

In the oxidation of Fe^{2+} to Fe^{3+} there occurs the release of 1 electron; this is observed for the metals of the transition series of the periodic table (e.g., Fe, Co) which can undergo univalent oxidation and can exist at two levels of oxidation differing by 1 electron. Although univalent oxidation is common among inorganic compounds, in the oxidation and reduction of organic molecules the reaction usually involves a bivalent oxidation; i.e., 2 electrons are transferred. Examples of such bivalent oxidation-reduction are the reversible reactions involving hydroquinone and quinone, lactic acid and pyruvic acid, succinic acid and fumaric acid.

Each of the oxidation reactions involving these organic compounds is a reversible reaction, but, just as with the oxidation of Fe^{2+} to Fe^{3+}, the reactions will not proceed to an appreciable extent unless there is present an electron acceptor, i.e., an oxidizing agent, for the oxidation process; similarly, there must be present an electron donor, i.e., a reducing agent, for the reverse reaction. In writing these oxidation reactions, the hydro-

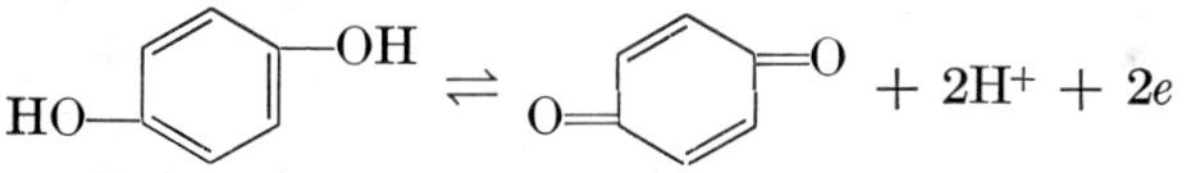

Hydroquinone Quinone

$$\begin{array}{c} CH_3 \\ | \\ H-C-OH \\ | \\ COOH \end{array} \rightleftharpoons \begin{array}{c} CH_3 \\ | \\ C=O \\ | \\ COOH \end{array} + 2H^+ + 2e$$

Lactic acid Pyruvic acid

$$\begin{array}{c} CH_2COOH \\ | \\ CH_2COOH \end{array} \rightleftharpoons \begin{array}{c} HOOCCH \\ \| \\ HCCOOH \end{array} + 2H^+ + 2e$$

Succinic acid Fumaric acid

gen atoms lost by the reductant are denoted $H^+ + e$ to emphasize the release of electrons in such processes. As will be seen on p. 319, reactions are known in which electron transfer from a reductant to an oxidant is concomitant with hydrogen transfer, and the protons are not released into solution.

For some bivalent oxidations involving organic compounds, it has been shown that an intermediate compound is formed which has lost only 1 electron. Michaelis[8] and Elema proposed that a stepwise univalent oxidation occurs in such reactions. The principle may be illustrated by the reaction studied by Michaelis—the oxidation of tetraphenyl-*p*-

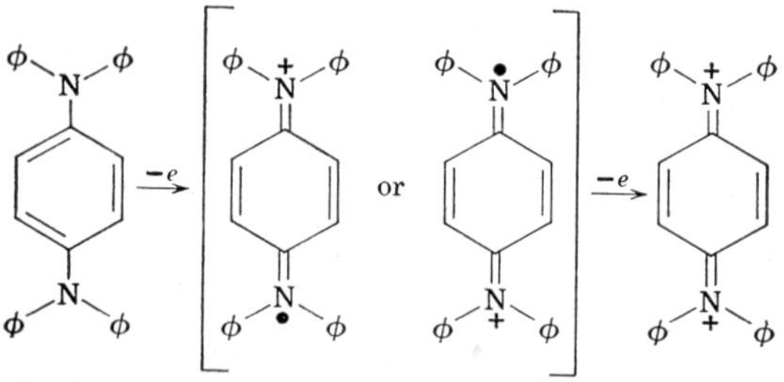

Tetraphenyl-*p*-phenylenediamine Semiquinone Tetraphenyl-*p*-quinonediimine

phenylenediamine to its corresponding quinonoid form. It will be noted from the reaction sequence shown that univalent oxidation leads to an intermediate compound, termed by Michaelis a "semiquinone," which may be written as one of two equivalent structures. These two structures differ from each other in the assignment of an unshared electron (denoted

[8] L. Michaelis. *Chem. Revs.,* **16,** 243 (1935); *Am. Scientist,* **34,** 573 (1946).

by a dot) to one or another of the 2 nitrogen atoms. The semiquinone should not be considered simply a mixture of the two forms, but rather a single intermediate of the two. Substances whose formulae may be written in two or more forms with regard to the distribution of electrons in the molecule are termed "resonance" hybrids, and the phenomenon of resonance which they exhibit serves to stabilize the structure. For this reason the semiquinone derived from tetraphenyl-p-phenylenediamine can be demonstrated experimentally. Under suitable conditions, other semi-quinones also have sufficient stability to permit their experimental study. It may be added, however, that the existence of semiquinones does not prove their formation by stepwise univalent electron transfer.[9]

Oxidation-Reduction Potentials

It is important to define the relative tendency of a series of oxidants to act as electron acceptors, or of the corresponding series of reductants to act as electron donors. Such quantitative comparison is possible on the basis of the property of oxidation-reduction systems termed the oxidation-reduction potential.

The concept of the potential of an oxidation-reduction system may be illustrated by considering a solution containing Fe^{2+}, which has a certain tendency to release electrons and pass over into Fe^{3+}; similarly, the Fe^{3+} has a certain tendency to accept electrons and pass over into Fe^{2+}. The solution thus contains the Fe^{2+}-Fe^{3+} oxidation-reduction system. On placing into the solution a chemically inert metal such as gold or platinum, electrons can leave the metal (termed an electrode) and go into the solution, or electrons may pass from the solution into the metal. There will be, in effect, a difference in the electron pressure of the metallic electrode and that of the Fe^{2+}-Fe^{3+} oxidation-reduction system. In order to determine the potential of the Fe^{2+}-Fe^{3+} system, the assembly must be so arranged that the metal dipping into the solution is connected to another electrode dipping into an oxidation-reduction system of known potential. To complete the circuit, the two solutions are connected by means of a salt bridge (e.g., agar gel containing KCl); this permits the migration of ions but prevents the chemical interaction of the two oxidation-reduction systems. Between the two metallic elec-trodes of the assembly is inserted an instrument, termed a potentiometer, for measuring the difference in electric potential (measured in volts) between the two "half-cells." In Fig. 2, the second oxidation-reduction system is the hydrogen-hydrogen ion system. In this half-cell, hydrogen ion tends to accept electrons from the electrode, and hydrogen tends to

[9] F. H. Westheimer, in W. D. McElroy and B. Glass, *The Mechanism of Enzyme Action*, Johns Hopkins Press, Baltimore, 1954.

donate electrons to the electrode. If an electric current were allowed
to flow in the complete assembly, electrons would move from the hydrogen
half-cell to the Fe^{2+}-Fe^{3+} half-cell. However, if this tendency for
electron flow is exactly opposed by means of the potentiometer, the
difference in electrical potential of the two oxidation-reduction systems
can be measured. The operation of this assembly fulfills the requirement
of thermodynamic reversibility (cf. p. 229), except for the effect of

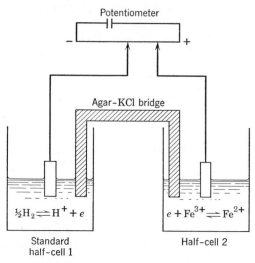

Fig. 2. Schematic representation of assembly for measurement of oxidation-reduction potentials.

irreversible diffusion at the liquid junctions. This effect ("liquid-
junction potential") may be reduced to a small value by using high
concentrations of KCl in the salt bridge.

In order to compare the potentials of different oxidation-reduction
systems, it is necessary to refer all of them to a common standard whose
potential is arbitrarily defined as zero under specified conditions. The
standard oxidation-reduction system is the hydrogen half-cell (termed the
hydrogen electrode) where the reaction is $\frac{1}{2}H_2 \rightleftharpoons H^+ + e$; by definition,
the potential of this system is zero at all temperatures when an inert
metallic electrode dips into a solution of unit activity with respect to
protons, i.e., pH 0, in equilibrium with hydrogen gas at a pressure of
1 atmosphere. Clearly, it is not necessary that the reference half-cell in
the complete assembly be the hydrogen system; any other oxidation-
reduction system whose potential has been accurately established with
reference to the standard hydrogen electrode may be used instead. The
experimental value for the difference in potential between the two half-

cells can then be used for the calculation of the oxidation-reduction potential of the system in the Fe^{2+}-Fe^{3+} half-cell with reference to the hydrogen electrode. In a similar manner, the potential of any oxidation-reduction system can be determined if that system can accept or donate electrons reversibly at metallic electrodes. Such oxidation-reduction systems are termed electromotively active systems. A more detailed discussion of the properties of such systems may be found in Clark's book.[10]

The difference in potential between the Fe^{2+}-Fe^{3+} half-cell and the standard hydrogen electrode is given by the formula

$$E_h = E_0 + \frac{RT}{n\mathfrak{F}} \ln \frac{(Fe^{3+})}{(Fe^{2+})}$$

where E_h is the observed difference in potential (in volts), R is the gas constant (8.314 absolute joules per degree per mole), T is the absolute temperature, n is the number of electrons per gram equivalent (in this reaction it equals unity), and $\mathfrak{F}$ is the faraday (96,496 absolute joules per absolute volt equivalent) and is defined as the amount of electricity (in ampere seconds) required to liberate one gram equivalent of a univalent element in electrolysis. The logarithmic term refers to the ratio of the activities of the two components of the oxidation-reduction system; by convention, the product of oxidation is placed in the numerator, thus defining the sign of the potential in relation to the standard hydrogen electrode. In general, one writes the above equation as follows:

$$E_h = E_0 + \frac{RT}{n\mathfrak{F}} \ln \frac{(\text{oxid})}{(\text{red})} = E_0 + \frac{2.303RT}{n\mathfrak{F}} \log \frac{(\text{oxid})}{(\text{red})}$$

At 30° C, $2.303RT/n\mathfrak{F}$ has a value of 0.06 volt when $n = 1$, and of 0.03 when $n = 2$. For the derivation of this fundamental relationship, see Clark.[10]

According to the convention used by biochemists, and by many physical chemists, E_h becomes more positive when the ratio of (oxid) to (red) is increased; also, if oxidation-reduction system A has a more negative value of E_h than does oxidation-reduction system B, system A will tend to reduce system B. Thus the system with the more negative potential has the greater tendency to donate electrons. Many physical chemists employ the opposite convention, which assigns the more negative potential to the system that has the greater tendency to accept electrons;[11] the "oxidation potentials" given by this convention are equal in magnitude to the "reduction potentials" used by biochemists, but of opposite sign. In 1953, it was recommended by the International Union

[10] W. M. Clark, *Topics in Physical Chemistry*, 2nd Ed., Chapter 21, Williams and Wilkins Co., Baltimore, 1952.

[11] W. M. Latimer, *The Oxidation States of the Elements and Their Potentials in Aqueous Solutions*, Prentice-Hall, Englewood Cliffs, N. J., 1952.

of Pure and Applied Chemistry that "reduction potentials" be used for the designation of the electrode potentials of oxidation-reduction systems (cf. Latimer[12]). In the biochemical literature, such "reduction potentials" are termed "oxidation-reduction potentials."

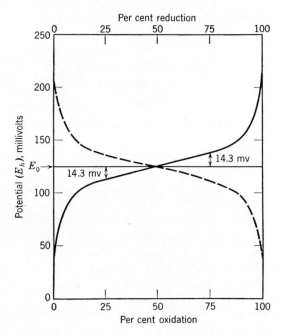

Fig. 3. Potentiometric titration of the reduced form of an oxidation-reduction system with an oxidizing agent (solid line). The curve shown is characteristic of any bivalent oxidation-reduction where semiquinone formation is not observed. For any given oxidation-reduction system, the absolute value of the potential for half-oxidation depends on the nature of the system and on the pH of the solution (cf. text). The broken line describes the potentiometric titration of the oxidized form with a reducing agent (abscissa at top of figure).

The meaning of the term E_0 becomes apparent if one considers the situation when (oxid) = (red). Under these circumstances, $E_h = E_0$, and thus E_0 may be defined as the potential (with reference to the standard hydrogen electrode) established by an oxidation-reduction system when the activities of the oxidized and reduced forms are equal. This value is characteristic of each oxidation-reduction system and gives a measure of the relative ability of that system to accept or donate electrons in oxidation-reduction reactions. With dilute solutions, it is customary to use the molar concentrations of the components in place of the activities.

The significance of E_0 may be visualized more clearly from the result

12 W. M. Latimer, *J. Am. Chem. Soc.*, **76**, 1200 (1954).

of an electrometric titration experiment. If to a half-cell containing the reduced form of an oxidation-reduction system one adds increasing quantities of a strong oxidizing agent, then the curve that relates the extent of oxidation (denoted as per cent oxidation on the abscissa) to the E_h of the half-cell has the form shown in Fig. 3. At the point at which 50 per cent oxidation has been effected, there is an inflection in the curve, and E_h equals E_0. It will be noted that the curve relating the

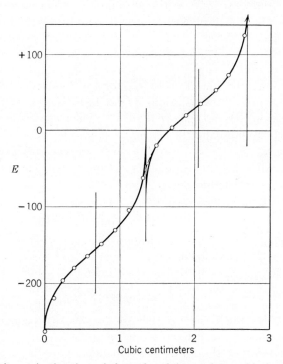

Fig. 4. Potentiometric titration of the reduced form of an oxidation-reduction system (pyocyanine) with an oxidizing agent (ferricyanide ion) at pH 1.82. In this titration, the separation of the discrete univalent oxidation steps is apparent; the form largely present at 50 per cent oxidation is the semiquinone. [From E. A. H. Friedheim and L. Michaelis, *J. Biol. Chem.*, **91**, 355 (1931).]

reduction of the oxidized form of the oxidation-reduction system to the potential has the same shape as the curve describing the reverse process. The slope of such curves in the region of the inflection point is directly related to the number of electrons involved in the oxidation-reduction; if the curve in Fig. 3 is taken to represent a bivalent oxidation or reduction, the corresponding curve for a univalent process would be somewhat more steep at the inflection point. The shape of a potentiometric titration curve therefore offers information about the appearance of semiquinone forms in the course of a bivalent oxidation. In Fig. 4, the graph shows an electrometric titration curve that is composed of two separate univalent oxidation steps which are clearly separated. However, under conditions where the semiquinone does not appear, the two univalent titration curves merge into one another to give the characteristic curve for a bivalent oxidation reaction.

The potentiometric titration of the Fe^{2+}-Fe^{3+} system indicates that at $25°$ C the value of E_0 for this system is 0.771 volt (771 millivolts) more positive than the E_0 for the standard hydrogen electrode. This value may therefore be termed the "normal oxidation-reduction potential" of the Fe^{2+}-Fe^{3+} system at $25°$ C. The normal potentials of other electromotively active oxidation-reduction systems are denoted in a similar manner.

If one examines the variation of E_0 for the Fe^{2+}-Fe^{3+} system as a function of the pH of the solution, it will be found that the E_0 is the same over a wide pH range (pH 0 to 5). Such constancy of E_0 with changes in pH is not found, however, in oxidation-reduction systems in which hydrogen ions enter into the over-all chemical reaction that describes the half-cell. The simplest reaction in which this occurs is the hydrogen electrode reaction itself. Here

$$E_h = \frac{RT}{n\mathcal{F}} \ln \frac{(H^+)}{P_{H_2}^{1/2}}$$

where P_{H_2} denotes the pressure of hydrogen gas. Since the standard hydrogen electrode is defined with reference to hydrogen gas at unit pressure, at $30°$ C, $E_h = 0.06 \log (H^+)$, or $E_h = -0.06 \, p$H. Thus at pH 7 the potential of the hydrogen electrode is -0.420 volt (or -420 millivolts). This variation of the potential of the hydrogen electrode with pH provides the basis for the use of the hydrogen electrode for accurate determination of pH (cf. p. 19).

It was noted earlier that the oxidation and reduction of organic substances frequently involves the appearance or disappearance of hydrogen ions. Such oxidation-reduction systems are the predominant ones in biological reactions, and their E_0 values will show variation with pH. For example, in the oxidation of succinate ion to fumarate ion, 2 protons and 2 electrons are released, and, if the "half-cell" is considered as a unit, one must take into account the $\frac{1}{2}H_2 \rightleftharpoons H^+ + e$ system. A simple way of considering the oxidation of succinate is to separate the liberation of H^+ from the oxidation-reduction as shown. The hypothetical intermediate

$$\begin{array}{ccc}
\begin{array}{l}
H \\
H:\overset{..}{\underset{..}{C}}:COO^- \\
H:\overset{..}{\underset{..}{C}}:COO^- \\
H
\end{array}
&
\xrightarrow{-2H^+}
\left[
\begin{array}{l}
H \\
:\overset{..}{\underset{..}{C}}:COO^- \\
:\overset{..}{\underset{..}{C}}:COO^- \\
H
\end{array}
\right]
&
\xrightarrow{-2e}
\begin{array}{l}
H \\
{}^-OOC:\overset{..}{\underset{..}{C}} \\
\overset{..}{\underset{..}{C}}:COO^- \\
H
\end{array}
\end{array}$$

Succinate   Fumarate

(in brackets) may be formally considered the conjugate base of succinate. One may write the oxidation of hydroquinone to quinone in a similar manner.

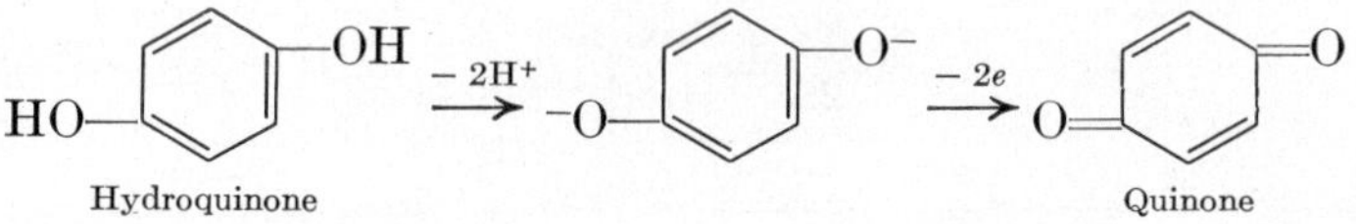

If, in the course of an oxidation or a reduction, there is formed a new group, capable of acting as an acid or a conjugate base, this will find expression in the shape of the pH-dependence curve of the potential at a fixed ratio of (oxid) to (red). Examples of such reactions are the oxidation of an aldehyde hydrate to the corresponding carboxylic acid (e.g., oxidation of acetaldehyde to acetate ion) or the reduction of quinone to hydroquinone. Therefore consideration must be given to the acidic dissociation constant of the new group produced. Clearly, at pH values more acid than the pK' of the new group, the contribution of the new group to the hydrogen ion activity of the half-cell will be different from the contribution at pH values more alkaline than the pK'. Consequently, in plotting the potential for 50 per cent oxidation as a function of pH, breaks will be observed in the curve whenever the curve passes through a pH region in which a pK' is involved.

To illustrate this, it will be convenient to consider the reaction

$$H_2 \text{ red} \rightarrow \text{Oxid} + 2H^+ + 2e$$

where the reduced form (H_2 red) of the oxidation-reduction system is a weak dibasic acid that dissociates as follows:

$$H_2 \text{ red} \rightleftharpoons H \text{ red}^- + H^+$$

$$H \text{ red}^- \rightleftharpoons \text{red}^{2-} + H^+$$

The dissociation constants of H_2 red will be described by K_1' and K_2'.

$$K_1' = \frac{[H^+][H \text{ red}^-]}{[H_2 \text{ red}]} \qquad K_2' = \frac{[H^+][\text{red}^{2-}]}{[H \text{ red}^-]}$$

The total stoichiometric concentration of the reduced form is denoted by [red], which is equal to $[H_2 \text{ red}] + [H \text{ red}^-] + [\text{red}^{2-}]$. Therefore the electrode equation of the oxidation-reduction system,

$$E_h = E_0 + \frac{RT}{2\mathfrak{F}} \ln \frac{[\text{oxid}][H^+]^2}{[H_2 \text{ red}]}$$

may be written as follows:

$$E_h = E_0 + \frac{RT}{2\mathfrak{F}} \ln \frac{[\text{oxid}]}{[\text{red}]} + \frac{RT}{2\mathfrak{F}} \ln \left[[H^+]^2 + K_1'[H^+] + K_1'K_2' \right]$$

At low pH values the magnitude of $[H^+]^2$ will be appreciably greater than $K_1'[H^+]$ and much greater than $K_1'K_2'$. Under these circumstances the electrode equation will be

$$E_h = E_0 + \frac{RT}{2\mathfrak{F}} \ln \frac{[\text{oxid}]}{[\text{red}]} + \frac{RT}{2\mathfrak{F}} \ln [H^+]^2$$

At 30° C,

$$E_h = E_0 + 0.03 \log \frac{[\text{oxid}]}{[\text{red}]} - 0.06\ p\text{H}$$

When $[\text{oxid}]/[\text{red}]$ is a constant, the potential will vary with pH in a linear manner, and the slope of the line will be -0.06. At a higher pH value, where $K_1'[H^+]$ is much larger than $[H^+]^2$ or $K_1'K_2'$, the slope of the line will be -0.03. Extrapolation of the two slopes to the point

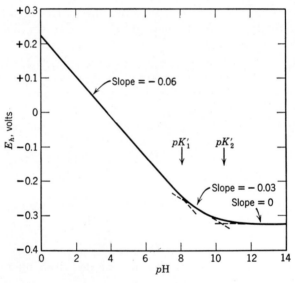

Fig. 5. Dependence of potential for half-oxidation of anthraquinone-2,6-disulfonate on pH. [From J. B. Conant et al., *J. Am. Chem. Soc.*, **44**, 1382 (1922).]

of intersection of the two lines will give the pK_1' of the dibasic acid (H_2 red). At high pH values, $K_1'K_2'$ will be much greater than $[H^+]^2$ or $K_1'[H^+]$, and the pH-dependence curve will have a slope of zero; the value of pK_2' may then be determined by extrapolation as before (cf. Fig. 5).

In the linear portions of the pH-dependence curve, the potential (at 30° C) varies with pH according to the equation

$$\frac{\Delta E_h}{\Delta p\text{H}} = -\frac{0.06a}{n}$$

where a denotes the number of hydrogen ions released in an oxidation reaction and n is the number of electrons involved in the process.

Since, in the consideration of biological oxidation-reduction reactions, it is important to compare the potentials for 50 per cent oxidation at a physiological pH value, such as pH 7, it is customary to refer to the "midpoint" potential at a given pH by the symbol E_0' (or E_m). Thus, for a solution buffered at pH 7,

$$E_h(pH\ 7) = E_0'(pH\ 7) + \frac{0.06}{n} \log \frac{[\text{oxid}]}{[\text{red}]}$$

The term E_0 is reserved for the midpoint potential of an oxidation-reduction system at pH 0.

One may set up tables of the magnitude of E_0' at physiological pH values for a variety of oxidation-reduction systems of biological interest. Some of the currently accepted potentials are given in Table 2; more data (some of which have undergone revision) may be found in the

Table 2. Electrode Potentials of Some Oxidation-Reduction Systems of Biochemical Interest

System	Temperature, °C	E_0, volts	E_0' (pH 7), volts
Hydrogen-hydrogen ion	30	0	−0.420
Formate-carbon dioxide	30		−0.42
β-Hydroxybutyrate-acetoacetate	38		−0.293
Diphosphopyridine nucleotide (oxidant)	30		−0.32
Riboflavin (oxidant)	30		−0.208
Phthiocol (oxidant)	30	+0.299	−0.180
Lactate-pyruvate	25		−0.19
Malate-oxaloacetate	25		−0.166
Yellow enzyme (oxidant)	30		−0.123
Pyocyanine (oxidant)	30	+0.366	−0.032
Succinate-fumarate	?		0.00
2-Methyl-1,4-naphthoquinone (oxidant)	?	+0.422	
Methylene blue (oxidant)	30		+0.011
Myoglobin-metmyglobin	30		+0.046
Ascorbic acid (reductant)	30	+0.390	+0.058
Alloxan (oxidant)	30	+0.364	+0.062
Hemoglobin-methemoglobin	30		+0.139
Ferrocytochrome c (reductant)	30	+0.464	+0.26
Hydrogen peroxide-oxygen	25	+0.682	
Hydroquinone-quinone	25	+0.699	
Ferrocytochrome a (reductant)	20		+0.29
3,4-Dihydroxy-L-phenylalanine (reductant)	30	+0.80	+0.38
Adrenalin (reductant)	30	+0.809	+0.38
Ferrous-ferric	25	+0.771	
Water-oxygen	25		+0.815

book by Lardy.[13]   It is likely that many of the oxidation-reduction potentials now used in biochemistry may require correction when they are redetermined more accurately.

Free-Energy Changes in Oxidation-Reduction

Data of the kind given in Table 2 permit one to predict the direction of interaction of any two oxidation-reduction systems.   As noted before (cf. p. 293), when one system has a more positive ("higher") electrode potential than another system, it is a stronger oxidizing agent; i.e., its tendency to take up electrons is greater than that of the system of "lower" electrode potential.   This statement does not imply that two oxidation-reduction systems of different potential will, in all cases, interact; the difference in potential is related to the free-energy change in a bimolecular reaction involving the oxidized form of one system and the reduced form of the other system, but not to the rate of their interaction.   The relationship between oxidation-reduction potential and free-energy change may be made apparent by considering two oxidation-reduction systems designated $A_r \rightleftharpoons A_o$ and $B_r \rightleftharpoons B_o$ respectively.   The subscript r denotes the reduced forms and the subscript o denotes the oxidized forms. Let us assign to the reaction $A_r \rightleftharpoons A_o$ a value of E_0 of -0.200 volt $(30°)$, and to the reaction $B_r \rightleftharpoons B_o$ an E_0 of -0.100 volt $(30°)$.   The reversible bimolecular reaction

$$A_r + B_o \rightleftharpoons A_o + B_r$$

in which the valence change is 2 for both oxidation-reduction systems will be characterized by an equilibrium constant (concentrations assumed to be equal to activities):

$$K = \frac{[A_o][B_r]}{[A_r][B_o]}$$

It will be obvious that, under conditions at which $[A_o] = [A_r]$, K will be equal to $[B_r]/[B_o]$; when $[B_r] = [B_o]$, K will be equal to $[A_o]/[A_r]$. If the bimolecular reaction is allowed to proceed until equilibrium is attained, the potential will be given by the equation

$$E_h = -0.200 + \frac{0.06}{n} \log \frac{[A_o]}{[A_r]} = -0.100 + \frac{0.06}{n} \log \frac{[B_o]}{[B_r]}$$

Thus

$$-0.100 - (-0.200) = \frac{0.06}{n} \left(\log \frac{[A_o]}{[A_r]} - \log \frac{[B_o]}{[B_r]} \right)$$

Hence

$$\Delta E_0 = 0.100 = \frac{0.06}{n} \log \frac{[A_o][B_r]}{[A_r][B_o]} = \frac{0.06}{n} \log K$$

[13] H. A. Lardy, *Respiratory Enzymes*, Burgess Publishing Co., Minneapolis, 1949.

More generally, one may state that

$$\Delta E_0 = \frac{RT}{n\mathfrak{F}} \ln K \qquad \text{or} \qquad n\mathfrak{F}\, \Delta E_0 = RT \ln K$$

From the earlier discussion of the relationship between the free-energy change in a reversible chemical reaction and the equilibrium constant (cf. p. 231), $\Delta F^\circ = -RT \ln K$, it follows that

$$\Delta F^\circ = -n\mathfrak{F}\, \Delta E_0$$

To express the free-energy change in terms of absolute calories per mole, the value of the faraday must be taken as 23,063 cal per volt equivalent. Therefore, for a potential difference of 1 volt, when n equals unity, the free-energy change is $-23,063$ absolute calories per mole.

In the bimolecular reaction discussed above,

$$\Delta F^\circ_{303} = -2 \times 23,063 \times 0.100 = -4613 \text{ cal}$$

The reaction is therefore an exergonic process, and may occur spontaneously; however, the rate of the reaction will be determined by the energy of activation (p. 265), and a catalyst may be required to allow it to proceed at a measurable rate. Clearly, one may calculate the free-energy change for each of the component oxidation-reduction systems by means of the equation $\Delta F^\circ = -n\mathfrak{F}E_0$, and obtain the value of ΔF° for the bimolecular reaction by difference. Thus $\Delta F^\circ = \Delta F^\circ$ (B system) $- \Delta F^\circ$ (A system) $= 4613 - (+9226) = -4613$ cal.

For a reaction conducted at a pH value where the midpoint potentials of the interacting systems differ from the E_0 values, the standard free-energy change is given by the term $-n\mathfrak{F}\Delta E_0{}'$, and is sometimes denoted by the symbol $\Delta F'$ (the free-energy change for a reaction in which all reactants except H$^+$ are in their standard states; cf. p. 236). The values of $\Delta F'$ (at a given pH) and of ΔF° may be different, since the dependence of the midpoint potential on pH may be different for the two interacting oxidation-reduction systems.

The above relationship between oxidation-reduction potential and free energy provides another experimental technique for the determination of ΔF° in reversible reactions involving valence change. The values thus obtained may then be compared with the results of calculation of ΔF° from thermal data by the equation $\Delta F^\circ = \Delta H^\circ - T\, \Delta S^\circ$, discussed on p. 236. Such a comparison was made for the succinate-fumarate oxidation-reduction system.[14] In these studies, the value of E_0 was obtained by extrapolation to pH 0 from the midpoint potential determined in the presence of the enzyme succinic dehydrogenase (p. 344) at pH 7.2 and 25° C; the magnitude of ΔF° calculated from the potential was found to be in excellent agreement with that derived from values for ΔH° and ΔS°, in accord with the view (cf. p. 211) that the enzyme does not alter the position of the equilibrium, but merely hastens its attainment.

[14] H. Borsook and H. F. Schott, *J. Biol. Chem.*, **92**, 535, 559 (1931).

Biological Oxidation-Reduction Systems

The foregoing considerations are of special importance in the study of biochemical oxidation-reduction reactions; the midpoint potentials of many systems cannot be measured easily potentiometrically since these systems are not electromotively active and do not establish stable potentials at metallic electrodes. However, if an oxidation-reduction system of unknown potential reacts reversibly, in the presence of a suitable catalyst, with another system of known potential, then a determination of the concentrations of the four components at equilibrium will permit the calculation of the equilibrium constant, and thus give the potential of the unknown system. In conducting such experiments, it is desirable to select systems that are not too far apart on the potential scale; otherwise the activity ratios (as a first approximation, the concentration ratios) will be difficult to determine accurately. Furthermore, it is convenient to work under conditions at which the ratio of concentrations of the components of one system is equal to unity (e.g., $[A_o] = [A_r]$). At equilibrium, therefore,

$$E_h = E_0' \text{ (system } A \text{)} = E_0' \text{ (system } B \text{)} + \frac{0.06}{n} \log \frac{[B_o]}{[B_r]}$$

This principle was employed by Thunberg[15] for the determination of the normal potential of the succinate-fumarate equilibrium in the presence of succinic dehydrogenase of washed muscle tissue; here the system of

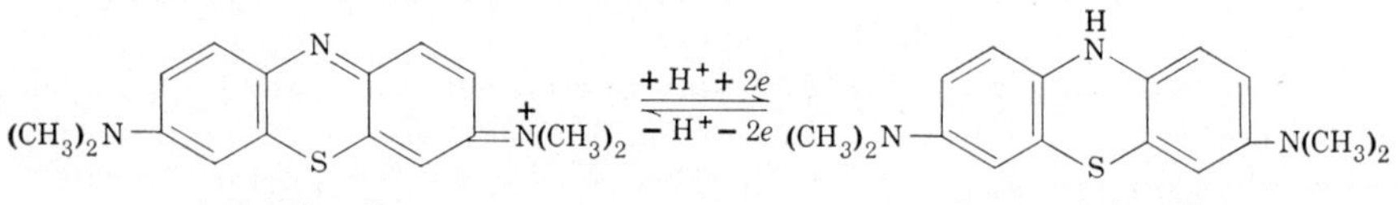

Methylene blue   Leucomethylene blue

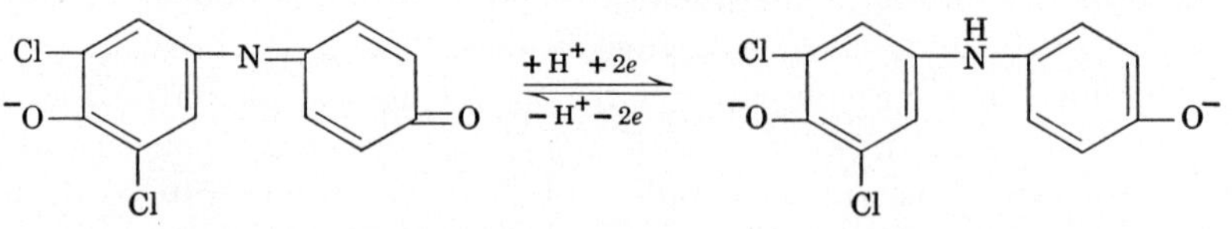

2,6-Dichlorophenolindophenol   Leuco-2,6-dichlorophenol-
(blue)   indophenol (colorless)

known potential was composed of the oxidized and reduced forms of the dye methylene blue, which served as an oxidation-reduction indicator. The oxidized form of methylene blue is colored, whereas the reduced form (leucomethylene blue) is colorless. Methylene blue is but one of a

[15] T. Thunberg, *Skand. Arch. Physiol.*, **46**, 339 (1925).

large number of organic dyes that form electromotively active oxidation-reduction systems; another is 2,6-dichlorophenolindophenol [E_0'(pH 7, 30° C) = +0.217 volt]. We owe to Clark and to Michaelis most of our knowledge about the oxidation-reduction potentials of these indicators, which have proved extremely useful in the study of biological oxidations.

In concluding this section on biological oxidation-reduction, it is appropriate to re-emphasize the fact that a favorable difference in potential does not, in itself, guarantee that the exergonic reaction will take place. For example, the reaction between succinic acid and methylene blue is a thermodynamically possible reaction; however, appreciable reaction cannot be demonstrated unless a catalytic system is present. In the presence of the specific catalysts, equilibrium is established in a measurable time. Here, again, one must consider not only the thermodynamic properties of the reaction but also the equally, if not more important, kinetic aspects of the reaction.

In succeeding chapters, some of the enzymes that catalyze oxidation-reduction reactions will be considered. It will be seen that the reactants combine with the catalytic protein to form oxidation-reduction systems composed of the oxidized and reduced forms of a conjugated protein, analogous to the methemoglobin-hemoglobin system (p. 299). Under these circumstances, the E_0' of the conjugated protein will depend on the relative magnitude of the dissociation constants of the two forms of the conjugated protein.

$$K_o = \frac{[\text{Protein}][\text{oxid}]}{[\text{Protein-oxid}]} \qquad K_r = \frac{[\text{Protein}][\text{red}]}{[\text{Protein-red}]}$$

If, for example, the reduced form is bound more tightly to the protein than the oxidized form (K_r less than K_o), the E_0' of the conjugated protein system will be more positive than that of the protein-free oxidation-reduction system. This follows from the relationship

$$E_0' \text{ (conjugated protein)} = E_0' \text{ (protein-free system)} + \frac{0.06}{n} \log \frac{K_o}{K_r}$$

For a more complete discussion of this important relationship, see Clark et al.,[16] who applied it to the experimental study of the oxidation-reduction potentials of hemochromogens. The dependence of the oxidation-reduction potentials of conjugated proteins on the relative magnitude of K_o and K_r is of considerable importance in the enzymic catalysis of biological oxidations, since the electron transfer usually involves the reaction of a conjugated protein (in either the reduced or the oxidized state) with an appropriate electron acceptor or electron donor (cf. p. 322).

[16] W. M. Clark et al., *J. Biol. Chem.*, **135**, 543 (1940).

Biological Electron Carrier Systems

The study of the oxidation-reduction reactions that may proceed in living systems has as its primary aim the elucidation of the mechanisms whereby the energy made available in oxidation reactions is utilized for the chemical and physical work of organisms. Among the most important advances in biochemistry has been the identification of a number of oxidation-reduction systems whose biological function appears to be the transfer of electrons from metabolites (e.g., succinic acid, lactic acid) to molecular oxygen.

The electron transfer systems of special interest in biochemistry are those that may be termed "carriers." Such a carrier system (C) must be capable of reacting with two different oxidation-reduction systems, A and B, so that the oxidized form of C (C_o) will rapidly oxidize the reduced form of system A (A_r) and the reduced form of C (C_r) will in turn be rapidly oxidized by the oxidized form of system B (B_o). Schematically, this may be represented as:

(1) $\qquad\qquad\qquad A_r + C_o \rightleftharpoons A_o + C_r$
(2) $\qquad\qquad\qquad B_o + C_r \rightleftharpoons B_r + C_o$

The net effect of the carrier system is therefore to transfer electrons from A_r to B_o; this may be visualized by means of a notation used by Baldwin.[17]

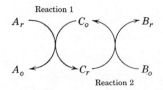

In the succeeding three chapters, primary consideration will be given to three important groups of electron carriers and to the enzyme proteins that catalyze the oxidation-reduction reactions in which these carriers participate. These groups of carriers are (1) the pyridine nucleotides, (2) the flavin nucleotides, and (3) the cytochromes. The approximate oxidation-reduction potentials (at pH 7, 30° C) of these three types of electron carriers, in relation to the comparable E_0' values of the hydrogen and oxygen electrodes, are as follows:

O_2 electrode ($H_2O \rightleftharpoons \frac{1}{2}O_2 + 2H^+ + 2e$)	+0.81 volt
Cytochrome c	+0.26
Flavin nucleotides	−0.22
Pyridine nucleotides	−0.32
Hydrogen electrode ($H_2 \rightleftharpoons 2H^+ + 2e$)	−0.42

[17] E. Baldwin, *Dynamic Aspects of Biochemistry*, 2nd Ed., Cambridge University Press, Cambridge, 1952.

These E_0' values lead one to expect that the reduced form of the pyridine nucleotides should serve as a good reductant of the oxidized forms of the flavin nucleotides or of cytochrome c, but the oxidized pyridine nucleotides would not be reduced appreciably by the reduced forms of the other two systems. Similarly, the reduced flavin nucleotides could be oxidized by oxidized cytochrome c, but reduced cytochrome c would not be oxidized to an appreciable extent by the oxidized forms of the flavin nucleotide and pyridine nucleotide systems. The thermodynamic conclusions drawn from the values for the potentials also suggest that the reduced forms of all three electron carrier systems may react with molecular oxygen as the electron acceptor. It must be remembered, however, that these conclusions give no information concerning the rates of the thermodynamically possible reactions. In fact, of the reduced forms of the three electron carrier systems mentioned above, only the reduced flavin nucleotides will react at a rapid rate with O_2 in the absence of added catalyst; it may be said, therefore, that the reduced flavin nucleotides are "autoxidizable." This autoxidation leads to the formation of H_2O_2 and may be written

$$FlavinH_2 + O_2 \rightarrow Flavin + H_2O_2$$

which may be considered as the summation of the two reactions:

$$FlavinH_2 \rightleftharpoons Flavin + 2H^+ + 2e$$

$$O_2 + 2H^+ + 2e \rightarrow H_2O_2$$

As will be evident from the subsequent discussion, however, the major pathway for electron transfer to molecular oxygen in aerobic organisms involves the autoxidation not of the flavin nucleotides, but of iron-porphyrin compounds. These apparent discrepancies between the chemical potentialities of the individual electron carrier systems and their role in biological systems are a direct consequence of the relative rates of the enzyme-catalyzed reactions in which they participate. Therefore the discussion of the electron carrier systems cannot be separated from a consideration of the specific enzyme proteins involved in their reactions.

Although the pyridine nucleotides, the flavin nucleotides, and the cytochromes represent the most important biological electron transfer systems of which there is some knowledge, it must be stressed that they are not necessarily the only ones that function in living organisms. Other oxidation-reduction systems that have been considered as possible electron carriers in biological oxidations are (1) the ascorbic acid-dehydroascorbic acid system (cf. Table 2); (2) the system involving the sulfhydryl and disulfide forms of glutathione (p. 136), the $E_0'(pH\ 7)$ of which is not known, but estimated to be about -0.1 volt; (3) the system involving the sulfhydryl and disulfide forms of lipoic acid (also named thioctic acid), the potential of which also is unknown, but believed to be about -0.4 volt; (4) the catechol-*o*-quinone system $[E_0'(pH\ 7) = ca.\ +0.33$ volt]. Some of the evidence in favor of the participation of these systems in biological oxidations will be considered later in this book.

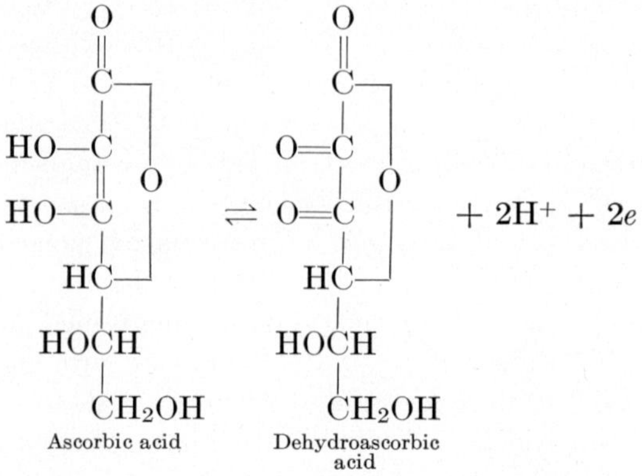

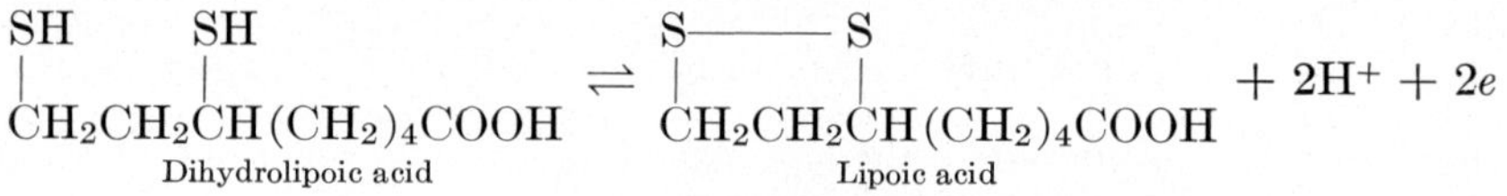

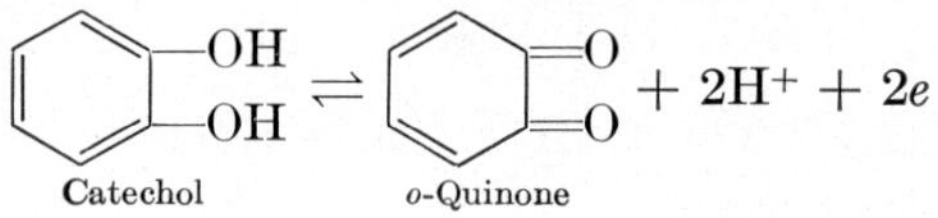

$$
\begin{array}{ccc}
\text{Ascorbic acid} & \rightleftharpoons & \text{Dehydroascorbic acid} \\
\end{array}
+ 2H^+ + 2e
$$

$$
\underset{\text{Dihydrolipoic acid}}{\overset{\text{SH}\quad\text{SH}}{|\quad\quad|}{CH_2CH_2CH(CH_2)_4COOH}}
\;\rightleftharpoons\;
\underset{\text{Lipoic acid}}{\overset{\text{S}\!-\!\!-\!\!-\!\text{S}}{|\quad\quad|}{CH_2CH_2CH(CH_2)_4COOH}}
\;+\;2H^+ + 2e
$$

$$
\text{Catechol} \;\rightleftharpoons\; \text{\textit{o}-Quinone} \;+\; 2H^+ + 2e
$$

12 ·

Pyridine Nucleotides
and
Dehydrogenases

The Pyridine Nucleotides [1, 2]

Diphosphopyridine Nucleotide. The study of the pyridine nucleotides may be said to have begun with Buchner's work on the preparation, from yeast, of a cell-free extract that was capable of converting glucose to ethyl alcohol. The enzyme system involved in this fermentation reaction was given the name "zymase." In 1904 Harden and Young found that the ability of such an extract to ferment glucose was lost when the extract was dialyzed, but could be restored by the addition of the dialyzable material. [3] They concluded that a substance of low molecular weight (which they found to be stable to heat) served as a cofactor in alcoholic fermentation by yeast. This dialyzable material was named cozymase, and was classified as a coenzyme, a term introduced by Bertrand to denote substances of low molecular weight essential for enzyme action (cf. p. 220). It has now become possible in many instances to replace the vague term "coenzyme" by more informative chemical names and to define the chemical role of these accessory substances.

The study of the chemical nature of cozymase was taken up by H. von Euler in 1923. By 1932 evidence had accumulated that cozymase was related to the adenylic acid obtained from muscle (adenosine-5'-phosphate). The nature of cozymase was more definitely established as a result of the discovery by Warburg that mammalian erythrocytes contain a thermostable, dialyzable factor which is required for the aerobic oxidation of glucose-6-phosphate to 6-phosphogluconic acid. In 1934 Warburg and Christian isolated this cofactor from erythrocytes and demonstrated that it was a compound formed by the union of 1 molecule

[1] T. P. Singer and E. B. Kearney, *Advances in Enzymol.,* **15,** 79 (1954).

[2] E. Racker, *Physiol. Revs.,* **35,** 1 (1955).

[3] A. Harden, *Alcoholic Fermentation,* 3rd Ed., Longmans, Green and Co., London, 1923.

$$
\begin{array}{ccc}
\text{CHO} & & \text{COOH} \\
| & & | \\
(\text{CHOH})_4 & + \tfrac{1}{2}\text{O}_2 \rightarrow & (\text{CHOH})_4 \\
| & & | \\
\text{CH}_2\text{OPO}_3\text{H}_2 & & \text{CH}_2\text{OPO}_3\text{H}_2 \\
\text{Glucose-6-phosphate} & & \text{6-Phosphogluconic acid}
\end{array}
$$

of adenine, 2 pentose units (presumably D-ribose), 3 equivalents of phosphoric acid, and 1 molecule of the amide of nicotinic acid (pyridine-3-carboxylic acid).[4] This demonstration of the presence of nicotinamide

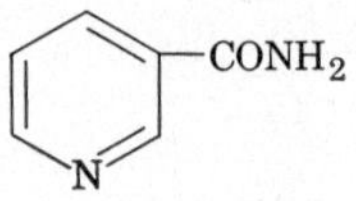

Nicotinic acid amide
(nicotinamide)

in the cofactor from erythrocytes was followed by the discovery in 1937 that nicotinic acid is effective in the prevention of the dietary deficiency in dogs known as "black tongue" and of the human nutritional disease known as pellagra (Chapter 39). It had been shown in 1936 that cozymase is a growth factor for *Hemophilus influenzae,* and later work demonstrated that nicotinamide is required by other microorganisms as well.

The discovery of nicotinamide in the cofactor from erythrocytes led Euler to test for the presence of this substance as a component of his purified cozymase preparations, and, when the result was positive, the close similarity between the two cofactors was established. On the basis of work done primarily by Euler, Schlenk, and their associates, the chemical structure of cozymase was shown to be that represented in the accompanying formula. It will be noted that in the compound a unit of the nucleotide adenosine-5'-phosphate (AMP) is joined by a pyrophosphate linkage to the 5'-phosphate of nicotinamide-D-ribotide, which, though not derived from nucleic acids, may also be termed a nucleotide (nicotinamide mononucleotide, abbreviated NMN). After the establishment of the constitution of cozymase it became the practice to refer to it as diphosphopyridine nucleotide (DPN). Until recently, other names such as coenzyme I (abbreviated Co I) or codehydrogenase I were also used. DPN is especially abundant in yeast (ca. 1 mg per gram fresh weight), and a satisfactory method for its isolation from this source has been described.[5] Among animal tissues, retina is characterized by a high DPN content (ca. 2 mg per gram dry weight).

The pyrophosphate linkage of DPN may be cleaved by an enzyme

[4] O. Warburg et al., *Biochem. Z.,* **282,** 157 (1935).

[5] A. Kornberg and W. E. Pricer, Jr., *Biochem. Preparations,* **3,** 20 (1953).

preparation (nucleotide pyrophosphatase) from potatoes to yield AMP and NMN.[6] A different enzyme (DPNase), found in animal tissues and in the mold *Neurospora crassa*, hydrolyzes DPN to form nicotinamide. The DPNase of some animal tissues (beef spleen, pig brain)

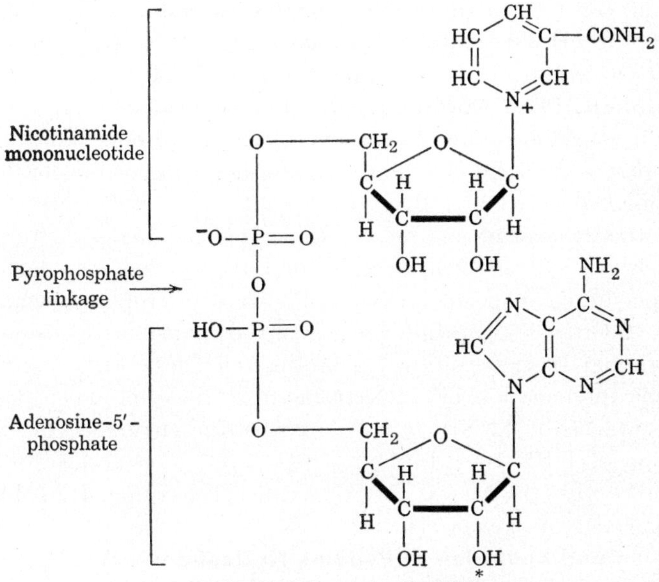

Diphosphopyridine nucleotide (DPN)

catalyzes not only the hydrolysis of the glycosidic bond involving nicotinamide, but also the replacement of the nicotinamide group in DPN by structurally related pyridine derivatives such as 3-acetylpyridine and isonicotinhydrazide.[7] 3-Acetylpyridine has been shown to be an

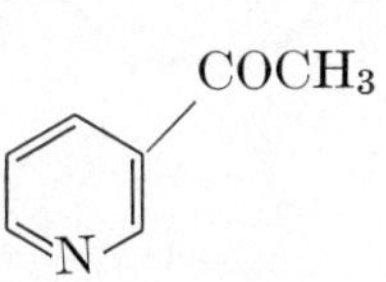

3-Acetylpyridine 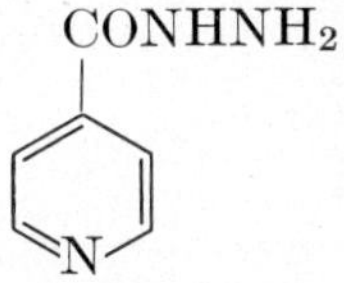   Isonicotinhydrazide

"antimetabolite" of nicotinamide, since it produces symptoms of nicotinic acid deficiency (Chapter 39) when it is fed to mice.[8] Isonicotinhydrazide has been used in the treatment of tuberculosis.

The biosynthesis of DPN probably occurs by means of the following

[6] A. Kornberg and W. E. Pricer, Jr., *J. Biol. Chem.*, **182**, 763 (1950).

[7] N. O. Kaplan et al., *Science*, **120**, 437 (1954); L. J. Zatman et al., *J. Biol. Chem.*, **209**, 453, 467 (1954).

[8] D. W. Woolley, *J. Biol. Chem.*, **157**, 455 (1945).

reaction involving adenosine triphosphate (ATP):

$$NMN + ATP \rightleftharpoons DPN + \text{pyrophosphate}$$

This reaction is catalyzed by the enzyme DPN pyrophosphorylase, preparations of which have been obtained from yeast and pig liver.[9] The equilibrium constant of the reaction for the synthesis of DPN is approximately 0.5 at pH 7.4, and the reverse reaction (the pyrophosphorolysis of DPN) can be demonstrated readily.

Triphosphopyridine Nucleotide. It will be recalled that the cofactor obtained by Warburg from erythrocytes contains 3 phosphoric acid units in place of the 2 in DPN. This triphosphopyridine nucleotide (TPN) has the same structure as DPN, with the addition of the third phosphoryl group at the 2′ position of the ribose portion of adenosine (denoted by an asterisk in the structural formula for DPN). This was demonstrated by the specific cleavage of TPN by nucleotide pyrophosphatase to give NMN and adenosine-2′,5′-diphosphate (2′,5′-diphosphoadenosine).[10] The various animal tissues examined contain much less TPN than DPN; a satisfactory preparation of TPN from sheep liver has been described.[11] The biosynthesis of TPN probably involves the enzyme-catalyzed phosphorylation of DPN by ATP.[12]

Until recently, TPN was often termed coenzyme II (abbreviated Co II) or codehydrogenase II.

Oxidation and Reduction of Pyridine Nucleotides. With the discovery by Warburg of the presence of nicotinamide in TPN, there emerged the important finding that the oxidation of glucose-6-phosphate in the pres-

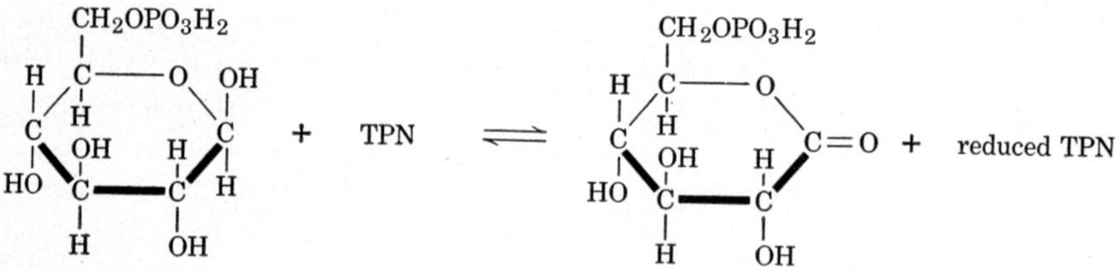

Glucose-6-phosphate
(pyranose form)

6-Phosphoglucono-
δ-lactone

ence of erythrocytes involves the enzyme-catalyzed reduction of the pyridine ring of TPN by glucose-6-phosphate. Later work showed that in this oxidation-reduction reaction the pyranose form (cf. p. 403) of

[9] A. Kornberg, *J. Biol. Chem.*, **182**, 779 (1950).

[10] A. Kornberg and W. E. Pricer, Jr., *J. Biol. Chem.*, **186**, 557 (1950); L. Heppel et al., *Biochem. J.*, **60**, 19 (1955).

[11] A. Kornberg and B. L. Horecker, *Biochem. Preparations*, **3**, 24 (1953).

[12] A. Kornberg, *J. Biol. Chem.*, **182**, 805 (1950); T. P. Wang and N. O. Kaplan, *ibid.*, **206**, 311 (1954); **211**, 465 (1954).

glucose-6-phosphate is dehydrogenated to 6-phosphogluconolactone (probably the δ-lactone).[13] The lactone readily undergoes hydrolysis to give 6-phosphogluconic acid.

Reduced TPN is not autoxidizable to any appreciable extent, and the oxidation of reduced TPN must be effected by the oxidized form of another oxidation-reduction system; in mammalian erythrocytes this appears to involve an enzyme-catalyzed bimolecular reaction between reduced TPN and an appropriate flavin nucleotide. The TPN system thus acts as an electron carrier between the glucose-6-phosphate system and the flavin nucleotide system.

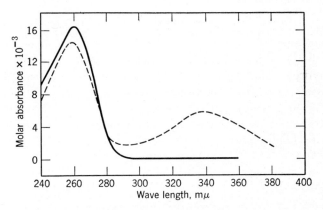

Fig. 1. Absorption spectra of triphosphopyridine nucleotide (solid line) and of reduced triphosphopyridine nucleotide (dash line).

The quantitative observation of the conversion of TPN to its reduced form is facilitated by a striking difference in the absorption spectra of the two forms. It will be noted from Fig. 1 that reduced TPN has a distinct absorption band with a maximum at 340 mμ and that this band is absent in the spectrum of the oxidized form. The same spectral differences may be demonstrated with DPN and its reduced form. Karrer has shown that the appearance of the absorption band at 340 mμ upon reduction of DPN or TPN can be simulated in a model system using the methiodide of nicotinamide, a derivative of nicotinamide in which the pyridine nitrogen has been converted to the quaternary pyridinium form. Upon reduction of the quaternary base with alkaline hydrosulfite ($Na_2S_2O_4$), the corresponding hydropyridine compound is formed; this has a distinctive absorption band at 360 mμ.

Although Karrer's work led to the recognition that the oxidation and

13 O. Cori and F. Lipmann, *J. Biol. Chem.*, **194**, 417 (1952); A. F. Brodie and F. Lipmann, *ibid.*, **212**, 677 (1955).

reduction of DPN and TPN involves the pyridine ring, the structure of the hydropyridine compound formed on reduction was not clarified until later,[14] and it was demonstrated that the reduction of DPN by $Na_2S_2O_4$ leads to the addition of hydrogen at the 4 position of the pyridine ring.[15]

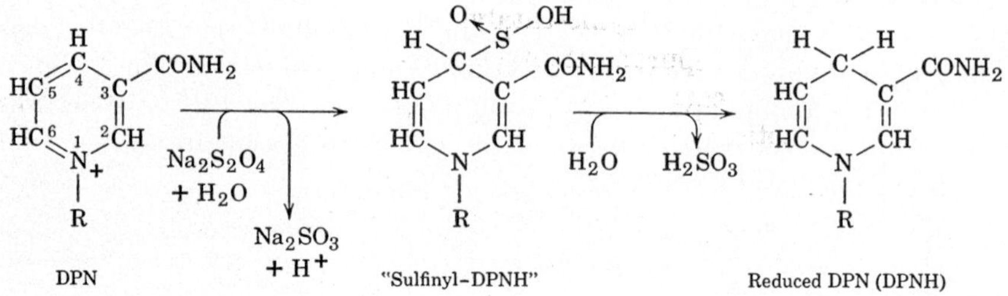

DPN   "Sulfinyl–DPNH"   Reduced DPN (DPNH)

It will be seen that, in the reduction, only one atom of hydrogen is added to the pyridine ring, although two electrons are transferred to the ring; a hydrogen ion appears in the medium. The formation of one equivalent of H^+ in the reduction of DPN may be demonstrated quantitatively; if the reaction with $Na_2S_2O_4$ is conducted in the presence of bicarbonate, there is liberated one equivalent of CO_2, which can be determined manometrically. Hence the oxidation-reduction system involving DPN (or TPN) may be written

$$DPN^+ + 2H^+ + 2e \rightleftharpoons DPNH + H^+$$

Reference will be found in the literature to the reduced form of DPN as "$DPNH_2$," and Warburg refers to "dihydropyridin" in writing of reduced pyridine nucleotides. In considering the oxidation-reduction reaction, however, it is clear that only one hydrogen atom is added to the pyridine ring in the course of the reduction of DPN or TPN; consequently, the reduced forms of these compounds are termed DPNH and TPNH respectively.

The oxidation-reduction potential (E_0') of the DPN and TPN systems at pH 7 and 30° C is about -0.32 volt.[16] The pH-dependence of E_0' is -0.03 volt per pH unit, in accordance with the considerations presented on p. 297. DPNH and TPNH can be oxidized by ferricyanide, o-quinones, and some oxidation-reduction indicators (not methylene blue); as mentioned before, the reduced pyridine nucleotides do not react directly with molecular oxygen.

[14] M. E. Pullman et al., *J. Biol. Chem.*, **206**, 129 (1954); G. W. Rafter and S. P. Colowick, *ibid.*, **209**, 773 (1954).

[15] M. B. Yarmolinsky and S. P. Colowick, *Biochim. et Biophys. Acta*, **20**, 177 (1956); G. Pfleiderer et al., *Biochem. Z.*, **328**, 187 (1956).

[16] K. Burton and T. H. Wilson, *Biochem. J.*, **54**, 86 (1953); F. L. Rodkey, *J. Biol. Chem.*, **213**, 777 (1955).

As shown on p. 312, in the reduction of DPN$^+$ by $Na_2S_2O_4$, an intermediate is formed by the addition of an —SO_2H group to the 4 position of the pyridine ring. Other addition reactions of DPN$^+$ have also been demonstrated. For example, DPN$^+$ combines with cyanide ions to form a cyano derivative which exhibits an absorption band at 325 mμ.[17]

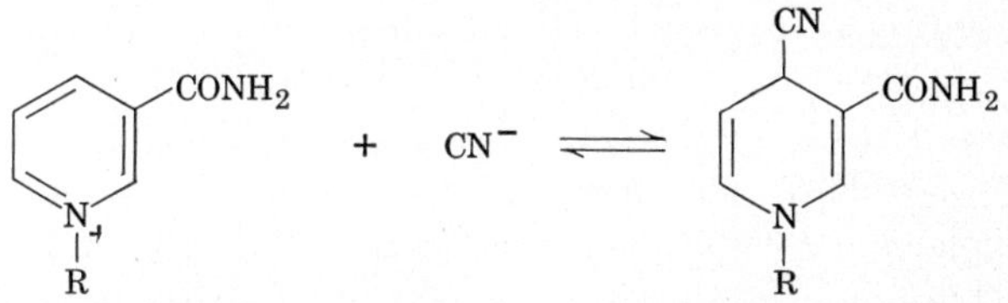

Several carbonyl compounds (e.g., dihydroxyacetone) also form similar addition compounds with DPN$^+$.[18] In these addition reactions, as in the reduction of DPN$^+$, the quaternary nitrogen of DPN$^+$ is converted to a tertiary nitrogen, with the appearance of an absorption band in the region 320 to 360 mμ. As will be seen from the subsequent discussion in this chapter, addition at the 4 position of the pyridine ring may be important in the enzymic catalysis of reactions involving the pyridine nucleotides.

The Dehydrogenases[2, 19]

If purified TPN is added to glucose-6-phosphate, no reaction occurs unless a specific protein is also added to serve as the enzymic catalyst. This enzyme protein has been termed glucose-6-phosphate dehydrogenase (Warburg referred to it as *Zwischenferment*), and preparations of this enzyme have been obtained from yeast and from erythrocytes. The bimolecular oxidation-reduction reaction catalyzed by glucose-6-phosphate dehydrogenase was shown on p. 310. The reaction

Glucose-6-phosphate + TPN$^+$ + H_2O $\rightleftharpoons$

6-Phosphogluconic acid + TPNH + H$^+$

is strongly exergonic, and the reverse reaction, the reduction of 6-phosphogluconic acid by TPNH, cannot be effected readily; this does not mean, however, that the forward reaction is thermodynamically irreversible. The reversibility of the enzymic reaction involving glucose-6-phosphate and 6-phosphogluconolactone has been demonstrated;[20] the

---

[17] S. P. Colowick et al., *J. Biol. Chem.*, **191**, 447 (1951); A. San Pietro, *ibid.*, **217**, 579 (1955).

[18] R. M. Burton and N. O. Kaplan, *J. Biol. Chem.*, **206**, 283 (1954); R. M. Burton et al., *Arch. Biochem. and Biophys.*, **70**, 87, 107 (1957).

[19] F. Schlenk, in J. B. Sumner and K. Myrbäck, *The Enzymes*, Chapter 52, Academic Press, New York, 1951.

[20] B. L. Horecker and P. Z. Smyrniotis, *Biochim. et Biophys. Acta*, **12**, 98 (1953).

hydrolysis of the lactone is an exergonic reaction, and thus pulls the equilibrium between glucose-6-phosphate and 6-phosphogluconolactone farther to the right. It may be added that ox liver contains a glucose dehydrogenase that catalyzes the reaction

$$\text{D-Glucopyranose} + \text{DPN}^+ \rightleftharpoons \text{D-Gluconolactone} + \text{DPNH} + \text{H}^+$$

As in the reaction catalyzed by glucose-6-phosphate dehydrogenase, the lactone is hydrolyzed to gluconic acid.[21] Although this hydrolysis occurs spontaneously, it is accelerated by an enzyme named "lactonase."

Glucose-6-phosphate dehydrogenase is specific in its catalytic action for the bimolecular oxidation-reduction involving glucose-6-phosphate and TPN. The sugar phosphate cannot be replaced by other substances, nor can TPN be replaced by DPN. The enzyme is a representative of a group named dehydrogenases and, in particular, of the dehydrogenases that catalyze bimolecular oxidation-reduction reactions between a metabolite system and the DPN or TPN system. The existence of many dehydrogenases, in a variety of biological systems, came to be recognized as a result of the work of Thunberg.[22] He observed the rate and extent of decolorization of methylene blue by extracts or homogenates of various tissues under anaerobic conditions in the presence of metabolites such as lactic acid and malic acid. This technique, known as the Thunberg method, led to the discovery, in animals, in plants, and in microorganisms, of a large number of enzymes that catalyze the dehydrogenation of various metabolites. It became evident from later investigations that the dehydrogenase-catalyzed transfer of electrons from a metabolite to a pyridine nucleotide was not followed directly by a transfer to methylene blue, but that other carrier systems, such as the flavin nucleotides, were interposed between the DPN (or TPN) system and the oxidation-reduction indicator. In addition, the biocatalytic dehydrogenation of certain metabolites (e.g., succinic acid) cannot be identified with enzymes which catalyze a bimolecular oxidation-reduction involving a pyridine nucleotide. As a consequence, reference will be found in the literature to dehydrogenases for which the immediate electron acceptor is still uncertain. In some cases future studies may show that a pyridine nucleotide is in fact a participant in the dehydrogenase-catalyzed reaction. For example, although it was long known that oxidized glutathione (GSSG) is reduced by extracts of plant and animal tissues, the participation of a pyridine nucleotide was discovered much later, with the demonstration of an enzyme (glutathione reductase) that catalyzes the oxidation of

[21] H. J. Strecker and S. Korkes, *J. Biol. Chem.*, **196**, 769 (1952); N. G. Brink, *Acta Chem. Scand.*, **7**, 1090 (1953).

[22] T. Thunberg, *Skand. Arch. Physiol.*, **40**, 1 (1920).

TPNH (not DPNH) by GSSG.[23] Subsequently, preparations of gluta-thione reductase obtained from yeast and liver were found to catalyze the oxidation of both reduced nucleotides, although the reaction with TPNH was more rapid.[24]

Many of the pyridine nucleotide-dependent dehydrogenases are rela-tively specific for the DPN system, and others are specific for the TPN system; for some enzymes of this group either nucleotide system is effective, although a difference in rate is usually observed. It should be added, however, that crude preparations of a dehydrogenase occasionally catalyze reactions with both nucleotide systems, but, on further purifica-tion, specificity with respect to DPN or TPN becomes evident. In regard to the specificity of the dehydrogenases toward the metabolite systems, the apparent sharp specificity of glucose-6-phosphate dehy-drogenase toward glucose-6-phosphate is the exception rather than the rule. Many instances of relative specificity (cf. p. 276) for metabolites are known; for example, partially purified glucose dehydrogenase (ox liver) catalyzes the oxidation of xylose (p. 410) at about one-fourth the rate for glucose. As with all enzymes, the unequivocal study of the specificity of dehydrogenases depends on the availability of highly puri-fied preparations. It has been observed frequently that closely related metabolites are oxidized (or reduced) by a pyridine nucleotide system in the presence of relatively crude dehydrogenase preparations from different biological sources. The question then arises whether enzymes of the same specificity are involved, even though the names assigned to the enzyme preparations from different sources refer to different metab-olites. For this reason, the nomenclature of some of the less thoroughly purified dehydrogenases is uncertain.

In Table 1 are listed some of the better-known dehydrogenases, together with the metabolite system with which they are usually associ-ated, and the specificity for the pyridine nucleotide system. Where either pyridine nucleotide can serve as a reaction partner, the specificity is indicated by the relative effectiveness of DPN and TPN (for further details see Mehler et al.[25]).

For the experimental observation of oxidation-reduction reactions in which the DPN or the TPN system participates, advantage is taken of the striking difference in the absorption spectra of the reduced and oxidized forms of the pyridine nucleotides. At 340 mμ, reduction of

[23] L. W. Mapson and D. R. Goddard, *Biochem. J.,* **49**, 592 (1951); E. E. Conn and B. Vennesland, *J. Biol. Chem.,* **192**, 17 (1951); T. W. Rall and A. L. Lehninger, *ibid.,* **194**, 119 (1952).

[24] E. Racker, *J. Biol. Chem.,* **217**, 855 (1955).

[25] A. H. Mehler et al., *J. Biol. Chem.,* **174**, 961 (1948).

Table I. Dehydrogenases that Catalyze Oxidation-Reduction Reactions between a Metabolite System and a Pyridine Nucleotide System

Enzyme and Source	Metabolite System	Specificity for DPN or TPN
Alcohol dehydrogenase		
(yeast)	CH_3CH_2OH/CH_3CHO	DPN
(liver)	$—CH_2OH/—CHO$	DPN
Aldehyde dehydrogenase	$—CHO/—COO^-$	
(liver)		DPN
(yeast)		TPN > DPN
Formaldehyde dehydrogenase(liver)	HCHO/Formate	DPN
Formic dehydrogenase (peas)	Formate/CO_2	DPN
Glucose dehydrogenase (liver)	D-Glucopyranose/ D-Gluconolactone	DPN or TPN
Glucose-6-phosphate dehydrogenase (erythrocytes, yeast)	D-Glucopyranose-6-phosphate/6-Phospho-D-gluconolactone	TPN
Glutamic dehydrogenase	L-Glutamate/α-Ketoglutarate + NH_4^+	
(liver)		DPN > TPN
(higher plants)		DPN
(bacteria)		TPN
Glutathione reductase (plant and animal tissues)	Glutathione/Oxidized glutathione	TPN > DPN
Glyceraldehyde-3-phosphate dehydrogenase (muscle, yeast)	D-Glyceraldehyde-3-phosphate + phosphate/D-1, 3-Diphosphoglyceric acid	DPN
Glycerophosphate dehydrogenase (muscle)	L-α-Glycerophosphate/ Dihydroxyacetone phosphate	DPN
Glyoxylic reductase (plants)	Glycolate/Glyoxylate	DPN
β-Hydroxyacyl-CoA dehydrogenase (liver)	L-β-Hydroxybutyryl-CoA/ Acetoacetyl-CoA	DPN
β-Hydroxybutyric dehydrogenase (liver)	D-β-Hydroxybutyrate/ Acetoacetate	DPN
β-Hydroxybutyryl-CoA dehydrogenase (liver)	D-β-Hydroxybutyryl-CoA/ Acetoacetyl-CoA	DPN
Isocitric dehydrogenase	d-Isocitrate/Oxalosuccinate	
(heart)		TPN
(animal tissues)		DPN
(yeast)		DPN
Lactic dehydrogenase	L-Lactate/Pyruvate	
(heart)		DPN > TPN
(muscle, liver)		DPN
Malic dehydrogenase (muscle)	L-Malate/Oxaloacetate	DPN > TPN

DPN$^+$ (or TPN$^+$) leads to an increase in absorbance; reoxidation of DPNH (or TPNH) causes a decrease in absorbance (cf. Fig. 2).

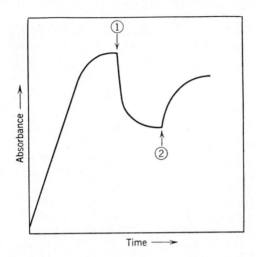

Fig. 2. Changes in absorbance (cf. p. 72) at 340 mμ as a function of time in the reduction or oxidation of DPN (or TPN). Initially, the specific dehydrogenase, DPN, and the reduced form of the metabolite system are present. At arrow 1, equilibrium has been attained; the addition at this point of the oxidized form of the metabolite system causes the reoxidation of some of the DPNH. At arrow 2, more of the reduced form of the metabolite system is added, and DPN is again reduced to DPNH.

Mechanism and Kinetics of Dehydrogenase Action. Among the pyridine nucleotide-dependent dehydrogenases, the largest number of known enzymes catalyze oxidation-reduction reactions involving alcohols and the corresponding aldehydes or ketones, and reactions involving aldehydes (or their derivatives) and the corresponding carboxylic acids (or their derivatives). Representatives of the first group are the alcohol dehydrogenases of yeast and of liver, and, of the second group, glyceraldehyde-3-phosphate dehydrogenase (from yeast and from muscle). The intensive study of the mechanism and kinetics of the action of these highly purified enzymes has contributed much to the understanding of the way in which other dehydrogenases function as specific catalysts in oxidation-reduction reactions.

Alcohol dehydrogenase catalyzes the reaction

$$CH_3CH_2OH + DPN^+ \rightleftharpoons CH_3CHO + DPNH + H^+$$

When the enzyme is present in a concentration much less than that of the reactants (cf. p. 211), the equilibrium constant of the reaction

$(25°\text{ C})$ is

$$K = \frac{[CH_3CHO][DPNH][H^+]}{[CH_3CH_2OH][DPN^+]} = 1 \times 10^{-11}\ M$$

It will be seen that the equilibrium in the reaction as written on p. 317 is far to the left, and that the enzyme could be named more properly "aldehyde reductase." In a buffered solution at pH 8, $[H^+] = 10^{-8}$, and the quotient $[CH_3CHO][DPNH]/[CH_3CH_2OH][DPN^+]$ equals about 0.001. Clearly, this quotient depends on pH and the oxidation of ethanol is favored by the addition of hydroxide ions.

In other enzyme-catalyzed oxidations of alcohols by DPN^+, the equilibrium constant also is in favor of DPNH oxidation. At $25°$ C, the equilibrium constants (in the direction of DPN^+ reduction) for the reactions catalyzed by glyoxylic reductase,[26] malic dehydrogenase,[27]

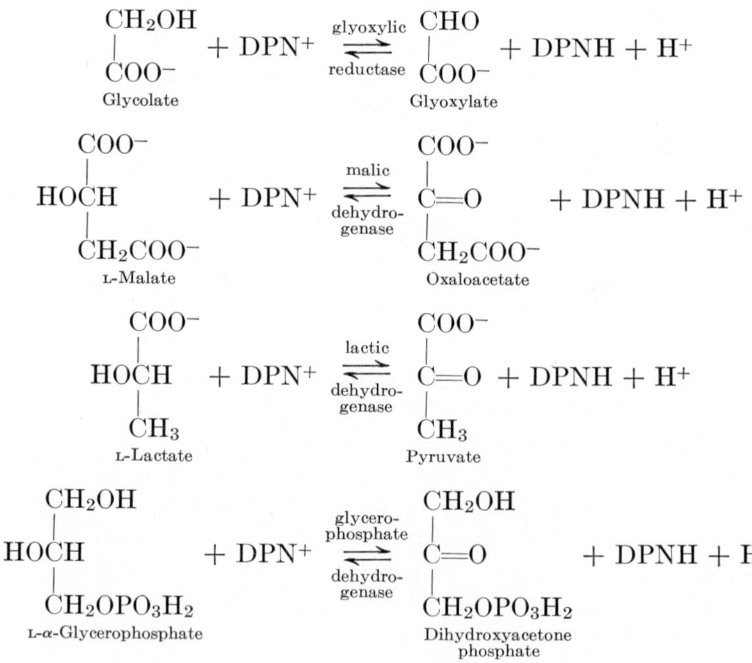

$$\begin{array}{c} CH_2OH \\ | \\ COO^- \\ \text{Glycolate} \end{array} + DPN^+ \underset{\text{reductase}}{\overset{\text{glyoxylic}}{\rightleftharpoons}} \begin{array}{c} CHO \\ | \\ COO^- \\ \text{Glyoxylate} \end{array} + DPNH + H^+$$

$$\begin{array}{c} COO^- \\ | \\ HOCH \\ | \\ CH_2COO^- \\ \text{L-Malate} \end{array} + DPN^+ \underset{\substack{\text{dehydro-}\\ \text{genase}}}{\overset{\text{malic}}{\rightleftharpoons}} \begin{array}{c} COO^- \\ | \\ C{=}O \\ | \\ CH_2COO^- \\ \text{Oxaloacetate} \end{array} + DPNH + H^+$$

$$\begin{array}{c} COO^- \\ | \\ HOCH \\ | \\ CH_3 \\ \text{L-Lactate} \end{array} + DPN^+ \underset{\substack{\text{dehydro-}\\ \text{genase}}}{\overset{\text{lactic}}{\rightleftharpoons}} \begin{array}{c} COO^- \\ | \\ C{=}O \\ | \\ CH_3 \\ \text{Pyruvate} \end{array} + DPNH + H^+$$

$$\begin{array}{c} CH_2OH \\ | \\ HOCH \\ | \\ CH_2OPO_3H_2 \\ \text{L-α-Glycerophosphate} \end{array} + DPN^+ \underset{\substack{\text{dehydro-}\\ \text{genase}}}{\overset{\substack{\text{glycero-}\\ \text{phosphate}}}{\rightleftharpoons}} \begin{array}{c} CH_2OH \\ | \\ C{=}O \\ | \\ CH_2OPO_3H_2 \\ \text{Dihydroxyacetone} \\ \text{phosphate} \end{array} + DPNH + H^+$$

lactic dehydrogenase,[28] and glycerophosphate dehydrogenase[29] are about

[26] I. Zelitch, *J. Biol. Chem.*, **216**, 553 (1955).

[27] F. B. Straub, *Z. physiol. Chem.*, **275**, 63 (1942); K. Burton and T. H. Wilson, *Biochem. J.*, **54**, 86 (1953).

[28] J. B. Neilands, *J. Biol. Chem.*, **199**, 373 (1952); D. M. Gibson et al., *ibid.*, **203**, 397 (1953); M. T. Hakala et al., *ibid.*, **221**, 191 (1956).

[29] T. Baranowski, *J. Biol. Chem.*, **180**, 535 (1949); G. Beisenherz et al., *Z. Naturforsch.*, **8b**, 555 (1953).

$2 \times 10^{-15} M, 8 \times 10^{-13} M, 3 \times 10^{-12} M$, and $7 \times 10^{-12} M$ respectively.

Crystalline preparations of alcohol dehydrogenase have been obtained from yeast[30] and from horse liver;[31] the two proteins are markedly different in their properties. Yeast alcohol dehydrogenase acts on ethanol more rapidly than on higher alcohols (e.g., *n*-propanol, *n*-butanol), whereas the liver enzyme has a broader specificity toward carbinol compounds, and even acts on long-chain primary alcohols such as vitamin A (Chapter 27). The yeast enzyme has a particle weight of 150,000, whereas the value for the liver enzyme is 73,000. The two enzyme preparations also differ in their response to inhibitors such as iodoacetate. Zinc has been found to be a constituent of both alcohol dehydrogenases,[32] as well as of some other pyridine nucleotide-dependent dehydrogenases (e.g., muscle lactic dehydrogenase).

An important property of alcohol dehydrogenase (from yeast and from liver), and of other dehydrogenases, is that they catalyze not only electron transfer but also direct hydrogen transfer (cf. p. 290). This discovery, made by Vennesland, Westheimer, and their associates,[33] has provided unequivocal evidence in favor of the view advanced in 1912 by H. Wieland, on the basis of experimental data that were later shown to be fallacious,[34] that hydrogen transfer occurs in dehydrogenation reactions. Vennesland and Westheimer showed that, when ethanol labeled with deuterium (D) reacts with DPN^+ in the presence of alcohol dehydrogenase, the isotope content of the reduced pyridine nucleotide is consistent with a direct transfer of deuterium, and excludes the participation of the protons of the medium in the transfer. In the reverse reaction, when acetaldehyde reacts with deuteroDPNH (produced in the forward reaction), the deuterium is transferred directly to the metabolite and appears in the ethanol. Furthermore, in the enzyme-catalyzed process, deuterium is added to the pyridine ring in a stereospecific manner; the oxidation of deuteroethanol leads to the formation of only one of the two possible stereoisomers of deuteroDPNH that differ in the relative location of the deuterium and hydrogen atoms at the 4 position of the ring (see equation shown on p. 320). The same isomer is produced in the reduction of DPN^+ by labeled L-malate or L-lactate, catalyzed by malic dehydrogenase or lactic dehydrogenase respectively.[35] On the

[30] E. Negelein and H. J. Wulff, *Biochem. Z.*, **293**, 351 (1937); E. Racker, *J. Biol. Chem.*, **184**, 313 (1950).

[31] R. K. Bonnichsen, *Acta Chem. Scand.*, **4**, 715 (1950).

[32] B. L. Vallee and F. L. Hoch, *J. Biol. Chem.*, **225**, 185 (1957).

[33] B. Vennesland and F. H. Westheimer, in W. D. McElroy and B. Glass, *The Mechanism of Enzyme Action*, Johns Hopkins Press, Baltimore, 1954.

[34] L. J. Gillespie and T. H. Liu, *J. Am. Chem. Soc.*, **53**, 3969 (1931).

[35] F. A. Loewus et al., *J. Biol. Chem.*, **202**, 699 (1953); **212**, 787 (1955).

other hand, in the reactions catalyzed by β-hydroxysteroid dehydrogenase (cf. p. 651), glucose dehydrogenase, and glyceraldehyde-3-phosphate dehydrogenase (cf. p. 324), the other isomer of deuteroDPNH (with D and H interchanged) is formed.[36] When DPN+ is reduced by

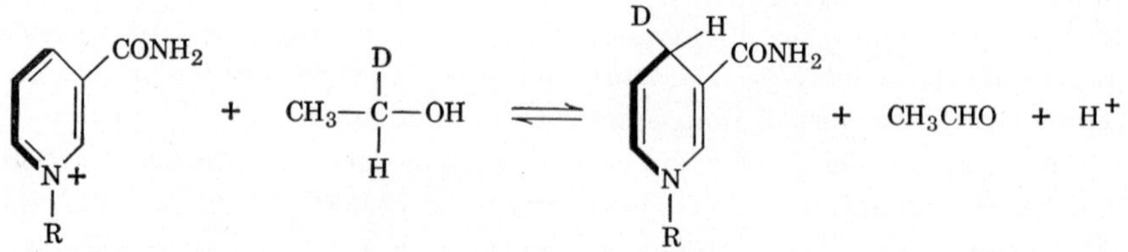

$Na_2S_2O_4$ in D_2O, a mixture of the two isomers is obtained. To explain the stereospecificity of the enzyme-catalyzed hydrogen transfer, it has been suggested[37] that alcohol dehydrogenase combines with ethanol and DPN+ in a manner that facilitates the addition of the metabolite molecule at the 4 position of the pyridine ring to form an intermediate similar to the addition compounds of DPN+ discussed previously (cf. p. 313).

Although the mechanism of alcohol dehydrogenase action has not been elucidated fully, it is clear that the function of the enzyme protein is to combine with DPN+ (or DPNH) and with ethanol (or acetaldehyde) so as to decrease the energy of activation for hydrogen transfer. In general, the effectiveness of a pyridine nucleotide-dependent dehydrogenase as a catalyst depends on a specific interaction with the DPN or TPN system, and with the appropriate metabolite system. As will be seen from Table 1, several dehydrogenases are specific for the oxidation of only one enantiomorph of a given metabolite (e.g., L-lactate, D-β-hydroxy-butyrate, d-isocitrate), and must therefore combine specifically with this enantiomorph. The stereochemical specificity of the enzymic transfer of hydrogen from the metabolite to DPN, or from DPNH to the oxidized form of the metabolite, is further evidence of specific interaction of dehydrogenases with the components of the appropriate metabolite system and of the pyridine nucleotide system.

For some DPN-dependent dehydrogenases, it has been possible to estimate the stoichiometry and equilibrium constants in the binding of DPN+ and DPNH by the enzyme protein. With yeast alcohol dehydrogenase, 4 molecules of pyridine nucleotide are bound per unit of 150,000; the corresponding enzyme from liver binds 2 molecules of DPN+ (or DPNH) per unit of 73,000. The participation of zinc ions in this binding is suggested by the finding that the combining weight for Zn is

---

[36] P. Talalay et al., *J. Biol. Chem.*, **212**, 801 (1955); H. R. Levy et al., *ibid.*, **222**, 685 (1956); **228**, 85 (1957); F. A. Loewus et al., *ibid.*, **223**, 589 (1956).

[37] R. M. Burton and N. O. Kaplan, *J. Biol. Chem.*, **211**, 447 (1954).

about 35,000 for both enzyme preparations.[38] The dissociation constant of the protein-DPNH complex, in the case of yeast alcohol dehydrogenase (ADH), was found to be 1.3×10^{-5} M. The dissociation constant of the ADH-DPN$^+$ complex was estimated to be 2.6×10^{-4} M.[39] Occasional reference will be found in the enzyme literature to DPN or TPN as the "coenzyme" or the "prosthetic group" of a particular dehydrogenase. However, if DPN is to be considered in this way, because of its binding by yeast ADH, then acetaldehyde must also be so considered, since the dissociation constant of the ADH-CH$_3$CHO complex is approximately 1.8×10^{-4} M. The practice of referring to the ADH-DPN complex as the enzyme (or holoenzyme) and to ADH as the apoenzyme (cf. p. 220) tends to obscure the fact that ADH catalyzes a bimolecular oxidation-reduction reaction (e.g., between CH$_3$CHO and DPNH), and that both reactants are specifically bound by the enzyme protein.

In some instances (e.g., muscle glyceraldehyde-3-phosphate dehydrogenase), the dissociation constant of the protein-DPN complex is so small that the conjugated protein is isolated (cf. p. 324). As will be seen from the later discussion of the flavoproteins and the iron-porphyrin enzymes, they represent conjugated proteins in which a component of an oxidation-reduction system (flavin nucleotide, heme) is bound even more tightly to a specific protein. For the economy of a living cell it may be important for the pyridine nucleotides to be bound relatively loosely by the dehydrogenases, so that these electron carriers can shuttle back and forth among the numerous specific dehydrogenases,[40] and for the flavin nucleotides and iron-porphyrins to be bound more firmly to the proteins that catalyze electron transfer to oxygen, to increase the efficiency of this process. Nevertheless, these considerations should not obscure the fact that in all these instances the electron carrier system bound to the protein participates in a bimolecular oxidation-reduction reaction with another oxidation-reduction system that is also bound by the specific protein.

It will be recalled that the dissociation constant of an enzyme-substrate complex is given by the Michaelis constant (K_m) only when k_2 is much greater than k_3, as defined on p. 255. Although this situation may apply to some enzymes, it does not hold for liver alcohol dehydrogenase, as shown by Theorell and Chance.[41] Their experiments involved rapid measurement of changes in the absorption spectra of free and bound DPNH (cf. p. 315) and took advantage of the fact that the

[38] F. L. Hoch and B. L. Vallee, *J. Biol. Chem.*, **221**, 491 (1956); K. Wallenfels et al., *Biochem. Z.*, **329**, 17, 31, 59 (1957).

[39] J. E. Hayes, Jr., and S. F. Velick, *J. Biol. Chem.*, **207**, 225 (1954); A. P. Nygaard and H. Theorell, *Acta Chem. Scand.*, **9**, 1551 (1955).

[40] A. P. Nygaard and W. J. Rutter, *Acta Chem. Scand.*, **10**, 37 (1956).

[41] H. Theorell and B. Chance, *Acta Chem. Scand.*, **5**, 1127 (1951).

absorption maximum of free DPNH is shifted from 340 mμ to 325 mμ when DPNH is bound to liver ADH (the yeast enzyme does not show this effect). Subsequent studies by Theorell et al.,[42] by the measurement of the fluorescence of free and bound DPNH, gave somewhat different values of the kinetic constants. Although the data may require further revision, they illustrate several important principles that are not likely to be vitiated by more accurate determinations in the future.

The reduction of acetaldehyde by DPNH in the presence of liver alcohol dehydrogenase (enzyme concentration much smaller than that of the reactants) has been formulated as follows:

(1) $\text{ADH} + \text{DPNH} \underset{k_2}{\overset{k_1}{\rightleftharpoons}} \text{ADH-DPNH}$

(2) $\text{ADH-DPNH} + \text{CH}_3\text{CHO} + \text{H}^+ \underset{k_6}{\overset{k_4}{\rightleftharpoons}} \text{ADH-DPN}^+ + \text{CH}_3\text{CH}_2\text{OH}$

(3) $\text{ADH-DPN}^+ \underset{k_5}{\overset{k_3}{\rightleftharpoons}} \text{ADH} + \text{DPN}^+$

ADH refers to the portion of the protein that binds 1 DPN$^+$ or DPNH molecule, and the k's denote the velocity constants of the individual reactions. No compound of ADH with CH_3CHO is included, because the kinetic data indicate that the rate of its dissociation is more rapid than the dissociation of ADH-DPN$^+$, which is rate-limiting (cf. p. 256). Similarly, in the reverse direction, the rate of dissociation of ADH-DPNH is rate-limiting, and no ADH-ethanol compound is included. However, this does not mean that such ADH-metabolite complexes are not formed. The experimentally determined rate constants at about pH 7 and 25° C are:[42]

$$k_1 = 3.7 \times 10^6 \ M^{-1} \ \text{sec}^{-1} \qquad k_4[\text{H}^+] = 2.4 \times 10^5 \ M^{-1} \ \text{sec}^{-1}$$

$$k_2 = 1.6 \ \text{sec}^{-1} \qquad\qquad\quad k_5 = 3 \times 10^5 \ M^{-1} \ \text{sec}^{-1}$$

$$k_3 = 37 \ \text{sec}^{-1} \qquad\qquad\quad k_6 = 3.5 \times 10^3 \ M^{-1} \ \text{sec}^{-1}$$

From these kinetic data, the dissociation constant of ADH-DPNH ($K_r = k_2/k_1$) may be calculated to be about $0.4 \times 10^{-6} \ M$, and that of ADH-DPN$^+$ ($K_o = k_3/k_5$) to be about $1.2 \times 10^{-4} \ M$. This shows that DPNH is bound by liver ADH much more firmly than is DPN$^+$. The ratio of K_o/K_r is about 300, and substitution of this value in the equation given on p. 303 permits the calculation of the oxidation-reduction potential of the conjugated protein. If -0.32 volt is taken as the value of E_0' (pH 7, 25°) for the free DPN system, the corresponding value for the liver ADH-DPN system is about -0.24 volt.

The equilibrium constant of the bimolecular oxidation-reduction reac-

[42] H. Theorell et al., *Acta Chem. Scand.*, **9**, 1148 (1955).

tion (the summation of the above reactions 1, 2, and 3)

$$DPNH + CH_3CHO + H^+ \rightleftharpoons DPN^+ + CH_3CH_2OH$$

is given by the quotient $k_2 k_5 k_6 / k_1 k_3 k_4$, and may be calculated from the kinetic data to be about 0.5×10^{-11}, in reasonably good agreement with the result of direct measurement of the concentrations of the reactants at equilibrium (cf. p. 318). If the enzyme concentration is increased, the apparent equilibrium constant also is increased.

The above kinetic data may be used for the calculation of K_m values for DPNH and acetaldehyde in the forward reaction, and for DPN^+ and ethanol in the reverse reaction; the Michaelis constants obtained may then be compared with the K_m values determined from the measurement of initial rates when one reaction partner is present in excess and the concentration of the other is varied (cf. p. 252). With liver alcohol dehydrogenase, $K_m(DPNH)$ determined in the latter manner is about $1 \times 10^{-5} M$; this denotes the concentration of DPNH required for half-maximal velocity when acetaldehyde is present in excess. In a similar manner, K_m(acetaldehyde) may be determined in the presence of excess DPNH, and equals about $1 \times 10^{-4} M$. In the reverse reaction, $K_m(DPN^+)$ and K_m(ethanol) have been found to be about $1 \times 10^{-5} M$ and $6 \times 10^{-4} M$ respectively.

Clearly, in the reaction between DPNH and acetaldehyde, catalyzed by small concentrations of liver alcohol dehydrogenase, the Michaelis constant for DPNH is not the same as the dissociation constant of ADH-DPNH (k_2/k_1). It will be recalled that $K_m = (k_2 + k_3)/k_1$ and that $K_m = k_2/k_1$ only when k_2 is much greater than k_3 (cf. p. 255). The above kinetic data show that in this system k_3 is greater than k_2, and therefore K_m approximates $k_3/k_1 = 37/(3.7 \times 10^6) = 1 \times 10^{-5}$, in excellent agreement with the value determined by direct measurement of K_m. The K_m values for the three other components may be calculated from the kinetic data: K_m(acetaldehyde) $= k_3/k_4[H^+] = 1.5 \times 10^{-4} M$; $K_m(DPN^+) = k_2/k_5 = 5 \times 10^{-6} M$; K_m(ethanol) $= k_2/k_6 = 5 \times 10^{-4} M$. These values agree reasonably well with those determined directly.

As mentioned earlier, valuable information about the mechanism of dehydrogenase action has come from studies not only with alcohol dehydrogenase, but also glyceraldehyde-3-phosphate dehydrogenase. The latter enzyme (also named triose phosphate dehydrogenase, TDH), which performs an important role in the anaerobic breakdown of glucose (Chapter 19), has been isolated in crystalline form from yeast[43] and from muscle.[44] Although not identical, the proteins from the two sources

---

[43] O. Warburg and W. Christian, *Biochem. Z.*, **303**, 40 (1939); G. W. Rafter and E. G. Krebs, *Arch. Biochem.*, **29**, 233 (1950).

[44] G. T. Cori et al., *J. Biol. Chem.*, **173**, 605 (1948).

are similar in many respects; they both have a particle weight of about 130,000 by ultracentrifugal analysis, and do not differ greatly in amino acid composition.[45]   Both proteins bind DPN[46] (3 molecules per unit of about 130,000); in fact, when the enzyme from rabbit muscle was first isolated in crystalline form, it was found to contain DPN.[47]   The pyridine nucleotide can be readily dissociated from the conjugated protein by treatment with charcoal, which strongly adsorbs DPN.   The active enzyme (from yeast and muscle) contains sulfhydryl groups, which are readily oxidized by oxygen, and some of which are essential for catalytic activity.   They may be regenerated, with concomitant restoration of activity, by treatment with sulfhydryl compounds such as cysteine or 2,3-dimercaptopropanol.   As with other enzymes whose catalytic action requires the presence of intact sulfhydryl groups, glyceraldehyde-3-phosphate dehydrogenase is protected by agents (e.g., ethylenediamine-tetraacetate) that bind metal ions, and is strongly inhibited by iodoacetate (cf. p. 325).

Warburg found that the reaction catalyzed by glyceraldehyde-3-phosphate dehydrogenase involves the participation of inorganic phosphate, and the work of Negelein and Brömel[48] showed that the product of the reaction is 1,3-diphosphoglyceric acid.   The latter discovery represents one of the most important advances in the understanding of the

$$\begin{array}{c}\text{CHO}\\|\\\text{HCOH}\\|\quad\text{OH}\\|\quad|\\\text{CH}_2\!-\!\text{OP}\!=\!\text{O}\\|\\\text{OH}\end{array}\;+\;\text{DPN}^+\;+\;\text{H}_3\text{PO}_4\;\rightleftharpoons\;\begin{array}{c}\text{O}\quad\text{OH}\\\|\quad|\\\text{C}\!-\!\text{OP}\!=\!\text{O}\\|\\\quad\text{OH}\\\text{HCOH}\\|\quad\text{OH}\\|\quad|\\\text{CH}_2\!-\!\text{OP}\!=\!\text{O}\\|\\\text{OH}\end{array}\;+\;\text{DPNH}\;+\;\text{H}^+$$

D-Glyceraldehyde-   D-1,3-Diphospho-
3-phosphate   glyceric acid

mechanism of coupling between biological oxidations and endergonic reactions, and is discussed more fully later (Chapter 15).

In attempting to interpret the mechanism of the reaction catalyzed by glyceraldehyde-3-phosphate dehydrogenase, Warburg assumed that an intermediate 1,3-diphosphoglyceraldehyde was formed by addition of the elements of phosphoric acid to the aldehyde group, followed by an

[45] S. F. Velick and S. Udenfriend, *J. Biol. Chem.*, **203**, 575 (1953).

[46] S. F. Velick et al., *J. Biol. Chem.*, **203**, 527, 545, 563 (1953); J. B. Fox, Jr., and W. B. Dandliker, *ibid.*, **221**, 1005 (1956).

[47] J. F. Taylor et al., *J. Biol. Chem.*, **173**, 619 (1948).

[48] E. Negelein and H. Brömel, *Biochem. Z.*, **303**, 132 (1939).

enzyme-catalyzed dehydrogenation of this intermediate. Later experimental data were incompatible with this hypothesis; it has been replaced by the view that an "acyl-enzyme" is formed in the dehydrogenation reaction, and that 1,3-diphosphoglyceric acid arises by phosphorolysis of the acyl-enzyme:[49]

$$RCHO + DPN^+ + enzyme\text{-}H \rightleftharpoons RCO\text{-}enzyme + DPNH + H^+$$

$$RCO\text{-}enzyme + H_3PO_4 \rightleftharpoons RCO\text{—}OPO_3H_2 + enzyme\text{-}H$$

The mechanism whereby the 3-phosphoglyceryl-enzyme compound is formed has not been elucidated completely,[50] but the work of Racker suggests that the aldehyde and the enzyme-DPN$^+$ complex interact, with the reduction of the pyridine nucleotide and attachment of the acyl group to the enzyme, as shown in Fig. 3. Racker has proposed that the

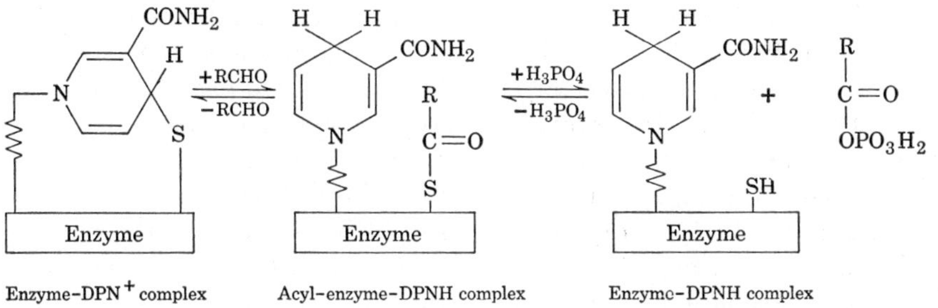

Fig. 3. Postulated mechanism of aldehyde oxidation by glyceraldehyde-3-phosphate dehydrogenase.

acyl group is linked to the enzyme by a thiol ester bond, involving the sulfhydryl group of glutathione bound to the dehydrogenase.[51] This hypothesis is supported by the observation that compounds known to combine with sulfhydryl groups (iodoacetate, p-chloromercuribenzoate) and to inactivate the enzyme affect the broad 360 mμ absorption of the enzyme-DPN$^+$ complex. It has also been shown that, in the absence of DPN$^+$ (removed by charcoal), 1,3-diphosphoglyceric acid reacts with the enzyme to form a stable acyl-enzyme which can be isolated in crystalline form.[52]

The intermediate formation of acyl-enzyme compounds is also observed

[49] E. Racker and I. Krimsky, *J. Biol. Chem.,* **198,** 731 (1952); J. Harting and S. F. Velick, *ibid.,* **207,** 867 (1954); O. Warburg et al., *Z. Naturforsch.,* **12b,** 47 (1957).

[50] P. D. Boyer and H. L. Segal, in W. D. McElroy and B. Glass, *Mechanism of Enzyme Action,* Johns Hopkins Press, Baltimore, 1954.

[51] E. Racker, in S. Colowick et al., *Glutathione,* Academic Press Inc., New York, 1954.

[52] I. Krimsky and E. Racker, *Science,* **122,** 319 (1955).

in the oxidation of other aldehydes (acetaldehyde, glyceraldehyde) by glyceraldehyde-3-phosphate dehydrogenase. For example, the enzyme catalyzes the formation of acetyl phosphate (CH_3CO—OPO_3H_2) from acetaldehyde and phosphate in the presence of DPN^+; on treatment of the DPN^+-free enzyme with acetyl phosphate, an acetyl-enzyme is obtained. Of the several known substrates of the enzyme, glyceraldehyde-3-phosphate is the one oxidized most rapidly, about 1000 times as much enzyme being required for a comparable rate of oxidation of glyceraldehyde.[53] When the enzyme is saturated with respect to glyceraldehyde-3-phosphate and to DPN^+, the turnover number is about 8000 molecules of DPN^+ per minute per unit of 130,000 (pH 8.6, 27° C).

In the early studies on glyceraldehyde-3-phosphate dehydrogenase, Warburg showed that, when phosphate (Na_2HPO_4) is replaced by arsenate (Na_2HAsO_4), the product of the reaction is D-3-phosphoglyceric acid. With the recognition of the acyl-enzyme as an intermediate in the reaction, this effect has been interpreted as an arsenolysis of the acyl-enzyme to form a carboxyl arsenate group ($—CO—OAsO_3{}^{2-}$) in the oxidation product. However, this group appears to be much more unstable in water than is the carboxyl phosphate group of 1,3-diphosphoglyceric acid, and rapidly undergoes hydrolysis to 3-phosphoglyceric acid and arsenate. In this connection, it should be added that the enzyme-DPN^+ complex catalyzes the hydrolysis of acetyl phosphate. Glyceraldehyde-3-phosphate dehydrogenase is therefore an enzyme that catalyzes not only oxidation reactions involving aldehydes and DPN^+, but also transfer reactions in which acyl groups react with phosphate (phosphorolysis) or with water (hydrolysis).

The importance of sulfhydryl groups in the action of glyceraldehyde-3-phosphate dehydrogenase invites the question whether analogous acyl-enzyme compounds having thiol ester bonds are formed in the action of other dehydrogenases that catalyze reactions between aldehydes and a pyridine nucleotide. Although this is likely for liver aldehyde dehydrogenase,[54] the evidence is not so extensive as for glyceraldehyde-3-phosphate dehydrogenase. With liver formaldehyde dehydrogenase, glutathione is a specific cofactor, and the possibility exists that a thiol ester (S-formyl glutathione) is formed by the dehydrogenation of the corresponding semimercaptal of formaldehyde.[55]

Enzymes similar to the glyceraldehyde-3-phosphate dehydrogenases of yeast and muscle have been found in other biological systems,

---

[53] C. F. Cori et al., *Biochim. et Biophys. Acta,* **4,** 160 (1950).

[54] E. Racker, *J. Biol. Chem.,* **177,** 883 (1949); L. P. Kendal and A. N. Ramanathan, *Biochem. J.,* **52,** 430 (1952).

[55] P. Strittmatter and E. G. Ball, *J. Biol. Chem.,* **213,** 445 (1955).

including plant tissues. In addition, however, leaves contain glyceraldehyde-3-phosphate dehydrogenases that are specific for TPN^+.[56]

Coupled Enzyme Reactions Involving Pyridine Nucleotides. In the oxidation-reduction reaction between 1,3-diphosphoglyceric acid and DPNH, catalyzed by small amounts of glyceraldehyde-3-phosphate dehydrogenase, the concentration ratio [glyceraldehyde-3-phosphate] $[DPN^+][HPO_4^{2-}]/[1,3$-diphosphoglycerate$][DPNH]$ is near unity at pH 7 and 25° C; the value of E_0' for the metabolite system has been calculated to be about -0.29 volt. Analogous calculation (cf. p. 300) of the E_0' values at pH 7 and 25° C for other metabolite systems, based on the value of -0.32 volt for the DPN or TPN system, has given the following potentials:[57]

L-Malate $\rightleftharpoons$ Oxaloacetate	-0.17 volt
L-Lactate $\rightleftharpoons$ Pyruvate	-0.19
L-α-Glycerophosphate $\rightleftharpoons$ Dihydroxyacetone phosphate	-0.19
Ethanol $\rightleftharpoons$ Acetaldehyde	-0.20

Although none of these systems is electroactive at metallic electrodes (cf. p. 302), potentiometric measurements have been performed in the presence of the appropriate enzyme system and of an electroactive oxidation-reduction system (a mediator) which facilitates electron exchange between the metabolite system and the metallic electrode. In several instances, the results agree well with the potentials calculated from the equilibrium concentration ratios in a reaction with an oxidation-reduction system of known potential. However, both the equilibrium data and the direct potentiometric measurements in the presence of mediators are subject to some uncertainty, and the above E_0' values must be considered approximations.

In the enzyme-catalyzed reaction of glyceraldehyde-3-phosphate, DPN^+, and phosphate to form 1,3-diphosphoglyceric acid, equilibrium is established when only partial conversion of the initial reactants has occurred. In contrast to the result of such an isolated enzyme experiment, when this reaction takes place during the fermentation of glucose to alcohol, it proceeds nearly to completion. To achieve this complete conversion, energy must be put into the system. Part of this energy is provided by the exergonic reduction of acetaldehyde by DPNH (cf. p. 318), catalyzed by alcohol dehydrogenase. This exergonic reaction drives the oxidation of glyceraldehyde-3-phosphate to completion in the manner illustrated on p. 328. The free energy change in the coupled reaction glyceraldehyde-3-phosphate + phosphate + acetaldehyde → 1,3-diphosphoglyceric acid + ethanol may be estimated from the above

[56] B. Axelrod et al., *J. Biol. Chem.*, **202**, 619 (1952).
[57] K. Burton and T. H. Wilson, *Biochem. J.*, **54**, 86 (1953).

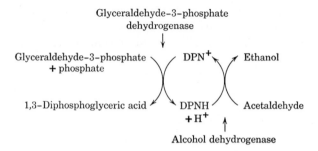

values of E_0' for the two metabolite systems. Since $\Delta F' = -n\mathfrak{F}\,\Delta E_0'$ (cf. p. 301), the standard free-energy change $(\Delta F')$ in the reaction (at pH 7 and 25° C) is approximately $-2 \times 23,063 \times [\,(-0.20) - (-0.29)\,] = -4150$ cal.

Coupled reactions of this type are sometimes termed "pyridine nucleotide-linked dismutations" or "coenzyme-linked dismutations." In the scheme shown above, the DPN system functions as an electron carrier from glyceraldehyde-3-phosphate to acetaldehyde, and the dismutation involves the operation of 2 catalytic proteins. The components of the DPN system may be considered to shuttle back and forth between these proteins; hence a small quantity of the pyridine nucleotide causes the transformation of much larger amounts of glyceraldehyde-3-phosphate and of acetaldehyde.

Another example of a DPN-linked dismutation is provided by the conversion of acetaldehyde to ethanol and acetic acid by extracts of animal tissues. This Cannizzaro reaction was thought for some time to be catalyzed by a single enzyme, termed "aldehyde mutase," but Racker[54] has shown that the reaction involves the coupled action of alcohol dehydrogenase and acetaldehyde dehydrogenase, as indicated.

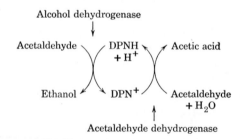

Other Pyridine Nucleotide-Dependent Dehydrogenases. It will be noted that Table 1 includes several enzymes in addition to those already mentioned in this chapter. Most of these will be discussed later in relation to the metabolic pathways in which they participate. For example, glutamic dehydrogenase plays an important role in amino acid metabolism, isocitric dehydrogenase is a key enzyme in the citric acid cycle, and β-hydroxyacyl-CoA dehydrogenases are participants in the breakdown and synthesis of fatty acids. Other pyridine nucleotide-dependent dehydrogenases will be encountered in the discussion of the role of several important metabolic intermediates, such as shikimic acid and orotic acid.

Two other metabolic processes, to be considered in relation to the aerobic oxidation of carbohydrates to CO_2 and H_2O, also involve the participation of DPN-dependent dehydrogenases. These processes are the oxidation of pyruvic acid to acetyl-CoA and CO_2, and the oxidation of α-ketoglutaric acid to succinyl-CoA and CO_2. Both involve the participation of lipoic acid (cf. p. 306), and it is believed that a "dihydrolipoic acid dehydrogenase" catalyzes the bimolecular oxidation-reduction reaction between DPN^+ and reduced lipoic acid.[58]

To these dehydrogenases may be added enzymes that catalyze the reaction

$$TPNH + DPN^+ \rightleftharpoons DPNH + TPN^+$$

Such enzymes, termed "pyridine nucleotide transhydrogenases," have been found in animal tissues and in *Pseudomonas fluorescens*. It has been suggested that, in animal tissues, transhydrogenase catalyzes hydrogen transfer between bound and free nucleotides.[59] Transhydrogenase also may permit the oxidation of TPNH by O_2 via electron transfer pathways specific for the aerobic oxidation of DPNH (cf. p. 371).[60]

[58] I. C. Gunsalus, in W. D. McElroy and B. Glass, *Mechanism of Enzyme Action*, Johns Hopkins Press, Baltimore, 1954.

[59] N. O. Kaplan et al., *J. Biol. Chem.*, **195**, 107 (1952); **205**, 1, 17, 31 (1953).

[60] E. G. Ball and O. Cooper, *Proc. Natl. Acad. Sci.*, **43**, 357 (1957).

In 1879 Blyth described the isolation from milk of a yellow pigment (named lactochrome) which showed a striking green fluorescence. This pigment was not studied further until 1925, when Bleyer and Kallman re-examined its properties. During the period 1932–1934, several pigments with similar optical properties were discovered in heart muscle extracts, in egg yolk, and in other tissues. Various names were given to these yellow substances (cytoflave, lyochromes), and, although it was later found that not all these pigments are flavins, it soon became clear that flavins occur in all cellular systems that have been examined. By 1936 the chemical nature of the yellow pigment of egg yolk and of milk had been established, largely through the work of Kuhn and Karrer; it was also shown that this pigment, named riboflavin, is identical with

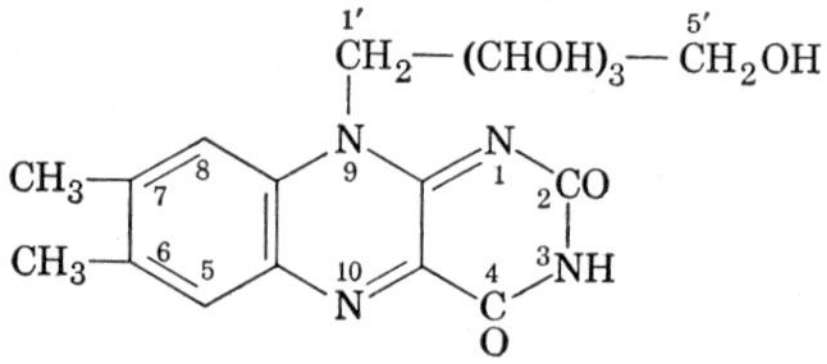

$$\text{CH}_2\text{— (CHOH)}_3\text{— CH}_2\text{OH}$$

Riboflavin

vitamin B_2 (Chapter 39). In riboflavin, a sugar residue, D-ribitol, is attached to an isoalloxazine ring; the compound may therefore be named 6,7-dimethyl-9-(1'-D-ribityl)isoalloxazine. It will be noted that the linkage between the sugar and the heterocyclic unit is not a glycosidic one, as in the nucleosides derived from the nucleic acids or in the pyridine nucleotides.

An important contribution to the elucidation of the structure of riboflavin came from the studies of Warburg and Christian on the mechanism of the oxidation of glucose-6-phosphate by mammalian erythrocytes. They showed in a memorable paper[1] that, for the oxidation of glucose-6-phosphate by atmospheric oxygen or, under anaerobic conditions, by methylene blue, a material present in red cells was required. This material was also found to be especially abundant in yeast, from which it was isolated in the form of a yellow pigment bound to a protein. Warburg and Christian named this conjugated protein the "yellow enzyme." The pigment could be removed from the protein by treatment of the yellow enzyme with methanol at 38° C. The protein-free pigment was converted by various reducing agents to a colorless (leuco) form, and the reduced pigment could be reoxidized by molecular oxygen.

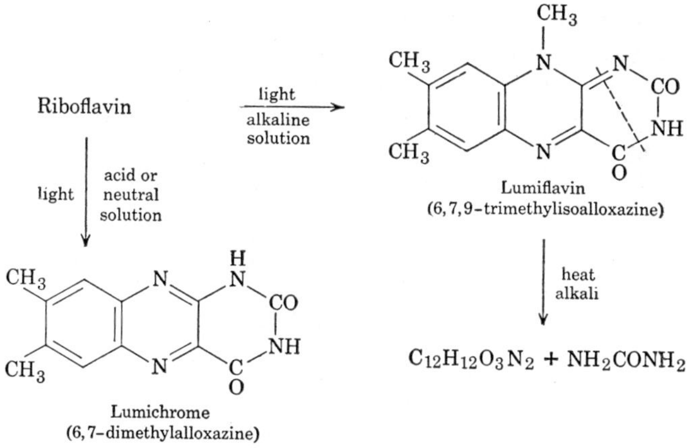

Riboflavin $\xrightarrow[\text{solution}]{\substack{\text{light} \\ \text{alkaline}}}$ Lumiflavin (6,7,9-trimethylisoalloxazine)

Riboflavin $\xrightarrow[\substack{\text{acid or} \\ \text{neutral} \\ \text{solution}}]{\text{light}}$ Lumichrome (6,7-dimethylalloxazine)

Lumiflavin $\xrightarrow[\text{alkali}]{\text{heat}}$ $C_{12}H_{12}O_3N_2 + NH_2CONH_2$

The protein-free pigment showed a green fluorescence upon irradiation with ultraviolet or blue light (4400 to 5400 A), while the conjugated protein did not. In the course of their study of the chemical nature of the yellow pigment, Warburg and Christian discovered that it was converted, on irradiation in alkaline solution, to a substance of the composition $C_{13}H_{12}O_2N_4$. When this material was heated with alkali, urea was formed. With these facts before him, Kuhn examined the effect of irradiation on the flavin pigment from egg yolk and found that it behaved in the same manner as Warburg's pigment; the product of irradiation in alkali was named lumiflavin. At acid or neutral pH values, irradiation of riboflavin results in the formation of lumichrome, a derivative of alloxazine.

After the nature of lumiflavin had been established, it became evident that the oxidation or reduction of the flavin involves the dehydrogenation or hydrogenation of the isoalloxazine ring. The flavin oxidation-reduction system is electroactive at a metallic electrode; for riboflavin, $E_0' = -0.185$ volt (pH 7, 20° C). Evidence has been presented in favor of

[1] O. Warburg and W. Christian, *Biochem. Z.*, **254**, 438 (1932).

the view that, in the reduction of the isoalloxazine ring, the addition
of electrons occurs in two separate steps, with the intermediate formation of a semiquinone[2] (cf. p. 290).

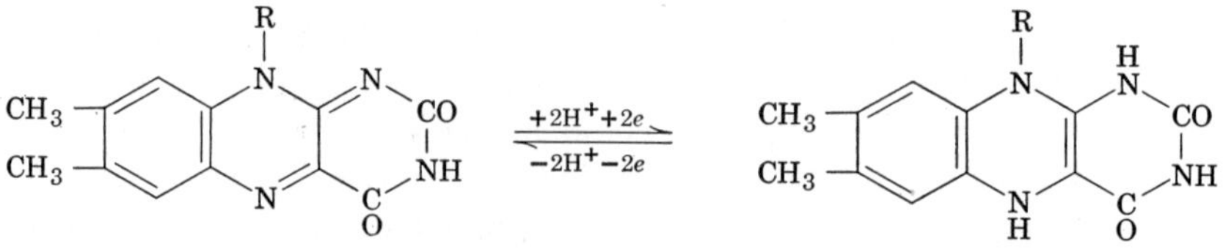

Oxidized flavin   Reduced flavin

Flavin Mononucleotide (FMN). Although riboflavin was first thought
to be the prosthetic group of the yellow enzyme, the work of Theorell[3] led
to the recognition that it is riboflavin-5′-phosphate. Since the flavin
phosphate is composed of a base (dimethylisoalloxazine), a sugar (ribi-

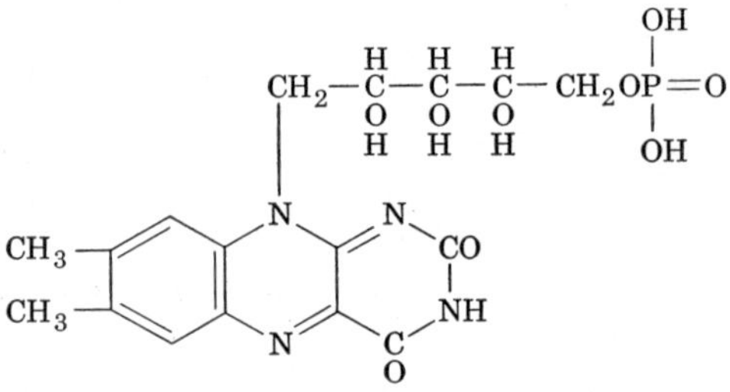

Riboflavin phosphate (flavin mononucleotide)

tol), and phosphate, it may be termed a nucleotide (flavin mononucleotide, FMN). Crystalline preparations of the yellow enzyme have been
obtained in various stages of purity; the most highly purified material
has a particle weight of about 100,000, and contains 2 molecules of FMN
per molecule of this weight.[4]

Upon dialysis of the yellow enzyme against dilute acid, or by precipitation of the protein with ammonium sulfate at pH 2.5, the pigment is
removed from the conjugated protein. The flavin-free protein does not
replace the yellow enzyme in the oxidation of glucose-6-phosphate by
oxygen or by methylene blue; when the isolated FMN is added to the
flavin-free protein, the catalytic activity is restored (cf. Fig. 1). In this
respect, FMN is much more effective than riboflavin,[5] indicating that
the presence of the phosphate in the 5′ position is important in the
binding of the flavin to the protein.

[2] H. Beinert, *J. Biol. Chem.,* **225,** 465 (1957).
[3] H. Theorell, *Biochem. Z.,* **278,** 263 (1935).
[4] H. Theorell and Å. Åkeson, *Arch. Biochem. and Biophys.,* **65,** 439 (1956).
[5] R. Kuhn and H. Rudy, *Ber. chem. Ges.,* **69B,** 2557 (1936).

The value of E_0' (pH 7, 30° C) for the FMN oxidation-reduction system is -0.219 volt;[6] when the flavin is attached to the protein portion of the yellow enzyme, however, the comparable value of E_0' is more positive (-0.123 volt);[7] reduced FMN is bound more tightly to the

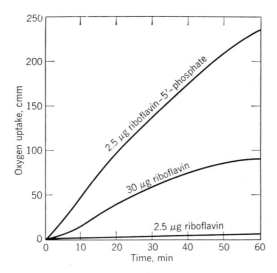

Fig. 1. Catalytic effect of riboflavin-5'-phosphate and of riboflavin on the oxidation of glucose-6-phosphate by oxygen, in the presence of the flavin-free protein of the yellow enzyme, TPN^+, and glucose-6-phosphate dehydrogenase. (From R. Kuhn and H. Rudy.[5])

protein than is oxidized FMN (cf. p. 303). The binding of the flavin to the protein also causes a shift in the absorption spectrum of FMN (cf. Fig. 2).

By taking advantage of the quenching of the fluorescence of FMN when it is bound in the yellow enzyme, Theorell and Nygaard[8] have determined the dissociation constant in the reaction

$$\text{FMN} + \text{protein} \underset{k_2}{\overset{k_1}{\rightleftharpoons}} \text{Yellow enzyme}$$

and have found it to be less than 10^{-12} M at pH 9 and 23° C; k_1 (the rate of association) is 1.4×10^6 M^{-1} sec^{-1}, and k_2 (the rate of dissociation) is less than 10^{-6} sec^{-1}. The dissociation constant ($K = k_2/k_1$) may be contrasted with the value for K_m, determined by holding the concentration of all components, including that of the flavin-free protein,

[6] H. J. Lowe and W. M. Clark, *J. Biol. Chem.*, **221**, 983 (1956).

[7] C. S. Vestling, *Acta Chem. Scand.*, **9**, 1600 (1955).

[8] H. Theorell and A. P. Nygaard, *Acta Chem. Scand.*, **8**, 877, 1649 (1954); **9**, 1587 (1955).

at a relatively high level, and varying the concentration of FMN (cf. Fig. 3). From a measurement of the concentration of FMN sufficient to permit half-maximal velocity, the value of K_m for the yellow enzyme was found to be $6 \times 10^{-8} M$ at pH 8.3.

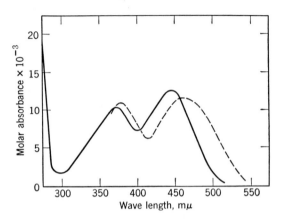

Fig. 2. Absorption spectra of flavin mononucleotide (solid line) and of old yellow enzyme (dash line).

As noted above, the yellow enzyme is a catalyst in the oxidation of glucose-6-phosphate, with either oxygen or methylene blue (MeB) serving as the ultimate electron acceptor. It will be recalled from p. 313 that the dehydrogenation of glucose-6-phosphate is effected in a reaction with TPN$^+$. Consequently, the role of the yellow enzyme is to catalyze electron transfer from TPNH to oxygen or to methylene blue, as indicated in the following equations.

(1) Glucose-6-phosphate + TPN$^+$ $\rightleftharpoons$
  6-Phosphogluconolactone + TPNH + H$^+$

(2) TPNH + H$^+$ + FMN $\rightleftharpoons$ TPN$^+$ + FMNH$_2$

(3a) FMNH$_2$ + O$_2$ $\rightarrow$ FMN + H$_2$O$_2$

(3b) FMNH$_2$ + MeB $\rightleftharpoons$ FMN + MeBH + H$^+$

Since $E_0'(p\text{H } 7)$ for the TPN system is about -0.32 volt, reduced TPN should be able to reduce FMN. Reaction 2 does not occur at a rapid rate, however, unless FMN is bound to its specific protein to form a flavoprotein such as the yellow enzyme. Since reaction 1 is catalyzed by another specific protein, glucose-6-phosphate dehydrogenase, it will be seen that the reaction of glucose-6-phosphate with oxygen or methylene blue involves the cooperative action of two specific proteins. In addition, the reduced form of FMN serves as the electron donor to oxygen or methylene blue. Thus one may say that the yellow enzyme is the catalyst for the reaction by which TPNH is converted to TPN$^+$, i.e., the summation of reactions 2 and 3a or 3b. It is therefore largely a matter of definition whether the conjugated flavoprotein as a whole is designated as "the enzyme." In the sequence of reactions under discussion, the definition depends on the nature of the chemical reaction to which reference is made; for this reason, it is desirable, whenever possible, to specify precisely the nature of the bimolecular oxidation-reduction reaction in question.

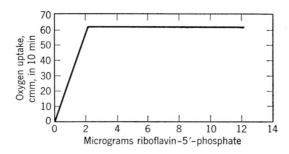

Fig. 3. Effect of increasing amounts of riboflavin-5'-phosphate on the rate of the aerobic oxidation of glucose-6-phosphate. (From H. Theorell.[3])

The biological conversion of riboflavin to flavin phosphate appears to be effected by an enzyme-catalyzed reaction in which adenosine triphosphate (ATP) serves as the phosphorylating agent:

$$\text{Riboflavin} + \text{ATP} \rightarrow \text{FMN} + \text{ADP}$$

A preparation of the enzyme (named "flavokinase") which catalyzes the phosphorylation reaction has been obtained from yeast.[9]

Flavin Adenine Dinucleotide (FAD). After the discovery of the yellow enzyme, other flavoproteins were found;[10] one enzyme, also studied by Warburg and Christian, catalyzes the oxidation of D-amino acids by oxygen, and is therefore termed D-amino acid oxidase. The presence of this enzyme in animal tissues was discovered by Krebs in 1933, and a purified preparation was obtained by Warburg from sheep kidneys. The reaction of D-amino acids and O_2 in the presence of the flavoprotein may be written as in the equations shown on p. 336. The product of the enzyme-catalyzed dehydrogenation has been assumed to be the imino acid, but it may be the tautomeric α,β-unsaturated amino acid bound to the enzyme. Whatever the structure of the intermediate may be,

[9] E. B. Kearney and S. Englard, *J. Biol. Chem.*, **193**, 821 (1951).

[10] H. Theorell, in J. B. Sumner and K. Myrbäck, *The Enzymes,* Chapter **55**, Academic Press, New York, 1951.

$$\begin{array}{ccc} \text{COOH} & & \text{COOH} \\ | & & | \\ \text{HC—NH}_2 + O_2 & \rightarrow & \text{C=NH} + H_2O_2 \\ | & & | \\ \text{R} & & \text{R} \end{array}$$

$$\begin{array}{ccc} \text{COOH} & & \text{COOH} \\ | & & | \\ \text{C=NH} + H_2O & \rightarrow & \text{C=O} + NH_3 \\ | & & | \\ \text{R} & & \text{R} \end{array}$$

it is unstable in water and is rapidly hydrolyzed to the corresponding keto acid.

When D-amino acid oxidase was treated with ammonium sulfate at pH 2.5, the conjugated flavoprotein was separated into a flavin-free protein and a protein-free flavin.[11] However, the flavin was not FMN,

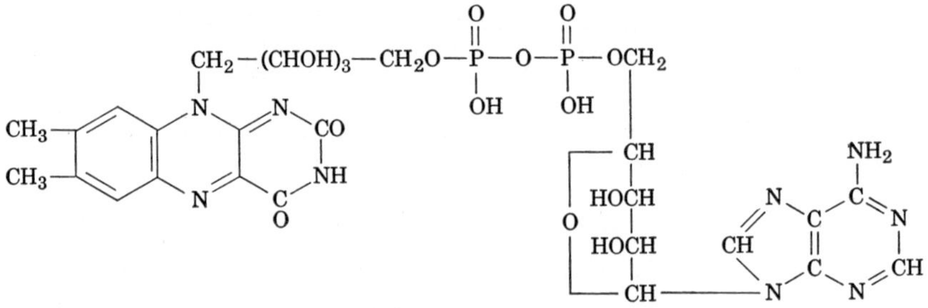

Flavin adenine dinucleotide (FAD)

but a compound in which 1 molecule of FMN is linked to a molecule of adenosine-5′-phosphate (AMP); this new flavin nucleotide was named flavin adenine dinucleotide (abbreviated FAD).

FAD has been obtained in highly purified form by chromatography and by paper electrophoresis.[12] Its structure has been definitely established by chemical synthesis in Todd's laboratory.[13] FAD is cleaved by the enzyme nucleotide pyrophosphatase (cf. p. 309) to yield the component mononucleotides FMN and AMP. It is probably synthesized in biological systems by the reaction of FMN with ATP, catalyzed by the enzyme FAD pyrophosphorylase (partially purified from yeast[14]):

$$\text{FMN} + \text{ATP} \rightleftharpoons \text{FAD} + \text{pyrophosphate}$$

The flavin-free protein of D-amino acid oxidase has been purified

[11] O. Warburg and W. Christian, *Biochem. Z.*, **298**, 150, 368 (1938).

[12] L. G. Whitby, *Biochem. J.*, **54**, 437 (1953); O. Walaas and E. Walaas, *Acta Chem. Scand.*, **10**, 118 (1956).

[13] S. M. H. Christie et al., *J. Chem. Soc.*, **1954**, 46.

[14] A. W. Schrecker and A. Kornberg, *J. Biol. Chem.*, **182**, 795 (1950).

appreciably, and measurements of K_m(FAD) for this enzyme preparation at pH 8.3 and 38° C have given values near 1.4×10^{-7} M (cf. Stadie and Zapp[15]). In the oxidation of D-amino acids, the FAD of D-amino acid oxidase functions as an electron carrier from the amino acid to O_2, in a manner analogous to the role of the FMN of the yellow enzyme in the transfer of electrons from TPNH to O_2. It must be emphasized that the specific capacity to catalyze the bimolecular reaction between FAD and a D-amino acid resides in the specific protein to which the FAD is attached. This specificity is extremely sharp with regard to the configuration of the amino acid; L-amino acids are not attacked. Among the inhibitors of D-amino acid oxidase is the antimalarial drug atebrin (quinacrine), which may act by competing with FAD for the protein.[16] In contrast to the yellow enzyme from yeast, D-amino acid oxidase is fluorescent, as is free FAD; this has been interpreted to indicate that in D-amino acid oxidase the N^3 position of the isoalloxazine ring (cf. p. 330) is not bound to the protein.[17] In the yellow enzyme, this position is probably involved in the linkage of FMN to the protein.

Several other flavoproteins that catalyze the oxidation of amino acids also have been described. These include an L-amino acid oxidase from rat kidney (contains FMN as the prosthetic group) and a glycine oxidase (contains FAD). The various amino acid oxidases will be discussed further in Chapter 31 in connection with their possible roles in the intermediate metabolism of amino acids.

After the identification of FAD as the prosthetic group of D-amino acid oxidase, Haas[18] found in yeast a FAD-flavoprotein that catalyzes the oxidation of TPNH by molecular oxygen. This newer flavoprotein was named the "new yellow enzyme" to distinguish it from the FMN-containing "old yellow enzyme" of yeast. Also, Warburg and Christian showed that the protein portion of the old yellow enzyme could be combined with FAD to form an artificial flavoprotein that catalyzes the oxidation of TPNH by O_2.

Other Catalytic Flavoproteins. In addition to those already mentioned, many other catalytic flavoproteins have been identified in biological systems, and a selected list is given in Table 1. FMN and FAD are the only naturally occurring flavin nucleotides of known structure identified as components of flavoproteins; the possibility exists, however, that other flavins may serve as prosthetic groups. Some flavoproteins have been reported to contain flavins other than FMN or FAD, but the nature of the prosthetic groups in these enzymes has not been

15 W. C. Stadie and J. A. Zapp, *J. Biol. Chem.*, **150**, 165 (1943).

16 L. Hellerman et al., *J. Biol. Chem.*, **163**, 553 (1946).

17 O. Walaas and E. Walaas, *Acta Chem. Scand.*, **10**, 122 (1956).

18 E. Haas, *Biochem. Z.*, **298**, 378 (1938).

elucidated. In general, the protein portion of a catalytic flavoprotein is relatively specific for either FMN or FAD, although instances are known (e.g., TPNH-cytochrome c reductase of swine liver) in which the isolated flavoprotein contains one of these nucleotides, but, after removal of the prosthetic group, the flavin-free protein forms an active flavoprotein with either nucleotide.[19]

Among the flavoproteins listed in Table 1 is glycolic acid oxidase,[20] which may play an important role in the respiration of higher plants. It catalyzes the oxidation of glycolate to glyoxylate (cf. p. 318) with

Table I.   Some Catalytic Flavoproteins

| | Prosthetic Groups | |
Name and Source	Flavin	Other
Old yellow enzyme (yeast)	FMN	
D-Amino acid oxidase (sheep kidney)	FAD	
New yellow enzyme (yeast)	FAD	
L-Amino acid oxidase (rat kidney)	FMN	
L-Amino acid oxidase (snake venom)	FAD	
Glycine oxidase (swine kidney)	FAD	
D-Aspartic acid oxidase (rabbit kidney)	FAD	
Glycolic acid oxidase (spinach)	FMN	
Glucose oxidase (*Penicillium notatum*)	FAD	
Xanthine oxidase (milk)	FAD	Molybdenum, iron
Aldehyde oxidase (swine liver)	FAD	Molybdenum, heme?
TPNH-nitrate reductase (*Neurospora crassa*)	FAD	Molybdenum
Hydrogenase (*Clostridium pasteurianum*)	FAD	Molybdenum
TPNH-cytochrome c reductase (yeast)	FMN	
Diaphorase (swine heart)	FAD	
DPNH-cytochrome c reductase (heart)	?	Iron
Succinic dehydrogenase (beef heart)	?	Iron
Acyl-CoA dehydrogenases (beef liver)		
"Green enzyme"	FAD	Copper
"Yellow enzyme"	FAD	Iron?

the production of H_2O_2, which oxidizes glyoxylate further to formate, CO_2, and H_2O. This enzyme provides a counterpart to glyoxylic reductase whose action appears to be limited to the reduction of glyoxylate by DPNH. Glycolic acid oxidase also has been identified in mammalian liver.[21]

It will have been noted that in the direct oxidation of a reduced flavin by O_2 one of the products is H_2O_2. This property of flavins assumed

[19] B. L. Horecker, *J. Bol. Chem.*, **183**, 593 (1950).
[20] I. Zelitch and S. Ochoa, *J. Biol. Chem.*, **201**, 707 (1953).
[21] E. Kun et al., *J. Biol. Chem.*, **210**, 269 (1954).

some interest when it was discovered that *Penicillium notatum* contained a yellow protein (notatin) which, in the presence of D-glucose, appeared to be an antibacterial agent. The subsequent identification of notatin and glucose oxidase explained the mode of antibacterial action, since the oxidation of glucose by O_2 in the presence of notatin results in the formation of bactericidal amounts of H_2O_2. Glucose oxidase is a relatively specific catalyst for the oxidation of β-D-glucopyranose (cf. p. 310) to δ-D-gluconolactone,[22,23] which readily undergoes hydrolysis to gluconic acid. Other flavoproteins (e.g., xanthine oxidase) that catalyze the formation of H_2O_2 have also been shown to act as antibacterial agents.

The catalytic flavoproteins listed in Table 1 include several that contain, in addition to FAD, a metal ion such as molybdenum (Mo). One of these is xanthine oxidase, a catalyst for the oxidation of hypoxanthine to xanthine and uric acid (Chapter 33); this enzyme (from milk) was studied by Ball[24] and has been obtained in crystalline form.[25] The recognition of Mo as a constituent of xanthine oxidase stems from studies on a dietary factor that is required for normal levels of this enzyme in the liver of young rats.[26] Subsequent studies showed that the xanthine oxidases from milk and liver are metalloflavoproteins.[27] Although the enzyme from milk is named xanthine oxidase, highly purified preparations also catalyze the oxidation of aldehydes (e.g., acetaldehyde) and of DPNH. The corresponding enzyme preparation from liver oxidizes hypoxanthine, aldehydes, and DPNH; it is similar in many respects to liver aldehyde oxidase.[28] The crystalline xanthine oxidase from milk contains iron in addition to FAD and Mo, in the approximate molar ratio 4:1:0.7 respectively. The manner in which these three components may cooperate to catalyze the oxidation of the substrates by O_2 has not been elucidated as yet.

Another catalytic metalloflavoprotein shown to contain molybdenum is TPNH-nitrate reductase,[29] which appears to catalyze electron transfer in the sequence TPNH $\rightarrow$ FAD (or FMN) $\rightarrow$ Mo $\rightarrow$ NO_3^- and leads to the reduction of nitrate to nitrite (Chapter 28). It has been suggested

[22] R. Bentley and A. Neuberger, *Biochem. J.*, **45**, 584 (1949).

[23] D. Keilin and E. F. Hartree, *Biochem. J.*, **42**, 221 (1948); **50**, 331 (1951).

[24] E. G. Ball, *J. Biol. Chem.*, **128**, 51 (1939).

[25] P. G. Avis et al., *J. Chem. Soc.*, **1955**, 1100; **1956**, 1212, 1219.

[26] D. A. Richert and W. W. Westerfeld, *J. Biol. Chem.*, **203**, 915 (1953); E. C. De Renzo et al., *J. Am. Chem. Soc.*, **75**, 753 (1953); *Advances in Enzymol.*, **17**, 293 (1956).

[27] B. Mackler et al., *J. Biol. Chem.*, **210**, 149 (1954); R. K. Kielley, *ibid.*, **216**, 405 (1955); C. N. Remy et al., *ibid.*, **217**, 293 (1955).

[28] H. R. Mahler et al., *J. Biol. Chem.*, **210**, 465 (1954); J. Hurwitz, *ibid.*, **212**, 757 (1955); F. Bergmann and S. Dikstein, *ibid.*, **223**, 765 (1956).

[29] D. J. D. Nicholas and A. Nason, *J. Biol. Chem.*, **207**, 353; **211**, 183 (1954).

that molybdenum operates in this sequence as the Mo^{5+}-Mo^{6+} oxidation-reduction system.[30]   The enzyme hydrogenase of some bacteria also appears to be a molybdoflavoprotein.

The Role of Flavoproteins in Respiration.   Interest in the catalytic flavoproteins stems from the possibility that certain of them may be important links in the transfer of electrons from metabolites and pyridine nucleotides to the ultimate electron acceptor in biological oxidations, molecular oxygen.   In particular, the recognized role of the pyridine nucleotides makes it essential to know how rapidly DPNH or TPNH can interact with the FMN or FAD of suitable flavoproteins and how fast the reduced flavins of the conjugated proteins can react with O_2. Obviously, the over-all rate of cellular respiration is determined by the slowest reaction.   If the observed rate of respiration of a given cell is more rapid than either the reduction of the flavin of a component flavoprotein by reduced pyridine nucleotides or the oxidation of the reduced flavin by oxygen, then it is unlikely that the flavoprotein in question is an important electron carrier in the direct transfer of electrons from DPNH or TPNH to O_2.   The discussion that follows illustrates an experimental approach to this important problem.

If one defines the bimolecular velocity constant for the reduction of a flavin by reduced pyridine nucleotide as k_r, and the velocity constant for the oxidation of a reduced flavin by O_2 as k_o, the data of Warburg and Christian show that, for the old yellow enzyme, at pH 7.4 and 25° C, $k_r = 6 \times 10^6 \ M^{-1} \ min^{-1}$ and $k_o = 1 \times 10^5 \ M^{-1} \ min^{-1}$.   The corresponding values for the new yellow enzyme are 2.2×10^7 and 1.4×10^4 respectively.   For the experimental procedure and mode of calculation employed in obtaining these data, see Warburg and Christian.[11]   In the transfer of electrons to O_2, the new yellow enzyme is therefore only one-seventh as effective as the old yellow enzyme $(1 \times 10^5 \div 1.4 \times 10^4 = 7)$. Theorell has shown that, in a system containing glucose-6-phosphate, glucose-6-phosphate dehydrogenase, TPN^+, and the protein portion of the old yellow enzyme, 1 μg of FMN $(2.2 \times 10^{-6}$ millimole) causes an uptake of 2.7 cmm of O_2 $(1.2 \times 10^{-4}$ millimole) per minute.   The turnover number of the old yellow enzyme is therefore about 55, and that of the new yellow enzyme must be one-seventh of this, namely 8.   If methylene blue is added, the rate of oxygen uptake is greatly increased, since the reaction of reduced flavin with methylene blue is extremely rapid, and the reduced methylene blue is oxidized very rapidly by molecular oxygen.

The values of 55 and 8 for the turnover numbers of the two yellow enzymes are extremely low, and the question arises whether electron

[30] D. J. D. Nicholas and H. M. Stevens, *Nature,* **176.** 1066 (1955).

carriers of such low effectiveness can be the sole link between DPNH or TPNH and O_2 in biological oxidations. This question was examined by Warburg with several bacteria, such as *Lactobacillus delbruckii*, which normally grow under anaerobic conditions and apparently do not contain measurable amounts of heme pigments. In the presence of oxygen, a slow respiration is observed, and H_2O_2 is formed. On the basis of the spectroscopic examination of the bacteria, it was estimated that a cell suspension characterized by an O_2 uptake of 1 cmm per ml per min contained 6×10^{-4} millimole of a flavin (nature unknown) per milliliter. This would correspond to a turnover number of 30, and it may well be that, under exceptional metabolic circumstances, flavoproteins such as the yeast yellow enzymes may serve *in vivo* as direct electron carriers to molecular oxygen. However, it is well known that yeast respires much more rapidly than could be accounted for simply on the basis of a direct transfer of electrons from the reduced flavins of the old and new yellow enzymes to molecular oxygen.

Electron Transfer from Pyridine Nucleotides to Cytochrome c. The respiration of yeast, and of all other normally aerobic cells, is extremely sensitive to the addition of cyanide; 0.45×10^{-5} M cyanide is sufficient to decrease the rate of respiration of baker's yeast to 50 per cent of its normal value. It will be recalled that the heme proteins readily combine with cyanide (cf. p. 178). Warburg showed that most of the cyanide inhibition of oxygen uptake by cells is due to interference with the normal operation of the iron-porphyrin proteins concerned with electron transfer to oxygen. In parallel studies, Keilin demonstrated that cyanide inhibits the enzymic oxidation by molecular oxygen of reduced cytochromes, the best known of which is cytochrome c (p. 350). Much attention has been devoted to the elucidation of the enzymic mechanisms of electron transfer from metabolites to cytochrome c; since the initial oxidation of many metabolites involves hydrogen transfer to DPN^+ or TPN^+, efforts were made to find enzyme systems that effect rapid electron transfer from DPNH and TPNH to oxidized cytochrome c. It is now known that catalytic flavoproteins participate in this process, and accelerate the reaction

$$\text{DPNH (or TPNH)} + 2CyFe^{3+} \rightleftharpoons$$
$$\text{DPN}^+ \text{ (or TPN}^+) + 2CyFe^{2+} + H^+$$

where $CyFe^{3+}$ and $CyFe^{2+}$ denote the oxidized and reduced forms of cytochrome c respectively. Flavin-containing enzyme preparations from a variety of biological sources have been found to function as catalysts in this reaction. These enzyme preparations have been termed DPNH (or TPNH)-cytochrome c reductases.

One of the first flavoproteins of this group to be discovered was isolated from yeast.[31]   This flavoprotein, now termed TPNH-cytochrome c reductase, is more sensitive to denaturation than the old yellow enzyme, and hence had escaped detection in the earlier work of Warburg and others. In contrast to the old and new yellow enzymes, yeast cytochrome c reductase reacts rapidly with cytochrome c. The velocity constant for the oxidation, by $CyFe^{3+}$, of the $FMNH_2$ in cytochrome c reductase $(k_o = 5.3 \times 10^9 \ M^{-1} \ min^{-1})$ is 180,000 times that of the old yellow enzyme. For the direct interaction of the reduced form of the cytochrome c reductase with oxygen, $k_o = 8 \times 10^3$, a value about one-tenth that for the autoxidation of the old yellow enzyme. With TPNH as the electron donor, $k_r = 8.5 \times 10^7$; the rate of the reduction of the cytochrome c reductase is about 14 times faster than that of the old yellow enzyme. However, with DPNH as the electron donor, the reduction of the FMN of the cytochrome c reductase is extremely slow. The efficiency of this flavoprotein in catalyzing the electron transfer from TPNH to cytochrome c may be seen from its turnover number of 1300; this value is based on the assumption that the flavoprotein has a molecular weight of 78,000. A cytochrome c reductase with a similar specificity for TPNH was later isolated from liver,[19] but the prosthetic group was found to contain FAD in place of FMN.

$$H^+ + TPNH \quad\diagdown\diagup\quad FMN \quad\diagdown\diagup\quad 2CyFe^{2+} + 2H^+$$

$$TPN^+ \diagup\diagdown FMNH_2 \diagup\diagdown 2CyFe^{3+}$$

The determination of the $K_m(FMN)$ for the yeast TPNH-cytochrome c reductase gave a value of approximately $1 \times 10^{-9} \ M$, which is lower than that found for the old yellow enzyme (cf. p. 334). Although no data are available for the dissociation constant of TPNH-cytochrome c reductase, it has been suggested that in this enzyme the flavin is bound to the protein even more tightly than in the old yellow enzyme. It would appear that, in the reduction of the FMN portion, TPNH is attached to the flavoprotein, and it has been surmised (but not yet demonstrated experimentally) that direct hydrogen transfer to FMN takes place. Although the intimate mechanism whereby TPNH-cytochrome c reductase acts has not been elucidated, the catalytic role of this enzyme may be described by means of a scheme in which the protein portion of the flavoprotein is considered a specific catalyst for two bimolecular oxidation-reduction reactions, and the TPN, FMN, and cytochrome c systems are the reactants.

The two cytochrome c reductases isolated by Haas et al.[31] and by

[31] E. Haas et al., *J. Biol. Chem.*, **143**, 341 (1942).

Horecker[19] from yeast and from liver appear to be specific for the TPN system. However, it has long been known that preparations of some animal tissues (e.g., heart muscle) do not oxidize TPNH rapidly, but effect the rapid oxidation of DPNH. Furthermore, for the oxidation of DPNH by O_2 in the presence of swine heart preparations, cytochrome c is required.[32] Although a flavoprotein (diaphorase; cf. Table 1) had been isolated from heart muscle,[33] and shown to oxidize DPNH rapidly, the reduced flavoprotein did not react effectively with oxidized cytochrome c. Thus diaphorase itself did not meet the requirements of a DPNH-cytochrome c reductase. However, when DPNH was oxidized by the FAD of diaphorase, and the reduced FAD reoxidized by methylene blue in the presence of O_2, a very rapid aerobic oxidation of DPNH was observed (maximum turnover number of about 8500).

An important advance in the elucidation of the enzymic mechanism of electron transfer from DPNH to cytochrome c was made by the isolation of a soluble DPNH-cytochrome c reductase from heart muscle,[34] and the recognition that it is a metalloflavoprotein containing iron; a flavin/iron ratio of 1:4 has been reported. After treatment with acid, or with agents that bind iron tightly (e.g., citrate), the ability of the enzyme to react with cytochrome c was almost completely lost, whereas the rate of electron transfer from DPNH to dyes ("diaphorase activity") was unaffected. This finding led to the conclusion that the role of the iron in the intact DPNH-cytochrome c reductase is to facilitate electron transfer from the reduced flavin to cytochrome c.[35] It appears unlikely that free ferrous ions transfer electrons to oxidized cytochrome c, since the potential of the Fe^{2+}-Fe^{3+} system is much more positive than that of the cytochrome c system (cf. p. 299). The possibility exists that complexes of iron with anions are effective in the enzymic electron transfer; such complexes generally have potentials more negative than the Fe^{2+}-Fe^{3+} system. Another possibility is that the metal ion in DPNH-cytochrome c reductase serves to effect a tighter binding of the flavin to the catalytic protein.

Much further work is needed to clarify the biological role of the metalloflavoproteins, especially in relation to the function of the metal ions.[36] Nevertheless, it is clear that metabolic pathways are available for the transfer of electrons from TPNH or DPNH to cytochrome c via flavins as electron carriers. As will be seen from the discussion in the

[32] E. E. Lockhart and V. R. Potter, *J. Biol. Chem.,* **137,** 1 (1941).

[33] F. B. Straub, *Biochem. J.,* **33,** 787 (1939); H. S. Corran et al., *ibid.,* **33,** 793 (1939); N. Savage, *ibid.,* **67,** 146 (1957).

[34] H. Edelhoch et al., *J. Biol. Chem.,* **197,** 97 (1952); H. R. Mahler et al., *ibid.,* **199,** 585 (1952); B. de Bernard, *Biochim. et Biophys. Acta,* **23,** 510 (1957).

[35] H. R. Mahler and D. G. Elowe, *J. Biol. Chem.,* **210,** 165 (1954).

[36] H. R. Mahler, *Advances in Enzymol.,* **17,** 233 (1956).

next chapter, additional electron carrier systems appear to be interposed
between the pyridine nucleotides and cytochrome c systems. It must
also be borne in mind that the sequence of electron transport described
above for yeast, liver, and heart muscle preparations does not necessarily
apply to all cells and tissues, and that alternative pathways may exist
in nature. It would be premature to conclude, therefore, that the pyridine nucleotide-cytochrome c reductases isolated thus far are the only
types of enzymic catalysts for electron transfer between the pyridine
nucleotides and the cytochromes.

Other Metalloflavoproteins. In the early studies (Battelli and Stern,
Thunberg) on the dehydrogenation of metabolites by tissue preparations,
it was recognized that succinate is rapidly converted to fumarate (cf.
p. 286) by suspensions of minced muscle; the enzyme responsible for this
effect was termed succinic dehydrogenase. Because of the difficulties
encountered in demonstrating succinic dehydrogenase activity in aqueous
extracts of animal tissues, for many years the literature on this subject
was unclear and often contradictory. More recent work has led to the
isolation of enzyme preparations (from a defatted mitochondrial fraction
of beef heart and from yeast) that contain flavin and nonheme iron in a
1:4 ratio.[37] These preparations catalyze electron transfer from succinate
to the oxidation-reduction indicator phenazine methosulfate, but not to
several other dyes (e.g., methylene blue) or to cytochrome c. As will be
seen on p. 355, the reduction of cytochrome c by succinate, in the presence
of heart muscle preparations, involves the coupled action of several
electron carrier systems. Since the purified succinic dehydrogenase
preparation catalyzes not only the dehydrogenation of succinate, but also
the reduction of fumarate by the reduced form of a dye, there is no need
to assume the presence of a separate "fumaric hydrogenase" in animal
tissues; such an enzyme was first reported to be present in yeast.[38]
Although FAD was found to be the flavin component of the yeast enzyme
preparation, the nature of the flavin in heart muscle succinic dehydrogenase has not been established as yet.

Among the first enzymes to be identified as metalloflavoproteins are
two important participants in the metabolism of fatty acids. These two
enzymes catalyze the dehydrogenation of CoA thiol esters of fatty acids[39]
to form the corresponding α,β-unsaturated acyl-CoA derivatives in the
following reaction:

$$RCH_2CH_2CO\text{-}CoA + FAD \rightleftharpoons RCH{=}CHCO\text{-}CoA + FADH_2$$

[37] T. P. Singer et al., *Arch. Biochem. and Biophys.*, **62**, 497 (1956); *J. Biol. Chem.*,
223, 599 (1956); *Advances in Enzymol.*, **18**, 65 (1957).

[38] F. G. Fischer et al., *Ann. Chem.*, **552**, 203 (1942).

[39] D. E. Green et al., *J. Biol. Chem.*, **206**, 1 (1954); F. L. Crane et al., *ibid.*, **218**,
701 (1956).

Both enzyme preparations have been isolated from beef liver mitochondria and found to contain FAD; they differ in color, however, one of them being green, the other yellow. The green enzyme contains copper in a ratio of Cu^{2+} to FAD of 2:1. The enzymic mechanism for the oxidation of the $FADH_2$ of these metalloflavoproteins by cytochrome c is unclear; it has been reported that an additional flavoprotein, termed the "electron-transferring flavoprotein," is involved.[40] The role of the acyl-CoA dehydrogenases (also termed acyl dehydrogenases) in the metabolic breakdown and synthesis of fatty acids will be considered later (Chapter 25).

From the discussion in this chapter it would appear, therefore, that at least three types of catalytic flavoproteins may be distinguished. The first group, which includes the old yellow enzyme, D-amino acid oxidase, and glucose oxidase, mediates rapid electron transfer between a metabolite and molecular oxygen, without the apparent participation of any other electron carrier. The second group of flavoproteins catalyzes electron transfer between DPNH or TPNH and cytochrome c (the pyridine nucleotide-cytochrome c reductases) or another one-electron acceptor (e.g., TPNH-nitrate reductase); such enzymes appear to require the presence of a metal ion for electron transfer to these oxidants, although the role of the metal has not been clarified completely. The third group catalyzes the oxidation of metabolites by various electron acceptors (e.g., xanthine oxidase, succinic dehydrogenase, acyl-CoA dehydrogenase), with the participation of metal ions in a manner whose details remain to be elucidated.

Role of Flavin in Bioluminescence. Many organisms are known to emit light; among those studied most intensively from this point of view are the firefly (*Photinus pyralis*), the crustacean *Cypridina hilgendorfii*, and the marine bacterium *Achromobacter fischerii*.[41] Cell-free extracts of these three luminous organisms exhibit luminescence under suitable conditions. Although the chemical events in bioluminescence are not understood fully, in general it appears that the biochemical process involves the action of an enzyme (luciferase) on a pigment (luciferin) to form an intermediate, which in the presence of O_2 forms a chemiluminescent substance. An example of nonbiological chemiluminescence is that of 3-aminophthalhydrazide in the presence of H_2O_2.[42]

Of special interest for the present discussion is the finding that bacterial luciferin appears to be $FMNH_2$. A partially purified luciferase prepara-

[40] F. L. Crane and H. Beinert, *J. Biol. Chem.*, **218**, 717 (1956).

[41] E. N. Harvey, *Bioluminescence*, Academic Press, New York, 1942; W. D. McElroy and B. L. Strehler, *Bact. Revs.*, **18**, 177 (1954); W. D. McElroy, *Harvey Lectures*, **51**, 240 (1957).

[42] H. D. K. Drew, *Trans. Faraday Soc.*, **35**, 207 (1939).

tion (from *Achromobacter fischerii*) catalyzes a light-emitting reaction in the presence of $FMNH_2$, O_2, and a long-chain fatty aldehyde (e.g., dodecyl aldehyde, palmitaldehyde).[43] Apparently, luminescence involves an enzyme-catalyzed electron transfer from $FMNH_2$ to O_2; the role of the aldehyde is not yet clear, but the compound is consumed during the light-emitting process, possibly through oxidation by the H_2O_2 produced in the aerobic oxidation of $FMNH_2$.

The chemical nature of firefly luciferin is unknown; its structure may be related to that of the flavins. Firefly luciferase has been obtained in crystalline form.[44] For the maximum luminescent activity of this enzyme, ATP and Mg^{2+} must be present, and it is probable that the reduced firefly luciferin reacts with ATP to form an "AMP-luciferin" which becomes chemiluminescent on oxidation by oxygen.[45]

[43] W. D. McElroy and A. A. Green, *Arch. Biochem. and Biophys.*, **56**, 240 (1955); J. R. Totter and M. J. Cormier, *J. Biol. Chem.*, **216**, 801 (1955); M. J. Cormier et al., *Arch. Biochem. and Biophys.*, **63**, 414 (1956).

[44] A. A. Green and W. D. McElroy, *Biochim. et Biophys. Acta*, **20**, 170 (1956).

[45] W. D. McElroy and A. A. Green, *Arch. Biochem. and Biophys.*, **64**, 257 (1956).

14 ·   Metal-Containing Oxidases

In the previous two chapters, consideration was given to the enzymes that catalyze electron transfer reactions involved in the dehydrogenation of metabolites (e.g., lactic acid, glyceraldehyde-3-phosphate, amino acids, hypoxanthine) and of reduced pyridine nucleotides. Since, in aerobic biological systems, the ultimate electron acceptor in respiration is molecular oxygen, one may turn next to the enzymes that catalyze the transfer of electrons to oxygen. As noted in the discussion of the flavoproteins, the reduced flavins react with oxygen, but at a rate insufficient to account for the respiration of aerobic cells. The central position in the direct reaction with molecular oxygen must rather be assigned to metal-containing proteins which transfer electrons from carriers such as reduced cytochrome c to O_2. These oxidases are related in many respects to enzymes that catalyze oxidation-reduction reactions involving hydrogen peroxide (the peroxidases and catalases).

Cytochrome Oxidase. Of the known metal-containing oxidases, those with iron-porphyrins as prosthetic groups have been studied most extensively. The decisive role of iron compounds in the utilization of O_2 by aerobic cells was suggested by early work on the effect of cyanide on respiration. For example, the concentration of cyanide sufficient to decrease the respiration of the sea urchin egg by 50 per cent is 0.5×10^{-5} M. Similar low concentrations of cyanide are effective in causing the "half-inhibition" of the respiration of erythrocytes, yeast, some lactic acid bacteria, etc. From such data Warburg concluded that cyanide, which was known to block many autoxidation reactions catalyzed by iron compounds (e.g., the oxidation of cysteine to cystine), also blocked the action of an iron-containing enzyme which catalyzed the direct electron transfer to molecular oxygen. He termed this enzyme *Atmungsferment* ("respiratory enzyme") and provided evidence for the view that it was a heme protein. In 1926 he showed that the oxygen uptake of a yeast

(*Torula utilis*) is inhibited by carbon monoxide and that the extent of the inhibition depends on the ratio of CO to O_2 in the medium. It will be recalled (cf. p. 176) that carbon monoxide readily combines with ferroheme derivatives such as hemoglobin.

In the study of the *Atmungsferment*, Warburg took advantage of the important discovery, made by Haldane and Smith in 1896, that carbon

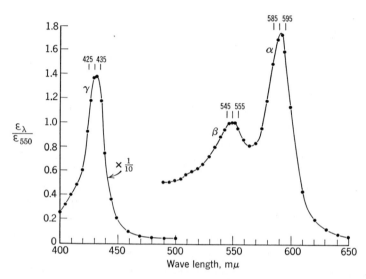

Fig. 1. Relative photochemical absorption spectrum of the CO-compound in baker's yeast (from Castor and Chance[3]). The ordinate gives the ratio of the specific absorbance at any wave length to the specific absorbance at 550 mμ. The Soret band (γ) has been depressed by a factor of 10.

monoxide-hemoglobin could be dissociated by visible light. He showed that the inhibition of yeast respiration by CO also was counteracted by light, and proceeded to measure the relative effectiveness of various wave lengths of light on the presumed dissociation of the CO-heme compound in yeast. Since the photochemical efficiency of a given wave length is proportional to the extent to which it is absorbed, the curve obtained by plotting wave length against relative photochemical efficiency should represent the absorption spectrum of the CO-compound dissociated by light. In the visible region of the spectrum there was found a large absorption band at 435 mμ, which corresponds to the Soret band (cf. p. 168) of heme compounds; this supports the view that the "respiratory enzyme" is a heme protein. Three other bands were found in the visible region, with maxima at 600 mμ (α-band), 550 mμ (β-band), and 525 mμ

(β'-band). For an account of the methods used in this research see Warburg.[1]

Since the work of Warburg, an improved method for the determination of the photochemical action spectrum of CO-inhibited respiration has been developed by Chance;[2,3] in Fig. 1 is shown the spectrum of the photosensitive CO-compound in baker's yeast, with maxima at about 430, 550, and 590 mμ. For heart muscle preparations and mouse ascites tumor cells, a peak at 430 mμ was also found. However, with some bacteria (e.g., *Acetobacter suboxydans*), the action spectrum has maxima at 417, 535, and 568 mμ, suggesting that in such organisms the CO-sensitive iron-porphyrin respiratory pigment is different from the type found in yeast and animal tissues.

The decisive advance in the elucidation of the respiratory function of the CO-sensitive heme pigments was made in 1925 by Keilin,[4] who rediscovered the cellular pigments he termed cytochromes. They had been first described in 1882–1886 by MacMunn, and were originally named histohematins (or myohematins); in a book[5] published posthumously MacMunn wrote:

A good deal of discussion has taken place over this pigment, and the name of Hoppe-Seyler has prevented the acceptance of the writer's views. The chemical position is undoubtedly weak, but doubtless in time this pigment will find its way into the text-books.

The Cytochromes

Keilin showed that, under suitable conditions, suspensions of many animal tissues (e.g., muscle, brain) and of microorganisms exhibit a characteristic multibanded spectrum, and demonstrated that the absorption bands could be assigned to at least three different heme proteins, which he named cytochromes a, b, and c respectively. In heart muscle preparations, these ferroheme compounds exhibited the following absorption maxima:

Cytochrome a: α-band, 605 mμ; β-band, (?); γ-band, 452 mμ.

Cytochrome b: α-band, 564 mμ; β-band, 530 mμ; γ-band, 432 mμ.

Cytochrome c: α-band, 550 mμ; β-band, 521 mμ; γ-band, 415 mμ.

[1] O. Warburg, *Heavy Metal Prosthetic Groups,* Oxford University Press, London, 1949.

[2] B. Chance, *J. Biol. Chem.,* **202**, 383, 397, 407 (1953).

[3] L. N. Castor and B. Chance, *J. Biol. Chem.,* **217**, 453 (1955).

[4] D. Keilin, *Proc. Roy. Soc.,* **98B**, 312 (1925); D. Keilin and E. C. Slater, *Brit. Med. Bull.,* **9**, 89 (1953).

[5] C. A. MacMunn, *Spectrum Analysis Applied to Biology and Medicine,* Longmans, Green and Co., London, 1914.

Keilin later found that heart muscle preparations contain a cytochrome with an absorption spectrum (α-band, 600 mμ; γ-band, 448 mμ) similar to that of cytochrome a, but which differs from cytochrome a in being sensitive to CO. This pigment was denoted cytochrome a_3 and appears to be identical with the cytochrome oxidase of heart muscle; the evidence will be discussed on p. 354. In Fig. 2 is shown the multibanded spectrum

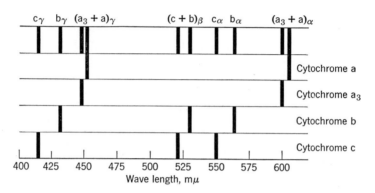

Fig. 2. Cytochrome system of heart muscle preparations. The top series of bands shows the multibanded spectrum of such preparations; the lower bands indicate their assignment to the individual cytochromes. [From D. Keilin and E. F. Hartree, *Proc. Roy. Soc.,* **127B,** 167 (1939).]

of the cytochromes of heart muscle preparations, together with the assignment of the bands to the individual pigments. The absorption bands indicated in Fig. 2 refer to the ferrous forms of the cytochromes; on oxidation, the α- and β-bands become faint, and only weak absorption is seen in the region 500 to 600 mμ.

Cytochrome c.[6] Of the three cytochromes originally identified in heart muscle preparations, the one about which the most is known is cytochrome c; it is readily extractable from tissues and is quite stable. Crystalline preparations of cytochrome c have been obtained from king penguin muscle, from fish muscle, from beef heart, from swine heart, and from baker's yeast.[7] However, there has been some uncertainty about the homogeneity of purified preparations of this conjugated protein. Preparations having 0.34 per cent Fe were long considered to be pure; later work gave material of 0.43 per cent Fe, and the more recent use of ion-exchange resins has yielded cytochrome c preparations having

[6] H. Theorell, *Advances in Enzymol.,* **7,** 265 (1947); K.-G. Paul, in J. B. Sumner and K. Myrbäck, *The Enzymes,* Chapter 56A, Academic Press, New York, 1951.

[7] G. Bodo, *Nature,* **176,** 829 (1955); B. Hagihara et al., *ibid.,* **178,** 629, 630, 631 (1956); **179,** 249 (1957).

0.465 per cent Fe.[8] The particle weight of cytochrome c is about 13,000, in agreement with the minimal molecular weight calculated from an iron content of 0.43 per cent. Hence only one iron atom is present per molecule of the heme protein. Cytochrome c has an isoelectric point of pH 10.65,[9] consistent with a relatively high content of lysine (about 20 residues per unit of 13,000).

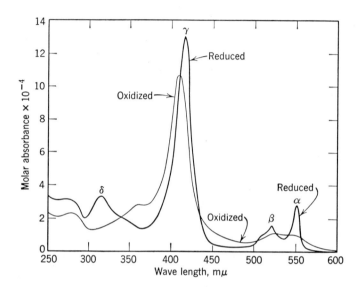

Fig. 3. Absorption spectra of oxidized and of reduced cytochrome c from horse heart; this preparation contained 0.45 per cent iron. [From D. Keilin and E. C. Slater, *Brit. Med. Bull.*, **9**, 89 (1953).]

Cytochrome c preparations from horse heart and from beef heart have been the ones studied most thoroughly; they were found to be very similar in physical and chemical properties to each other, and to preparations obtained from other animals (salmon, chicken). In addition, pigments having the absorption maxima characteristic of ferrocytochrome c have been identified in other animals, in plants, and in bacteria. Clearly, heme pigments with the spectroscopic properties of heart muscle cytochrome c are very widely distributed in nature. It is the practice to refer to such pigments as "cytochrome c," although they differ in several respects from the heart muscle preparation.

The porphyrin of cytochrome c is a derivative of protoporphyrin IX (p. 165), and is joined to the protein by two thioether linkages involving the sulfur of two cysteine residues in the peptide chain, as shown in the

[8] E. Margoliash, *Biochem. J.*, **56**, 529, 535 (1954).
[9] H. Tint and W. Reiss, *J. Biol. Chem.*, **182**, 385, 397 (1950).

accompanying formula. Convincing evidence for this mode of linkage, originally proposed by Theorell, came from the work of Paul,[10] who found that the treatment of cytochrome c with silver salts, known to cleave thioether linkages under mild conditions, liberated an optically

Cytochrome c

active hematoporphyrin IX (p. 167). The optical activity arises from the fact that the hematoporphyrin, like cytochrome c, has two substituents with centers of asymmetry (designated by means of asterisks in the formula given above). On partial degradation of beef cytochrome c

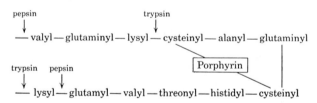

Probable amino acid sequence in beef cytochrome c

by the proteinases pepsin and trypsin, heme-containing fragments (hemopeptides) of the original molecule are formed; the amino acid sequence shown is believed to describe the segment of the protein to which the porphyrin is attached.[11] It is of interest that the amino acid sequence in the comparable peptic degradation product of salmon cytochrome c appears to be the same as that in the hemopeptide from the bovine material; in chicken cytochrome c, the alanine residue of the beef hemo-

[10] K.-G. Paul, *Acta Chem. Scand.*, **5**, 389 (1951).

[11] H. Tuppy and S. Paleus, *Acta Chem. Scand.*, **9**, 353, 365 (1955).

peptide appears to be replaced by a serine residue. Cytochrome c contains 3 or 4 histidine residues, and it is probable that the imidazolyl groups of 2 of these are linked to the iron to form a hemochromogen.[12]

At physiological pH values, the 6 coordinate valences of the iron of cytochrome c are satisfied by the 4 nitrogens of the porphyrin and probably by 2 imidazolyl groups of the proteins, thus explaining the failure of cytochrome c to combine with O_2 or with CO (cf. p. 172). Ferrocytochrome c can be oxidized nonenzymically to the ferric form by ferricyanide; ferricytochrome c can be reduced to the ferrous form by a variety of reagents, including p-phenylenediamine, cysteine, ascorbic acid, and catechol. The E_0' (30° C) of cytochrome c is about $+0.26$ volt over the pH range 2 to 7.8; in the region pH 7.8 to 10, the potential for 50 per cent reduction has a -0.06 slope[13] (cf. p. 298).

It was noted before that cytochrome c is readily extractable from tissues. Spectroscopic studies have shown that, in addition to this soluble pigment, heart muscle preparations contain a very similar substance (α-band, 554 mμ; β-band, 524 mμ; γ-band, 418 mμ) which is extracted less easily. This pigment has been named cytochrome c_1 (formerly cytochrome e), and is considered an endogenous form of cytochrome c.[14] Like cytochrome c, this component is not autoxidizable and does not appear to react with CO or with cyanide; however, cytochrome c_1 is thermolabile, in contrast to cytochrome c.

Several types of bacteria contain heme pigments which, in their ferrous form, exhibit absorption maxima similar to those of heart muscle cytochrome c or c_1.[15] These include heme proteins termed cytochrome c_2 (from *Rhodospirillum rubrum*), cytochrome c_3 (from *Desulfovibrio desulfuricans*), and cytochromes c_4 and c_5 (from *Azotobacter vinelandii*). In general, these bacterial cytochromes differ from mammalian cytochrome c in their chemical properties (e.g., isoelectric point, oxidation-reduction potential), and are not reactive in the presence of the mammalian enzyme systems that effect the oxidation or reduction of heart cytochrome c. A heme pigment similar to mammalian cytochrome c, and named "cytochrome f," has also been identified in the leaves of higher plants; it appears to be confined to the chloroplasts.[16] In some microorganisms, usually classified as strict anaerobes (e.g., *Clostridia*), cytochromes are not detectable.

[12] E. Margoliash, *Nature*, **175**, 293 (1955).

[13] F. L. Rodkey and E. G. Ball, *J. Biol. Chem.*, **182**, 17 (1950).

[14] D. Keilin and E. F. Hartree, *Nature*, **176**, 200 (1955).

[15] L. P. Vernon and M. Kamen, *J. Biol. Chem.*, **211**, 643 (1954); J. R. Postgate, *J. Gen. Microbiol.*, **14**, 545; **15**, 186 (1956); A. Tissieres, *Biochem. J.*, **64**, 582 (1956).

[16] E. F. Hartree, *Advances in Enzymol.*, **18**, 1 (1957).

Cytochrome a and Related Pigments. It has long been known that preparations of animal tissues can catalyze the oxidation of dimethyl-*p*-phenylenediamine by oxygen. The enzyme system responsible for this reaction was named "indophenol oxidase," because of the formation of indophenol blue when the oxidation is conducted in the presence of α-naphthol.[17] Keilin's study of this enzyme system showed that the oxidation is mediated by cytochrome c, whose ferric form is reduced by dimethyl-*p*-phenylenediamine; the ferrocytochrome c then is reoxidized enzymically by O_2. The name cytochrome oxidase was assigned to the enzyme responsible for the oxidation of cytochrome c by oxygen, and there is considerable evidence for the view that the cytochrome oxidase of heart muscle is identical with cytochrome a_3.[18] As noted before (cf. p. 350), cytochrome a_3 was found to be associated with cytochrome a in heart muscle preparations. Although the two pigments have similar absorption maxima, and appear to be closely related functionally, they differ in the fact that cytochrome a does not react with O_2 or CO, whereas cytochrome a_3 is autoxidizable and forms a CO-compound with absorption maxima at 589 mμ and at 430 mμ. Since the photochemical action spectrum of the CO-compound of the "respiratory enzyme" in yeast and heart muscle preparations exhibits the same maxima (cf. p. 348), it has been concluded that cytochrome a_3 is identical with Warburg's *Atmungsferment*. Spectroscopic studies also indicate that, in cells containing cytochromes c (or c_1), a, and a_3, electron transfer from ferrocytochrome c (c^{2+}) to oxygen involves the reversible oxidation-reduction of the cytochrome a and a_3 systems, as shown. Ball[19] has estimated the E_0'

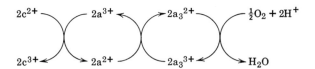

(pH 7.4, 20° C) of cytochrome a to be +0.29 volt. The potential of cytochrome a_3 is not known at present.

The study of cytochromes a and a_3 has been impeded by difficulties encountered in the extraction of these components from tissues. Cellular particles containing cytochrome oxidase activity may be dispersed with the aid of bile salts such as sodium cholate or deoxycholate, which emulsify lipids apparently associated with cytochromes a and a_3. By treatment of such dispersions with the proteinase trypsin, clear aqueous

[17] W. Straus, *J. Biol. Chem.,* **207,** 733 (1954).

[18] D. Keilin and E. F. Hartree, *Proc. Roy. Soc.,* **127B,** 167 (1939); E. G. Ball et al., *J. Biol. Chem.,* **193,** 635 (1951); B. Chance, *ibid.,* **197,** 567 (1952).

[19] E. G. Ball, *Biochem. Z.,* **295,** 262 (1938).

solutions containing these cytochromes have been obtained.[20]   The
complete structure of the porphyrins of cytochromes a and a_3 has not
been established; these porphyrins appear to be closely related, but
possibly not identical, and are characterized by the presence of a side-
chain formyl group in place of one of the vinyl groups of protoporphyrin
(cf. p. 165).[21]

Some bacteria contain pigments similar to cytochrome a, and designated
cytochrome a_1 and cytochrome a_2.[22]   In *Acetobacter pasteurianum*,
cytochrome a_1 (α-band, 588 mμ) is the terminal respiratory enzyme; this
pigment forms a CO-compound that is dissociated by light.   However,
it does not catalyze the oxidation of mammalian cytochrome c by
oxygen.

Cytochrome b and Related Pigments.   Like cytochromes a and a_3,
cytochrome b is not readily extractable from tissues, and is thermolabile.
Little is known about its chemical nature, and most studies of this cytochrome component have been limited to spectrophotometric measurements.
At physiological pH values, cytochrome b does not react with CO or with
cyanide, but appears to be autoxidizable.   Its E_0' (pH 7.4, 20° C) has
been estimated to be about 0.00 volt.

Spectroscopic studies have shown that the cytochrome b of heart
muscle preparations is reduced by succinate, and that the oxidation of
ferrocytochrome b by oxygen involves the participation of cytochromes
c, a, and a_3. In some cellular systems (e.g., rat liver mitochondria),
electron transfer from succinate or DPNH to ferricytochrome c appears
to be mediated by heme proteins whose spectroscopic properties are
similar to the cytochrome b of heart muscle preparations.[23]   It will be
recalled that flavoprotein preparations have been obtained that catalyze
rapid electron transfer from reduced pyridine nucleotides to ferricytochrome c (cf. p. 343).   The possibility that, in living cells, one or more
additional electron carriers may be interposed between a flavin and
cytochrome c (or c_1) was raised by the discovery that treatment of heart
muscle preparations with naphthoquinones[24] or with 2,3-dimercapto-
propanol (BAL—British anti-Lewisite),[25] inhibits the reduction of
cytochrome c by succinate or by DPNH, but does not affect electron

[20] L. Smith and E. Stotz, *J. Biol. Chem.,* **209,** 819 (1954); L. Smith, *ibid.,* **215,**
833 (1955).

[21] W. A. Rawlinson and J. H. Hale, *Biochem. J.,* **45,** 247 (1949); I. T. Oliver and
W. A. Rawlinson, *ibid.,* **61,** 641 (1955); M. Morrison and E. Stotz, *J. Biol. Chem.,*
213, 373 (1955).

[22] L. Smith, *Bact. Revs.,* **18,** 106 (1954); *Arch. Biochem. and Biophys.,* **50,** 299
(1954); J. Barrett, *Biochem. J.,* **64,** 626 (1956).

[23] B. Chance and G. R. Williams, *J. Biol. Chem.,* **217,** 429 (1955).

[24] E. G. Ball et al., *J. Biol. Chem.,* **168,** 257 (1947).

[25] E. C. Slater, *Biochem. J.,* **45,** 14 (1949).

transfer from succinate or DPNH to cytochrome b, or from cytochrome c to oxygen. Subsequently, a similar effect was found with antimycin A (an antibiotic from a strain of *Streptomyces*).[26] The antibiotic does not inhibit the purified pyridine nucleotide-cytochrome c reductases. The action of antimycin A has been studied extensively, and it has been concluded that the antibiotic blocks electron transfer from cytochrome b to cytochrome c (or c_1). How this inhibition is effected is not known; a relation to the lipids apparently associated with cytochrome b is suggested by the report that the action of antimycin A is counteracted by vitamin E (Chapter 27).[27] The antimycin A-sensitive respiration of tissue preparations has been attributed therefore to the participation of cytochrome b in the sequence of electron transfer from metabolites to oxygen, and this pigment has been assigned the role of an electron carrier between flavins and cytochrome c.

Many biological systems have been shown to contain heme pigments whose properties indicate a similarity to heart muscle cytochrome b. Among these are cytochromes found in the microsomal fraction of liver preparations[28] (cytochrome m) and in insect tissues (cytochrome b_5).[29] Because of their spectroscopic resemblance, cytochrome b_5 has been considered to be closely related to cytochrome m. The absorption maxima of the reduced cytochrome from rabbit liver microsomes are: α-band, 557 mμ; β-band, 527 mμ; γ-band, 423 mμ. The corresponding values for the insect pigment are 557 mμ, 526 mμ, and 421 mμ. The oxidation-reduction potential (E_0') of cytochrome m has been estimated to be $+0.02$ volt (pH 7, 26° C). Like cytochrome b, these heme pigments do not combine with CO or with cyanide, and appear to be autoxidizable. However, antimycin A does not inhibit the oxidation of ferrocytochrome m (or b_5) by ferricytochrome c; this difference between the effect of antimycin A on the reduction of ferricytochrome c by enzyme preparations from mitochondria and from microsomes also has been observed with plant material.[30] Thus, although both mitochondria and microsomes from several types of organisms can effect electron transport from DPNH to cytochrome c, the properties of the intermediate electron carrier system in mitochondria appear to differ from the corresponding system in microsomes. Liver microsomes contain a FAD-flavoprotein that catalyzes the oxidation of DPNH only by cytochrome m

[26] V. R. Potter and A. E. Reif, *J. Biol. Chem.*, **194**, 287 (1952); **205**, 279 (1953); M. B. Thorn, *Biochem. J.*, **63**, 420 (1956).

[27] A. Nason and I. R. Lehman, *J. Biol. Chem.*, **222**, 511 (1956).

[28] C. F. Strittmatter and E. G. Ball, *Proc. Natl. Acad. Sci.*, **38**, 19 (1952); P. Strittmatter and S. F. Velick, *J. Biol. Chem.*, **221**, 253, 265 (1956); **228**, 785 (1957).

[29] A. M. Pappenheimer, Jr., and C. M. Williams, *J. Biol. Chem.*, **209**, 915 (1954).

[30] E. M. Martin and R. K. Morton, *Biochem. J.*, **62**, 696; **64**, 221, 687 (1956).

(but not by cytochrome c); however, since cytochrome m can react directly with cytochrome c, the electron transfer from DPNH to cytochrome c observed in the presence of the microsomal fraction appears to be effected via the endogenous cytochrome m. It has been suggested that in silkworm (*Cecropia*) pupae during diapause (Chapter 38), when their respiration is not inhibited by CO or by cyanide, cytochrome b_5 acts as a terminal respiratory enzyme in place of the cytochrome c-cytochrome oxidase system. Cytochrome b_5 was first thought to be identical with the pigment originally named cytochrome e (now recognized as cytochrome c_1; cf. p. 353), but this has been shown to be incorrect.

Prior to the identification of the cytochrome b_5 (or m) group of pigments, several other intracellular heme proteins had been reported to have properties similar to those of cytochrome b. Cytochrome b_1 (α-band, 558 mμ) has been found in several bacteria,[31] including *Corynebacterium diphtheriae*, and it has been suggested that the toxin elaborated by this pathogenic organism is related to the protein portion of cytochrome b_1.[32] Cytochrome b_2 (α-band, 557 mμ; β-band, 528 mμ) was found in baker's yeast, and is associated with preparations having dehydrogenase activity toward L-lactic acid.[33] The lactic dehydrogenase of yeast has been purified appreciably, and appears to be a conjugated protein containing nonheme iron, and having both flavin mononucleotide and heme as prosthetic groups.[34] The lactic dehydrogenase of yeast thus resembles the metalloflavoproteins (cf. p. 338), and differs from the enzyme found in mammalian tissues (cf. p. 318). Cytochrome b_3 (α-band, 560 mμ) has been identified in microsomes from the tissues of higher plants.[35] Cytochrome b_4 was reported to be present in some bacteria, but its properties suggest that it belongs more properly to the group of bacterial pigments related to cytochrome c (cf. p. 353). Cytochrome b_6 (α-band, 563 mμ) was found in the chloroplasts of some green plants, where it appears to be associated with cytochrome f (cf. p. 353).[36] The oxidation-reduction potential (pH 7, 25° C) of cytochrome b_6 has been estimated to be about -0.06 volt.

A pigment that resembles cytochrome b occurs in the hepatopancreas of the snail *Helix pomatia*, and has been named "cytochrome h"; it

[31] L. P. Vernon, *J. Biol. Chem.*, **222**, 1035 (1956).

[32] A. M. Pappenheimer, Jr., and E. D. Hendee, *J. Biol. Chem.*, **171**, 701 (1947).

[33] S. J. Bach et al., *Biochem. J.*, **40**, 229 (1946); J. Yamashita et al., *Nature*, **179**, 959 (1957).

[34] E. Boeri et al., *Arch. Biochem. and Biophys.*, **56**, 487 (1955); **60**, 463 (1956).

[35] R. Hill and R. Scarisbrick, *New Phytol.*, **50**, 98 (1951); E. M. Martin and R. K. Morton, *Nature* **176**, 113 (1955); *Biochem. J.*, **65**, 404 (1957).

[36] R. Hill, *Nature*, **174**, 501 (1954).

appears to be converted in the animal to helicorubin, a hemochromogen found in the gastrointestinal tract.[37]

Sequence of Electron Transport by the Cytochromes. There is little doubt that the respiration of most aerobic organisms and tissues proceeds via a cytochrome system. For example, Haas[38] showed that, if one measures the extent of light absorption of yeast cells at 550 mμ (position of the α-band of cytochrome c), in air all the cytochrome c is in the ferric form, whereas in nitrogen it is all in the ferrous form. Haas estimated the concentration of cytochrome c to be about 1×10^{-5} millimole per milliliter of cell suspension. He then determined the rate of reduction of cytochrome c when cyanide was added to a suspension of yeast cells to prevent reoxidation of the reduced form of the pigment. From these kinetic measurements he calculated that the reversible oxidation and reduction of cytochrome c should permit an O_2 uptake of 0.32 cmm of O_2 per milliliter of cell suspension. Direct measurement gave a value of 0.34 cmm, and it was concluded, therefore, that nearly all of the respiration of the yeast cells proceeded via cytochrome c. Furthermore, yeast cells grown in the presence of the acridine dye acriflavine lose the capacity to synthesize components of the cytochrome system, including cytochrome oxidase; the dwarf colonies ("petite" yeast) that result exhibit a marked reduction (ca. 95 per cent) in oxygen uptake.[39] Additional evidence for the important role of cytochrome c in biological oxidation is provided by a comparison of the Q_{O_2} values (cf. p. 288) of various tissues of the rat with the corresponding values for the cytochrome c content of these tissues (Table 1). However, as will be seen later (cf. p. 359), the most direct evidence of the participation of the cytochromes in electron transport to oxygen has come from the spectrophotometric studies of Keilin and Chance.

It will be recalled that, of the known cytochromes of animal tissues, cytochrome c is the only one that is readily extractable, and that the other cytochrome components (b, a, a$_3$) of a preparation of heart muscle or rat liver mitochondria are bound more firmly to the organized structures of the cells. For many years (Battelli and Stern, 1910; Warburg, 1913) it has been recognized that the rapid oxidation of a metabolite such as succinate by O_2 in the presence of a tissue preparation depends on the structural integrity of a catalytic unit now known to constitute a multienzyme system. The complete catalytic system for the oxidation of succinate by O_2 (originally termed "succinoxidase") is localized in discrete intracellular structures. In rat liver cells, succinoxidase activity

[37] J. Keilin, *Biochem. J.,* **64,** 663 (1956); *Nature,* **180,** 427 (1957).

[38] E. Haas, *Naturwissenschaften,* **22,** 207 (1934).

[39] P. P. Slonimski, in *Adaptation in Micro-organisms,* Cambridge University Press, Cambridge, 1953; B. Ephrussi, *Naturwissenschaften,* **43,** 505 (1956).

Table I. Comparison of Cytochrome c Concentration and Oxygen Consumption in Various Rat Tissues [40]

Tissue	Approximate Q_{O_2}	Cytochrome c, μg per gram dry weight
Erythrocytes	0.1	8
Skin	1.5	51
Muscle	6	381
Brain	10	375
Liver	10+	607
Kidney	20	1433
Heart	30+	1940

is associated with the mitochondria,[41] and in heart muscle it is localized in particles ("sarcosomes") that correspond cytologically to the mitochondria of other tissues.

Keilin showed that it is possible to separate "succinoxidase" into two component systems, one of which may be called the dehydrogenase system and the other the oxidase system. When succinic acid is oxidized anaerobically by methylene blue in the presence of the succinoxidase system, the band of reduced cytochrome b disappears, whereas the bands of cytochromes c, a, and a_3 remain unchanged. On the other hand, the catalytic activity of components a and a_3 may be measured by using p-phenylenediamine as the substrate and cytochrome c as an electron carrier; here p-phenylenediamine replaces the succinate-cytochrome b system. The activity of this oxidase system, i.e., cytochromes c, a, and a_3, is influenced by a variety of factors, especially the concentration of phosphate, which do not alter the activity of the dehydrogenase system. The functional integrity of the complete succinoxidase system appears to depend on the presence of phospholipids. As mentioned before, electron transfer from succinate to cytochrome c probably involves a flavin, cytochrome b, and an antimycin A-sensitive factor that links cytochrome b to cytochrome c.[42] The sequence of electron transfer to oxygen in the succinoxidase system appears to be as follows: succinate $\rightarrow$ flavin $\rightarrow$ cytochrome b $\rightarrow$ cytochrome c $\rightarrow$ cytochrome a $\rightarrow$ cytochrome $a_3 \rightarrow O_2$.

Similarly, with liver mitochondria, which effect the rapid oxidation of DPNH by oxygen, a chemical dissection of the "DPNH oxidase" system has been achieved,[43] and the experimental evidence is consistent with

[40] D. Drabkin, in F. J. W. Roughton and J. C. Kendrew, *Hemoglobin*, Butterworths Scientific Publications, London, 1949.

[41] G. H. Hogeboom et al., *J. Biol. Chem.*, **172**, 619 (1948); **183**, 123 (1950).

[42] H. W. Clark et al., *J. Biol. Chem.*, **210**, 851, 861 (1954).

[43] D. E. Green, in O. H. Gaebler, *Enzymes: Units of Biological Structure and Function*, Academic Press, New York, 1956.

the following sequence of electron transfer: DPNH → flavin → cytochrome b → cytochrome c (or c_1) → cytochrome a → cytochrome a_3 → O_2. If values are assumed for the E_0' (pH 7) of the DPN system (-0.32 volt), the flavin system (-0.1 volt), cytochrome b (0.00 volt), cytochrome c ($+0.26$ volt), and cytochrome a ($+0.29$ volt), electron transfer to O_2 ($E_0' = +0.81$ volt) seems to be effected in stages by means of carriers of successively more positive potential. These steps are exergonic reactions, and, as will be seen in the next chapter, several of them are coupled to the endergonic phosphorylation of adenosine diphosphate to form adenosine triphosphate.

The most incisive recent data on the sequence of electron transfer in tissue preparations and in intact cells have come from the work of Chance, who has developed rapid and sensitive spectrophotometric methods to observe changes in the oxidation-reduction state of the component electron carriers.[44] The methods depend on the determination of the difference in the absorbance of a tissue preparation or a cell suspension in which the carriers are fully oxidized and one in which they are partially or fully reduced. Examples of such "difference spectra" are given in Fig. 4, which describes the effect of oxygen deprivation and of treatment with antimycin A on the oxidation state of the electron carriers in rat liver mitochondria.[45] It will be seen that, when the mitochondria are made anaerobic, all the detectable carrier systems become reduced, as shown by the positive increment in the absorbance at 340 mμ (DPNH), 445 mμ (cytochrome a_3, γ-band), 550 mμ (cytochrome c, α-band), and 605 mμ (cytochrome a, α-band), as well as the decrease in absorbance at about 460 mμ (flavin). It will be recalled that the reduction of flavins causes a decrease in their absorption in the visible region of the spectrum (p. 331). If aerobic mitochondria are allowed to act on β-hydroxybutyrate (p. 316) in the presence of antimycin A, increases in the extent of reduction are observed only for cytochrome b (α-band, 563 mμ, γ-band, 430 mμ), and the flavin and DPN systems. Under these conditions, cytochromes c, a, and a_3 are in the oxidized state, and electron transfer from cytochrome b to cytochrome c has been inhibited.

In the enzymic oxidation of a relatively large amount of a metabolite (e.g., succinate, β-hydroxybutyrate) by O_2, under conditions where the concentration of these reactants is not rate-limiting, each of the components of the electron transfer system is present at a stationary ratio of oxidant to reductant. This ratio is different from that found at thermodynamic equilibrium, which is approximated more closely under anaerobic conditions, as described by curve 1 in Fig. 4. Under aerobic

[44] B. Chance, *Science,* **120,** 767 (1954); B. Chance and G. R. Williams, *Advances in Enzymol.,* **17,** 65 (1956).
[45] B. Chance and G. R. Williams, *J. Biol. Chem.,* **217,** 395 (1955).

conditions, the stationary ratio oxidant/reductant is characteristic of the steady state determined by the rates of electron transfer in the individual steps of the sequence (cf. p. 243). The method developed by Chance permits estimates to be made of the steady-state ratios of the electron

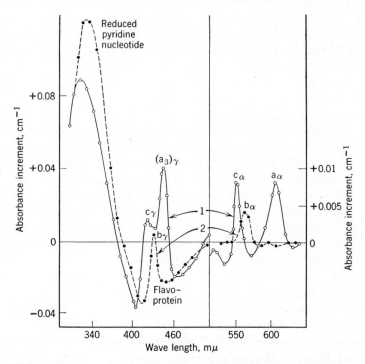

Fig. 4. Difference spectra for the respiratory carrier systems in rat liver mitochondria. The solid curve 1 represents the difference between the reduced and oxidized forms that is made evident by removal of oxygen. The dashed curve 2 represents the difference spectrum obtained when aerobic mitochondria act on β-hydroxybutyrate in the presence of antimycin A. (From Chance and Williams.[45])

carrier systems under a variety of experimental conditions. For example, curve 2 in Fig. 4 shows that antimycin A increases the steady-state reduction of cytochrome b. In the aerobic oxidation of succinate, by a heart muscle succinoxidase preparation, the percentages of oxidation of cytochromes a_3, a, and c in the steady state are approximately 86, 74, and 83 respectively.[46] The predominance of the ferric forms of these electron carriers is consistent with the finding that their ferrous forms are oxidized at rates about 100 to 400 times more rapid than the initial dehydrogenation of succinate. Thus, in the steady state of the operation

[46] B. Chance, *J. Biol. Chem.,* **197,** 567 (1952); *Nature,* **169,** 215 (1952).

of the succinoxidase system, the transfer of electrons from ferrocytochrome c to oxygen appears to "pull" the equivalent transfer of electrons from succinate. Similarly, the steady-state levels of oxidation for the electron carriers in rat liver mitochondria during the oxidation of β-hydroxybutyrate by O_2 also indicate that the oxidation of ferrocytochrome c by oxygen is much more rapid than the reduction of ferricytochrome c by electrons derived from the metabolite.[47] Other important studies of the steady-state kinetics in cell preparations and with purified enzymes have been discussed by Chance.[48]

It will be evident from the foregoing discussion that the researches of Keilin, Chance, and others have shown that, in general, the cytochromes related to cytochrome a serve as electron carriers between cytochrome c (or c_1) and oxygen, and that the cytochromes related to cytochrome b are closer to the dehydrogenase-catalyzed reactions in the sequence of electron transfer. Although the main outlines of the sequence have been worked out for the aerobic oxidation of metabolites such as succinate and β-hydroxybutyrate by heart muscle and liver mitochondria, points of uncertainty still remain. Among these are the role of cytochrome c_1, of cytochrome b, and of the metalloflavoproteins. It should be recognized that the oxidation of all metabolites may not require the participation of the complete sequence of electron carriers; for example, it is likely that the oxidation of ascorbic acid in animal tissues may proceed via cytochrome c and cytochrome oxidase only. Furthermore, the discussion of the properties of the individual cytochromes has indicated that alternate pathways of electron transfer must be considered. The occurrence of different mechanisms in widely different biological forms is extremely probable, and even in the case of mammalian tissues the microsomes (which contain cytochrome m or b_5) may have an electron transfer mechanism different from that of the mitochondria of the same cell type. For this reason, it is not advisable to generalize too extensively about the manner in which the various cytochromes of microorganisms, plants, and animals function to effect the oxidation of metabolites by oxygen. Much further work on the characterization of the individual cytochromes is needed.

The Peroxidases and Catalases [49]

Peroxidases. The peroxidases and catalases are iron-porphyrin-containing enzymes that catalyze reactions in which hydrogen peroxide is an electron acceptor. The peroxidases are conjugated proteins found

---

[47] B. Chance and G. R. Williams, *J. Biol. Chem.*, **217**, 409 (1955).

[48] B. Chance, in W. D. McElroy and B. Glass, *Mechanism of Enzyme Action*, Johns Hopkins Press, Baltimore, 1954.

[49] H. Theorell, in J. B. Sumner and K. Myrbäck, *The Enzymes*, Chapter 56B. Academic Press, New York, 1951.

largely in plant tissues. However, at least two peroxidases have been obtained from animals: lactoperoxidase (present in milk) and verdoperoxidase (or myeloperoxidase, in leucocytes). Peroxidase activity has also been found in the adrenal medulla. The type reaction catalyzed by these enzymes may be written

$$AH_2 + H_2O_2 \rightarrow A + 2H_2O$$

where AH_2 may be a phenol, p-aminobenzoic acid, p-phenylenediamine, ascorbic acid, or leuco forms of oxidation-reduction indicators; ferrocytochrome c also is oxidized.

The peroxidase that has been studied most closely is horseradish peroxidase, crystallized by Theorell. This conjugated protein contains 1.47 per cent hemin (p. 178) and has a molecular weight of about 40,000; there is present 1 atom of Fe per molecule of protein. Treatment with acetone-HCl at $-15°$ C causes a dissociation of the peroxidase; the iron-porphyrin remains in solution, and the pigment-free protein is precipitated. The protein fraction is inactive catalytically, but, if hemin (prepared from hemoglobin) is added to a solution of the protein at pH 7.5, the original catalytic activity is largely restored. Peroxidase is, therefore, a protein comparable to methemoglobin in which the iron is also in the ferric state. Methemoglobin itself exhibits peroxidatic activity, but only to a limited degree, and the full catalytic activity of the peroxidases depends on the presence of the specific proteins characteristic of these metalloporphyrin enzymes. If the ferric complexes of porphyrins other than protoporphyrin IX are employed in the "resynthesis" of peroxidase, some catalytic activity is found; however, this is much less than the activity noted with hemin.

The oxidation-reduction potential of horseradish peroxidase has been determined by Harbury,[50] who has reported a value for E_0'(pH 7.0, 30° C) of -0.27 volt. This potential is more negative than those found for other well-defined heme compounds, and may be compared with values for E_0' (pH 7, 30° C) of $+0.05$ volt, $+0.14$ volt, and $+0.26$ volt for the myoglobin, hemoglobin, and cytochrome c systems respectively. These differences in potential, as well as in other properties, suggest that the mode of linkage between the iron-porphyrin and protein parts of peroxidase is different from that in any of the other three conjugated proteins. Like hemoglobin and myoglobin, ferroperoxidase combines reversibly with cyanide and with CO. It is of interest that not only the CO-compound of ferroperoxidase undergoes reversible photodissociation (cf. p. 177), but also the cyanide compound exhibits this property.[51]

[50] H. A. Harbury, J. Am. Chem. Soc., **75**, 4625 (1953); J. Biol. Chem., **225**, 1009 (1957).

[51] D. Keilin and E. F. Hartree, Biochem. J., **61**, 153 (1955).

The work of Chance[52] has provided important knowledge of the mechanism whereby horseradish peroxidase exerts its catalytic action. Upon the addition of H_2O_2 to peroxidase, a primary addition complex is formed which has a green color (absorption maxima at 410 and 665 mμ). This peroxidase-H_2O_2 complex (complex I) is formed extremely rapidly ($k_1 = 9 \times 10^6$ M^{-1} sec^{-1}), and is dissociated to peroxidase and H_2O_2 much more slowly (k_2 about 3 sec^{-1}). In the presence of an electron donor such as p-aminobenzoic acid (AH$_2$), complex I is rapidly converted ($k_3 = 5 \times 10^4$ M^{-1} sec^{-1}) into a pale-red complex II (absorption maxima at 418, 527, and 555 mμ). The further reaction of complex II with the substrate, to regenerate the enzyme, is slower ($k_4 = 2 \times 10^3$ M^{-1} sec^{-1}) than the transformation of complex I into complex II; hence complex II is the apparent "Michaelis complex" in the peroxidase-catalyzed reaction (cf. p. 256). Similar enzyme-substrate compounds are formed with alkyl hydrogen peroxides such as methyl hydrogen peroxide (CH_3OOH), but the rates of formation and of decomposition are different from those found for the H_2O_2 compound. The nature of the chemical changes undergone by the peroxidase molecule in the catalytic process has not been elucidated,[53] but it has been suggested that the following sequence of reactions occurs in the peroxidase-catalyzed oxidation of an electron donor by H_2O_2 (or by ROOH):

$$\underset{\text{(brown)}}{\text{Peroxidase-H}_2\text{O}} + \text{H}_2\text{O}_2 \underset{k_2}{\overset{k_1}{\rightleftharpoons}} \underset{\text{(green)}}{\text{Peroxidase-H}_2\text{O}_2 \text{ (complex I)}} + \text{H}_2\text{O}$$

$$\underset{\text{(green)}}{\text{Complex I}} + \text{AH}_2 \overset{k_3}{\longrightarrow} \underset{\text{(pale red)}}{\text{Complex II}} + \text{AH} \cdot + \text{H}_2\text{O}$$

$$\text{Complex II} + \text{AH} \cdot + \text{AH}_2 \overset{k_4}{\longrightarrow} \text{Peroxidase-H}_2\text{O} + \text{A} + \text{AH}_2$$

In these reactions, AH· denotes the half-oxidized electron donor molecule.

The physiological function of the peroxidases is not clear. It may be that in plants these enzymes catalyze the oxidation of metabolites by means of H_2O_2 produced in the direct reaction of reduced flavins with oxygen (cf. p. 305). In wheat germ a peroxidase appears to be involved in the oxidation of TPNH by molecular oxygen,[54] and in *Pseudomonas fluorescens* a peroxidase appears to be specific for the oxidation of the cytochrome c-like pigment of this organism.[55] In respect to the peroxi-

[52] B. Chance, *Arch. Biochem.*, **22**, 224 (1949); *Science*, **109**, 204 (1949).

[53] B. Chance and R. R. Fergusson, in W. D. McElroy and B. Glass, *Mechanism of Enzyme Action*, Johns Hopkins Press, Baltimore, 1954; P. George, in D. E. Green, *Currents in Biochemical Research*, Interscience Publishers, New York, 1956.

[54] E. E. Conn et al., *J. Biol. Chem.*, **194**, 143 (1952).

[55] H. M. Lenhoff and N. O. Kaplan, *J. Biol. Chem.*, **220**, 967 (1956).

dase of mammalian leucocytes, it has been suggested that this enzyme may inactivate toxic substances through oxidation by H_2O_2.[56]

Catalases. The best known of the reactions catalyzed by the catalases is the decomposition of H_2O_2 according to the equation

$$2H_2O_2 \rightarrow 2H_2O + O_2$$

This equation describes a bimolecular oxidation-reduction in which one molecule of peroxide is oxidized to O_2 and the other is reduced to water.

Catalases have been obtained in crystalline form from several animal tissues and from bacteria. The first crystallization of a catalase was performed by Sumner and Dounce,[57] who obtained it from beef liver. Catalase crystals have also been prepared from erythrocytes and from the livers of various animals. The crystalline catalases obtained from various biological sources, including bacteria, have similar chemical properties. All the preparations that have been studied appear to have a molecular weight near 250,000, and to contain 4 iron atoms per protein molecule. Like the peroxidases, the catalases are conjugated proteins in which the iron-porphyrin is in the ferric state; the prosthetic group is the ferric complex of protoporphyrin IX.

It was long thought that the primary biological function of the catalases was to destroy H_2O_2, which is toxic to living systems. More recent studies of Keilin and of Chance demonstrated that these enzymes may have a broader physiological function. Keilin and Hartree[58] showed that, if catalase and ethanol are added to a system in which H_2O_2 is produced (e.g., the oxidation of glucose to gluconic acid by notatin; cf. p. 339), the alcohol is oxidized to acetaldehyde.

$$CH_3CH_2OH + H_2O_2 \rightarrow CH_3CHO + 2H_2O$$

This equation corresponds to the type of reaction catalyzed by the peroxidases, and indicates that catalases and peroxidases are more similar in their mode of action than had been thought previously (cf. Keilin and Hartree[59]). For this reason, these two types of enzymes are considered to belong to a single group, termed "hydroperoxidases." The catalases and peroxidases exhibit differences in specificity for the electron donor; in contrast to liver catalase, horseradish peroxidase does not catalyze the oxidation of ethanol by H_2O_2.

At low concentrations of a peroxide (H_2O_2 or ROOH), catalase forms an enzyme-substrate compound spectroscopically similar to "complex I"

[56] K. Agner, *J. Exptl. Med.*, **92**, 337 (1950).
[57] J. B. Sumner and A. L. Dounce, *J. Biol. Chem.*, **121**, 417 (1937).
[58] D. Keilin and E. F. Hartree, *Biochem. J.*, **39**, 293 (1945).
[59] D. Keilin and E. F. Hartree, *Biochem. J.*, **49**, 88 (1951); **60**, 310 (1955).

of the peroxidases.[60] The reaction with H_2O_2 is very rapid (rate

$$\text{Catalase} + \text{HOOR} \rightleftharpoons \text{Catalase-OOR}$$

constant, ca. $1 \times 10^7\ M^{-1}\ sec^{-1}$). The oxidation of ethanol by the catalase-H_2O_2 complex has a rate constant of about $1 \times 10^3\ M^{-1}\ sec^{-1}$; higher alcohols ($n$-butanol, isoamyl alcohol) are oxidized at slower rates.

$$\text{Catalase-OOR} + CH_3CH_2OH \rightarrow \text{Catalase} + CH_3CHO + ROH + H_2O$$

In the presence of relatively high concentrations of H_2O_2, a catalase-peroxide complex effects the dehydrogenation of H_2O_2 in a manner analogous to the dehydrogenation of a primary alcohol. The reaction of the

$$\text{Catalase-OOR} + H_2O_2 \rightarrow \text{Catalase} + O_2 + ROH + H_2O$$

catalase-H_2O_2 complex with another molecule of H_2O_2 is an extremely rapid process (rate constant, ca. $2 \times 10^7\ M^{-1}\ sec^{-1}$).

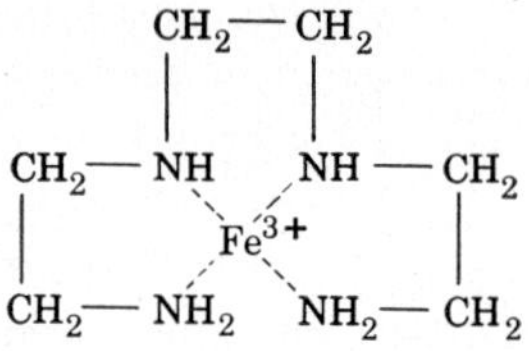

Ferric complex of triethylene tetramine

It is of interest that the ferric complex of triethylene tetramine catalyzes the decomposition of H_2O_2 with a turnover number of about 100,000;[61] however, this value is still much lower than that of catalase (ca. 2 to 5 million).

Copper-Containing Oxidases [62]

Among the copper-containing proteins that act as catalysts in oxidation reactions those most studied are the polyphenol oxidases (also termed phenol oxidases or tyrosinases), which are widely distributed in plant and animal tissues.[63] The copper of polyphenol oxidase, like that in the hemocyanins (cf. p. 180), is not linked to the protein through a por-

[60] B. Chance, *J. Biol. Chem.*, **180**, 947 (1949); **182**, 643, 649 (1950); B. Chance et al., *Arch. Biochem. and Biophys.*, **37**, 301, 322 (1952).

[61] J. H. Wang, *J. Am. Chem. Soc.*, **77**, 822 (1955).

[62] C. R. Dawson and W. B. Tarpley, in J. B. Sumner and K. Myrbäck, *The Enzymes*, Vol. II, Chapter 57, Academic Press, New York, 1951.

[63] J. M. Nelson and C. R. Dawson, *Advances in Enzymol.*, **4**, 99 (1944); H. S. Mason, *ibid.*, **16**, 105 (1955).

phyrin; thus far, no non-amino acid organic constituent has been identified as a component of these enzymes. When a highly purified preparation of polyphenol oxidase (from potatoes) is dialyzed against a 0.01 *M* cyanide solution, the copper is removed, and the remaining protein is inactive as a catalyst; if the copper ion is restored, the enzymic activity is again demonstrable.[64] In the oxidation of a polyphenol such as catechol to the corresponding quinone, the cupric form of the enzyme is reduced to the cuprous form, and this, in turn, is reoxidized by oxygen.

Catechol *o*-Quinone

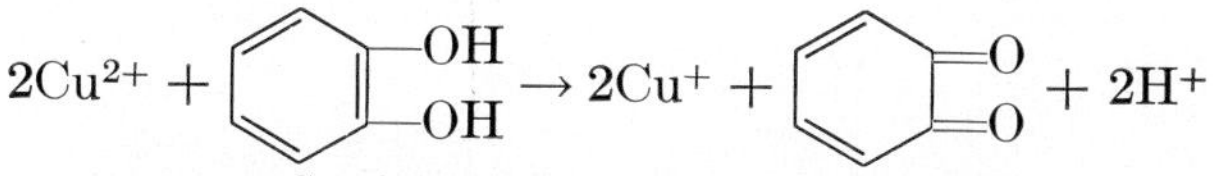

$$2Cu^{+} + 2H^{+} + \tfrac{1}{2}O_2 \rightarrow 2Cu^{2+} + H_2O$$

Monophenols are also oxidized in the presence of the enzyme, but the reaction is slow, probably because of the necessity for the formation of a small quantity of the corresponding *o*-diphenol which causes a more rapid oxidation of the monophenol. Extensive studies by Raper[65] showed that the first product of the action of polyphenol oxidase on L-tyrosine was the corresponding diphenol, 3,4-dihydroxy-L-phenylalanine (dopa). The further enzymic oxidation of this diphenol leads

L-Tyrosine 3,4-Dihydroxy-L-phenylalanine

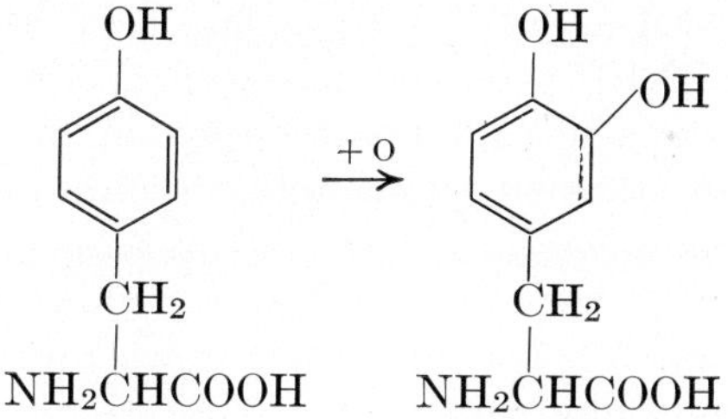

to the formation of the corresponding *o*-quinone which undergoes a complex series of reactions to form highly insoluble dark pigments termed melanins. Since L-tyrosine is a natural substrate for the polyphenol oxidase of potatoes, this oxidative process serves to explain the characteristic blackening of cut raw potatoes on exposure to air. Melanin formation is also observed in animals; here, in addition to polyphenol oxidase, another enzyme, termed "dopa oxidase," has been identified.[66] Although it has been suggested that, in higher plants, the polyphenol

[64] F. Kubowitz, *Biochem. Z.*, **299**, 32 (1938).
[65] H. S. Raper, *Physiol. Revs.*, **8**, 245 (1928).
[66] A. B. Lerner et al., *J. Biol. Chem.*, **187**, 793 (1950).

oxidases serve as important links in electron transport from metabolites to oxygen, the status of this question is uncertain.

Another copper-containing enzyme which may be of greater importance in the respiration of higher plants is ascorbic acid oxidase. This enzyme has been obtained in highly purified form from several plants, notably squash; the copper appears to be firmly bound to the protein.[67] On oxidation, ascorbic acid is converted to dehydroascorbic acid, the two compounds forming a reversible oxidation-reduction system (cf. p. 306).

It has long been known that extracts of plant tissues contain an enzyme (dehydroascorbic reductase) that catalyzes the reduction of dehydroascorbic acid (DHA) to ascorbic acid (AA) by glutathione.[68]

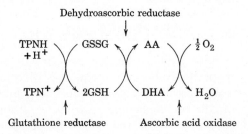

Studies on the respiration of pea seedlings[69] have suggested that a multi-enzyme system composed of glutathione reductase (p. 314), dehydro-ascorbic reductase, and ascorbic acid oxidase may catalyze the transfer of electrons from TPNH to oxygen, as shown in the accompanying diagram. It is difficult to assess the relative contribution of this alternative pathway of electron transfer to the total respiration of the seedlings, as compared to the pathway involving flavins and the cytochromes.

The presence of copper in some metalloflavoproteins has been mentioned previously (cf. p. 345); the enzyme uricase is also believed to be a copper-containing protein.

A general point of some interest in regard to the known metal-containing oxidases is that the processes catalyzed by various members of this group of enzymes may involve different modes of reaction of molecular oxygen.[70] Thus, in the oxidation of a phenol to an o-diphenol (e.g., tyrosine to "dopa") by O_2, 1 atom of the O_2 molecule is added to the substrate (S), and the other is reduced to water: $SH + O_2 + 2e + 2H^+ \rightleftharpoons SOH + H_2O$. This process may be contrasted with that catalyzed by a metal-containing oxidase such as cytochrome oxidase; here both oxygen atoms are reduced to water by the transfer of 4 electrons

[67] M. Joselow and C. R. Dawson, *J. Biol. Chem.,* **191,** 1, 11 (1951).

[68] E. M. Crook and E. J. Morgan, *Biochem. J.,* **38,** 10 (1944).

[69] L. W. Mapson and E. M. Moustafa, *Biochem. J.,* **62,** 248 (1956).

[70] H. S. Mason, *Science,* **125,** 1185 (1957).

and the addition of 4 protons: $O_2 + 4e + 4H^+ \rightleftharpoons 2H_2O$. As will be seen in Chapter 32, a third type of reaction involving O_2 is catalyzed by enzymes (homogentisic acid oxidase, protocatechuic acid oxidase) believed to be metal-proteins; in these reactions, both atoms of the O_2 molecule appear to be added to the substrate.

15 ·

Coupled Enzyme-Catalyzed Reactions

Although individual enzymes may be studied as separate entities, it should be recognized that within a living cell they do not act independently of one another. In general, the linking of separate enzyme-catalyzed chemical reactions is made possible by the utilization of a product of one reaction as a substrate in another reaction. Such linking or "coupling" of enzyme-catalyzed reactions is perhaps the most distinctive biochemical attribute of living matter. It will be evident from the previous discussion that the specificity of the individual enzymes determines the nature and rate of a coupled reaction sequence. The specificity exhibited in such linked reactions is therefore even more sharply defined than that of each individual reaction. The morphological distribution of the component enzymes and substrates in a living cell will also influence the direction and pace of linked reactions. Clearly, if a given enzyme is localized in the nucleus of a cell, and another enzyme is localized in certain formed elements (e.g., mitochondria) in the cytoplasm, it is unlikely that the two biocatalysts will participate in a coupled reaction. The last factor is of obvious importance in assessing the possible physiological role of a coupled reaction artificially created *in vitro* by the combination of two enzyme-catalyzed reactions. In a sense, therefore, the knowledge of the component enzymes of a cell and the study of their properties in purified form are necessary but not ultimate steps in the understanding of their physiological role. When a biochemist mixes several purified enzymes in an attempt to reconstruct the catalytic apparatus within the living cell, he is proceeding from an analysis of the enzymic composition of the cell to a synthetic approach. However, the results of such artificial syntheses can only serve as working hypotheses which ultimately must be tested with the living cell or with intact cellular structures (nuclei, mitochondria, etc.) as the experimental material.

An outstanding example of a coupled sequence of enzyme-catalyzed reactions, localized in an intracellular component, is the aerobic oxidation of metabolites by liver mitochondria. As shown by electron microscopy, which permits magnifications up to about 100,000 diameters, mitochondria possess a distinctive structure, characterized by a double membrane and by striking internal lamination.[1] When liver is ground carefully ("homogenized"), and the resulting mixture of intracellular particles (nuclei, mitochondria, microsomes, etc.) is separated as well as possible by fractional centrifugation, the succinoxidase system is found to be associated with the mitochondrial fraction (cf. p. 358). Mitochondria also are able to perform the aerobic oxidation of many metabolites (e.g., β-hydroxybutyrate) that react with a pyridine nucleotide in dehydrogenase-catalyzed reactions. It is generally agreed that these aerobic oxidations are performed by an organized catalytic unit which is present in mitochondria and which comprises the enzymes required for the coupled electron transfer from DPNH to oxygen.

It is not yet possible to specify completely the nature of the electron carriers and catalytic proteins involved in the aerobic oxidation of succinate or of DPNH by liver mitochondria (cf. p. 359). Enough is known, however, to justify the assumption that the sequence of electron transfer involves a flavin system and cytochromes b, c, a, and a_3. The pathway of electrons from a metabolite (AH_2) to O_2 may be represented as shown in the accompanying diagram, where the oxidized flavin is

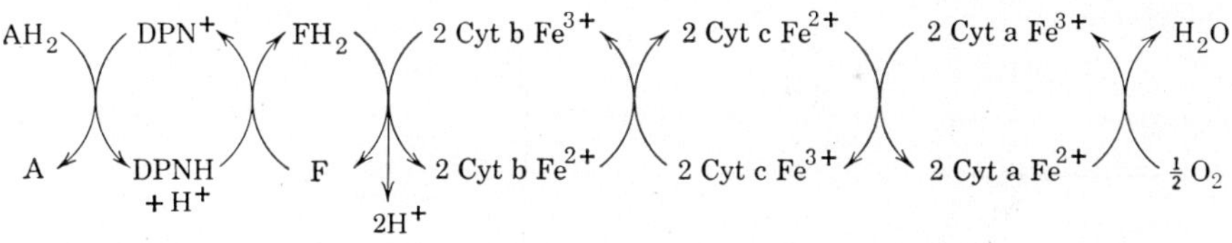

denoted F. If it is assumed that the oxidation-reduction potentials of the electron carrier systems within the mitochondria are not very different from the E_0' values for the isolated systems, this scheme indicates that the sequence of electron transfer proceeds through steps of successively more positive potential. In Table 1 are given the approximate values of $\Delta E_0'$ (pH 7, 30° C) for the several successive steps between DPNH and O_2, together with the values of $\Delta F'$ (cf. p. 301) calculated from these differences in potential. It should be emphasized that such assumptions about the magnitude of the potentials of intracellular oxidation-reduction systems are fraught with uncertainty, because of factors such as the effect of binding by catalytic proteins (cf. p. 303), and the

---

[1] G. E. Palade, in O. H. Gaebler, *Enzymes: Units of Structure and Function,* Academic Press, New York, 1956.

fact that the scheme describes a steady-state system that has been shown to be reversible.

If one accepts the values in Table 1 as a basis for further discussion, it will be seen that the total free-energy change (ca. −50 kcal) in the transfer of 2 electrons from DPNH to an oxygen atom is effected in a series of exergonic steps. When suitable coupling mechanisms are available, the energy released in some of these steps may be used to drive endergonic reactions. As will be seen later in this chapter, the aerobic oxidation of DPNH and of succinate by liver mitochondria is coupled to the phosphorylation of adenosine diphosphate, an endergonic process. In considering the values for $\Delta F'$ given in Table 1, it should be remembered

Table I.   Stepwise Electron Transfer from DPNH to Oxygen

Oxidation-Reduction System	Approximate E_0' (pH 7, 30° C), volts	$\Delta E_0'$ (pH 7), volts	$\Delta F'_{303}$ (pH 7) per Electron Pair, kcal per mole
DPN system	−0.3		
		+0.2	−9.2
Flavin system	−0.1		
		+0.1	−4.6
Cytochrome b	0.0		
		+0.25	−11.6
Cytochrome c	+0.25		
		+0.05	−2.3
Cytochrome a	+0.3		
		+0.5	−23.1
Oxygen	+0.8		
		+1.1	−50.8

that they suggest only the magnitude of the energy change in each step of the postulated sequence of electron transfer; they do not give information about the manner in which the liberated energy may be used to drive endergonic processes. Such transfer of energy can take place only through well-defined chemical intermediates, and specific enzymes must be available to catalyze the formation of such intermediates. An important task of biochemistry has been, and continues to be, the elucidation of the nature and function of intermediates that link exergonic oxidation reactions to endergonic processes.

The manner in which the energy released in an enzyme-catalyzed exergonic process may be transferred, in a coupled reaction, to an endergonic process is strikingly illustrated by the studies of Meyerhof, Needham, and Warburg on the mechanism of the oxidation of glyceraldehyde-3-phosphate to 3-phosphoglyceric acid in yeast or muscle extracts. In 1937 Meyerhof and Needham independently found that for every molecule of aldehyde oxidized to the acid there was a concomitant conversion of one molecule of adenosine diphosphate (ADP) to adenosine triphosphate (ATP). It will be recalled that, when the enzymic oxidation of glyceraldehyde-3-phosphate occurs in the presence of inorganic phosphate, the product is 1,3-diphosphoglyceric acid (p. 324). The

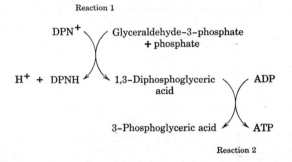

Reaction 1

Reaction 2

diphosphoglyceric acid then reacts with ADP in another enzyme-catalyzed reaction to form 3-phosphoglyceric acid and ATP; the reaction involved is a transphosphorylation, and the enzyme that catalyzes it may be termed ATP-phosphoglycerate transphosphorylase or phosphoglycerate kinase.[2] The coupled reaction may be written as shown.

Meyerhof determined the concentrations of the reactants at equilibrium (pH 7.8, 20° C) and found that

$$\frac{[\text{3-Phosphoglyceric acid}][\text{ATP}][\text{DPNH}]}{[\text{Glyceraldehyde-3-phosphate}][\text{phosphate}][\text{ADP}][\text{DPN}^+]} = 3 \times 10^3$$

From this value for the ratio of equilibrium concentrations, the free-energy change $\Delta F'$ was calculated to be -4.7 kcal;[3] this value refers to the reaction with all reactants except the hydrogen ion in their standard states (cf. p. 236). For the purposes of thermodynamic calculations, the coupled reaction may be considered to be the composite of three processes: (1) the reduction of DPN$^+$ to DPNH; (2) the oxidation of glyceraldehyde-3-phosphate to 3-phosphoglyceric acid; (3) the condensation of ADP and phosphate to form ATP. Meyerhof attempted to calculate the magnitude of $\Delta F'$ for process (3) by means of the relationship $\Delta F' = \Delta F'_1 + \Delta F'_2 + \Delta F'_3$, where the subscripts refer to the partial reactions indicated above. From a value (now known to be incorrect) of E_0' for the DPN system, $\Delta F'_1$ was calculated to be about $+13.5$ kcal, and by means of several assumptions $\Delta F'_2$ was estimated to be -30.1 kcal. Thus $-4.7 = +13.5 - 30.1 + \Delta F'_3$, giving a value of $+11.9$ kcal for the reaction $\text{ADP}^{3-} + \text{HPO}_4^{2-} + \text{H}^+ \rightarrow \text{ATP}^{4-} + \text{H}_2\text{O}$, with all

[2] T. Bücher, *Biochim. et Biophys. Acta*, **1**, 292 (1947).

[3] O. Meyerhof, *Ann. N. Y. Acad. Sci.*, **45**, 377 (1944).

reactants except H^+ in their standard states. The reverse reaction, the hydrolysis of ATP, would therefore be accompanied by a $\Delta F'_{293}$ of about -12 kcal per mole.

Although the value of -12 kcal for the $\Delta F'$ (pH ca. 7.5) in the hydrolysis of ATP was long accepted as a basis for the calculation of energy relations in biochemical processes, it is probably incorrect. The uncertainties in the experimental determination of equilibrium concentrations, and in the calculation of $\Delta F'_1$ and $\Delta F'_2$, serve as a warning against the ready acceptance of free-energy values obtained in the manner described above, and underline the need for accurate thermodynamic data for substances of biochemical interest. A critical evaluation of some of the data available in 1952 was made by Burton and Krebs,[4] whose paper deserves careful study.

Because of the importance of ATP as a participant in many biochemical reactions, there has been much interest in the magnitude of $\Delta F'$ (pH ca. 7.5) for its hydrolysis to ADP and inorganic phosphate. The value of about -12 kcal, cited above, had also been derived from a calorimetric determination of ΔH and the assumption that ΔS is very small (cf. p. 241). However, more critical studies of the enthalpy change in the hydrolysis of ATP (cf. p. 228) have shown that ΔH_{293} (pH 8) is about -5 kcal, a value much lower than that accepted previously. Furthermore, recent estimates of $\Delta F'$ for the hydrolysis of ATP, derived from equilibrium studies analogous to those of Meyerhof but with different enzyme-catalyzed reactions involving ATP, have given values of about -9 kcal[4] and of -8 kcal.[5] Consequently, the magnitude of the free-energy change in the hydrolysis of ATP is uncertain at present, although it is extremely probable that the frequently assumed value of -12 kcal is much too high, and that the correct value is near -8 kcal.

Despite the uncertainty in the values assigned to $\Delta F'$, $\Delta F'_1$, $\Delta F'_2$, and $\Delta F'_3$ in the coupled reaction catalyzed by glyceraldehyde-3-phosphate dehydrogenase and ATP-phosphoglycerate transphosphorylase, it is clear that 1,3-diphosphoglyceric acid fulfills the role of an intermediate that makes possible the transfer of energy from an energy-yielding oxidation to energy-requiring processes. In this coupled reaction, the energy made available by the exergonic oxidation of glyceraldehyde-3-phosphate to 3-phosphoglyceric acid is utilized, in large part, to drive two endergonic reactions, the reduction of DPN^+ and the phosphorylation of ADP. As will be seen from the discussion of the pathways of carbohydrate metabolism in yeast and in muscle, the energy put into the DPN and ATP systems is available for other coupled reactions. For

[4] K. Burton and H. A. Krebs, *Biochem. J.*, **54**, 94 (1953).

[5] L. Levintow and A. Meister, *J. Biol. Chem.*, **209**, 265 (1954); E. A. Robbins and P. D. Boyer, *ibid.*, **224**, 121 (1957).

example, in yeast, DPNH is reoxidized to DPN$^+$ by acetaldehyde, in the presence of alcohol dehydrogenase, and ethanol is formed (cf. p. 476). Similarly, in muscle extracts, DPNH is reoxidized to DPN$^+$ in the bimolecular reaction catalyzed by lactic dehydrogenase, and pyruvic acid is reduced to lactic acid (cf. p. 490).

Adenosine triphosphate participates in a variety of biochemical processes in which the energy acquired in the coupled reaction discussed above can be used for chemical work. For example, in the presence of the enzyme hexokinase, ATP can phosphorylate glucose to form glucose-6-phosphate in the reaction

$$\text{Glucose} + \text{ATP}^{4-} \rightleftharpoons \text{Glucose-6-phosphate}^{2-} + \text{ADP}^{3-} + \text{H}^+$$

The equilibrium in this reaction is far to the right, and the magnitude of the free-energy change may be estimated by considering the transphosphorylation as composed of (1) the hydrolysis of ATP to ADP and phosphate and (2) the condensation of glucose and inorganic phosphate to glucose-6-phosphate and water, i.e., the reverse of hydrolysis. The $\Delta F'$ of the latter process has been estimated to be about $+3$ kcal per mole.[6] If $\Delta F'$ for the hydrolysis of ATP is assumed to be -8 kcal per mole, the standard free-energy change at pH 7.5 and 20° C equals $(+3 - 8)$, or about -5 kcal per mole. This type of calculation is permitted by the nature of the thermodynamic data, and should not be interpreted to mean that, in the transphosphorylation reaction, there occurs a hydrolysis of ATP, followed by a condensation reaction to give glucose-6-phosphate. However, all such calculations should be made with due regard to the uncertainties in the available free-energy data.

In addition to its role in the phosphorylation of glucose, ATP participates in many other transphosphorylation reactions.[7] Some of these will be discussed later in connection with the metabolism of carbohydrates, of lipids, of amino acids, and of nucleic acids. The role of ATP in the biosynthesis of pyridine nucleotides and of flavin nucleotides was mentioned previously (cf. pp. 310, 335). Another example of the synthesis of a "coenzyme" from a vitamin is the biochemical conversion of pyridoxal (vitamin B$_6$, Chapter 39) to pyridoxal phosphate in the presence of ATP.[8]

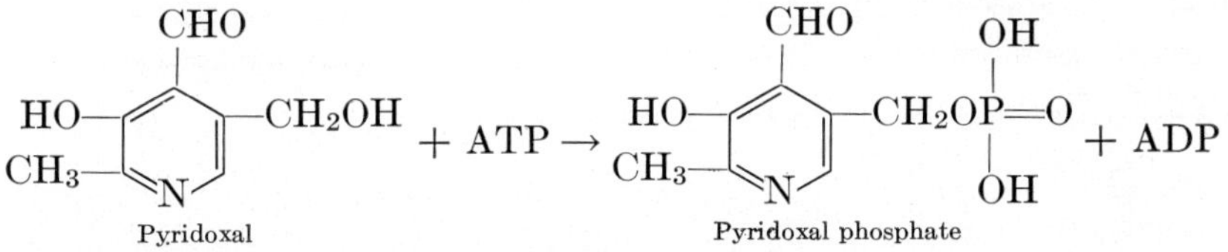

Pyridoxal + ATP → Pyridoxal phosphate + ADP

[6] O. Meyerhof and H. Green, *J. Biol. Chem.*, **178**, 655 (1949).

[7] S. P. Colowick, in J. B. Sumner and K. Myrbäck, *The Enzymes*, Chapter 46, Academic Press, New York, 1951.

[8] J. Hurwitz, *J. Biol. Chem.*, **205**, 935 (1953).

As noted above, the phosphorylation of glucose by ATP is a strongly exergonic reaction, with the equilibrium far in the direction of the formation of glucose-6-phosphate. Similar equilibria apply to transphosphorylation reactions in which phosphate is transferred from ATP to an aliphatic hydroxyl group in compounds other than glucose. Several enzyme-catalyzed reactions are known, however, in which the transfer of phosphate from ATP is not exergonic. One example is the reaction

3-Phosphoglycerate^{3-} + ATP^{4-} $\rightleftharpoons$

$$\text{1,3-Diphosphoglycerate}^{4-} + \text{ADP}^{3-}$$

(cf. reaction 2 in the diagram shown on p. 373). The standard free-energy change (at 25°C) for this reaction has been reported to be +4.8 kcal. Hence, if the value of −8 kcal is assumed for $\Delta F'$ (pH 7.5) in the hydrolysis of ATP to ADP and phosphate, the corresponding value for the hydrolysis of 1,3-diphosphoglyceric acid to 3-phosphoglyceric acid and phosphate is about −13 kcal per mole. Another example of a reaction in which phosphate transfer from ATP is not accompanied by a negative $\Delta F'$ is the reaction of creatine with ATP to form creatine phosphate (p. 379) and ADP; this reaction is catalyzed by the enzyme ATP-creatine transphosphorylase.[9] $\Delta F'$ (pH 7.5) for the reaction

Creatine^{+} + ATP^{4-} $\rightleftharpoons$ Creatine phosphate^{-} + ADP^{3-} + H^{+}

has been estimated (from equilibrium studies) to be about +3 kcal, giving a value of $\Delta F'$ of about −11 kcal for the hydrolysis of creatine phosphate to creatine and phosphate, again assuming a value of −8 kcal for the hydrolysis of ATP.

It should be added that the hydrolysis of ADP to adenosine monophosphate (AMP) and phosphate appears to have a $\Delta F'$ value similar to that for the hydrolysis of the terminal pyrophosphate bond of ATP. This is suggested by the fact that in the transphosphorylation reaction catalyzed by the enzyme myokinase

2 ADP^{3-} $\rightleftharpoons$ AMP^{2-} + ATP^{4-}

the equilibrium constant is not far from unity.

Coupled enzyme-catalyzed reactions are known in which the conversion of ATP to ADP and phosphate is linked to the synthesis of thiol esters of coenzyme A (p. 206). For example, the coupled process

Acetate^{-} + CoA + ATP^{4-} $\rightleftharpoons$ Acetyl-CoA + ADP^{3-} + HPO$_4$$^{2-}$

has a $\Delta F'$ of about zero. It may be concluded therefore that $\Delta F'$ (pH 7.5) for the hydrolysis of acetyl-coenzyme A to acetate and coenzyme A is approximately the same as that for the hydrolysis of ATP to ADP and

[9] S. A. Kuby et al., *J. Biol. Chem.*, **209**, 191; **210**, 65, 83 (1954).

phosphate.[10]   Another enzyme-catalyzed reaction, of general importance in intermediate metabolism, and involving coenzyme A, is the process

$$\text{Succinate}^{2-} + \text{CoA} + \text{ATP}^{4-} \rightleftharpoons$$
$$\text{Succinyl-CoA}^{-} + \text{ADP}^{3-} + \text{HPO}_4{}^{2-}$$

The equilibrium constant in the direction shown was found to be about 0.3, corresponding to a $\Delta F'$ (pH 7.4) of about $+0.7$ kcal.[11]   Thus the reverse of the two reactions written above, involving the cleavage of acetyl-CoA or of succinyl-CoA, provides mechanisms for the generation of a pyrophosphate bond of ATP.   As will be seen later, these two thiol esters of coenzyme A arise by the oxidative decarboxylation of pyruvate (cf. p. 481) and of α-ketoglutarate (cf. p. 505) respectively, and therefore represent additional intermediates that link exergonic oxidation reactions to the endergonic phosphorylation of ADP.

Because of the manifold biochemical reactions involving the pyrophosphate bonds of ATP, and their synthesis in coupled reactions driven by exergonic oxidation processes, it may be said that ATP serves as a "funneling agent" of energy from biological oxidations to a variety of important metabolic processes.   In addition to the reactions mentioned above, and the many others that will be encountered in later pages of this book, it may be noted, for example, that ATP appears to participate in the biological transformation of chemical energy to electrical energy. Thus Nachmansohn[12] has shown that the discharge of electricity by the electric organ of the fish *Electrophorus electricus* is related to the hydrolysis of acetylcholine (p. 275), which is resynthesized from choline and acetate in a chemical process requiring the presence of ATP and coenzyme A.

"Energy-Rich" Bonds.   In the foregoing discussion of the equilibria in transphosphorylation reactions involving ATP, it was noted that the reported values for $\Delta F'$ (ca. pH 7.5) of hydrolysis of phosphate esters such as glucose-6-phosphate fell in the range -2 to -4 kcal per mole, whereas the values for the hydrolysis of susbtances such as ATP, 1,3-diphosphoglyceric acid, creatine phosphate, or acetyl-coenzyme A are probably in the range -7 to -13 kcal per mole.   Some years ago, it was suggested[13] that a distinction be made between bonds whose $\Delta F'$ of hydrolysis fell into these two groups of values; the phosphate ester bond of substances such as glucose-6-phosphate was designated an "energy-poor" or "low-energy" phosphate bond, and the pyrophosphate bonds of ATP or the carboxyl phosphate bond of 1,3-diphosphoglyceric

[10] K. Burton, *Biochem. J.*, **59**, 44 (1955).
[11] S. Kaufman and S. G. A. Alivisatos, *J. Biol. Chem.*, **216**, 141 (1955).
[12] D. Nachmansohn, *Harvey Lectures*, **49**, 57 (1955).
[13] F. Lipmann, *Advances in Enzymol.*, **1**, 99 (1941).

acid were termed "energy-rich" or "high-energy" phosphate bonds. This distinction was extended to include bonds in which a phosphoryl group was not a participant; for example, the peptide bond linking two amino acids was considered an "energy-poor" bond ($\Delta F' =$ ca. -3 kcal), and the thiol ester bond of acetyl-CoA an "energy-rich" bond ($\Delta F' =$ ca. -8 kcal). These views were advanced at a time when the value for $\Delta F'$ (pH 7.5) for the hydrolysis of ATP was believed to be about -12 kcal per mole, and most of the values of $\Delta F'$ for the hydrolysis of other compounds having "energy-rich" bonds had been calculated from equilibrium data by means of this figure. The more recent recognition that the value of $\Delta F'$ for the hydrolysis of ATP is probably much lower than -12 kcal (cf. p. 374) has narrowed the gap between "energy-rich" and "energy-poor" bonds. Furthermore, calorimetric studies of some reactions usually considered to involve the hydrolysis of "energy-poor" bonds (e.g., the hydrolysis of a CO—NH linkage) gave ΔH_{298} values of about -6 kcal,[14] and similar ΔH values were found for the hydrolysis of "energy-rich" pyrophosphate bonds,[15] suggesting that a sharp line of demarcation between "energy-poor" and "energy-rich" bonds does not exist.

Among the "energy-rich" phosphate bonds were listed not only the pyrophosphate bonds of ATP, but also those of other pyrophosphate compounds, including inorganic pyrophosphate. Like 1,3-diphosphoglyceric acid (p. 324), acetyl phosphate ($CH_3CO—OPO_3{}^{2-}$) may be considered to have an "energy-rich" carboxyl phosphate bond.[16] A third type of compound having an "energy-rich" phosphate bond is the phosphate ester of an enol, as in phosphoenolpyruvate; the hydrolysis of this compound is strongly exergonic, having a $\Delta F'$ (ca. pH 7.5) of about -13 kcal per mole (assuming -8 kcal for the hydrolysis of ATP). Phosphoenolpyruvic acid is formed from 2-phosphoglyceric acid by a dehydration reaction catalyzed by the enzyme enolase (cf. p. 472).

$$
\begin{array}{ccc}
\text{COOH} & \text{COOH} & \text{COOH} \\
| & | & | \\
\text{HCOPO}_3\text{H}_2 \xrightarrow{-\text{H}_2\text{O}} & \text{COPO}_3\text{H}_2 \xrightarrow{+\text{H}_2\text{O}} & \text{C}=\text{O} + \text{H}_3\text{PO}_4 \\
| & \| & | \\
\text{CH}_2\text{OH} & \text{CH}_2 & \text{CH}_3 \\
\text{2-Phosphoglyceric} & \text{Phosphoenolpyruvic} & \text{Pyruvic} \\
\text{acid} & \text{acid} & \text{acid}
\end{array}
$$

Other "energy-rich" bonds are the phosphoamide linkages in creatine phosphate and in arginine phosphate, thiol ester linkages (RCO—SR')

[14] J. M. Sturtevant, *J. Am. Chem. Soc.*, **75**, 2016 (1953).

[15] N. S. Ging and J. M. Sturtevant, *J. Am. Chem. Soc.*, **76**, 2087 (1954).

[16] F. Lipmann, *Advances in Enzymol.*, **6**, 231 (1946).

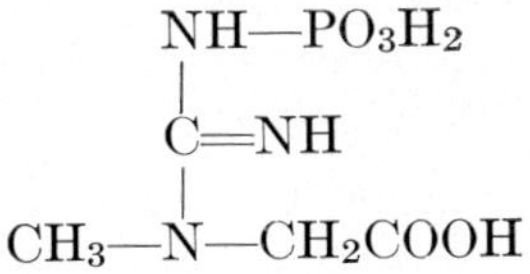

$$NH-PO_3H_2$$
$$|$$
$$C{=}NH$$
$$|$$
$$NH$$
$$|$$
$$(CH_2)_3$$

$$NH-PO_3H_2$$
$$|$$
$$C{=}NH$$
$$|$$
$$CH_3-N-CH_2COOH \qquad NH_2-CH-COOH$$

Creatine phosphate 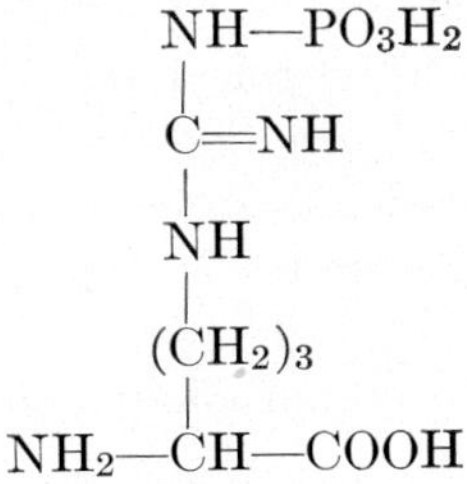   Arginine phosphate

as in acetyl-CoA or S-acetylglutathione (cf. p. 479), and acyl imidazole bonds as in N-acetylimidazole (cf. p. 67).

The relatively large negative free-energy change in the hydrolysis of the various "energy-rich" bonds has been attributed to an increased "resonance stability" of the products of hydrolysis, and to electrostatic repulsion between the groups joined by the "energy-rich" bond.[17] If one considers the hydrolysis of a carboxyl phosphate, the resultant carboxylate ion may be written either

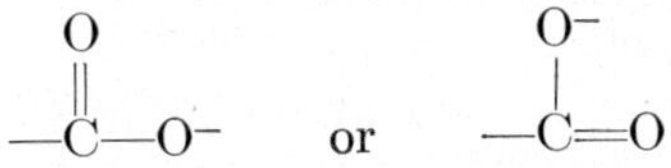

$$\begin{matrix} O \\ \| \\ -C-O^- \end{matrix} \quad \text{or} \quad \begin{matrix} O^- \\ | \\ -C{=}O \end{matrix}$$

The actual electronic configuration of the carboxylate ion is intermediate between these two possible structures; the resulting "resonance hybrid" is more stable, i.e., it is at a lower energy level, than either of the two forms written above.[18] In a similar manner, the phosphate ion formed on hydrolysis may be considered as being stabilized by resonance among a number of electronic configurations which contribute to its structure. In the carboxyl phosphate group, however, such stabilization becomes impossible because of the incompatibility of complete resonance in the constituent carboxyl and phosphate residues. For further discussion of the role of resonance in the determination of the properties of the compounds with "energy-rich" phosphate bonds, see the articles by Kalckar and by Oesper.[19]

Although the term "energy-rich bond" has been applied to a linkage whose hydrolytic cleavage is accompanied by a $\Delta F'$ (ca. pH 7.5) of about -10 kcal per mole, it is important to recognize that the energy change depends on the structure of the compound that is hydrolyzed, and of the products of hydrolysis. Some biochemists refer to an "energy-rich"

[17] T. L. Hill and M. F. Morales, *J. Am. Chem. Soc.*, **73**, 1656 (1951).

[18] G. W. Wheland, *Resonance in Organic Chemistry*, John Wiley & Sons, New York, 1955.

[19] H. M. Kalckar, *Chem. Revs.*, **28**, 71 (1941); *Ann. N. Y. Acad. Sci.*, **45**, 395 (1944); P. Oesper, *Arch. Biochem.*, **27**, 255 (1950).

bond by placing a "wriggle" between the atoms it is considered to join (e.g., ATP = adenosine-P$\sim$P$\sim$P), but the use of this symbol may give the misleading idea that the energy released on hydrolysis is concentrated in one chemical bond. Furthermore, with some compounds whose hydrolysis appears to be accompanied by a relatively large negative $\Delta F'$, it is difficult to specify the "energy-rich" bond; examples are the diacylamides and sulfonium compounds.

$$RCO\!-\!NH\!-\!COR + H_2O \rightarrow RCO\!-\!NH_2 + RCOOH$$

$$R\!-\!\overset{+}{S}\!-\!R' + OH^- \rightarrow R\!-\!S\!-\!R' + ROH$$
$$\underset{R}{\vert}$$

It should be added that the term "bond energy" as used by some biochemists in connection with "energy-rich" and "energy-poor" bonds has a meaning different from "bond energy" as defined in physical chemistry, where it refers to the mean $\Delta H°$ required to break a bond between 2 atoms. Thus the bond energy of the O—H bond is 110 kcal per mole, and that of the C—C bond is 58 kcal per mole; more energy is required to break the O—H bond.

Some of the compounds that contain phosphate bonds whose hydrolysis is accompanied by large negative $\Delta F'$ are extremely unstable in acid solution. The pyrophosphate bonds of ATP are cleaved by brief treatment with N hydrochloric acid at 100° C; the N—P bonds of creatine phosphate and of arginine phosphate are even more sensitive to acid, and the carboxyl phosphate appears to be still more labile. It will be recalled, however, that the magnitude of the free-energy change in a reaction (at a given pH and temperature) does not give information about the rate of the reaction; this is determined by the energy of activation under the conditions employed (cf. p. 265). The stability of compounds containing "energy-rich" bonds varies greatly, depending on the conditions of hydrolysis. For example, whereas phosphoamides are stable in alkali and extremely acid-labile, thiol esters such as acetyl-CoA are relatively stable at acid and neutral pH values, and are rapidly hydrolyzed in alkaline solution.

Phosphorylation of ADP Coupled to Electron Transport. As noted before, 1,3-diphosphoglyceric acid serves as an intermediate in linking the exergonic dehydrogenation of a metabolite (glyceraldehyde-3-phosphate) to the endergonic phosphorylation of ADP to form ATP. Such coupling of the oxidation of a metabolite to the generation of pyrophosphate bonds is sometimes termed "substrate-linked phosphorylation"; another example is the phosphorylation of ADP coupled to the oxidative decarboxylation of pyruvate or of α-ketoglutarate. However, in aerobic cells these mechanisms of oxidative phosphorylation of ADP are responsible for only a small fraction of the total amount of ATP synthesized. The greater part of the generation of the pyrophosphate bonds of ATP is coupled to the operation of the enzymic mechanisms for electron transfer to oxygen from pyridine nucleotides or from metabolites such as succinate. This type of process is sometimes termed "respiratory chain phosphorylation."

Numerous investigators have shown that, under suitable experimental conditions, the aerobic respiration of cells and of tissue preparations is linked to the uptake of inorganic phosphate, which appears in combination with organic constituents, as in phosphorylated sugars or in creatine phosphate.[20] It was soon found that the respiration is responsible for the generation of the pyrophosphate bonds of ATP, and that the transphosphorylation from ATP to a suitable phosphate acceptor (e.g., glucose, creatine) is independent of the oxidation. Later work showed that ADP is the specific substrate in oxidative phosphorylation,[21] and much attention was therefore devoted to the estimation of the stoichiometric relation between the equivalents of ADP phosphorylated and the atoms of oxygen taken up (or electron pairs transferred to oxygen) in the aerobic oxidation of a metabolite. This relation is usually termed the "P/O ratio," since it denotes the number of atoms of inorganic phosphorus incorporated into organic phosphates per atom of oxygen consumed. The determination of P/O ratios is complicated by the hydrolytic cleavage of the pyrophosphate bonds of ATP (cf. p. 489); to reduce this loss of ATP, fluoride (ca. 0.04 M) is usually added as an inhibitor of the enzymes that hydrolyze ATP. Also, an efficient transphosphorylating system, such as the hexokinase-catalyzed reaction (p. 375), is frequently coupled to the generation of ATP, which is thus "trapped" in a rapid transphosphorylation reaction (e.g., as glucose-6-phosphate). Many studies of oxidative phosphorylation have been performed by the use of inorganic phosphate labeled with the radioactive isotope P^{32} (cf. p. 392), and by the determination of the radioactivity in the organic phosphates formed.

Although respiratory chain phosphorylation has been demonstrated with preparations of various animal tissues, the most extensive information has been obtained in studies with the mitochondrial fraction of rat liver. Of special importance was the demonstration by Friedkin and Lehninger[22] that liver mitochondria effect phosphorylation coupled to the oxidation of DPNH by O_2. Subsequent studies by Lehninger[23] gave

[20] V. A. Belitzer, *Enzymologia*, **6**, 1 (1939); S. P. Colowick et al., *J. Biol. Chem.*, **133**, 359 (1940); S. Ochoa, *ibid.*, **151**, 493 (1943).

[21] E. C. Slater and F. A. Holton, *Biochem. J.*, **55**, 530 (1953).

[22] M. Friedkin and A. L. Lehninger, *J. Biol. Chem.*, **178**, 611 (1949).

[23] A. L. Lehninger, *Harvey Lectures*, **49**, 176 (1955).

P/O values of about 2.6 for this oxidation, under conditions which favored the penetration of DPNH into the mitochondria, and in which the ATP was trapped by means of the hexokinase-catalyzed reaction. If β-hydroxybutyrate was used as the electron donor, a similar P/O ratio was obtained, indicating that the coupled phosphorylation was associated with the oxidation of endogenous DPNH by O_2. The use of β-hydroxybutyrate as a substrate for studies of oxidative phosphorylation by liver mitochondria has the advantage that the product of its enzymic dehydrogenation, acetoacetate, is not metabolized further in this system. The finding of a P/O ratio greater than 2 has been interpreted to mean that the actual value is 3, and the lower experimental figure is attributed to the partial loss of ATP by hydrolysis. The P/O value of 3 in the aerobic oxidation of DPNH has been generally accepted as a basis for further work. One may therefore write the reaction (P_i denotes inorganic phosphate)

$$DPNH + H^+ + \tfrac{1}{2}O_2 + 3ADP + 3P_i \rightarrow DPN^+ + H_2O + 3ATP$$

If the standard free-energy change at pH 7 ($\Delta F'$) for the aerobic oxidation of DPNH is taken to be about -50 kcal per mole (cf. p. 372), and the value for the synthesis of ATP is assumed to be about $+8$ kcal per mole (cf. p. 374), it may be calculated that the thermodynamic efficiency of oxidative phosphorylation is about 50 per cent. It was noted earlier in this chapter that the energy made available in the aerobic oxidation of DPNH by liver mitochondria is released in "packets," corresponding to successive steps in the sequence of electron transport. Through experiments in which one of the steps is blocked, or a portion of the sequence has been bypassed, important advances have been made toward the location of the particular electron transfer steps that are coupled to the phosphorylation of ADP.

There is considerable evidence to show that one equivalent of ATP is formed per atom of oxygen consumed in the oxidation of ferrocytochrome c by O_2.[24] When ascorbic acid is used as the electron donor with rat liver mitochondria, this substance reduces ferricytochrome c nonenzymically (cf. p. 353), thus bypassing the electron carrier systems of more negative potential (cytochrome b, flavin, DPN). Other compounds (e.g., 3,4-dihydroxy-L-phenylalanine) that reduce ferricytochrome c may be used in place of ascorbic acid.[25] Since the aerobic oxidation of ascorbic acid by the cytochrome oxidase system is accompanied by a P/O ratio of nearly 1, it has been concluded that one of the three sites of phosphorylation in the respiratory chain lies between ferrocytochrome c and oxygen.

---

[24] S. O. Nielsen and A. L. Lehninger, *J. Biol. Chem.*, **215**, 555 (1955); C. Cooper and A. L. Lehninger, *ibid.*, **219**, 519 (1956).

[25] G. F. Maley and H. A. Lardy, *J. Biol. Chem.*, **210**, 903 (1954).

The allocation of one of the three sites of oxidative phosphorylation to the ferrocytochrome c → O_2 span of the electron transport sequence supports the view that the other two sites lie between DPNH and ferricytochrome c. Thus experiments with rat liver mitochondria, in which the cytochrome oxidase system had been blocked by cyanide and ferricytochrome c served as the electron acceptor, gave P/O values approaching 2 for the oxidation of β-hydroxybutyrate.[26] A tentative assignment of one of the two phosphorylation sites suggested by this P/O value is between DPNH and the antimycin-sensitive step[27] (cytochrome b?; p. 356); the other may be at the reaction between ferrocytochrome b and ferricytochrome c.[28] This assignment is in agreement with the finding that the aerobic oxidation of succinate by mitochondria gives P/O values between 1 and 2, suggesting only two sites of oxidative phosphorylation. Since the enzymic dehydrogenation of succinate does not involve a pyridine nucleotide system (cf. p. 344), it may be inferred that a phosphorylation site near the DPNH → flavin step of the respiratory chain has been bypassed in the aerobic oxidation of this metabolite (Fig. 1).

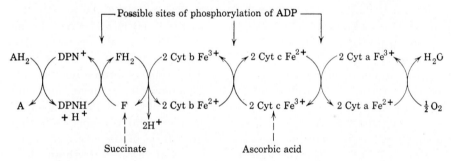

Fig. 1. Possible sites of coupling of phosphorylation with electron transport in liver mitochondria.

Further important information about the probable sites of oxidative phosphorylation has come from the spectroscopic studies of Chance and Williams[29] on the steady-state levels of the electron carrier systems in liver mitochondria. Earlier work[30] had shown that the rate of electron transport from DPNH to O_2 is controlled by the concentration of ADP and of inorganic phosphate. When ADP is added to a suitable preparation

26 B. Borgström et al., *J. Biol. Chem.*, **215**, 571 (1955).

27 J. H. Copenhaver and H. A. Lardy, *J. Biol. Chem.*, **195**, 225 (1952).

28 B. Chance and G. R. Williams, *J. Biol. Chem.*, **217**, 429 (1955).

29 B. Chance and G. R. Williams, *J. Biol. Chem.*, **217**, 409, 439 (1955); *Advances in Enzymol.*, **17**, 65 (1956).

30 H. A. Lardy and H. Wellman, *J. Biol. Chem.*, **195**, 215 (1952).

of mitochondria in the presence of phosphate, the rate of oxygen uptake is increased about tenfold. This increased respiration is accompanied by distinctive changes in the steady-state ratio of the oxidized to reduced forms (cf. p. 360) of the DPN, flavin, cytochrome b, and cytochrome c systems, all of which become more oxidized. By estimating the steady-state ratios under a variety of experimental conditions, Chance and Williams have inferred that ADP exerts its effect on the rate of electron transfer at the three oxidation-reduction reactions indicated in Fig. 1, and that these reactions may represent the three sites of oxidative phosphorylation in liver mitochondria.

It may be added that oxidative phosphorylation has been demonstrated with intracellular particles from the microorganisms *Alcaligenes fecalis*[31] and *Azotobacter vinelandii*,[32] and from plant cells.[33] The addition of polynucleotides to the enzyme system from *Alcaligenes fecalis* promotes oxidative phosphorylation. It is also of interest that oxidative phosphorylation in liver mitochondria appears to be largely associated with the oxidation of DPNH rather than of TPNH.[34]

The nature of the intermediates responsible for the transfer of energy from the oxidation of the reduced electron carriers to the phosphorylation of ADP is unknown. The phosphate groups of DPN and FAD do not appear to participate in this process. Among the several hypotheses that have been proposed is the suggestion[35] that, on oxidation of the reduced form of an electron carrier, an "energy-rich" bond is formed between the oxidized form of the carrier and a mitochondrial component, and that the cleavage of this bond is coupled to the phosphorylation of ADP (cf. Lehninger[23]). Another hypothesis (Chance and Williams[29]) is that the "energy-rich" bond involves the reduced form of the electron carrier system. Whatever the intimate mechanisms of respiratory chain phosphorylation turn out to be, they appear to involve, in addition to the coupling reactions, separate bimolecular reactions for the phosphorylation of ADP.[36]

Clearly, the elucidation of the chemical nature of the intermediates responsible for the conservation of the free energy released on oxidation, and for its transfer to the phosphorylation of ADP, represents one of the

[31] G. B. Pinchot, *J. Biol. Chem.*, **205**, 65 (1953); *Biochim. et Biophys. Acta*, **23**, 660 (1957).

[32] I. A. Rose and S. Ochoa, *J. Biol. Chem.*, **220**, 307 (1956).

[33] J. Bonner and A. Millerd, *J. Histochem. and Cytochem.*, **1**, 254 (1953); E. E. Conn and L. C. T. Young, *J. Biol. Chem.*, **227**, 23 (1957).

[34] N. O. Kaplan et al., *Proc. Natl. Acad. Sci.*, **42**, 481 (1956).

[35] C. L. Wadkins and A. L. Lehninger, *J. Am. Chem. Soc.*, **79**, 1010 (1957).

[36] P. D. Boyer et al., *Nature*, **174**, 401 (1954); *J. Biol. Chem.*, **223**, 405 (1956); M. Cohn and G. R. Drysdale, *ibid.*, **216**, 831 (1955).

most challenging tasks of modern biochemistry. The difficulty of this problem has been great, especially because the mechanism of oxidative phosphorylation depends on the integrity of an organized multienzyme system that is damaged easily. However, the recent separation, from digitonin extracts of rat liver mitochondria, of particles that perform oxidative phosphorylation is an important advance toward the chemical dissection of this complex process.[37]

In the study of oxidative phosphorylation, advantage has been taken of the effect of a large variety of substances to dissociate ("uncouple") electron transfer from phosphorylation, permitting oxidation to occur but inhibiting the phosphorylation of ADP. Among these uncoupling agents is 2,4-dinitrophenol,[38] which is believed to accelerate the hydrolysis of ATP and of "energy-rich" bonds in substances involved in the transfer of energy from oxidation to phosphorylation. The addition of dinitrophenol increases the rate of oxygen uptake, presumably by eliminating the regulatory influence of inorganic phosphate and of phosphate acceptors (cf. p. 383). Calcium ion also acts as an uncoupling agent, probably by counteracting the effect of magnesium ion, which is essential for oxidative phosphorylation. Other uncoupling agents are the hormone thyroxine,[39] the anticoagulant dicumarol,[40] the antibiotic gramicidin, bilirubin,[41] adrenochrome, pentachlorophenol, and azide. Most of these substances are effective at relatively low concentrations (ca. 10^{-5} M). The elucidation of their mode of action as uncoupling agents depends on further chemical dissection of the multienzyme system involved in oxidative phosphorylation. That the mechanism whereby they act is not the same in all cases is indicated by the fact that uncoupling by thyroxine (which appears to alter the permeability of the mitochondrial membrane; cf. Chapter 38) is counteracted by glutathione, Mg^{2+}, or Mn^{2+}; none of these agents overcomes the effect of dinitrophenol.[42] Furthermore, the action of adrenochrome is counteracted by glutathione, but not by Mg^{2+} or Mn^{2+}.

The results discussed in this chapter make it clear that the coupled action of multienzyme systems is a distinctive attribute of the chemical activity of living matter, and that the intracellular integration of enzyme

[37] C. Cooper and A. L. Lehninger, *J. Biol. Chem.*, **219**, 489 (1956); J. L. Gamble, Jr., and A. L. Lehninger, *ibid.*, **223**, 921 (1956).

[38] W. F. Loomis and F. Lipmann, *J. Biol. Chem.*, **179**, 503 (1949); C. Cooper and A. L. Lehninger, *ibid.*, **224**, 547, 561 (1957).

[39] F. L. Hoch and F. Lipmann, *Proc. Natl. Acad. Sci.*, **40**, 909 (1954); G. F. Maley and H. A. Lardy, *J. Biol. Chem.*, **215**, 377 (1955).

[40] C. Martius and D. Nitz-Litzow, *Biochim. et Biophys. Acta*, **13**, 152, 289 (1954).

[41] R. Zetterström and L. Ernster, *Nature*, **178**, 1335 (1956).

[42] J. H. Park et al., *Biochim. et Biophys. Acta*, **22**, 403 (1956).

action is of decisive importance in the determination of metabolic pathways. The subsequent discussion of the intermediate metabolism of
carbohydrates, lipids, proteins, and other cell constituents will provide
many illustrations of the fact that the study of the integrated action of
multienzyme systems forms the basis of modern biochemistry.[43]

[43] M. Dixon, *Multi-Enzyme Systems,* Cambridge University Press, Cambridge,
1949.

Methods for the Study
of
Intermediate Metabolism

Although nongrowing organisms are characterized by a relative constancy with regard to the chemical composition of their cellular material, this is the expression of a balancing of many chemical reactions rather than of a static situation. For the maintenance of life, most of the constituents of cells must be rebuilt continually; to make this possible, chemical substances containing carbon, oxygen, hydrogen, nitrogen, and the other essential elements must be ingested and used for the synthesis of the carbohydrates, fats, proteins, nucleic acids, porphyrins, etc., required for the integrity of the biological unit. Obviously, during the process of growth, the existing cellular constituents must not only be rebuilt, but they must also be augmented by the synthesis of additional cellular material. Furthermore, in all organisms the energy derived from the breakdown of some of the foodstuffs must be made available to drive endergonic reactions, when external sources of energy (e.g., sunlight in photosynthesis) cannot be mobilized. These processes—the degradation of foodstuffs, the synthesis of cellular constituents, and the transfer of energy—are components of the "metabolism" (Greek, *metabole,* change) of biological systems, and are all dependent on the catalytic activity of enzymes. In the preceding chapters, emphasis was placed on the importance of studying the chemical action of purified enzymes, since the knowledge gained in this way is essential for an understanding of the role of the individual enzymes in the chemical dynamics of a biological unit. However, such knowledge, though essential, is not sufficient for an appreciation of the part that the individual enzymes play in the chemical transformation of a given substance in a particular living cell.

The study of the chemical degradations (sometimes termed "catabolism") and chemical syntheses (sometimes termed "anabolism") that occur in a living system must, of necessity, be examined in that living system. In other words, one must examine the fate of a chemical compound *in vivo* to ascertain the successive chemical reactions whereby it is converted to a variety of cellular constituents or to excretory products. Thus, for example, a portion of the nitrogen present in the proteins ingested by man will be excreted in the urine in the form of urea; another portion will, after a given time, be found in the protoporphyrin of the erythrocyte hemoglobin and in other nitrogenous constituents of the body. The study of the various biochemical transformations of a given dietary protein will then provide information about the "intermediate metabolism" of that protein in man. Entirely analogous considerations apply to any other biological form, whether it be another vertebrate, or a sea urchin egg, or a microorganism; however, the intermediate metabolism of a protein, or a carbohydrate, or a fat, or any of their chemical derivatives, must be examined for each type of organism separately. The intermediate metabolism of certain substances has frequently been found to follow similar pathways in widely different biological species. Such findings support the view that there is a unity in the mechanisms by which many fundamental biochemical processes are accomplished in organisms as diverse as a yeast cell and a mammal.

In the historical development of biochemistry, the discovery of chemical processes in whole organisms has usually preceded the study of the individual enzymes that catalyze the component chemical reactions. Perhaps the outstanding example of this is the development of knowledge concerning the fermentation of glucose to alcohol by yeast. In the chapters to follow, consideration will be given to some of the available knowledge in the field of intermediate metabolism. Whenever possible, attention will be directed to the enzymes involved in the biochemical reactions under discussion, but, as will become apparent, there are many reactions known to occur in living systems for which it is not possible at present to specify the component enzymes. Before examining, in turn, the metabolic transformations of carbohydrates, fats, proteins, and compounds related to each of these groups of substances, it may be appropriate to consider briefly some of the general experimental methods which have proved to be of value in this area of biochemistry.

Isotopic Tracer Technique

The primary objective in the study of the metabolic transformation of a particular chemical substance is to observe the fate of that substance *in vivo* under experimental conditions which cause a minimum of physiological disturbance to the test organism. For this reason, the most fruitful of the known methods for the study of metabolism is the "isotopic tracer technique"; here one or more of the atoms in the metabolite under study is "labeled" by means of one of the rare or artificially produced isotopes. For a historical sketch of the biological application of isotopes, see the articles by Hevesy.[1]

An isotope is one of a group of atomic species all members of which have the same number of protons in the nucleus; it differs from the other members of the group only in the number of neutrons in its nucleus. Thus two isotopes of an element have the same atomic number but different atomic mass. For example, nitrogen (atomic number 7) is found in nature both with a mass of 14 (designated N^{14}) and with a mass of 15 (designated N^{15}). These two naturally occurring nitrogen isotopes are "stable"; their nuclei do not undergo spontaneous decomposition. Atoms whose nuclei decompose spontaneously with the emission of radiation are termed radioactive isotopes. Most of the radioactive isotopes used in biochemical research do not occur in nature, but are created artificially by nuclear reactions.

Stable Isotopes. The stable isotopic elements of biochemical interest are H^2 (also designated by the symbol D, for deuterium), N^{15}, C^{13}, and O^{18}. These atoms exist in nature in the following relative abundance:

$$H^1/H^2 = 99.98/0.02$$
$$N^{14}/N^{15} = 99.63/0.37$$
$$C^{12}/C^{13} = 98.9/1.1$$
$$O^{16}/O^{18} = 99.8/0.2$$

Methods are available for the preparation of samples of each of these elements in which the natural abundance ratio has been altered in favor of the less abundant form, and one may say, therefore, that the element has been enriched with respect to its isotope content, or that the element has been "labeled." Such a labeled element may then be incorporated, by appropriate synthetic methods,[2] into a substance whose metabolic fate is to be investigated (e.g., N^{15} in the α-NH_2 group of an amino acid); the "isotopic" compound is introduced into the organism under study, and after a suitable time other compounds are isolated from the tissues and fluids of the organism, and their isotope content is determined. In order to measure the N^{15} concentration of a given material that contains nitrogen, one determines the ratio of the abundance of the two masses. This is performed in the mass spectrometer devised by Aston in 1919 and greatly improved since that date.[3] In principle, the mass spectrometer is an apparatus in which uncharged atoms or

---

[1] G. Hevesy, *Cold Spring Harbor Symposia Quant. Biol.*, **13**, 129 (1948); *J. Chem. Soc.*, **1951**, 1618.

[2] H. R. V. Arnstein and R. Bentley, *Quart. Revs.*, **4**, 172 (1950); S. L. Thomas and H. S. Turner, *ibid.*, **7**, 407 (1953).

[3] A. O. Nier, *Science*, **121**, 737 (1955).

molecules are converted into positively charged ions; these are accelerated into the field of a powerful magnet (cf. Fig. 1). In the magnetic field the ions will be deflected to an extent that will depend on their mass. The relative amounts of the ions of different mass may then be determined by collecting them on a plate and measuring the current produced. In the

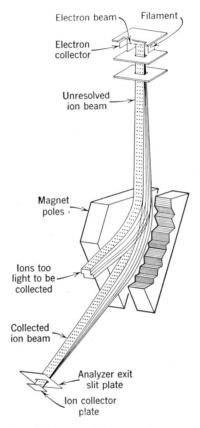

Fig. 1. Schematic drawing of the essential parts of a mass spectrometer tube. The ion source, the ion path, and the collector arrangement are enclosed in a tube that is pumped continuously with a high-vacuum pump. (From Nier.[3])

determination of the N^{15} content of an amino acid, the bound nitrogen first must be converted to nitrogen gas; this is introduced into the highly evacuated spectrometer tube, and the ratio of the masses 28 ($N^{14}N^{14}$) and 29 ($N^{15}N^{14}$) is measured. The concentration of O^{18} in a compound is estimated by conversion to CO_2 or CO; in the latter case, the ratio of masses 30 ($C^{12}O^{18}$) to 28 ($C^{12}O^{16}$) is determined. CO_2 has been used for the determination of C^{13}, and hydrogen gas for the determination of deuterium. In addition to the mass spectrometric method, deuterium may be determined by measurement of the density of water obtained upon the combustion of the deuterium-containing compound; the O^{18} content of water also can be determined by density measurements.

From the natural abundance data for nitrogen, given above, it is clear that 37 of every 10,000 nitrogen atoms are of mass 15. This abundance is more conveniently expressed as "atom per cent," which here would be 0.37. If one prepares a sample of nitrogen that has been enriched with respect to its N^{15} content so that its N^{15}/N^{14} ratio is 200/9800, i.e., it contains 2.00 atom per cent N^{15}, this value exceeds the normal abundance by 1.63 atom per cent. The sample is thus said to contain 1.63 atom per cent excess N^{15}. With modern mass spectrometers it is possible to measure the N^{15} concentration of a sample of nitrogen within about 0.003 atom per cent excess N^{15}.

The advantage of using the "atom per cent excess" to express N^{15} concentration may best be illustrated by means of an example. Suppose one dilutes 1 mole of a sample containing 2.00 atom per cent N^{15} with 9 moles of a sample having the normal abundance (0.37 atom per cent N^{15}). The resultant N^{15} concentration is

$$\frac{[(1 \times 2.00) + (9 \times 0.37)]}{10} = 0.53 \text{ atom per cent } N^{15}$$

which corresponds to 0.16 atom per cent excess N^{15}. If one employs instead the value 1.63 atom per cent excess for the undiluted sample, then this value simply may be divided by the molar dilution factor (10) to give the N^{15} concentration (in atom per cent excess) of the diluted sample. The latter procedure thus offers a convenient way of calculating the dilution of isotope in the course of any mixing process. As will be seen in later chapters, the presentation of isotope concentrations as atom per cent excess simplifies the evaluation of data obtained by the use of organic compounds labeled with N^{15}.

Radioactive Isotopes.[4]   The radioactive elements are, in many respects, more useful as tracers than the stable isotopes, since the analytical methods for their measurement are exceedingly sensitive. Some of the radioactive isotopes that have proved to be of the greatest value in biochemical work are listed in Table 1. The nuclear disintegration of these isotopes is accompanied by the emission of β^--rays (negatrons, mass 5.5×10^{-4}, charge -1) and γ-rays (photons, zero mass and charge). Other radioactive isotopes emit these and other types of radiation; for a discussion, see Friedlander and Kennedy.[5]   The energy of the radiation is

[4] M. D. Kamen, *Isotopic Tracers in Biology,* 3rd Ed., Academic Press, New York, 1957.

[5] G. Friedlander and J. W. Kennedy, *Nuclear and Radiochemistry,* John Wiley & Sons, New York, 1955.

Table I. Some Radioactive Isotopes Used in Biochemical Studies

Element	Mass Number	Type of Radiation	Half-Life
Hydrogen	3	β^-	12.5 yr
Carbon	14	β^-	5570 yr
Sodium	24	β^-, γ	15 hr
Phosphorus	32	β^-	14.3 days
Sulfur	35	β^-	87.1 days
Potassium	42	β^-, γ	12.5 hr
Calcium	45	β^-	164 days
Iron	59	β^-, γ	45.1 days
Cobalt	60	β^-, γ	5.2 yr
Iodine	131	β^-, γ	8.1 days

denoted in terms of the electron-volt (ev), which is defined as the kinetic energy acquired by an electron when it moves across a potential gradient of 1 volt. Usually the unit Mev (million electron-volts) is used. For example, the β-radiation of C^{14} has an energy of 0.155 Mev, and that of P^{32} an energy of 1.7 Mev. C^{14} is usually termed a "weak" β-emitter, and P^{32} a "strong" β-emitter. The radioactive hydrogen isotope tritium (H^3, T) is a very weak β-emitter, the energy of radiation being 0.0176 Mev. The radioactive decay of an isotope accords with the kinetics of a first-order reaction (cf. p. 244), and the time required for the loss of 50 per cent of its radioactivity ("half-life") is characteristic of each isotope. With the short-lived isotopes, the investigator must make the necessary corrections for the amount of radioactivity lost by decay during the experiment. This is clearly not necessary with C^{14}, which has been an extremely valuable isotopic marker in a variety of metabolic experiments.[6]

All the isotopes listed in Table 1 are produced artificially by means of nuclear reactions; for example, C^{14} is formed by the irradiation of N^{14} with neutrons produced in a nuclear reactor ("atomic pile"). In this nuclear reaction, protons are emitted, and it is therefore usually written $N^{14}(n,p)C^{14}$. P^{32} and S^{35} are made from S^{32} and Cl^{35} respectively by the same type of nuclear reaction.

The most widely used method for the determination of radioactive isotopes is based on the ability of the emitted radiation to ionize atoms in a suitable detection apparatus, such as the Geiger-Müller tube.[7] In this instrument (cf. Fig. 2), a difference in potential is applied across two electrodes separated by a gas (helium, argon). When the gas becomes ionized by radiation emitted by a radioactive substance, electric

[6] M. Calvin et al., *Isotopic Carbon*, John Wiley & Sons, New York, 1949.

[7] E. C. Pollard and W. L. Davidson, *Applied Nuclear Physics*, 2nd Ed., John Wiley & Sons, 1951.

current flows.   At a sufficiently high voltage (ca. 800 to 1500 volts) between the electrodes, a plateau is reached where the number of pulses of current is independent of the voltage and is proportional to the number of ionizing particles entering the tube.   If the tube is connected to a suitable metering device, the number of pulses per unit time can be counted, and the radioactivity of a sample may be given in terms of its "specific radioactivity," i.e., the number of counts per minute (cpm) per unit weight (milligram, micromole, etc.).   The relationship of this quantity to the number of disintegrations per unit time depends on the count-

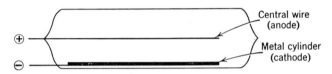

Fig. 2.   Schematic diagram of a simple Geiger-Müller tube.

ing efficiency of the system.   The absolute unit of disintegration rate is the curie; 1 millicurie (mc) $= 3.7 \times 10^7$ disintegrations per second; one microcurie (μc) $= 3.7 \times 10^4$ disintegrations per second.

The measurement of the radioactivity of a uniformly layered sample of solid material (e.g., $BaC^{14}O_3$) depends on many factors that must be taken into account, and for which corrections must be made.   Among these are: (1) the background count caused by radiation not emanating directly from the sample; (2) the spatial relation between the sample and the detector ("geometry" of the system); (3) the interaction of the radiation with the sample, as reflected in "self-absorption" and "back-scatter" of the radiation, and which varies with the thickness of the sample.   For a discussion of these and other corrections, see Francis et al.[8]   Procedures have been developed for the stepwise and nearly quantitative degradation of many carbon compounds, permitting the separate conversion of each carbon atom to CO_2, which may be introduced directly into the Geiger-Müller tube; in this procedure, the counting efficiency is much greater than with solid samples of $BaCO_3$.

The synthesis of many organic compounds containing radioactive or stable isotopes has been reported.   The conventions employed to designate the labeled atom are shown for various types of isotopic glycine.

Glycine-1-C^{14} $NH_2CH_2C^{14}OOH$

Glycine-2-C^{14} $NH_2C^{14}H_2COOH$

Glycine-N^{15} $N^{15}H_2CH_2COOH$

[8] G. E. Francis et al., *Isotopic Tracers,* University of London, The Athlone Press, London. 1954.

In some biochemical journals, however, the number designating the mass of the isotope is placed before the symbol for the element (e.g., $NH_2CH_2{}^{14}COOH$, $NH_2{}^{14}CH_2COOH$, $^{15}NH_2CH_2COOH$).

As in experiments with stable isotopes, the equation that describes the dilution of y milligrams of nonradioactive material by x milligrams of radioactive material having a specific activity of C_0 counts per minute per milligram is the following: $y = x[(C_0/C) - 1]$, where C is the specific activity of the diluted material (cf. p. 128).

Use of Isotopes in Biochemical Studies. Since it is the atomic number and not the mass that determines the chemical reactivity of an element, compounds differing only with respect to certain isotopic atoms have similar chemical properties, and thus will be subjected to similar metabolic transformations. In some instances, however, a labeled compound may be metabolized at a rate somewhat different from that for the unlabeled substance. For example, succinate containing **77** atom per cent excess deuterium in the methylene groups is oxidized by a heart muscle succinoxidase preparation at about **40** per cent of the rate for the unlabeled succinate.[9] Such "isotope effects" are roughly proportional to the difference in mass between two isotopes, and are especially marked for the hydrogen isotopes[10] (H, H^2, H^3), and less evident for the carbon isotopes (C^{12}, C^{13}, C^{14}).

When labeled compounds are employed in metabolic studies, one must be certain that the isotope does not "exchange" with the more abundant form present in the environment. For example, an amino acid labeled with deuterium in the α-NH_2 group will exchange deuterium ions with the hydrogen ions of the biological fluid.

$$R—ND_3{}^+ + 3H^+ \rightleftharpoons R—NH_3{}^+ + 3D^+$$

For this reason, amino acids labeled with deuterium in the α-NH_2 group are not likely to be useful in tracer studies of metabolism.

In the application of isotopes to the study of intermediate metabolism, the simplest type of problem is that represented by the question whether a certain organism can convert substance A to substance B. For example, the studies of Rose indicated that, in the growing rat, L-phenylalanine can be converted to L-tyrosine, since L-tyrosine could be omitted from the diet if sufficient amounts of L-phenylalanine were present. Definitive proof of this conversion came from the work of Moss and Schoenheimer, who prepared a sample of DL-phenylalanine in which the hydrogen atoms of the benzene ring had been replaced by deuterium, and fed the labeled amino acid to both growing and adult

[9] M. B. Thorn, *Biochem. J.,* **49**, 602 (1951).

[10] R. F. Glascock and W. G. Duncombe, *Biochem. J.,* **58**, 440 (1954); J. R. Rachele et al., *J. Am. Chem. Soc.,* **76**, 4342 (1954).

rats for various time intervals. After the rats had been sacrificed, a pure sample of L-tyrosine was isolated from an acid hydrolysate of the tissue proteins and was analyzed for deuterium. The isotope content of the tyrosine was such as to provide conclusive evidence for the conversion *in vivo* of the benzene ring of dietary L-phenylalanine to the phenol ring of tissue L-tyrosine. It must be emphasized, however, that this experiment offers no information about the route of the metabolic transformation of phenylalanine into tyrosine.

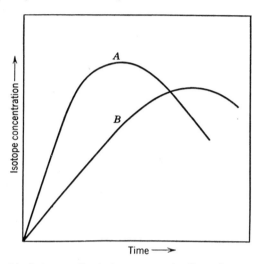

Fig. 3. Relationship between the isotope concentration of a precursor (*A*) and its metabolic product (*B*).

In studies of the metabolic conversion of compound A to compound B, it is desirable, whenever possible, to determine the isotope content of both A and B at increasing time intervals after the administration of A. If A is a specific precursor of B, the changes in the isotope content of the two compounds with time should be related to each other as shown in Fig. 3. For a discussion of the principles and application of this procedure, see Zilversmit et al.[11]

In attempts to broaden the knowledge of intermediate metabolism, intensive efforts were made during the period 1940–1950 to trace each available isotopic element from an administered metabolite to as many tissue constituents as could be isolated in a chemically homogeneous state. This type of experimentation has yielded many data of the greatest value. The discovery, by Shemin and Rittenberg,[12] that the nitrogen of glycine administered to rats appears in the pyrrole nitrogen of proto-

[11] D. B. Zilversmit et al., *J. Gen. Physiol.*, **26**, 325 (1943).
[12] D. Shemin and D. Rittenberg, *J. Biol. Chem.*, **166**, 621 (1946).

porphyrin IX, present in hemoglobin, is but one example; many others will be cited in subsequent chapters. The information gained in such exploratory investigations provides a basis for the more direct approach exemplified by the study of the conversion of phenylalanine to tyrosine. Furthermore, through systematic degradation of isotopic compounds isolated from a biological system, the labeled atoms may be identified, and their relation to a labeled atom in the administered precursor may be inferred. Thus the administration of C^{14}-labeled formate ($HC^{14}OO^-$) to a pigeon leads to the metabolic formation of labeled uric acid; chemical degradation of this product has shown that the C^{14} is largely located in carbons 2 and 8 of the purine ring (Chapter 33).

The introduction of isotopes into metabolites is the most important example of the "labeling" of chemical substances so that they may be followed more easily in metabolism. The labeling technique itself antedates the use of isotopes, however. For example, in 1904 Knoop described the metabolism of phenyl-substituted fatty acids in animals, and showed that the phenyl group could serve as a marker which would appear in the degradation product of the ingested fatty acid (Chapter 25). Labeling methods of this type involve the introduction into the organism of substances which may be "unphysiological," and which may occasionally be harmful to the organism. This criticism may also be made of isotope experiments in which the isotopic substance is present in extremely large amounts or the isotope concentration of the test substance is excessively high. Thus, if an organism is "flooded" with D_2O, it may be expected that the rates of many of the metabolic reactions will be different from the rates in the presence of very small amounts of D_2O. Similarly, large amounts of radioactivity may cause radiation effects which in turn will lead to an altered metabolic behavior. In general, therefore, the investigator prefers to use the smallest possible quantity of labeled compound.

Isotopic labeling has been used widely in attempts to determine the rates at which metabolic reactions proceed in an intact organism. Frequent reference will be found in the literature to the "turnover rate" of a substance, or the "biological half-life" of a substance. These terms usually refer to the rates at which an administered isotope leaves a given biological system. However, since assumptions are made about the mixing of the labeled material with the corresponding unlabeled biological constituent, and about the kinetics of *in vivo* processes, such values for "half-life" have questionable validity in many instances.[13] The interpretation of data of this kind is made very difficult by the complexity of the heterogeneous, multicompartment, steady-state systems found in living organisms.

[13] J. M. Reiner, *Arch. Biochem. and Biophys.* **46**, 53, 80 (1953).

Growth Studies

Despite the undisputed importance of the isotopic tracer technique, it would be incorrect to suppose that it is the only experimental approach to the study of intermediate metabolism in intact organisms. Many of the conclusions drawn from isotope experiments had been fore-shadowed by the results of the application of other methods. As mentioned earlier, the metabolic relation of phenylalanine to tyrosine emerged from studies of the growth of immature rats. This experimental procedure depends, first of all, on the recognition that a given constituent of the diet is indispensable for the normal growth of an organism. Subsequent investigations are directed to the search for other compounds that can, partially or fully, replace this dietary essential. This line of research has been especially fruitful in the study of the intermediate metabolism of microorganisms. Many bacteria, for example, have exacting nutritional requirements for certain amino acids or vitamins. Other bacteria or molds that are not so fastidious can be caused to "mutate" (by treatment with X-rays, ultraviolet light, or selective chemical agents) into strains (termed mutants or auxotrophs) which are then characterized by a newly acquired nutritional requirement. As is the case for nutritional experiments with the growing rat, the ability of substances to replace an essential nutrient in the culture medium of microorganisms may reveal metabolic relationships between the compounds tested for their growth-promoting capacity.[14]

Recent improvements in techniques for the growth of mammalian cells in tissue culture[15] have led to valuable studies on the nutritional requirements of such cells.[16]

Application of Surgical Techniques

Before the advent of the isotope technique, much information was gained about the intermediate metabolism of complex organisms, and especially animals, by the application of the methods of experimental surgery. For example, it was found that in the rat hepatectomy (surgical removal of the liver) causes an appreciable rise in the level of ammonia in the circulating blood, while the level of urea falls. This observation led to the conclusion that the liver is an important site of the utilization of ammonia for urea synthesis. Another experimental technique is the tapping of blood vessels leading to and from various organs to permit the injection of substances into the arteries and the

[14] D. D. Woods, *J. Gen. Microbiol.,* **9,** 151 (1953).
[15] E. N. Willmer, *Tissue Culture,* 2nd Ed., Methuen and Co., London, 1954.
[16] H. Eagle, *J. Biol. Chem.,* **214,** 839 (1955); *Science,* **122,** 501 (1955).

withdrawal of samples of blood for analysis from the veins. This method, termed the "angiostomy technique," has been used with singular success by London[17] and others on dogs.

Metabolic Abnormalities and Biochemical Genetics

The physiological dysfunction which results from the surgical removal of an internal organ may resemble pathological states observed in a diseased organism. Indeed, in higher vertebrates many diseases of the liver lead to metabolic changes similar to those noted after hepatectomy. Of the metabolic abnormalities of clinical importance in medicine, several are hereditary; they have been termed "inborn errors of metabolism" by Garrod.[18] Human beings who exhibit one or another of these metabolic disorders have served as valuable experimental subjects for the study of intermediate metabolism. For example, in the condition known as alcaptonuria, a substance (homogentisic acid) is excreted in the urine; this substance is absent in the urine of normal human subjects. The study of the nature and mode of formation of homogentisic acid has provided many of the basic data on the intermediate metabolism of tyrosine in animal organisms; these data, indicating that homogentisic acid is formed from tyrosine, have been confirmed and extended by the application of the isotope technique (Chapter 32).

The excretion of homogentisic acid by the alcaptonuric was explained by Garrod as the result of a hereditary inability to metabolize the compound further in the normal manner. This concept has been the basis for the modern development of the techniques of biochemical genetics which have, in the period since 1940, provided a most useful approach to the study of intermediate metabolism.[19] If one assumes that the biosynthesis of compound B from compound A must go through an unknown intermediate X according to the scheme $A \rightarrow X \rightarrow B$, and then observes that the ability of the organism to convert A into B is lost as the result of a mutation, it is often possible to demonstrate that the organism is still capable of the reaction $A \rightarrow X$, and to isolate and identify the unknown intermediate   Thus, in certain artificially induced mutant strains of the mold *Neurospora crassa*, it has been shown that 3-hydroxyanthranilic acid is an intermediate in the normal pathway for the synthesis of nicotinic acid from tryptophan (Chapter

[17] E. S. London, *Harvey Lectures*, **23**, 208 (1927–1928).

[18] A. E. Garrod, *Inborn Errors of Metabolism*, 2nd Ed., Oxford University Press, Oxford, 1923; H. Harris, *An Introduction to Human Biochemical Genetics*, Cambridge University Press, London, 1953.

[19] G. W. Beadle, *Chem. Revs.*, **37**, 15 (1945); R. P. Wagner and H. K. Mitchell, *Genetics and Metabolism*, John Wiley & Sons, New York, 1955.

32). Many other examples of this type will be encountered in later chapters. It may be mentioned here, moreover, that the combined efforts of genetics and biochemistry have helped to explain metabolic transformations not only in microorganisms, but in a number of higher plants and animals as well.

Metabolic abnormalities may also be induced artificially by the administration to test organisms of "metabolite antagonists." These are substances which, by virtue of a structural similarity to natural metabolites, interfere with one or more natural biochemical processes; presumably, the antagonist functions as an inhibitor of specific enzymic transformations (cf. p. 260). A stimulating discussion of this approach may be found in the book by Woolley.[20]

Perfusion of Excised Organs

Many important results pertaining to intermediate metabolism were obtained during the period 1900–1920 by the perfusion of isolated organs. In this experimental technique, an organ is carefully removed from an animal and placed in a closed system in which it may be perfused either by means of the animal's own blood or with a salt solution (physiological saline) whose electrolyte content approximates that of the blood. Such isotonic salt solutions were first prepared by Ringer (1882) and by Locke (1900), and many modifications of their solutions have been described in the later literature. Under the conditions of such experiments, the organ survives for an appreciable period of time; hence test substances may be introduced into the liquid entering the organ, and samples of the liquid that emerges from the organ may be withdrawn for analysis. It will be obvious, however, that this technique suffers from the disadvantage that the organ has been separated from the physiological environment in which it normally operates and from contact with circulating hormones which, as will be seen later, exert a profound influence on intermediate metabolism. Although the perfusion technique has been employed infrequently in recent years, its importance as a method for the study of intermediate metabolism in whole organs is now receiving renewed recognition.

Use of Various Tissue Preparations

Once a given organ or tissue has been implicated as the site of a biochemical transformation, this process may be investigated more closely by the use of tissue slices. When very thin slices of an organ are sus-

[20] D. W. Woolley, A Study of Antimetabolites, John Wiley & Sons, New York, 1952.

pended in an appropriate physiological saline solution, they will generally survive long enough to metabolize a chemical substance that has been added to the suspension fluid, and the fate of the added substance may be determined if suitable analytical procedures are available. An account of the techniques for the preparation and handling of tissue slices may be found in the book by Umbreit et al.[21] and the article by Elliott.[22] An important shortcoming of the tissue slice technique is the uncertainty whether the test compound can enter the cells of the slices. Thus failure to observe appreciable chemical conversion of a substance, when it is incubated with tissue slices, does not in itself prove that the substance is not an active metabolite in the cells of that organ; it may merely mean that the penetration of the substance into the cells did not occur, or was extremely slow.

Significant data about intermediate metabolism have also been gained from the use of tissue minces and homogenates, in which the cellular organization and even the individual cells have been largely destroyed. In particular, much work has been done with cell-free homogenates which essentially consist of suspensions of the solid components of protoplasm (mitochondria, microsomes, nuclear material, etc.) in a solution containing the soluble components of the cell. A discussion of the homogenate technique may be found in the book of Umbreit et al.[21] The work of Claude, Schneider, and others has provided methods for the separation, by differential centrifugation, of some of the particulate components of homogenates, and these have also been used to obtain important results on metabolic reactions performed by the enzymes present in these cellular constituents.[23]

Although many of the important enzymes of cells appear to be bound to the insoluble components found in homogenates, decisive data about intermediate metabolism may also be obtained by means of extracts containing the soluble components. Such cell-free extracts may be considered to represent solutions of enzymes present in the cells, but the natural morphological relationship among these enzymes has been completely destroyed. This places a serious limitation on the interpretation of the results obtained in terms of the chemical process that occurs in the intact cell; nevertheless, the study of the chemical reactions of which such extracts are capable has been of the greatest

[21] W. W. Umbreit et al., *Manometric Techniques and Tissue Metabolism,* 2nd Ed., Burgess Publishing Co., Minneapolis, 1949.

[22] K. A. C. Elliott, in S. P. Colowick and N. O. Kaplan, *Methods in Enzymology,* Vol. I, Academic Press, New York, 1955.

[23] A. L. Dounce, in J. B. Sumner and K. Myrbäck, *The Enzymes,* Vol. I, Academic Press, New York, 1950; E. L. Kuff and G. H. Hogeboom, in O. H. Gaebler, *Enzymes: Units of Biological Structure and Function,* Academic Press, New York, 1956.

value for the progress of biochemistry. These studies lead naturally to attempts to isolate, and to purify, the constituent enzymes. A study of the properties of the individual enzymes, and of their relationship to one another in coupled reactions, then can serve as the basis for the development of working hypotheses to explain the manner in which the enzymes cooperate in the intact cell.

It would be pointless to single out any one of the available experimental techniques for the study of intermediate metabolism as being uniquely sufficient for the elucidation of the chemical fate of a given chemical substance in a particular organism. Rather, each of the methods contributes importantly to such studies, and frequently data obtained by different techniques reinforce one another and thus become more meaningful. Furthermore, the several techniques can, in many instances, be combined; thus the isotope technique has been applied to good advantage, not only to metabolic experiments with intact animals, plants, or microorganisms, but also to studies with tissue homogenates, cell extracts, and specific enzyme systems prepared from these biological forms.

17 ·

Chemistry
of the
Carbohydrates

Before discussing the intermediate metabolism of the carbohydrates it is desirable to review briefly some of the salient features of the chemistry of this class of biochemical constituents. Valuable reference books on structural carbohydrate chemistry have been prepared by Percival[1] and by Pigman.[2]

The carbohydrates, as their name implies, are compounds composed of carbon, hydrogen, and oxygen, although, as will be seen later, certain members of this group also contain nitrogen or sulfur. In general, the substances belonging to this class of compounds may be divided into three broad categories. The first of these includes the so-called monosaccharides, among which are five-carbon compounds such as the pentoses (D-ribose is an example) and six-carbon compounds such as the hexoses (e.g., D-glucose). The second group of carbohydrates may be designated "oligosaccharides," which are composed of two or more monosaccharide units linked to one another through glycosidic linkage. Examples of oligosaccharides are sucrose (a disaccharide) and raffinose (a trisaccharide). No sharp line of distinction can be drawn between the oligosaccharides and the third group of carbohydrates, the polysaccharides, which represent large aggregates of monosaccharide units, joined through glycosidic bonds; the polysaccharides contain a great many of these units and, therefore, are substances of appreciable molecular weight.

Monosaccharides

Perhaps the most important of the known monosaccharides is D-glucose. It is found as such in the blood of all animals and in the sap of plants;

[1] E. G. V. Percival, *Structural Carbohydrate Chemistry,* Prentice-Hall, Inc., Englewood Cliffs, N. J., 1950.

[2] W. Pigman, *The Carbohydrates,* Academic Press, New York, 1957.

it also forms the structural unit of the most important polysaccharides. The work of Emil Fischer and others showed that D-glucose exists in solution largely in the form of a ring compound which is in equilibrium with a small amount of the corresponding open-chain form. The ring

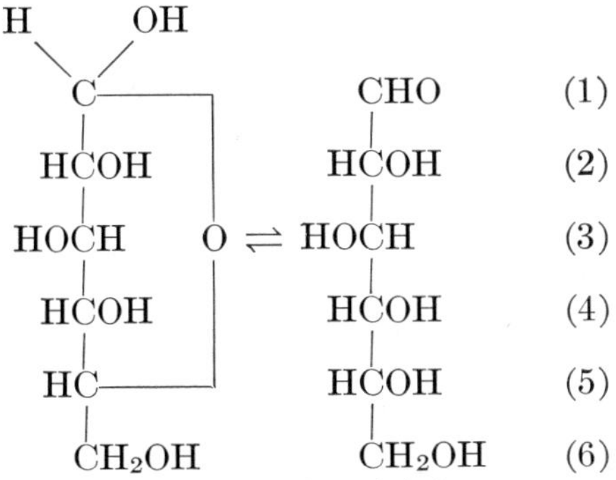

$$
\begin{array}{c}
\overset{\displaystyle H\qquad OH}{\underset{\displaystyle}{\diagdown\diagup}} \\
\end{array}
$$

C————	CHO	(1)
HCOH │	HCOH	(2)
HOCH O ⇌	HOCH	(3)
HCOH │	HCOH	(4)
HC————	HCOH	(5)
CH₂OH	CH₂OH	(6)

Pyranose form   Open-chain form
of D-glucose   of D-glucose

in this cyclic form of glucose is related to the heterocyclic compound pyrane, and is termed a "pyranose" ring. It will be noted that the open-chain form of D-glucose has 4 asymmetric carbon atoms and the cyclic form will be seen to have five centers of asymmetry. By convention, the assignment of the configuration of glucose and of other monosaccharides depends on the configuration about the highest-numbered asymmetric carbon atom. If the configuration about this carbon is the same as that in D-glyceraldehyde (cf. p. 79), the monosaccharide is designated a D-sugar. The enantiomorph of the D-sugar is related to L-glyceraldehyde in the same manner.

Since the open-chain formula of glucose has 4 asymmetric carbon atoms, it follows that there are 16 possible isomers of this sugar. Of the 8 isomers belonging to the D-series, 7 differ from D-glucose in the configuration about carbon atoms 2, 3, and 4; the names assigned to these isomers are given in Table 1, which presents the configurational relationships of the D-series of sugars. An excellent discussion of the stereochemistry of sugars may be found in the article by Hudson.[3]

The formation of the pyranose ring in the cyclization of a hexose introduces a fifth center of asymmetry at carbon atom 1. When the hydroxyl group of the cyclic D-glucose is *cis-* to the hydroxyl group at carbon atom 2, the compound is termed α-D-glucopyranose; if these 2 hydroxyl groups are *trans-* to one another, the compound is β-D-glucopyranose.

In 1927 Haworth proposed a valuable method for representing the cyclic forms of sugars; according to this method, α-D-glucopyranose is

[3] C. S. Hudson, *Advances in Carbohydrate Chem.*, **3**, 1 (1948).

Table I. Configurational Relationships of the D-Sugars

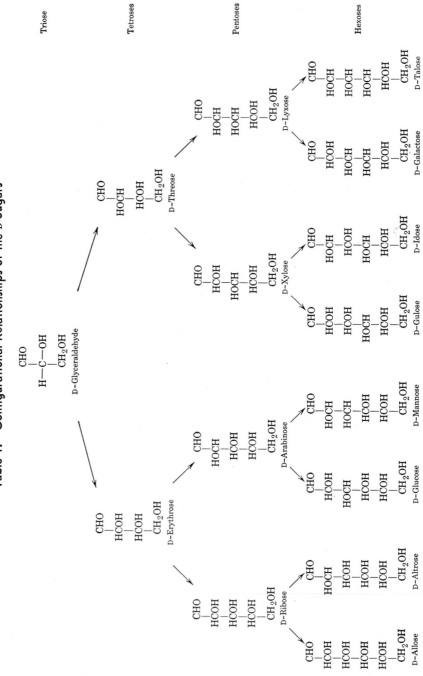

written as shown in the accompanying formulae. The plane of the
pyranose ring is considered to be perpendicular to that of the page on
which it is written, with the substituents above or below the plane of
the ring. In practice, the carbon atoms of the ring and the hydrogen
atoms are omitted, as shown in structure A; the formula also may be
inverted, as in structure B. Comparison of the Haworth formulation of
α-D-glucopyranose with that shown previously (cf. p. 403) might suggest,
at first glance, a discrepancy between the two. The reason for this may

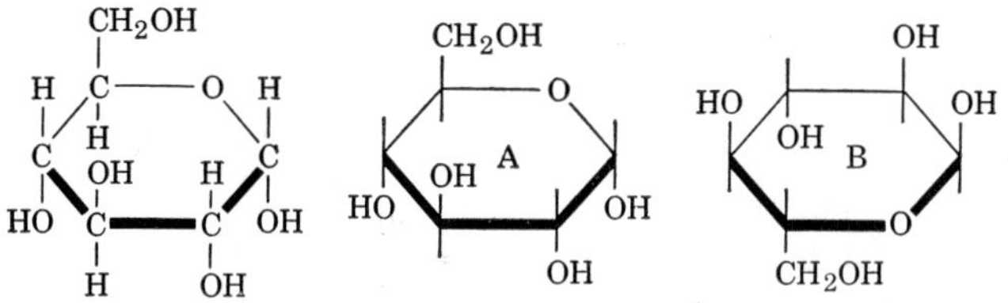

α-D-Glucopyranose

best be visualized by means of atomic models, but may also be appreciated by a consideration of the effect of bringing the ring oxygen atom
into the plane of the ring carbon atoms. This operation involves the
rotation of the bond between carbon 5 and the ring oxygen through
more than a right angle and therefore brings the hydrogen atom attached
to carbon 5 below the plane of the ring.

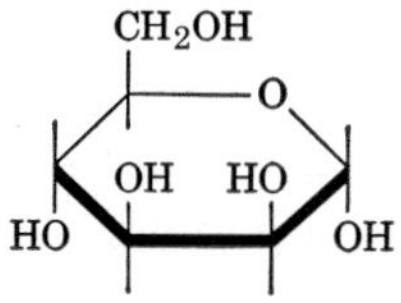

α-D-Mannopyranose 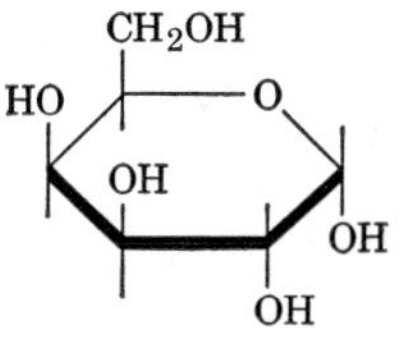   α-D-Galactopyranose

The other aldohexoses of greatest biochemical interest are D-mannose,
which is found in nature as a constituent of certain polysaccharides and
of glycoproteins, and differs from glucose in its configuration about carbon atom 2; and D-galactose, which is a component of the disaccharide
lactose (from milk) and of several polysaccharides, and differs from
glucose in its configuration about carbon 4.

The configuration about carbon atom 1 in the cyclic aldohexoses is
not stable but can readily pass from the α- to the β-form when the sugar
is put into solution. This is a consequence of the fact that the structure
about carbon 1 in the ring compound is that of an hemiacetal, and,
as mentioned earlier, in solution the ring compound is in equilibrium
with the open-chain aldehydic form. The open-chain form can be converted into either the α- or the β-form of the ring compound. When

α-D-glucopyranose is dissolved in water, it first shows a rotation of $[\alpha]_D^{20} = +112°$, but this value slowly falls to $+53°$ (Table 2). This change in rotation is termed "mutarotation," and is due to the establishment of the equilibrium between the α- and β-forms of the ring

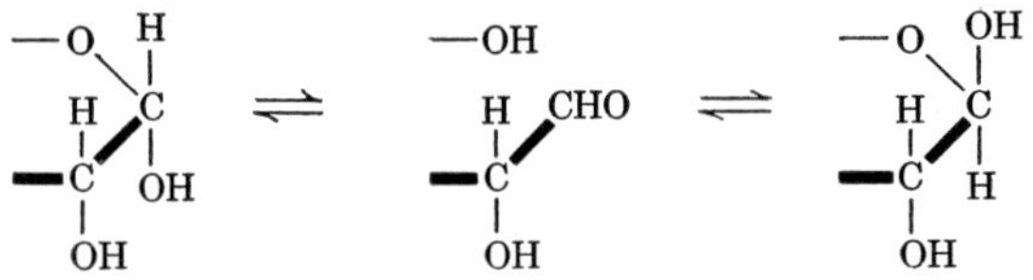

compound. A synthetic sample of β-D-glucopyranose has an initial $[\alpha]_D^{20}$ of $+19°$; hence the equilibrium in the mutarotation of D-glucose corresponds to a mixture of 36 per cent of the α-form and 64 per cent of the β-form. The rate of mutarotation is increased by the addition

Table 2. Optical Rotation of Some Sugars

Where two values are given for the α- or β-form of a sugar, the value after the arrow denotes the rotation of the equilibrium mixture formed by mutarotation. The rotations of nonreducing sugars are enclosed in brackets.

Sugar, grams per 100 ml H_2O	$[\alpha]_D^{20}$ α-Form	β-Form
D-Glucose (4)	$+112.2 \rightarrow +52.7$	$+18.7 \rightarrow +52.7$
D-Galactose (4)	$+150.7 \rightarrow +80.2$	$+52.8 \rightarrow +80.2$
D-Mannose (4)	$+29.3 \rightarrow +14.2$	$-17.0 \rightarrow +14.2$
D-Fructose (4)		$-132.2 \rightarrow -92.4$
L-Arabinose (4)		$+190.6 \rightarrow +104.5$
D-Ribose (4)	$-23.1 \rightarrow -23.7$	
D-Xylose (4)	$+93.6 \rightarrow +18.8$	
L-Fucose (4)	$-152.6 \rightarrow -75.9$	
Maltose $\cdot H_2O$ (4)		$+111.7 \rightarrow +130.4$
Cellobiose (8)		$+14.2 \rightarrow +34.6$
Lactose $\cdot H_2O$ (8)	$+85.0 \rightarrow +52.6$	
Melibiose $\cdot 2H_2O$ (4)		$+111.7 \rightarrow +129.5$
Sucrose (26)	[+66.53]	
Trehalose (7)	[+178.3]	
Raffinose (4)	[+105.2]	

of dilute acid or alkali. 2-Hydroxypyridine is an effective catalyst of mutarotation; its action appears to involve simultaneous acid and base catalysis (cf. p. 280). An enzyme (mutarotase), present in extracts of the mold *Penicillium notatum* and of some animal tissues (kidney, liver), also catalyzes the mutarotation of glucose.[4]

Since the ring forms of the sugars are in equilibrium with the cor-

[4] D. Keilin and E. F. Hartree, *Biochem. J.*, **50**, 341 (1952); A. S. Keston, *Science*, **120**, 355 (1954).

responding open-chain aldehydic forms, a suitable aldehyde reagent will react with the sugar and remove the open-chain form from the equilibrium. This permits the oxidation of glucose and of other aldoses by means of Fehling's solution (an alkaline solution of copper sulfate plus sodium potassium tartrate) ; the cupric ion is reduced to the cuprous form and appears as the red cuprous oxide. There are several modifications of Fehling's solution (e.g., Benedict's solution—an aqueous solution of copper sulfate, sodium citrate, and sodium carbonate). The reduction of cupric ions by glucose provides the basis for several excellent quantitative methods for the analysis of this substance in biological materials, such as blood. One of these is the procedure devised by Somogyi,[5] in which the cuprous ion formed on reduction is allowed to react with iodine, and the unreacted iodine is determined by titration with standard thiosulfate. These methods are not specific for glucose but will, in general, measure the total reducing capacity of the test sample. In addition to their oxidation by cupric ion, the reducing sugars can also be oxidized by the ferricyanide ion, which is reduced to ferrocyanide (Hagedorn-Jensen method). The reaction of aldohexoses with alkaline hypoiodite ($NaIO$), followed by an iodometric titration, provides the basis for still another analytical procedure (Willstätter-Schudel method). The flavoprotein notatin (p. 339), which is specific for β-D-glucopyranose, can be used for the enzymic determination of this hexose.

On treatment with strong acids, aldohexoses give rise to hydroxymethylfurfural, which, on further heating, is converted to levulinic acid.[6]

$$\begin{array}{c} CH\!\!-\!\!-\!\!CH \\ \parallel \quad \parallel \\ HOCH_2\!\!-\!\!C \quad\ C\,-\!CHO \\ \diagdown \ \diagup \\ O \end{array}$$

$$CH_3COCH_2CH_2COOH$$

Hydroxymethylfurfural   Levulinic acid

Hydroxymethylfurfural and the parent substance, furfural (formed by the treatment of aldopentoses with acid), react with a variety of compounds [α-naphthol, resorcinol, orcinol[7] (5-methylresorcinol), diphenylamine, benzidine, skatole, indole, etc.] to form colored products. Thus the Molisch reaction involves the treatment of a sugar with sulfuric acid, followed by the addition of a solution of α-naphthol. Another useful reagent is anthrone (see p. 408) ; after treatment with acid, a blue color is given by glucose, by other monosaccharides, and by oligo- and polysaccharides upon the addition of this reagent.[8]

[5] M. Somogyi, *J. Biol. Chem.*, **70**, 599 (1926) ; N. Nelson, *ibid.*, **153**, 375 (1944).

[6] F. H. Newth, *Advances in Carbohydrate Chem.*, **6**, 83 (1951).

[7] J. Brückner, *Biochem. J.*, **60**, 200 (1955).

[8] D. L. Morris, *Science*, **107**, 254 (1948).

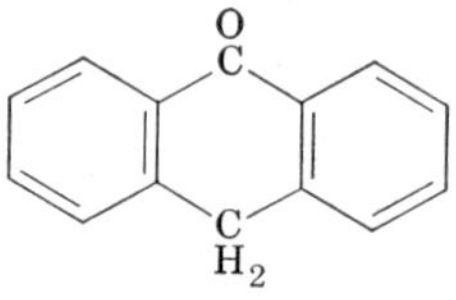

Anthrone

One of the most useful means for the characterization of the mono-saccharides was discovered by Emil Fischer in 1884 and involves the reaction of sugars such as glucose with phenylhydrazine to form crystal-line "osazones."[9]   Since D-mannose differs from D-glucose only in the configuration about carbon 2, the osazone formed from mannose is identical with that from glucose.   The osazone of D-galactose is a diastereo-isomer of glucosazone.

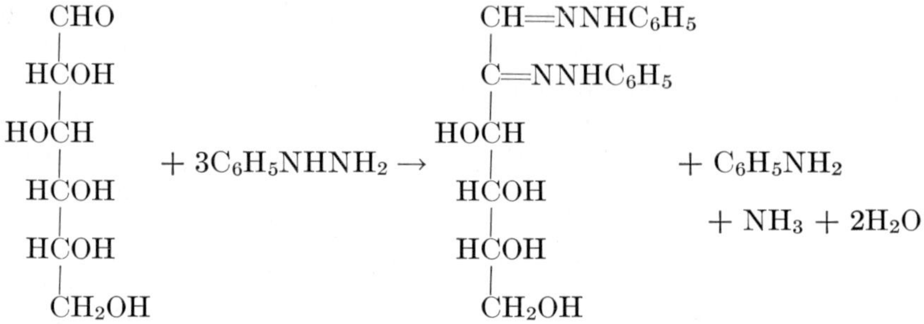

$$
\begin{array}{ccc}
\text{CHO} & & \text{CH}\!=\!\text{NNHC}_6\text{H}_5 \\
| & & | \\
\text{HCOH} & & \text{C}\!=\!\text{NNHC}_6\text{H}_5 \\
| & & | \\
\text{HOCH} & + 3\text{C}_6\text{H}_5\text{NHNH}_2 \rightarrow & \text{HOCH} \qquad + \text{C}_6\text{H}_5\text{NH}_2 \\
| & & | \\
\text{HCOH} & & \text{HCOH} \qquad + \text{NH}_3 + 2\text{H}_2\text{O} \\
| & & | \\
\text{HCOH} & & \text{HCOH} \\
| & & | \\
\text{CH}_2\text{OH} & & \text{CH}_2\text{OH} \\
\text{Glucose} & & \text{Glucosazone}
\end{array}
$$

If glucose is heated with methanol in the presence of HCl, the hydroxyl group on carbon 1 is substituted and a methylglucoside is obtained. Clearly, two such derivatives are possible; they are designated α-methyl-D-glucoside and β-methyl-D-glucoside respectively.   A more precise

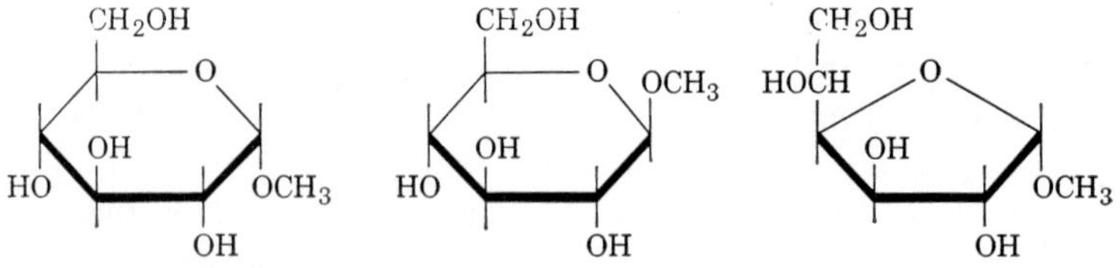

α-Methyl-D-glucoside   β-Methyl-D-glucoside   α-Methyl-D-glucofuranoside

designation of the α-methyl-D-glucoside so formed would be α-methyl-D-glucopyranoside, since the latter name specifies the nature of the ring. This designation is important, since treatment of glucose with methanol and HCl in the cold yields a glucoside in which the pyranose ring is replaced by the five-membered ring related to furane.   As may be seen

[9] E. G. V. Percival, *Advances in Carbohydrate Chem.*, **3**, 23 (1948).

from the formula for α-methyl-D-glucofuranoside, this type of ring formation involves the hydroxyl group at carbon 4, instead of carbon 5 as in the pyranosides. Analogous furanosides may be obtained from other monosaccharides.

Methylglucoside is perhaps the simplest example of a large group of substances in which the hydroxyl of the hemiacetal group at carbon 1 of a monosaccharide has been condensed with the hydroxyl group of an alcohol. Such derivatives are termed glycosides, and the linkage which joins the sugar to the alcohol is termed a glycosidic bond. The participation of the potential reducing group of a sugar in a glycosidic linkage abolishes its capacity to react with phenylhydrazine or with Fehling's solution, and the configuration of the ring compound is stabilized in either the α- or the β-form. When a glycosidic bond involves the union of two monosaccharides, a disaccharide results, and, when many monosaccharide units are joined in a linear array by means of glycosidic bonds, the resulting product is a polysaccharide. The glycosidic linkage occupies a place in carbohydrate chemistry analogous to the role of the peptide bond in protein chemistry.

Of the 8 D-aldohexoses listed on p. 404, only glucose, mannose, and galactose have been found in nature; the other 5 isomers have been synthesized, but have not been identified in biological material. Another important hexose found in nature is the ketohexose fructose, which has

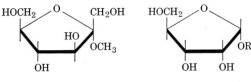

α-Methyl-D-fructofuranoside α-D-Ribofuranoside

a reducing group at carbon 2. The open-chain form of this hexose is in equilibrium with the corresponding pyranose and furanose forms; in solutions of the free sugar, the pyranose form predominates. However, when fructose participates in glycosidic linkage, as in the disaccharide sucrose (cf. p. 415), it is present in the furanose form. Fructose is found as such in seminal fluid,[10] and is a constituent of the polysaccharide inulin. Fructose can reduce cupric ions and reacts with phenylhydrazine to give the same osazone as that obtained from glucose and mannose. A ketohexose related to fructose is L-sorbose. Other naturally occurring ketoses are the seven-carbon sugars (ketoheptoses) D-mannoheptulose, found in the avocado, and D-sedoheptulose, found in plants of the *Sedum* family.

[10] T. Mann, *The Biochemistry of Semen*, Methuen and Co., London, 1954.

$$
\begin{array}{cccc}
\text{CH}_2\text{OH} & \text{CH}_2\text{OH} & \text{CH}_2\text{OH} & \text{CH}_2\text{OH} \\
| & | & | & | \\
\text{C}{=}\text{O} & \text{C}{=}\text{O} & \text{C}{=}\text{O} & \text{C}{=}\text{O} \\
| & | & | & | \\
\text{HOCH} & \text{HOCH} & \text{HOCH} & \text{HOCH} \\
| & | & | & | \\
\text{HCOH} & \text{HCOH} & \text{HOCH} & \text{HCOH} \\
| & | & | & | \\
\text{HCOH} & \text{HOCH} & \text{HCOH} & \text{HCOH} \\
| & | & | & | \\
\text{CH}_2\text{OH} & \text{CH}_2\text{OH} & \text{HCOH} & \text{HCOH} \\
 & & | & | \\
 & & \text{CH}_2\text{OH} & \text{CH}_2\text{OH} \\
\text{D-Fructose} & \text{L-Sorbose} & \text{D-Mannoheptulose} & \text{D-Sedoheptulose}
\end{array}
$$

A number of pentoses have been found in nature; perhaps the most important of these is D-ribose, a constituent of ribonucleic acids and of several nucleotides (ATP, DPN, etc.). The free sugar is largely in the pyranose form, but in glycosides ribose is present as a furanoside (p. 409). The closely related 2-deoxy-D-ribose, a constituent of deoxypentose nucleic acids (p. 191), also participates in glycosidic linkage as a furanoside. The natural occurrence of 5-methylthio-D-ribose was mentioned on p. 206. Two other aldopentoses that occur in nature are D-xylose (a constituent of plant polysaccharides), which differs from D-ribose in its configuration about carbon atom 3, and L-arabinose (found in combined form in various plant products), which differs from L-ribose in its configuration about carbon 2. The ketopentoses analogous to D-ribose and D-xylose are named D-ribulose and D-xylulose respectively.

$$
\begin{array}{cccc}
\text{CH}_2\text{OH} & \text{CHO} & \text{CH}_2\text{OH} & \text{CHO} \\
| & | & | & | \\
\text{C}{=}\text{O} & \text{HCOH} & \text{C}{=}\text{O} & \text{HCOH} \\
| & | & | & | \\
\text{HCOH} & \text{HOCH} & \text{HOCH} & \text{HOCH} \\
| & | & | & | \\
\text{HCOH} & \text{HCOH} & \text{HCOH} & \text{HOCH} \\
| & | & | & | \\
\text{CH}_2\text{OH} & \text{CH}_2\text{OH} & \text{CH}_2\text{OH} & \text{CH}_2\text{OH} \\
\text{D-Ribulose} & \text{D-Xylose} & \text{D-Xylulose} & \text{L-Arabinose}
\end{array}
$$

Several methylpentoses are found as constituents of plant products; among these are 6-deoxy-D-glucose (present as a glycoside in the bark of many species of *Cinchona*), L-fucose (found in bound form in marine algae and also in some mammalian polysaccharides), and L-rhamnose (present as a glycoside in various plant materials). The occurrence of L-fucose as an important constituent of the type specific human blood-group substances (p. 428) is of special interest.

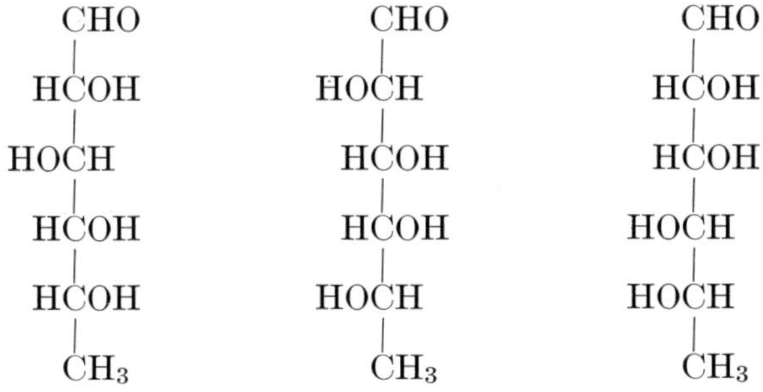

$$
\begin{array}{ccc}
\text{CHO} & \text{CHO} & \text{CHO} \\
| & | & | \\
\text{HCOH} & \text{HOCH} & \text{HCOH} \\
| & | & | \\
\text{HOCH} & \text{HCOH} & \text{HCOH} \\
| & | & | \\
\text{HCOH} & \text{HCOH} & \text{HOCH} \\
| & | & | \\
\text{HCOH} & \text{HOCH} & \text{HOCH} \\
| & | & | \\
\text{CH}_3 & \text{CH}_3 & \text{CH}_3 \\
\text{6-Deoxy-D-glucose} & \text{L-Fucose} & \text{L-Rhamnose}
\end{array}
$$

Oxidation of the reducing group at position 1 of glucopyranose gives gluconolactone (probably a δ-lactone), which is hydrolyzed to gluconic acid; as was seen earlier, this oxidation is catalyzed by enzymes such as glucose oxidase (notatin). Another oxidation product of D-glucose, found as a constituent of certain polysaccharides and as an excretion product in animals, is glucuronic acid, formed by oxidation of the CH_2OH in the 6 position to a carboxyl group. An analogous uronic acid is obtained from galactose and is termed galacturonic acid; it is found as a constituent of fruit pectins. Another uronic acid found in nature is mannuronic acid, derived from mannose and found in polysaccharides of brown marine algae. The lactones derived from the uronic acids usually are γ-lactones.

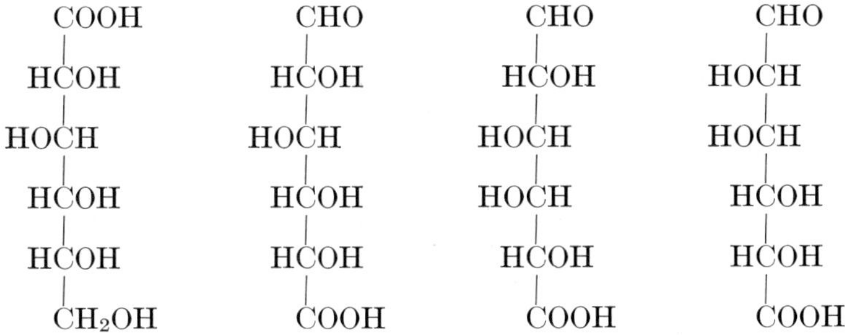

$$
\begin{array}{cccc}
\text{COOH} & \text{CHO} & \text{CHO} & \text{CHO} \\
| & | & | & | \\
\text{HCOH} & \text{HCOH} & \text{HCOH} & \text{HOCH} \\
| & | & | & | \\
\text{HOCH} & \text{HOCH} & \text{HOCH} & \text{HOCH} \\
| & | & | & | \\
\text{HCOH} & \text{HCOH} & \text{HOCH} & \text{HCOH} \\
| & | & | & | \\
\text{HCOH} & \text{HCOH} & \text{HCOH} & \text{HCOH} \\
| & | & | & | \\
\text{CH}_2\text{OH} & \text{COOH} & \text{COOH} & \text{COOH} \\
\text{D-Gluconic} & \text{D-Glucuronic} & \text{D-Galacturonic} & \text{D-Mannuronic} \\
\text{acid} & \text{acid} & \text{acid} & \text{acid}
\end{array}
$$

Mild reduction of the monosaccharides leads to the formation of polyhydroxy alcohols in which the reducing group (CHO or CO) of the sugar has been replaced by an alcohol group. Among the compounds of this type are several naturally occurring hexahydric alcohols related to the hexoses (see Lohmar and Goepp[11]). Thus D-mannitol is an important constituent of brown algae, and D-sorbitol is found in many fruits. It will be recalled that in riboflavin the sugar residue is derived

[11] R. Lohmar and R. M. Goepp, Jr., Advances in Carbohydrate Chem., 4, 211 (1949).

from a pentahydric alcohol related to D-ribose, and therefore is termed D-ribitol (cf. p. 330).

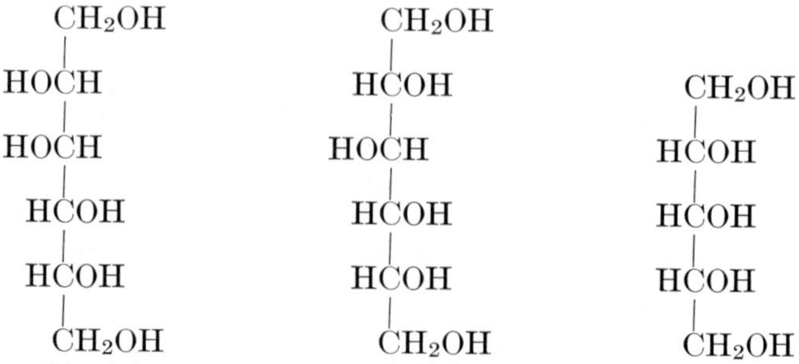

D-Mannitol   D-Sorbitol   D-Ribitol

Closely related to the hexahydric straight-chain alcohols are the cyclic inositols (see Fletcher[12]). The most important of the isomeric inositols is the optically inactive *meso*-inositol (also called *myo*-inositol), which is

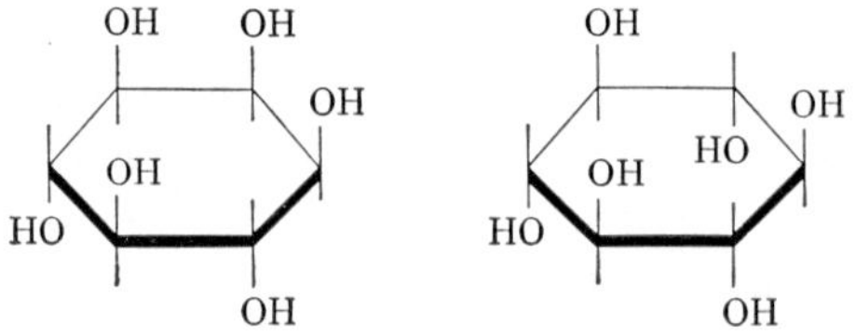

meso-Inositol   Scyllitol

widely distributed among plants and animals; it is present in large amounts (ca. 1 gram per 100 ml) in boar semen.[10] Another of the isomeric inositols (scyllitol) has been identified as a constituent of dogfish liver and cartilage and of several plants.

An important derivative of D-glucose is the amino sugar 2-amino-2-deoxy-D-glucose, usually termed D-glucosamine, a component of several polysaccharides (cf. p. 423). Another amino sugar that is a structural unit of certain polysaccharides is galactosamine or chondrosamine

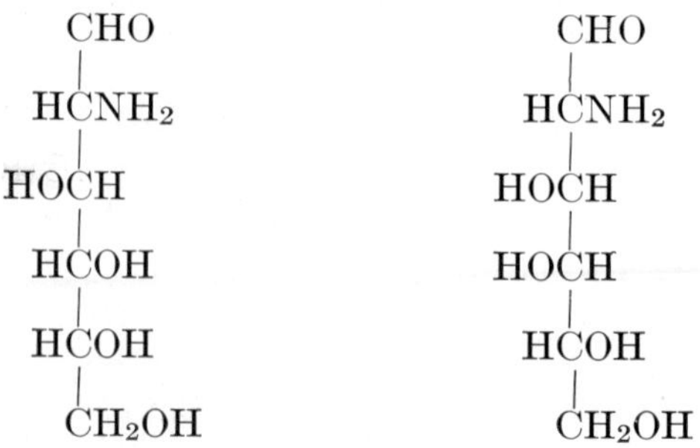

D-Glucosamine   D-Galactosamine

[12] H. G. Fletcher, Jr., *Advances in Carbohydrate Chem.*, **3**, 45 (1948).

(2-amino-2-deoxy-D-galactose). Glucosamine and galactosamine may be determined colorimetrically by treatment with acetylacetone, followed by the addition of p-dimethylaminobenzaldehyde.[13] These two amino sugars occur in polysaccharides in the form of their N-acetyl derivatives, which can also be determined by a colorimetric method.[14] Valuable reviews on the chemistry of the 2-amino sugars have been prepared by Foster and Stacey[15] and by Kent and Whitehouse.[16] It may be added that a 3-amino sugar (3-amino-3-deoxy-D-ribose) has been shown to be a constituent of the antibiotic puromycin (p. 206), and that N-methyl-L-glucosamine is a constituent of the antibiotic streptomycin.

Many of the monosaccharides mentioned above have been isolated from biological sources not only as such, but also in the form of phosphoric acid esters. Since the work of Harden and Young (ca. 1910), who identified fructose-1,6-diphosphate as an intermediate in the fermentation of glucose by yeast, numerous other sugar phosphates have been found in nature. As will be seen from the later discussion of the metabolic pathways in the breakdown and synthesis of carbohydrates, phosphorylated derivatives of several monosaccarides (glucose, galactose, mannose, fructose, ribose, glucosamine, etc.) are important intermediates in carbohydrate metabolism.

As with other compounds of biochemical interest, the separation, identification, and estimation of monosaccharides (and their derivatives) have been notably furthered by the introduction of chromatographic techniques.[17] For paper chromatography (p. 116), a variety of solvents (e.g., phenol-water) has been used, and the chromatograms are sprayed with a reagent such as an ammoniacal solution of silver nitrate (reduction to silver); another type of reagent depends on the reaction of aromatic amines (e.g., aniline) or phenols (e.g., orcinol) with furfural derivatives produced on treatment of sugars with acid (cf. p. 407). Sugar phosphates may be identified on paper chromatograms by treatment with an acid solution of ammonium molybdate to hydrolyze the ester and to form the blue phosphomolybdate.[18] In chromatographic studies, advantage has been taken of the formation of a complex ion between a molecule of boric acid and two neighboring cis-hydroxyl groups;[19] if a sugar has such a structure, its R_F value (cf. p. 118) in a

[13] C. J. M. Rondle and W. T. J. Morgan, $Biochem. J.$, **61**, 586 (1955).

[14] J. L. Reissig et al., $J. Biol. Chem.$, **217**, 959 (1955).

[15] A. B. Foster and M. Stacey, $Advances in Carbohydrate Chem.$, **7**, 247 (1952).

[16] P. W. Kent and M. W. Whitehouse, $Biochemistry of the Amino Sugars$, Butterworth's Scientific Publications, London, 1955.

[17] F. A. Isherwood, $Brit. Med. Bull.$, **10**, 202 (1954); G. N. Kowkabany, $Advances in Carbohydrate Chem.$, **9**, 303 (1954); W. W. Binkley, $ibid.$, **10**, 55 (1955).

[18] C. S. Hanes and F. A. Isherwood, $Nature$, **164**, 1107 (1949).

[19] C. A. Zittle, $Advances in Enzymol.$, **12**, 493 (1951).

given solvent is markedly altered by the presence of boric acid. The chromatographic separation of sugars and their derivatives may be effected on columns of various adsorbents (carbon, fuller's earth clay), and is useful for the isolation and purification of relatively large quantities of material. With sugars that form boric acid complexes, anion-exchange resins (p. 122) can be used.

Oligosaccharides

As noted earlier, the oligosaccharides are glycosides in which a hydroxyl group of one monosaccharide has condensed with the reducing group of another. If two sugar units are joined in this manner, a disaccharide results; a linear array of three monosaccharides joined by glycosidic bonds is a trisaccharide, and so forth.

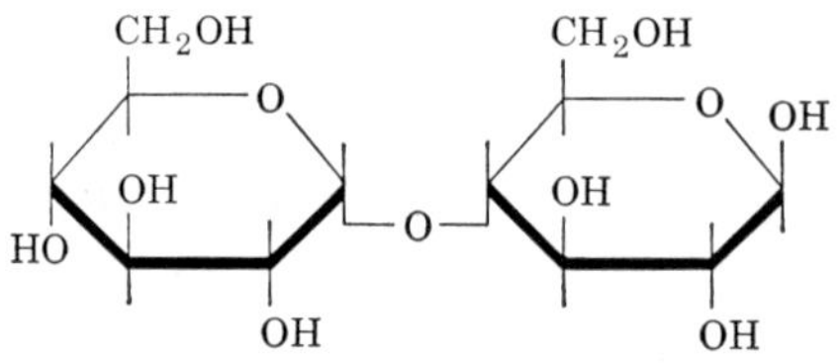

Maltose (β–form)

Among the disaccharides is the reducing sugar maltose, a product of the partial degradation of polysaccharides such as starch. In maltose one molecule of D-glucopyranose is joined through the hydroxyl group at carbon 1 by means of an α-glycosidic linkage to the hydroxyl located at carbon 4 of a second molecule of D-glucose. Maltose may therefore be termed 4-(α-D-glucopyranosyl)-D-glucopyranose. In the formula shown, the configuration about the reducing group is given as β, since this is the form in which maltose is usually obtained. As with other reducing sugars, a solution of the β-form shows mutarotation.

Although maltose is not found as such in nature, another disaccharide, D-lactose, occurs in the milk of mammals. On hydrolysis, lactose gives D-glucose and D-galactose; in the intact disaccharide, these two monosaccharides are also joined by means of a 1,4-glycosidic bond, the carbon 1 of galactose being linked to carbon 4 of glucose by an oxygen bridge. However, the configuration about carbon 1 of the galactose unit is β; hence lactose is a β-glycoside, and may be designated 4-(β-D-galactopyranosyl)-D-glucopyranose. In contrast to cow's milk, human milk contains, in addition to lactose, other oligosaccharides such as L-fucosyllactose, in which L-fucose (p. 411) is linked to the hydroxyl group at carbon 2 of the galactose residue.[20]

[20] D. J. Bell, *Ann. Reps.*, **52**, 333 (1956).

Another 1,4-β-glycoside of biochemical interest is cellobiose, a disaccharide formed on the degradation of the important polysaccharide cellulose. On hydrolysis, cellobiose yields D-glucose and may therefore be designated 4-(β-D-glucopyranosyl)-D-glucopyranose. Cellobiose and maltose are identical in structure except for the mode of linkage between the glucose units. The three disaccharides mentioned above (maltose,

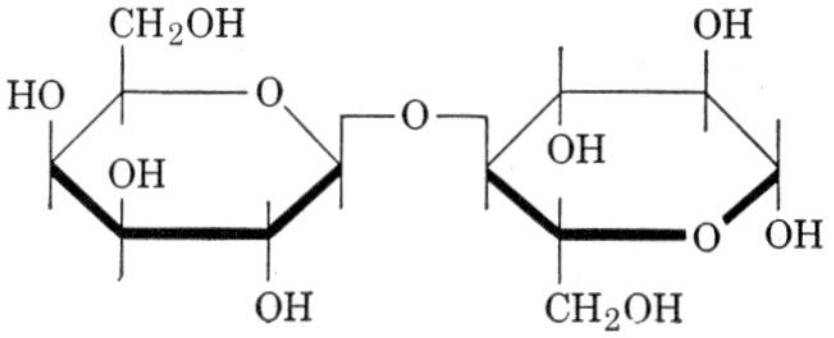

Lactose (β-form) 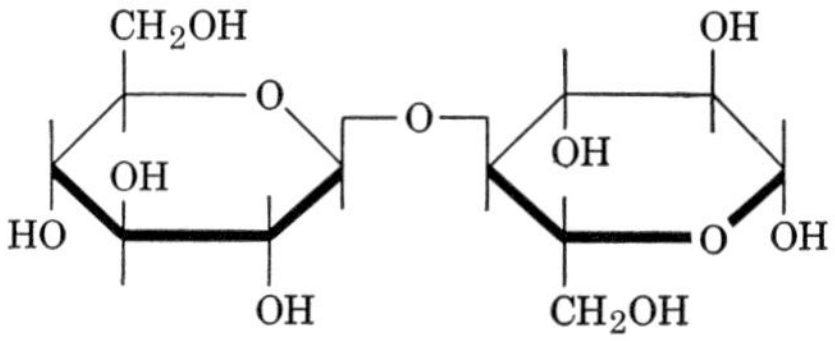   Cellobiose (β-form)

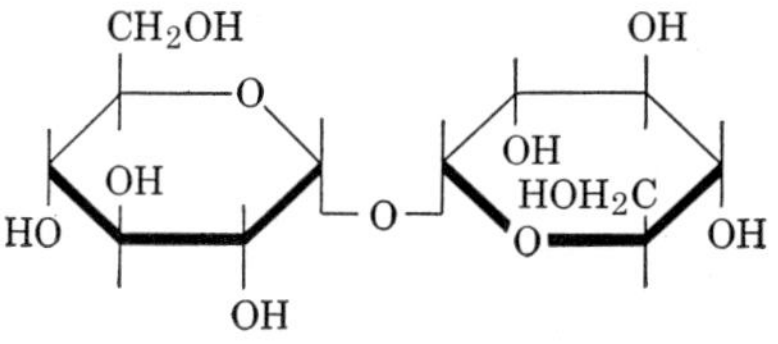

Trehalose 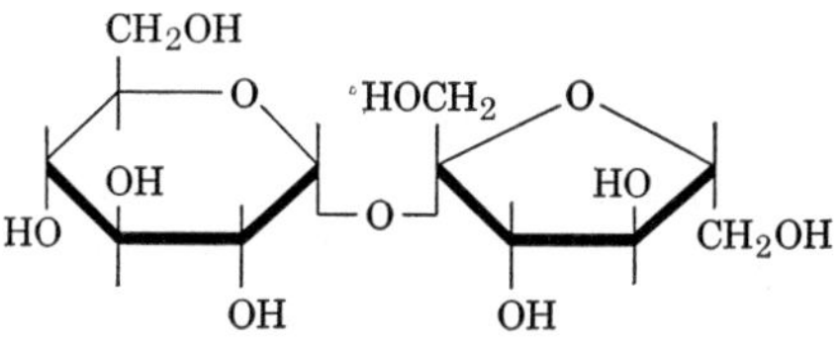   Sucrose

lactose, cellobiose) are all reducing sugars and form characteristic osazones. On the other hand, the disaccharide sucrose is not a reducing sugar, since the glycosidic bond involves the hydroxyl at carbon 1 of D-glucopyranose and the hydroxyl at carbon 2 of D-fructofuranose, thus blocking the reducing groups of both monosaccharides. Sucrose may be designated α-D-glucopyranosyl-β-D-fructofuranoside, as indicated in the formula. Sucrose is found as such in all photosynthetic plants, and is perhaps the most important of the low-molecular-weight carbohydrates in the natural diet of animals. The current world production of sucrose is approximately 35 million tons per year; one-third is made from sugar beets and two-thirds from sugar cane.

Another naturally occurring, nonreducing disaccharide is trehalose, found in fungi and yeasts, which has been formulated 1-(α-D-glucopyranosyl-α-D-glucopyranoside. Trehalose has been identified as the principal carbohydrate component of the blood (hemolymph) of a variety of insects.[21]

Among the other disaccharides of biochemical interest is gentiobiose, a constituent of the natural glycoside amygdalin (p. 416); gentiobiose is designated 6-(β-D-glucopyranosyl)-D-glucopyranose. Another disaccharide characterized by the presence of a 1,6-glycosidic bond is melibiose,

[21] G. R. Wyatt and G. F. Kalf, *J. Gen. Physiol.*, **40**, 833 (1957).

which is 6-(α-D-galactopyranosyl)-D-glucopyranose. Melibiose occurs in certain plant products (beet molasses, cottonseed hulls) as a constituent of the trisaccharide raffinose. Other disaccharides with 1,6-glycosidic

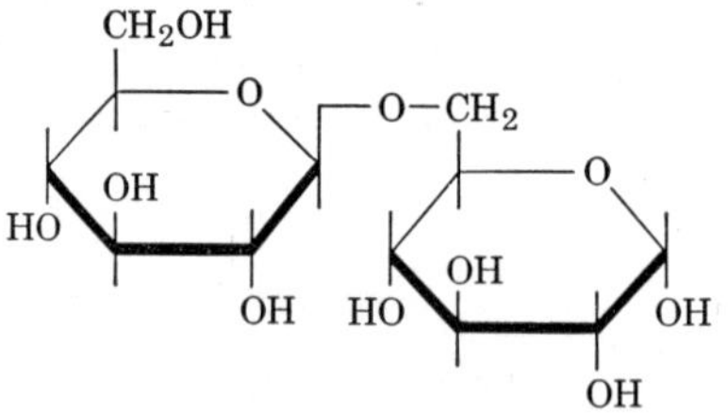

Gentiobiose (α-form)

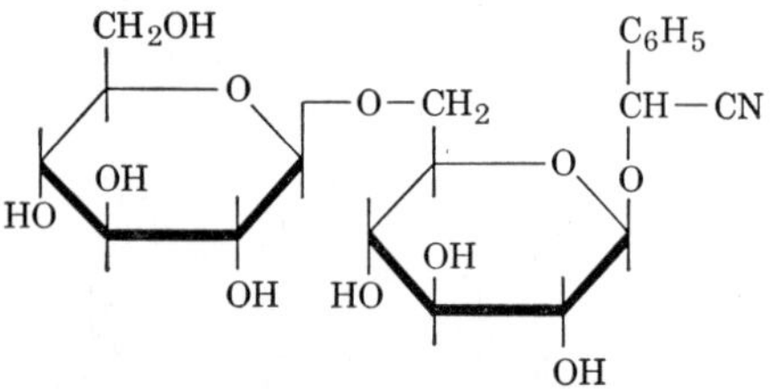

Amygdalin

linkages are primeverose (6-(β-D-xylopyranosyl)-D-glucopyranose), vicianose (6-(β-L-arabopyranosyl)-D-glucopyranose), and rutinose (6-(β-L-rhamnosyl)-D-glucopyranose).

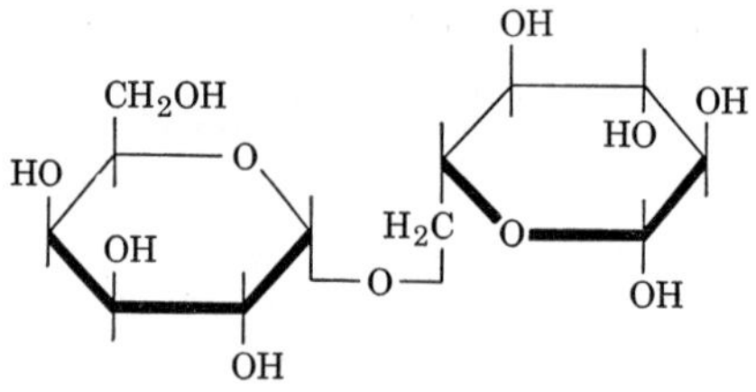

Melibiose (β-form)

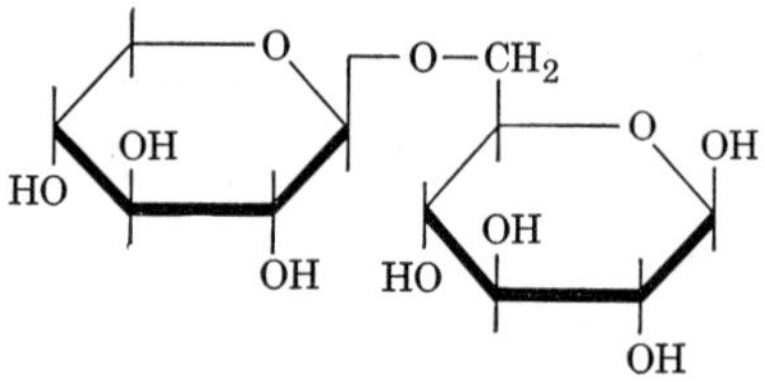

Primeverose (β-form)

The naturally occurring trisaccharides include the nonreducing sugar gentianose, composed of 2 molecules of glucose and 1 of fructose, and raffinose, which on hydrolysis yields glucose, fructose, and galactose. In

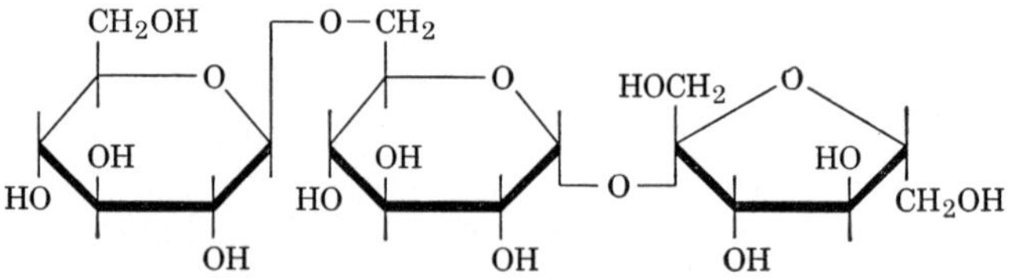

Gentianose

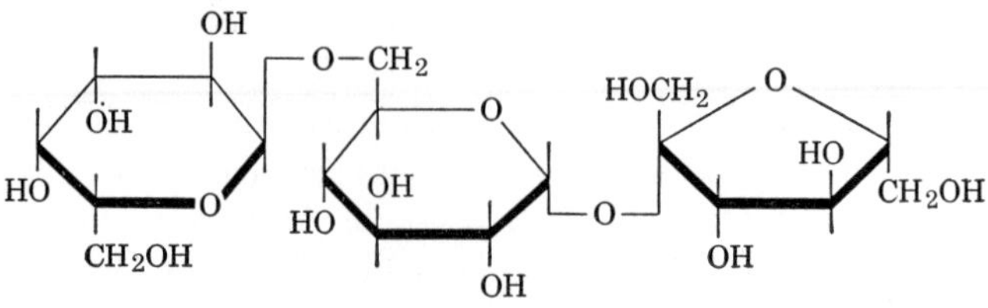

Raffinose

naming trisaccharides and higher oligosaccharides, the nature of each glycosidic bond is denoted as shown in the designation of raffinose as α-D-galactopyranosyl-$(1\rightarrow6)$-α-D-glucopyranosyl-$(1\rightarrow2)$-β-D-fructofuranoside. Gentianose and raffinose[22] have been isolated only from plants. It is noteworthy that the variety of oligosaccharides in the plant kingdom appears to be considerably greater than that found in the tissues of animals.

Polysaccharides

The polysaccharides may be separated roughly into two broad groups, the so-called "skeletal" or "structural" polysaccharides, which serve as rigid mechanical structures in plants and animals, and "nutrient" polysaccharides, which act as a metabolic reserve of monosaccharides in plants and animals. In addition to the substances that may readily be fitted into one or another of these two groups, there are still other polysaccharides, principally derived from bacteria and fungi.

Because of their importance in metabolism, the nutrient polysaccharides will be considered first. In plants the representatives of this group are the starches and inulin. The starches occur in the form of grains in many parts of plants and are especially abundant in embryonic tissues (e.g., potato tubers, or rice, wheat, or corn seeds) where they serve as reserve stores of carbohydrate for the nutrition of the developing plant. The starch grains of plants differ in size and shape and may be identified microscopically. Nearly all starches are composed of a mixture of two different kinds of polysaccharides, both of which yield D-glucose on complete hydrolysis, and are termed amyloses and amylopectins respectively. The amyloses give a deep-blue color with iodine, and the amylopectins give a red to purple color with this reagent. Potato starch contains about 20 per cent of the amylose component, and many other starches have a similar proportion of amylose; a notable exception is the starch of waxy corn, which is practically free of amylose. Methods are available for the separation of the amyloses and amylopectins from one another, and studies have been conducted on the mode of linkage of the glucose units in each type of polysaccharide.

Preparations of potato amylose may be fractionated into components which have particle weights ranging from about 4000 to 150,000, whereas the amyloses of seeds may contain components as large as 400,000. The amyloses are therefore inhomogeneous in composition. However, the mode of linkage of the monosaccharide units appears to be the same for all the components since enzymic hydrolysis (by glycosidases known as

[22] D. French, *Advances in Carbohydrate Chem.*, **9**, 149 (1954).

amylases) in all cases yields maltose as the principal product (p. 433). Since maltose is $\alpha(1\rightarrow4)$glucosylglucose, there must be present in amylose $\alpha(1\rightarrow4)$-glycosidic linkages.   Conclusive evidence that the glucose units of amylose are joined by such $(1\rightarrow4)$ bonds was obtained by means of the methylation technique developed by Haworth for the determination of the structure of oligo- and polysaccharides.   In this pro-

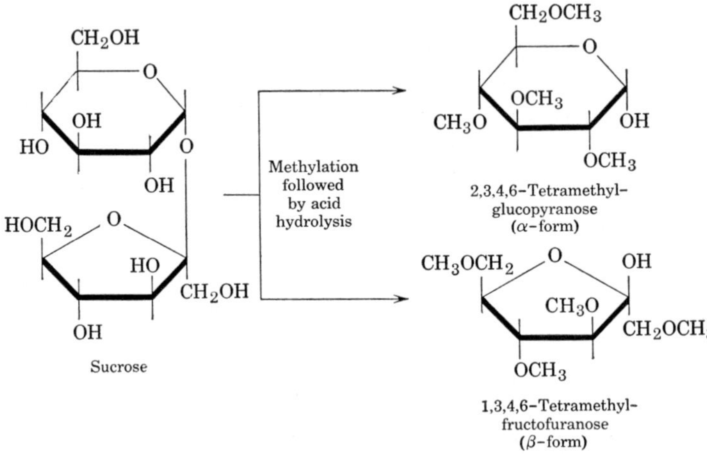

cedure the carbohydrate is treated with dimethyl sulfate $[(CH_3)_2SO_4]$, which reacts with the free hydroxyl groups to form ether groups $(-OCH_3)$ stable to hydrolysis with acid. For example, the methylation of sucrose gives an octamethylsucrose which on hydrolysis yields 2,3,4,6-tetramethylglucopyranose   and   1,3,4,6-tetramethylfructofuranose,   as shown. These products can arise only if the glycosidic bond of sucrose links carbon 1 of glucose to carbon 2 of fructose. If amylose is treated in a similar manner, the principal product is 2,3,6-trimethylglucose. In addition, a small amount (about 0.5 per cent of the total product) of 2,3,4,6-tetramethylglucose is formed. This result may be explained best by the formulation of the amyloses as long chains of glucose units joined together by means of $\alpha(1\rightarrow4)$-glycosidic bonds; the glucose unit at the nonreducing end of the polysaccharide chain is thus converted to the tetramethylglucose, and the relative proportion of this product to the trimethylglucose formed gives a measure of the length of the polysaccharide chain. Clearly the glucose unit at the reducing end of the amylose is converted to a 1,2,3,6-tetramethylglucose unit on methylation, but the $-OCH_3$ at carbon 1 is cleaved upon hydrolysis of the methylated amylose. This "end group method" for polysaccharides has permitted the estimation of the average chain length of several amylose prepara-

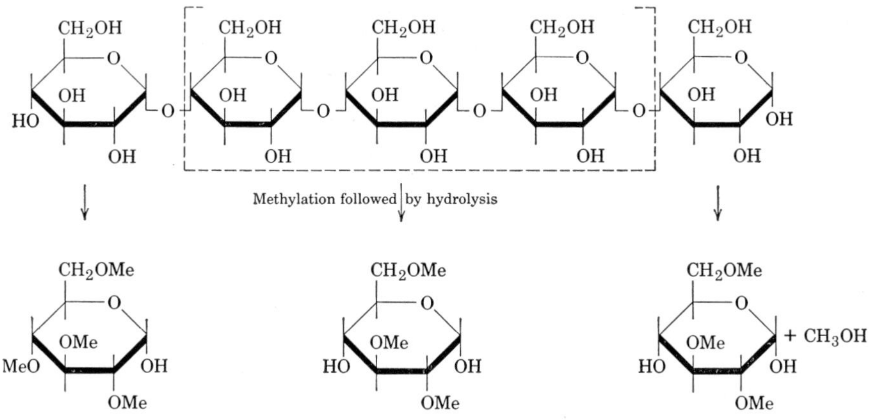

2,3,4,6–Tetramethyl-
glucopyranose   2,3,6–Trimethylglucopyranose

tions; an amylose of molecular weight about 35,000 has about 200 glucose units.

When the end group assay is applied to preparations of amylopectin, the products are 2,3,6-trimethylglucose (about 91 per cent), 2,3,4,6-tetramethylglucose (about 4 per cent) and 2,3-dimethylglucose (about 5 per cent). The isolation of a relatively large quantity of tetramethyl-glucose indicates that the chain of glucose units linked by (1→4)-glycosidic bonds must be shorter in amylopectin than in amylose.

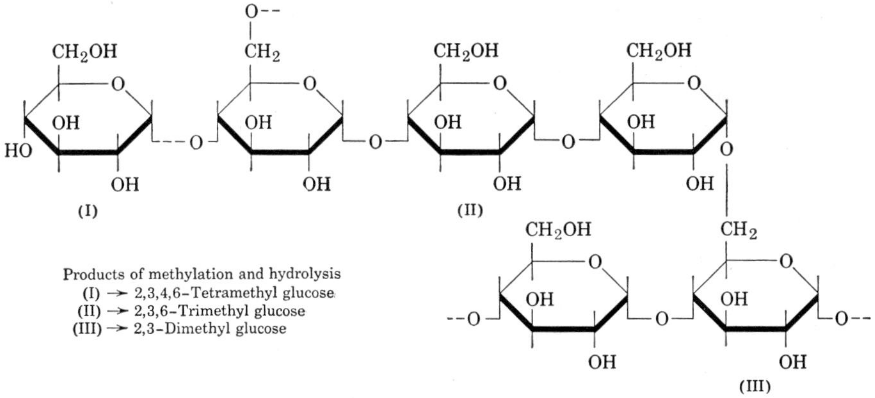

Products of methylation and hydrolysis
(I) → 2,3,4,6-Tetramethyl glucose
(II) → 2,3,6-Trimethyl glucose
(III)→ 2,3-Dimethyl glucose

Furthermore, the formation of the dimethylglucose shows that the 6 position of some of the glucose units in amylopectin is also involved in glycosidic linkage. Thus, the 6-hydroxyl of these glucose units partici-pates in (1→6)-glycosidic bonds which serve to cross-link the individual short chains (about 24 to 30 glucose units). This results in a ramified structure. The partial structure of an amylopectin, shown on p. 419, is intended only as an approximation since it is possible that a few cross-linkages involving hydroxyls at positions 2 and 3 may also be present. Indeed, evidence for the presence of a few $\alpha(1\to3)$-glycosidic bonds has come from the isolation of 3-(α-D-glucopyranosyl)-D-glucose (nigerose) from partial hydrolysates of amylopectin.[23]

It will be clear from the relatively large amount of dimethylglucose found by the end group assay of amylopectin that there are a considerable number of cross links (largely $(1\to6)$-glycosidic bonds). The amylopectin of rice starch (molecular weight about 500,000) appears to have 80 to 90 cross-linked chains, each of which represents a linear array of about 30 glucose units joined by $(1\to4)$-glycosidic bonds. However, amylopectins obtained from different starches exhibit varying degrees of ramification. As with the amyloses, a given preparation of an amylopectin may consist of particles of varying molecular weight, and these variations are probably the reflection of differences in the extent of ramification. Excellent reviews on the chemistry of the starches may be found in the articles by Hassid[24] and by Meyer and Gibbons.[25]

Another method for the determination of the length of $(1\to4)$-glycosidic chains in polysaccharides involves the use of periodate.[26] It will be recalled that this reagent cleaves carbon—carbon bonds when both

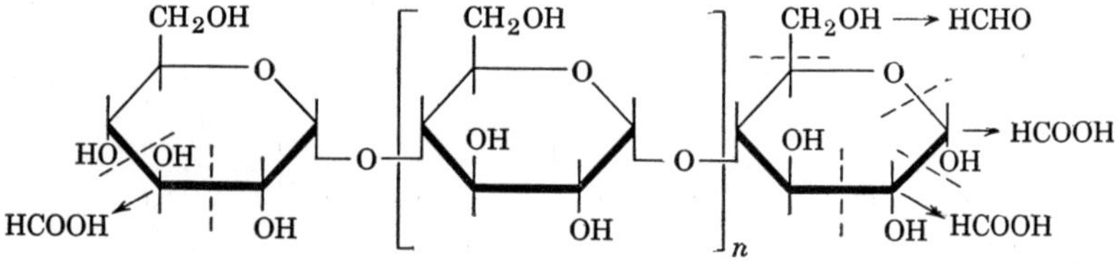

carbons bear free hydroxyl groups (cf. p. 56). If amylose is treated with periodate, all such linkages are split, in the manner shown, to yield 3 moles of formic acid per amylose chain. One mole of formic acid arises from the terminal nonreducing end of the chain, and 2 moles come from the terminal reducing end of the chain. The formic acid is estimated by titration. With amylopectin, which is almost free of terminal reducing groups, only one mole of formic acid is formed per $(1\to4)$-glycosidic chain. The periodate method of end group assay is less

[23] M. L. Wolfrom and A. Thompson, *J. Am. Chem. Soc.*, **78**, 4116 (1956).

[24] W. Z. Hassid, *Federation Proc.*, **4**, 227 (1945); in H. Gilman, *Organic Chemistry*, Vol. IV, Chapter 9, John Wiley & Sons, New York, 1953.

[25] K. H. Meyer and G. C. Gibbons, *Advances in Enzymol.*, **12**, 341 (1951).

[26] J. M. Bobbitt. *Advances in Carbohydrate Chem.*, **11**, 1 (1956).

time-consuming than the methylation technique of Haworth; the results obtained by the two methods have been essentially concordant.[27]

As noted above, another nutrient polysaccharide found among plants is inulin, which occurs in artichokes, dahlia bulbs, etc., and which yields D-fructose on hydrolysis. The application of the Haworth end group assay method to this polysaccharide has indicated that inulin represents a linear array of about 33 fructofuranose units joined together by means of $\beta(2\rightarrow1)$-glycosidic linkages. There appear to be a small number of D-glucose units in inulin.[28]

In the carbohydrate metabolism of animals, the important reserve polysaccharides are members of the group of substances given the collective name "glycogen." Glycogen is closely related in chemical structure to amylopectin; it gives a brown color with iodine. The glycogens appear to be much larger in molecular size than the amylopectins; particle weights of the order of 1 to 4 million have been reported.

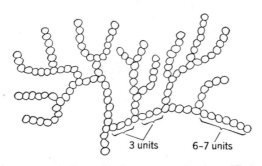

Fig. 1. Schematic representation of glycogen molecule. [From K. H. Meyer, *Advances in Enzymol.*, **3**, 109 (1943).]

The glycogens from numerous animal tissues have been subjected to methylation and hydrolysis, to periodate oxidation, or to successive enzymic degradation (cf. p. 444), and the results indicate that this group of polysaccharides is characterized by a highly ramified structure (cf. Fig. 1), in which straight-chain arrays of 11 to 18 D-glucopyranose units (in $\alpha(1\rightarrow4)$-glycosidic linkage) are cross-linked by means of $\alpha(1\rightarrow6)$-glycosidic bonds.[29]

Glycogen may be isolated by treatment of animal tissues (liver, muscle) with hot concentrated NaOH, in which it is stable, followed by

[27] A. L. Potter and W. Z. Hassid, *J. Am. Chem. Soc.*, **70**, 3488 (1948); D. J. Manners and A. R. Archibald, *J. Chem. Soc.*, **1957**, 2205.

[28] A. Palmer, *Biochem. J.*, **48**, 389 (1951); E. L. Hirst, *Proc. Chem. Soc.*, **1957**, 193.

[29] M. Schlamowitz, *J. Biol. Chem.*, **188**, 145 (1951); M. Abdel-Akher and F. Smith, *J. Am. Chem. Soc.*, **73**, 994 (1951); B. Illingworth et al., *J. Biol. Chem.*, **199**, 631 (1952)

precipitation by alcohol. Among the methods for the determination of glycogen are colorimetric procedures involving iodine or anthrone as the reagent.[30]

The most important of the so-called structural polysaccharides is the cellulose of plants. On complete hydrolysis of cellulose, D-glucose is formed; partial hydrolysis of the polysaccharide gives the β-glycoside cellobiose. The principal product obtained from cellulose by the Haworth end group assay method is 2,3,6-trimethylglucose; at most, about 0.5 per cent of tetramethylglucose is found. It may be concluded, therefore, that cellulose represents a linear array of D-glucopyranose units joined by $\beta(1\rightarrow4)$-glycosidic bonds. Studies on the particle weight of various celluloses, as determined in the ultracentrifuge, have given values varying between 100,000 and 2,000,000. The large particle weights found for "native" cellulose are a consequence of the aggregation of individual glycosidic chains (molecular weight about 35,000); it has been suggested that in such aggregates there is a parallel orientation of the chains with respect to one another.

In higher plants (e.g., maple, wheat, sugar cane), cellulose is accompanied by polymeric noncarbohydrate material termed lignin, which may represent 15 to 30 per cent of the dry weight.[31] The structure of the lignins is unknown, but it is believed that p-hydroxyphenylpropanes derived from coniferyl alcohol, or some closely related compound, are the fundamental repeating units; methoxy groups usually are present

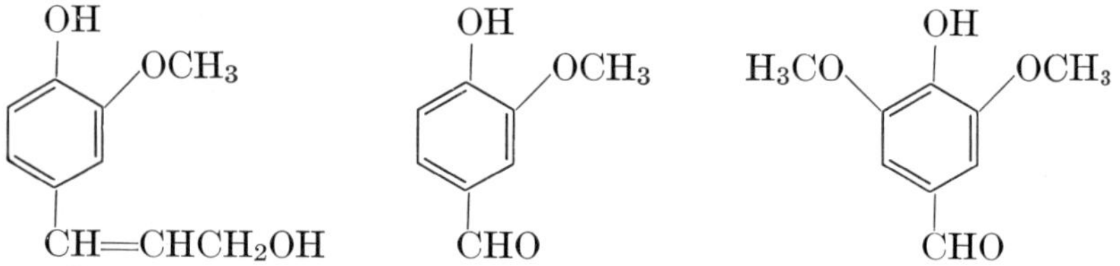

OH	OH	OH
OCH₃	OCH₃	H₃CO OCH₃
CH=CHCH₂OH	CHO	CHO
Coniferyl alcohol	Vanillin	Syringaldehyde

ortho to the phenolic hydroxyl group. Oxidation of lignin preparations (from wheat) with nitrobenzene in alkaline solution produces p-hydroxybenzaldehyde, vanillin, and syringaldehyde.

An important structural polysacharide of yeast is mannan, composed of D-mannose units linked largely by $(1\rightarrow2)$- and $(1\rightarrow6)$-glycosidic bonds. Mannan is present in the cell wall, and constitutes about 16 per cent of the dry weight of baker's yeast.[32] A related group of mannans occurs

[30] J. van der Vies, *Biochem. J.*, **57**, 410 (1954); N. V. Carroll et al., *J. Biol. Chem.*, **220**, 583 (1956).

[31] K. Freudenberg, *Fortschritte der Chemie organischer Naturstoffe*, **11**, 53 (1954); W. J. Schubert and F. F. Nord, *Advances in Enzymol.*, **18**, 349 (1957).

[32] G. Falcone and W. J. Nickerson, *Science*, **124**, 272 (1956).

in the ivory nut; the D-mannopyranose units of these polysaccharides are joined by $\beta(1\rightarrow4)$-glycosidic bonds.

Another structural polysaccharide of plant tisues is xylan[33] (associated with cellulose in wood) which on complete hydrolysis is largely converted to D-xylose. These pentose units are believed to be joined in chains of 20 to 40 D-xylopyranose units by means of $\beta(1\rightarrow4)$-glycosidic bonds; there is evidence for cross-linkage between such straight chains by means of $(1\rightarrow3)$-glycosidic linkages. In addition to D-xylose units, xylan (from wheat straw) contains L-arabinose units.

Many plant tissues, and especially fruit, contain representatives of yet another group of structural polysaccharides, termed pectic acids,[34] which appear to be long chains of D-galacturonic acid units (pyranose form) joined in $\alpha(1\rightarrow4)$-glycosidic linkage; the molecular weight of the pectic acids from various fruits ranges between 25,000 and 100,000. These acids are found as components of the plant materials named "pectins," which also contain polysaccharides composed of galactose (galactans) or arabinose units (arabans).

A second polysaccharide in which the repeating unit is a uronic acid is alginic acid, found in the brown marine algae; here D-mannuronic acid units are joined to one another by means of $\beta(1\rightarrow4)$-glycosidic linkages to form long chains.[35] L-Guluronic acid (the uronic acid derived from L-gulose; cf. p. 404) also is present in alginic acid. A third group of plant polysaccharides that contain uronic acid units are the "hemicelluloses" of woody tisues; on acid hydrolysis, these materials yield D-glucuronic acid and D-xylose.[36]

An important structural polysaccharide of invertebrates is the substance termed chitin, which is found in large amounts in the shells of

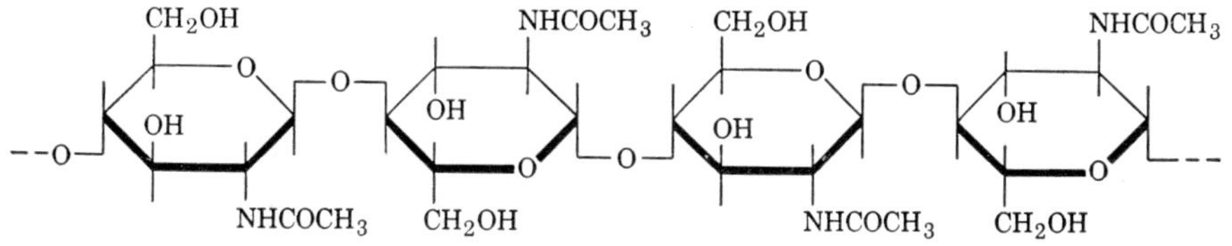

Chitin

lobsters and crabs. Chitin apparently consists of units of N-acetyl-D-glucosamine joined to one another by means of $\beta(1\rightarrow4)$-glycosidic bonds.

Among the animal carbohydrates that may be thought of as structural

[33] R. L. Whistler, *Advances in Carbohydrate Chem.*, **5**, 269 (1950); W. J. Polglase, *ibid.*, **10**, 283 (1955).

[34] E. L. Hirst and J. K. N. Jones, *Advances in Carbohydrate Chem.*, **2**, 235 (1946).

[35] T. Mori, *Advances in Carbohydrate Chem.*, **8**, 316 (1953).

[36] R. Montgomery et al., *J. Am. Chem. Soc.*, **78**, 2837 (1956).

polysaccharides are hyaluronic acid and the chondroitin sulfates; these substances are members of a group designated "mucopolysaccharides," in which amino sugars and uronic acids are the principal units of structure.[37] Hyaluronic acid is a collective term given to the muco-polysaccharide obtained from tissues such as the vitreous body of the eye, the umbilical cord, and the synovial fluid of joints. The high viscosity of synovial fluid and its role as a biological lubricant is largely a consequence of its hyaluronic acid content (ca. 0.03 per cent). Hyaluronic acid also appears to serve as a cementing substance ("ground

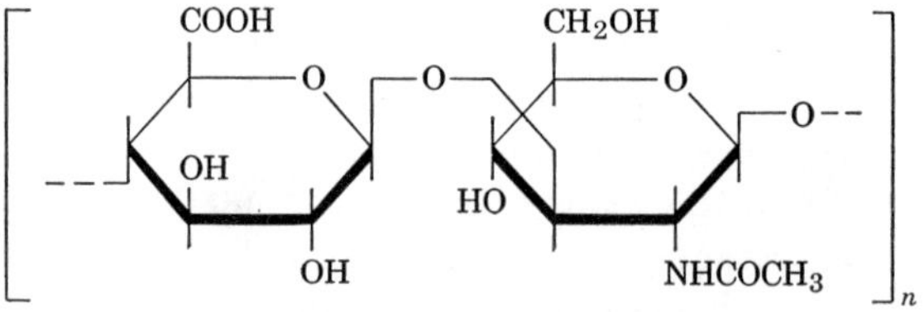

Probable structure of hyaluronic acid

substance") in the subcutaneous tissue. As judged by physical-chemical studies, hyaluronic acid preparations behave as highly asymmetric particles of considerable weight (100,000 to 4 million).[38] This muco-polysaccharide is composed of units of D-glucuronic acid and N-acetyl-D-glucosamine, and appears to be a linear polymer in which the disaccharide N-acetylhyalobiuronic acid[39] is the principal repeating unit. Hyalo-biuronic acid has been isolated from partial hydrolysates of hyaluronic acid and shown[40] to be 3-(β-D-glucopyranosyl uronic acid)-2-amino-2-deoxy-D-glucopyranose. The sulfuric acid ester of hyaluronic acid is termed "mucoitin sulfate"; its presence in gastric mucosa has been reported.

The group of sulfated mucopolysaccharides includes chondroitin sulfate A (present in cartilage, adult bone, cornea), chondroitin sulfate B (present in skin, tendons, heart valves), and chondroitin sulfate C (present in cartilage, tendons).[41] On hydrolysis, chondroitin sulfates A and C yield approximately equivalent amounts of D-glucuronic acid, D-galactosamine, acetic acid, and sulfuric acid. A disaccharide (chon-drosine) has been isolated from partial acid hydrolysates; its structure is similar to that of hyalobiuronic acid, except for the presence of a galactosamine residue in place of the glucosamine residue.[42] Hyaluronic

---

[37] K. Meyer, *Harvey Lectures*, **51**, 88 (1957).

[38] T. C. Laurent, *J. Biol. Chem.*, **216**, 263 (1955); L. Varga, *ibid.*, **217**, 651, (1955); J. W. Rowen et al., *Biochem. et Biophys. Acta*, **19**, 480 (1956).

[39] B. Weissmann et al., *J. Biol. Chem.*, **208**, 417 (1954).

[40] B. Weissmann and K. Meyer, *J. Am. Chem. Soc.*, **76**, 1753 (1954).

[41] K. Meyer et al., *Biochem. et Biophys. Acta*, **21**, 506 (1956).

[42] E. A. Davidson and K. Meyer, *J. Am. Chem. Soc.*, **76**, 5686 (1954).

acid and chondroitin sulfates A and C have, therefore, a similar fundamental structure in their polysaccharide chains. The name chondroitin has been given to preparations of cartilage mucopolysaccharide composed of glucuronic acid and galactosamine units, but which contain little or no sulfate.[43] The uronic acid of chondroitin sulfate B appears to be L-iduronic acid[44] (derived from L-idose; cf. p. 404).

Animal tissues (liver, lung, spleen, etc.) contain a group of mucopolysaccharides denoted "heparin" (see review by Foster and Huggard[45]); these substances are potent inhibitors of blood coagulation (Chapter 29). The complete hydrolysis of heparin gives glucuronic acid, glucosamine, acetic acid, and sulfuric acid. The last-named component appears to be linked not only to the sugar hydroxyl groups, but also to the amino group of the glucosamine units to form sulfamic acid groups ($-NHSO_2OH$). The particle weight of heparin is about 17,000. A heparin-like material containing galactosamine in place of glucosamine has been described;[43] it may be identical with chondroitin sulfate B.

Many of the mucopolysaccharides are present in the tissues as prosthetic groups of conjugated proteins to which the terms "glycoproteins," "mucoproteins," and "mucins" have been applied.[47] A portion of the chondroitin sulfate of cartilage is bound to protein,[48] and heparin is probably present in the tissues in the form of a carbohydrate-protein complex. Among the mucoproteins is included a variety of conjugated proteins in which the carbohydrate is a neutral polysaccharide, containing hexosamine and other sugar residues, but no glucuronic acid or sulfate. Such mucoproteins are present in the α_1- and α_2-globulin fractions of human plasma (cf. p. 19).[49] The α_1-mucoprotein has been obtained in crystalline form and found to contain about 17 per cent hexose and 12 per cent hexosamine. Its particle weight is about 44,000. This protein appears in the urine of patients with proteinuria. A different mucoprotein has been isolated from the urine of normal human subjects.[50] Other conjugated proteins containing a neutral mucopolysaccharide as the prosthetic group have been obtained from submaxillary mucosa and from egg white. The mucoprotein from the latter source is termed

[43] E. A. Davidson and K. Meyer, *J. Biol. Chem.*, **211**, 605 (1954).

[44] P. Hoffman et al., *Science*, **124**, 1252 (1956).

[45] A. B. Foster and A. J. Huggard, *Advances in Carbohydrate Chem.*, **10**, 335 (1955).

[46] R. Marbet and A. Winterstein, *Helv. Chim. Acta*, **34**, 2311 (1951).

[47] K. Meyer, *Advances in Protein Chem.*, **2**, 249 (1945); M. Stacey, *Advances in Carbohydrate Chem.*, **2**, 161 (1946).

[48] J. Shatton and M. Schubert, *J. Biol. Chem.*, **211**, 565 (1954).

[49] K. Schmid, *J. Am. Chem. Soc.*, **75**, 60 (1953); *Biochim. et Biophys. Acta*, **21**, 399 (1956).

[50] I. Tamm and F. L. Horsfall, Jr., *J. Exp. Med.*, **95**, 71 (1952).

"ovomucoid" and is an inhibitor of pancreatic trypsin (Chapter 29). Ovomucoid contains N-acetylglucosamine and mannose in a molar ratio of 1:1, and has a particle weight of about 28,000.[51]

The above mucoproteins from plasma, urine, submaxillary gland, and egg white all are characterized by the presence of an acetylhexosamine (presumed to be N-acetyl-D-glucosamine) and a hexose (mannose, galactose) in the polysaccharide portion. In addition, common constituents of these conjugated proteins are L-fucose (p. 411) and sialic acid;[52] the structure of the latter substance is probably that shown in the accompanying formula.[53] On hydrolysis by alkali or by a glycosidase present in some bacteria, sialic acid yields pyruvic acid and N-acetyl-D-mannosamine; the latter epimerizes readily to acetylglucosamine.

$$\underset{\text{Sialic acid (N-acetylneuraminic acid)}}{\overset{\displaystyle \overset{\text{COCH}_3}{|}}{\underset{\overbrace{\qquad\qquad\text{O}\qquad\qquad}}{\text{HOOC}-\underset{|}{\overset{|}{\underset{\text{OH}}{\text{C}}}}-\text{CH}_2-\underset{|}{\overset{|}{\underset{\text{OH}}{\text{CH}}}}-\underset{|}{\overset{|}{\underset{\text{NH}}{\text{CH}}}}-\text{CH}-\underset{|}{\overset{|}{\underset{\text{OH}}{\text{CH}}}}-\underset{|}{\overset{|}{\underset{\text{OH}}{\text{CH}}}}-\text{CH}_2\text{OH}}}}$$

Sialic acid appears to be identical with "lactaminic acid," a constituent of cow's colostrum[54] (milk formed immediately after birth), and with "gynaminic acid," a constituent of human milk.[55] It is probably the N-acetyl derivative of "neuraminic acid," a cleavage product of the gangliosides[56] (Chapter 23). The N-glycolyl ($HOCH_2CO-$) derivative of neuraminic acid has been identified in mucoprotein from pig submaxillary gland. The detection of neuraminic acid derivatives is facilitated by their direct reaction with p-dimethylaminobenzaldehyde to form a purple compound.

The manner in which sialic acid and the other monosaccharide units of the mucoproteins are bound to each other, and to the protein portion, has not been elucidated.[57] It is of interest that the ability of several mucoproteins to inhibit the clumping of red cells (hemagglutination) induced by heat-treated influenza virus particles appears to be associated

[51] H. Lineweaver and C. W. Murray, *J. Biol. Chem.*, **171**, 565 (1947).

[52] G. Blix et al., *Nature*, **175**, 340 (1955).

[53] A. Gottschalk, *Yale J. Biol. Med.*, **28**, 525 (1956); R. Heimer and K. Meyer, *Proc. Natl. Acad. Sci.*, **42**, 728 (1956).

[54] R. Kuhn and R. Brossner, *Ber. chem. Ges.*, **89**, 2471 (1956).

[55] F. Zilliken et al., *Arch. Biochem. and Biophys.*, **63**, 394 (1956).

[56] E. Klenk and H. Faillard, *Z. physiol. Chem.*, **298**, 230 (1954); E. Klenk, *Angew. Chem.*, **68**, 349 (1956); E. Klenk and G. Uhlenbruck, *Z. physiol. Chem.*, **305**, 224 (1956); **307**, 266 (1957).

[57] A. Gottschalk, *Biochim. et Biophys. Acta*, **20**, 560 (1956); **24**, 649 (1957).

with the sialic acid portion. *Vibrio cholerae* contains an enzyme ("receptor destroying enzyme") that abolishes this property of mucoproteins by splitting off the sialic acid portion.

Among the mucoproteins may also be included the "blood-group substances."[58] In 1900, Landsteiner[59] showed that the tendency of human erythrocytes to agglutinate differs depending on the presence in the red cells of a blood-group substance A or a blood-group substance B, and on the nature of the substances ("isoagglutinins") in the serum that cause agglutination. This discovery led to the recognition of four genetically controlled blood-group characters, denoted A, B, AB, or O (cf. Table 3). The erythrocytes of group A individuals are agglutinated

Table 3. Classification of Blood-Group Substances

Blood Group	Serum Isoagglutinins	Agglutination of Red Cells of Type A	B	AB	O
A	β	−	+	+	−
B	α	+	−	+	−
AB	none	−	−	−	−
O(H)	α and β	+	+	+	−

by group B or O serum, and group A serum (contains β-isoagglutinins) agglutinates red cells of group B and AB only. Group B cells are agglutinated by group A or O serum, and group B serum (contains α-isoagglutinins) agglutinates only A or AB cells. Group AB serum does not contain either agglutinin, and group AB cells are agglutinated by sera of all the other three types. Group O red cells are not agglutinated by sera of the other three groups, and group O serum contains both α- and β-isoagglutinins. Group O cells contain a blood-group substance designated "O" or "H." If the red cells of one of the blood-group types is injected into an animal, the type specific mucoprotein acts as an antigen and elicits the formation in the recipient of an antibody that acts as an agglutinin. The action of normal and of induced agglutinins is inhibited by the corresponding antigenic mucoprotein. Thus preparations of blood-group B substance inhibit the isohemagglutination of group B cells by natural human β-isoagglutinin or by the antibody β-agglutinin produced in an animal by injection of group B cells. Since the early work of Landsteiner, blood-group characters other than A, B, AB, and O have been discovered; among these is the "Lewis" character, associated with the Le group substance.

The type specific blood-group substances are not only found in the

[58] E. A. Kabat, *Blood Group Substances,* Academic Press, New York, 1956.

[59] K. Landsteiner, *The Specificity of Serological Reactions,* Rev. Ed., Harvard University Press, Cambridge, 1945.

red cells of individuals belonging to these individual types, but are also present in various body fluids (e.g., gastric juice, saliva, ovarian cyst fluid) from which active mucoprotein preparations have been obtained and partially purified. The work of Morgan and his associates on the purification and the chemical study of the blood-group substances A, H, and Le (obtained from ovarian cyst fluid of appropriate individuals) has shown that they are all mucopolysaccharide-protein complexes. Acid hydrolysates of these preparations contain hexosamine (ca. 35 per cent), L-fucose (ca. 13 per cent), galactose (ca. 17 per cent), and a variety of α-amino acids (ca. 40 per cent).[60] The blood-group B substance has a higher proportion of fucose (ca. 19 per cent) and gives less hexosamine (ca. 21 per cent) on hydrolysis.[61] The hexosamine fraction of the acid hydrolysates contains both glucosamine and galactosamine; the glucosamine/galactosamine ratio is in the range 1.4 to 2.8.[62] It is probable that a portion of the hexosamine arises by the decomposition of N-acetylhexosamine derivatives similar to sialic acid.

The antigenic capacity of the blood-group substances to elicit the production of specific antibodies in suitable animals is exhibited by several other types of polysaccharides. Among them are bacterial polysaccharides;[63] those found in various strains of *Pneumococcus* have been studied most intensively. These polysaccharides are specifically precipitated when they are added to the serum of an immunized animal. The work of Avery, Heidelberger, and their associates showed that the differences in the antigenic behavior of various types of pneumococci were related to differences in the nature of the polysaccharide present in the capsule which surrounds the virulent form of these organisms. Preparations of capsular polysaccharide from type I pneumococci gave, on hydrolysis, glucosamine and glucuronic acid. The type II polysaccharide contains residues of glucose, glucuronic acid, and L-rhamnose (p. 411); this material appears to be a highly branched structure, with glucose residues involved in both $(1\rightarrow4)$- and $(1\rightarrow6)$-glycosidic bonds.[64] The type III polysaccharide appears to be composed of 3-(glucopyranosyl) glucuronic acid units joined by $(1\rightarrow4)$-glycosidic bonds.[65] The type VIII polysaccharide contains residues of D-glucose, D-galactose, and D-glucuronic acid.

Certain bacterial cells, belonging to the group designated *Leuconostoc*,

[60] D. Aminoff et al., *Biochem. J.*, **46**, 426 (1950); E. F. Annison and W. T. J. Morgan, *ibid.*, **50**, 460; **52**, 247 (1952).

[61] R. A. Gibbons and W. T. J. Morgan, *Biochem. J.*, **57**, 283 (1954).

[62] S. Leskowitz and E. A. Kabat, *J. Am. Chem. Soc.*, **76**, 4887 (1954).

[63] M. Burger, *Bacterial Polysaccharides*, Charles C Thomas, Springfield, 1950

[64] K. Butler and M. Stacey, *J. Chem. Soc.*, **1955**, 1537.

[65] R. E. Reeves and W. F. Goebel, *J. Biol. Chem.*, **139**, 511 (1941).

elaborate polysaccharides (named dextrans) composed of D-glucopyranose units largely joined by $\alpha(1\to6)$-glycosidic linkages, although preparations with high proportions of $(1\to3)$ and $(1\to4)$ bonds have also been obtained.[66] Other microorganisms (e.g., *Bacillus subtilis, Bacillus mesentericus*) form polysaccharides (named levans) composed of D-fructofuranose units largely linked by $\beta(2\to6)$-glycosidic bonds. The enzymic synthesis of dextrans and levans is discussed on p. 451. The dextrans are antigenic substances, and they elicit the formation of antibodies (antidextrans) upon injection into human subjects. It is of interest that oligosaccharides with $\alpha(1\to6)$-glycosidic bonds (as in isomaltose, 6-(α-D-glucopyranosyl)-D-glucopyranose) inhibit the precipitation of $(1\to6)$-dextrans by human antidextrans produced in response to the injection of such $(1\to6)$-dextrans.[67] Synthetic polyglucoses with $(1\to6)$-glycosidic bonds also react with antibody to type II pneumococcal polysaccharide,[68] which contains $(1\to6)$ linkages.

[66] A. Jeanes et al., *J. Am. Chem. Soc.*, **76**, 5041 (1954).

[67] P. Z. Allen and E. Kabat, *J. Am. Chem. Soc.*, **78**, 1890 (1956).

[68] M. Heidelberger and A. C. Aisenberg, *Proc. Natl. Acad. Sci.*, **39**, 453 (1953); M. Heidelberger, *Ann. Rev. Biochem.*, **25**, 641 (1956).

Enzymic Cleavage and Synthesis of Glycosidic Bonds

18 ·

Among the monosaccharides, D-glucose occupies a unique place in the metabolism of most biological forms. The chemical transformations of this sugar lead to the release of energy which can be used to drive endergonic reactions in nearly all organisms. In the preceding chapter, it was noted that glucose occurs in nature, not only in the free state, but also as a component of oligosaccharides and polysaccharides. In order to make the monosaccharide available for metabolic transformation, the glycosidic linkages of these polymeric sugars must be broken. This cleavage of glycosidic linkages is effected in biological systems by two general mechanisms. The first involves the hydrolysis of a glycosidic

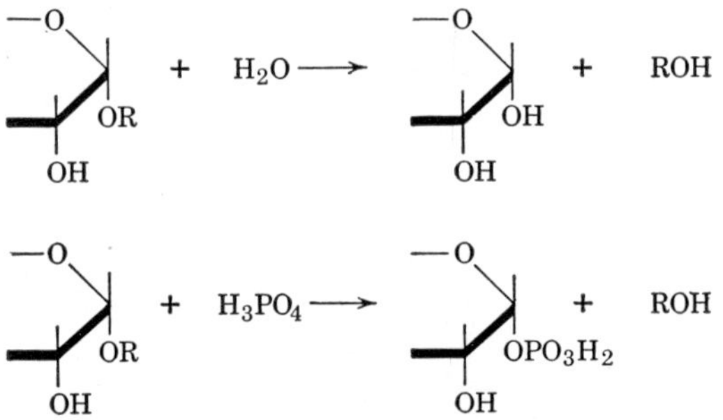

bond, with the incorporation, into the hydrolytic products, of the elements of water. The second general mechanism involves the "phosphorolysis" of a glycosidic bond, i.e., the addition of the elements of phosphoric acid. Both general types of reaction are catalyzed by specific enzymes.

Glycosidases [1]

The glycosidases (also termed carbohydrases) catalyze the hydrolysis of glycosidic bonds. The specificity of these enzymes may be defined in

[1] W. W. Pigman, *J. Research Natl. Bur. Standards,* **30,** 257 (1943).

terms of the structural factors that determine whether a given glycosidase will act at a particular glycosidic linkage. These factors may be listed as follows:

1. The nature of the monosaccharide that donates the reducing group involved in the glycosidic bond. For example, among the enzymes that act at glycosidic bonds involving the aldohexoses, separate glycosidases (glucosidases and galactosidases) hydrolyze glucosides and galactosides.

2. The configuration (α or β) about the carbon atom of the potential reducing group. Separate enzymes (α-glucosidases and β-glucosidases) act on α-glucosides and on β-glucosides.

3. The configuration (D or L) of the monosaccharide bearing the potential reducing group. Most of the known glycosidases act at linkages in which a D-monosaccharide provides the reducing group.

4. The size of the heterocyclic oxygen ring. Usually the carbohydrases that act on aldohexosides require the presence of a pyranose ring, whereas the enzymic hydrolysis of ketohexosides requires the substrate to be in the furanose form.

The carbohydrases may be separated into two broad groups; those that catalyze the hydrolysis of glycosidic bonds in simple glycosides or in oligosaccharides, and those that catalyze the hydrolysis of the glycosidic bonds of polysaccharides. The term "glycosidase" is frequently assigned to the first group only; the other enzymes are often called "polysaccharidases."

One of the important results of the synthetic work of Emil Fischer in the carbohydrate field was the recognition that α-D-glucosides are attacked by different enzymes from those that act on β-D-glucosides. In fact, the systematic study of enzyme specificity may be said to have begun with Fischer's demonstration in 1894 that yeast extracts which did not act on β-methylglucoside hydrolyzed α-methylglucoside and maltose. On the other hand, an extract of almonds caused the hydrolysis of the β-glucoside but did not affect the α-glucoside. Since this work, many studies[2] have been made of the specificity of α- and β-glucosidases from various sources; these enzymes have been purified only partially, and there has been considerable controversy in the literature about the identity or nonidentity of various enzyme materials. For example, although it appeared likely that the same α-glucosidase of yeast acts on α-methylglucoside and on maltose, it was suggested that there is another enzyme (named maltase) specifically adapted to the hydrolysis of maltose. More recent studies, to be discussed later (cf. p. 453), have shown that a

[2] W. W. Pigman, *Advances in Enzymol.*, **4**, 41 (1944); A. Gottschalk, *Advances in Carbohydrate Chem.*, **5**, 49 (1950).

specific action on maltose may not be a hydrolytic one. The β-glucosidases are widely distributed in seeds, molds, and bacteria;[3] they have also been found in marine invertebrates. The best-studied representative of this group is derived from almonds; it was named emulsin by Liebig and Wohler in 1840. The substrate used by these early workers was the plant glycoside amygdalin (p. 416), which is cleaved at both β-glycosidic bonds, with the formation of two equivalents of glucose and one equivalent of d-mandelic acid nitrile; the latter is further decomposed to form benzaldehyde and HCN. The work of Helferich and others has shown that the

$$\text{Amygdalin} \rightarrow 2 \text{ Glucose} + \underset{\text{OH}}{\overset{\text{CHCN}}{\bigcirc}} \rightarrow C_6H_5CHO + HCN$$

nonsugar portion (the "aglucone") of a β-glucoside may be varied considerably in substrates of the enzyme (cf. p. 276). β-Glucosidases such as emulsin also act on a variety of oligosaccharides containing a β-glucosidic link (e.g., cellobiose).

Two groups of enzymes are specifically adapted to the hydrolysis of α- and β-galactosides. The α-galactosidases occur principally in yeasts, molds, and bacteria, and, since they cleave melibiose (p. 416), frequently are termed melibiases. Representatives of the β-galactosidases[4] are also widespread among microorganisms; a typical substrate is lactose (p. 415), and these enzymes also are termed lactases.

Another group of β-glycosidases of some interest includes the enzymes that catalyze the hydrolysis of β-glucuronides, and are, therefore, named β-glucuronidases.[5] β-D-Glucuronides are formed in animals by the condensation of D-glucuronic acid with a variety of aromatic hydroxyl compounds such as borneol, sterols, phenol (cf. p. 537).

For the quantitative estimation of the rate of β-glycosidase-catalyzed reactions, it has proved convenient to employ as a substrate the appropriate glycoside in which the aglycone is o-nitrophenol or p-nitrophenol. Since free o- or p-nitrophenol, in alkaline solution, forms a yellow nitrophenolate ion, the extent of the hydrolysis of o- or p-nitrophenyl-β-glycosides may be followed colorimetrically. With β-glucuronides, phenolphthalein has been used as the chromogenic aglycone. A valuable method for the measurement of the rate of release of free glucose from a glucoside takes advantage of the specificity of glucose oxidase (cf. p. 339).

Few glycosidases have been studied as extensively as the yeast enzyme that causes the hydrolysis of sucrose to glucose and fructose. Since this

---

[3] S. Veibel, in J. B. Sumner and K. Myrbäck, *The Enzymes,* Chapter 16, Academic Press, New York, 1950.

[4] S. A. Kuby and H. A. Lardy, *J. Am. Chem. Soc.,* **75,** 890 (1953).

[5] W. H. Fishman, *Advances in Enzymol.,* **16,** 361 (1955).

hydrolysis leads to a change in optical rotation of the reaction mixture from a positive to a negative value, the enzyme was first named invertase.[6] Despite the extensive studies conducted on invertase, only partial purification of the enzyme has been achieved thus far; purified preparations of yeast invertase contain mannan[7] (p. 422). Invertase also has been termed saccharase, sucrase, and β-fructosidase. The last of these names is the most descriptive, because the enzyme is specifically adapted to the hydrolysis of β-D-fructofuranosides. In addition to its action on sucrose, invertase causes the hydrolysis of the trisaccharide raffinose to melibiose and fructose. It is of interest that a sucrose-hydrolyzing enzyme is found in the intestinal mucosa of many animals; since maltose also is hydrolyzed, this enzyme appears to be an α-glucosidase rather than a β-fructosidase.

When yeast invertase acts on sucrose in water labeled with O^{18}, the isotope does not appear in the hydroxyl at carbon 1 of the resulting glucopyranose, indicating that the cleavage occurs between carbon 2 of the β-fructofuranosyl group and the glycosidic oxygen[8] (cf. formula on p. 415). This finding is consonant with the ability of invertase preparations to catalyze the transfer of fructofuranosyl groups not only to water (hydrolysis), but also to various alcohols and sugars, by "transglycosidation" (or "transglycosylation") reactions. As mentioned previously (cf. p. 273), such "transfer" reactions are catalyzed by many enzymes frequently classified as hydrolases; the action of glycosidases as transglycosidases will be discussed later in this chapter.

Polysaccharidases.[9] The best known of these enzymes are the amylases, which act on starch and glycogen. Wheat amylase was one of the first enzymes to be identified; it was discovered by Kirchhoff in 1811. Amylases are found in many plant tissues and in the saliva and pancreas of animals. In the course of the action of the amylases on a polysaccharide such as amylose, four changes in the properties of the reaction mixture are usually noted: (1) a decrease in viscosity, denoting the cleavage of the polysaccharide chain; (2) loss of the capacity to give a blue color with iodine; (3) appearance of reducing groups; and (4) formation of maltose and, in addition, of larger oligosaccharides of varying chain length (dextrins). Among the known amylases, there are two broad groups, designated α- and β-amylases respectively.[10] Here

[6] C. Neuberg and I. Mandl, in J. B. Sumner and K. Myrbäck, *The Enzymes,* Chapter 14, Academic Press, New York, 1950.

[7] E. Fischer and L. Kohtès, *Helv. Chim. Acta,* **34,** 1123, 1134 (1951); J. A. Cifonelli and F. Smith, *J. Am. Chem. Soc.,* **77,** 5682 (1955).

[8] D. E. Koshland, Jr., and S. S. Stein, *J. Biol. Chem.,* **208,** 139 (1954).

[9] P. Bernfeld, *Advances in Enzymol.,* **12,** 379 (1951); D. J. Manners, *Ann. Reps.,* **50,** 288 (1954); *Quart. Revs.,* **9,** 73 (1955).

[10] R. H. Hopkins, *Advances in Enzymol.,* **6,** 389 (1946).

the designation α or β does not refer to the configuration of the glycosidic bond that is hydrolyzed; both types of enzymes hydrolyze $\alpha(1\rightarrow4)$-glucosidic linkages.

The β-amylases rapidly hydrolyze the amylose fraction of starch to maltose. This conversion is practically quantitative, and negligible amounts of dextrins are formed; under some conditions, however, the cleavage does not proceed to completion.[11] In the course of the action of the β-amylases on amylose the capacity to give a blue color with iodine is lost rather slowly, indicating the presence of large chains which are eventually broken down completely to give the disaccharide. When the β-amylases act on amylopectin, the hydrolysis proceeds to about 50 to 60 per cent of the theoretical maximum (calculated as maltose). These enzymes attack polysaccharides from the nonreducing end of the chain, cleaving alternate $\alpha(1\rightarrow4)$-glycosidic bonds and hydrolyzing off maltose units. This action can be practically complete with the straight-chain amylose, but with the branched-chain amylopectin the enzymic action stops at the points of branching, i.e., at the $(1\rightarrow6)$-glycosidic bonds (cf. Fig. 1). End group assay of the "limit" dextrins formed upon degradation of amylopectin by β-amylases is in agreement with this interpretation. The β-amylase of sweet potatoes has been obtained in crystalline form,[12] and malt β-amylase also has been crystallized.[13]

In contrast to the β-amylases, the α-amylases cause a rapid loss of the capacity of amylose to give a blue color with iodine, and the rate of appearance of maltose is very slow. Here the attack on the polysaccharide appears to be at glycosidic linkages in the interior of the chain (cf. Fig. 2), with the formation of oligosaccharides (e.g., the trisaccharide maltotriose) which are cleaved slowly to maltose and glucose.[14] In further contrast to the β-amylases, the α-amylases can hydrolyze $\alpha(1\rightarrow4)$ bonds of amylopectins on either side of the $(1\rightarrow6)$ branch points, forming $(1\rightarrow6)$ linked oligosaccharides as small as pentasaccharides. This extensive shortening of the chain length leads to the rapid loss of viscosity. Hence the α-amylases are also termed "dextrinogenic" or "liquefying" amylases. The α-amylases of malt, *Bacillus subtilis*, swine pancreas, and human saliva have been obtained in crystalline form.[15] Although these enzyme proteins are not identical, they exhibit the same action on the components of starch. The α-amylases are activated by chloride ions.[16]

[11] S. Peat et al., *J. Chem. Soc.*, **1952**, 722; E. F. Neufeld and W. Z. Hassid, *Arch. Biochem. and Biophys.*, **59**, 405 (1955).

[12] A. K. Balls et al., *J. Biol. Chem.*, **173**, 9 (1948); S. Englard and T. P. Singer, *ibid.*, **187**, 213 (1950).

[13] K. H. Meyer et al., *Helv. Chim. Acta*, **34**, 316 (1951).

[14] R. Bird and R. H. Hopkins, *Biochem. J.*, **56**, 86 (1954).

[15] K. H. Meyer, *Angew. Chem.*, **63**, 153 (1951); *Experientia*, **8**, 405 (1952).

[16] Y. Muus et al.. *Arch. Biochem. and Biophys.*, **65**, 268 (1956).

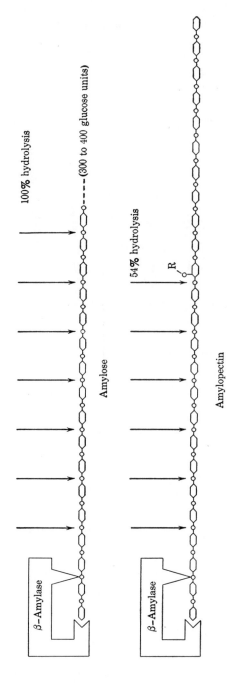

Fig. 1. Mode of action of β-amylase on amylose and amylopectin. The R denotes a branched chain. [From W. Z. Hassid and R. H. McCready, *J. Am. Chem. Soc.*, **65**, 1157 (1943).]

In higher animals the amylase of saliva initiates the hydrolytic attack on the dietary polysaccharides (starch and glycogen); this digestive process is continued by the amylase present in the pancreatic juice secreted into the small intestine. The resulting maltose is hydrolyzed by intestinal α-glucosidase to glucose, which is absorbed in the intestine (cf. p. 492). In addition to amylase and glucosidase, which are restricted

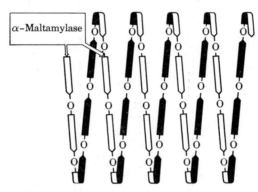

Fig. 2. Proposed helical structure of amylose chain, and suggested mode of action of α-amylase. [From C. S. Hanes, *New Phytol.,* **36,** 189 (1937).]

in their action to α(1→4)-glucosidic bonds, intestinal mucosa contains an enzyme ("oligo-1,6-glucosidase") that is specific for the hydrolysis of α(1→6)-glucosidic linkages.[17] This enzyme hydrolyzes the (1→6) bond of isomaltose ((1→6)-glucosylglucose) and of larger oligosaccharides, thus providing an enzymic mechanism for the complete degradation, in the intestinal tract, of ingested amylopectins and glycogens to free glucose. A similar enzyme is present in muscle extracts and is named "amylo-1,6-glucosidase."[18]   However, this enzyme cannot act as a "debranching" agent until a terminal glucose unit in α(1→6) linkage has been exposed through prior degradation of the α(1→4) linkages in the branch (cf. p. 445). Enzymes analogous to the intestinal oligo-1,6-glucosidase have been identified in extracts of beans and potatoes,[19] and have been named "R enzymes."

Some bacteria (e.g., *Bacillus macerans*) contain an amylase that acts on starch to produce a mixture of water-soluble dextrins,[20] some of which may be obtained in the form of crystalline nonreducing compounds.

[17] J. Larner and C. M. McNickle, *J. Biol. Chem.,* **215,** 723 (1955); J. Larner and R. E. Gillespie, *ibid.,* **223,** 709 (1956).

[18] G. T. Cori and J. Larner, *J. Biol. Chem.,* **188,** 17 (1951); J. Larner and L. H. Schliselfeld, *Biochim. et Biophys. Acta,* **20,** 53 (1956).

[19] P. N. Hobson et al., *J. Chem. Soc.,* **1951,** 1451; S. Peat et al., *ibid.,* **1954,** 4440.

[20] E. B. Tilden and C. S. Hudson, *J. Bact.,* **43,** 527 (1942).

These crystalline dextrins were first described by Schardinger in 1908, and are therefore termed Schardinger dextrins. On exhaustive methylation, followed by hydrolysis, only 2,3,6-trimethylglucose is obtained; it would appear, therefore, that the Schardinger dextrins are closed-ring structures in which glucose units (about 6) are joined by means of $\alpha(1\rightarrow4)$-glucosidic bonds. Evidence has been presented in favor of the view that the amylase of *B. macerans* catalyzes a series of transglucosidation reactions (cf. p. 451) in which the enzyme attacks the sixth glucosidic bond from the nonreducing end of the amylose chain, and produces a new glucosidic bond between carbon 1 of the sixth glucosyl unit and carbon 4 of the terminal glucosyl unit.[21] Such a sequence of cyclization reactions would be favored by the helical structure proposed for amylose by Hanes (cf. Fig. 2). The blue color given by amylose with iodine is probably a consequence of the deposition of iodine molecules in the interior of the polysaccharide helix.

It is known that some invertebrates have digestive enzymes which enable them to degrade structural polysaccharides such as cellulose and chitin. Thus the hepatopancreatic juice of the snail *Helix pomatia* contains enzymes designated cellulase and chitinase.[22] The action of cellulase on cellulose leads to the formation of cellobiose; chitin is split by chitinase to form N-acetylglucosamine. Cellulases appear to be widespread among anaerobic microorganisms found in the soil and in the digestive tract of herbivorous animals. The ability of termites to destroy wood appears to depend upon the enzymic activity of microorganisms that inhabit the gut of these insects.

A polysaccharide-splitting enzyme of some interest in animal physiology is hyaluronidase, which causes the degradation of hyaluronic acid by hydrolysis of the glycosidic bonds involving the reducing group of N-acetylglucosamine; oligosaccharides of varying chain length are formed, and these products can be further split to N-acetylglucosamine and glucuronic acid by a β-glucuronidase.[23] However, the N-acetylhyalobiuronic acid (p. 424) produced in the enzymic breakdown of hyaluronic acid by testicular hyaluronidase appears to be resistant to β-glucuronidase. It is of interest that hyaluronidase preparations from several bacteria do not produce N-acetylhyalobiuronic acid, but instead an unsaturated derivative of this compound is formed. In addition to its occurrence in animal tissues, notably testes, and in some bacteria, hyaluronidase activity has been found in snake venoms. The possible

[21] D. French, *Advances in Carbohydrate Chem.*, **12**, 190 (1957).

[22] M. V. Tracey, *Biochem. Soc. Symposia*, **11**, 49 (1953); *Biochem. J.*, **61**, 579 (1955).

[23] K. Meyer et al., *J. Biol. Chem.*, **192**, 275 (1951); A. Linker et al., *ibid.*, **213**, 237 (1955).

importance of hyaluronidase arises from its property to act as a "spreading factor"; i.e., it increases the diffusion of foreign materials (bacterial toxins, dyes, etc.) injected into the skin.[24]

Another enzyme, also believed to act on mucopolysaccharides, is lysozyme.[25] This enzyme is found in the mucosal secretions of man (tears, nasal mucosa) and in egg white, and has the property of lysing bacteria, such as *Micrococcus lysodeikticus*. The lysozyme of egg white has been crystallized by several investigators; the simplest procedure is that of Fevold and Alderton.[26] Lysozyme has also been isolated in crystalline form from papaya latex, where it represents about one-third of the soluble protein.[27] Lysozyme is a basic protein (isoelectric point pH 10.5 to 11.0) of relatively low molecular weight (about 17,500).

Plants, fungi, and bacteria contain enzymes (pectic enzymes[28]) which catalyze the hydrolytic cleavage of the pectic substances (polygalacturonic acids partially esterified by methanol). The enzyme denoted "pectinase" cleaves the chain to galacturonic acid and digalacturonic acid.[29] The pectic enzymes are important in the industrial processing of fruit juices and other beverages.

Phosphorylases

Although it was long known that extracts of animal tissues such as liver and muscle contain enzymes capable of causing the scission of the glycosidic bonds of glycogen, until about 1935 it was incorrectly thought that the breakdown of glycogen in these tissues was effected by amylases analogous to those discussed in the previous section of this chapter. In that year Cori and Parnas, working independently, showed that inorganic phosphate was an obligatory participant in the degradation of glycogen, and that a phosphorylated monosaccharide was formed in the reaction. The most decisive advance in the understanding of the role of phosphate in the breakdown of glycogen by muscle extracts was made by Cori et al.,[30] who identified the phosphorylated sugar as glucose-1-phosphate (α-D-glucopyranose-1-phosphate). The enzymic conversion of a part of the glycogen molecule to glucose-1-phosphate may be written as shown. This process has been designated "phosphorolysis," and the enzymes that catalyze such reactions are termed "phosphorylases." The salient dif-

[24] F. Duran-Reynals et al., *Ann. N. Y. Acad. Sci.,* **52,** 943 (1950).

[25] H. L. Fevold, *Advances in Protein Chem.,* **6,** 187 (1951).

[26] H. L. Fevold and G. Alderton, *Biochem. Preparations,* **1,** 67 (1949).

[27] E. L. Smith et al., *J. Biol. Chem.,* **215,** 67 (1955).

[28] Z. I. Kertesz and R. J. McColloch, *Advances in Carbohydrate Chem.,* **5,** 79 (1950); H. Lineweaver and E. F. Jansen, *Advances in Enzymol.,* **11,** 267 (1951).

[29] H. J. Phaff and A. L. Demain, *J. Biol. Chem.,* **218,** 875 (1956).

[30] C. F. Cori et al., *J. Biol. Chem.,* **121,** 465 (1937).

ference between the chemical reactions catalyzed by the amylases and the phosphorylases is the introduction, in the presence of the amylases, of the elements of water into the glycosidic bond that is broken, whereas, with the phosphorylases, the elements of phosphoric acid are introduced.

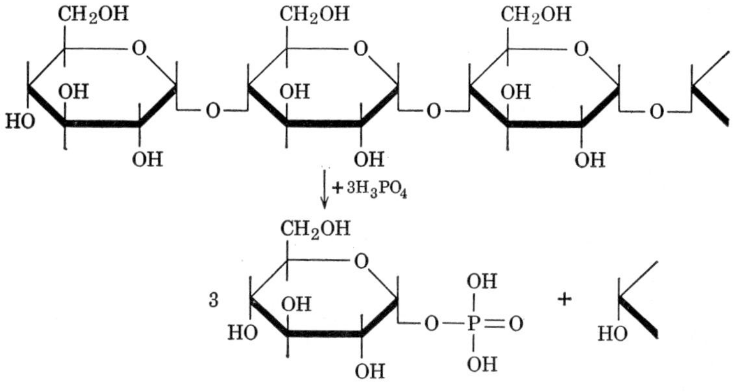

Glucose-1-phosphate

Arsenate can be used in place of phosphate in the phosphorylase-catalyzed reactions, but the resulting organic arsenate (e.g., glucose-1-arsenate) is rapidly hydrolyzed by water (cf. p. 326).

Phosphorylases have been found in extracts of many animal tissues (muscle, liver, heart, brain), of yeast, and of many higher plants (e.g., peas, potatoes). The work of Hanes[31] showed that the phosphorylases of plants convert starch to glucose-1-phosphate.

The study of the phosphorylases reached a high point in 1943, when the enzyme of rabbit muscle was obtained in the form of a crystalline protein (cf. p. 23) of particle weight about 500,000.[32] This protein represents about 2 per cent of the total protein material in the muscle extract. When the crystalline material became available, many of the results obtained with less homogeneous preparations of muscle phosphorylase were re-examined. For example, it had been found that the crude enzyme was inactive unless adenosine-5'-phosphate (AMP) was added. With the crystalline enzyme, there was appreciable activity in the absence of added AMP, although the addition of the nucleotide increased the activity somewhat. This contrast in the behavior of the two phosphorylase preparations became understandable when it was observed that the crystalline enzyme (named "phosphorylase a") was converted by a tissue enzyme, possibly a tissue proteinase, into a form

[31] C. S. Hanes, *Proc. Roy. Soc.,* **129B,** 174 (1940).
[32] A. A. Green and G. T. Cori, *J. Biol. Chem.,* **151,** 21 (1943); B. A. Illingworth and G. T. Cori, *Biochem. Preparations,* **3,** 1 (1953).

(phosphorylase b) that is inactive in the absence of added AMP. Although it was first thought that in the conversion of phosphorylase a to phosphorylase b an essential prosthetic group was removed, later work[33] showed that this conversion involves the cleavage of phosphorylase a into halves (particle weight ca. 250,000) as judged by ultracentrifugal studies. The enzyme responsible for this effect is now termed the "phosphorylase-rupturing" enzyme (PR enzyme).[34] Before phosphorylase a can be crystallized from a muscle extract, the PR enzyme must be removed; this separation of the two enzymes can be effected by isoelectric precipitation of the PR enzyme at pH 6.0. The possibility that the PR enzyme may be a proteolytic enzyme is indicated by the fact that crystalline pancreatic trypsin converts phosphorylase a to phosphorylase b without appreciable destruction of the potential phosphorylase activity. Phosphorylase b has also been obtained in crystalline form.[35]

Preparations of crystalline muscle phosphorylase a contain 4 moles of pyridoxal phosphate (p. 375) per unit of 500,000. Removal of the pyridoxal phosphate results in the loss of phosphorylase activity, which is restored by the addition of the cofactor.[36] Phosphorylase b contains 2 moles of pyridoxal phosphate per unit of 250,000. The role of pyridoxal phosphate in the catalytic action of muscle phosphorylase has not been elucidated as yet.

As noted above, phosphorylase b is activated by the addition of AMP. However, the reconversion of muscle phosphorylase b to phosphorylase a is an enzymic process that depends on the presence of adenosine triphosphate (ATP) and Mg^{2+} or Mn^{2+}.[37]

Similar relationships between inactive and active phosphorylase apply to the enzymes obtained from liver and heart.[38] The active form of liver phosphorylase (particle weight ca. 240,000) has been purified appreciably from dog liver.[39] It is inactivated by an accompanying liver enzyme in a process that causes no change in particle weight but involves the liberation of inorganic phosphate (2 moles per unit of 240,000), suggesting that the active liver phosphorylase is a phosphoprotein which is dephosphorylated by the inactivating enzyme. The conversion of the inactive dephosphorylated enzyme to the active form is effected by an enzyme

[33] P. J. Keller and G. T. Cori, *Biochim. et Biophys. Acta*, **12**, 235 (1953).

[34] P. J. Keller and G. T. Cori, *J. Biol. Chem.*, **214**, 127, 135 (1955).

[35] E. H. Fischer and E. G. Krebs, *J. Biol. Chem.*, **231**, 65 (1958).

[36] T. Baranowski et al., *Biochim. et. Biophys. Acta*, **25**, 16 (1957); C. F. Cori and B. Illingworth, *Proc. Natl. Acad. Sci.*, **43**, 547 (1957).

[37] E. H. Fischer and E. G. Krebs, *J. Biol. Chem.*, **216**, 121 (1955); E. G. Krebs and E. H. Fischer, *Biochim. et Biophys. Acta*, **20**, 150 (1956).

[38] T. W. Rall et al., *J. Biol. Chem.*, **218**, 483 (1956); *Biochim. et Biophys. Acta*, **20**, 69 (1956); E. W. Sutherland and T. W. Rall, *J. Am. Chem. Soc.*, **79**, 3608 (1957).

[39] E. W. Sutherland and W. D. Wosilait, *J. Biol. Chem.*, **218**, 459 (1956).

system that requires ATP and Mg^{2+}, as in the case of the enzyme from skeletal muscle; AMP does not activate liver phosphorylase. The activation of liver phosphorylase is influenced by the hormones epinephrine and glucagon (Chapter 38). In the presence of ATP, Mg^{2+}, and either epinephrine or glucagon, the sedimentable fraction of liver homogenates forms a cyclic adenosine-3',5'-phosphate (p. 204) which stimulates the production of active phosphorylase by the soluble fraction of such homogenates.

The study of the kinetics and equilibria in the reaction catalyzed by crystalline muscle phosphorylase a led to results of considerable general significance. Although for the enzyme-catalyzed hydrolysis of glycosidic bonds the position of the equilibrium is far in the direction of hydrolysis, the reaction catalyzed by phosphorylase is characterized by an extremely mobile equilibrium that can readily be approached from either direction. The equilibrium constant for the phosphorolysis may be written

$$K' = \frac{[\text{Glucose-1-phosphate}]^n}{[\text{Polysaccharide}][\text{inorganic P}]^n}$$

Since, during the reaction, the molar concentration of the polysaccharide changes only slightly compared with the concentrations of glucose-1-phosphate and of inorganic phosphate, K' may be calculated from the equilibrium ratio of glucose-1-phosphate to inorganic P. At $30°$ C, the ratio $[\text{glucose-1-phosphate}^-]/[\text{H}_2\text{PO}_4{}^-]$ is about 0.088.[40] The ratio of total glucose-1-phosphate to total phosphate varies with pH since the pK_2 values ($30°$ C) of these two substances are 6.51 and 7.19 respectively.[41]

It will be clear from the above equilibrium ratio that the free-energy change in the phosphorolysis is small. In fact, the phosphorolysis is an endergonic reaction; $\Delta F°$ at $30°$ C is about $+1.5$ kcal per mole. Under these conditions, therefore, it is the formation of the polysaccharide from glucose-1-phosphate that is exergonic.

Muscle phosphorylase a is inhibited by a variety of chemical agents.

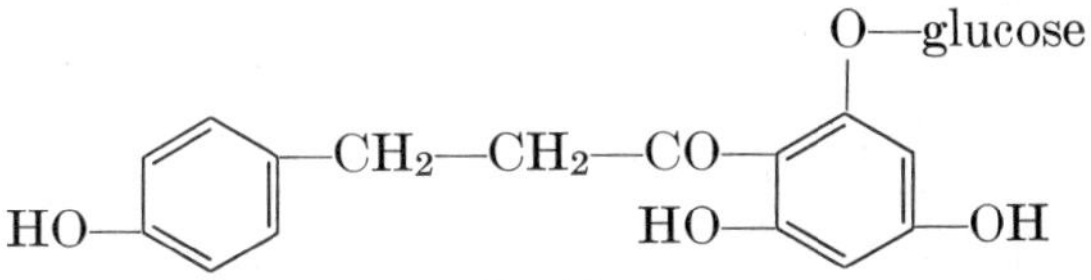

Phlorizin

Glucose is a competitive inhibitor with respect to glucose-1-phosphate; β-glycerophosphate and the plant glucoside phlorizin are noncompetitive inhibitors.

[40] W. E. Trevelyan et al., *Arch. Biochem. and Biophys.*, **39**, 419 (1952).
[41] J. H. Ashby et al., *Biochem. J.*, **59**, 203 (1955).

Of special importance with respect to the activity of crystalline muscle phosphorylase a is the absence of a reaction if the enzyme is added to pure glucose-1-phosphate. Synthesis of a polysaccharide ensues only if small quantities of glycogen or starch also are added (Fig. 3). With very

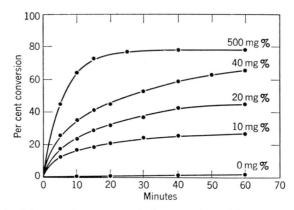

Fig. 3. Effect of increased amounts of glycogen (in milligrams per cent) on the rate of conversion of glucose-1-phosphate to polysaccharide by crystalline muscle phosphorylase. [From G. T. Cori et al., *Federation Proc.,* **4,** 234 (1945).]

small amounts of glycogen (about 10 mg per cent) equilibrium is not attained; with 40 mg per cent of glycogen the reaction reaches equilibrium at a rate that falls off more rapidly than can be accounted for on the basis of first-order kinetics; with 500 mg per cent of glycogen, the reaction proceeds at maximal rate and is kinetically of first order throughout its course. Under these conditions, the turnover number of muscle phosphorylase is about 40,000.

The work of the Cori group explained the role of the added polysaccharide as an activator by showing that it is actually a participant in the reaction, and that the function of the enzyme is to catalyze the interaction of glucose-1-phosphate with the nonreducing ends of the branches of the activating polysaccharide (Fig. 4). Branched-chain polysaccharides such as amylopectin or glycogen are good activators, whereas the straight-chain amylose has little or no effect. The "priming" efficiency of a polysaccharide is thus a function of the number of nonaldehydic terminal glucose units. It is of interest that the polysaccharide formed when muscle phosphorylase a acts on glucose-1-phosphate cannot itself serve as an activator in the reaction; this is in accord with the data (from end group assay) that show the polysaccharide to be a straight-chain amylose of 80 to 200 glucose units. Like the amylose of starch, the polysaccharide formed by phosphorylase gives a pure blue color with iodine. This means that crystalline muscle phosphorylase is restricted in its action to the synthesis of $\alpha(1\rightarrow4)$-glucosidic bonds. The enzyme is also specific for α-D-glucopyranose-1-phosphate; no other sugar phosphate that has been tested can be substituted.

The restriction in the specificity of phosphorylase to the synthesis of $(1\rightarrow4)$-glucosidic bonds raises the question: How are the $(1\rightarrow6)$-glucosidic bonds of muscle glycogen synthesized? Obviously the action of

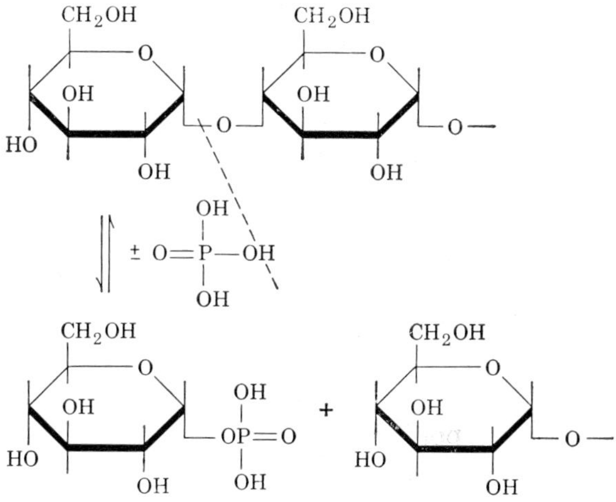

Fig. 4. Action of phosphorylase at nonreducing end of activating polysaccharide.

muscle phosphorylase must be supplemented by another enzyme-catalyzed reaction in which branching is induced, since muscle tissue itself contains little or no polysaccharides of the amylose type. Crude phosphorylase preparations from animal tissues such as liver and heart and from yeast cause the formation of branched polysaccharides, and contain a separate "branching" enzyme. By allowing muscle phosphorylase to catalyze the addition of C^{14}-labeled glucosyl units (of C^{14}-glucose-1-phosphate) to the outer branches of "primer" glycogen, and then by treatment of the labeled polysaccharide with branching enzyme (from liver) in the absence of phosphate, it was shown that isotopic $(1\rightarrow6)$-linked glucosyl units are formed.[42] This indicates that the branching enzyme catalyzes transglucosidation reactions (cf. p. 451) in which short segments of a long $(1\rightarrow4)$-linked amylose chain are transferred to the 6-hydroxyl of glucose units in the chain; the $(1\rightarrow4)$-linked chains are shortened and extensive branching at $(1\rightarrow6)$ linkages is effected (Fig. 5).

Many of the conclusions drawn from work on muscle phosphorylase also apply to potato phosphorylase. Crystalline preparations of the

[42] J. Larner, *J. Biol. Chem.*, **202**, 491 (1953).

latter enzyme have been described.[43] With potato phosphorylase, a straight-chain amylose is produced from glucose-1-phosphate, and a priming substance must be present; however, for the action of the plant enzyme, oligosaccharides containing 4 to 5 glucose units can serve as activators.[44] Another important difference between the two enzyme preparations is that the potato enzyme shows maximal activity in the absence of added AMP.

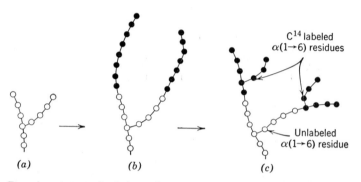

Fig. 5. Branch point synthesis by radioactive labeling technique. (a) Incompletely degraded glycogen segment (nonreducing end). (b) Glycogen segment with labeled outer chains. (c) Glycogen segment after action of branching enzyme. ○, unlabeled glucose residue; ●, C[14]-labeled glucose residue. (From Larner.[42])

The principal polysaccharide of potato starch is of the amylopectin type; from potato extracts an enzyme (named the "Q enzyme") has been obtained[45] which, in conjunction with purified potato phosphorylase, converts glucose-1-phosphate to a branched-chain polysaccharide that gives a red color with iodine. The Q enzyme appears to act as a transglucosidase that transfers short chains of (1→4)-glucosyl units to the 6-hydroxyl of other glucosyl units of an amylose chain, as in the case of the comparable liver branching enzyme.

The recognition of the mode of action of muscle phosphorylase, amylo-1,6-glucosidase, and β-amylase has permitted the use of these enzymes as reagents for the stepwise degradation of glycogen preparations.[46] The structural specificity of these three enzymes is summarized in Fig. 6. The combined action of phosphorylase and the (1→6)-glucosidase leads to the nearly complete degradation of glycogen to glucose-1-phosphate

[43] E. H. Fischer and H. M. Hilpert, *Experientia, 9,* 176 (1953); H. Baum and G. A. Gilbert, *Nature, 171,* 983 (1953).

[44] M. A. Swanson and C. F. Cori, *J. Biol. Chem., 172,* 815 (1948).

[45] S. Peat, *Advances in Enzymol., 11,* 339 (1951); G. A. Gilbert and A. D. Patrick, *Biochem. J., 51,* 81 (1952).

[46] B. Illingworth et al., *J. Biol. Chem., 199,* 631 (1952); J. Larner et al., *ibid.,* **199,** 641 (1952).

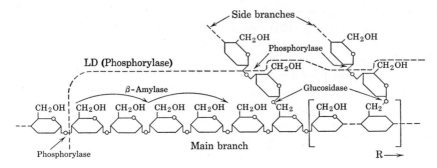

Fig. 6. Structural model of a portion of a branched polysaccharide showing the sites of enzymic action. LD corresponds to the limit dextrin formed by exhaustive action of phosphorylase. R refers to the reducing end of the polysaccharide. [From G. T. Cori and J. Larner, *J. Biol. Chem.*, **188**, 17 (1951).]

(phosphorolysis of (1→4)-glucosyl bonds) and to glucose (hydrolysis of (1→6) bonds); the ratio of glucose to glucose-1-phosphate liberated as each tier of glucosyl residues is removed gives a measure of the extent of branching (cf. Fig. 7). The results of stepwise enzymic degradation

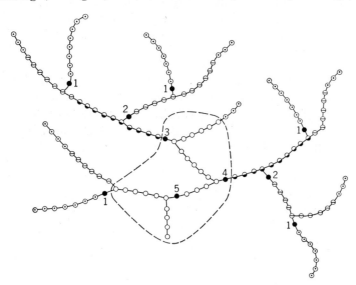

Fig. 7. Model of segment of rabbit muscle glycogen (150 glucose residues) containing 5 tiers. The portion enclosed by dash lines corresponds to the limit dextrin that would be produced after alternating treatment with phosphorylase (3 times) and amylo-1,6-glucosidase (twice). ⊙, ⊖, ⊘, glucose residues removed by first, second, and third degradation with phosphorylase respectively; ● at numbers 1 and 2, glucose residues removed by first and second degradation with the glucosidase respectively; ● at numbers 3, 4, and 5, glucose residues involved in (1→6) linkage and potentially susceptible to attack by the glucosidase. (From Larner et al.[46])

are in good agreement with data obtained by methylation (p. 418) or by periodate oxidation (p. 420); values of 7 to 13 glucosyl residues for the outer chains of glycogens, and of 3 to 5 residues for the inner chains, were obtained.

In a few cases of a group of human abnormalities known as "glycogen storage" disease, in which there are deposited unusually large amounts of glycogen in several tissues, the outer (1→4) chains were found to be much shorter than the normal average.[47] In the form of the disease characterized by glycogen storage in all tissues, and especially in muscle, the abnormality may be a consequence of a deficiency in amylo-1,6-glucosidase. Where glycogen storage is restricted to liver and kidney, it may be associated with a deficiency in glucose-6-phosphatase. This enzyme is responsible for the final step in the conversion of glycogen to glucose in the liver (cf. p. 497), and the absence of glucose-6-phosphatase may be expected to cause an increase in the amount of liver glycogen.

In what has gone before, attention has been focused on the phosphoro-lytic cleavage of polysaccharides. Evidence is at hand that a similar mode of enzymic action applies, at least in some organisms, to the break-down (and synthesis) of disaccharides, notably sucrose. It will be recalled that the hydrolysis of sucrose by invertase proceeds far in the direction of the split products; attempts to effect appreciable reversion of the enzymic hydrolysis have proved unsuccessful. In 1943, however, Doudoroff et al.[48] showed that dried preparations of the organism *Pseudomonas saccharophila* convert sucrose to glucose-1-phosphate and fructose and that this phosphorolysis is readily reversible (cf. Fig. 8). The enzyme ("sucrose phosphorylase") responsible for the catalysis of the reaction is an "adaptive enzyme"; it is produced in appreciable amounts when the culture medium for the organism contains sucrose or an oligosaccharide that can give rise to sucrose (e.g., raffinose). The enzyme does not appear in readily detectable amounts, however, if the organism is grown in the presence of glucose, maltose, or starch as the sole source of carbon. At present, partially purified preparations of the enzyme are available from *P. saccharophila* and from *Leuconostoc mesenteroides*. If arsenate is used in place of phosphate, free glucose is formed from sucrose, since the intermediate glucose-1-arsenate is rapidly hydrolyzed by water (cf. p. 326).

Sucrose phosphorylase has no detectable action on starch, maltose, lactose, or raffinose. Also, if glucose-1-phosphate is replaced by galactose-

[47] G. T. Cori, *Harvey Lectures,* **48,** 145 (1954); B. Illingworth et al., *J. Biol. Chem.,* **218,** 123 (1956).
[48] M. Doudoroff et al., *J. Biol. Chem.,* **148,** 67 (1943).

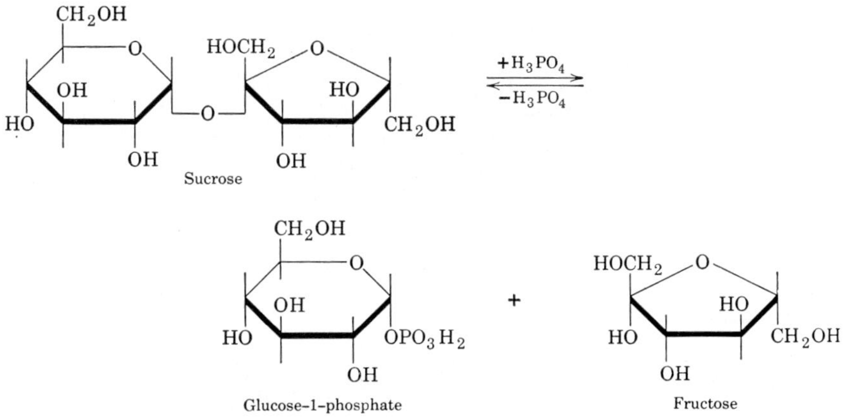

Fig. 8. Action of sucrose phosphorylase.

1-phosphate or mannose-1-phosphate, no reaction with fructose can be demonstrated. However, fructose may be replaced by one of several monosaccharides as shown in the reactions given below.

(I) α-D-Glucose-1-phosphate + L-sorbose ⇌

α-D-Glucopyranosyl-α-L-sorbofuranoside + phosphate

(II) α-D-Glucose-1-phosphate + D-xylulose ⇌

α-D-Glucopyranosyl-β-D-xylulofuranoside + phosphate

(III) α-D-Glucose-1-phosphate + L-arabulose ⇌

α-D-Glucopyranosyl-α-L-arabulofuranoside + phosphate

(IV) α-D-Glucose-1-phosphate + L-arabinose ⇌

3-(α-D-Glucopyranosyl)-L-arabinopyranose + phosphate

The structures of the four disaccharides synthesized in the above reactions are shown in the formulae on p. 448.

It will be noted that in these reactions α-glucosidic bonds are involved in the interconversion of α-D-glucose-1-phosphate and disaccharides. In contrast to this retention of configuration is the reaction catalyzed by an enzyme ("maltose phosphorylase") present in *Neisseria meningitides*:

4-(α-D-Glucopyranosyl)-D-glucopyranose + phosphate ⇌

β-D-Glucose-1-phosphate + D-glucose

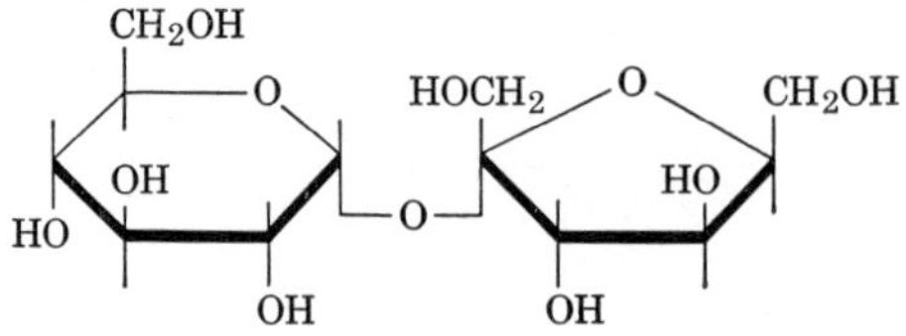

In the reverse reaction, D-xylose can be used in place of D-glucose, but α-D-glucose-1-phosphate does not serve as a substrate.[49]

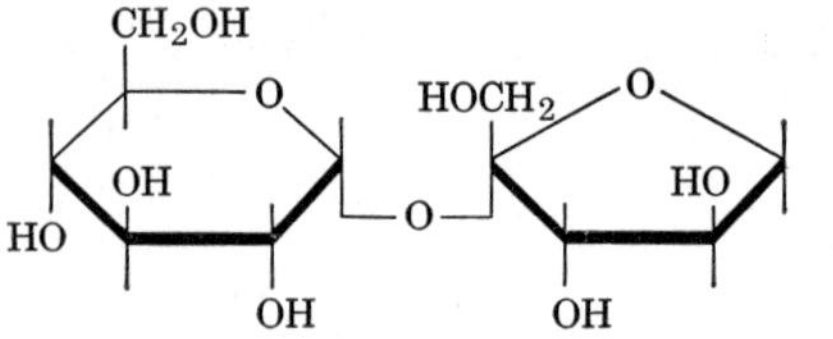

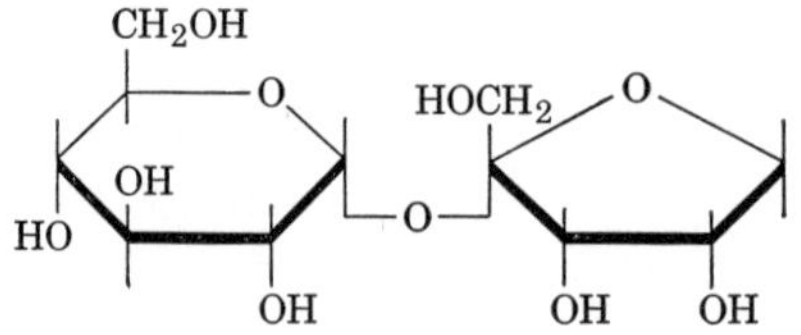

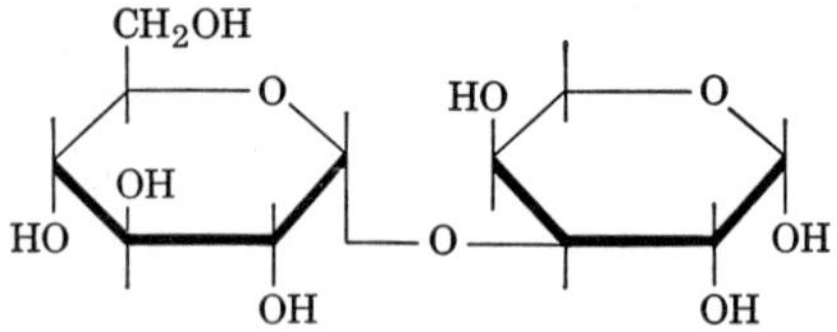

Important conclusions about the mechanism of the action of sucrose phosphorylase emerged from studies in which the phosphorolysis of sucrose was studied in the presence of phosphate containing P^{32}. Doudoroff et al.[50] found that, if one adds glucose-1-phosphate and radioactive phosphate to the enzyme, in the absence of a ketose, there occurs a rapid exchange of the radioactive P between the glucose-1-phosphate and the inorganic phosphate, indicating that the following reaction had occurred:

Glucose-1-phosphate + enzyme ⇌ Glucosyl-enzyme + phosphate

In the synthesis of a disaccharide, therefore, the glucose-enzyme complex then reacts with a "glucose acceptor" such as fructose. This finding led to the examination of the action of sucrose phosphorylase on sucrose in the presence of a ketohexose such as sorbose, but in the absence of phosphate. In this system it was found that the glucose moiety was transferred from the fructose part of sucrose to sorbose to form a new disaccharide, a glucosylsorboside:

Glucosyl-1-fructoside + sorbose ⇌ Glucosyl-1-sorboside + fructose

It follows from the above that the action of the enzyme is to catalyze the reaction of the "activated" aldehydic group of D-glucose with a suitable acceptor, and that this activation can be effected by converting glucose to either glucose-1-phosphate or to a glucoside. Hence phosphate

[49] C. Fitting and M. Doudoroff, J. Biol. Chem., 199, 153, 573 (1952); E. W. Putman et al., J. Am. Chem. Soc., 77, 4351 (1955).

[50] M. Doudoroff et al., J. Biol. Chem., 168, 725 (1947).

is not an indispensable component of the enzyme-catalyzed reaction, and the term "sucrose phosphorylase" is too restrictive. In the phosphorolysis of sucrose, phosphate serves as the acceptor of glucose but other substances (e.g., sorbose) can also serve in this capacity. If one considers the sugar—phosphate bond of glucose-1-phosphate to be formally equivalent to the glycosidic bond of a disaccharide, the function of the enzyme may be described more properly as the catalysis of a replacement reaction, in which one component of a glucosidic bond is replaced by another, with a relatively small over-all free-energy change. Replacement reactions of this type have been termed "transglycosidation" (or "transglycosylation") reactions, and sucrose phosphorylase is more properly named a "transglucosidase," since it can cause glucose, bound in glycosidic linkage, to combine with a variety of glucose acceptors.[51] Indeed, among these acceptors may possibly be included water, since sucrose phosphorylase preparations from *Leuconostoc mesenteroides* catalyze slow hydrolysis of sucrose and of glucose-1-phosphate at pH 6.6.[52] It should be added that the above conclusions do not appear to apply to maltose phosphorylase, which does not catalyze an exchange between P^{32}-labeled phosphate and β-D-glucose-1-phosphate.

The mechanism proposed by Doudoroff et al.[50] for the action of sucrose phosphorylase apparently does not strictly apply to the phosphorolysis of starch or glycogen by muscle or potato phosphorylase. Cohn and Cori[53] have shown that, when glucose-1-phosphate is incubated with muscle phosphorylase a (or potato phosphorylase) and radioactive inorganic phosphate in the absence of a priming polysaccharide, the glucose-1-phosphate does not become radioactive. It would appear, therefore, that these phosphorylases do not catalyze an exchange between the inorganic phosphate and the organic phosphate, and that here the presence of phosphate (or of glucose-1-phosphate) is indispensable for enzyme action. However, Cohn[54] has provided evidence to indicate that muscle phosphorylase and sucrose phosphorylase attack glucose-1-phosphate at the same linkage. By using inorganic phosphate labeled with O^{18}, she showed that with both enzymes the cleavage of glucose-1-phosphate occurs between carbon 1 of glucose and the oxygen of the phosphate group (cf. Fig. 9). A similar cleavage occurs upon hydrolysis catalyzed by H^+. On the other hand, when glucose-1-phosphate is subjected to enzymic hydrolysis in the presence of H_2O^{18} and the reaction is catalyzed

[51] W. Z. Hassid and M. Doudoroff, *Advances in Enzymol.*, **10**, 123 (1950); H. M. Kalckar, in W. D. McElroy and B. Glass, *Mechanism of Enzyme Action*, Johns Hopkins Press, Baltimore, 1954.

[52] R. Weinberg and M. Doudoroff, *J. Bact.*, **68**, 381 (1954).

[53] M. Cohn and G. T. Cori, *J. Biol. Chem.*, **175**, 89 (1948).

[54] M. Cohn, *J. Biol. Chem.*, **180**, 771 (1949).

by phosphatases, the cleavage occurs between the oxygen at carbon 1 and the phosphorus atom. The phosphatases will be discussed later (Chapter 24); for the present it may suffice to call attention to the difference between their action and that of the phosphorylases.

Another important group of phosphorylases are those that catalyze the phosphorolysis of nucleosides. It was shown by Kalckar[55] that the

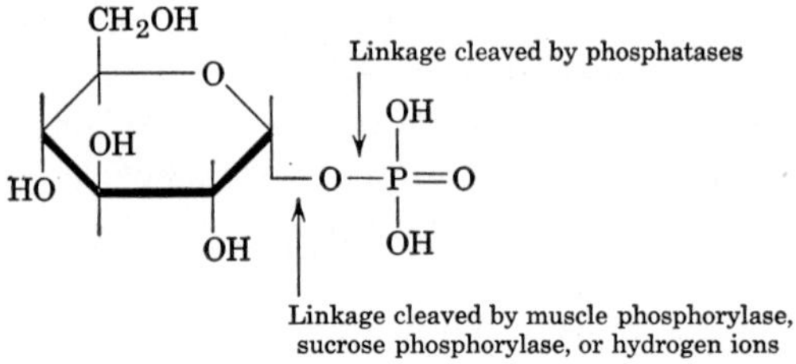

Linkage cleaved by phosphatases

Linkage cleaved by muscle phosphorylase, sucrose phosphorylase, or hydrogen ions

Fig. 9. Mode of action of several enzymes on glucose-1-phosphate.

nucleosidases of liver and spleen, thought for many years to be hydrolytic enzymes, were in fact phosphorylases which act in reversible reactions of the type:

Inosine + phosphate $\rightleftharpoons$ Hypoxanthine + ribose-1-phosphate

The equilibrium in this reaction was found to be in favor of synthesis of the nucleoside. The nucleoside phosphorylases, and related enzymes, are discussed more fully in Chapter 35 in relation to their role in the intermediate metabolism of nucleic acids.

Before concluding this section on the phosphorylases, further attention may be given to the problem of the biosynthesis of sucrose. Although the presence of sucrose phosphorylase in some microorganisms provides an enzymic mechanism for the formation of this important disaccharide from glucose-1-phosphate and fructose, this pathway does not appear to be significant in sucrose synthesis by higher plants. The work of Leloir, Cardini, and others[56] has shown that extracts of plant tissues contain an enzyme ("UDPG-fructose transglycosylase") that catalyzes the transfer of the glucosyl residue of uridine diphosphate glucose (UDPG; cf. p. 205) to fructose, thus forming sucrose and uridine diphosphate (UDP). Other ketosugars (L-sorbose, D-xylulose, D-rhamnulose) also serve as acceptors of the glucosyl group of UDPG to form the corresponding disaccharides. Some plant preparations also catalyze the formation of sucrose phosphate

[55] H. M. Kalckar, *Federation Proc.*, **4**, 248 (1945).

[56] C. E. Cardini et al., *J. Biol. Chem.*, **214**, 149 (1955); L. F. Leloir and C. E. Cardini, *ibid.*, **214**, 157 (1955); R. C. Bean and W. Z. Hassid, *J. Am. Chem. Soc.*, **77**, 5737 (1955); D. P. Burma and D. C. Mortimer, *Arch. Biochem. and Biophys.*, **62**, 16 (1956); J. F. Turner, *Biochem. J.*, **67**, 450 (1957).

from UDPG and fructose-6-phosphate (p. 458); sucrose phosphate is hydrolyzed to sucrose by an enzyme in plants. The various enzymes responsible for these reactions have not yet been purified. UDPG probably arises by the reaction of glucose-1-phosphate with uridine tri-

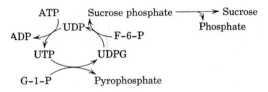

phosphate (UTP). The probable sequence of reactions in the synthesis of sucrose from glucose-1-phosphate (G-1-P) and fructose-6-phosphate (F-6-P) by higher plants is shown in the accompanying scheme. Other enzymic reactions involving glycosidic derivatives of UDP are discussed on p. 464.

Transglycosidases

It was seen above that the action of sucrose phosphorylase does not depend on the presence of phosphate and that this enzyme is more accurately classified as a transglycosidase. This is by no means the first recorded example of an enzyme that catalyzes the replacement of one component of a glycosidic bond by another. Since the beginning of the century (Beijerinck, 1910), it was known that certain bacteria make polysaccharides if they are grown on sucrose, but not if they are grown on a mixture of glucose and fructose. For example, *Leuconostoc mesenteroides* synthesizes dextran from sucrose. As noted earlier (cf. p. 429), dextran is a polysaccharide in which D-glucopyranose units are joined by means of $\alpha(1\rightarrow6)$-glycosidic linkages, with occasional cross-linking to form $\alpha(1\rightarrow3)$- and $\alpha(1\rightarrow4)$-bridges. A number of investigators have shown that, in the absence of phosphate, cultures of *L. mesenteroides* catalyze the reaction

$$n \text{ Sucrose } \rightarrow n \text{ Fructose } + (\text{glucose})_n$$

In this synthesis, the fructose units of sucrose are replaced by glucose units in a series of transglucosidation reactions. The enzyme responsible for dextran formation has been named dextran sucrase.[57] Under favorable conditions, dextrans of average particle weight 75,000 are formed.[58] If dextrans of low molecular weight or sugars such as isomaltose, maltose, or glucose are present in addition to sucrose, dextran sucrase causes the

[57] E. J. Hehre, *Advances in Enzymol.,* **11**, 297 (1951).
[58] H. M. Tsuchiya et al., *J. Am. Chem. Soc.,* **77**, 2412 (1955).

formation of glucosyl derivatives of these acceptors. A by-product of the dextran sucrase reaction is leucrose (5-(α-D-glucopyranosyl)-D-fructose).[59]

Similar polysaccharide synthesis has been noted with *Bacillus subtilis,* and other organisms, with the important difference that, in place of dextran, the polysaccharide levan is formed. Since levan is a fructosan in which the D-fructofuranose units are joined by means of $(2 \rightarrow 6)$-glycosidic linkages, it is apparent that a transfructosidation reaction occurs as follows:

$$n \text{ Sucrose } \rightarrow n \text{ Glucose } + (\text{fructose})_n$$

Clearly, in levan formation sucrose serves as a fructoside, whereas in dextran formation it serves as a glucoside. The enzyme responsible for levan formation from sucrose has been named levan sucrase.[60] A preparation from *Aerobacter levanicum* catalyzes the transfer of the β-fructofuranosyl group of raffinose (p. 416) to xylose, with the formation of α-D-xylopyranosyl-β-D-fructofuranoside, or to galactose, yielding α-D-galactopyranosyl-β-D-fructofuranoside.[61]

Dextrans and levan are rather special types of polysaccharides, since they give no color with iodine and are not attacked by amylases. It may be asked, therefore, whether the mechanism of transglycosidation in the absence of phosphate is also operative in the synthesis of polysaccharides that resemble the amyloses or amylopectins. The actual occurence of such transformations in bacterial systems has been demonstrated by Hehre,[62] who found that cell-free extracts of *Neisseria perflava* catalyze the reaction

$$n \text{ Sucrose } \rightarrow n \text{ Fructose } + (\text{glucose})_n$$

The polysaccharide formed in this reaction resembles amylopectin in giving a brown color with iodine and is attacked by amylases. End group assay showed this polysaccharide to be composed of short chains, each of which contains 11 to 12 glucose units linked by $(1 \rightarrow 4)$-glucosidic bonds, with $(1 \rightarrow 6)$ bonds at the branch points. Apparently two enzymes cooperate to cause the branching. Hehre has named the enzyme preparation responsible for these transglycosidation reactions amylosucrase. Another case of transglycosidation leading to the synthesis of a starchlike polysaccharide was discovered by Monod and Torriani in 1948, and examined further by Doudoroff et al.[63] Monod observed that certain

[59] F. H. Stodola et al., *J. Am. Chem., Soc.,* **78,** 2514 (1956).

[60] S. Hestrin et al., *Biochem. J.,* **64,** 340, 351 (1956).

[61] G. Avigad et al., *Biochim. et Biophys. Acta,* **20,** 129 (1956); D. S. Feingold et al., *J. Biol. Chem.,* **224,** 295 (1957).

[62] E. J. Hehre, *J. Biol. Chem.,* **177,** 267 (1949).

[63] M. Doudoroff et al., *J. Biol. Chem.,* **179,** 921 (1949).

strains of *Escherichia coli* act on maltose; glucose is formed, but the amount of the free hexose (determined by means of glucose oxidase) is equivalent to only one-half of the maltose that has disappeared. Here the cleavage of maltose is accomplished not by a hydrolytic mechanism, but by a transglycosidation leading to the formation of a polysaccharide which gives a blue color with iodine. The enzyme involved has been named amylomaltase, and the reaction that it catalyzes may be written:

$$n \text{ Maltose} \rightarrow n \text{ Glucose} + (\text{glucose})_n$$

Doudoroff et al.[63] showed this reaction to be reversible. Monod's data reopened the problem whether the production of glucose from maltose by bacteria other than *E. coli* is due to α-glucosidases or to enzymes which are in fact transglucosidases.

Since none of the known transglycosidases has been purified appreciably to date, their relationship to other enzymes present in the bacterial extracts and acting on glycosidic bonds cannot be specified. However, the discovery of these enzymes is of general significance because it demonstrates that the synthesis of glycosidic bonds in all living systems does not necessarily involve the direct participation of phosphate. The above discussion brings to the fore the important generalization that some biological systems contain enzymes which can catalyze the formation of polysaccharides of the amylose type by the two following mechanisms:

(1) Glucose-1-phosphate $\rightarrow$ Polysaccharide + phosphate

(2) Glucosyl-1-glycoside $\rightarrow$ Polysaccharide + sugar

In both instances, the reactivity of the carbon 1 of glucose is enhanced by the conversion of glucose to a derivative which can serve as a substrate for a transglycosidation reaction characterized by a relatively small change in free energy. It must be stressed that in order to make this derivative from free glucose energy is required; as will be seen from the discussion in the next chapter, this energy may be derived from the cleavage of one of the pyrophosphate bonds of adenosine triphosphate. However, once this derivative is formed, and if suitable catalysts are present in the biological system, the synthesis of polysaccharide may be effected by exergonic replacement reactions.

Earlier in this chapter it was mentioned that the formation of cyclic dextrins by *Bacillus macerans* amylase (cf. p. 436) is a transglucosidation reaction; enzyme preparations from this organism also catalyze transglucosidation reactions in which linear polyglucoses interact with each other to form a mixture of shorter and longer chains.[64] A similar

[64] E. Norberg and D. French, *J. Am. Chem. Soc.*, **72**, 1202 (1950); D. French et al., *ibid.*, **76**, 2387 (1954).

transglucosidase has been found in potatoes and named "D enzyme." It converts $\alpha(1\rightarrow4)$-oligosaccharides to glucose and to longer $\alpha(1\rightarrow4)$ chains.[65]

Among the transglucosidases are also the branching enzymes of animal and plant tissues (cf. p. 443); these enzymes catalyze the transfer of oligosaccharide units from $\alpha(1\rightarrow4)$- to $\alpha(1\rightarrow6)$-glucosidic bonds. A similar type of reaction is effected by enzymes found in the molds *Aspergillus niger* and *Aspergillus oryzae*, which convert maltose to $\alpha(1\rightarrow6)$-oligosaccharides such as panose (α-D-glucopyranosyl-$(1\rightarrow6)$- α-D-glucopyranosyl-$(1\rightarrow4)$-α-D-glucopyranose) and the related trisaccharide in which both glycosidic linkages are $(1\rightarrow6)$ bonds.[66] Preparations from *A. oryzae* also catalyze the transfer of glucosyl groups from maltose to the 3 position of a glucose unit.[67]

In considering the specificity of the so-called transglycosidases, it must be recognized that the enzymes usually classified as hydrolases because they catalyze the hydrolysis of particular glycosidic bonds also catalyze transglycosidation reactions involving these bonds.[68] If one considers the function of a glycosidase to be the activation of a glycosidic bond in a hydrolytic reaction, where water serves as the acceptor, this activation also facilitates reactions in which the hydroxyl groups of alcohols, monosaccharides, or oligosaccharides serve as acceptors. This has been clearly demonstrated for invertase[69] (p. 433), which acts as a transfructosidase, and transfers β-fructofuranosyl units from sucrose to a suitable acceptor. The relative extent of transfer and hydrolysis depends on the concentration of the reactants, the nature of the acceptor (other than water), and other experimental conditions. β-Glucosidases (e.g., emulsin; p. 432) also catalyze transglycosidation reactions, in which glucosyl units are transferred.[70] Other types of transglycosidation reactions catalyzed by glycosidase preparations are the enzymic transfer to suitable acceptors of β-glucuronic acid units from β-glucuronides,[71] and the transfer of galactosyl units from lactose.[72] Furthermore, in the action of testicular

[65] S. Peat et al., *J. Chem. Soc.,* **1956**, 44, 53.

[66] S. C. Pan et al., *J. Am. Chem. Soc.,* **73**, 2547 (1951); J. H. Pazur and D. French, *J. Biol. Chem.,* **196**, 265 (1952).

[67] J. H. Pazur et al., *J. Am. Chem. Soc.,* **79**, 625 (1957).

[68] J. Edelman, *Advances in Enzymol.,* **17**, 189 (1956).

[69] J. S. D. Bacon, *Ann. Reps.,* **50**, 281 (1954); *Biochem. J.,* **57**, 320 (1954); P. J. Allen and J. S. D. Bacon, *ibid.,* **63**, 200 (1956).

[70] J. E. Courtois and M. Leclerc, *Bull. soc. chim. biol.,* **38**, 365 (1956); E. M. Crook and B. A. Stone, *Biochem. J.,* **65**, 1 (1957).

[71] W. H. Fishman and S. Green, *J. Am. Chem. Soc.,* **78**, 880 (1956).

[72] M. Aronson, *Arch. Biochem. and Biophys.,* **39**, 370 (1952); J. H. Pazur, *J. Biol. Chem.,* **208**, 439 (1954).

hyaluronidase (p. 437) on mucopolysaccharides, transglycosidation reactions have been shown to occur.[73]

It follows therefore that no sharp line of demarcation can be drawn between enzymes that catalyze hydrolysis of glycosidic bonds and those that catalyze transglycosidation reactions. Some of the enzymes originally named glycosidases effect transfer reactions in addition to hydrolysis, and some of the enzymes named transglycosidases (e.g., sucrose phosphorylase; p. 449) appear to catalyze hydrolysis. It is probable that the specificity of the transglycosidases strongly favors the replacement reaction over hydrolysis under the experimental conditions usually employed. However, the unequivocal study of the relation of transglycosidation to hydrolysis by such enzymes must await their purification.

As will be seen later, other so-called hydrolases, notably the esterases, phosphatases, and peptidases, catalyze replacement reactions. Under suitable conditions, some of these enzymes appear to act solely as catalysts of transfer reactions, and the extent of hydrolysis is small.

[73] B. Weissmann, *J. Biol. Chem.*, **216**, 783 (1955); P. Hoffman et al., *ibid.*, **219**, 653 (1956).

19 ·

Fermentation and Glycolysis

Mention has already been made of the important place occupied in the history of biochemistry by studies of the fermentation of glucose to ethanol and CO_2. In 1810 Gay-Lussac showed that the equation $C_6H_{12}O_6 \rightarrow 2C_2H_5OH + 2CO_2$ describes the over-all reaction. The work of Cagniard-Latour, Schwann, and Kützing showed, in 1837, that the phenomenon of alcoholic fermentation involves the participation of living yeast cells; these investigators and many who followed them believed that the act of fermentation is indissolubly linked with the life of the yeast cell. Foremost among the later students of this subject was Pasteur, who made many decisive discoveries about the chemical activity of microorganisms. Of special importance was his demonstration in 1861 that the production of alcohol from glucose by yeast is a process that does not require the participation of atmospheric oxygen; i.e., it is an anaerobic process. This led to the epoch-making generalization that the act of fermentation is an expression of the ability of organisms to draw nourishment and energy from glucose in the absence of oxygen; as Pasteur termed it, fermentation is associated with "la vie sans air." Pasteur's studies showed that the anaerobic breakdown of sugar by various microorganisms leads to the formation, not only of ethanol, but also of other products: lactic acid, succinic acid, butyric acid, glycerol. All these anaerobic transformations of sugar were subsumed under the general heading of fermentations, and it has become customary to refer to "alcoholic fermentation," "lactic acid fermentation," etc.

With prophetic insight, Pasteur recognized that living cells which require oxygen for normal growth and function also possess the capacity to derive energy from glucose by degrading it under anaerobic conditions. Work during the succeeding 100 years amply demonstrated the correctness of this view that aerobic cells, both of unicellular and of multicellular organisms, can perform "fermentations" as well as the aerobic oxidation of glucose and other metabolites. The systematic study of the enzymes responsible for the catalysis of these metabolic processes began only after 1897, when Buchner succeeded in obtaining from yeast a cell-free extract which was able to convert glucose to ethanol (cf. p. 214). A valuable summary of the researches of Buchner and of his contemporaries may be found in the monograph by Harden.[1] A review on yeast fermentations is that of Nord and Weiss.[2]

The early workers recognized that yeast extracts ferment not only glucose, but also fructose, mannose, sucrose, and maltose, the last two sugars presumably being first hydrolyzed by glycosidases to form the component monosaccharides. Primary attention was given to the fermentation of glucose by such extracts, and during the period 1900 to 1950 many distinguished biochemists participated in the elucidation of the mechanism of alcoholic fermentation. After Meyerhof found that extracts of mammalian muscle cause the anaerobic degradation of glycogen to lactic acid ("glycolysis"), the study of anaerobic glycolysis and of alcoholic fermentation developed in parallel; the results obtained with muscle extracts illumined the problems encountered in yeast fermentation, and vice versa. It will be convenient for the present discussion to consider first the salient facts about the anaerobic breakdown of glucose and other monosaccharides in microorganisms and then to examine the situation as it applies to mammalian muscle and other animal tissues.

Fermentation of Hexoses by Yeast

An important initial step in the study of the mode of action of yeast extracts on glucose was taken by Harden and Young in 1905. They showed that the production of CO_2 from glucose began at a rapid rate, but quickly fell off unless inorganic phosphate were added. This is shown in Fig. 1, which illustrates the dependence of the rate of fermentation (as measured by CO_2 evolution) on the presence or absence of added inorganic phosphate. Harden and Young also found that, in the course of the fermentation, the added phosphate disappeared. They concluded therefore that it was being converted to organic phosphate, and succeeded in isolating a hexose diphosphate (Harden-Young ester), later shown to be α-D-fructofuranose-1,6-diphosphate. Harden and Young suggested that the following equation described the fermentation:

$$2C_6H_{12}O_6 + 2H_3PO_4 \rightarrow$$
$$2CO_2 + 2C_2H_5OH + C_6H_{10}O_6(PO_3H_2)_2 + 2H_2O$$

[1] A. Harden, *Alcoholic Fermentation*, 3rd Ed., Longmans, Green and Co., London, 1923.

[2] F. F. Nord and S. Weiss, in J. B. Sumner and K. Myrbäck, *The Enzymes*, Chapter 64, Academic Press, New York, 1951.

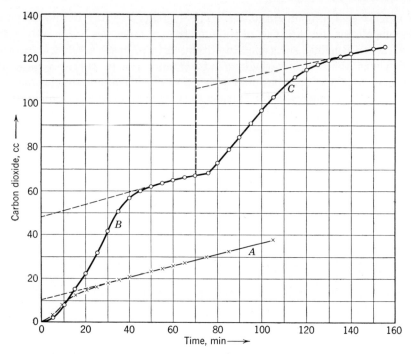

Fig. 1. Rate of evolution of carbon dioxide in fermentation of glucose by a yeast extract. Curve *A*, no phosphate added; curve *B*, phosphate added; curve *C*, second addition of phosphate 70 min after start of experiment. (From A. Harden.[1])

Later, two other phosphorylated sugar derivatives were isolated; they proved to be D-glucopyranose-6-phosphate (Robison ester) and D-fructofuranose-6-phosphate (Neuberg ester).

Fructose-1,6-diphosphate   Glucose-6-phosphate   Fructose-6-phosphate

In the formulae for the sugar phosphates, the phosphoric acid residue is written in the undissociated form. This practice will be followed for convenience only; at physiological pH values, extensive dissociation of the $-OPO_3H_2$ group occurs since the pK_1' and pK_2' values of the sugar phosphates are near pH 2 and 6 respectively.

The question to be considered next is the metabolic relationship of these three phosphorylated hexoses to glucose. It will be recalled that Harden and Young had found that dialysis of a yeast extract destroyed its capacity to ferment glucose (cf. p. 307); one constituent of the dialysate was later shown to be the cofactor diphosphopyridine nucleotide (DPN). This is not the only substance essential for fermentation that is lost on dialysis; other substances are certain inorganic ions, thiamine pyrophosphate (p. 475), and adenosine-5′-triphosphate (ATP) or the closely related adenosine-5′-diphosphate (ADP) and adenosine-5′-monophosphate (AMP). If to a dialyzed yeast extract one adds glucose and inorganic phosphate, no phosphorylated sugars can be demonstrated in the mixture. However, upon the addition of ATP and Mg^{2+} ions, glucose is phosphorylated by the transfer of the terminal phosphate of ATP to the 6-hydroxyl of glucose to form glucose-6-phosphate. The

$$\text{Glucose} + \text{ATP} \rightleftharpoons \text{Glucose-6-phosphate} + \text{ADP}$$

discovery of this transphosphorylation reaction stems from the work of Meyerhof, who in 1927 named the enzyme that catalyzes it "hexokinase." This enzyme is representative of a group of transphosphorylases that catalyze the transfer of the terminal phosphate of ATP to a suitable acceptor; such enzymes are frequently denoted "kinases," a prefix being added to indicate the nature of the substance that is phosphorylated by ATP. A more descriptive designation of hexokinase might be ATP-hexose transphosphorylase.

At first, the hexokinase reaction was thought to be

$$2 \text{ Glucose} + \text{ATP} \rightarrow 2 \text{ Glucose-6-phosphate} + \text{AMP}$$

Later work showed, however, that crude hexokinase preparations contain an enzyme (myokinase, adenylate kinase) that catalyzes the reaction: $2 \text{ ADP} \rightleftharpoons \text{ATP} + \text{AMP}$.[3] Thus the presence of myokinase leads to the conversion of 2 moles of glucose to glucose-6-phosphate per mole of ATP converted to AMP in a process linked by ADP. Myokinase is not restricted to muscle, as its name suggests, but is widely distributed in biological systems. It may be termed more correctly ATP-AMP transphosphorylase, and is a member of a group of enzymes that catalyze the interconversion of nucleotides (Chapter 35). Crystalline myokinase has been prepared from rabbit muscle.

Yeast hexokinase has been obtained in crystalline form[4] (particle weight ca. 97,000); it has been reported to be a glycoprotein with man-

[3] S. P. Colowick and H. M. Kalckar, *J. Biol. Chem.*, **148**, 117, 127 (1943); L. Noda and S. A. Kuby, *ibid.*, **226**, 541, 551 (1957).

[4] L. Berger et al., *J. Gen. Physiol.*, **29**, 379 (1946); M. Kunitz and M. R. McDonald, *ibid.*, **29**, 393 (1946).

nose units as constituents of the polysaccharide chain.[5] The enzyme catalyzes the reaction of ATP with glucose, fructose, and mannose; the K_m value for mannose is similar to that for glucose (ca. 10^{-4} M), whereas K_m for fructose is about 10^{-3} M.[6] With fructose and mannose, the corresponding 6-phosphates also are formed. N-Acetylglucosamine does not serve as a substrate, but glucosamine is converted to glucosamine-6-phosphate. Mg^{2+} is essential for the action of hexokinase. Although the phosphorylation of glucose by ATP is a strongly exergonic reaction (cf. p. 375), its reversibility has been demonstrated experimentally,[7] and it is not "irreversible," as sometimes stated. Animal tissues contain hexokinases that differ in many respects from yeast hexokinase, and enzyme preparations specific for glucose (glucokinase) or fructose (fructokinase) have been described (cf. p. 500). Specific glucokinases have been reported for some microorganisms, and a specific fructokinase has been found in pea seeds.[8]

Glucose-6-phosphate was first isolated by Robison[9] as part of a mixture which also contained fructose-6-phosphate; subsequent work by Lohmann[10] showed that there is an enzyme in muscle extracts, later also found in plants, which catalyzes the attainment of a mobile equilibrium between these two sugar phosphates. This enzyme has been named

$$\text{Glucose-6-phosphate} \rightleftharpoons \text{Fructose-6-phosphate}$$

phosphohexoisomerase (or phosphoglucoisomerase); at equilibrium there is about 70 per cent glucose-6-phosphate and 30 per cent fructose-6-phosphate (pH 8, 30° C). The reaction proceeds via an enediol intermediate, as shown.

$$\underset{\displaystyle -\!\overset{\displaystyle |}{\text{C}}\text{H}\!-\!\text{CHO}}{\overset{\displaystyle \text{OH}}{}} \rightleftharpoons \underset{\displaystyle -\!\overset{\displaystyle |}{\text{C}}\!=\!\text{CHOH}}{\overset{\displaystyle \text{OH}}{}} \rightleftharpoons \underset{\displaystyle -\!\overset{\displaystyle ||}{\text{C}}\!-\!\text{CH}_2\text{OH}}{\overset{\displaystyle \text{O}}{}}$$

It will be recalled that Harden and Young isolated fructose-1,6-diphosphate from the fermentation of glucose by yeast. The formation of this derivative involves an enzyme-catalyzed transfer of phosphate from ATP to fructose-6-phosphate. Thus, to prepare glucose for fermentative breakdown, two separate transphosphorylation reactions involving ATP are required. The reaction by which fructose-6-phosphate

[5] H. Boser, Z. physiol. Chem., **300**, 1 (1955).

[6] M. W. Slein et al., J. Biol. Chem., **186**, 763 (1950).

[7] J. L. Gamble, Jr., and V. A. Najjar, Science, **120**, 1023 (1954); J. Biol. Chem., **217**, 595 (1955).

[8] A. Medina and A. Sols, Biochim. et Biophys. Acta, **19**, 378 (1956).

[9] R. Robison, The Significance of Phosphoric Esters in Metabolism, New York University Press, New York, 1932.

[10] K. Lohmann, Biochem. Z., **262**, 137 (1933).

is converted to the 1,6-diphosphate is much like the hexokinase reaction and is characterized by a large negative $\Delta F'$ value. The enzyme that catalyzes the formation of fructose-1,6-diphosphate is termed phosphohexokinase (or phosphofructokinase); it has not been studied extensively.

$$\text{Fructose-6-phosphate} + \text{ATP} \rightleftharpoons \text{Fructose-1,6-diphosphate} + \text{ADP}$$

Apparently, inosine triphosphate (ITP) and uridine triphosphate (UTP) also donate their terminal phosphoryl groups to fructose-6-phosphate in analogous reactions.[11]   Although enzymes (termed nucleoside diphosphokinases) are known that catalyze the reaction[12]

$$\text{ITP (or UTP)} + \text{ADP} \rightleftharpoons \text{IDP (or UDP)} + \text{ATP}$$

they do not seem to be involved in the transfer of phosphate from ITP and UTP to fructose-6-phosphate.

As indicated above, the equilibrium in the phosphohexokinase reaction is far in the direction of fructose-1,6-diphosphate.   In biological systems, the conversion of this compound back to fructose-6-phosphate is effected by a relatively specific phosphatase (fructose-1,6-diphosphatase), identified in plants and in animal tissues.[13]

It is appropriate at this point to discuss the relation of glucose-6-phosphate to glucose-1-phosphate (cf. p. 438), the initial product of the phosphorolytic cleavage of starch (in plants) and of glycogen (in muscle). Glucose-1-phosphate is readily converted to glucose-6-phosphate through the catalytic agency of an enzyme named phosphoglucomutase, which has been obtained in purified form from yeast and has been crystallized from extracts of rabbit muscle.[14]   Its particle weight is about 74,000.   At equilibrium about 94.5 per cent of glucose-6-phosphate and 5.5 per cent of glucose-1-phosphate are present; $\Delta F' = -1.7$ kcal per mole (pH 7.5, $30°$ C) for the conversion of the 1-ester to the 6-ester.   The presence of cysteine and of magnesium ions is essential for enzymic activity, although crude enzyme preparations are also activated by manganese or cobalt ions.   Sutherland et al.[15] have shown that, in order for the enzymic interconversion of the two glucose phosphates to be effected, there must be present a catalytic amount of glucose-1,6-diphosphate, and that the function of the enzyme is to catalyze a transphosphorylation in which a phosphate group is transferred from the diphosphate to a monophosphate. This mechanism of the phosphoglucomutase reaction was confirmed in

[11] K. Ling and H. A. Lardy, *J. Am. Chem. Soc.*, **76**, 2842 (1954).

[12] P. Berg and W. K. Joklik, *J. Biol. Chem.*, **210**, 657 (1954).

[13] G. Gomori, *J. Biol. Chem.*, **148**, 139 (1943); B. M. Pogell and R. W. McGilvery, *ibid.*, **208**, 149 (1954); L. C. Mokrasch and R. W. McGilvery, *ibid.*, **221**, 909 (1956).

[14] V. A. Najjar, *J. Biol. Chem.*, **175**, 281 (1948).

[15] E. W. Sutherland et al., *J. Biol. Chem.*, **180**, 1285 (1949).

studies with isotopic glucose-1-phosphate, labeled with C^{14} and with P^{32}. The initial recognition of glucose-1,6-diphosphate as a cofactor in the phosphoglucomutase reaction stems from the work of Cardini et al.,[16]

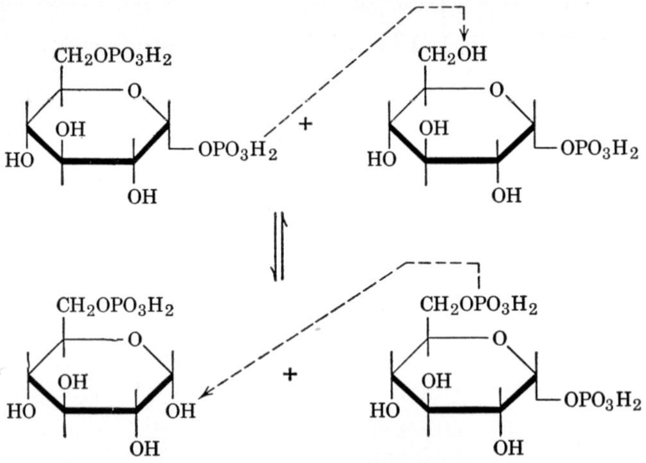

who pointed out that the usual preparations of glucose-1-phosphate contain enough of the diphosphate as an impurity to permit the reaction to proceed. Thus, in the over-all conversion of the 1-ester to the 6-ester, the latter compound arises directly from the dephosphorylation of the cofactor, and a new molecule of the diphosphate is formed from the 1-phosphate. Moreover, the enzyme protein participates in this phosphate transfer, and is dephosphorylated or phosphorylated.[17] Thus the phosphorylated phosphoglucomutase (the phosphoryl group is probably bound to the β-hydroxyl of a serine residue) donates phosphate to glucose-1-phosphate (G-1-P) to form glucose-1,6-diphosphate (G-1,6-P); the resulting dephosphorylated enzyme accepts a phosphate from G-1,6-P to form glucose-6-phosphate (G-6-P). It may be added that yeast and

$$\text{G-1-P} + \text{enzyme-P} \rightleftharpoons \text{G-1,6-P} + \text{enzyme}$$

$$\text{Enzyme} + \text{G-1,6-P} \rightleftharpoons \text{Enzyme-P} + \text{G-6-P}$$

muscle contain an enzyme (glucose-1-phosphate kinase) that catalyzes the phosphorylation of G-1-P by ATP to form G-1,6-P.[18] Furthermore, a glucose-1-phosphate transphosphorylase present in bacteria and in muscle catalyzes the reaction[19]

$$2 \text{ G-1-P} \rightleftharpoons \text{G-1,6-P} + \text{glucose}$$

[16] C. E. Cardini et al., *Arch. Biochem.*, **22**, 87 (1949).

[17] V. A. Najjar and M. E. Pullman, *Science*, **119**, 631 (1954).

[18] A. C. Paladini et al., *Arch. Biochem.*, **23**, 55 (1949).

[19] J. B. Sidbury et al., *J. Biol. Chem.*, **222**, 89 (1956).

The probable metabolic relations, in yeast cells, among the various hexoses and hexose phosphates discussed above are summarized in Fig. 2. These compounds are linked to a polysaccharide such as starch through the phosphorylase-catalyzed reaction of glucose-1-phosphate. Since the reactions linking the polysaccharide, glucose-1-phosphate, and glucose-

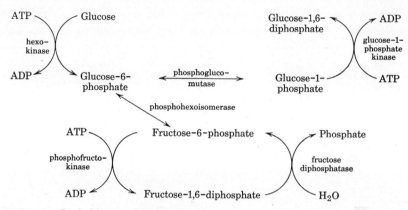

Fig. 2.   Probable metabolic relations among hexose phosphates in yeast.

6-phosphate, are freely reversible in the presence of the appropriate enzymes, one may begin with glucose-6-phosphate and form polysaccharide. This was achieved experimentally with partially purified enzymes from muscle.[20]

Enzymic Transformations of Other Hexose Phosphates

In addition to glucose and fructose, other monosaccharides are metabolized by microorganisms or animal tissues under anaerobic conditions. It was mentioned before that crystalline yeast hexokinase catalyzes the phosphorylation of mannose by ATP to form mannose-6-phosphate. The enzymic conversion of this sugar phosphate to fructose-6-phosphate has been shown to be effected by an enzyme found in muscle extracts and presumed to be in yeast as well. This enzyme has been termed phosphomannose isomerase.[21] At equilibrium, about 40 per cent mannose-6-phosphate and 60 per cent fructose-6-phosphate are present (pH 8, 30° C).

The fermentation of galactose requires an initial phosphorylation by ATP, catalyzed by the enzyme galactokinase. The product of this reaction, galactose-1-phosphate[22] (not galactose-6-phosphate) is con-

[20] S. P. Colowick and E. W. Sutherland, *J. Biol. Chem.*, **144**, 423 (1942).

[21] M. W. Slein, *J. Biol. Chem.*, **186**, 753 (1950).

[22] R. E. Trucco et al., *Arch. Biochem.*, **18**, 137 (1948).

verted to glucose-1-phosphate in a series of reversible reactions that involves uridine diphosphate glucose (UDPG; cf. p. 205) as a cofactor.[23] First, galactose-1-phosphate reacts with UDPG to form glucose-1-phosphate and UDP-galactose (a galactosyl residue in place of the glucosyl residue in the formula for UDPG on p. 205). The enzyme that catalyzes this reaction has been termed a "uridyl transferase," because a uridine monophosphoryl group is transferred reversibly from UDPG to galactose-1-phosphate.[24] The UDP-galactose is then subjected to a remarkable

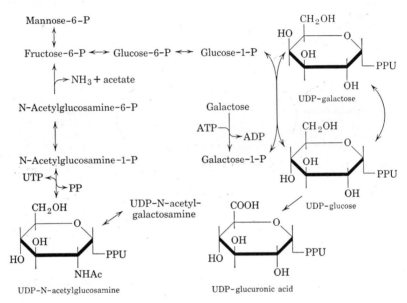

Fig. 3. Enzyme-catalyzed interconversions of hexose monophosphates. The phosphoryl groups are denoted P, uridyl groups U, and acetyl groups Ac.

enzymic transformation in which the configuration about carbon 4 of the galactosyl residue undergoes Walden inversion to form a glucosyl residue. The enzyme system responsible for this inversion has been named "galactowaldenase" or "UDP-galactose 4-epimerase." It is probable that the process involves intermediate oxidation and reduction, since DPN^+ is a cofactor for the enzyme-catalyzed Walden inversion.[25]

These conclusions about the initial steps in the fermentation of galactose by yeast are summarized in Fig. 3. They also apply to the metab-

[23] L. F. Leloir, *Advances in Enzymol.*, **14**, 193 (1953).

[24] H. M. Kalckar, in W. D. McElroy and B. Glass, *The Mechanism of Enzyme Action*, Johns Hopkins Press, Baltimore, 1954.

[25] E. S. Maxwell, *J. Am. Chem. Soc.*, **78**, 1074 (1956); H. M. Kalckar and E. S. Maxwell, *Biochim. et Biophys. Acta*, **22**, 588 (1956).

olism of galactose in animal tissues. Of special interest is the discovery by Kalckar et al.[26] that, in the hereditary childhood disease known as galactosemia (characterized by abnormal galactose metabolism), the uridyl transferase activity of several tissues (erythrocytes, liver) is greatly lowered, leading to an accumulation of galactose-1-phosphate if galactose or lactose is fed.

It will be recalled that UDPG is a participant in the biosynthesis of sucrose from glucose-1-phosphate and fructose-6-phosphate (cf. p. 450); yeast extracts also catalyze the reaction of UDPG with glucose-6-phosphate to form the nonreducing disaccharide trehalose phosphate[27] (cf. p. 415). It is probable that UDP derivatives also are involved in the biosynthesis of lactose in the mammary gland;[28] the galactose portion of the disaccharide appears to arise from phosphorylated hexoses, whereas the glucose portion is derived from free glucose.

Among the UDP derivatives found in yeast, in higher plants, and in mammalian tissues is UDP-N-acetylglucosamine, in which a pyrophosphate bond joins UMP and N-acetylglucosamine-1-phosphate; this UDP derivative appears to be an intermediate in the biosynthesis of chitin[29] (p. 423). Extracts of liver and swine kidney contain enzymes that catalyze the formation of fructose-6-phosphate, ammonia, and acetate from N-acetylglucosamine-6-phosphate, as well as the conversion of the last-named compound to the corresponding 1-phosphate.[30] N-Acetylglucosamine-6-phosphate can arise by enzymic transfer of the acetyl group of acetyl-CoA (cf. p. 482) to glucosamine-6-phosphate,[31] which appears to be formed from fructose-6-phosphate by a reaction involving glutamine;[32] the enzymic breakdown of glucosamine involves its prior conversion to glucosamine-6-phosphate, which is deaminated to fructose-6-phosphate.[33]

N–Acetylglucosamine-6-phosphate ← (Acetyl–CoA / CoA) — Glucosamine-6-phosphate ← (+ glutamine) / (→ NH₃) — Fructose-6-phosphate

[26] H. M. Kalckar et al., *Biochim. et Biophys. Acta,* **20,** 262 (1956); *Physiol. Revs.,* **38,** 77 (1958).

[27] L. F. Leloir and E. Cabib, *J. Am. Chem. Soc.,* **75,** 5445 (1953).

[28] J. E. Gander et al., *Arch. Biochem. and Biophys.,* **60,** 259 (1956); H. G. Wood et al., *J. Biol. Chem.,* **226,** 1023 (1957).

[29] L. Glaser and D. H. Brown, *J. Biol. Chem.,* **228,** 729 (1957).

[30] L. F. Leloir and C. E. Cardini, *Biochim. et Biophys. Acta,* **20,** 33 (1956).

[31] T. C. Chou and M. Soodak, *J. Biol. Chem.,* **196,** 105 (1952); E. A. Davidson et al., *ibid.,* **226,** 125 (1957).

[32] B. M. Pogell and R. M. Gryder, *J. Biol. Chem.,* **228,** 701 (1957).

[33] D. G. Comb and S. Roseman, *Biochim. et Biophys. Acta,* **21,** 193 (1956); J. B. Wolfe et al., *Arch. Biochem. and Biophys.,* **64,** 480, 489 (1956).

In the reversible conversion of N-acetylglucosamine-6-phosphate to the 1-phosphate, glucose-1,6-diphosphate acts as a cofactor,[34] presumably in a manner analogous to its role in the phosphoglucomutase reaction (cf. p. 461). As with glucose-1-phosphate, N-acetylglucosamine-1-phosphate participates in an enzyme-catalyzed reaction with UTP to form UDP-acetylglucosamine and pyrophosphate; similarly, with glucosamine-1-phosphate, UDP-glucosamine is formed.[35] Evidence also has been obtained for the formation of UDP-acetylgalactosamine from UDP-acetylglucosamine by enzymes analogous to those discussed above for the interconversion of UDPG and UDP-galactose. These enzymic pathways thus serve to link phosphorylated hexoses in the anaerobic metabolism of glucose with the synthesis of the 2-amino-2-deoxyhexoses present in various polysaccharides (cf. Fig. 3).

It will be seen from the above discussion that at least two types of enzyme-catalyzed uridyl transfer reactions are known, in both of which a pyrophosphate bond of a UDP derivative is cleaved. One of these is typified by the reaction

$$
\text{Uridine}\underset{\overset{|}{OH}}{\overset{\overset{O}{\parallel}}{P}}\!\!-\!\!O\!\!\underset{\overset{|}{OH}}{\overset{\overset{O}{\parallel}}{-P}}\!\!-\!\!O\!\!-\!\!\text{sugar}_1 + \text{sugar}_2\!\!-\!\!O\!\!\underset{\overset{|}{OH}}{\overset{\overset{O}{\parallel}}{-P}}\!\!-\!\!OH \rightleftharpoons
$$

$$
\text{Uridine}\underset{\overset{|}{OH}}{\overset{\overset{O}{\parallel}}{-P}}\!\!-\!\!O\!\!\underset{\overset{|}{OH}}{\overset{\overset{O}{\parallel}}{-P}}\!\!-\!\!O\!\!-\!\!\text{sugar}_2 + \text{sugar}_1\!\!-\!\!O\!\!\underset{\overset{|}{OH}}{\overset{\overset{O}{\parallel}}{-P}}\!\!-\!\!OH
$$

the arrows denoting the site of cleavage. The second type of reaction involves the cleavage of UTP by a sugar phosphate:[36]

$$
\text{Uridine}\underset{\overset{|}{OH}}{\overset{\overset{O}{\parallel}}{-P}}\!\!-\!\!O\!\!\underset{\overset{|}{OH}}{\overset{\overset{O}{\parallel}}{-P}}\!\!-\!\!O\!\!\underset{\overset{|}{OH}}{\overset{\overset{O}{\parallel}}{-P}}\!\!-\!\!OH + \text{sugar}\!\!-\!\!O\!\!\underset{\overset{|}{OH}}{\overset{\overset{O}{\parallel}}{-P}}\!\!-\!\!OH \rightleftharpoons
$$

$$
\text{Uridine}\underset{\overset{|}{OH}}{\overset{\overset{O}{\parallel}}{-P}}\!\!-\!\!O\!\!\underset{\overset{|}{OH}}{\overset{\overset{O}{\parallel}}{-P}}\!\!-\!\!O\!\!-\!\!\text{sugar} + \text{HO}\!\!\underset{\overset{|}{OH}}{\overset{\overset{O}{\parallel}}{-P}}\!\!-\!\!O\!\!\underset{\overset{|}{OH}}{\overset{\overset{O}{\parallel}}{-P}}\!\!-\!\!OH
$$

Evidence for these two mechanisms comes from isotope experiments in which C^{14}-labeled glucose-1-phosphate or P^{32}-labeled pyrophosphate

[34] J. L. Reissig, *J. Biol. Chem.*, **219**, 753 (1956).

[35] F. Maley et al., *J. Am. Chem. Soc.*, **78**, 5303 (1956).

[36] A. Munch-Peterson, *Acta Chem. Scand.*, **9**, 1523 (1955).

was used. It is of interest to note the similarity between the above reactions and the pyrophosphorolysis of DPN and FAD (cf. pp. 310, 336). An analogous reaction appears to be important in the synthesis of phospholipids; here cytidine triphosphate and choline phosphate react to give cytidine diphosphate choline and pyrophosphate (cf. p. 616). Still another reaction of this type is that between guanosine triphosphate and mannose-1-phosphate to form guanosine diphosphate mannose[37] (p. 205). In addition to the above metabolic reactions of UDP derivatives, it has been shown that the 6 position of the glucosyl residue of UDPG is oxidized enzymically by DPN^+ to yield UDP-glucuronic acid[38] (cf. Fig. 3).

The enzymes operative in several of the transformations shown in Fig. 3 have not been purified extensively, and future work may make necessary some revision of the scheme. Nevertheless, these reactions underline the importance of uridine nucleotides in carbohydrate metabolism; other aspects of the metabolism of these nucleotides will be considered in Chapter 35.

Cleavage of Hexose Diphosphate

Attention may next be given to the metabolic steps that lead to the cleavage of the carbon skeleton of fructose-1,6-diphosphate and the formation of ethanol and CO_2. A clue to the nature of the intermediate products came from the work of Neuberg, who showed in 1918 that, if one added sodium sulfite (Na_2SO_3) to the fermenting yeast extract, there appeared equivalent quantities of acetaldehyde (in the form of its bisulfite derivative) and of glycerol. Under these conditions the amount of alcohol and CO_2 formed was markedly reduced. This "sulfite fermentation" method provided the basis for the development of an industrial process for the manufacture of glycerol. Neuberg's finding indicated that acetaldehyde was probably the precursor of ethanol in the fermentation, and that the glycerol had been derived from three-carbon units formed by cleavage of the hexose. On the basis of these and other results, Neuberg proposed a scheme of alcoholic fermentation which was accepted until about 1930; as a result of subsequent work, largely by Meyerhof and his associates, it has been supplanted and will not be discussed here.

Neuberg's demonstration of the role of acetaldehyde as an intermediate came from the use of sulfite as a trapping agent; the decisive advance in the elucidation of the precursors of acetaldehyde emerged from the use of enzyme inhibitors. In 1930 it was observed that the addition of fluoride ions to fermenting yeast extracts led to the accumulation of a

[37] A. Munch-Peterson, *Acta Chem. Scand.,* **10,** 928 (1956).

[38] J. Strominger et al., *J. Biol. Chem.,* **224,** 79 (1957); E. S. Maxwell et al., *Arch. Biochem. and Biophys.,* **65,** 2 (1956).

phosphoglyceric acid, later identified as D-3-phosphoglyceric acid (3-phos-phoryl-D-glyceric acid). The same compound was found to accumulate in fluoride-poisoned muscle extracts undergoing glycolysis. Accordingly, attention was directed to the reactions leading from fructose-1,6-diphosphate to 3-phosphoglyceric acid. In 1934 Meyerhof and Lohmann[39] showed that fructose-1,6-diphosphate is converted by muscle extracts to 2 moles of triose phosphate, thus providing experimental proof for a view expressed by Embden in 1913. The further study of this cleavage showed that the fructose-1,6-diphosphate is converted to equivalent amounts of D-glyceraldehyde-3-phosphate and dihydroxyacetone phosphate by a specific enzyme, now termed "aldolase."[40] The unequivocal chemical synthesis of these two trioses has been achieved by Fischer and his associates.[41]

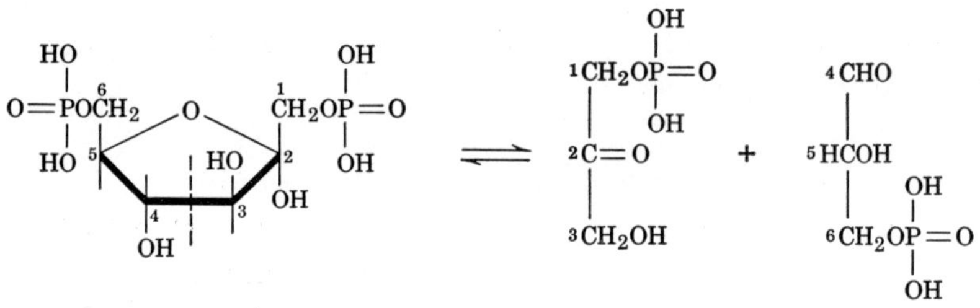

Fructose-1,6-diphosphate   Dihydroxyacetone   D-Glyceraldehyde-
                                      phosphate   3-phosphate

As is indicated in the equation, the cleavage between carbons 3 and 4 of the hexose unit occurs in a reaction which is the reverse of an aldol condensation. The equilibrium constant in this cleavage, as catalyzed by partially purified preparations of aldolase, is 1.2×10^{-4} (38° C, pH 7.3); under the conditions used, 89 per cent of fructose-1,6-diphosphate and 11 per cent of the triose phosphates are present at equilibrium.[42] Thus the equilibrium is far to the side of the hexose diphosphate, and aldolase should readily catalyze the exergonic condensation of the two triose phosphates to form fructose-1,6-diphosphate by an aldol condensation. In fact, Fischer and Baer[43] showed that, in dilute alkali, D-glyceraldehyde and dihydroxyacetone condense to form a mixture of fructose and sorbose, no enzyme being required for this reaction. A similar condensa-

---

[39] O. Meyerhof and K. Lohmann, *Biochem. Z.,* **271**, 89 (1934).

[40] O. Meyerhof, in J. B. Sumner and K. Myrbäck, *The Enzymes,* Chapter 48, Academic Press, New York, 1951.

[41] C. E. Ballou and H. O. L. Fischer, *J. Am. Chem. Soc.,* **77**, 3329 (1955); **78**, 1659 (1956).

[42] O. Meyerhof and R. Junowicz-Kocholaty, *J. Biol. Chem.,* **149**, 71 (1943).

[43] H. O. L. Fischer and E. Baer, *Helv. Chim. Acta,* **19**, 519 (1936).

tion reaction had been effected by E. Fischer and Tafel in 1895. The aldolase-catalyzed reaction appears to be specific for the condensation of dihydroxyacetone phosphate with one of a variety of aldehydes;[44] thus, if D-glyceraldehyde is present, fructose-1-phosphate is formed. With only one known exception, all the condensation reactions found to be catalyzed by aldolase lead to the *trans*-configuration of the hydroxyls at carbons 3 and 4 of the resulting hexose phosphates (see formula of fructose-1,6-diphosphate). Isotope studies have suggested that the enzyme combines with dihydroxyacetone phosphate in such a way as to labilize one of the 2 hydrogen atoms on carbon 3 in a stereospecific manner.[45]

Aldolase activity has been found not only in muscle and yeast extracts but in extracts of higher plants as well. Crystalline preparations of aldolase have been obtained from muscle by several investigators.[46, 47] The particle weight of rabbit muscle aldolase is about 149,000.

Although crystalline aldolase preparations can cleave fructose-1-phosphate to dihydroxyacetone phosphate and glyceraldehyde, it appears likely that in some tissues (mammalian liver) a separate "fructose-1-phosphate aldolase" is present which effects this reaction[48] (cf. p. 494).

Examination of the structure of the two isomeric triose phosphates formed by the cleavage of hexose diphosphate shows a structural relation resembling that observed in the isomerism of glucose and fructose. As noted above, there is an enzyme (phosphohexoisomerase) which catalyzes the reversible isomerization of glucose-6-phosphate to fructose-6-phosphate. An isomerase which catalyzes the interconversion of glyceraldehyde-3-phosphate and dihydroxyacetone phosphate is present in extracts of muscle and of yeast; this enzyme, called triose phosphate isomerase or phosphoglyceroisomerase, has been crystallized from muscle.[49] The equilibrium concentrations are 4 per cent glyceraldehyde phosphate and 96 per cent dihydroxyacetone phosphate; $\Delta F' = $ ca. -1.8 kcal (pH 8, 25° C) per mole.[50] Therefore, if an aldolase preparation contains appreciable amounts of the isomerase, nearly all the glyceraldehyde phosphate arising from hexose diphosphate will be converted to dihydroxyacetone phosphate. In fact, the first crude preparations of aldolase did yield

[44] T. Tung et al., *Biochim. et Biophys. Acta,* **14,** 488 (1954); A. L. Lehninger and J. Sice, *J. Am. Chem. Soc.,* **77,** 5343 (1955).

[45] I. A. Rose and S. V. Rieder, *J. Am. Chem. Soc.,* **77,** 5764 (1955); B. Bloom and Y. J. Topper, *Science,* **124,** 982 (1956).

[46] T. Baranowski and T. R. Niederland, *J. Biol. Chem.,* **180,** 543 (1949).

[47] G. Beisenherz et al., *Z. Naturforsch.,* **8b,** 555 (1953).

[48] F. Leuthardt et al., *Helv. Chim. Acta,* **36,** 227 (1953); **37,** 1734 (1954).

[49] E. Meyer-Arendt et al., *Naturwissenschaften,* **40,** 59 (1953).

[50] P. Oesper and O. Meyerhof, *Arch. Biochem.,* **27,** 223 (1950).

nearly 2 moles of dihydroxyacetone phosphate; this mixture of aldolase and isomerase was originally termed "zymohexase," but the term has now been abandoned. Triose phosphate isomerase has a remarkable catalytic activity; its turnover number at 26° C is nearly a million moles of substrate per minute per 100,000 grams of protein.

The demonstration that glyceraldehyde-3-phosphate is an intermediate in alcoholic fermentation was a consequence of its synthesis by Fischer and Baer in 1932, and of the finding by Smythe and Gerischer in 1933 that this substance is readily fermented by yeast. From these and subsequent studies it became clear that, of the two triose phosphates formed upon cleavage of hexose diphosphate, it is the glyceraldehyde phosphate that is converted to alcohol via acetaldehyde. The immediate fate of glyceraldehyde-3-phosphate was elucidated in Warburg's laboratory through the isolation of a crystalline glyceraldehyde-3-phosphate dehydrogenase from yeast; this enzyme, also called triose phosphate dehydrogenase, catalyzes the conversion of glyceraldehyde-3-phosphate to 1,3-diphosphoglyceric acid (p. 324). As noted previously, the dehydrogenase has also been crystallized from rabbit muscle.

$$\text{Glyceraldehyde-3-phosphate} + H_3PO_4 + DPN^+ \rightleftharpoons$$
$$\text{1,3-Diphosphoglyceric acid} + DPNH + H^+$$

Of special importance in relation to the effect of phosphate in the experiment of Harden and Young (cf. p. 457) is the fact that the uptake of inorganic phosphate during the fermentation of glucose is associated with the oxidation of glyceraldehyde-3-phosphate; when the supply of inorganic phosphate is exhausted, the fermentation halts at the stage of hexose diphosphate. The presence of inorganic phosphate is indispensable for the removal of glyceraldehyde phosphate from the equilibria catalyzed by aldolase and by triose phosphate isomerase, since the energetic relationships in the aldolase-catalyzed reaction are such that, if the triose phosphates are not removed, hexose diphosphate accumulates.

The reaction catalyzed by glyceraldehyde phosphate dehydrogenase has been discussed previously in relation to its coupling with the transfer of the 1-phosphate group of 1,3-diphosphoglyceric acid to ADP (cf. p. 373). This transphosphorylation is catalyzed by ATP-phosphoglyceric transphosphorylase (or 3-phosphoglycerate kinase), an enzyme obtained in crystalline form from yeast and from muscle.[47, 51] This enzyme, like other transphosphorylases, requires the addition of magnesium (or manganese) ions for activity. In the reaction catalyzed by the enzyme, the equilibrium for the equation shown is far to the right ($K' = 3.3 \times 10^3$, pH 7, 25° C).

[51] T. Bücher, *Biochim. et Biophys. Acta,* **1,** 292 (1947).

$$
\begin{array}{ccc}
\begin{matrix} \text{OC—OPO}_3\text{H}_2 \\ | \\ \text{HCOH} \\ | \\ \text{CH}_2\text{OPO}_3\text{H}_2 \end{matrix} & + \text{ADP} \rightleftharpoons & \begin{matrix} \text{COOH} \\ | \\ \text{HCOH} \\ | \\ \text{CH}_2\text{OPO}_3\text{H}_2 \end{matrix} \quad + \text{ATP}
\end{array}
$$

1,3-Diphosphoglyceric   3-Phosphoglyceric
acid   acid

Since 2 triose phosphate molecules arise from 1 molecule of glucose, the last reaction should give rise to 2 moles of ATP per mole of hexose fermented. Clearly, the rapid removal of D-glyceraldehyde-3-phosphate from the reaction catalyzed by its isomerase will tend to convert nearly all the dihydroxyacetone phosphate to glyceraldehyde phosphate. In the multienzyme system, and in the absence of side reactions, 1 mole of glucose will yield 2 moles of D-3-phosphoglyceric acid, and thus 2 moles of ATP. It will be recalled that, in order to convert a mole of glucose to hexose diphosphate, 1 mole of ATP is required in each of the two separate transphosphorylation reactions; the action of ATP-phosphoglyceric transphosphorylase regenerates these 2 moles of ATP. In the presence of catalytic amounts of ATP and an adequate supply of inorganic phosphate, therefore, a suitable yeast extract will convert a large quantity of glucose to 3-phosphoglyceric acid. The last compound accumulates in fermenting yeast extracts poisoned with fluoride; as will be seen from the subsequent discussion, fluoride blocks an enzyme involved in the conversion of 3-phosphoglyceric acid to acetaldehyde.

The work of Lohmann, Meyerhof, and Kiessling (1934–1936) showed that, if 3-phosphoglyceric acid is added to a dialyzed yeast or muscle extract, another phosphate compound (phosphoenolpyruvic acid) arises. In order to explain the formation of the new compound from 3-phosphoglyceric acid, it was necessary to assume the intermediate formation of 2-phosphoglyceric acid (2-phosphoryl-D-glyceric acid), and experimental evidence for its presence in the incubation mixture soon followed. The

$$
\begin{array}{ccc}
\begin{matrix} \text{COOH} \\ | \\ \text{HCOH} \\ | \\ \text{CH}_2\text{OPO}_3\text{H}_2 \end{matrix} \rightarrow & \begin{matrix} \text{COOH} \\ | \\ \text{HC—OPO}_3\text{H}_2 \\ | \\ \text{CH}_2\text{OH} \end{matrix} \rightarrow & \begin{matrix} \text{COOH} \\ | \\ \text{C—OPO}_3\text{H}_2 \\ \| \\ \text{CH}_2 \end{matrix} + \text{H}_2\text{O}
\end{array}
$$

D-3-Phosphoglyceric   D-2-Phosphoglyceric   Phosphoenol-
acid   acid   pyruvic acid

conversion of 3-phosphoglyceric acid to phosphoenolpyruvic acid involves two successive reactions. The transphosphorylation reaction by which 2-phosphoglyceric acid is formed is analogous to the reaction catalyzed by phosphoglucomutase, where glucose-1-phosphate is converted into glucose-6-phosphate; the enzyme that acts on 3-phosphoglyceric acid is termed phosphoglyceromutase. At equilibrium, the ratio of the 3-phospho compound to the 2-phospho derivative is about 5 (pH 6.8,

$37°$ C).[52] A crystalline preparation of phosphoglyceromutase from yeast has been described.[53]

It will be recalled that, for the action of phosphoglucomutase, catalytic amounts of glucose-1,6-diphosphate are required. An exactly analogous situation applies to the action of phosphoglyceromutase, where 2,3-diphosphoglyceric acid participates in the reaction.[54] The natural occur-

$$
\begin{array}{cccc}
\text{COOH} & \text{COOH} & \text{COOH} & \text{COOH} \\
| & | & | & | \\
\text{HC} - \text{OPO}_3\text{H}_2 \;+\; \text{HCOH} & & \text{HC} - \text{OPO}_3\text{H}_2 \;+\; \text{HC} - \text{OPO}_3\text{H}_2 \\
| \qquad\qquad\quad | & & | \qquad\qquad\quad | \\
\text{CH}_2\text{OPO}_3\text{H}_2 \quad \text{CH}_2\text{OPO}_3\text{H}_2 & \rightleftharpoons & \text{CH}_2\text{OH} \qquad \text{CH}_2\text{OPO}_3\text{H}_2
\end{array}
$$

rence of 2,3-diphosphoglyceric acid has been known since 1925, when Greenwald discovered its presence in erythrocytes. However, the demonstration of its role in the phosphoglyceromutase reaction was the first indication of its possible metabolic function. The 2,3-diphosphoglyceric acid of erythrocytes may arise through the action of an enzyme which catalyzes the conversion of 1,3-diphosphoglyceric acid to the 2,3-diphospho compound.[55]

The reaction leading from 2-phosphoglyceric acid to phosphoenolpyruvic acid is a dehydration; the enzyme (termed enolase) that catalyzes it has been obtained by Warburg and Christian[56] as a crystalline mercury derivative (particle weight ca. 65,000). This mercury compound is inactive as an enzyme, but active enolase may readily be obtained from the crystalline material by removal of the mercury ion, and the addition of magnesium ions (or manganese or zinc ions). In the presence of phosphate, enolase is strongly inhibited by fluoride. For this reason it is believed that the normal activator of the enzyme is magnesium, since magnesium fluorophosphate is only slightly dissociated. As mentioned previously, the addition of fluoride to yeast or muscle extracts leads to the accumulation of 3-phosphoglyceric acid. This result is understandable in the light of the strong inhibition of enolase by fluoride, since the equilibrium between the 2-phosphoglyceric and 3-phosphoglyceric acids is in favor of the latter.

At pH 7.5 and $25°$ C, the value of $\Delta F'$ in the enolase-catalyzed reaction is about -1 kcal per mole.[57] The dehydration reaction leads to the conversion of a compound having an "energy-poor" phosphate bond to one that has an "energy-rich" bond and liberates a relatively

[52] R. W. Cowgill and L. I. Pizer, *J. Biol. Chem.*, **223**, 885 (1956).

[53] V. W. Rodwell et al., *Biochim. et Biophys. Acta*, **20**, 394 (1956).

[54] E. W. Sutherland et al., *J. Biol. Chem.*, **181**, 153 (1949).

[55] S. Rapoport and J. Luebering, *J. Biol. Chem.*, **183**, 507 (1950).

[56] O. Warburg and W. Christian, *Biochem. Z.*, **310**, 384 (1942).

[57] F. Wold and C. E. Ballou, *J. Biol. Chem.*, **227**, 301 (1957).

large amount of energy on hydrolysis. Clearly, in the conversion of 2-phosphoglyceric acid to phosphoenolpyruvic acid there must occur a redistribution of the total energy of the molecule (cf. p. 378).

It was noted earlier that in dialyzed yeast extracts 3-phosphoglyceric acid is converted to phosphoenolpyruvic acid. If ADP is added, there occurs a transphosphorylation reaction in which ATP and pyruvic acid are the products. This reaction is catalyzed by a transphosphorylase

$$
\begin{array}{cc}
\text{COOH} & \text{COOH} \\
| & | \\
\text{C}{-}\text{OPO}_3\text{H}_2 + \text{ADP} \rightleftharpoons \text{C}{=}\text{O} \quad + \text{ATP} \\
\| & | \\
\text{CH}_2 & \text{CH}_3 \\
\text{Phosphoenol-} & \text{Pyruvic} \\
\text{pyruvic acid} & \text{acid}
\end{array}
$$

(ATP-phosphopyruvic transphosphorylase or pyruvate kinase) which, like the other known enzymes of this group, requires magnesium ions. A similar Mg^{2+}-activated enzyme is found in muscle, but it also requires the presence of potassium ions; the activity of the muscle enzyme is depressed by sodium and calcium ions (cf. Chapter 36). The equilibrium constant ($pH\ 7, 30°$ C) of the reaction is about 2×10^3 in the direction of pyruvic acid and ATP.[50] An important consequence of the ATP-phosphopyruvic transphosphorylase reaction is the formation of 2 moles of ATP per mole of glucose fermented. Thus, in the conversion of glucose to pyruvic acid in the course of alcoholic fermentation, there is a net gain of 2 "energy-rich" phosphate bonds per mole of sugar fermented.

At this point attention may be given to an interesting problem which faced students of alcoholic fermentation for many years. It has long been known that with living yeast alcoholic fermentation continues rapidly until all the glucose is metabolized, and in such a fermentation system the concentration of inorganic phosphate is not a limiting factor. On the other hand, with yeast extracts, even if the sugar is in large excess, the fermentation ceases when the inorganic phosphate is used up, and there is an accumulation of hexose diphosphate which is fermented very slowly under these conditions. The reason for this difference in behavior was discovered by Meyerhof,[58] who showed that in living yeast the excess ATP arising during the fermentation of glucose is not permitted to accumulate but is rapidly hydrolyzed by a specific phosphatase that causes the removal of the terminal phosphate group, thus forming ADP and inorganic phosphate. The enzyme causing the hydrolytic cleavage of ATP to ADP and phosphate is termed adenosine triphosphatase (ATP-ase). As a consequence of this hydrolysis, inor-

[58] O. Meyerhof, J. Biol. Chem., **180**, 575 (1949).

ganic phosphate is always available for the formation of 1,3-diphospho-glyceric acid. However, the ATP-ase of yeast is very unstable, and is largely inactivated in the preparation of the extract; the enzyme is inhibited by urethan or toluene, or by drying the yeast cells. For this reason, during fermentation by the yeast extract, ATP accumulates and the inorganic phosphate disappears. If, however, one adds to an extract that has stopped fermenting a purified preparation of an ATP-hydrolyz-ing enzyme from another source (e.g., potatoes), then the fermentation is rapidly restored. Under these conditions, hexose diphosphate is rapidly fermented by the yeast extract, and the rate is comparable to that observed in the presence of inorganic phosphate. The potato enzyme catalyzes the hydrolysis of both pyrophosphate linkages of ATP, thus converting it to adenylic acid (AMP); the addition of too much of this enzyme to the yeast extract will destroy all the available ATP. It is clear from the foregoing that the presence of ATP-ase in yeast cells (or the addition of the enzyme to a yeast extract) maintains a balance between the phosphorylation of glucose, for which ATP is required, and the phosphorylation of glyceraldehyde-3-phosphate, for which inorganic phosphate is required.

The importance of the series of enzyme-catalyzed reactions considered thus far in this chapter lies not only in its role in the fermentative breakdown of hexoses, but also in its relation to the synthesis of hexoses from smaller units. The conversion of 1 mole of glucose to 2 moles of pyruvate is an exergonic process (cf. p. 491) which can be reversed only if the multienzyme system is coupled to reactions that provide energy. It is probable that, in the metabolic synthesis of hexose phosphates by many biological systems, the sequence from phosphoenolpyruvate to glucose-6-phosphate is the reverse of that in the breakdown, except for the conversion of fructose-1,6-diphosphate to fructose-6-phosphate, which is catalyzed by a specific phosphatase (cf. p. 461). Although the possibility of an enzymic phosphorylation of pyruvate by ATP has been demonstrated,[59] it is believed that the major pathway for the conversion of pyruvate to phosphoenolpyruvate is a different one, and involves the participation of oxaloacetic acid (cf. p. 513).

Formation of Acetaldehyde and Ethanol

As mentioned before, the anaerobic breakdown of glyceraldehyde-3-phosphate by yeast leads to ethanol and CO_2 via pyruvic acid and acetaldehyde. It has long been known from the work of Neuberg (1911) that yeast can cause the decarboxylation of pyruvic acid to acetaldehyde

[59] H. A. Lardy and J. A. Ziegler, *J. Biol. Chem.*, **159**, 343 (1945).

and CO_2. In 1932 it was shown that washed yeast cells lose the

$$CH_3COCOOH \rightarrow CH_3CHO + CO_2$$

capacity to perform this reaction, and it was established that a diffusible cofactor was required for the decarboxylation. Since the enzyme which catalyzes the reaction had been termed "carboxylase" (pyruvic decarboxylase would be more precise), the cofactor was named cocarboxylase. Lohmann and Schuster[60] isolated cocarboxylase and showed it to be

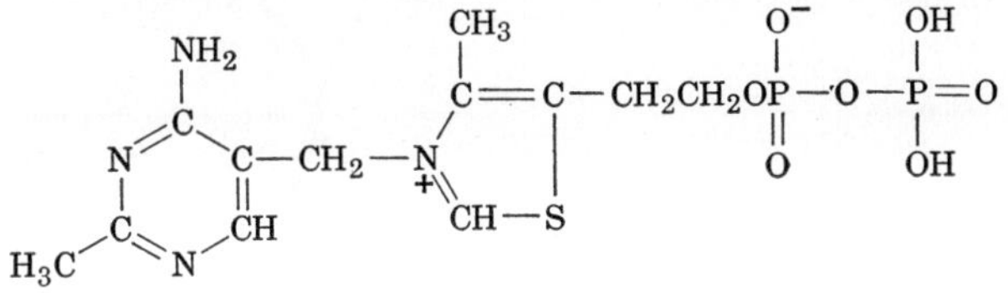

Thiamine pyrophosphate

thiamine pyrophosphate. Thiamine itself is a vitamin (vitamin B_1); its physiological role will be discussed in Chapter 39. The phosphorylation of thiamine to give cocarboxylase may be effected either chemically, or enzymically with ATP as the phosphorylating agent; extracts of brain and other tissues can serve as sources of the specific transphosphorylating enzymes.

The purest preparations of yeast carboxylase obtained thus far contain magnesium, and this ion is required for enzyme action. It may be added that the enzymic decarboxylation of keto acids other than pyruvic acid also requires cocarboxylase as a cofactor (cf. p. 504). However, the chemical mechanism whereby thiamine pyrophosphate (TPP) acts as a cofactor is not yet understood. It has been suggested that in the decarboxylation of pyruvate by yeast carboxylase, an "activated acetaldehyde" (possibly the carbanion CH_3CO^-) linked to TPP occurs as an intermediate, and that this hypothetical acetaldehyde-TPP compound reacts with H^+ to give free acetaldehyde and to regenerate TPP (cf. p. 480).

The final step in the sequence of reactions in alcoholic fermentation is the reduction of acetaldehyde to ethanol. From the previous discussion of the dehydrogenases, it will be recalled that alcohol dehydrogenase catalyzes the reaction

$$CH_3CHO + DPNH + H^+ \rightleftharpoons CH_3CH_2OH + DPN^+$$

Acetaldehyde   Ethanol

In the conversion of glyceraldehyde-3-phosphate to 3-phosphoglyceric acid, DPN^+ was reduced to DPNH. In the reduction of acetaldehyde to alcohol, the DPN^+ is regenerated. Thus, so long as both dehydrogenase-

[60] K. Lohmann and P. Schuster, *Biochem. Z.*, **294**, 188 (1937).

catalyzed reactions are proceeding, only a catalytic amount of DPN is required to convert a relatively large amount of glyceraldehyde-3-phosphate to ethanol.

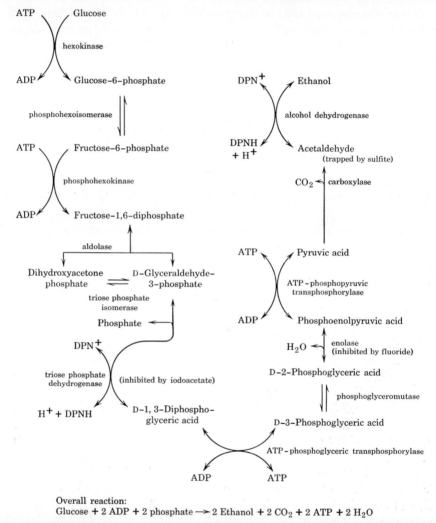

Overall reaction:
Glucose + 2 ADP + 2 phosphate $\longrightarrow$ 2 Ethanol + 2 CO_2 + 2 ATP + 2 H_2O

Fig. 4. Pathway of anaerobic breakdown of glucose to ethanol and carbon dioxide in yeast.

The current knowledge about the sequence of reactions in alcoholic fermentation is summarized in the scheme shown in Fig. 4. Since much of this scheme grows out of the work and theories of Embden and Meyerhof, it is frequently termed the "Embden-Meyerhof" scheme.

It was indicated at the beginning of this chapter that many of the reactions in the fermentation of glucose by yeast also are essential steps in the anaerobic breakdown of glycogen by muscle extracts (cf. p. 490). The sequence of enzyme-catalyzed reactions from glucose-6-phosphate to pyruvate also has been demonstrated for other plant and animal cells. For example, pea seeds contain all the enzymes necessary for the conversion of fructose-1,6-diphosphate to pyruvate by the metabolic route shown in Fig. 4.[61] The validity of the Embden-Meyerhof scheme does not rest solely upon the identification of the component enzymes, or the effect of inhibitors such as iodoacetate or fluoride, but is also supported by isotope studies. Thus the fermentation of glucose labeled with C^{14} in carbons 3 and 4 leads to the formation of carboxyl-labeled lactate[62] (in *Lactobacillus casei;* cf. p. 126) or $C^{14}O_2$ (in yeast) as predicted by the scheme. However, similar isotope experiments with other microorganisms that are known to contain enzymes usually associated with the Embden-Meyerhof pathway have given labeling data incompatible with the scheme, and have shown that alternative enzymic mechanisms of glucose breakdown are operative.[63] As will be seen later (Chapter 21), in some biological systems the Embden-Meyerhof pathway may be subsidiary to other routes of carbohydrate metabolism. Nevertheless, the general significance of the scheme presented in Fig. 4 is beyond question, and its development represents a magnificent chapter in the history of biochemistry.

Formation of Glycerol

With the scheme in Fig. 4 as a background, it is possible to return to a consideration of Neuberg's finding that, in the presence of sulfite, acetaldehyde (in the form of the bisulfite addition product) and glycerol are formed. The trapping of the acetaldehyde prevents its reduction by DPNH, thus blocking the regeneration of the DPN$^+$ needed for the oxidation of glyceraldehyde-3-phosphate. Under these circumstances an alternative metabolic pathway for the oxidation of DPNH comes into play. This probably involves the reduction of dihydroxyacetone phosphate by DPNH in the presence of alcohol dehydrogenase. (In muscle extracts this reaction is effected by α-glycerophosphate dehydrogenase, which is not present in appreciable amounts in yeast.) As a consequence, glycerophosphate is formed in amounts equivalent to the quantity of acetaldehyde trapped and of CO_2 released. Hydrolysis of the accumu-

[61] P. K. Stumpf, *J. Biol. Chem.,* **182,** 261 (1950); B. Axelrod and R. S. Bandurski, *ibid.,* **204,** 939 (1953).

[62] M. Gibbs et al., *J. Biol. Chem.,* **184,** 545 (1950).

[63] I. C. Gunsalus et al., *Bact. Revs.,* **19,** 79 (1955).

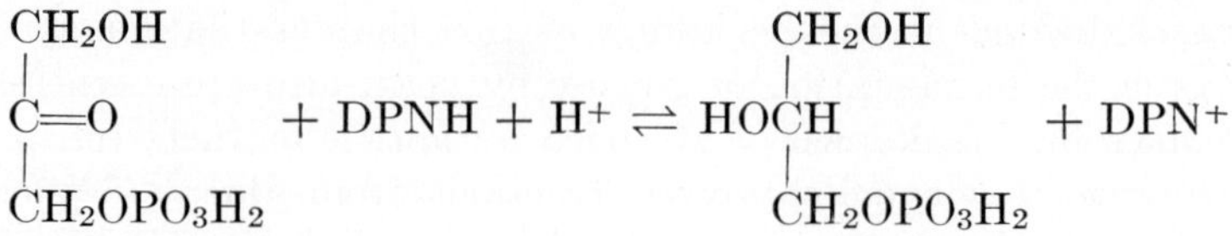

$$\begin{array}{c} CH_2OH \\ | \\ C{=}O \\ | \\ CH_2OPO_3H_2 \end{array} \quad + DPNH + H^+ \rightleftharpoons \quad \begin{array}{c} CH_2OH \\ | \\ HOCH \\ | \\ CH_2OPO_3H_2 \end{array} \quad + DPN^+$$

Dihydroxyacetone
phosphate   L-α-Glycero-
phosphate

lated glycerophosphate by phosphatases then leads to the formation of the glycerol obtained in Neuberg's "sulfite fermentation." The over-all

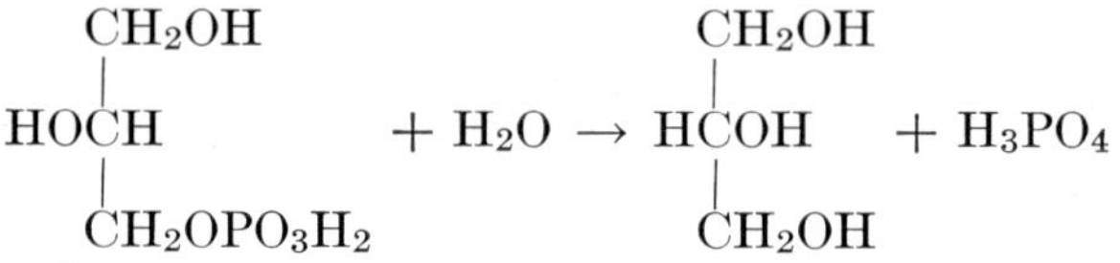

$$\begin{array}{c} CH_2OH \\ | \\ HOCH \\ | \\ CH_2OPO_3H_2 \end{array} \quad + H_2O \rightarrow \quad \begin{array}{c} CH_2OH \\ | \\ HCOH \\ | \\ CH_2OH \end{array} \quad + H_3PO_4$$

Glycerophosphate   Glycerol

fermentation process in the presence of sulfite approximates the equation

$$Glucose \rightarrow Glycerol + CO_2 + \ acetaldehyde$$

This is sometimes referred to as Neuberg's "second form" of fermentation, the "first form" being the production of alcohol and CO_2 according to the Gay-Lussac equation. In both, the pH of the medium is kept at about 5 to 6; when, however, the fermentation of glucose by yeast is conducted in an alkaline medium, there occurs Neuberg's "third form" of fermentation which may be described by the equation

$$2 \ Glucose \rightarrow 2 \ Glycerol + 2CO_2 + \ acetic \ acid + ethanol$$

If sulfite is added to glycolyzing muscle extracts, where DPNH is normally reoxidized by pyruvic acid with lactic dehydrogenase (cf. p. 318) as the catalyst, the pyruvic acid is trapped as the bisulfite compound. Under these circumstances, dihydroxyacetone phosphate is reduced by DPNH in the presence of glycerophosphate dehydrogenase to glycerophosphate, and equal amounts of glycerophosphate and of pyruvic acid are formed from fructose-1,6-diphosphate. The fact that, in yeast fermentation, sulfite does not trap pyruvic acid but acetaldehyde has been attributed to the ability of yeast to ferment the bisulfite addition compound of pyruvic acid.

Other Anaerobic Transformations of Pyruvic Acid

As will be seen in the next chapter, the conversion of glucose units to pyruvate in aerobic biological systems is followed by the oxidation of pyruvate by oxygen to CO_2 and H_2O. However, in anaerobic organisms, or in aerobic cells operating under anaerobic conditions, several enzymic pathways are known for the transformation of pyruvate.

Because of the presence of carboxylase in yeast cells, they can convert pyruvic acid to acetaldehyde and CO_2. In mammalian muscle, pyruvic acid is converted under anaerobic conditions to L-lactic acid.

It was once believed that the lactic acid formed in glycolysis arose from methylglyoxal by the action of the enzyme glyoxalase, present in yeast, muscle and other animal tissues, and plants. Although this view was abandoned after the work of Meyerhof, the action of glyoxalase has been studied extensively. Thus Lohmann[64] demonstrated that glutathione (p. 136) is an essential cofactor for glyoxalase. The role of the peptide in the enzymic reaction was elucidated by Racker,[65] who showed that two steps were involved. In the first step, catalyzed by an enzyme named "glyoxalase I," methylglyoxal and glutathione (GSH) react to

$$
\begin{array}{ccc}
\text{CHO} & \text{CO—SG} & \text{COOH} \\
| & | & | \\
\text{C}{=}\text{O} \xrightarrow{+\ \text{GSH}} & \text{HCOH} \xrightarrow[-\ \text{GSH}]{+\ \text{H}_2\text{O}} & \text{HCOH} \\
| & | & | \\
\text{CH}_3 & \text{CH}_3 & \text{CH}_3 \\
\text{Methylglyoxal} & \text{S-Lactyl-} & \text{D-Lactic acid} \\
& \text{glutathione} &
\end{array}
$$

form S-lactylglutathione, which is cleaved by a second enzyme (glyoxalase II) to D-lactic acid and GSH. Glyoxalase II thus functions as a thiolesterase. Despite their wide distribution, these enzymes do not appear to fit into any of the currently accepted schemes of carbohydrate metabolism.[66]

D-Lactic acid (or the DL-form) appears as the sole or chief end product of glucose breakdown by the group of microorganisms termed "lactic acid bacteria" (cf. p. 126). These organisms contain a DPN-linked lactic dehydrogenase specific for D-lactic acid, in addition to an L-lactic dehydrogenase; it is probable that the formation of DL-lactic acid[67] is a consequence of the coupled action of both dehydrogenases, since it is dependent on the presence of DPN.[68] Other lactic dehydrogenases have also been identified, among them the hemeflavoprotein of yeast related to cytochrome b_2 (cf. p. 357).

In addition to its conversion to acetaldehyde or lactic acid, pyruvic acid is transformed to acetylmethylcarbinol (acetoin) by a variety of microorganisms. This process was discovered by Neuberg[69] for yeast,

[64] K. Lohmann, *Biochem. Z.*, **254**, 332 (1932).

[65] E. Racker, *J. Biol. Chem.*, **190**, 685 (1951); T. Wieland et al., *Biochem. Z.*, **327**, 393; **328**, 239 (1956).

[66] E. Racker, in S. P. Colowick et al., *Glutathione*, Academic Press, New York, 1954.

[67] E. L. Tatum et al., *Biochem. J.*, **30**, 1892 (1936).

[68] S. Kaufman et al., *J. Biol. Chem.*, **192**, 301 (1951).

[69] C. Neuberg and J. Hirsch, *Biochem. Z.*, **115**, 282 (1921).

and in the light of present knowledge may be explained by assuming that yeast carboxylase catalyzes the formation of a reactive acetaldehyde (perhaps bound to thiamine pyrophosphate, TPP) which combines with free acetaldehyde formed by the decarboxylation of another molecule of pyruvate, as shown in the accompanying scheme. It is not clear whether a protein catalyst besides carboxylase is involved, although it

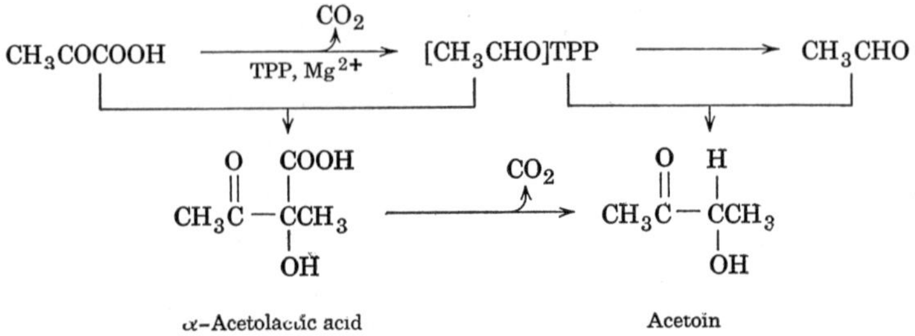

$$CH_3COCOOH \xrightarrow[\text{TPP, Mg}^{2+}]{CO_2} [CH_3CHO]TPP \longrightarrow CH_3CHO$$

$$\underset{\overset{|}{\text{OH}}}{\overset{\overset{\text{O}}{\|} \quad \text{COOH}}{CH_3C - CCH_3}} \xrightarrow{CO_2} \underset{\overset{|}{\text{OH}}}{\overset{\overset{\text{O}}{\|} \quad \overset{\text{H}}{\overset{|}{}}}{CH_3C - CCH_3}}$$

α–Acetolactic acid   Acetoin

is probable that a second enzyme (termed "carboligase") may effect the condensation reaction. Aldehydes (RCHO) other than acetaldehyde can serve as "acceptors" of the reactive acetaldehyde, thus leading to a variety of acyloins ($CH_3COCHOHR$). These products are optically active; for example, the acetylphenylcarbinol obtained from pyruvate and benzaldehyde, on catalytic hydrogenation in the presence of methylamine, yields *l*-ephedrine.

In *Aerobacter aerogenes* and *Proteus morganii*, acetoin formation from pyruvate involves *d*-α-acetolactate as an intermediate;[70] decarboxylation of this compound gives acetoin. Here pyruvate acts as the "acceptor" of the reactive acetaldehyde, as shown. Several bacteria contain enzyme systems for the reduction of acetoin to $CH_3CHOHCHOHCH_3$ (2,3-butanediol), which can be converted chemically to $CH_2{=}CHCH{=}CH_2$ (butadiene), a substance of importance in the manufacture of synthetic rubber ("Buna" rubber). Acetoin and 2,3-butanediol are related metabolically to diacetyl ($CH_3COCOCH_3$),[71] which can serve as an "acceptor" in an acyloin condensation to form $(CH_3CO)_2C(OH)CH_3$ (diacetylmethylcarbinol). Animal tissues also contain enzymes that catalyze the anaerobic decarboxylation of pyruvic acid with the formation of acetoin or α-acetolactate.[72] In all cases, TPP and Mg^{2+} are essential cofactors.

Another product of the anaerobic dissimilation of pyruvate is acetate, which is formed in many microbial fermentations. In some organisms,

[70] E. Juni, *J. Biol. Chem.*, **195**, 715 (1952); Y. Kobayashi and G. Kalnitsky, *ibid.*, **211**, 473 (1954).

[71] E. Juni and G. A. Heym, *J. Bact.*, **71**, 425; **72**, 746 (1956).

[72] R. S. Schweet et al., in W. D. McElroy and B. Glass, *Phosphorus Metabolism*, Vol. I, Johns Hopkins Press, Baltimore, 1951; E. Juni and G. A. Heym, *J. Biol. Chem.*, **218**, 365 (1956).

acetaldehyde arising from the decarboxylation of pyruvate is oxidized to acetate by pyridine nucleotide-linked acetaldehyde dehydrogenase (p. 328); in others, the "activated acetaldehyde" (presumably bound to TPP) is oxidized by electron acceptor systems of the bacterial cells.

Of special importance are the enzymic mechanisms, found in some microorganisms (*Escherichia coli, Streptococcus fecalis*) and in some animal tissues (e.g., swine heart), that catalyze the conversion of pyruvate to acetyl-coenzyme A (acetyl-CoA). The work of Korkes et al.[73] and of Gunsalus[74] has shown that, in addition to TPP, Mg^{2+},

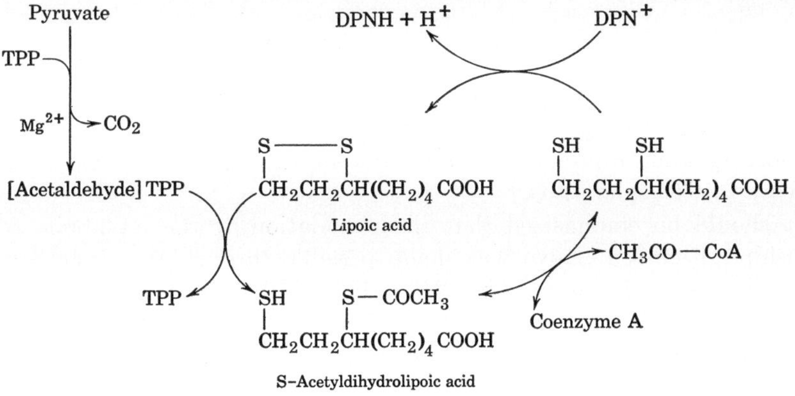

Fig. 5. Postulated mechanism for the enzymic conversion of pyruvate to acetyl-CoA and CO_2.

and coenzyme A (p. 206), the required cofactors include DPN^+ and lipoic acid (thioctic acid; p. 306). The discovery of the last-named substance stems from studies on a bacterial growth factor that is essential for pyruvate oxidation by *S. fecalis*, or to replace acetate for *Lactobacillus casei*. Although the enzymes participating in the conversion of pyruvate to acetyl-CoA have not been purified extensively, the available data are consistent with the sequence of reactions shown in Fig. 5. According to this scheme, acetyldihydrolipoic acid[75] is formed by the reaction of lipoic acid with the activated acetaldehyde-TPP compound; this reaction involves the reductive cleavage of the disulfide bond with the concomitant formation of an S-acetyl group (note analogy to postulated mechanism of glyceraldehyde-3-phosphate dehydrogenase; cf. p. 325). Enzymic transfer of the S-acetyl group to coenzyme A gives

[73] S. Korkes et al., *J. Biol. Chem.*, **193**, 721 (1951); **195**, 541 (1952).

[74] I. C. Gunsalus, in W. D. McElroy and B. Glass, *The Mechanism of Enzyme Action*, Johns Hopkins Press, Baltimore, 1954.

[75] I. C. Gunsalus et al., *J. Am. Chem. Soc.*, **78**, 1763 (1956).

acetyl-CoA and reduced lipoic acid (dihydrolipoic acid). Such "thio-transacetylases" appear to be widely distributed, and several enzymes of different specificity have been found.[76] The reduced lipoic acid is oxidized by DPN$^+$ (in the presence of dihydrolipoic dehydrogenase) to the disulfide form. Hence, if an enzymic mechanism is available for the regeneration of DPN$^+$, the conversion of pyruvate to CO_2 and acetyl-CoA can be effected in the presence of catalytic amounts of thiamine pyrophosphate, lipoic acid, and DPN$^+$. Korkes et al.[73] showed that this conversion can be coupled to the oxidation of DPNH by pyruvate in the presence of lactic dehydrogenase to give the following over-all reaction:

$$\text{2 Pyruvate + coenzyme A} \rightarrow \text{Acetyl-CoA} + CO_2 + \text{lactate}$$

As will be seen in the next chapter, the aerobic conversion of pyruvate to acetyl-CoA and CO_2, in which DPNH is oxidized by O_2 via the cytochrome system, represents a key step in the metabolic oxidation of glucose to CO_2 and H_2O.

It should be emphasized that the elucidation of the metabolic relationships discussed above was made possible through the discovery of coenzyme A by Lipmann[77] in 1947. This achievement, and the subsequent determination of the chemical structure of coenzyme A, have had a profound influence on the development of several areas of biochemistry. Coenzyme A is a derivative of the vitamin pantothenic acid (Chapter 39), which is linked to β-mercaptoethylamine by a CO—NH bond.[78] The work of Lynen[79] demonstrated that acetyl-CoA is a thiol ester involving the sulfhydryl group of β-mercaptoethylamine (see complete structure of coenzyme A on p. 206):

$$\text{Adenyl-pyrophosphoryl-pantothenyl—NHCH}_2\text{CH}_2\text{S—COCH}_3$$

It is worthy of note that, in addition to pantothenic acid, three other substances classified as vitamins (thiamine, lipoic acid, and nicotinamide) are related to participants in the enzymic conversion of pyruvate in biological systems.

Prior to the discovery of coenzyme A, Lipmann observed that in *Lactobacillus delbruckii* the oxidation of pyruvate depends on the presence of phosphate, and demonstrated that the product is acetyl phosphate[80] ($CH_3CO—OPO_3{}^{2-}$). Subsequent work showed that bacteria contain

[76] R. O. Brady and E. R. Stadtman, *J. Biol. Chem.,* **211,** 621 (1954).

[77] F. Lipmann, *Science,* **120,** 855 (1954).

[78] J. Baddiley, *Advances in Enzymol.,* **16,** 1 (1955).

[79] F. Lynen et al., *Ann. Chem.,* **574,** 1 (1951); F. Lynen, *Harvey Lectures,* **48,** 210 (1954).

[80] F. Lipmann, *Advances in Enzymol.,* **6,** 231 (1946).

an enzyme named "phosphotransacetylase" (apparently not present in animal tissues or yeast) that catalyzes the reversible transfer of the acetyl group from acetyl-CoA to phosphate:[81]

$$\text{Acetyl-CoA} + \text{phosphate} \rightleftharpoons \text{Acetyl phosphate} + \text{coenzyme A}$$

Acetyl phosphate is hydrolyzed by a specific phosphatase to acetate and phosphate.

It should be added that, although the discovery of acetyl phosphate as a metabolic intermediate came from studies with *L. delbruckii*, this organism generates acetyl phosphate from pyruvate by a mechanism that does not appear to involve either lipoic acid or coenzyme A.[82] Furthermore, in several bacteria (*Clostridium kluyverii*, *Escherichia coli*), acetyl-CoA can arise from acetaldehyde by a mechanism that is independent of lipoic acid, by means of the reaction:[83]

$$CH_3CHO + \text{coenzyme A} + DPN^+ \rightleftharpoons \text{Acetyl-CoA} + DPNH + H^+$$

This formation of a thiol ester in an oxidation catalyzed by an aldehyde dehydrogenase is analogous to the process effected by glyceraldehyde-3-phosphate dehydrogenase (cf. p. 325). In *E. coli*, the conversion of pyruvate to ethanol appears to involve the reverse of the reaction shown above; acetyl-CoA and acetaldehyde are intermediates.[84] Another microbial fermentation of pyruvate, by a mechanism not clearly understood, is the "phosphoroclastic" reaction in *E. coli* yielding acetate and formate:

$$CH_3COCOOH \rightarrow CH_3COOH + HCOOH$$

Phosphate, coenzyme A, and thiamine pyrophosphate are required as cofactors; it is probable that acetyl phosphate is formed as an intermediate, and is hydrolyzed to acetate.[85] *E. coli* also contains a "hydrogenlyase," which catalyzes the reversible decomposition of formic acid to molecular hydrogen and CO_2. With extracts of *Clostridium butylicum*, H_2 and CO_2 are also produced from pyruvic acid, but here formic acid does not appear to be an intermediate.

The hydrolysis of acetyl-CoA and of acetyl phosphate is accompanied by a large negative change in free energy (cf. p. 378), and the utilization of acetate for their synthesis must be coupled to the exergonic cleavage of a pyrophosphate bond of ATP. In *E. coli*, an enzyme system named

[81] E. R. Stadtman et al., *J. Biol. Chem.*, **191**, 365 (1951); **196**, 535 (1952).

[82] L. P. Hager et al., *Federation Proc.*, **13**, 734 (1954).

[83] R. M. Burton and E. R. Stadtman, *J. Biol. Chem.*, **202**, 873 (1953).

[84] E. A. Dawes and S. M. Foster, *Biochim. et Biophys. Acta*, **22**, 253 (1956).

[85] H. J. Strecker, *J. Biol. Chem.*, **189**, 815 (1951).

"acetokinase" catalyzes the reaction:[86]

$$\text{Acetate} + \text{ATP} \rightleftharpoons \text{Acetyl phosphate} + \text{ADP}$$

Acetokinase appears to be limited to organisms that contain phospho-transacetylase, and can acetylate coenzyme A by means of acetyl phosphate. A more general reaction for the synthesis of acetyl-CoA from acetate and coenzyme A is the following (demonstrated for yeast and liver[87]):

$$\text{Acetate} + \text{coenzyme A} + \text{ATP} \rightleftharpoons \text{Acetyl-CoA} + \text{AMP} + \text{pyrophosphate}$$

In this "acetate-activating" reaction, it is probable that an intermediate adenyl acetate (acetyl-AMP) is formed,[88] and bound to the enzyme, as shown by an exchange of P^{32}-labeled pyrophosphate with ATP in the

$$
\text{Adenosine—O}\overset{\overset{\text{O}}{\|}}{\underset{\underset{\text{OH}}{|}}{\text{P}}}\text{—O—}\overset{\overset{\text{O}}{\|}}{\underset{\underset{\text{OH}}{|}}{\text{P}}}\text{—O—}\overset{\overset{\text{O}}{\|}}{\underset{\underset{\text{OH}}{|}}{\text{P}}}\text{—OH} + \text{CH}_3\text{COOH} \rightleftharpoons
$$

$$
\text{Adenosine—O}\overset{\overset{\text{O}}{\|}}{\underset{\underset{\text{OH}}{|}}{\text{P}}}\text{—O—COCH}_3 + \text{HO—}\overset{\overset{\text{O}}{\|}}{\underset{\underset{\text{OH}}{|}}{\text{P}}}\text{—O—}\overset{\overset{\text{O}}{\|}}{\underset{\underset{\text{OH}}{|}}{\text{P}}}\text{—OH}
$$

absence of an acyl acceptor (e.g., coenzyme A). Presumably this intermediate reacts with coenzyme A to form acetyl-CoA and AMP. It will be seen from the later discussion that, in the activation of the carboxyl groups of fatty acids (Chapter 25) and of amino acids (Chapter 29), a similar mechanism appears to be operative. In studies of such "activated" acyl groups (in compounds such as adenyl acetate, acetyl-CoA, or acetyl phosphate), a valuable analytical reagent is hydroxylamine (NH_2OH), which serves as an artificial acceptor of the acyl group. At pH values near 7, hydroxamic acids (RCO—NHOH) are formed; these give a distinctive red complex with ferric ion in acid solution.[89]

Anaerobic Carbohydrate Metabolism of Muscle[90]

Glycogen is the chief carbohydrate of skeletal muscle, there being relatively little free glucose in this tissue. Thus the sequence of reactions

[86] I. A. Rose et al., *J. Biol. Chem.*, **211**, 737 (1954).

[87] M. E. Jones et al., *Biochim. et Biophys., Acta*, **12**, 141 (1953).

[88] P. Berg, *J. Biol. Chem.*, **222**, 991, 1015 (1956).

[89] F. Lipmann and L. C. Tuttle, *J. Biol. Chem.*, **159**, 21 (1945).

[90] F. Dickens, in J. B. Sumner and K. Myrbäck, *The Enzymes*, Chapter 63, Academic Press, New York, 1951.

in anaerobic glycolysis begins with glycogen and terminates with lactic acid, 2 moles of L-lactic acid arising from each glucose unit of the polysaccharide. The pathway of anaerobic glycolysis in skeletal muscle has attracted considerable attention because of the intimate relationship of this chemical conversion to the physiological phenomenon of muscular contraction. The first decisive experiments to link these two events were performed in 1907 by Fletcher and Hopkins, who worked with isolated frog muscles. They found that, if a muscle is electrically stimulated in the absence of oxygen, contraction occurs and lactic acid accumulates in the course of this anaerobic contraction. If the anaerobic stimulation is continued too long, however, the muscle eventually fails to respond; it is then said to be "fatigued." When the fatigued muscle is exposed to oxygen, the tissue may recover its ability to contract, and the accumulated lactic acid disappears. In the course of aerobic contraction, no appreciable accumulation of lactic acid can be noted.

A significant advance in the biochemical study of anaerobic glycolysis was made by Meyerhof, who prepared cell-free extracts of the muscles of frogs and other animals and showed that these extracts could convert glycogen, in a stoichiometric manner, to lactic acid. Dialysis of the muscle extracts destroyed their capacity to cause glycolysis, but this could be restored by the addition of a "cozymase" preparation from yeast.

From the studies on alcoholic fermentation, it had been known since 1905 that phosphate compounds play an important part in the anaerobic breakdown of carbohydrates. Much attention was therefore given to the organic phosphate compounds of muscle, and it was found in 1927 that ice-cold extracts of the muscle of vertebrates contain an acid-labile substance, identified as creatine phosphate (also termed phosphocreatine; cf. formula on p. 379). The term "phosphagen" has been applied to creatine phosphate and to related compounds. The standard free energy of hydrolysis at pH 7.5 and 25° C has been estimated to be about -13 kcal per mole for creatine phosphate and for other phosphoamides. Although this value may be subject to revision (cf. p. 376), it clearly places such phosphoamides among the substances having "energy-rich" bonds. Compounds of this type (the simplest example is amidophosphoric acid, $H_2N-PO_3H_2$) are stable in alkaline solution, but extremely labile at acid pH values.

Most of the creatine of the striated, smooth, and cardiac muscles of vertebrates is present in the form of creatine phosphate. It was once believed that, in invertebrates, this phosphagen is replaced only by arginine phosphate (or phosphoarginine; p. 379), which has been isolated from the muscle of some crustaceans.[91] However, more recent chro-

[91] O. Meyerhof and K. Lohmann, *Biochem. Z.,* **196**, 49 (1928); A. H. Ennor et al., *Biochem. J.,* **62**, 358 (1956).

matographic studies have shown that several annelids contain, as their principal muscle phosphagen, the guanidine phosphate glycocyamine phosphate or taurocyamine phosphate.[92] A phosphodiester of guanidinoethanol and serine ("lombricine") has been isolated from earthworms;[93] the phosphagen derived from lombricine is phosphorylated at the guanidino group.

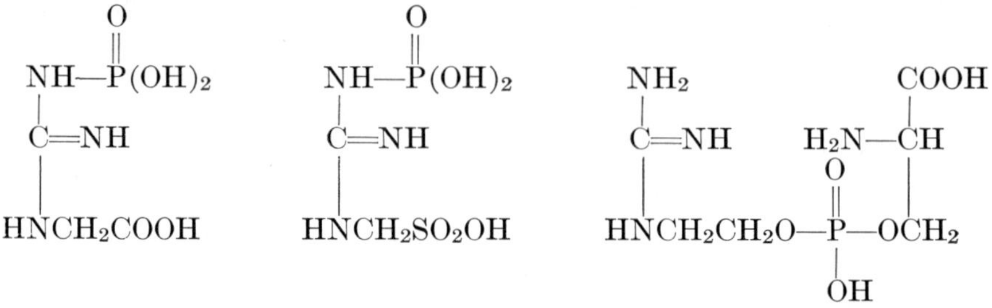

$$\begin{array}{ccc}
\overset{\overset{\displaystyle O}{\parallel}}{NH-P(OH)_2} & \overset{\overset{\displaystyle O}{\parallel}}{NH-P(OH)_2} & NH_2 \\
| & | & | \\
C=NH & C=NH & C=NH \\
| & | & | \\
HNCH_2COOH & HNCH_2SO_2OH & HNCH_2CH_2O-P-OCH_2 \\
\end{array}$$

Glycocyamine phosphate	Taurocyamine phosphate	Lombricine

The discovery of creatine phosphate in vertebrate muscles soon was followed by the recognition of its role in muscular contraction. This emerged especially clearly in 1930 from the experiments of Lundsgaard, who showed that, if a muscle is poisoned with iodoacetate, electric stimulation still causes contraction but lactic acid is not formed. However, in the contraction of iodoacetate-poisoned muscles, the creatine phosphate disappears and is replaced by equivalent amounts of creatine and inorganic phosphate. Moreover, the amount of creatine phosphate that disappears is proportional to the amount of muscular work done; when the supply of the phosphagen is exhausted, the muscle no longer responds to stimulation and is said to be in a state of "rigor." It followed from this important work that muscular contraction depended only indirectly on the formation of lactic acid in the course of glycolysis, and more directly on the supply of creatine phosphate in the muscle.

The chemical role of creatine phosphate became clearer when Lohmann[94] showed that muscle extracts are able to convert this substance to creatine and inorganic phosphate, but lose the capacity to do so after dialysis. However, upon the addition of ADP, there occurs a transphosphorylation reaction leading to the formation of ATP. This reaction is

$$\text{Creatine phosphate} + \text{ADP} \rightleftharpoons \text{Creatine} + \text{ATP}$$

catalyzed by the enzyme ATP-creatine transphosphorylase (or creatine

[92] G. E. Hobson and K. R. Rees, *Biochem. J.,* **61,** 549 (1955).

[93] N. V. Thoai and Y. Robin, *Biochim. et Biophys. Acta,* **14,** 76 (1954); C. Rey, *ibid.,* **19,** 300 (1956).

[94] K. Lohmann, *Biochem. Z.,* **271,** 264 (1934).

kinase), which has been crystallized from rabbit muscle.[95] Its particle weight is about 81,000. Magnesium ions are essential for the reaction, and they markedly influence the position of the equilibrium; at 0.002 M Mg^{2+}, the equilibrium ratio of concentrations in the phosphorylation of creatine by ATP is about 0.6. A similar dependence on Mg^{2+} concentration appears to apply to other enzymic reactions involving ATP, and it is likely that a Mg^{2+} complex of ATP is the reactive species. The apparent dissociation constant $[Mg^{2+}][ATP^{4-}]/[Mg\text{-}ATP^{2-}]$ is about $1 \times 10^{-3} M$; the comparable value for a $Mg\text{-}ADP^-$ complex is about $3 \times 10^{-3} M$. In some calculations of the equilibria and energy relations in enzyme-catalyzed transphosphorylation reactions of ATP, the effect of the binding of magnesium ions has been neglected.

Many of the properties of ATP-creatine transphosphorylase also are exhibited by ATP-arginine transphosphorylase (arginine kinase, arginine phosphokinase), present in the muscle of some invertebrates (e.g., crayfish).[96] The latter enzyme is specific for arginine and a few closely related compounds; it does not catalyze the phosphorylation of creatine, of glycocyamine, or of taurocyamine. Annelid worms contain enzymes that effect the phosphorylation of glycocyamine and of taurocyamine by ATP.[97]

The occurrence of the ATP-creatine transphosphorylase reaction makes it possible to understand the iodoacetate effect observed by Lundsgaard in terms of an inhibition of glyceraldehyde-3-phosphate dehydrogenase (cf. p. 325), and a block in the resynthesis of ATP from ADP. Under these circumstances, when the supply of creatine phosphate has been exhausted, hexose phosphates accumulate.

The studies summarized in the foregoing clearly pointed to the possibility that ATP may be the active chemical agent in providing energy for muscular contraction. When in 1939 Engelhardt[98] reported that preparations of the contractile protein "myosin" (which represents about 70 per cent of the muscle proteins) were able to effect the hydrolysis of ATP, it was suggested that the chemical energy released upon the hydrolytic cleavage of the terminal pyrophosphate bond of ATP could somehow be transformed into mechanical work. Subsequent research, especially by Straub and Szent-Gyorgi,[99] showed that the material previously termed myosin is, in fact, a combination ("actomyosin") of

[95] S. A. Kuby et al., *J. Biol. Chem.*, **209**, 191; **210**, 65, 83 (1954).

[96] J. F. Morrison et al., *Biochem. J.*, **65**, 143, 153 (1957).

[97] G. E. Hobson and K. R. Rees, *Biochem. J.*, **65**, 305 (1957).

[98] W. A. Engelhardt, *Yale J. Biol. and Med.*, **15**, 21 (1942).

[99] A. Szent-Gyorgi, *Chemistry of Muscular Contraction*, 2nd Ed., Academic Press, New York, 1951.

two separable proteins, myosin and actin. Myosin[100] is a fibrous protein (particle weight of rabbit myosin, ca. 850,000; axial ratio, ca. 100). On treatment with trypsin or with chymotrypsin, myosin is converted to smaller units, as judged by a decrease in viscosity;[101] the products have been termed "meromyosins." Actin can exist in two forms, a globular (G) and a fibrous (F) form. G-Actin (particle weight of dimeric form, ca. 140,000) is converted to F-actin in a process induced by ATP in the presence of neutral salts, and in the conversion one equivalent of ATP is dephosphorylated to ADP.[102] In solution, myosin and actin interact to form an artificial actomyosin having some of the properties of the natural complex; this complex is dissociated by ATP,[103] with a loss in the high viscosity and strong birefringence of flow exhibited by actomyosin solutions.[104] Threads of actomyosin can be prepared; when these are treated with ATP (ca. 0.005 M), in the presence of $MgCl_2$ and KCl, they contract to about one-half their original length. The addition of ATP-creatine transphosphorylase and creatine phosphate causes a partial relaxation of the contracted fiber. Although these phenomena are of considerable interest, their significance for the physiological contraction of muscle fibers is uncertain.

In addition to myosin and actin, muscle fibers contain a globulin named tropomyosin (particle weight, ca. 60,000), which resembles myosin in several of its properties.[105]

The adenosine triphosphatase (ATP-ase) activity of myosin is activated by Ca^{2+} ions and inhibited by Mg^{2+} ions.[106] Myosin ATP-ase hydrolyzes ATP to ADP and phosphate; if myokinase (p. 459) is present, AMP is produced. Myosin ATP-ase is limited in its action to the hydrolysis of nucleoside triphosphates and of inorganic triphosphate; it does not hydrolyze ADP, pyrophosphate, or phosphate esters of organic alcohols.

There has been much discussion[107] of the question whether the hydrolysis of ATP by myosin ATP-ase is the immediate source of chemical energy for muscular contraction, but no definitive answer can be given

---

[100] K. Bailey, in H. Neurath and K. Bailey, *The Proteins,* Vol. IIB, Chapter 24, Academic Press, New York, 1954.

[101] J. Gergely, *J. Biol. Chem.,* **200,** 543 (1953); **212,** 165 (1955).

[102] W. F. H. M. Mommaerts, *J. Biol. Chem.,* **198,** 459 (1952).

[103] J. Gergely, *J. Biol. Chem.,* **220,** 917 (1956).

[104] A. Weber, *Biochim. et Biophys. Acta,* **19,** 345 (1956).

[105] K. Bailey, *Biochem. J.,* **43,** 271 (1948).

[106] D. M. Needham, *Advances in Enzymol.,* **13,** 151 (1952); W. F. H. M. Mommaerts and I. Green, *J. Biol. Chem.,* **208,** 833 (1954).

[107] A. V. Hill et al., *Proc. Roy. Soc.,* **137B,** 40 (1950); S. V. Perry, *Physiol. Revs.,* **36,** 1 (1956); M. F. Morales, in O. H. Gaebler, *Enzymes: Units of Biological Structure and Function,* Academic Press, New York, 1956.

at present. Of considerable importance in this connection is the observation[108] that, after single contractions of muscle fibers under suitable conditions, no changes in the content of creatine phosphate, ATP, or ADP appear to occur. However, inorganic phosphate is liberated, suggesting that it is derived from an organic phosphate compound more directly concerned with contraction, and which may be formed in a reaction involving ATP.

Muscle tissue contains another ATP-ase, associated with the sarcosomes (cf. p. 359); in contrast to the enzyme of the myofibrils, it is activated by Mg^{2+}.[109] It may be added that enzymes which hydrolyze ATP have been found in nearly all animal and plant tissues examined. Some enzyme preparations, such as that from the potato, catalyze the hydrolysis of both pyrophosphate bonds of ATP with the formation of AMP and 2 equivalents of inorganic phosphate. To distinguish these enzymes from the ATP-ases of muscle, they are termed "apyrases" (a contraction of adenylpyrophosphatases). The available data suggest that the enzymic removal of both phosphate groups of ATP may involve the successive action of a nucleotide pyrophosphatase which catalyzes the reaction $ATP + H_2O \rightarrow AMP +$ pyrophosphate, and of a pyrophosphatase, which hydrolyzes inorganic pyrophosphate to 2 equivalents of phosphate.[110]

From the discussion of alcoholic fermentation, it became evident that the conversion of glucose to pyruvic acid leads to the net synthesis of 2 moles of ATP from ADP per mole of glucose degraded. The situation is somewhat different with regard to the amount of ATP synthesized per glucosyl unit of glycogen when the polysaccharide is converted to lactic acid in muscle extracts. As mentioned earlier, the work of numerous investigators established the identity of many of the enzymic steps in alcoholic fermentation and anaerobic glycolysis. The sequence of reactions in the Embden-Meyerhof scheme for the conversion of glycogen to lactic acid in muscle extracts is given in Fig. 6. Animal tissues other than muscle also exhibit appreciable anaerobic glycolysis. Among these tissues, retina, brain, embryonic tissues, and certain tumors are outstanding in the rate at which they produce lactic acid in the absence of oxygen.

A comparison of the schemes for alcoholic fermentation and for the breakdown of glycogen in muscle shows a number of important differences. In muscle, the fact that glycogen is the initial substrate means

[108] A. Fleckenstein et al., *Nature,* **174,** 1081 (1954).

[109] W. W. Kielley and O. Meyerhof, *J. Biol. Chem.,* **174,** 387 (1948); S. V. Perry, *Biochim. et Biophys. Acta,* **8,** 499 (1952).

[110] L. A. Heppel and R. J. Hilmoe, *J. Biol. Chem.,* **202,** 217 (1953); M. Johnson et al., *Biochem. J.,* **54,** 625 (1953).

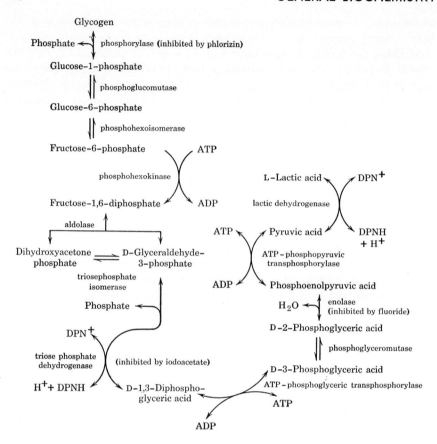

Overall reaction:
$(C_6H_{10}O_5)$ + 3 ADP + 3 phosphate $\rightarrow$ 2 lactic acid + 3 ATP + 2 H_2O

Fig. 6. Pathway of anaerobic glycolysis in muscle.

that only 1 mole of ATP is required per glucosyl unit converted, whereas in yeast, where free glucose has to be phosphorylated, 2 moles of ATP were needed. However, in muscle, an additional equivalent of inorganic phosphate is required for the phosphorolytic cleavage of glycogen. Since in both sequences 4 moles of ATP are formed from ADP per mole of glucose converted, the over-all reaction in muscle may be written

Glucosyl unit + ATP + 3 phosphate + 3 ADP $\rightarrow$

2 Lactic acid + 4 ATP + 2 H_2O

whereas the reaction in yeast, discussed earlier, is

Glucose + 2 ATP + 2 phosphate + 2 ADP $\rightarrow$

2 Ethanol + 2 CO_2 + 4 ATP + 2 H_2O

Thus, in the conversion of glycogen to lactic acid, in muscle extracts, there is a net gain of 3 "energy-rich" phosphate bonds in the form of ATP per glucosyl unit degraded. With glucose as the starting material, the net gain is only 2 "energy-rich" bonds, since ATP is required for the hexokinase reaction. The free-energy change in the conversion of 1 glucosyl unit of glycogen to 2 molecules of lactate (pH 7, 25° C, reactants at 0.01 M) has been estimated to be ca. −57 kcal per mole of glucose equivalent.[111] If ΔF for the reaction ADP + phosphate → ATP + H_2O (under the above conditions) is assumed to be about +11 kcal per mole, the gain of 33 kcal represents an efficiency of 58 per cent. However, the values used for the calculation are uncertain (cf. p. 374), and this estimate of the thermodynamic efficiency of glycolysis should not be considered more than a rough approximation.

It was noted before that, in muscle, creatine phosphate serves as a source of phosphate for the synthesis of ATP. In fact, the muscle of vertebrates contains relatively small amounts of ATP (frog muscle contains ca. 0.4 millimole of ATP per 100 grams) but has larger amounts of creatine phosphate (frog muscle contains ca. 1.8 millimoles of creatine phosphate per 100 grams). It was seen that in the over-all process leading from glycogen to lactic acid there is a net gain of 3 equivalents of ATP; after a brief contraction, the ATP interacts with creatine to regenerate creatine phosphate. From the data of Lundsgaard, who showed that, per mole of lactic acid formed, nearly 2 moles of creatine phosphate are synthesized, it would appear that the system works with high efficiency. Since the resynthesis of creatine phosphate occurs under anaerobic conditions, it is customary to refer to the period immediately following anaerobic contraction as one of "anaerobic recovery." The chemical events during anaerobic contraction and anaerobic recovery may be summarized as follows:

Contraction: Glycogen → Lactic acid
             Creatine phosphate → Creatine + phosphate
             ATP unchanged

Recovery: Glycogen → Lactic acid
             Creatine + phosphate → Creatine phosphate
             ATP unchanged

Thus glycolysis provides energy both for the anaerobic contraction and for the anaerobic recovery. The energy obtained from the breakdown of glycogen to lactic acid is used for the synthesis of ATP, and during the period of anaerobic recovery drives the synthesis of creatine phosphate. The enzymic reaction of creatine phosphate with ADP returns this energy to the ATP-requiring reactions essential for glycolysis.

[111] K. Burton and H. A. Krebs, *Biochem. J.,* **54,** 94 (1953).

Since, for glycolysis, inorganic phosphate is also required (for the phosphorolysis of glycogen and the oxidation of glyceraldehyde phosphate), there must be a balance in muscle, as in yeast, between the synthesis of ATP and its hydrolysis by ATP-ase.

When an isolated frog muscle is stimulated to contract in the presence of oxygen, no lactic acid is formed. Also, if a muscle that has been contracting under anaerobic conditions is placed in oxygen, the lactic acid that has accumulated disappears and glycogen is formed. This phenomenon is usually referred to as "oxidative recovery." However, there is considerable doubt whether this pathway of oxidative recovery occurs to a significant extent in mammalian muscles *in vivo*. Cori and Cori have shown that lactic acid rapidly diffuses out of muscle into the blood stream, which carries it to the liver; here lactic acid is converted to glycogen.[112] The glycogen of mammalian muscle arises from the glucose carried to it from the liver by the blood; the utilization of blood glucose for glycogen synthesis involves, as a first step, the formation of glucose-6-phosphate through the catalytic agency of muscle glucokinase. Although this enzyme, like other animal hexokinases (cf. p. 500), has not been purified extensively, it appears to be distinct from an enzyme specific for fructose (fructokinase). The conversion of glucose-6-phosphate to glycogen via glucose-1-phosphate requires the participation of phosphoglucomutase, phosphorylase, and branching enzyme (cf. p. 443). The over-all process of the uptake of glucose by muscle, and its utilization for glycogen formation, have been studied extensively *in vitro* with excised rat diaphragm. The cyclic process summarized in the accompanying scheme is frequently termed the "Cori cycle."

$$\text{Muscle glycogen} \rightarrow \text{Blood lactic acid}$$
$$\uparrow \qquad\qquad\qquad \downarrow$$
$$\text{Blood glucose} \leftarrow \text{Liver glycogen}$$

Carbohydrate Metabolism of Liver and Other Tissues

In the mammalian organism, therefore, there is a close interdependence between the carbohydrate metabolism of muscle and of liver. The liver occupies a central place in the metabolism of all foodstuffs, since the products of their degradation in the gastrointestinal tract are carried to it from the small intestine by the portal circulation. Cori showed that glucose and other monosaccharides (e.g., galactose, fructose) are absorbed in the intestine at a characteristic rate that is essentially independent of sugar concentration.[113] Although this suggests that the rate-limiting reaction is a hexokinase-catalyzed phosphorylation of the sugars, and

[112] C. F. Cori, *Biol. Symposia*, **5**, 131 (1941).
[113] C. F. Cori, *J. Biol. Chem.*, **66**, 691 (1925).

experimental evidence consistent with this view is available,[114] other data[115] make the present status of this question uncertain. If phosphorylated sugars are formed as intermediates in intestinal absorption, they must be dephosphorylated (presumably by intestinal phosphatases) before the free sugars enter the circulation.

In the liver, glucose is converted in large part to glycogen. Liver glycogen was discovered in 1855 by Claude Bernard, who recognized that it is a major reserve carbohydrate of animals. The metabolic formation of glycogen from glucose is frequently termed "glycogenesis." In fasted animals, glycogen formation can be induced by the feeding not only of materials that can be hydrolyzed to glucose and other monosaccharides such as fructose but of various other materials as well. A number of L-amino acids (e.g., alanine, serine, glutamic acid), upon deamination in the liver, give rise to substances (e.g., pyruvic acid, α-ketoglutaric acid) that can be converted in the liver to the glucosyl units of glycogen. In addition, substances such as glycerol (derived from fats), dihydroxyacetone, or lactic acid can all give rise to glycogen deposition in the liver. Such noncarbohydrate precursors are termed glycogenic (or glucogenic) compounds; for historical reasons this designation is restricted to substances that cause a demonstrable net synthesis of glycogen or of glucose in fasting or in diabetic animals. The process of glycogen formation from these precursors is known as glyconeogenesis. The synthesis of glycogen in the liver by the processes of glycogenesis and of glyconeogenesis is counteracted by the conversion of glycogen to glucose (glycogenolysis) and the degradation of glycogen to pyruvic acid (glycolysis).

The sugars and glucogenic substances brought to the liver not only are stored as liver glycogen, but are in part extensively oxidized to provide energy for the maintenance of endergonic processes. However, the storage of glucose in the form of a reserve carbohydrate enables an animal to draw upon its liver glycogen during periods of stress (e.g., starvation) when more glucose is required for the body economy than is provided by ingested foodstuffs.

In examining the process of glycogenesis, one may consider first the fate of absorbed glucose or fructose. In the liver, these two monosaccharides are phosphorylated by ATP through the agency of separate transphosphorylases termed glucokinase and fructokinase. Like yeast hexokinase (p. 459), liver glucokinase catalyzes the conversion of glucose to glucose-6-phosphate; however, liver fructokinase converts fructose to fructose-1-phosphate. Liver contains an aldolase that cleaves fructose-

[114] M. P. Hele, *Biochem. J.,* **55,** 857, 864 (1953).

[115] A. Sols, *Biochim. et Biophys. Acta,* **19,** 144 (1956); R. K. Crane and S. M. Krane, *ibid.,* **20,** 568 (1956).

1-phosphate to dihydroxyacetone phosphate and glyceraldehyde, and it appears that glyceraldehyde is either reduced by liver alcohol dehydrogenase (p. 319) to glycerol, or is phosphorylated to form glyceraldehyde-3-phosphate. Clearly, this triose phosphate can also arise from dihydroxyacetone phosphate by the action of triose phosphate isomerase. Condensation of the two triose phosphates by fructose-1,6-diphosphate

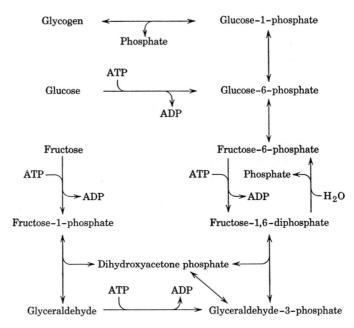

Fig. 7. Possible metabolic relations of glucose, fructose, and glycogen in mammalian liver.

aldolase (p. 468) gives this hexose diphosphate, which is hydrolyzed to fructose-6-phosphate by a specific phosphatase abundant in mammalian liver. The conversion of fructose-6-phosphate to glycogen then proceeds by the enzymic pathway via glucose-6-phosphate and glucose-1-phosphate, as discussed previously, with the participation of the characteristic liver phosphorylase (cf. p. 440). The possible metabolic relationships among glucose, fructose, and glycogen in mammalian liver may be summarized as shown in Fig. 7. Evidence in favor of the pathway suggested for the conversion of fructose to glycogen has come from studies[116] with fructose labeled with C^{14} in carbon 1. An enzymic pathway for the conversion of glucose to fructose, of possible metabolic significance in some animal tissues, is the reduction of glucose by TPNH to yield

[116] H. G. Hers. *J. Biol. Chem.* **214**, 373 (1955).

D-sorbitol (p. 412), which is oxidized to fructose by a DPN-dependent dehydrogenase (sorbitol dehydrogenase).[117]

By the administration of a single dose of C^{14}-labeled glucose to intact rats, Stetten and Stetten[118] have shown that there is initially a replacement of the glucosyl units in the outer tiers of the branched structure of liver glycogen (cf. p. 445). With increasing time, the inner tiers of the polysaccharide become labeled, and eventually the specific radioactivity of the peripheral glucosyl units is less than that of the limit dextrin obtained by the action of β-amylase or of phosphorylase. These results indicate that liver glycogen is rapidly synthesized and degraded, the most rapid metabolic turnover occurring at the peripheral glucosyl units. With muscle glycogen, rapid replacement of the outer glucosyl units is observed, but the inner tiers do not become labeled as rapidly as in liver.

It was noted before that, in addition to dietary monosaccharides, lactate and pyruvate can be converted in animals to liver glycogen. For example, in muscular contraction, lactate is produced and liberated into the circulation, as shown by a rise in the level of lactate in the blood during exercise. Smaller amounts of lactate are also formed by glycolysis in many other tissues (cf. p. 499). The lactate is largely removed from the blood by the liver, and in this organ it is converted to glycogen. The available evidence points to the initial oxidation of lactate to pyruvate, followed by the conversion of pyruvate to oxaloacetate and phosphoenolpyruvate (cf. p. 513), and the reactions of the Embden-Meyerhof scheme leading from phosphoenolpyruvate to glyceraldehyde-3-phosphate. The triose phosphate is then converted to glycogen as shown in Fig. 7. Clearly, this reversal of carbohydrate breakdown to pyruvate is an endergonic process, and is coupled to the enzymic mechanisms for the generation of ATP (cf. p. 380).

Although there is no doubt of the conversion of blood lactic acid to liver glycogen in the intact animal, pyruvic acid, which is an obligatory intermediate in the reversal of anaerobic glycolysis, also participates in metabolic reactions other than the formation of phosphoenolpyruvic acid and related intermediates of glycolysis. This has been clearly demonstrated in experiments[119] in which lactic acid or pyruvic acid labeled with C^{13} in the α-carbon (i.e., $CH_3C^{13}HOHCOOH$ or $CH_3C^{13}OCOOH$) was administered to rats depleted of liver glycogen by a prolonged fast. The liver glycogen was then isolated, glucose was obtained by hydrolysis,

[117] R. L. Blakley, *Biochem. J.,* **49,** 257 (1951); H. G. Hers, *Biochim. et Biophys. Acta,* **22,** 202 (1956).

[118] M. R. Stetten and D. Stetten, Jr., *J. Biol. Chem.,* **207,** 331 (1954); **213,** 723 (1955); **222,** 587 (1956); **232,** 489 (1958).

[119] V. Lorber et al., *J. Biol. Chem.,* **183,** 517 (1950); Y. J. Topper and A. B. Hastings, *ibid.,* **179,** 1255 (1949).

and the C^{13} content of the carbon atoms of the hexose was determined by means of a series of degradation reactions. The important result of these experiments was the finding of C^{13} in all the carbon atoms of glucose, with a preponderance of isotope in carbons 2 and 5. If lactic acid had been transformed to glycogen by the direct route, isotope should have appeared only in the 2 and 5 positions, as shown. The presence of appreciable quantities of C^{13} in the other 4 carbon atoms indicates that lactic acid or one of its metabolic products participated in other reactions

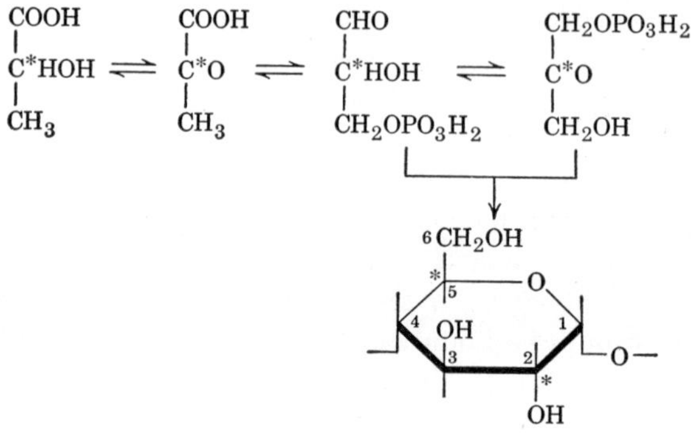

$$
\begin{array}{ccccccc}
\text{COOH} & & \text{COOH} & & \text{CHO} & & \text{CH}_2\text{OPO}_3\text{H}_2 \\
| & & | & & | & & | \\
\text{C*HOH} & \rightleftharpoons & \text{C*O} & \rightleftharpoons & \text{C*HOH} & \rightleftharpoons & \text{C*O} \\
| & & | & & | & & | \\
\text{CH}_3 & & \text{CH}_3 & & \text{CH}_2\text{OPO}_3\text{H}_2 & & \text{CH}_2\text{OH}
\end{array}
$$

Glucosyl unit of glycogen

which led to the observed distribution of the isotopic label, and it was estimated that no more than about one-sixth or one-seventh of the administered isotopic compounds could have been converted to glycogen by the direct route outlined above. It must be emphasized that this conclusion does not invalidate the view that glycogen is resynthesized from pyruvic acid by a reversal of anaerobic glycolysis; it does indicate, however, that in its metabolic transformations pyruvic acid participates in other reactions which lead to the appearance of C^{13} in all of its carbon atoms. As will be seen from the discussion in the next chapter, these reactions are related to the aerobic metabolism of pyruvic acid. More recent studies[120] with liver slices from fasted rats have shown that about one-fourteenth of the labeled pyruvate (in this case $CH_3C^{14}OCOOH$) used by the slices for glycogen synthesis was directly converted to glucosyl units. With slices from fed rats, whose liver glycogen is higher than in the fasted state, even less (about one-fiftieth) of the pyruvate-2-C^{14} was converted to glycogen prior to labeling of the other two carbons of the pyruvate molecule.

Although the mechanism for the synthesis of glycogen from glucose appears to be present in nearly all animal tissues, the most important sites of this process are the liver and muscles. The liver is exceptional,

[120] B. R. Landau et al., *J. Biol. Chem.*, **214**, 525 (1955).

however, in the ready mobilization of glycogen for body needs. As might be expected from the previous discussion, the level of liver glycogen depends on the rate of feeding of carbohydrate (and other glycogenic substances) to an animal, and on the rate of utilization of glucose by that animal. In a fasted animal the liver glycogen may drop to about 1 per cent of the weight of the fresh liver, whereas, after the administration of a large amount of carbohydrate, it may in some instances rise to 10 to 15 per cent. Although the muscle glycogen may also fluctuate according to the nutritional state of the animal, such widely disparate extremes are not observed in muscle tissue. Prolonged exercise, however, will lead to a decrease in the glycogen content of skeletal muscle. On the other hand, the glycogen of heart muscle does not decrease during starvation; rather, slight increases have been noted.

The work of Cori and his associates has shown that the mobilization of glucose from glycogen in the liver is effected by the following sequence of enzyme-catalyzed reactions:

Glycogen → Glucose-1-phosphate → Glucose-6-phosphate → Glucose

The last of the reactions is catalyzed by a phosphatase present in liver. This enzyme (glucose-6-phosphatase) has been partially purified and is without action on a variety of phosphate esters, including fructose-6-phosphate.[121]

Of the three reactions between glycogen and glucose, given above, the first two are readily reversible, and only in the hydrolysis of glucose-6-phosphate is the equilibrium very far to the right. In the steady state of glycogenolysis in the liver, the rate of glucose production is determined by the activity of glucose-6-phosphatase; the level of this activity in rat livers increases over the normal value after the animals have been fasted, and is markedly influenced by hormonal imbalance (Chapter 38).[122] In some cases of von Gierke's disease (cf. p. 446), in which the liver glycogen content is high and the blood sugar level is low, little glucose-6-phosphatase activity was found.[123]

The glucose formed by glycogenolysis is, in large part, released into the blood, which carries it to the other tissues. One of the remarkable control mechanisms of animals is concerned with the glucose level of the circulating blood. In normal human beings, the glucose content of whole blood is 70 to 110 mg of reducing substances (calculated as glucose) per 100 cc of blood. This is usually expressed as 70 to 110 mg per cent. When glucose is fed in large amounts (1 to 2 grams per kilogram of body

[121] M. A. Swanson, *J. Biol. Chem.,* **184,** 647 (1950); R. K. Crane, *Biochim. et Biophys. Acta,* **17,** 443 (1955).

[122] J. Ashmore et al., *J. Biol. Chem.,* **218,** 77 (1956).

[123] G. T. Cori and C. F. Cori, *J. Biol. Chem.,* **199,** 661 (1952).

weight) to a normal subject, the blood sugar level mounts rapidly and may reach nearly 200 mg per cent within 1 hr, and then returns rapidly to the normal value within the next 2 hr (Fig. 8). If glucose is injected intravenously, the blood sugar level may reach 300 mg per cent. When such elevated blood sugar levels are attained, the situation is described as one of hyperglycemia. Should the rate of glucose utilization by the tissues exceed the rate of the supply of glucose into the circulation,

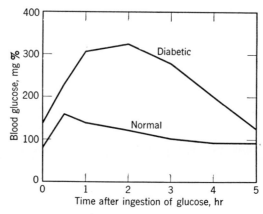

Fig. 8. Sugar tolerance curves of normal and diabetic human subjects. The data refer to the arterial blood sugar levels after the ingestion of 100 grams of glucose.

the blood sugar level may drop below 70 mg per cent; this condition is termed hypoglycemia. If there is a physiological defect in the subject, so that his tissues are unable to metabolize glucose in a normal manner, the hyperglycemia resulting from a sugar meal may be sustained for a period much longer than 2 hr; under these circumstances glucose will be eliminated by the kidneys and will appear in the urine (glycosuria). Thus, in the metabolic disease known as diabetes mellitus, hyperglycemia and glycosuria are the consequence of the administration of glucose (Fig. 8). The failure of diabetic subjects to maintain their blood sugar level at a normal value is a reflection of their deficiency in the protein hormone insulin, elaborated by the pancreas. Upon the injection of insulin into the blood stream of a diabetic, the circulating glucose level returns to a normal value. If too much insulin is administered, a hypoglycemic state may be induced. It should be added that insulin is not the only hormone concerned with the regulation of the level of blood sugar (Chapter 38).

The measurement of the response to the administration of a test dose of sugar thus serves as a useful index of the physiological state of the subject with respect to his ability to metabolize carbohydrates.

The curves shown in Fig. 8 are usually termed "sugar tolerance curves."

The various metabolic events that contribute to the maintenance of a steady-state concentration of glucose in mammalian blood are summarized in the accompanying scheme.

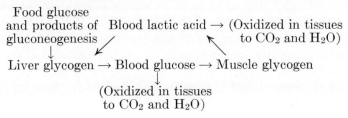

As mentioned before, a number of tissues are exceptional in having a high rate of anaerobic glycolysis, leading to the production of blood lactate. Among these are embryonic and tumor tissues,[124] brain tissue,[125] retina, and bone marrow (cf. Table 1). Although many of the enzymes cited in Fig. 6 have been identified in these biological systems, a satisfactory explanation of their high glycolytic rate is not yet possible. A stimulating hypothesis, which suggests that the origin of tumor cells is a consequence of irreversible damage to the aerobic respiratory mechanisms of normal tissue cells, has been developed by Warburg.[126]

Table I. Approximate Rate of Anaerobic Glycolysis

Tissue (rat)	Rate†	Tissue (rat)	Rate†
Retina	3.5	Placenta	0.7
Jensen sarcoma	1.6	Spleen	0.35
Embryo	1.0	Spermatozoa	0.25
Bone marrow	1.0	Liver	0.15
Brain	0.9	Erythrocytes	0.015

† The values are given in micromoles of acid (assumed to be lactic acid) formed per hour per milligram dry weight of tissue incubated at about 38° C in the absence of oxygen (N_2 is used). Such data are frequently obtained by measurement in a Warburg apparatus of the CO_2 produced from a bicarbonate buffer (cf. p. 288), and are often given in cubic millimeters of CO_2 (1 micromole of acid is equivalent to 22.4 cmm of gas at standard temperature and pressure).

In most instances, the glycolytic enzymes of mammalian tissues other than muscle and liver have not been purified or characterized satisfac-

[124] O. Warburg, *Stoffwechsel der Tumoren*, J. Springer, Berlin, 1926; *The Metabolism of Tumours*, translated by F. Dickens, Constable, London, 1930.

[125] J. H. Quastel, *Physiol. Revs.*, **19**, 135 (1939).

[126] O. Warburg, *Science*, **123**, 309 (1956); O. Warburg et al., *Z. Naturforsch.*, **11b**, 657 (1956).

torily. In all cases, the utilization of glucose appears to involve a glucokinase-catalyzed reaction. The relative glucokinase activity of various rat tissues may be listed as follows: brain, 100; stomach, 65; heart, 55; small intestine, 43; kidney, 28; muscle, 22. In contrast to the corresponding enzymes of liver and muscle, the hexokinase of brain appears to resemble that of yeast in its ability to catalyze the phosphorylation both of glucose and of fructose. Brain hexokinase is largely associated with cellular particles;[127] many of the other enzymes involved in anaerobic glycolysis appear to be in the soluble material of the cellular cytoplasm.[128]

In seminal tissue, blood glucose is converted to fructose (cf. p. 409). This conversion may be effected either via glucose-6-phosphate and fructose-6-phosphate (which is hydrolyzed to fructose) or via D-sorbitol (cf. p. 495). The transformation of blood glucose to fructose also occurs in the placenta of ungulates; in this group of mammals, fructose forms the larger part of the fetal blood sugar, and arises from the glucose of the maternal blood.[129]

[127] R. K. Crane and A. Sols, *J. Biol. Chem.*, **203**, 273 (1953); **206**, 925 (1954).

[128] G. A. LePage and W. C. Schneider, *J. Biol. Chem.*, **176**, 1021 (1948); H. G. Hers et al., *Bull. soc. chim. biol.*, **33**, 21 (1951).

[129] A. S. Huggett et al., *J. Physiol.*, **113**, 258 (1951); M. W. Neil et al., *Biochem. J.*, **65**, 35p (1957).

Aerobic Breakdown of Carbohydrates

It was noted in the preceding chapter that, when an isolated muscle contracts in the presence of oxygen, lactic acid is not produced in appreciable amounts. This does not mean that the metabolic pathway from glycogen to pyruvic acid is different under aerobic conditions, but rather that the extent of formation of lactic acid from pyruvic acid is markedly decreased as a consequence of at least two factors. First, the presence of oxygen leads to the reoxidation of DPNH (formed by the oxidation of glyceraldehyde phosphate) to DPN[+], and makes DPNH unavailable for the reduction of pyruvic acid to lactic acid (cf. p. 490). A second, and perhaps more important, reason for the failure of lactic acid to accumulate under aerobic conditions is the rapid oxidation of pyruvic acid itself in the presence of oxygen; this oxidation is primarily responsible for the respiratory CO_2 arising from the complete oxidation of carbohydrates. Therefore the discussion of the aerobic metabolism of carbohydrates essentially revolves about the mechanisms for the oxidation of pyruvic acid to CO_2 and water.

The oxidation of pyruvic acid by oxygen in muscle, and in many other biological systems, represents the most important component pathway from glucose to CO_2 and H_2O. It occupies a central place not only in the oxidative metabolism of carbohydrates but, as will be seen in subsequent chapters, of lipids and of amino acids as well.

The Citric Acid Cycle [1,2]

An important step in the study of the complete oxidation of pyruvic acid was taken in 1935 by Szent-Gyorgi and his associates, who studied the respiration of minced pigeon breast muscle, a tissue chosen because

[1] H. A. Krebs, *Advances in Enzymol.*, **3**, 191 (1943); *Harvey Lectures*, **44**, 165 (1950); in D. M. Greenberg, *Chemical Pathways of Metabolism*, Vol. I, Academic Press, New York, 1954.

[2] C. Martius and F. Lynen, *Advances in Enzymol.*, **10**, 167 (1950); S. Ochoa, *ibid.*, **15**, 183 (1954).

of its relatively high rate of respiration. They found that the rate of oxygen uptake fell off slowly with time, but that the original rate could be restored by the addition of small quantities of salts of one of the following four-carbon dicarboxylic acids: succinic acid, fumaric acid, malic acid, or oxaloacetic acid. Of special importance was the fact that the increase in oxygen uptake was much greater than that required for the oxidation of the added dicarboxylic acid. It had been known from the work of Thunberg and others that muscle contains enzymes such as succinic dehydrogenase (p. 344), fumarase (p. 234), and malic dehydrogenase (p. 318). It was also recognized from the work of Keilin that the succinic dehydrogenase was linked to the cytochrome system (cf. p. 359). Szent-Gyorgi's experiments suggested, therefore, that these various enzyme systems had a catalytic effect on the aerobic respiration of the muscle tissue. The importance of the succinic dehydrogenase system was underlined by the fact that the addition of malonate inhibited the catalytic effect of the addition of any one of the four-carbon dicarboxylic acids. These compounds were assumed to be converted into each other in a sequence of enzyme-catalyzed reactions, as shown.

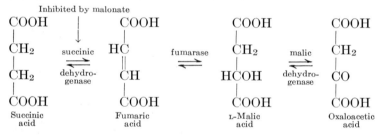

From the measurement of the amount of oxygen taken up and the amount of CO_2 produced, the respiratory quotient (CO_2/O_2) was found to be close to unity, thus supporting the view that the principal substance undergoing oxidation was related to the carbohydrates. The oxidation of carbohydrate by oxygen may be written as follows:

$$(CH_2O)_n + nO_2 \rightarrow nCO_2 + nH_2O$$

The results of Szent-Gyorgi et al. were put on a firmer basis in 1936 by the experiments of Stare and Baumann, who confirmed the finding that the specific enzymes that act on the four-carbon dicarboxylic acids serve as catalysts in the aerobic oxidation of carbohydrates. Later studies, notably by Krebs, demonstrated that the respiration of minced pigeon breast muscle was increased not only by the addition of the 4-carbon acids, but also by other substances, such as citric acid, α-keto-glutaric acid, pyruvic acid, as well as the amino acids L-glutamic acid and

L-aspartic acid. However, before these catalytic effects could be understood, additional facts had to be accumulated.

These came in part from the work of Martius and Knoop (1937) on the oxidation of citric acid by muscle tissues. Although Thunberg had shown earlier that citric acid can serve as a substrate for biological oxidations, the nature of the enzyme-catalyzed reactions involved in its transformation emerged more clearly when it was found that citric acid is oxidized to α-ketoglutaric acid, with the intermediate formation of d-isocitric acid.

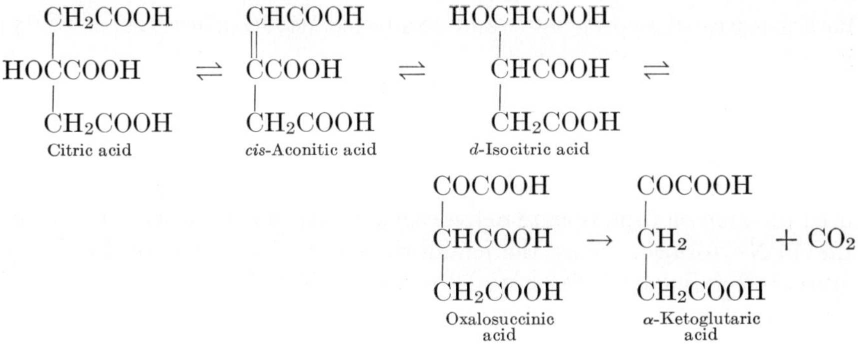

$$
\begin{array}{ccc}
\text{CH}_2\text{COOH} & \text{CHCOOH} & \text{HOCHCOOH} \\
| & \| & | \\
\text{HOCCOOH} \;\rightleftharpoons\; & \text{CCOOH} \;\rightleftharpoons\; & \text{CHCOOH} \;\rightleftharpoons\; \\
| & | & | \\
\text{CH}_2\text{COOH} & \text{CH}_2\text{COOH} & \text{CH}_2\text{COOH} \\
\text{Citric acid} & cis\text{-Aconitic acid} & d\text{-Isocitric acid}
\end{array}
$$

$$
\begin{array}{ccc}
\text{COCOOH} & \text{COCOOH} & \\
| & | & \\
\text{CHCOOH} \;\rightarrow\; & \text{CH}_2 & +\;\text{CO}_2 \\
| & | & \\
\text{CH}_2\text{COOH} & \text{CH}_2\text{COOH} & \\
\text{Oxalosuccinic} & \alpha\text{-Ketoglutaric} & \\
\text{acid} & \text{acid} &
\end{array}
$$

It will be noted from the accompanying scheme that cis-aconitic acid is the dehydration product of the isomeric compounds citric acid and d-isocitric acid; these three substances are converted into one another in the presence of an enzyme named aconitase. On the basis of its specificity aconitase may be classed, along with fumarase and enolase, among the enzymes (hydrases) that catalyze dehydration reactions. At pH 7.4 and 25° C, the equilibrium mixture contains 90.9 per cent citric acid, 6.2 per cent d-isocitric acid, and 2.9 per cent cis-aconitic acid.[3] Aconitase has been purified from swine heart,[4] and shown to be activated by ferrous ions and reducing agents (e.g., cysteine). It appears that a complex between Fe^{2+} and each acid exists, and that the enzyme catalyzes their interconversion, via a common intermediate, while the metal complex is bound to the protein.[5] Therefore the free acids are in equilibrium with a common intermediate, and the conversion of free citric acid to free d-isocitric acid does not involve free cis-aconitic acid. The representation of the reaction sequence shown above is used only for

[3] H. A. Krebs, *Biochem. J.*, **54**, 78 (1953).

[4] J. M. Buchanan and C. B. Anfinsen, *J. Biol. Chem.*, **180**, 47 (1949); J. F. Morrison, *Biochem. J.*, **56**, 99; **58**, 685 (1954).

[5] J. F. Speyer and S. R. Dickman, *J. Biol. Chem.*, **220**, 193 (1956); S. Englard and S. P. Colowick, *ibid.*, **226**, 1017 (1957).

convenience, and should be understood to mean that a substance bound to the enzyme is in equilibrium with free *cis*-aconitic acid.

The oxidation of *d*-isocitric acid to oxalosuccinic acid involves the participation of a pyridine nucleotide system (cf. p. 316). TPN-specific isocitric dehydrogenases have been isolated from swine heart and from yeast, and DPN-specific enzymes have been found in several animal tissues.[6] The decarboxylation of oxalosuccinic acid to α-ketoglutaric acid is effected by an enzyme named oxalosuccinic decarboxylase; it has been found in many animal tissues and requires Mn^{2+} for activity.[7] Since a highly purified enzyme preparation from swine heart exhibits both isocitric dehydrogenase and oxalosuccinic decarboxylase activity, it has been concluded[8] that a single enzyme catalyzes the reaction

d-Isocitric acid $+ TPN^+ \rightleftharpoons$
$$\alpha\text{-Ketoglutaric acid} + CO_2 + TPNH + H^+$$

The reversibility of this reaction has been demonstrated by Ochoa, who used the glucose-6-phosphate dehydrogenase system (cf. p. 313) to reduce the TPN$^+$ formed. Since the equilibrium in the reduction of TPN$^+$ by glucose-6-phosphate is far in the direction of TPNH, the "CO_2 fixation" by α-ketoglutarate is pulled by the removal of TPN$^+$ from the equilibrium in the reaction written above (cf. accompanying diagram).

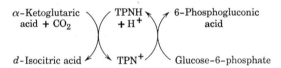

At the time of the work of Martius and Knoop, it was already known that muscle tissue can cause the decarboxylation of α-ketoglutaric acid to succinic acid. This reaction could serve as a link between the meta-

$$\alpha\text{-Ketoglutaric acid} + \tfrac{1}{2}O_2 \rightarrow \text{Succinic acid} + CO_2$$

bolic transformations of the tricarboxylic acids and of the four-carbon dicarboxylic acids. The work of Green et al.[9] and of others demonstrated that cocarboxylase (thiamine pyrophosphate, TPP) and Mg^{2+} are obligatory cofactors in the operation of a coupled reaction sequence involving successive decarboxylation and oxidation. The over-all reaction is inhibited by arsenite. After the studies of Lipmann, Lynen, and Ochoa

[6] S. Ochoa, *J. Biol. Chem.*, **174**, 133 (1948); A. Kornberg and W. E. Pricer, Jr., *ibid.*, **189**, 123 (1951); G. W. E. Plaut and S. C. Sung, *ibid.*, **207**, 305 (1954).

[7] S. Ochoa and E. Weisz-Tabori, *J. Biol. Chem.*, **174**, 123 (1948).

[8] J. Moyle and M. Dixon, *Biochem. J.*, **63**, 548, 552 (1956); G. Siebert et al., *J. Biol. Chem.*, **226**, 965, 977 (1957).

[9] D. E. Green et al., *J. Biol. Chem.*, **140**, 683 (1941).

on the role of coenzyme A in the oxidative decarboxylation of pyruvic acid (cf. p. 482), it was shown that succinyl-CoA is an intermediate in the decarboxylation of α-ketoglutaric acid,[10] and that lipoic acid and DPN$^+$ are participants in the reaction. From the important work of Kaufman et al.[11] it is now recognized that the oxidative decarboxylation of α-ketoglutarate by heart muscle preparations resembles in many respects the conversion of pyruvate to acetyl-CoA (cf. p. 481). A partially purified "α-ketoglutaric dehydrogenase" preparation requires TPP, Mg^{2+}, and lipoic acid to effect the reaction

$$\alpha\text{-Ketoglutaric acid} + DPN^+ + \text{coenzyme A} \rightarrow$$

$$\underset{\text{Succinyl-CoA}}{\overset{\displaystyle CH_2COOH}{\underset{\displaystyle |}{CH_2CO-SCH_2CH_2NHR}}} + CO_2 + DPNH + H^+$$

In the formula of succinyl-CoA shown, the group R denotes the remainder of the molecule of coenzyme A (p. 206).

It has been assumed, but not yet established experimentally, that, as in the oxidation of pyruvate, the above reaction proceeds by a sequence of steps in which a compound of TPP and succinyl semialdehyde ($HOOCCH_2CH_2CHO$) is formed by decarboxylation of α-ketoglutarate and reacts with lipoic acid to form a S-succinyl derivative of dihydrolipoic acid. This is thought to be followed by the transfer of the succinyl group to coenzyme A, and the reoxidation of dihydrolipoic acid by DPN$^+$. Two enzymic routes are available for the conversion of succinyl-CoA to succinate in crude preparations from heart muscle. One of these is hydrolysis of the thiol ester bond by a thiol esterase ("deacylase").[12] The second involves a coupled reaction in which ADP is phosphorylated to form ATP. The enzyme system responsible for this

$$\text{Succinyl-CoA} + ADP + \text{phosphate} \rightleftharpoons \text{Succinate} + \text{coenzyme A} + ATP$$

reaction has been separated from the α-ketoglutaric dehydrogenase system described above, and has been termed the "phosphorylating enzyme" (P enzyme).[13] The dehydrogenase and phosphorylating systems have been identified in animal tissues (heart muscle), plants (spinach), and bacteria (*Escherichia coli*). It appears that, with preparations of the P enzyme from heart muscle, guanosine diphosphate (or inosine diphosphate) rather than ADP is the initial phosphate acceptor;[14] the resulting

[10] D. R. Sanadi and J. W. Littlefield, *J. Biol. Chem.*, **193**, 683 (1951).

[11] S. Kaufman et al., *J. Biol. Chem.*, **203**, 869 (1953).

[12] J. Gergely et al., *J. Biol. Chem.*, **198**, 323 (1952).

[13] H. Hift et al., *J. Biol. Chem.*, **204**, 565 (1953); S. Kaufman, *ibid.*, **216**, 153 (1955).

[14] D. R. Sanadi et al., *J. Biol. Chem.*, **218**, 505 (1956).

GTP (or ITP) reacts with ADP in the presence of nucleoside diphospho-kinase (p. 461) to form ATP. The purified P enzyme preparations from heart muscle appear to be specific for succinate. The equilibrium ratio [succinyl-CoA] [ADP] [phosphate]/[succinate] [ATP] [coenzyme A] is about 0.3 at pH 7.4 and 20° C; hence the value of $\Delta F'$ in the hydrolysis of succinyl-CoA to succinate and coenzyme A is of the same order of magnitude as in the hydrolysis of ATP to ADP and phosphate (cf. p. 377). The conversion of α-ketoglutarate to succinyl-CoA by heart muscle preparations, when coupled to the action of the phosphorylating enzyme, can lead to the generation of ATP from ADP and phosphate. In contrast to the phosphorylation of ADP coupled to the respiratory chain, this oxidative phosphorylation is not "uncoupled" by dinitrophenol. Like the conversion of glyceraldehyde-3-phosphate to 3-phosphoglyceric acid, the oxidation of α-ketoglutarate to succinate and CO_2 is coupled to a "substrate-linked" phosphorylation (cf. p. 380).

What proved to be perhaps the most decisive discovery in the study of the mechanism of the aerobic oxidation of carbohydrates was provided by Krebs in 1937 when he showed that minced pigeon breast muscle can convert oxaloacetic acid to citric acid. This conversion of a four-carbon acid into a six-carbon compound clearly involved the addition of two carbons from some metabolite, and Krebs suggested that the source of these two carbons might be pyruvic acid, which suffered decarboxylation in the process. It is now known that the substance derived from pyruvic acid, and which condenses with oxaloacetic acid, is acetyl-CoA (p. 482). This has been demonstrated convincingly by Stern and Ochoa[15] through the crystallization from swine heart of an enzyme ("condensing enzyme") that catalyzes the reaction:

$$\text{Oxaloacetic acid} + \text{acetyl-CoA} + H_2O \rightleftharpoons \text{Citric acid} + \text{coenzyme A}$$

The reaction is strongly exergonic in the direction of citrate synthesis ($\Delta F' =$ ca. -7 kcal per mole at pH 7.2, 22° C). The enzyme appears to be widely distributed among animal and plant tissues, as well as some microorganisms. If its action is coupled to that of phosphotransacetylase (p. 483), acetyl phosphate can serve as an acetyl donor to oxaloacetate. The metabolic interrelationships of pyruvic acid, oxaloacetic acid, and citric acid are summarized in Fig. 1. In the presence of ATP and the "acetate activating" system (cf. p. 484), acetate is converted to acetyl-CoA and thus can be utilized for citric acid synthesis.

It will be noted that the reaction catalyzed by the condensing enzyme involves the attachment of the methyl carbon of the acetyl group to oxaloacetic acid. The reaction differs, therefore, from acetylation reac-

[15] J. R. Stern et al., *J. Biol. Chem.*, **191**, 161; **193**, 691, 703 (1951); **198**, 313 (1952).

tions in which acetyl-coenzyme A donates an acetyl group to amines such as sulfanilamide or to alcohols such as choline with the formation of acetylsulfanilamide or acetylcholine respectively (cf. p. 578). Although the formation of citrate involves a different type of chemical reaction from that in the acetylation of sulfanilamide, acetyl-coenzyme A is the "acetyl" donor in both. This result must be attributed to a characteristic difference in the specificity of the two enzyme systems concerned.

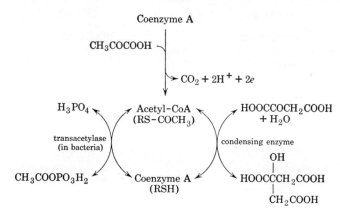

Fig. 1. Role of coenzyme A in the metabolic relations among pyruvic acid, oxalo-acetic acid, and citric acid.

On the basis of the facts available in 1937, Krebs[16] proposed a metabolic cycle involving citric acid as an intermediate; this scheme (cf. Fig. 2) has been variously termed the "citric acid cycle," the "Krebs cycle," and the "tricarboxylic acid cycle." In what follows, the first of these names will be used. In the form given in Fig. 2, the scheme includes information gained since it was originally proposed by Krebs.

The experimental basis offered by Krebs for the operation of the citric acid cycle in pigeon breast muscle was summarized by him under four headings: (1) the catalytic effect of citric acid on the respiration of pigeon breast muscle is of the same order of magnitude as that of succinic acid and the other 4-carbon dicarboxylic acids; (2) there is a rapid oxidation of citric, isocitric, cis-aconitic, and α-ketoglutaric acids by pigeon breast muscle; (3) citric acid is synthesized from oxaloacetic acid; and (4) under aerobic conditions, succinic acid is formed oxidatively either from fumaric acid or from oxaloacetic acid even in the presence of 0.01 M malonate, which specifically blocks succinic dehydrogenase to about 90 per cent. This last point is of special importance, since it shows that, under conditions where the conversion of fumaric acid to

[16] H. A. Krebs and W. A. Johnson. *Enzymologia*, **4**, 148 (1937).

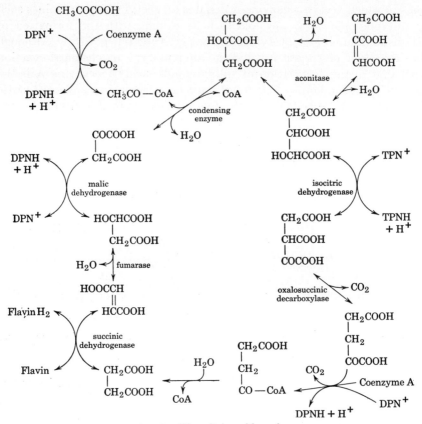

Fig. 2. The citric acid cycle.

succinic acid by succinic dehydrogenase is blocked, there is another metabolic pathway for the formation of succinic acid. In fact, any one of the di- or tricarboxylic acids that stimulates the aerobic respiration of muscle will give rise to succinic acid in the presence of malonate. However, under these conditions, the respiration ceases when all of the substance added has been converted, in a stoichiometric manner, to succinic acid.

Examination of the scheme in Fig. 2 shows that it satisfies the stoichiometric requirements for the oxidation of pyruvic acid by molecular oxygen:

$$CH_3COCOOH + 5O \rightarrow 3CO_2 + 2H_2O$$

The uptake of 5 atoms of oxygen clearly corresponds to the removal of 5 pairs of electrons during the clockwise operation of the citric acid cycle. Although the manner in which each pair of electrons is transferred to oxygen is not completely elucidated, the earlier discussion of biological oxidations points to cytochrome oxidase as the immediate catalyst of the electron transfer to oxygen. Each of the 5 atoms of oxygen that are reduced may be considered to combine with 2 hydrogen atoms to form water. Since, as written, 3 equivalents of water are taken up during the operation of the cycle, the net change corresponds to the formation of 2 moles of water per mole of pyruvic acid oxidized.

It is of the utmost significance to the physiological economy of aerobic cells that the enzymes of the citric acid cycle are associated in cytoplasmic particles (liver mitochondria, muscle sarcosomes) with the enzymes of the respiratory chain of electron transfer from reduced pyridine nucleotides and flavins to oxygen. In Chapter 15, attention was called to the integration of the enzymic mechanisms of electron transfer with those for the phosphorylation of ADP. The close association of the citric acid cycle with this multienzyme system provides a means for the continuous reduction of electron carriers, thus transferring energy from pyruvate to these oxidation-reduction systems; in the presence of oxygen, the electron carriers are reoxidized, and energy is further transferred to ATP by respiratory chain phosphorylation of ADP. Consequently, in the steady state of aerobic oxidation of metabolites via the citric acid cycle, catalytic amounts of the various cofactors (coenzyme A, pyridine nucleotides, etc.) suffice to effect the synthesis of relatively large amounts of ATP which are needed to drive the resynthesis of essential cellular components (proteins, polysaccharides, etc.) in the steady state of biological turnover.

A significant metabolic aspect of the citric acid cycle is that the equilibrium in the oxidative decarboxylation of α-ketoglutaric acid is so far in the direction of succinic acid as to make the operation of the cycle essentially unidirectional. Krebs[17] has pointed out that several metabolic cycles have one or more reactions that are, for practical purposes, "irreversible." It is probable that the regulation of the rate of such "irreversible" steps determines the physiological activity of some cycles, and is an important factor in the maintenance of steady-state levels of metabolites (homeostasis).

The scheme in Fig. 2 shows how a small quantity of oxaloacetic acid, or a substance that can give rise to this compound, can cause the oxidation of a much larger amount of pyruvic acid by minced pigeon breast muscle. If malonic acid is added, the regeneration of oxaloacetic acid is inhibited in this tissue, and respiration is thereby inhibited. As noted earlier, the addition of oxaloacetic acid (or of fumaric, malic, citric, or α-ketoglutaric acid) will restore respiration only until all the added substrate has been completely converted to succinic acid. However,

[17] H. A. Krebs, *Enzymologia*, **12**, 88 (1946).

the addition of very large amounts of any of these compounds, or of succinic acid itself, can completely reverse the malonate effect since the competitive inhibition of succinic dehydrogenase by malonate is overcome by high concentrations (10 to 20 times that of the inhibitor) of succinate.

Another inhibitor of the citric acid cycle is fluoroacetate (FCH_2COO^-), which in biological systems gives rise to the formation of fluorocitrate.[18] This product is formed by the enzyme-catalyzed condensation of fluoro-acetyl-CoA and oxaloacetate,[19] and inhibits competitively the action of aconitase.[20] Fluoroacetic acid has been found to occur naturally in the leaves of a South African plant (*Dichapetalum cymosum*); these leaves are toxic to animals that eat them.

Formation of Four-Carbon Dicarboxylic Acids by CO₂ Fixation

In contrast to the behavior of muscle preparations, minced pigeon liver is able to oxidize pyruvate in the presence of malonate, or if no four-carbon dicarboxylic acids are added. This is not to be taken as indicating that the citric acid cycle is inoperative in pigeon liver minces; the difference in the response to malonate is a consequence of the fact that pigeon liver (as well as mammalian kidney and liver) can synthesize four-carbon dicarboxylic acids from pyruvic acid if CO_2 is present.

The first clear indications of such "CO_2 fixation" came from studies with bacterial systems.[21] It had been known that "propionic acid bacteria" (found in Gruyère and Emmentaler cheese and elsewhere), when grown in a medium buffered with phosphate and containing glycerol as the carbon source, produce propionic acid in almost quantitative yield. Wood and Werkman[22] found that, when the phosphate is replaced by carbonate, succinic acid is formed in addition to propionic acid, and, for every equivalent of succinic acid formed, one equivalent of CO_2 disappears. By the use of $C^{13}O_2$, they demonstrated that the succinic acid contained C^{13} in the carboxyl carbons. Since this result suggested the biological fixation of CO_2 by a three-carbon compound to yield a four-carbon dicarboxylic acid, Wood and Werkman offered the hypothesis that pyruvic acid (derived from glycerol) combined with CO_2 to form oxaloacetic acid; this condensation has come to be called the Wood-

---

[18] R. A. Peters, *Advances in Enzymol.*, **18**, 113 (1957).

[19] R. O. Brady, *J. Biol. Chem.*, **217**, 213 (1955); A. Marcus and W. B. Elliott, *ibid.*, **218**, 823 (1956).

[20] J. F. Morrison and R. A. Peters, *Biochem. J.*, **58**, 473 (1954).

[21] M. F. Utter and H. G. Wood, *Advances in Enzymol.*, **12**, 41 (1951).

[22] H. G. Wood and C. H. Werkman, *Biochem. J.*, **32**, 1262 (1938); **34**, 7 (1940); H. G. Wood et al., *J. Biol. Chem.*, **139**, 365, 377 (1941).

Werkman reaction. The formation of succinic acid was thought to involve the reactions shown.

$$
\begin{array}{ccccccccc}
\text{COOH} & & \text{COOH} & & \text{COOH} & & \text{COOH} & & \text{COOH} \\
| & & | & & | & & | & & | \\
\text{CH}_3 & & \text{CH}_2 & & \text{CH}_2 & & \text{HC} & & \text{CH}_2 \\
| & \xrightarrow{+\,CO_2} & | & \xrightarrow{+\,2H} & | & \xrightarrow{-\,H_2O} & \| & \xrightarrow{+\,2H} & | \\
\text{CO} & & \text{CO} & & \text{HCOH} & & \text{CH} & & \text{CH}_2 \\
| & & | & & | & & | & & | \\
\text{COOH} & & \text{COOH} & & \text{COOH} & & \text{COOH} & & \text{COOH} \\
\text{Pyruvic} & & \text{Oxaloacetic} & & \text{Malic} & & \text{Fumaric} & & \text{Succinic} \\
\text{acid} & & \text{acid} & & \text{acid} & & \text{acid} & & \text{acid}
\end{array}
$$

It will be noted that the conversion of pyruvic acid to oxaloacetic acid by CO_2 fixation is the reverse of a decarboxylation of the keto acid. Enzymes that catalyze this decarboxylation (oxaloacetic decarboxylases) are widely distributed in biological systems; purified preparations have been obtained from plant and animal tissues, and from bacteria.[23] By means of labeled CO_2, it was shown that such preparations catalyze the incorporation of labeled carbon into the carboxyl adjacent to the methylene group of oxaloacetate.

$$C^*O_2 + CH_3COCOOH \rightleftharpoons HOOC^*CH_2COCOOH$$

The wider importance of the fixation of CO_2 to form four-carbon acids became evident with the demonstration that it also occurred in some animal tissues.[24] When pigeon liver preparations are incubated with pyruvic acid and isotopic CO_2 ($C^{13}O_2$, $C^{14}O_2$, or $C^{11}O_2$), the isotope appears in the carboxyl groups of the four-carbon dicarboxylic acids and in α-ketoglutaric acid. Since the α-ketoglutaric acid only contains isotope in the carboxyl group adjacent to the carbonyl group, it was believed for a time that the conversion of pyruvic acid to α-ketoglutaric acid could not involve any symmetrical intermediates such as citric acid, and that citric acid is not in the direct metabolic pathway, as indicated in Fig. 2. Ogston,[25] however, called attention to the fact that, although citric acid is a symmetrical compound, the enzyme which causes its metabolic transformation is not. Hence the enzyme-catalyzed conversion of a symmetrical molecule such as citric acid labeled asymmetrically with an isotope might be expected to take an asymmetric course, provided the substrate has a specific spatial relationship to the enzyme at three points in the enzyme-substrate complex (cf. p. 278). Experimental evidence for the formation of such isotopically asymmetric citric acid by rat liver

[23] B. Vennesland et al., *J. Biol. Chem.*, **178**, 301 (1949); S. Ochoa et al., *ibid.*, **174**, 979 (1948); L. O. Krampitz and C. H. Werkman, *Biochem. J.*, **35**, 595 (1941).

[24] E. A. Evans, Jr., and L. Slotin, *J. Biol. Chem.*, **141**, 439 (1941); H. G. Wood et al., *ibid.*, **142**, 31 (1942).

[25] A. G. Ogston, *Nature*, **162**, 963 (1948).

homogenates was provided soon thereafter,[26] and the fixation of isotopic CO_2 was formulated as shown.

$$\left.\begin{array}{l}\text{Pyruvic acid} \\ + \ C^{14}O_2\end{array}\right\} \rightarrow \begin{array}{l}CH_2C^{14}OOH \\ | \\ \star COCOOH\end{array} \rightarrow \begin{array}{l}CH_2C^{14}OOH \\ | \\ HOCCOOH \\ | \\ CH_2COOH\end{array} \rightarrow \begin{array}{l}COC^{14}OOH \\ | \\ CH_2\star \\ | \\ CH_2COOH\end{array}$$

Subsequent studies on the oxaloacetic decarboxylase systems of animal tissues (pigeon liver) and of plants (wheat germ) have shown[27] that the reversible decarboxylation needs a nucleotide such as inosine triphosphate (ITP) or ATP, and that the product of this decarboxylation is phosphoenolpyruvic acid (p. 471). In these enzyme systems, the fixation of CO_2 by phosphoenolpyruvic acid is coupled to phosphate transfer to IDP; the interconversion of the ATP and ITP systems has been attributed to the action of nucleoside diphosphokinase (p. 461). Plant tissues

$$\begin{array}{l}CH_2COOH \\ | \\ CO \\ | \\ COOH\end{array} \quad \overset{ITP \quad CO_2}{\underset{Mn^{2+} \quad IDP}{\rightleftarrows}} \quad \begin{array}{l}CH_2 \\ || \\ C-OPO_3H_2 \\ | \\ COOH\end{array}$$

Oxaloacetic acid   Phosphoenolpyruvic acid

(spinach leaves, wheat germ) also contain another enzyme system that catalyzes the formation of oxaloacetic acid from phosphoenolpyruvic acid and CO_2 in the absence of added nucleotides, and with the liberation of inorganic phosphate.[28] This CO_2 fixation is essentially irreversible, and it may account for the accumulation in leaves of relatively large amounts of the organic acids of the citric acid cycle (cf. p. 516).

Another enzyme system for the decarboxylation of a four-carbon dicarboxylic acid to pyruvic acid and CO_2 is the "malic enzyme," which effects the oxidative decarboxylation of malic acid.[29] This reaction requires Mn^{2+} and involves the obligatory participation of the TPN system; it cannot be imitated by combining purified malic dehydrogenase and oxaloacetic decarboxylase. The reaction mediated by the

$$\text{Malic acid} + TPN^+ \rightleftharpoons \text{Pyruvic acid} + CO_2 + TPNH + H^+$$

[26] V. R. Potter and C. Heidelberger, *Nature*, **164**, 180 (1949); V. Lorber et al., *J. Biol. Chem.*, **185**, 689 (1950).

[27] M. F. Utter and K. Kurahashi, *J. Biol. Chem.*, **207**, 787, 821 (1954); T. T. Tchen and B. Vennesland, *ibid.*, **213**, 533 (1955); K. Kurahashi et al., *ibid.*, **226**, 1059 (1957).

[28] R. S. Bandurski, *J. Biol. Chem.*, **217**, 137 (1955); T. T. Tchen et al., *ibid.*, **213**, 547 (1955).

[29] S. Ochoa et al., *J. Biol. Chem.*, **174**, 979 (1948); **187**, 849, 863, 891 (1950); S. Ochoa, in J. B. Sumner and K. Myrbäck, *The Enzymes*, Chapter 72, Academic Press, New York, 1952.

"malic enzyme" is readily reversible. If glucose-6-phosphate and its specific dehydrogenase are present, a mechanism is available for the reduction of TPN^+ (cf. p. 504), and the fixation of CO_2 by pyruvic acid to form malic acid ensues. With some exceptions,[30] preparations of the "malic enzyme" decarboxylate oxaloacetic acid to yield pyruvic acid. It will be noted that the oxidative decarboxylation of malic acid by the "malic enzyme" resembles the oxidative decarboxylation of isocitric acid (cf. p. 504). "Malic enzyme" activity has been found in many biological systems, including plants and bacteria.[31]

From the above discussion it may be concluded that two enzymic mechanisms are present in animal tissues for the decarboxylation of four-carbon dicarboxylic acids. It has been suggested that the conversion of pyruvate to phosphoenolpyruvate involves the cooperation of these two enzyme systems, and that this route may be more important than the direct reversal of the ATP-pyruvic transphosphorylase reaction (cf. p. 473). According to this hypothesis,[32] the "malic enzyme" and malic dehydrogenase convert pyruvate and CO_2 to oxaloacetate, which is decarboxylated by oxaloacetic decarboxylase in the reaction that requires ITP or ATP.

$$Pyruvate + TPNH + H^+ + CO_2 \rightarrow Malate + TPN^+$$

$$Malate + TPN^+ \rightarrow Oxaloacetate + TPNH + H^+$$

$$Oxaloacetate + ITP \rightarrow Phosphoenolpyruvate + CO_2 + IDP$$

$$IDP + ATP \rightarrow ITP + ADP$$

$$Pyruvate + ATP \rightarrow Phosphoenolpyruvate + ADP$$

Relation of Acetate to the Biosynthesis of Carbohydrates

The place of acetate in the intermediate metabolism of carbohydrates is of special interest in that its administration does not increase the amount of liver glycogen in a fasted animal or enhance glycosuria in a diabetic animal. Although it is not glycogenic by these criteria, acetic acid can provide carbon atoms for the synthesis of glycogen, since, if $C^{13}H_3COOH$ is given to a fasting rat, isotopic carbon is found in all the carbon atoms of the glucose units; with $CH_3C^{13}OOH$, the isotope appears in the 3 and 4 positions.[33] The administration of radioactive

[30] P. Faulkner, *Biochem. J.,* **64**, 430; *Nature,* **178**, 921 (1956); H. J. Saz and J. A. Hubbard, *J. Biol. Chem.,* **225**, 921 (1957).

[31] L. M. Kraemer et al., *J. Biol. Chem.,* **188**, 583 (1951).

[32] H. A. Krebs, *Bull. Johns Hopkins Hosp.,* **95**, 45 (1954).

[33] H. G. Wood, *Cold Spring Harbor Symposia Quant. Biol.,* **13**, 201 (1948).

bicarbonate also leads to the appearance of C^{14} in the 3 and 4 positions of the glucose units of liver glycogen.[34]   As pointed out by Bloch,[35] there is no inconsistency between these data from isotope experiments and the failure of acetic acid to behave as a glycogenic substance, as defined above.   The formation of glycogen from pyruvic acid (or from compounds that are readily converted to pyruvic acid) can be accomplished by a reversal of the reactions operative in glycogenolysis.   Thus the administration of such glycogenic substances to fasting or diabetic animals can force the synthesis of hexose units.   On the other hand, the carbon atoms of acetic acid can be converted to pyruvic acid only by way of the citric acid cycle via condensation of acetyl-CoA with oxaloacetic acid.   Consequently, the formation *in vivo* of glycogen from acetic acid is primarily dependent not upon the amount of acetic acid available but upon the entrance of acetic acid into the citric acid cycle and the rate at which pyruvate can be formed thereby.

It will be instructive to trace the path of acetate labeled in the methyl carbon or the carboxyl carbon as this metabolite passes through the citric acid cycle (cf. Fig. 3).   Note that the phosphoenolpyruvate formed after one turn of the cycle is so labeled that its carboxyl carbon contains isotope from the carbonyl carbon of acetyl-CoA, and its other two carbon atoms contain the label originally present in the methyl group.   If this labeled phosphoenolpyruvate is converted to glucosyl units, carbons 3 and 4 of glucose will be labeled by the isotope from the carboxyl group of acetate and the other four carbon atoms of glucose will contain isotope derived from the methyl carbon.

It is important to recognize that although citrate is a symmetrical molecule, the isotope derived from a labeled precursor is not randomized; as mentioned previously, citrate is metabolized in an asymmetric manner, and bound to the enzyme surface at three enzymic groups that differ in their catalytic properties.   On the other hand, isotope present in succinate is randomized, presumably because free succinate is released from the enzyme system that converts α-ketoglutarate to fumarate.

Upon completion of the first turn of the cycle, the oxaloacetate becomes labeled, and a second turn of the cycle will lead to the distribution of isotope from the methyl-carbon of acetate among all three carbon atoms of phosphoenolpyruvate, the smallest amount of isotope being in the pyruvate carboxyl group.   It will be recalled that, when pyruvate-2-C^{13} ($CH_3C^{13}OCOOH$) is administered to rats, the liver glycogen is found to be labeled not only in carbons 2 and 5 of the glucosyl units, but also in the other four carbon atoms as well (cf. p. 496).   It can now be seen that the appearance of C^{13} in carbons 3 and 4 of glucose is a consequence of the entrance of pyruvate into the citric acid cycle, through

[34] N. Lifson et al., *J. Biol. Chem.*, **188**, 491 (1951).
[35] K. Bloch, *Physiol. Revs.*, **27**, 574 (1947).

the formation of $CH_3C^{13}O$-CoA. Clearly, the appearance of C^{13} in carbons 2 and 5 of glucose can result from the direct utilization of pyruvate-2-C^{13} for the synthesis of phosphoenolpyruvate-2-C^{13} (cf. p.

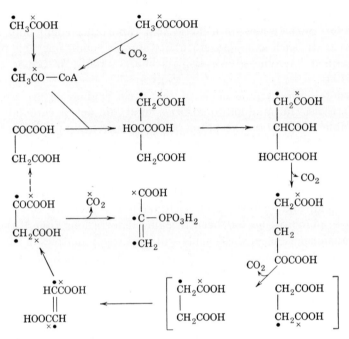

Fig. 3. Labeling of oxaloacetate upon completion of one turn of the citric acid cycle after the entrance of a labeled acetyl group derived from acetate or from pyruvate. The broken arrow denotes the entrance of labeled oxaloacetate into a second turn of the cycle.

473). If the labeled pyruvate participates in a CO_2-fixation reaction leading either to malate or to oxaloacetate, $HOOCCH_2C^{13}OCOOH$ will be formed. One turn of the citric acid cycle will convert this to $HOOCC^{13}H_2C^{13}OCOOH$, which gives rise to glucose-1,2,5,6-C^{13}.

From the foregoing, it will be evident that the fixation of labeled CO_2 (e.g., $C^{14}O_2$) into oxaloacetate or malate, followed by the formation of a symmetrical 4-carbon compound such as succinate (cf. Fig. 3), should lead to the labeling of liver glycogen in carbons 3 and 4 of the glucosyl units.

The Citric Acid Cycle in Other Biological Systems

After the proposal of the citric acid cycle in 1937, there was much discussion about its validity, but there can be little doubt at present that it represents the principal metabolic pathway for the aerobic oxidation of pyruvic acid in mammalian tissues. Although the information about the carbohydrate metabolism of invertebrates is less extensive, the available evidence also points to the operation of the cycle in their tissues.[36] It should be added, however, that some animal tissues appear to have a relatively low capacity to oxidize pyruvate or acetate via the citric acid cycle. Such tissues form lactic acid (and other compounds derived from pyruvate, such as L-alanine) under aerobic conditions; this phenomenon, termed "aerobic glycolysis," is characteristic of tumor tissues[37] (cf. p. 499).

In general, the organic acids of the citric acid cycle are present in animal tissues in minimal quantities, and do not accumulate to an appreciable extent; an exception is the occurrence of relatively large amounts of citric acid in bone and in the prostate gland.[38] On the other hand, the leaves of many species of plants contain considerable quantities of malic acid and citric acid, in addition to other organic acids such as oxalic acid, succinic acid, and, in certain species, cis-aconitic acid, isocitric acid, and tartaric acid. Although the presence of these components in plant tissues has been recognized for a long time,[39] the metabolic transformations of these acids still are largely matters of conjecture. The studies by Vickery and his associates[40] have provided evidence for the view that some of the organic acids may be involved in enzyme-catalyzed reactions of the citric acid cycle, and the enzymes of the cycle have been identified in green leaves.[41] Of special interest is the demonstration that, in excised leaves of *Bryophyllum calycinum* (a succulent herb of the *Crassulaceae* family), there occurs a diurnal variation in the level of malic acid. In the dark, this level rises, with a concomitant fall in the starch content; during the day, when photosynthetic processes are operative, the level of malic acid falls, and the starch content is increased, as shown in Fig. 4. It will be noted that the rise in organic acid content is accompanied by a significant drop in pH. For further discussion of these phenomena, see the references cited above, and the textbook by Bonner.[42]

The most striking data in favor of the operation of the citric acid cycle in plant tissues has come from studies with cellular particles prepared from etiolated seedlings of the mung bean (*Phaseolus aureus*); these

---

[36] K. R. Rees, *Biochem. J.,* **55,** 478 (1953).

[37] H. Busch and H. A. Baltrush, *Cancer Research,* **14,** 448 (1954).

[38] T. Mann and C. Lutwak-Mann, *Physiol. Revs.,* **31,** 27 (1951).

[39] T. A. Bennet-Clark, *Ann. Rev. Biochem.,* **6,** 579 (1937); H. B. Vickery and G. W. Pucher, *ibid.,* **9,** 529 (1940).

[40] H. B. Vickery and M. D. Abrahams, *J. Biol. Chem.,* **180,** 37 (1949); G. W. Pucher et al., *Plant Physiol.,* **24,** 610 (1949).

[41] D. O. Brummond and R. H. Burris, *J. Biol. Chem.,* **209,** 755 (1954).

[42] J. Bonner, *Plant Biochemistry,* Academic Press, New York, 1950.

particles show many of the properties of liver mitochondria in their action on intermediates of the cycle.[43]

Although enzymes of the citric acid cycle have been demonstrated in many microorganisms, and it is probable that the cycle serves as one of the pathways for the aerobic oxidation of metabolites in some bacteria,

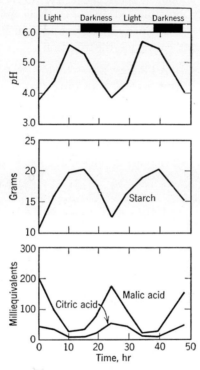

Fig. 4. Diurnal variation of organic acids and starch of excised leaves of *Bryophyllum calycinum*. The data for starch, malic acid, and citric acid are given per kilogram of fresh weight of leaf. [From H. B. Vickery, *Plant Physiol.*, **27**, 9 (1952).]

alternative pathways are known in several instances to be of greater significance than the citric acid cycle. It should be noted that several components of the cycle (e.g., α-ketoglutaric acid, oxaloacetic acid) are important in amino acid metabolism (Chapter 31), and the principal function of the microbial enzymes concerned with their conversion may be related to protein metabolism rather than to the oxidation of acetyl groups derived from pyruvic acid.[44]

[43] A. Millerd et al., *Proc. Natl. Acad. Sci.*, **37**, 855 (1951); *Arch. Biochem. and Biophys.*, **42**, 149 (1953).

[44] H. A. Krebs et al., *Biochem. J.*, **51**, 614 (1952).

Other Metabolic Conversions of Acids of the Citric Acid Cycle

It was seen above that the "condensing enzyme" which catalyzes the reversible formation of citric acid from acetyl-CoA and oxaloacetic acid is widely distributed among aerobic cells. However, it does not appear to represent the only possible catalyst for citric acid breakdown and synthesis in animal tissues, since an enzyme system has been obtained[45] (from swine liver) that catalyzes the reaction

Citrate + coenzyme A + ATP $\rightleftharpoons$
$$\text{Acetyl-CoA} + \text{oxaloacetate} + \text{ADP} + \text{phosphate}$$

In some microorganisms (e.g., *Pseudomonas*), citrate and isocitrate undergo the following reversible reactions,[46] catalyzed by "citritase" and "isocitritase" respectively. These reactions are slightly exergonic in the direction written. Coenzyme A does not appear to be involved.

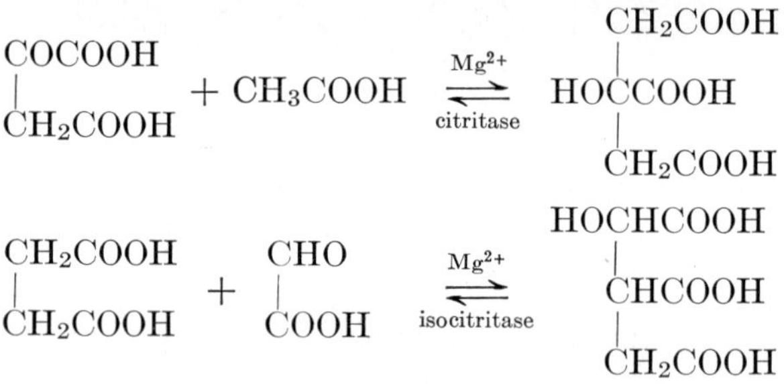

$$\begin{array}{l} \text{COCOOH} \\ | \\ \text{CH}_2\text{COOH} \end{array} + \text{CH}_3\text{COOH} \underset{\text{citritase}}{\overset{\text{Mg}^{2+}}{\rightleftharpoons}} \begin{array}{l} \text{CH}_2\text{COOH} \\ | \\ \text{HOCCOOH} \\ | \\ \text{CH}_2\text{COOH} \end{array}$$

$$\begin{array}{l} \text{CH}_2\text{COOH} \\ | \\ \text{CH}_2\text{COOH} \end{array} + \begin{array}{l} \text{CHO} \\ | \\ \text{COOH} \end{array} \underset{\text{isocitritase}}{\overset{\text{Mg}^{2+}}{\rightleftharpoons}} \begin{array}{l} \text{HOCHCOOH} \\ | \\ \text{CHCOOH} \\ | \\ \text{CH}_2\text{COOH} \end{array}$$

In many molds (e.g., *Aspergillus niger*), citric acid is a major end product of the oxidative metabolism of acetate. For the synthesis of citrate, oxaloacetate is required, and it has been suggested that such a 4-carbon dicarboxylic acid may arise by the condensation of two C_2 units. This hypothesis, derived from the work of Thunberg and Wieland, has recurred at intervals in the biochemical literature;[47] one formulation of the Thunberg-Wieland cycle (or dicarboxylic acid cycle) is given in the scheme on p. 519. Although isotope studies with molds gave data that were interpreted to indicate the condensation of two C_2 units

[45] P. A. Srere and F. Lipmann, *J. Am. Chem. Soc.*, **75**, 4874 (1953).

[46] S. Dagley and E. A. Dawes, *Biochim. et Biophys. Acta,* **17**, 177 (1955); R. W. Wheat and S. J. Ajl, *J. Biol. Chem.*, **217**, 897, 909 (1955); H. J. Saz and E. P. Hillary, *Biochem. J.*, **62**, 563 (1956); R. A. Smith et al., *Biochim. et Biophys. Acta,* **19**, 567 (1956).

[47] T. K. Walker, *Advances in Enzymol.*, **9**, 537 (1949); J. W. Foster et al., *Proc. Natl. Acad. Sci.*, **35**, 663 (1949); **36**, 219 (1950); W. E. Jefferson and J. W. Foster, *J. Bact.*, **65**, 587 (1953).

to form a C_4 acid, later work showed that other explanations of the results were equally valid.

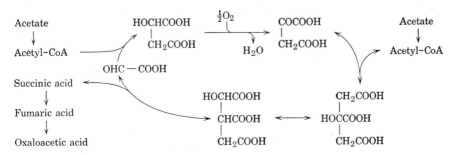

Dicarboxylic acid cycle

Of special importance in this connection was the discovery of a microbial enzyme system ("malate synthetase") that effects the condensation of acetate (presumably via acetyl-CoA) with glyoxylic acid to form malic acid,[48] a reaction formally analogous to the enzymic condensation of acetyl-CoA with oxaloacetic acid to form citric acid (p. 506).

Fig. 5. The glyoxylic acid cycle.

In microorganisms that contain malate synthetase and isocitritase, a "glyoxylic acid cycle" (Fig. 5) may be operative for the oxidative conversion of 2 molecules of acetate to 1 of succinic acid. It will be noted from Fig. 5 that, in the glyoxylic acid cycle, the isocitritase and malate synthetase reactions replace the steps from isocitric acid to malic acid in the citric acid cycle. The oxidation of succinic acid to fumaric acid would explain the formation of the latter compound from C_2 compounds in molds such as *Rhizopus nigricans;* further oxidation of the

48 H. L. Kornberg and H. A. Krebs, *Nature,* **179**, 988 (1957); D. T. O. Wong and S. J. Ajl, *J. Am. Chem. Soc.,* **78**, 3230 (1956); *Science,* **126**, 1013 (1957).

C_4 acid to oxaloacetic acid would permit the net formation of 1 molecule of citric acid from 3 molecules of acetate, as in *Aspergillus*.

Another product of the carbohydrate metabolism of some fungi (*Aspergillus terreus*) is itaconic acid, which probably arises by the enzymic decarboxylation of *cis*-aconitic acid.[49]

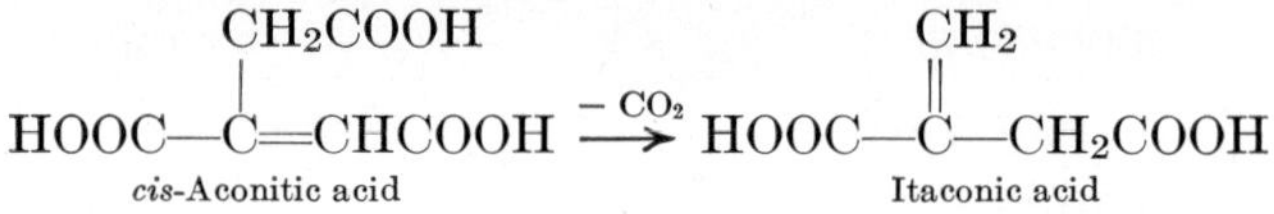

$$\underset{cis\text{-Aconitic acid}}{\overset{\displaystyle CH_2COOH}{HOOC-C\!\!=\!\!CHCOOH}} \xrightarrow{-CO_2} \underset{Itaconic\ acid}{\overset{\displaystyle CH_2}{HOOC-C-CH_2COOH}}$$

Oxalic acid (HOOC—COOH) is a further product of the oxidation of carbohydrates and of acetate by fungi such as *Aspergillus niger*.[50] It is probably formed by the oxidation of glyoxylic acid (OHC—COOH); this may arise either by the oxidation of glycolic acid (HOCH$_2$COOH), catalyzed by glycolic acid oxidase (p. 338), or by enzymic cleavage of isocitric acid or of oxaloacetic acid.[51] Some fungi decarboxylate oxalic acid to yield formic acid and CO_2.

Energy Relations in Carbohydrate Metabolism

In order to discuss the energy relations in the metabolic breakdown of carbohydrates, it may be useful to summarize schematically the processes involved in the oxidation of glucose to CO_2 and water. As will be seen from the subsequent discussion of the metabolism of fats and of proteins,

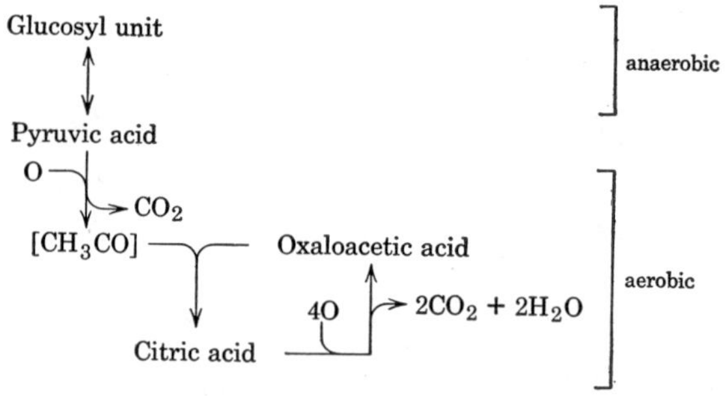

several intermediates in the scheme shown in Fig. 2 may be derived from, or be converted to, fatty acids or amino acids. Thus acetyl-CoA is an important intermediate in the oxidation and in the synthesis of fatty acids. Also, the keto acids pyruvic acid, oxaloacetic acid, and α-keto-glutaric acid are closely related in metabolism to a variety of L-amino acids, notably alanine, serine, cysteine, aspartic acid, glutamic acid,

[49] R. Bentley and C. P. Thiessen, *J. Biol. Chem.*, **226**, 673, 689, 703 (1957).
[50] W. W. Cleland and M. J. Johnson, *J. Biol. Chem.*, **220**, 595 (1956).
[51] O. Hayaishi et al., *J. Am. Chem. Soc.*, **78**, 5126 (1956).

among others. Consequently, although the intermediate metabolism of carbohydrates is considered separately from the metabolism of fats and proteins, this separation is made only for convenience; in the intact cell, there are many metabolic processes which link the metabolism of carbohydrates with that of other cell constituents and of other nutrient materials.

As noted earlier, in the oxidative breakdown of carbohydrate to CO_2 and water, ΔF° in the reaction

$$C_6H_{12}O_6 + 6O_2 \rightarrow 6CO_2 + 6H_2O$$

is approximately -690 kcal per mole. It was seen that this process may be considered to begin with the anaerobic degradation of glucose units to pyruvic acid, and in muscle extracts the process of anaerobic glycolysis from glycogen to lactic acid may be described by the reaction

$$(C_6H_{10}O_5) + H_2O \rightarrow 2CH_3CHOHCOOH$$

The free-energy change in this process is approximately -57 kcal per mole, a major part of which (ca. 60 per cent) is used by muscle cells for the resynthesis of ATP from ADP. In the aerobic oxidation of pyruvate to CO_2 and H_2O by means of the citric acid cycle, 5 atoms of oxygen are required per molecule of pyruvate (cf. p. 508) and are reduced by electron transfer from DPNH, TPNH, or a reduced flavin. As seen before, this electron transfer involves the respiratory chain of catalysts, and is coupled in liver mitochondria and muscle sarcosomes with the phosphorylation of ADP.

The studies performed by Ochoa[52] have shown that, with cell-free extracts of cat heart muscle, the oxidation of pyruvate to CO_2 and H_2O is accompanied by the generation of about 15 "energy-rich" phosphate bonds per mole of pyruvate. This value may be compared with the result of a calculation from data on the yield of ATP in the individual reactions of the citric acid cycle. Determinations of the P/O ratio in the oxidation of DPNH by oxygen have given values approaching 3; the P/O for the flavoprotein-dependent oxidation of succinate to fumarate by oxygen is probably 2 (cf. p. 383). In the conversion of α-ketoglutarate to succinate, 1 ATP is generated by a "substrate-linked" phosphorylation. These data are summarized[53] in Table 1, and it will be seen that the total number of "energy-rich" bonds generated in the five oxidative steps of the citric acid cycle is calculated to be 15, in excellent agreement with the value found by Ochoa.

In the oxidation of glucose to CO_2 and H_2O, 12 oxygen atoms are

[52] S. Ochoa, J. Biol. Chem., 151, 493 (1943).

[53] F. E. Hunter, in W. D. McElroy and B. Glass, Phosphorus Metabolism, Vol. I, Johns Hopkins Press, Baltimore, 1951.

required per molecule of hexose; 10 of these are needed for the oxidation of 2 molecules of pyruvate, with a concomitant synthesis of about 30 molecules of ATP from ADP. The other 2 oxygen atoms are required for the reoxidation of the 2 DPNH molecules (per hexose unit) formed in the oxidation of glyceraldehyde-3-phosphate (cf. p. 324); this yields an additional 6 molecules of ATP by coupling with the respiratory chain. Furthermore, there is a net yield of 2 moles of ATP (from ADP) per mole of hexose in the anaerobic conversion of glucose to pyruvate (cf. p. 490), giving a total of 38 "energy-rich" bonds. For complete oxidation of a glucosyl unit of glycogen the calculated total is 39 "energy-rich" bonds, since the net yield of ATP in anaerobic glycolysis is 3 moles per mole of hexose unit. If a value of about $+11$ kcal per mole is assumed for the phosphorylation of ADP under the conditions of glucose oxidation in the cell (cf. p. 491), the oxidation of 1 mole of glucose to CO_2 and H_2O may be expected to be accompanied by the transfer of about 420 kcal to the synthesis of ATP. This corresponds to an efficiency of about 60 per cent.

Table I. Oxidative Phosphorylation in Operation of Citric Acid Cycle

No.	Reaction	P/O ratio
1	Pyruvic acid $+ DPN^+ \rightarrow CH_3CO- + DPNH + H^+$	0
	$DPNH + H^+ + \frac{1}{2}O_2 \rightarrow DPN^+ + H_2O$	3
2	Isocitric acid $+ TPN^+ \rightarrow$ Oxalosuccinic acid $+ TPNH + H^+$	0
	$TPNH + H^+ + \frac{1}{2}O_2 \rightarrow TPN^+ + H_2O$	3
3	α-Ketoglutaric acid $+ DPN^+ \rightarrow$ Succinic acid $+ DPNH + H^+$	1
	$DPNH + H^+ + \frac{1}{2}O_2 \rightarrow DPN^+ + H_2O$	3
4	Succinic acid $+ \frac{1}{2}O_2 \rightarrow$ Fumaric acid $+ H_2O$	2
5	Malic acid $+ DPN^+ \rightarrow$ Oxaloacetic acid $+ DPNH + H^+$	0
	$DPNH + H^+ + \frac{1}{2}O_2 \rightarrow DPN^+ + H_2O$	3

From the values for the free-energy changes in the breakdown of glucose (cf. p. 521) it is clear that the aerobic oxidation of glucose yields approximately 12 times more energy per mole than does the process of anaerobic glycolysis. In other words, to perform a given amount of work, a muscle operating aerobically might be expected to oxidize much less glucose than in anaerobic work. In this connection it is of interest that under anaerobic conditions the rate of consumption of carbohydrate by muscle tissue is approximately six to eight times that observed under aerobic conditions. It would appear, therefore, that the operation of the aerobic mechanisms of carbohydrate breakdown inhibits the rate of conversion of glucose to pyruvic acid. This inhibition, by oxygen, of the rate of carbohydrate breakdown is frequently called the Pasteur effect.[54] In 1861, Pasteur found, in his studies on alcoholic fermentation, that under anaerobic conditions much more sugar was taken up, per quantity of yeast present, than was consumed in the presence of air. This effect, later termed by Warburg the "Pasteur reaction," has been observed with many types of cells from a variety of organisms, including animals and plants.

The Pasteur effect appears to be an expression of the close interrelation between the cellular mechanisms of anaerobic glycolysis, responsible for the conversion of glucose to pyruvate, and of the citric acid cycle, which causes the generation of ATP by the aerobic oxidation of pyruvate. The mechanism of the effect has not been elucidated, and several theories have been advanced in efforts to explain it. Meyerhof's studies on the Pasteur effect in muscle led him to suggest that it is a consequence of the resynthesis of carbohydrate under oxidative conditions, the result being a decrease in the net rate of glycolysis. From his data he concluded that the ratio

$$\frac{\text{pyruvic acid converted to carbohydrate}}{\text{pyruvic acid oxidized to } CO_2 \text{ and } H_2O}$$

is approximately 5. A similar value has been calculated on the basis of Ochoa's data on the oxidative generation of the pyrophosphate bonds of ATP. If the assumption is made that 4 moles of ATP are required for the reversal of the glycolytic breakdown of 1 mole of a glucosyl unit to 2 moles of pyruvic acid (cf. p. 490), it follows that the oxidation of 2 moles of pyruvic acid will provide sufficient ATP, i.e., approximately 30 pyrophosphate bonds, to permit the conversion of about 14 moles of pyruvic acid to glycogen, corresponding to a value of about 7 for the above ratio.

Although Meyerhof's hypothesis may have limited validity in explaining the Pasteur effect in muscle, it does not appear to apply to many other biological systems that exhibit the effect. For this reason, consideration has been given to the suggestion that in the presence of oxygen one of the early steps in anaerobic glycolysis is inhibited, with a resultant decrease in the over-all rate at which pyruvic acid is formed.[55] Thus the decreased utilization of glucose in the presence of oxygen may be a consequence of an inhibition of the reaction catalyzed by hexokinase. It will be recalled that this reaction depends on the availability of ATP. Since the steady-state levels of ATP, ADP, and inorganic phosphate at the cellular sites of anaerobic glycolysis and of respiratory chain phosphorylation influence the rates of these processes (cf. p. 383), the possi-

[54] K. C. Dixon, *Biol. Revs.*, **12**, 431 (1937).

[55] A. C. Aisenberg and V. R. Potter, *J. Biol. Chem.*, **224**, 1115 (1957).

bility exists that the Pasteur effect is caused by differences in the intracellular localization of these phosphate compounds under aerobic and anaerobic conditions.[56] Such a hypothesis also provides an explanation of the observation made by Crabtree[57] that the endogenous respiration of tumor tissues is inhibited by glycolysis induced by the addition of glucose. The close connection between glucose utilization and oxidative phosphorylation is also indicated by the finding that the Pasteur effect in yeast and other organisms is counteracted by the "uncoupling" agent 2,4-dinitrophenol[58] (cf. p. 385).

[56] E. Racker, *Harvey Lectures,* **51,** 143 (1957).

[57] H. G. Crabtree, *Biochem. J.,* **23,** 536 (1929).

[58] O. Meyerhof and S. Fiala, *Biochim. et Biophys. Acta,* **6,** 1 (1950); F. Lynen and R. Koenigsberger, *Ann. Chem.,* **573,** 60 (1951).

21 · Alternative Pathways of Carbohydrate Metabolism

Although the Embden-Meyerhof scheme of anaerobic breakdown of glucose (the glycolytic pathway) unquestionably represents the principal route of conversion of carbohydrates to pyruvic acid in many biological systems, including animal and plant tissues and some microorganisms, it is by no means the only known metabolic route for this conversion. The occurrence of alternative pathways was indicated by early observations that reagents such as iodoacetate, arsenite, or fluoride, which block component reactions in the glycolytic pathway, do not inhibit glucose utilization completely; in some systems the inhibition is relatively slight. One of these alternative routes of glucose metabolism, of importance in plants, some animal tissues, and several types of microorganisms, involves the oxidation of glucose-6-phosphate to 6-phosphogluconic acid, which is in turn converted to pentose phosphates. Knowledge of this pathway has emerged from the initial studies of Warburg, Dickens, Lipmann, and Dische; it has been elucidated largely through the later efforts of Cohen, Horecker, and Racker. In the biochemical literature, this alternative route has been given various names, including the "Warburg-Dickens pathway," the "hexose monophosphate oxidation shunt," and the "pentose phosphate pathway." In the present discussion, the last of these designations will be used. As will be seen later in this chapter, additional metabolic mechanisms of glucose breakdown, other than the glycolytic and pentose phosphate pathways, are also known.

The Pentose Phosphate Pathway[1]

It will be recalled that 6-phospho-D-gluconolactone is the product of the oxidation of D-glucopyranose-6-phosphate by TPN$^+$ in the pres-

[1] F. Dickens, *Brit. Med. Bull.*, **9**, 105 (1953); E. Racker, *Advances in Enzymol.*, **15**, 141 (1954); *Harvey Lectures*, **51**, 143 (1957); B. L. Horecker and A. H. Mehler, *Ann. Rev. Biochem.*, **24**, 207 (1955); S. S. Cohen, in D. M. Greenberg, *Chemical Pathways in Metabolism*, Vol. I, Academic Press, New York, 1954.

ence of glucose-6-phosphate dehydrogenase, and that the lactone is hydrolyzed to form 6-phospho-D-gluconic acid (p. 313). This dehydrogenase has been found in many animal tissues (it is especially high in adrenal cortex),[2] and in higher plants, yeast, and numerous other microorganisms. In addition to its formation by the oxidation of glucose-6-phosphate, 6-phosphogluconic acid can arise in molds and bacteria by enzymic phosphorylation of D-gluconic acid by ATP; a "gluconokinase" has been demonstrated in microorganisms adapted to utilize gluconic acid as a nutrient carbohydrate.[3] The conversion of glucose to gluconic acid is effected by a microbial glucose oxidase (p. 339). It is of interest that mammalian liver also contains an enzyme that catalyzes the oxidation of glucose to gluconic acid. When isotopic gluconic acid is administered to an intact rat, some of the isotope appears in the tissue glycogen; rat liver and kidney exhibit gluconokinase activity.[4]

The studies of several investigators have shown that yeast, *Escherichia coli,* and extracts of many animal and plant tissues contain another enzyme, named 6-phosphogluconic dehydrogenase, which, in the presence of TPN[+], catalyzes the oxidative decarboxylation of 6-phosphogluconic acid; the enzyme is activated by Mg^{2+} or Mn^{2+}. It would appear that this reaction proceeds in two steps; first, a phosphoketogluconic acid (possibly 6-phospho-3-ketogluconic acid) is formed, and this compound then loses CO_2 to form the phosphoketopentose D-ribulose-5-phosphate. The likelihood exists that these two steps are catalyzed by a single enzyme, analogous to the enzymes that cause the oxidative decarboxylation of malic acid or of isocitric acid (cf. p. 513).

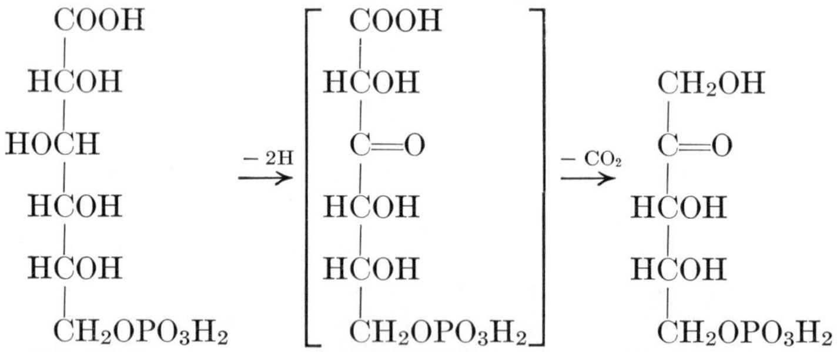

6-Phosphogluconic acid   6-Phospho-3-keto-gluconic acid   Ribulose-5-phosphate

[2] G. E. Glock and P. McLean, *Biochem. J.,* **56,** 171 (1954); T. L. Kelly et al., *J. Biol. Chem.,* **212,** 545 (1955).

[3] S. S. Cohen, *J. Biol. Chem.,* **189,** 617 (1951); D. B. M. Scott and S. S. Cohen, *Biochem. J.,* **55,** 23, 33 (1953).

[4] M. R. Stetten and D. Stetten, Jr., *J. Biol. Chem.,* **187,** 241 (1950); I. G. Leder, *ibid.,* **225,** 125 (1957).

D-Ribulose-5-phosphate is a key intermediate in the pentose phosphate pathway. By the action of the widely distributed enzyme ribose-5-phosphate isomerase,[5] it is converted to D-ribose-5-phosphate; at equilibrium, the ratio of ketose to aldose is about 1:3. The similarity of this reaction to those catalyzed by phosphohexoisomerase (p. 460) and by triose phosphate isomerase (p. 469) is readily apparent. Ribose-5-phosphate is converted to ribose-1-phosphate in the presence of phosphoglucomutase, which thus exhibits "phosphoribomutase" activity. Ribose-1,5-diphosphate is a cofactor, and acts in a manner analogous to that of glucose-1,6-diphosphate in the enzymic interconversion of glucose-6-phosphate and glucose-1-phosphate (cf. p. 461). As will be seen in Chapter 35, the incorporation of ribosyl units into ribonucleic acids involves the participation of ribose-5-phosphate or of ribose-1-phosphate.

Another important reaction undergone by ribulose-5-phosphate is its isomerization to D-xylulose-5-phosphate by an enzyme (phosphoketo-

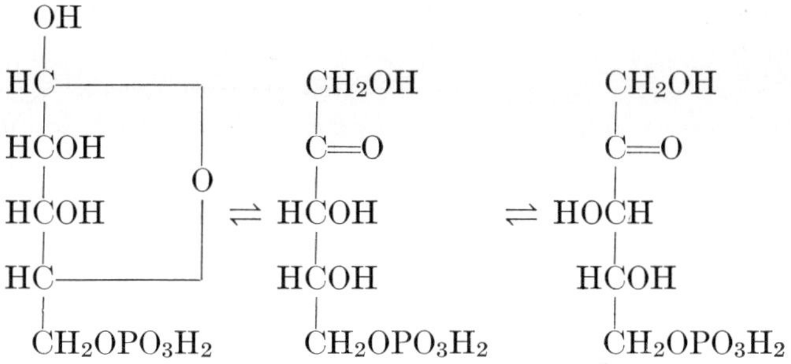

| | Ribose-5-phosphate | Ribulose-5-phosphate | Xylulose-5-phosphate |

pentoepimerase or xylulose-5-phosphate isomerase) found in animal and plant tissues and in microorganisms; at equilibrium (pH 7.5, 37° C), the ratio of xylulose-5-phosphate to ribulose-5-phosphate is about 1.4.[6]

In plants, ribulose-5-phosphate is also converted to D-ribulose-1,5-diphosphate through phosphorylation by ATP, in a reaction catalyzed by the enzyme "phosphoribulokinase."[7] Of particular importance to the photosynthesis of carbohydrates is the enzymic cleavage of ribulose-1,5-diphosphate by the addition of CO_2 and the formation of 2 molecules of D-3-phosphoglyceric acid. The enzyme system responsible for this

[5] B. L. Horecker et al., J. Biol. Chem., **193**, 371, 383 (1951); B. Axelrod and R. Jang, ibid., **209**, 847 (1954).

[6] P. A. Srere et al., Arch. Biochem. and Biophys., **59**, 535 (1955); J. Hurwitz and B. L. Horecker, J. Biol. Chem., **223**, 993 (1956); F. Dickens and D. H. Williamson, Biochem. J., **64**, 567 (1956); G. Ashwell and J. Hickman, J. Biol. Chem., **226**, 65 (1957).

[7] J. R. Quayle et al., J. Am. Chem. Soc., **76**, 3610 (1954); B. L. Horecker et al., J. Biol. Chem., **218**, 769, 785 (1956).

process has been named ribulose diphosphate carboxylase (or ribulose diphosphate dismutase).[8]

$$\begin{array}{ccc}
CH_2OPO_3H_2 & & \\
| & & COOH \\
C{=}O & & | \\
| & +H_2O & | \\
HCOH & + CO_2 \xrightarrow{\ \ \ \ } & 2\ HCOH \\
| & & | \\
HCOH & & CH_2OPO_3H_2 \\
| & & \\
CH_2OPO_3H_2 & & \\
\end{array}$$

Ribulose-1,5-diphosphate   3-Phosphoglyceric acid

In *Escherichia coli*, ribulose-5-phosphate also can arise either from ribose by conversion of ribose-5-phosphate (formed by enzymic phosphorylation with ATP)[9] or through the phosphorylation of ribulose by ATP. The two kinases involved are termed ribokinase and ribulokinase respectively. *E. coli* is able to interconvert D-arabinose (p. 404) and

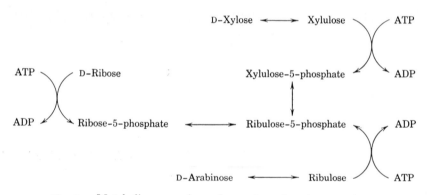

Fig. 1.   Metabolic conversions of D-pentoses in microorganisms.

D-ribulose.[10]   Microorganisms (cf. Fig. 1) also can utilize D-xylose (p. 410); the initial step appears to be isomerization to xylulose, followed by enzymic phosphorylation by ATP to form xylulose-5-phosphate.[11] In higher plants, the interconversion of arabinose and xylose may be effected by the reactions of their UDP derivatives (cf. p. 464); thus UDP-xylose is transformed to UDP-arabinose in the mung bean.[12]   In

[8] A. Weissbach et al., *J. Biol. Chem.*, **218**, 795 (1956) ; J. Mayaudon et al., *Biochim. et Biophys. Acta*, **23**, 342 (1957).

[9] C. Long, *Biochem. J.*, **59**, 322 (1955).

[10] S. S. Cohen, *J. Biol. Chem.*, **201**, 71 (1953).

[11] J. O. Lampen, *J. Biol. Chem.*, **204**, 999 (1953).

[12] V. Ginsburg et al., *Proc. Natl. Acad. Sci.*, **42**, 333 (1956) ; *J. Biol. Chem.*, **223**, 977 (1956).

higher animals, ribose is utilized preferentially, although xylose also is metabolized; arabinose and xylose are frequently found in the urine after the ingestion of large quantities of fruits or berries.

Conversion of Pentose Phosphate to Hexose Phosphate.   Although the reactions linking glucose-6-phosphate and the pentose phosphates are reversible, the over-all equilibrium is far in the direction of the latter, and the reversal of the process requires the expenditure of energy. A different route is available for the conversion of pentose phosphate to hexose phosphate, thus completing a cyclic pathway (cf. p. 531).   The resynthesis of hexose phosphate is initiated by the cleavage of xylulose-5-phosphate by the widely distributed enzyme transketolase,[13] which has been crystallized from yeast.   As its name suggests, this enzyme catalyzes the transfer of a ketol group ($-COCH_2OH$) from xylulose-5-phosphate (it was first thought that ribulose-5-phosphate is a substrate) to a suitable acceptor aldehyde.   A variety of aldehydes, including ribose-5-phosphate, can serve as reaction partners; others are glyceraldehyde-3-phosphate, glyceraldehyde, and glycolaldehyde.   The type reaction catalyzed by transketolase is shown.   The crystalline enzyme contains

$$
\begin{array}{c}
CH_2OH \\
| \\
C=O \\
| \\
HOCH \\
| \\
R
\end{array}
+
\begin{array}{c}
CHO \\
| \\
R'
\end{array}
\rightleftharpoons
\begin{array}{c}
CHO \\
| \\
R
\end{array}
+
\begin{array}{c}
CH_2OH \\
| \\
C=O \\
| \\
HOCH \\
| \\
R'
\end{array}
$$

thiamine pyrophosphate (TPP), which is essential (in addition to Mg^{2+}) for activity.   This suggests that, in the action of transketolase, an "active glycolaldehyde" may be bound to TPP, in analogy to the postulated mechanism of decarboxylation of pyruvate by yeast carboxylase (cf. p. 475).   Whereas transketolase does not decarboxylate pyruvate, it catalyzes the decarboxylation of hydroxypyruvate ($HOCH_2COCOO^-$), if a suitable aldehyde is present to accept the ketol group.   Thus the combined action of carboxylase and of transketolase converts hydroxypyruvate to the 4-carbon keto sugar erythrulose and CO_2.[14]   Hydroxypyruvate may arise in metabolism by several enzymic processes, such as the dehydrogenation of glycerate, or the deamination of serine.

$$
2HOCH_2COCOOH \rightarrow HOCH_2CO\overset{\displaystyle OH}{\overset{\displaystyle |}{C}}HCH_2OH + 2CO_2
$$

Hydroxypyruvic acid   Erythrulose

---

[13] B. L. Horecker et al., *J. Biol. Chem.*, **205**, 661 (1953); G. de la Haba et al., *ibid.*, **214**, 409 (1955).

[14] F. Dickens and D. H. Williamson, *Nature*, **178**, 1349 (1956).

In the operation of the pentose phosphate pathway, the transketolase-catalyzed reaction between xylulose-5-phosphate and ribose-5-phosphate is of special importance. The products are D-sedoheptulose-7-phosphate[15] and D-glyceraldehyde-3-phosphate. Sedoheptulose and the

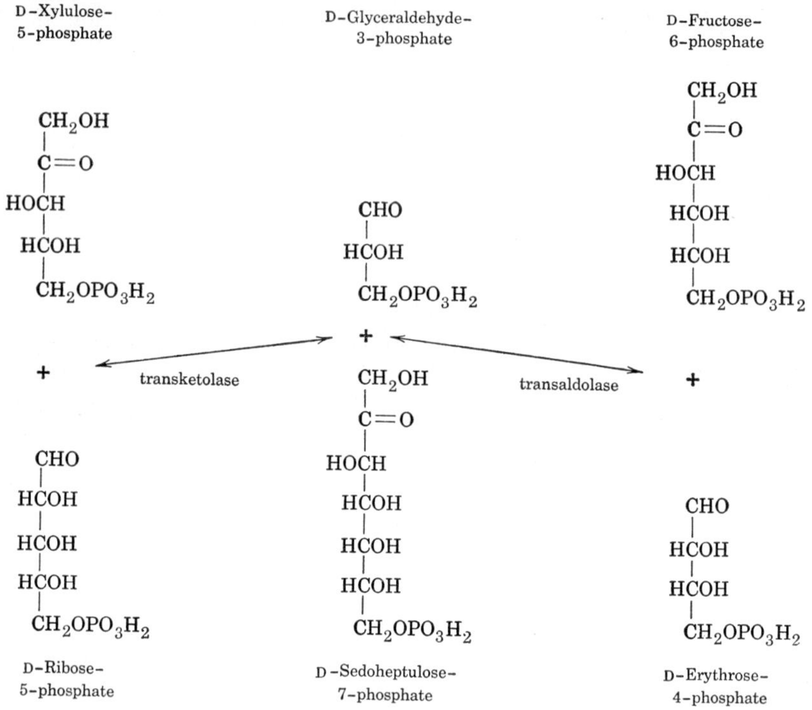

D-Xylulose-
5-phosphate

D-Glyceraldehyde-
3-phosphate

D-Fructose-
6-phosphate

CH$_2$OH
|
C=O
|
HOCH
|
HCOH
|
CH$_2$OPO$_3$H$_2$

CHO
|
HCOH
|
CH$_2$OPO$_3$H$_2$

CH$_2$OH
|
C=O
|
HOCH
|
HCOH
|
HCOH
|
CH$_2$OPO$_3$H$_2$

+ ←

+   transketolase   CH$_2$OH   transaldolase   +
|
C=O
|
HOCH

CHO
|
HCOH
|
HCOH
|
HCOH
|
CH$_2$OPO$_3$H$_2$

HCOH
|
HCOH
|
HCOH
|
CH$_2$OPO$_3$H$_2$

CHO
|
HCOH
|
HCOH
|
CH$_2$OPO$_3$H$_2$

D-Ribose-
5-phosphate

D-Sedoheptulose-
7-phosphate

D-Erythrose-
4-phosphate

isomeric mannoheptulose are 7-carbon sugars found in plant materials (p. 409), and sedoheptulose phosphate is an intermediate in photosynthesis (p. 551). Both sedoheptulose-7-phosphate and fructose-6-phosphate can serve as donors of a ketol group in reactions catalyzed by transketolase; these compounds have the same configuration about carbon 3 as does xylulose-5-phosphate.

In the presence of glyceraldehyde-3-phosphate, the heptulose phosphate is cleaved by the enzyme transaldolase[16] in such a manner that the dihydroxyacetone portion is transferred to the triose phosphate. This enzyme (purified from yeast and identified in plant and animal tissues) appears to be specific for sedoheptulose-7-phosphate and fructose-6-phosphate as donors of the dihydroxyacetone group, and for glyceralde-

[15] B. L. Horecker et al., *J. Biol. Chem.*, **205**, 661 (1953); **223**, 1009 (1956).
[16] B. L. Horecker and P. Z. Smyrniotis, *J. Biol. Chem.*, **212**, 811 (1955); C. E. Ballou et al., *J. Am. Chem. Soc.*, **77**, 5967 (1955).

hyde-3-phosphate, D-erythrose-4-phosphate, and ribose-5-phosphate as acceptors. Since no cofactors appear to be required for the action of purified transaldolase, it has been suggested that an enzyme-dihydroxy-acetone complex is formed (cf. p. 469), and that the triose group is then transferred to the acceptor aldehyde.

A different type of cleavage of xylulose-5-phosphate occurs in *Lactobacillus pentosus* (grown on L-arabinose or D-xylose) which leads to the formation of acetyl phosphate and a triose phosphate.[17] In this reaction,

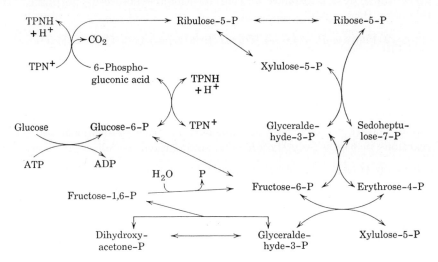

Fig. 2.   Enzyme-catalyzed reactions of the pentose phosphate pathway.

which requires the presence of TPP, a phosphorolysis of the pentose phosphate occurs, with the conversion of the ketol group of xylulose-5-phosphate to acetyl phosphate. An analogous reaction, in which fruc-

Xylulose-5-phosphate + phosphate →
$\qquad$ Acetyl phosphate + triose phosphate

tose-6-phosphate is cleaved by phosphorolysis to yield acetyl phosphate and erythrose-4-phosphate, is effected by an enzyme preparation from *Acetobacter xylinum*.[18]

It will be recalled that fructose-6-phosphate is converted to glucose-6-phosphate by the action of phosphohexoisomerase, thus completing the cycle in the pentose phosphate pathway (cf. Fig. 2). In the reactions discussed thus far, the net result of the metabolism of glucose-6-phosphate via this pathway is:

[17] E. C. Heath et al., *J. Biol. Chem.*, **231**, 1009, 1031 (1958).
[18] M. Schramm et al., *J. Biol. Chem.*, **233**, 1283 (1958).

$$\text{Hexose-P} + O_2 \rightarrow \text{Pentose-P} + CO_2 + H_2O$$

$$2 \text{ Pentose-P} \rightarrow \text{Hexose-P} + \text{tetrose-P}$$

$$\text{Pentose-P} + O_2 \rightarrow \text{Tetrose-P} + CO_2 + H_2O$$

However, the tetrose phosphate does not accumulate, and it has been inferred that transketolase catalyzes a reaction between erythrose-4-phosphate and another molecule of xylulose-5-phosphate to form glyceraldehyde-3-phosphate and an additional fructose-6-phosphate. In this case, the over-all process is:

$$2 \text{ Pentose-P} + O_2 \rightarrow \text{Hexose-P} + \text{triose-P} + CO_2 + H_2O$$

In the scheme given in Fig. 2, provision is also made for the isomerization of glyceraldehyde-3-phosphate to dihydroxyacetone phosphate (cf. p. 469), followed by the enzymic condensation of the two trioses to form fructose-1,6-diphosphate, which is hydrolyzed by the specific fructose diphosphatase to give another molecule of fructose-6-phosphate. The reactions in Fig. 2 may therefore be summarized as follows:

$$6 \text{ Hexose-P} + 6 \text{ } O_2 \rightarrow 6 \text{ Pentose-P} + 6 \text{ } CO_2 + 6 \text{ } H_2O$$

$$4 \text{ Pentose-P} \rightarrow 2 \text{ Hexose-P} + 2 \text{ tetrose-P}$$

$$2 \text{ Pentose-P} + 2 \text{ tetrose-P} \rightarrow 2 \text{ Hexose-P} + 2 \text{ triose-P}$$

$$2 \text{ Triose-P} + H_2O \rightarrow \text{Hexose-P} + \text{phosphate}$$

$$\text{Hexose-P} + 6 \text{ } O_2 \rightarrow 6 \text{ } CO_2 + 5 \text{ } H_2O + \text{phosphate}$$

The stoichiometry of the complete cycle indicates that for every 6 glucose molecules that enter via glucose-6-phosphate, 6 molecules of CO_2 are produced. Thus the scheme provides a mechanism for the total oxidation of a glucose molecule to CO_2; at each oxidative decarboxylation, carbon 1 of the hexose is converted to CO_2, and, as the other glucose carbons pass through the cycle, they are successively transformed into carbon 1 of fructose-6-phosphate, and subsequently removed by oxidative decarboxylation.

The validity of the formulation of the pentose phosphate cycle is supported by isotope experiments of Horecker et al.,[19] who incubated preparations of rat liver or of pea tissues with ribose-1-C^{14}, isolated glucose-6-phosphate from the mixture, and determined the distribution of C^{14} among the carbon atoms of the hexose. The finding that the isotope was predominantly located in carbons 1 and 3 of glucose, and

[19] B. L. Horecker et al., *J. Biol. Chem.*, **207**, 393 (1954); M. Gibbs and B. L. Horecker, *ibid.*, **208**, 813 (1954).

that the specific radioactivity of carbon 1 was about three times that of carbon 3 was interpreted as follows. In reaction (1), the successive action of transketolase (TK) and transaldolase (TA) produces fructose-6-phosphate equally labeled in carbons 1 and 3. In reaction (2), fructose-6-phosphate labeled only in carbon 1 is produced from erythrose-4-phosphate and an additional pentose phosphate, thus largely accounting for the unequal labeling of carbons 1 and 3 of the hexose phosphate isolated. In reactions (1) and (2), the labeled carbons are denoted C*.

$$(1) \quad 2[\text{C*-C-C-C-C}] \xrightarrow{\text{TK}} [\text{C*-C-C*-C-C-C-C}] + [\text{C-C-C}] \xrightarrow{\text{TA}}$$
$$[\text{C*-C-C*-C-C-C}] + [\text{C-C-C-C}]$$

$$(2) \quad [\text{C*-C-C-C-C}] + [\text{C-C-C-C}] \xrightarrow{\text{TK}} [\text{C*-C-C-C-C-C}] + [\text{C-C-C}]$$

Significance of the Pentose Phosphate Pathway. Although the enzymes of the pentose phosphate pathway have been identified in various plant and animal tissues, and the labeling data discussed above are in accord with the operation of the cycle as outlined in Fig. 2, it is not possible at present to assess the quantitative importance of this oxidative pathway in relation to the Embden-Meyerhof glycolytic pathway and the citric acid cycle. There is evidence that the pentose phosphate pathway may be the more significant one in some plant tissues, especially leaves;[20] several intermediates of the pathway are actively metabolized and increase the oxygen uptake of leaf preparations. Since TPN^+ is essential for the operation of the pathway, and its level is usually much lower than that of DPN^+, the relative importance of the pentose phosphate cycle may be influenced by variations in the TPN^+ content of a tissue.

Efforts to determine the significance of the pentose phosphate pathway in the oxidation of glucose by animal tissues have indicated that in muscle the Embden-Meyerhof pathway (supplemented by the citric acid cycle) is the exclusive route, and that in liver about 90 per cent of the glucose metabolized is converted by reactions of the glycolytic pathway.[21] Most of these studies are based on measurement of differences in the rate of liberation of $C^{14}O_2$ from glucose-1-C^{14} and from glucose-6-C^{14}. A comparison of the two pathways will show that in the glycolytic route carbons 1 and 6 of glucose are both converted to the methyl carbon of pyruvic acid (cf. p. 468) and are therefore metabolized in the same manner, whereas in the pentose phosphate pathway carbons 1 and 6 of glucose are handled differently. This approach has yielded

[20] B. Axelrod and H. Beevers, *Ann. Rev. Plant Physiol.*, **7**, 267 (1956).

[21] J. Katz et al., *J. Biol. Chem.*, **214**, 853 (1955); J. Ashmore et al., *ibid.*, **220**, 619 (1956); **224**, 225 (1957).

valuable data[22] on the fraction of glucose oxidized to CO_2 via the two pathways, but the unequivocal interpretation of the results is made difficult by the many reactions that can lead to redistribution of the isotope (see Wood[23]). Although the pentose phosphate pathway appears to occupy a subsidiary place in the total glucose metabolism of mammalian liver, its occurrence there is indicated by the finding[24] that the incubation of liver slices with glucose-2-C^{14}, or the administration of this compound to intact rats, gives rise to glycogen labeled more extensively in carbon 1 than in carbon 6 of the glucosyl units; in the pentose phosphate pathway, the glucose-2-C^{14} may be expected to give pentose-1-C^{14}-phosphate, which would be converted to hexose as discussed above.

It is probable that in some mammalian cells and tissues the pentose phosphate pathway may be of greater significance than the glycolytic route. This appears to be the situation in lactating mammary glands, leucocytes, and adrenal cortex.[25]

Another aspect of the metabolic role of the pentose phosphate pathway is the question whether the D-ribosyl units of ribonucleic acids arise directly from glucose by loss of carbon 1 of the hexose, and utilization of the pentose phosphate without further cleavage of the carbon chain. Although this appears to be a major pathway in *Escherichia coli*,[26] it is probably less significant in animal tissues. Bernstein[27] has found that the administration of isotopic precursors to chicks gives a pattern of

$$
\begin{array}{ccc}
& & \text{CHO} \\
& & | \\
\text{CHO} & & \text{CH}_2 \\
| & \text{CHO} & | \\
\text{HCOH} + & | & \rightleftharpoons \text{HCOH} \\
| & \text{CH}_3 & | \\
\text{CH}_2\text{OPO}_3\text{H}_2 & & \text{HCOH} \\
& & | \\
& & \text{CH}_2\text{OPO}_3\text{H}_2
\end{array}
$$

2-Deoxy-D-ribose-5-phosphate

labeling in the ribose of nucleic acids best explained in terms of the condensation of a C_2 unit and a C_3 unit. For example, the pentose-5-phosphate may arise by the transketolase-catalyzed transfer of a ketol group from fructose-6-phosphate to glyceraldehyde-3-phosphate. In this

---

[22] B. Bloom and D. Stetten, Jr., *J. Biol. Chem.*, **212**, 555 (1955); J. A. Muntz and J. R. Murphy, *ibid.*, **224**, 971 (1957).

[23] H. G. Wood, *Physiol. Revs.*, **35**, 841 (1955).

[24] B. Bloom et al., *J. Biol. Chem.*, **215**, 461 (1955); **222**, 301 (1956).

[25] S. Abraham et al., *J. Biol. Chem.*, **211**, 31 (1954); R. V. Coxon and R. J. Robinson, *Proc. Roy. Soc.*, **145B**, 232 (1956).

[26] M. C. Lanning and S. S. Cohen, *J. Biol. Chem.*, **207**, 193 (1954); I. A. Bernstein, *ibid.*, **221**, 873 (1956).

[27] I. A. Bernstein, *J. Biol. Chem.*, **205**, 317 (1953).

connection, it is of interest that a widely distributed enzyme system catalyzes the reaction between acetaldehyde and glyceraldehyde-3-phosphate to form deoxyribose-5-phosphate;[28] the mechanism of this reaction (p. 534) has not been elucidated.

Other Pathways of Glucose Oxidation

In addition to the glycolysis-citric acid cycle and pentose phosphate pathways, which represent the two known pathways of glucose breakdown in animal tissues, other routes have been identified in some microorganisms.[29] One of these involves the conversion of 6-phosphogluconate (here formed by phosphorylation of gluconic acid by ATP) to 2-keto-3-deoxy-6-phosphogluconate by an enzyme system discovered by Entner and Doudoroff.[30] This reaction, which is of major importance

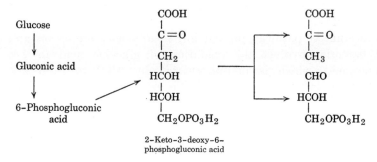

2-Keto-3-deoxy-6-
phosphogluconic acid

in *Pseudomonas fluorescens*, requires the presence of Fe^{2+} and glutathione (or cysteine). The hexose chain is then cleaved to form pyruvate and glyceraldehyde-3-phosphate by an aldolase-like reaction. Since the triose phosphate is converted to pyruvate, the net process is the same as in the Embden-Meyerhof pathway, but the mechanism is entirely different. Whereas the carboxyl group of pyruvate formed by glycolysis is derived from carbons 3 and 4 of glucose (p. 468), in the "Entner-Doudoroff" fermentation the carboxyl carbon of half the pyruvate formed is derived from carbon 1 of glucose.[31]

In this connection it is of interest to mention studies on the "heterolactic" fermentation of C^{14}-labeled glucose by *Leuconostoc mesenteroides*;[32] here 1 mole of glucose is converted to 1 mole each of lactic acid,

[28] E. Racker, *J. Biol. Chem.*, **196**, 347 (1952).

[29] I. C. Gunsalus et al., *Bact. Revs.*, **19**, 79 (1955).

[30] N. Entner and M. Doudoroff, *J. Biol. Chem.*, **196**, 853 (1952); J. MacGee and M. Doudoroff, *ibid.*, **210**, 617 (1954); R. Kovachevich and W. A. Wood, *ibid.*, **213**, 745, 757 (1955).

[31] M. Gibbs and R. D. DeMoss, *J. Biol. Chem.*, **207**, 689 (1954).

[32] I. C. Gunsalus and M. Gibbs, *J. Biol. Chem.*, **194**, 871 (1952).

ethanol, and CO_2. It had been assumed that the glycolytic pathway was followed in this conversion and that, per mole of glucose, 1 mole of pyruvate was reduced to lactate, the other being oxidized to ethanol and CO_2. If this were the case, the CO_2 should have been derived from carbons 3 and 4 of glucose, but it was found to have come from carbon 1; the carbinol carbon of ethanol and the carboxyl carbon of lactate were derived from carbons 3 and 4, as shown. In the light of the previous

$$\overset{1}{C}-\overset{2}{C}-\overset{3}{C}-\overset{4}{C}-\overset{5}{C}-\overset{6}{C} \quad \rightarrow \quad \overset{1}{C}O_2 + CH_3CH_2OH + HOO\overset{3}{C}CHOHCH_3$$

discussion, it would appear that glucose had been converted, via the pentose phosphate pathway, to CO_2 and xylulose-5-phosphate, which was then cleaved to C_2 and C_3 fragments (cf. p. 531). It is clear therefore that this heterolactic fermentation, although giving products whose formation might be interpreted in terms of the glycolytic pathway, actually follows a different route.

An alternative pathway present in *Pseudomonas fluorescens* and some other bacteria involves the oxidation of gluconic acid to 2-keto-D-gluconic acid, which is phosphorylated by ATP to form 2-keto-6-phosphogluconic acid; cleavage of this product eventually also yields 2 molecules of pyruvate.[33] In some strains of *Acetobacter*, 5-keto-D-gluconic acid is formed in addition to the 2-keto acid; in *Acetobacter melanogenum*, glucose is oxidized via gluconic acid and 2-ketogluconic acid to 2,5-diketogluconic acid, which is further oxidized to α-ketoglutaric acid.[34]

The oxidation of D-galactose by *Pseudomonas saccharophila* also appears to involve the intermediate formation of hexonic acids; enzymes have been identified for the conversion of the hexose to 2-keto-3-deoxy-D-galactonic acid via D-galactonolactone and D-galactonic acid. In the presence of ATP, the keto acid is cleaved to pyruvic acid and glyceraldehyde-3-phosphate.[35]

It has been suggested that a 2-ketohexonic acid may be cleaved in plant tissues by an aldolase-like enzyme to form hydroxypyruvic acid (p. 529). Since a DPN-specific glyceric dehydrogenase is known to reduce the latter compound to D-glyceric acid,[36] such a cleavage would provide a possible route for the formation of glyceric acid, which is present in appreciable amounts in some plants.

[33] S. A. Narrod and W. A. Wood, *J. Biol. Chem.*, **220**, 45 (1956); J. DeLey, *Biochim. et Biophys. Acta*, **13**, 302 (1954).

[34] D. Kulka and T. K. Walker, *Arch. Biochem. and Biophys.*, **50**, 169 (1954); H. Katznelson et al., *J. Biol. Chem.*, **204**, 43 (1953); *Nature*, **179**, 153 (1957).

[35] J. DeLey and M. Doudoroff, *J. Biol. Chem.*, **227**, 745 (1957).

[36] H. A. Stafford et al., *J. Biol. Chem.*, **207**, 621 (1954).

In addition to the metabolic oxidation of gluconic acid at carbon 2, enzymic mechanisms appear to be present in some biological systems for a similar oxidation of glucose to glucosone (formed chemically by acid hydrolysis of glucosazone).[37]

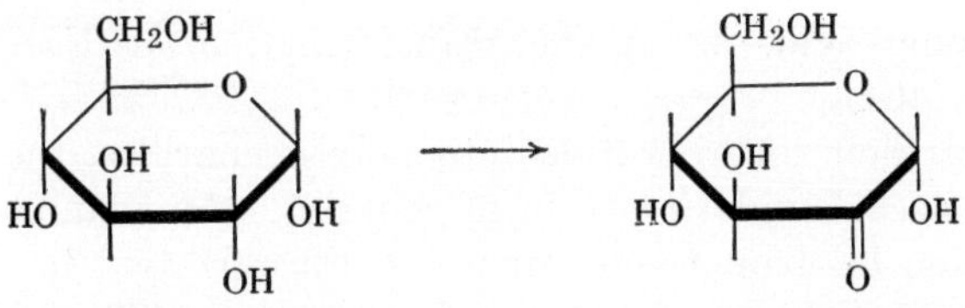

D-Glucose   D-Glucosone

Metabolism of Uronic Acids. It was seen earlier that D-glucuronic acid and D-galacturonic acid are important constituents of many polysaccharides (cf. p. 424). The available data clearly point to the conversion of glucose to glucuronic acid in animal tissues by a mechanism that does not involve fragmentation of the hexose chain,[38] and to the fact that the oxidation is effected by a DPN-dependent dehydrogenase acting on UDPG (cf. p. 467). Thus the conversion of glucose to glucuronic acid may be formulated: glucose → glucose-6-phosphate → glucose-1-phosphate → UDP-glucose → UDP-glucuronic acid → glucuronic acid.

Many aromatic compounds are excreted in the urine of man and animals as derivatives of D-glucuronic acid; these conjugates (glucuronides) are of two types: alcohols and phenols give rise to β-glycosides, and some carboxylic acids are conjugated as β-acylal compounds.[39]

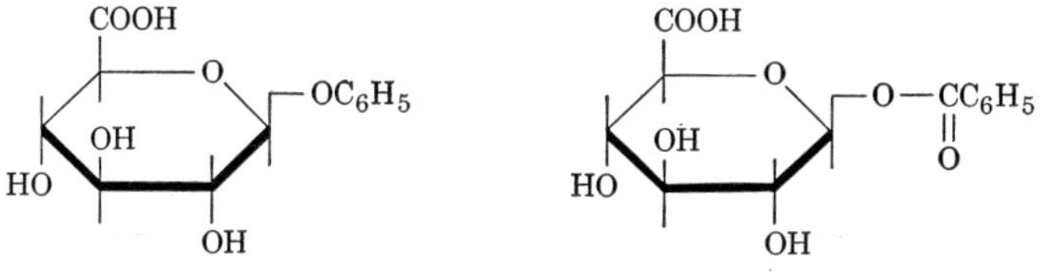

β-Phenylglucuronide β-Benzoylglucuronide

Such derivatives are formed in the liver by the reaction of UDP-glucuronic acid with the aglycone.[40] This enzymic process is an important physiological mechanism for the "detoxication" of many drugs. It is assumed that, as with UDPG, the configuration about carbon 1 of

[37] R. C. Bean and W. Z. Hassid, *Science,* **124,** 171 (1956).

[38] F. Eisenberg and S. Gurin, *J. Biol. Chem.,* **195,** 317 (1952); F. Eisenberg, *ibid.,* **212,** 501 (1955).

[39] R. S. Teague, *Advances in Carbohydrate Chem.,* **9,** 185 (1954).

[40] I. D. E. Storey and G. J. Dutton, *Biochem. J.,* **59,** 279 (1955); K. J. Isselbacher and J. Axelrod, *J. Am. Chem. Soc.,* **77,** 1070 (1955).

UDP-glucuronic acid is that of an α-glycoside. If this is so, an inversion of configuration occurs in the biosynthesis of the β-glucuronides.

Little is known at present about the mode of formation of D-galacturonic acid, but the possibility exists that this compound may be formed by Walden inversion about carbon 4 of the glucuronic acid portion of UDP-glucuronic acid, as in the transformation of UDPG to UDP-galactose (p. 464).

Aside from their incorporation into polysaccharides, the uronic acids can undergo decarboxylation to form pentoses. An example is the probable conversion by fruit tissues of D-galacturonic acid to L-arabinose;[41] these two sugars are components of pectin (p. 423). Similarly, the D-xylose of xylan appears to be derived from D-glucuronic acid by loss of carbon 6.

```
   CHO              CHO                CHO              CHO
    |                |                  |                |
  HCOH             HCOH               HCOH             HCOH
    |                |                  |                |
  HOCH    – CO₂    HOCH               HOCH    – CO₂    HOCH
    |      ⟶        |                  |      ⟶        |
  HOCH             HOCH               HCOH             HCOH
    |                |                  |                |
  HCOH            CH₂OH               HCOH            CH₂OH
    |                                   |
  COOH                                COOH
 D-Galacturonic   L-Arabinose      D-Glucuronic      D-Xylose
     acid                              acid
```

Aldonic acids occur as intermediates in the breakdown of pentoses by some microorganisms. Thus L-arabinose and D-arabinose are oxidized by *Pseudomonas saccharophila* via arabonic acid.[42]

```
  ┌─── CHOH         ┌─── C=O            COOH            COOH
  │     |           │     |              |               |
  │    HCOH         │    HCOH           HCOH            C=O
  │     |           │     |              |               |
 O│    HOCH       O│    HOCH   ⟶       HOCH   ---->    CH₂
  │     |           │     |              |               |
  └─── CH           └─── CH            HOCH            CH₂
        |                 |              |               |
      CH₂OH             CH₂OH          CH₂OH           COOH

  L-Arabinose       L-Arabono-        L-Arabonic     α-Ketoglutaric
                    γ-lactone            acid             acid
```

In the course of his extensive studies on the products of mold metabolism, Raistrick[43] showed that a strain of *Penicillium* converts glucose to a group of substances related to tetronic acid, including γ-methyl-

---

[41] C. G. Seegmiller et al., *J. Biol. Chem.*, **217**, 765 (1955).

[42] R. Weimberg and M. Doudoroff, *J. Biol. Chem.*, **217**, 607 (1955); N. J. Palleroni and M. Doudoroff, *ibid.*, **223**, 499 (1956).

[43] H. Raistrick, *Proc. Roy. Soc.*, **136B**, 481 (1949).

tetronic acid and carolic acid. Although these substances resemble the lactones of pentonic acids, no information is available about the mode of their biosynthesis.

$$\begin{array}{cc} \text{HO—C} \!\!=\!\!\text{CH} & \text{HO—C} \!\!=\!\!\text{C—COCH}_2\text{CH}_2\text{CH}_2\text{OH} \\ | \qquad | & | \qquad | \\ \text{CH}_3\text{—CH} \quad \text{CO} & \text{CH}_3\text{—CH} \quad \text{CO} \\ \diagdown \; \diagup & \diagdown \; \diagup \\ \text{O} & \text{O} \end{array}$$

γ-Methyltetronic acid   Carolic acid

Biosynthesis of Ascorbic Acid.[44] The vitamin L-ascorbic acid (p. 306) is derived from D-glucose in the rat and in plant tissues by a sequence of enzymic conversions in which the hexose carbon chain remains intact.[45] However, the administration of glucose-1-C^{14} to rats gave rise to ascorbic acid labeled in carbon 6. This remarkable transformation[46] involves the sequence of reactions shown in Fig. 3. It will be seen that D-glucose is converted to D-glucuronolactone, which is reduced to the lactone of an aldonic acid (L-gulonic acid) whose configuration is the same as that of L-gulose (cf. p. 404), the numbering of the carbon atoms now beginning with the carboxyl carbon. Oxidation of this lactone gives L-ascorbic acid, which can also arise by oxidation of L-galactono-γ-lactone, derived from D-galactose via D-galacturonic acid. The enzymes responsible for these conversions have not been characterized, but it appears likely that the reduction of the hexuronic acids to gulonolactone or galactonolactone is effected by a pyridine nucleotide-dependent dehydrogenase. Although the pathway outlined in Fig. 3 appears to occur in some plants (e.g., pea seedlings), it is uncertain whether it applies to others (e.g., strawberry).[47]

The enzymic formation of ascorbic acid from glucuronolactone has been demonstrated with liver preparations from several animals (rat, mouse, dog, rabbit); this conversion does not occur in the liver of the guinea pig, which requires a dietary source of the vitamin (cf. Chapter 39), and in which the formation of ascorbic acid from L-gulonolactone appears to be blocked.[48] Ascorbic acid is oxidized in animal tissues, with CO_2 and oxalic acid as products.

[44] L. W. Mapson, *Vitamins and Hormones,* **13,** 71 (1955).

[45] H. H. Horowitz et al., *J. Biol. Chem.,* **199,** 193 (1952); J. J. Burns and E. H. Mosbach, *ibid.,* **221,** 107 (1956).

[46] F. A. Isherwood et al., *Biochem. J.,* **56,** 1, 21 (1954); L. W. Mapson and F. A. Isherwood, *ibid.,* **64,** 13 (1956); J. J. Burns and C. Evans, *J. Biol. Chem.,* **223,** 897 (1956).

[47] F. A. Loewus et al., *J. Biol. Chem.,* **222,** 649 (1956); *Biochim. et Biophys. Acta,* **23,** 206 (1957); *J. Biol. Chem.,* **232,** 505, 521, 533 (1958).

[48] M. ul Hassan and A. L. Lehninger, *J. Biol. Chem.,* **223,** 123 (1956); J. J. Burns et al., *Science,* **124,** 1148 (1956); *Nature,* **180,** 553 (1957).

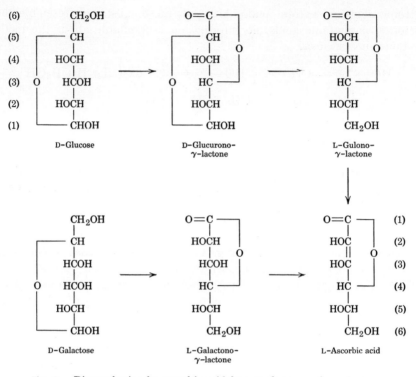

Fig. 3. Biosynthesis of L-ascorbic acid from D-glucose and D-galactose.

Formation of L-Xylulose. In the clinical condition known as pentosuria, human beings excrete abnormally large amounts of a dextrorotatory pentose identified as L-xylulose. This compound appears to arise by

decarboxylation of L-gulonic acid, which is derived from D-glucuronolactone.[49] Mammalian liver contains a DPN-dependent dehydrogenase that catalyzes the oxidation of the pentahydric alcohol xylitol

[49] O. Touster et al., *J. Biol. Chem.*, **215**, 677 (1955); *Biochim. et Biophys. Acta*, **25**, 196 (1957); J. J. Burns et al., *ibid.*, **25**, 647 (1957).

to D-xylulose, and a different TPN-dependent enzyme for the interconversion of xylitol and L-xylulose.[50]   It seems, therefore, that in
pentosuric subjects the normal metabolism of D-xylulose (or its 5-phos-
phate) via hexose-6-phosphate (cf. p. 531) is blocked; this leads to an
accumulation and excretion of L-xylulose.   Mammalian liver can effect
the phosphorylation (by ATP) of D-xylulose to D-xylulose-5-phosphate.[51]

   Formation of Cyclic Compounds from Glucose.   Some plants contain
relatively large amounts of the compound quinic acid (first isolated
from cinchona bark in about 1800); its structure is 1,3,4,5-tetrahydroxy-
cyclohexane-1-carboxylic acid.   A closely related substance, shikimic
acid (3,4,5-trihydroxy-Δ-1,6-cyclohexene-1-carboxylic acid) is less widely
distributed in nature.   Through studies with bacterial mutants, Davis[52]
has shown that shikimic acid is an intermediate in the biosynthesis of
aromatic compounds from glucose in *Escherichia coli;* this applies to
other microorganisms,[53] and to higher plants.[54]   Experiments on the
utilization of labeled glucose for the biosynthesis of shikimic acid (in a
mutant of *E. coli* that accumulates shikimic acid because its further
conversion is blocked) indicated that it is derived from 2-keto-3-deoxy-
7-phospho-D-glucoheptonic acid, as shown in Fig. 4.   This 7-carbon sugar
acid arises from D-erythrose-4-phosphate and phosphoenolpyruvic acid,
and is quantitatively converted (by extracts of an appropriate mutant)
to 5-dehydroshikimic acid (Fig. 4).[55]   The pattern of labeling of the
shikimic acid isolated in the isotope experiments is consistent with
the view that the tetrose phosphate had arisen from glucose via the
pentose phosphate pathway, and that the phosphoenolpyruvate came
from glucose by glycolysis according to the Embden-Meyerhof scheme.

   The conversion of dehydroshikimic acid to shikimic acid is effected
by a TPN-specific dehydrogenase ("dehydroshikimic reductase") present
in bacteria, yeast, and higher plants, but absent from animal tissues.[56]
Quinic acid probably arises by a similar reduction of the corresponding
5-dehydroquinic acid; the dehydrogenase that catalyzes this reaction has
been found in *Aerobacter,* but not in *E. coli,* and is DPN-specific.[57]   The
studies of Davis have shown that, in *E. coli,* 5-dehydroquinic acid is an
intermediate in the synthesis of 5-dehydroshikimic acid from carbohy-

[50] O. Touster et al., *J. Biol. Chem.,* **221,** 697 (1956); S. Hollmann and O. Touster, *ibid.,* **225,** 87 (1957).

[51] J. Hickman and G. Ashwell, *J. Am. Chem. Soc.,* **78,** 6209 (1956).

[52] B. D. Davis, *J. Biol. Chem.,* **191,** 315 (1951); *Harvey Lectures,* **50,** 230 (1956).

[53] E. L. Tatum et al., *Proc. Natl. Acad. Sci.,* **40,** 271 (1954).

[54] S. A. Brown and A. C. Neish, *Nature,* **175,** 688 (1955).

[55] P. R. Srinivasan et al., *J. Biol. Chem.,* **220,** 477; **223,** 913 (1956).

[56] H. Yaniv and C. Gilvarg, *J. Biol. Chem.,* **213,** 787 (1955).

[57] S. Mitsuhashi and B. D. Davis, *Biochim. et Biophys. Acta,* **15,** 268 (1954).

drate, and that the dehydration of dehydroquinic acid is catalyzed by the enzyme "5-dehydroquinase."[58] These metabolic relationships are

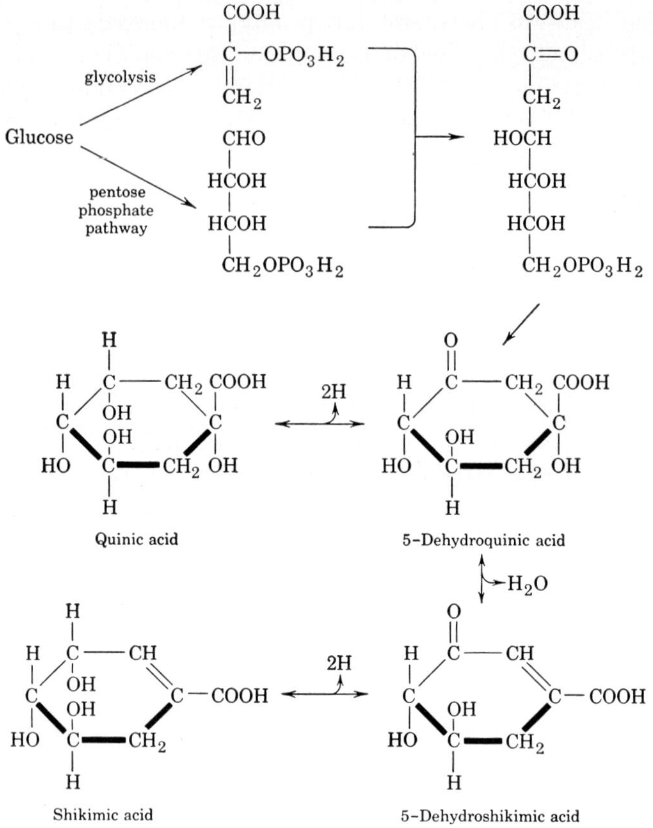

Fig. 4. Biosynthesis of quinic acid and shikimic acid from glucose.

summarized in Fig. 4. The further conversion of shikimic acid to aromatic amino acids is discussed in Chapter 32.

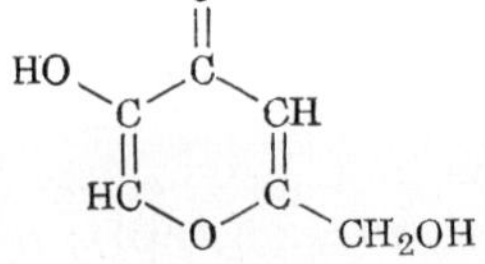

Kojic acid

Some molds and bacteria (*Aspergillus, Acetobacter*) convert glucose to kojic acid[59] (5-hydroxy-2-hydroxymethyl-γ-pyrone) largely without

[58] S. Mitsuhashi and B. D. Davis, *Biochim. et Biophys. Acta,* **15,** 54 (1954).
[59] A. Beélik, *Advances in Carbohydrate Chem.,* **11,** 145 (1956).

cleavage of the carbon chain, although a secondary pathway involving the condensation of C_3 units is also suggested by isotope studies.[60] Kojic acid appears to arise from some pentoses (D-ribose, D-xylose) by prior conversion to hexoses via the transketolase and transaldolase reactions. A number of γ-pyrones structurally related to kojic acid have been isolated from plants.

Metabolic Reduction of Hexoses

Among the hexahydric alcohols related to the naturally occurring hexoses, D-mannitol is of special interest because of its wide distribution among fungi, algae, and higher plants; in some organisms it appears to serve as a reserve carbohydrate. Although little is known about its metabolism, a dehydrogenase present in *Escherichia coli* has been found to catalyze the oxidation of mannitol-1-phosphate by DPN$^+$ to form fructose-6-phosphate;[61] this suggests a route of mannitol formation and

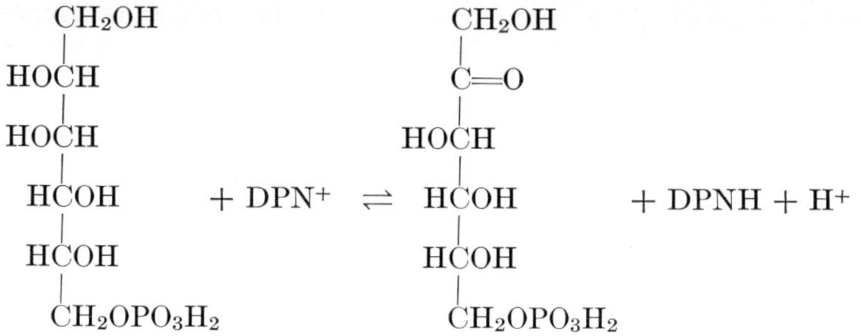

$$
\begin{array}{ccccc}
\text{CH}_2\text{OH} & & \text{CH}_2\text{OH} & & \\
| & & | & & \\
\text{HOCH} & & \text{C}=\text{O} & & \\
| & & | & & \\
\text{HOCH} & & \text{HOCH} & & \\
| & + \text{DPN}^+ & \rightleftharpoons & | & + \text{DPNH} + \text{H}^+ \\
\text{HCOH} & & \text{HCOH} & & \\
| & & | & & \\
\text{HCOH} & & \text{HCOH} & & \\
| & & | & & \\
\text{CH}_2\text{OPO}_3\text{H}_2 & & \text{CH}_2\text{OPO}_3\text{H}_2 & & \\
\text{Mannitol-1-phosphate} & & \text{Fructose-6-phosphate} & &
\end{array}
$$

of its fermentation by bacteria. The conversion of D-sorbitol to L-sorbose (p. 410) by *Acetobacter suboxydans* is of industrial importance, since the ketose is a valuable starting material in the chemical synthesis of L-ascorbic acid. Animal tissues (liver) also contain dehydrogenase activity toward hexahydric alcohols, but this appears to be limited to nonphosphorylated compounds such as D-sorbitol, which is converted to glucose; D-mannitol is not oxidized.[62]

It is probable that the cyclic hexahydric inositols (p. 412) also are derived from glucose, but little is known about the metabolic reactions involved. The conversion of glucose to inositol by microorganisms and

[60] H. R. V. Arnstein and R. Bentley, *Biochem. J.*, **54**, 508, 517 (1953); **62**, 403 (1956).

[61] J. B. Wolff and N. O. Kaplan, *J. Biol. Chem.*, **218**, 849 (1956).

[62] J. McCorkindale and N. L. Edson, *Biochem. J.*, **57**, 518 (1954).

by higher plants has been demonstrated; this transformation probably is also effected by some mammalian tissues. Isotope experiments on the conversion of C^{14}-labeled glucose to *myo*-inositol by yeast indicate that a direct cyclization of the hexose does not occur, and that inositol is formed by the condensation of fragments derived from the breakdown of glucose.[63]   Fischer[64] has suggested that inositol is an intermediate between carbohydrates and aromatic substances; this implies a metabolic relation of inositol to shikimic acid.

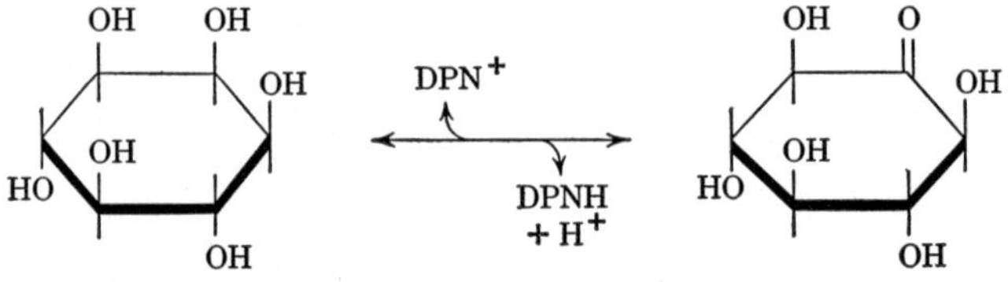

Myo-inositol   2-Keto-*myo*-inositol

Myo-inositol is converted to glucuronic acid by an enzyme system present in rat kidney,[65] and is metabolized by bacteria (*Acetobacter*) to yield a triose, CO_2, and water.   In the microbial breakdown of inositol, the initial attack involves the action of a DPN-dependent dehydrogenase to form 2-keto-*myo*-inositol; the interesting specificity of this enzyme has been established by Magasanik.[66]

[63] F. C. Charalampous, *J. Biol. Chem.*, **225**, 595 (1957).

[64] H. O. L. Fischer, *Harvey Lectures*, **40**, 156 (1945).

[65] F. C. Charalampous and C. Lyras, *J. Biol. Chem.*, **228**, 1 (1957).

[66] B. Magasanik, in S. Graff, *Essays in Biochemistry*, John Wiley & Sons, New York, 1956.

22 · Photosynthesis

In the preceding chapters considerable attention has been devoted to the metabolic pathways and energy changes in the oxidation of carbohydrates to CO_2 and water in biological systems. From the point of view of the maintenance of life on this planet, of even greater importance is the photosynthesis, by green plants, of carbohydrate from CO_2 and

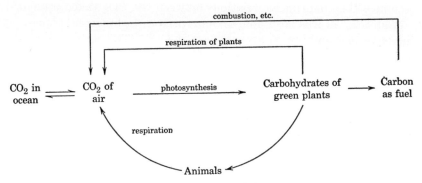

Fig. 1. The carbon cycle in nature.

water; this process is made possible by the presence of the chlorophylls (magnesium complexes of the pheophytins; p. 182). The light energy absorbed by these pigments is transformed by chlorophyll-containing cells into the chemical energy needed for the synthesis of carbohydrates. The importance of the photosynthetic process in the over-all cycle of the transformations of carbon in nature may be seen from the scheme shown in Fig. 1. Rabinowitch[1] has prepared a comprehensive treatise on photosynthesis; valuable monographs are those of Hill and Whittingham[2] and of Franck and Loomis.[3]

[1] E. I. Rabinowitch, *Photosynthesis*, Interscience Publishers, New York, 1945, 1951, 1956.
[2] R. Hill and C. P. Whittingham, *Photosynthesis*, Methuen and Co., London, 1955.
[3] J. Franck and W. E. Loomis, *Photosynthesis in Plants*, Iowa State College Press, Ames, 1949.

The decisive role of photosynthesis in nature may be said to have been discovered during the latter part of the eighteenth century, after the studies of Priestley and his contemporaries on the composition of the air. However, early in the seventeenth century van Helmont recognized that the soil was not the principal source of the food of green plants; some 100 years later Stephen Hales demonstrated that this source was the air. With the discovery of oxygen and the elucidation of the nature of combustion and of respiration, there arose the question of the mechanisms in nature for replenishing the supply of oxygen converted by animals to CO_2 and water. In a series of simple but brilliant experiments Priestley showed in 1771–1778 that green plants and certain green algae were able to reverse the respiratory process and to render air that was rich in CO_2 but depleted of oxygen capable of supporting combustion and respiration anew. This discovery was followed by the systematic studies of Jan Ingenhousz,[4] who in 1779 described the role of visible light in the conversion of CO_2 to oxygen. Some twenty years later, de Saussure determined the quantitative relations between the CO_2 taken up and the O_2 produced; it was also found that, in the dark, green plants, like animals, respire and thus convert oxygen to CO_2. The early investigators associated the phenomenon of CO_2 uptake with the green pigment, which was named chlorophyll in 1819. The definitive demonstration of the central role of chlorophyll in the absorption of light for photosynthesis came from the work of Engelmann in 1880. The elucidation of the chemical nature of the chlorophylls is largely due to the work of Willstätter and Hans Fischer during the period 1910 to 1940.

For a long time the only recognizable products of the photosynthetic process were the monosaccharides glucose and fructose, the disaccharide sucrose, and the polysaccharides (starch, etc.) which were known to be derivatives of glucose. For this reason, the process of photosynthesis has been written as the reverse of the oxidation of glucose, i.e.,

$$6CO_2 + 6H_2O \rightarrow C_6H_{12}O_6 + 6O_2$$

As will be seen later in this chapter, the chemical reaction written above is not entirely accurate, since there is good evidence that 12 molecules of water are required for the formation of 1 glucose unit, and 6 molecules of water appear among the products of the reaction.

$$6CO_2 + 12H_2O \rightarrow C_6H_{12}O_6 + 6O_2 + 6H_2O$$

Although the net change is the same in both equations, it is important to stress that an essential feature of the photosynthetic process in green plants is a photoreduction in which water serves as the ultimate hydrogen donor. Hydrogen gas can be used in place of water by some photo-

[4] H. S. Reed. *Jan Ingenhousz*, Chronica Botanica Co., Waltham, 1949.

synthetic bacteria; here no oxygen is produced during photosynthesis.

$$6CO_2 + 12H_2 \rightarrow C_6H_{12}O_6 + 6H_2O$$

In an examination of the available knowledge about the biochemical aspects of photosynthesis, consideration may be given first to the energetic efficiency of light in promoting this process. The chemical energy ($\Delta F°$) required for the synthesis of a mole of glucose from CO_2 and water is approximately 690 kcal, and it comes from the radiant energy of visible light ($\lambda = 4000$ to 7000 A). The emission of light occurs in the form of discrete "packets" of waves; these groups of light waves are termed photons, and the energy of a photon is equal to the product of its frequency (ν) and Planck's constant h (6.62×10^{-27} erg second). The frequency is the reciprocal of the wave length (in centimeters) times the velocity of light (3×10^{10} cm per second). The product $h\nu$ (or the quantum value) may be expressed in terms of either ergs or calories; 1 absolute calorie equals 4.184×10^7 ergs. According to Einstein's law of photochemical equivalence, a molecule will react only after it has absorbed one photon; hence, to react, one mole of substance must absorb 6.024×10^{23} (N) photons in a photochemical reaction. The total energy of this number of photons ($Nh\nu$) is termed an Einstein. In Table 1 the value of an Einstein (in calories) is presented for several wave lengths of visible monochromatic light. It will be noted that, the shorter the wave length, the larger the value of the Einstein. Each value in the final column of the table thus denotes the energy acquired by a mole of substance if it absorbs completely one Einstein of light of a given wave length.

Table I. Energy Values for Several Wave Lengths of Light

Wave Length, λ		Frequency per sec, ν	Quantum value of photon ($h\nu$), ergs	Einstein, cal per mole
A	Cm			
7500 (red)	$7.5 \ \times 10^{-5}$	4.00×10^{14}	2.65×10^{-12}	38,200
6500 (red)	$6.5 \ \times 10^{-5}$	4.58×10^{14}	3.03×10^{-12}	43,600
5900 (yellow)	$5.9 \ \times 10^{-5}$	5.08×10^{14}	3.36×10^{-12}	48,400
4900 (blue)	$4.9 \ \times 10^{-5}$	6.12×10^{14}	4.05×10^{-12}	58,300
3950 (ultraviolet)	3.95×10^{-5}	7.59×10^{14}	5.02×10^{-12}	72,200

From Einstein's law of photochemical equivalence it follows that there should be a direct relationship between the photosynthetic efficiency of different wave lengths of light and the absorption spectra of the chlorophylls (Fig. 2); i.e., the wave lengths that are absorbed more strongly by the chlorophyll pigments of a green leaf should be more effective in photosynthesis. Although this is largely true, it must be added that the light absorbed by other leaf pigments, notably the carotenoids (p. 652), may also contribute energy to the photosynthetic process. An additional possible role of the carotenoids is to protect the cell from destruction by photochemical reactions induced by illuminated chlorophyll.[5] With

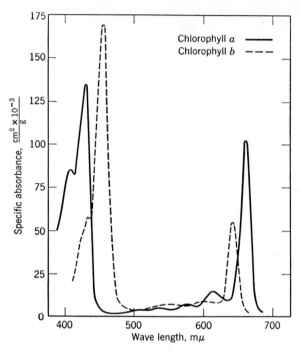

Fig. 2. Absorption spectra of chlorophylls a and b.

some photosynthetic microorganisms which contain both phycobilins (p. 168) and chlorophyll, the wave lengths absorbed by the phycobilins are more effective in photosynthesis; this has been taken to suggest a transfer of energy from the phycobilins to chlorophyll, which then participates in the chemosynthesis.[6]

In the cells of green leaves, the chlorophyll pigments are located in numerous disk-shaped structures termed chloroplasts (diameter, ca. 5 μ); disintegration of chloroplasts yields particles (grana) in which the pigments appear to be concentrated. In some photosynthetic algae (e.g., *Chlorella*), only one chloroplast is present. The blue-green algae and the photosynthetic bacteria do not contain discernible chloroplasts.

An important discovery in the study of the mechanism of photosynthesis was made by Blackman in 1905 when he found that, under certain

[5] M. Griffiths et al., *Nature,* **176,** 1211 (1955).
[6] L. R. Blinks, *Ann. Rev. Plant Physiol.,* **5,** 93 (1954).

conditions, photosynthesis cannot be accelerated by increasing the intensity of illumination. This result has been construed as evidence for a nonphotochemical reaction (dark reaction) as a component of the photosynthetic process. Experimental evidence for this view was provided by studies in which intermittent illumination was used; much more oxygen was produced under these conditions than was found upon continuous illumination with the same amount of light. Subsequent studies also showed that isotopic CO_2 was fixed by green plants in the absence of illumination. These findings led to the currently accepted view that some constituent of the plant fixes CO_2 in a nonphotochemical reaction, and that the energy obtained from the absorption of light by chlorophyll is made available for the reduction of the product of CO_2 fixation.

Strong support for this idea has been provided by work with the photosynthetic bacteria.[7] Some of the so-called purple bacteria contain pigments (bacteriochlorophylls) which permit a photochemical conversion leading from CO_2 to carbohydrate without the formation of oxygen. Such organisms require, however, the presence of reducing substances[8] such as H_2S or H_2. Thus, in the purple sulfur bacteria,

$$nCO_2 + 2nH_2S \rightarrow (CH_2O)_n + nH_2O + 2nS$$

This is formally analogous to the process of photosynthesis in green plants, which may be written

$$nCO_2 + 2nH_2O \rightarrow (CH_2O)_n + nH_2O + nO_2$$

On the basis of the results with the photosynthetic bacteria, the most general statement of the over-all process of photosynthesis is given by the reaction

$$nCO_2 + 2nH_2A \rightarrow (CH_2O)_n + nH_2O + 2nA$$

where H_2A is a specific hydrogen donor. In the instances cited above, H_2O, H_2S, and H_2 can serve as hydrogen donors in the appropriate organisms. In addition, organic substances (e.g., isopropanol $CH_3CHOHCH_3$) can also function in this capacity with certain purple bacteria; here the hydrogen donor is converted to acetone by a dehydrogenation reaction.[9]

Evidence for the view that photosynthesis in green plants involves the "photolysis" of water was provided by Ruben et al.,[10] who showed, by the use of water and CO_2 labeled with O^{18}, that the molecular oxygen which is a product of photosynthesis comes from the water while the oxygen of CO_2 enters into the organic compounds.

[7] C. B. van Niel, *Bact. Revs.*, **8**, 1 (1944); *Am. Scientist*, **37**, 371 (1949).
[8] M. D. Kamen, *Federation Proc.*, **9**, 543 (1950).
[9] H. Gest, *Bact. Revs.*, **15**, 183 (1951).
[10] S. Ruben et al., *J. Am. Chem. Soc.*, **63**, 877 (1941).

$$CO^{16}_2 + 2H_2O^{18} \rightarrow (CH_2O^{16}) + H_2O^{16} + O^{18}_2$$

$$CO^{18}_2 + 2H_2O^{16} \rightarrow (CH_2O^{18}) + H_2O^{18} + O^{16}_2$$

The fact that the photochemical reaction is basically a reduction process was also brought out by Hill's discovery in 1937 that isolated chloroplasts can, upon illumination, reduce ferric oxalate.[11] Subsequently, it was shown that quinone and a variety of organic dyes are reduced in this way, with the concomitant release of molecular oxygen. This reaction has been termed the "Hill reaction" or the "chloroplast reaction," and may be formulated as

$$A + H_2O \xrightarrow{\text{light}} AH_2 + \tfrac{1}{2}O_2$$

Here there is no CO_2 fixation, and no carbohydrate is formed.

From the preceding discussion, it follows that the biochemical aspects of photosynthesis may be considered under two headings: (1) the nature of the enzyme-catalyzed "dark reactions" that lead to CO_2 fixation, and (2) the mechanism whereby the light energy absorbed by chlorophyll is converted to chemical energy needed to drive these reactions.

Fixation of CO_2 and Carbohydrate Formation in Photosynthesis. Significant advances in the elucidation of the chemical reactions in the conversion of CO_2 and water to carbohydrate during photosynthesis have come from the work of Calvin and his associates.[12] These investigators have studied the radioactive substances formed from $C^{14}O_2$ by photosynthetic algae such as *Chlorella* or *Scenedesmus*. For this purpose, they devised a number of extremely ingenious techniques by which the chemical constituents present in the illuminated algae are subjected to two-dimensional paper chromatography and the radioactive components are detected by radioautography, i.e., by placing the chromatogram on a sheet of photographic paper.

If the algae are exposed to $C^{14}O_2$ in the dark, the isotopic carbon appears in succinic acid, fumaric acid, malic acid, and other dicarboxylic acids. This is consistent with the operation of CO_2-fixation reactions associated with intermediates of the citric acid cycle. On the other hand, after illumination for 30 to 90 sec, the major portion of the isotopic carbon is found in compounds identified as phosphoglyceric acid and hexose phosphates. Of special importance is the observation that, after an illumination of about 5 sec, most of the radioactive carbon is located in the carboxyl group of 3-phosphoglyceric acid. Since the radioactive hexoses that appear upon illumination for about 30 sec are largely labeled in carbons 3 and 4, it is reasonable to conclude that they arise

---

[11] R. Hill, *Advances in Enzymol.,* **12**, 1 (1951).

[12] M. Calvin, *J. Chem. Soc.,* **1956**, 1895.

from 3-phosphoglyceric acid by a reversal of the Embden-Meyerhof glycolytic pathway (p. 476), via glyceraldehyde-3-phosphate, fructose-1,6-diphosphate, fructose-6-phosphate, glucose-6-phosphate, and glucose-1-phosphate. The formation of starch is catalyzed by phosphorylase (p. 439), and the synthesis of sucrose involves enzyme-catalyzed reactions of UDP derivatives (p. 450). It will be recalled that in animal tissues the conversion of oligosaccharides to 3-phosphoglyceric acid is an exergonic process that requires DPN^+, ADP, and inorganic phosphate, and in which DPNH and ATP are formed. (It appears likely that in green leaves TPN^+ is effective in place of DPN^+.) Clearly, the reversal of this portion of the glycolytic pathway is an endergonic process that requires the presence of a reduced pyridine nucleotide (DPNH or TPNH) and of ATP. The probable source of these two components will become more evident from the subsequent discussion.

In regard to the mode of formation of the isotopic 3-phosphoglyceric acid from $C^{14}O_2$ after brief illumination, Calvin has presented evidence in favor of the view that ribulose-1,5-diphosphate is carboxylated to form an intermediate which is cleaved enzymically (cf. p. 527) to form 2 molecules of 3-phosphoglyceric acid. Thus the CO_2 acceptor in photosynthesis is thought to be ribulose-1,5-diphosphate, formed from ribulose-5-phosphate by enzymic phosphorylation with ATP. Since ribulose-5-phosphate is an important intermediate in the oxidative pentose phosphate pathway (p. 531), it follows that the components of this pathway are needed to regenerate ribulose-1,5-diphosphate as it is carboxylated and converted to carbohydrate via 3-phosphoglyceric acid. This was indicated by the appearance of C^{14}, after brief illumination, in compounds such as sedoheptulose phosphate. From the distribution of the isotope in the various radioactive intermediates,[13] Calvin has concluded that a "reductive pentose phosphate pathway" is operative in photosynthesis. A slightly modified version of this scheme is given in Fig. 3.

The stoichiometry of the reductive pentose phosphate cycle may be formulated in terms of the conversion of CO_2 and H (from TPNH) to glyceraldehyde-3-phosphate. It will be seen that, for the entrance of 3 molecules of CO_2 into the cycle, 3 molecules of ribulose-1,5-diphosphate are required. These give rise to 6 molecules of 3-phosphoglyceric acid, which is converted to glyceraldehyde-3-phosphate by a reversal of the glyceraldehyde-3-phosphate dehydrogenase reaction (cf. p. 373); this requires an equivalent amount of ATP and of reduced pyridine nucleotide. Of the 6 molecules of the triose phosphate formed, 5 are needed for the completion of the cycle, and 1 molecule can be utilized for carbo-

[13] J. A. Bassham et al., *J. Am. Chem. Soc.*, **76**, 1760 (1954); *Biochim. et Biophys. Acta*, **21**, 376 (1956); A. T. Wilson and M. Calvin, *J. Am. Chem. Soc.*, **77**, 5948 (1955).

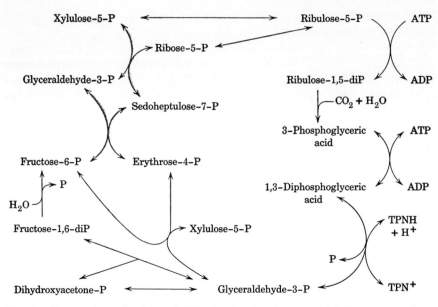

Fig. 3. Proposed mechanism of CO_2 fixation in photosynthesis by means of the reductive pentose phosphate cycle.

Table 2. Stoichiometry of the Reductive Pentose Phosphate Cycle in Photosynthesis

3 Pentose-P + 3 ATP → 3 Ribulose-diP + 3 ADP

3 Ribulose-diP + 3 CO_2 + 3 H_2O → 6 P-glycerate

6 P-glycerate + 6 ATP → 6 DiP-glycerate + 6 ADP

6 DiP-glycerate + 6 TPNH + 6 H^+ → 6 Glyceraldehyde-P + 6 TPN$^+$ + 6 P

2 Glyceraldehyde-P → 2 Dihydroxyacetone-P

2 Glyceraldehyde-P + 2 dihydroxyacetone-P → 2 Fructose-diP

2 Fructose-diP + 2 H_2O → 2 Fructose-P + 2 P

1 Fructose-P + 1 glyceraldehyde-P → 1 Pentose-P + 1 tetrose-P

1 Fructose-P + 1 tetrose-P → 1 Heptulose-P + 1 glyceraldehyde-P

1 Heptulose-P + 1 glyceraldehyde-P → 2 Pentose-P

---

3 CO_2 + 9 ATP + 5 H_2O + 6 TPNH + 6 H^+ →
                    1 Glyceraldehyde-P + 9 ADP + 6 TPN$^+$ + 8 phosphate

hydrate synthesis. These considerations are summarized in Table 2. It should be added that, although the reactions in Table 2 account for the appearance of the various labeled compounds during photosynthesis, the distribution of C^{14} in the glucose formed is not in satisfactory accord with the postulated scheme,[14] suggesting the occurrence of alternative light-dependent transformations of the products of CO_2 fixation. The operation of such alternative pathways is indicated by the finding[15] that brief illumination of *Chlorella* in the presence of $C^{14}O_2$ markedly increases the labeling of aspartic acid. The carbon chain of the amino acid probably is derived directly from oxaloacetic acid (Chapter 31) formed through CO_2 fixation by a 3-carbon compound. Some photosynthetic organisms (e.g., purple sulfur bacteria) do not store appreciable amounts of carbohydrate, and it is likely that the energy absorbed by their chlorophyll is utilized, in large part, for the synthesis of amino acids needed for protein formation.

Transformation of Light Energy into Chemical Energy in Photosynthesis.[16] The current view of the mechanism of photosynthesis assigns to illuminated chlorophyll the function of transforming light energy into chemical energy for the formation of reduced pyridine nucleotide and ATP. Little is known, however, about the chemical events in this transformation, or about the changes undergone by chlorophyll when it is illuminated. Upon illumination, chlorophyll can catalyze reversible oxidation-reduction reactions, and it is widely believed that the photochemical action of chlorophyll *in vivo* is to effect an electron transfer reaction, but the components of this reaction have not been identified.

It will be recalled that on illumination chloroplasts reduce the oxidized form of various oxidation-reduction systems (the Hill reaction). Vishniac and Ochoa[17] have shown that DPN^+ and TPN^+ can be reduced by illuminated grana from spinach leaves; with intact chloroplasts, TPN^+ is reduced preferentially. This example of a Hill reaction thus provides a mechanism for the generation of the TPNH required for the operation of the cycle shown in Fig. 3. It cannot be concluded, however, that TPN^+ is reduced directly by illuminated chlorophyll. Calvin[18] has suggested that the reduction involves the participation of lipoic acid (thioctic acid; p. 306), which is thought to be the direct electron acceptor from the illuminated chlorophyll system. The reduced lipoic acid may then form TPNH from TPN^+ as follows:

[14] M. Gibbs and O. Kandler, *Proc. Natl. Acad. Sci.*, **43**, 446 (1957).

[15] O. Warburg et al., *Z. Naturforsch.*, **12b**, 481 (1957).

[16] C. P. Whittingham, *Biol. Revs.*, **30**, 40 (1955); L. N. M. Duysens, *Ann. Rev Plant Physiol.*, **7**, 25 (1956).

[17] W. Vishniac and S. Ochoa, *J. Biol. Chem.*, **195**, 75 (1952).

[18] J. A. Bassham et al., *J. Am. Chem. Soc.*, **78**, 4120 (1956).

$$\text{TPN}^+ + \overset{\overset{\displaystyle SH}{\displaystyle |}}{C}H_2CH_2\overset{\overset{\displaystyle SH}{\displaystyle |}}{C}H(CH_2)_4COOH \rightarrow$$

$$\text{TPNH} + H^+ + \overset{\overset{\displaystyle S\text{------}S}{\displaystyle |\qquad\ |}}{C}H_2CH_2CH(CH_2)_4COOH$$

The nature of the electron donor that reacts directly with illuminated chlorophyll is also not clearly established. Since the O_2 produced in photosynthesis by green plants comes from water, it would appear that water is the source of the electrons, but it is possible that another oxidation-reduction reaction may intervene. As noted previously, in photosynthetic bacteria a photoreduction occurs without liberation of O_2. At present, therefore, the oxidation-reduction reaction catalyzed by illuminated chlorophyll may be written

$$A + BH \overset{\text{light}}{\longrightarrow} AH + B$$

where A is an unknown electron acceptor (possibly lipoic acid) and BH is an unknown electron donor (possibly water). It is assumed that A is regenerated in the reduction of TPN^+ (or DPN^+) by AH, and that the unknown oxidant B reacts in green plants with H_2O to form O_2, or in bacteria with another oxidizable substrate, thus regenerating BH.

$$4B + 2H_2O \rightarrow 4BH + O_2 \quad \text{(green plants)}$$
$$4B + 2H_2X \rightarrow 4BH + 2X \quad \text{(bacteria)}$$

From the above discussion it follows that the photochemical reduction of TPN^+ by the Hill reaction,

$$TPN^+ + H_2O \rightarrow TPNH + H^+ + \tfrac{1}{2}O_2$$

probably represents a coupled oxidation-reduction reaction.

Clearly, for the operation of the reductive pentose phosphate pathway, ATP is required as well as TPNH. Evidence has been presented that ATP is generated by the coupling of the phosphorylation of ADP to the oxidation of a portion of the reductant AH (or possibly TPNH) by an equivalent portion of the oxidant B. This process has been termed "photosynthetic phosphorylation" to distinguish it from the respiratory chain phosphorylation performed by mitochondria.[19] The electron carriers involved in this phosphorylation of ADP by illuminated chloroplasts have not been identified as satisfactorily as in the case of mitochondrial phosphorylation (cf. p. 371), but they appear to include a flavin system, vitamin K (menadione; p. 668), ascorbic acid, and possibly a cytochrome (cytochrome f; p. 353). Although the sequence of electron

[19] D. I. Arnon, *Science,* **122,** 9 (1955); D. I. Arnon et al., *Biochim. et Biophys. Acta,* **20,** 449, 462 (1956); *Nature,* **180,** 182 (1957); A. W. Frankel, *J. Biol. Chem.,* **222,** 823 (1956).

transfer from AH to B has not been elucidated, it is clear that a mechanism of oxidative phosphorylation is present in chloroplasts for the generation of ATP; in this system oxygen does not appear to be the terminal electron acceptor, as in mitochondria, but rather the unknown oxidant B.

A number of model experiments have been performed with preparations of chloroplasts and grana to demonstrate the possibility of coupling the photoreduction of pyridine nucleotides to ATP synthesis and to CO_2 fixation. Thus the photochemical reduction of DPN^+ by spinach grana has been coupled to the respiratory chain phosphorylation catalyzed by mitochondria from plant tissues,[20] and the photoreduction of TPN^+ has been coupled to the CO_2 fixation reaction catalyzed by the "malic enzyme" (cf. p. 512). These model experiments are further examples of the utilization of light energy to drive endergonic chemical processes in the presence of suitable enzymic catalysts.

It has been assumed that 3 molecules of ADP are phosphorylated per electron pair transferred in stepwise manner from AH to B; if this value is accepted as a basis for further calculation, an estimate can be made of the energy relations implicit in the photosynthetic conversion of CO_2 to triose phosphate according to the scheme in Fig. 3. It will be seen from the stoichiometry of the reductive pentose phosphate cycle (cf. p. 552) that 9 molecules of ATP are required in this scheme to convert 3 molecules of CO_2 to glyceraldehyde-3-phosphate. To generate this amount of ATP by photosynthetic phosphorylation, 3 molecules of pyridine nucleotide would be oxidized by the unknown electron acceptor B. Since 6 additional molecules of reduced pyridine nucleotide are also needed, the energy requirements of the reductive pentose phosphate cycle for the synthesis of a triose phosphate would be met by the photochemical reduction of 9 molecules of pyridine nucleotide. Hence, per molecule of CO_2 fixed, 3 molecules of reduced pyridine nucleotide must be formed by the transfer of 6 electrons made available by the action of illuminated chlorophyll. If the quantum efficiency of the photochemical process is such that the absorption of one photon leads to the transfer of one electron from BH to A, then 6 quanta of light would cause the fixation of 1 molecule of CO_2, and in green plants would cause the liberation of 1 molecule of O_2. This calculation rests on several unproven assumptions, and at present cannot be considered more than a plausible hypothesis.

A comparison of this calculated value with the results of direct experimental measurement of the quantum efficiency of photosynthesis is made difficult by the lack of concordance among the data reported by various investigators. In 1923, Warburg reported that, under suitable conditions, the absorption of 4 quanta of red light (6560 A) was sufficient to

[20] W. Vishniac and S. Ochoa, *J. Biol. Chem.*, **198**, 501 (1952).

cause the formation of 1 molecule of O_2 in the course of photosynthesis by *Chlorella*. Since the value for the Einstein at this wave length is 44 kcal per mole, the above result implies that the absorption of 176 kcal of light energy by the chlorophyll would lead to the production of 1 mole of oxygen. As seen earlier, the formation of 6 moles of oxygen in photosynthesis involves a $\Delta F°$ of approximately 690 kcal, or 115 kcal per mole of oxygen; Warburg's result, therefore, would indicate an efficiency of approximately 65 per cent, under the conditions of his experiments. This finding has been disputed by a number of investigators, whose results led them to conclude that the quantum efficiency in the photosynthesis of *Chlorella* was considerably lower; values of 6 to 12 quanta per molecule of O_2 produced were reported by Emerson and others (Chapters 10–13 in Franck and Loomis[3]). More recent measurements[21] are also in this range (ca. 7 to 9 quanta). A reinvestigation of the problem by Warburg,[22] with experimental techniques designed to eliminate the influence of respiration and of differences in the algae produced by different modes of illumination during their growth, led him to reiterate the earlier estimate of 4 quanta. Burk and Warburg[23] have reported a quantum yield of 1 under conditions of alternating light and dark periods. Since a quantum yield of about 3 represents 100 per cent efficiency, it was concluded that part of the necessary energy is supplied by light and part by respiration occurring in the dark periods.

In the foregoing discussion, the role of illuminated chlorophyll has been considered only in relation to its function in providing energy for CO_2 fixation. However, the studies of Warburg et al.[24] suggest that the pigment may exist in chloroplasts in the form of a CO_2-derivative (possibly a carboxylated chlorophyll a) which can donate CO_2 for the fixation reaction. It would appear, therefore, that the photosynthetic apparatus of the chloroplast is a highly integrated system in which chlorophyll may participate intimately both in the photolysis of water and in the CO_2 fixation reaction.

A valuable review on the enzymic reactions in photosynthesis has been prepared by Vishniac et al.[25]

[21] E. L. Yuan et al., *Biochim. et Biophys. Acta,* **17**, 185 (1955); J. A. Bassham et al., *ibid.,* **17**, 332 (1955).

[22] O. Warburg et al., *Z. Naturforsch.,* **8b**, 675 (1953); **11b**, 654 (1956); D. Burk et al., *Science,* **110**, 225 (1949).

[23] D. Burk and O. Warburg, *Z. Naturforsch.,* **6b**, 12 (1951); *Federation Proc.,* **10**, 169 (1951).

[24] O. Warburg et al., *Naturwissenschaften,* **43**, 237 (1956); *Z. Naturforsch.,* **11b**, 718 (1956); *Angew. Chem.,* **69**, 627 (1957).

[25] W. Vishniac et al., *Advances in Enzymol.,* **19**, 1 (1957).

23 ·

Chemistry
of Fats
and Phospholipids

Together with the proteins and carbohydrates, the lipids[1] form the bulk of the organic matter of living cells. As seen in earlier chapters, the proteins and carbohydrates may be defined on the basis of their relationship to particular structural units—amino acids or monosaccharides. The term "lipids" refers to a heterogeneous collection of biochemical substances which have in common the property of being variably soluble in organic solvents (e.g., methanol, ethanol, acetone, chloroform, ether, benzene); the lipids are, however, only sparingly soluble in water. It has become the practice to designate substances of the latter type as "hydrophobic," in contrast to materials that are soluble in water, or wettable by water, and hence "hydrophilic." Among the hydrophilic substances are included proteins (e.g., keratin) and polysaccharides (e.g., cellulose) that are insoluble in water but are capable of binding water.

Fats, Oils, and Waxes

The lipids may be separated into several groups on the basis of their chemical and physical properties. The representatives of the first general group may be termed "simple lipids" or "homolipids";[2] these are esters containing only carbon, hydrogen, and oxygen, and they yield, on complete hydrolysis, only fatty acids and an alcohol. The earliest investigations of the simple lipids were concerned with the so-called neutral fats and oils, in which the trihydric alcohol glycerol (discovered by Scheele in 1783) is joined by ester linkages to three fatty acid units. These ester linkages can be cleaved readily by alkaline hydrolysis (saponification)

[1] J. A. Lovern, *The Chemistry of Lipids of Biochemical Significance*, Methuen and Co., London, 1955; H. J. Deuel, *The Lipids*, Vol. I, Interscience Publishers, New York, 1951.

[2] H. H. Hutt, *Nature*, **175**, 303 (1955).

to yield the salts of the fatty acids (soaps). The distinction between

$$
\begin{array}{ccc}
CH_2OOCR & & CH_2OH + KOOCR \\
| & & | \\
CHOOCR' & + 3KOH \rightarrow & CHOH + KOOCR' \\
| & & | \\
CH_2OOCR'' & & CH_2OH + KOOCR''
\end{array}
$$

the fats and the oils is based on their physical state at ordinary temperatures, at which the fats are solids and the oils are liquids.

Fatty Acids. The groundwork on the nature of the fatty acids of the fats and oils was laid by Michel Eugene Chevreul (1786–1889) during the early part of the nineteenth century. Since that time much knowledge has accumulated[3] about the fatty acids formed by the saponification of simple lipids. As will be seen from the list in Table 1, an appreciable number of saturated fatty acids of the general formula $C_nH_{2n+1}COOH$ has been identified. Of these, palmitic acid is most widely distributed in natural fats. Saturated straight-chain fatty acids with an even number of carbon atoms (C_6 through C_{18}) have been found in fats and oils not only from animals and plants, but also from bacteria[4] and molds.[5] In addition, lipids from all these sources contain small amounts of saturated straight-chain fatty acids with an odd number of carbon atoms (C_5 through C_{17}). A variety of branched chain fatty acids having either an even or an odd number of carbon atoms has been identified as minor components of natural fats and oils. Among these are *iso*-valeric acid (from dolphin and porpoise blubber), 11-methyldodecanoic acid and 13-methyltetradecanoic acid (from butter fat[6]), and the 10-methyloctadecanoic acid (tuberculostearic acid) of tubercle bacilli.[7]

Many unsaturated straight-chain fatty acids (of both the even- and odd-numbered series) have been found in nature; among these oleic acid (*cis*-octadec-9-enoic acid) is almost universally present in natural fats. It represents the most abundant mono-unsaturated octadecanoic acid in animals and higher plants, whereas the isomeric *cis*-vaccenic acid (octadec-11-enoic acid) is the major monoethenoid C_{18} acid in bacteria.[8] Among the unsaturated branched-chain fatty acids found to occur naturally is a C_{27} acid (phthienoic acid) obtained from the lipids of virulent tubercle bacilli.[9] Other interesting members of this group are

[3] T. P. Hilditch, *The Chemical Constitution of Natural Fats*, 3rd Ed., John Wiley & Sons, New York, 1956; L. Crombie, *Ann. Reps.*, **52**, 296 (1956).

[4] K. Hofmann et al., *J. Biol. Chem.*, **217**, 49 (1955).

[5] J. Singh et al., *Biochem. J.*, **61**, 85 (1955).

[6] F. B. Shorland et al., *Biochem. J.*, **61**, 702 (1955).

[7] R. J. Anderson, *Harvey Lectures*, **35**, 271 (1940).

[8] H. Laser, *J. Physiol.*, **110**, 338 (1949); I. D. Morton and A. R. Todd, *Biochem. J.*, **47**, 327 (1950); K. Hofmann and F. Tausig, *J. Biol. Chem.*, **213**, 415 (1955).

[9] J. Cason et al., *J. Biol. Chem.*, **192**, 415 (1951); **220**, 893 (1956).

Table I. Some Fatty Acids Found in Natural Fats

	Some Sources
Saturated Fatty Acids	
Butyric acid	Butter, milk fat
Caproic acid (hexanoic)	Coconut, palm nut oil
Caprylic acid (octanoic)	Coconut, palm nut oil
Capric acid (decanoic)	Coconut, palm nut oil
Lauric acid (dodecanoic)	Laurel oil, spermaceti
Myristic acid (tetradecanoic)	Nutmeg butter
Palmitic acid (hexadecanoic)	Animal, plant, and bacterial fats
Stearic acid (octadecanoic)	Animal, plant, and bacterial fats
Arachidic acid (eicosanoic)	Peanut oil
Behenic acid (docosanoic)	Peanut oil
Lignoceric acid (tetracosanoic)	Peanut oil, rapeseed oil
Cerotic acid (hexacosanoic)	Wool fat

	Formula	
Butyric acid	$CH_3(CH_2)_2COOH$	
Caproic acid (hexanoic)	$CH_3(CH_2)_4COOH$	
Caprylic acid (octanoic)	$CH_3(CH_2)_6COOH$	
Capric acid (decanoic)	$CH_3(CH_2)_8COOH$	
Lauric acid (dodecanoic)	$CH_3(CH_2)_{10}COOH$	
Myristic acid (tetradecanoic)	$CH_3(CH_2)_{12}COOH$	
Palmitic acid (hexadecanoic)	$CH_3(CH_2)_{14}COOH$	
Stearic acid (octadecanoic)	$CH_3(CH_2)_{16}COOH$	
Arachidic acid (eicosanoic)	$CH_3(CH_2)_{18}COOH$	
Behenic acid (docosanoic)	$CH_3(CH_2)_{20}COOH$	
Lignoceric acid (tetracosanoic)	$CH_3(CH_2)_{22}COOH$	
Cerotic acid (hexacosanoic)	$CH_3(CH_2)_{24}COOH$	

Unsaturated Fatty Acids (Mono-, Di-, Tri-, and Tetraethenoid Acids)[†]

	Formula	Some Sources
Crotonic acid	$CH_3CH{=}CHCOOH$	Croton oil
Palmitoleic acid (hexadec-9-enoic)	$CH_3(CH_2)_5CH{=}CH(CH_2)_7COOH$	Animal, plant, and bacterial fats
Oleic acid (octadec-9-enoic)	$CH_3(CH_2)_7CH{=}CH(CH_2)_7COOH$	Animal, plant, and bacterial fats
cis-Vaccenic acid (octadec-11-enoic)	$CH_3(CH_2)_5CH{=}CH(CH_2)_9COOH$	Bacterial fats
Linoleic acid (octadeca-9,12-dienoic)	$CH_3(CH_2)_3(CH_2CH{=}CH)_2(CH_2)_7COOH$	Plant oils (linseed and cottonseed oils)
Eleostearic acid (octadeca-9,11,13-trienoic)	$CH_3(CH_2)_3(CH{=}CH)_3(CH_2)_7COOH$	Plant seed fats
Linolenic acid (octadeca-9,12,15-trienoic)	$CH_3(CH_2CH{=}CH)_3(CH_2)_7COOH$	Linseed oil
γ-Linolenic acid (octadeca-6,9,12-trienoic)	$CH_3(CH_2)_3(CH_2CH{=}CH)_3(CH_2)_4COOH$	Primrose seed oil
Octadeca-6,9,12,15-tetraenoic acid	$CH_3(CH_2CH{=}CH)_4(CH_2)_4COOH$	Herring oil
Arachidonic acid (eicosa-5,8,11,14-tetraenoic)	$CH_3(CH_2)_3(CH_2CH{=}CH)_4(CH_2)_3COOH$	Animal fats

† In designating the positions of the double bonds it is customary to number the fatty acid chain in accordance with the Geneva system (i.e., the carboxyl carbon is number 1) and to give only the lower number of each pair of carbon atoms that participates in an unsaturated linkage. The symbol Δ is sometimes used with a superscript denoting both carbon atoms joined by the double bond; thus palmitoleic acid might be termed $\Delta^{9:10}$-hexadecenoic acid.

two fatty acids of plant origin: chaulmoogric acid[10] (a cyclopentene derivative) and sterculic acid[11] (a cyclopropene derivative). A fatty acid related to sterculic acid is the saturated cyclopropane derivative lactobacillic acid[12] (phytomonic acid), which is a major constituent of the lipids of lactobacilli and of the plant pathogen *Agrobacterium* (*Phytomonas*) *tumefaciens*.

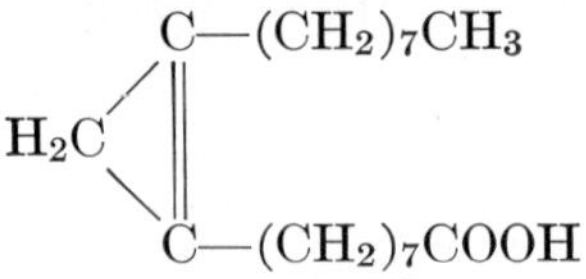

$$C—(CH_2)_7CH_3$$

$$H_2C$$

$$C—(CH_2)_7COOH$$
Sterculic acid

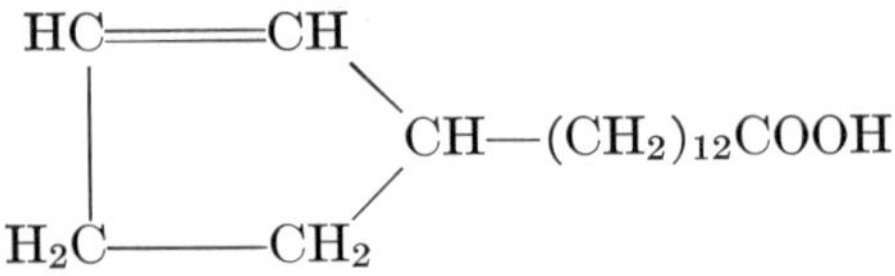

$$HC═══CH$$

$$CH—(CH_2)_{12}COOH$$

$$H_2C———CH_2$$
Chaulmoogric acid

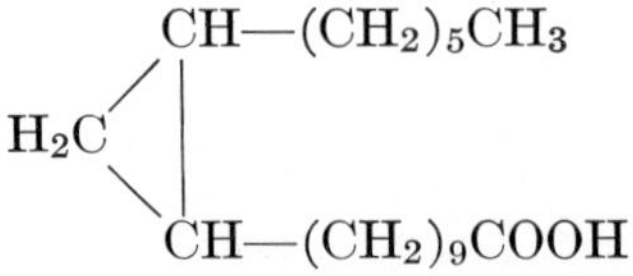

$$CH—(CH_2)_5CH_3$$

$$H_2C$$

$$CH—(CH_2)_9COOH$$
Lactobacillic acid

Examination of the structure of the unsaturated fatty acids containing one double bond (e.g., oleic acid or vaccenic acid) shows that two geometrical isomers (*cis* and *trans*) analogous to maleic acid and fumaric acid are possible. Most unsaturated fatty acids occur mainly in the *cis*-form; however, the *trans*-isomer of oleic acid (elaidic acid), *trans*-vaccenic acid, and other *trans*-unsaturated fatty acids have been detected

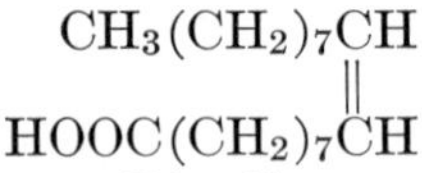

$$CH_3(CH_2)_7CH$$
$$HOOC(CH_2)_7CH$$
Oleic acid

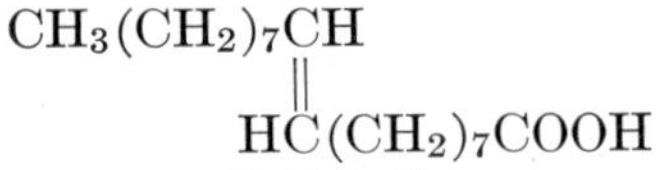

$$CH_3(CH_2)_7CH$$
$$HC(CH_2)_7COOH$$
Elaidic acid

in trace amounts in natural lipids. It is of special interest that *trans*-isomers have been found in relatively large amounts (up to about 20 per cent of the total fatty acids) in the body fats of ruminants and marsupials that have a rumen-like stomach.[13] The origin of the *trans*-forms is obscure, but it has been suggested that they arise from dietary *cis*-acids by the action of rumen bacteria.

The unsaturated fatty acids containing more than one double bond (e.g., linoleic, linolenic, γ-linolenic, and arachidonic acids) are important in animal metabolism, since these fatty acids apparently are not synthesized in animals at a rate sufficient to meet the needs of the body

[10] K. Mislow and I. V. Steinberg, *J. Am. Chem. Soc.*, **77**, 3807 (1955).

[11] J. R. Nunn, *J. Chem. Soc.*, **1952**, 313; P. K. Faure and J. C. Smith, *ibid.*, **1956**, 1818; K. Hofmann et al., *J. Am. Chem. Soc.*, **79**, 3608 (1957).

[12] K. Hofmann et al., *J. Biol. Chem.*, **195**, 473 (1952).

[13] L. Hartman et al., *Biochem. J.*, **61**, 603 (1955); **69**, 1 (1958).

economy. For normal growth, mice, rats, dogs, and probably human beings require a dietary source of at least one of these compounds.[14] Under certain conditions, some bacteria also require unsaturated fatty acids (e.g., oleic acid) in the culture medium for growth. Fatty acids that are required either in the diet of higher animals or in the culture media of bacteria have been termed "essential fatty acids." Among these should be included lipoic acid (thioctic acid; p. 306), which is an important cofactor in the oxidative decarboxylation of α-keto acids (cf. p. 481).

Animal tissues have also been found to contain unsaturated fatty acids other than those listed in Table 1. Among these fatty acids are members of the C_{20} and C_{22} series and which have 2, 3, 4, 5, or 6 double bonds.[15] Higher plants and microorganisms also contain highly unsaturated fatty acids including some with acetylenic (i.e., triple) bonds.[16] Examples are ximenynic acid (*trans*-octadec-11-en-9-ynoic acid; also called santalbic acid), which is the major component of the seed oils of the sandalwood[17] (*Santalum album*), and mycomycin (trideca-3(*trans*),5(*cis*),7,8-tetraene-10,12-diynoic acid),[18] an antibiotic produced by an actinomycete.

$$CH_3(CH_2)_5CH$$
$$\|$$
$$HCC\equiv C(CH_2)_7COOH$$

Ximenynic acid

$$CH\equiv CC\equiv CCH\equiv C\equiv CHCH$$
$$\|$$
$$HCCH$$
$$\|$$
$$HOOCCH_2CH$$

Mycomycin

Fatty acids containing a hydroxyl group have been isolated from higher plants (see Table 2) and an epoxy fatty acid (vernolic acid, 12,13-epoxyoctadec-9-enoic acid) has been reported to be the major acid in the seed oil of the plant *Vernonia anthelmintica*.[19] Among the more complex hydroxylated fatty acids found in nature is mycolic acid (approximate composition, $C_{88}H_{176}O_4$). One of the factors responsible for the virulence of mycobacteria (e.g., *Mycobacterium tuberculosis*) is a compound ("cord factor") formed by the esterification of 2 molecules of mycolic acid by the 6-hydroxyls of trehalose (p. 415).

Because of their structure, fatty acids exhibit a characteristic behavior at surfaces of water or at interfaces between aqueous and organic solvents. The long-chain fatty acids such as oleic acid may be considered to be

[14] H. J. Deuel and R. Reiser, *Vitamins and Hormones,* **13,** 29 (1955).

[15] J. M. Whitcutt and D. A. Sutton, *Biochem. J.,* **63,** 469 (1956); W. Montag et al., *J. Biol. Chem.,* **227,** 53 (1957); E. Klenk and J. Tomuschat, *Z. physiol. Chem.,* **308,** 165 (1957).

[16] J. D. Bu'Lock, *Quart. Revs.,* **10,** 371 (1956).

[17] F. D. Gunstone and W. C. Russell, *J. Chem. Soc.,* **1955,** 3782; J. Grigor et al., *ibid.,* **1955,** 1069.

[18] W. D. Celmer and I. A. Solomons, *J. Am. Chem. Soc.,* **75,** 1372 (1953).

[19] F. D. Gunstone, *J. Chem. Soc.,* **1954,** 1611.

composed of a hydrocarbon-like portion that is insoluble in water and soluble in organic solvents and of a polar carboxyl group that is soluble in water. As a consequence, these molecules will become oriented at a surface between water and benzene so that the hydrocarbon chains project

Table 2.   Oxygenated Derivatives of Stearic Acid Found in Plant Seed Oils

Ricinoleic acid	$CH_3(CH_2)_5\overset{\overset{\displaystyle OH}{\displaystyle |}}{CH}CH_2CH=CH(CH_2)_7COOH$
9-Hydroxyoctadec-12-enoic acid	$CH_3(CH_2)_4CH=CH(CH_2)_2\overset{\overset{\displaystyle OH}{\displaystyle |}}{CH}(CH_2)_7COOH$
9,10-Dihydroxystearic acid	$CH_3(CH_2)_7\overset{\overset{\displaystyle OH}{\displaystyle |}}{CH}—\overset{\overset{\displaystyle OH}{\displaystyle |}}{CH}(CH_2)_7COOH$
18-Hydroxyeleostearic acid	$\overset{\overset{\displaystyle OH}{\displaystyle |}}{CH_2}(CH_2)_3CH=CHCH=CHCH=CH(CH_2)_7COOH$
12,13-Epoxyoleic acid	$CH_3(CH_2)_4\overset{\overset{\displaystyle O}{\diagup\diagdown}}{CH—CH}CH_2CH=CH(CH_2)_7COOH$

into the organic solvent while the carboxyl groups are attracted to the aqueous layer. If a drop of oleic acid is placed on a water surface, the affinity of the carboxyl groups for water will cause the acid to spread. The attraction between the hydrocarbon residues of oleic acid is much greater than their affinity for water; the spreading of the film will therefore stop when a monomolecular layer is formed. By measurement of the area of the film, when it is subjected to sufficient pressure to align the hydrocarbon side chains parallel to one another, it is possible to calculate the cross-sectional dimension of a single fatty acid molecule in a surface film. Reference was made earlier (p. 155) to the fact that many proteins also spread as monolayers on water.

Analysis of Natural Fats and Oils. It must be emphasized that the saponifiable fats or oils obtained upon extraction of a plant or animal tissue with an organic solvent are not pure compounds but are mixtures of several more or less closely related triglycerides. Consequently, it has not been possible to establish the precise nature of each natural triglyceride in terms of the distribution of the fatty acids. Another factor that has complicated the structural analysis of glycerides is the tendency for acyl migration from one hydroxyl group of the glycerol molecule to another. The current views on this subject have been summarized by Deuel and Hilditch.[20]

Obviously, the triglycerides can vary considerably with respect to the nature and arrangement of the constituent fatty acid residues. For this reason, it is fairly difficult to characterize natural fats and oils in terms of the individual triglycerides they may contain. Some of the methods that may be used in the characterization of such naturally occurring mixtures are the following:

1. Determination of the saponification number, which may be defined as the number of milligrams of KOH necessary to neutralize the fatty acids liberated from 1 gram of a fat or oil mixture. This gives a measure of the amount of fatty acid formed after alkaline hydrolysis of a natural fat mixture. Since each equivalent of a triglyceride requires 3 equivalents of KOH (molecular weight 56), the average molecular weight of the mixed triglycerides is related to the saponification number as follows:

$$\text{Average molecular weight} = \frac{3 \times 56 \times 1000}{\text{Saponification number}}$$

From the average molecular weight, an estimate may be made of the average length of the fatty acid chains present in the mixed triglycerides.

2. Determination of the Reichert-Meissel number, defined as the number of cubic centimeters of 0.1 N NaOH required to neutralize the *volatile* fatty acids obtained from 5 grams of mixed triglycerides. Of the fatty acids listed in Table 1, those with fewer than 12 carbon atoms may be distilled with steam; the Reichert-Meissel number thus provides an estimate of the relative proportion of such short-chain fatty acids obtained upon saponification of the mixed triglycerides. For example, butter, which yields appreciable amounts of fatty acids of low molecular weight, has a high Reichert-Meissel number.

3. Fractional distillation of the methyl esters of fatty acids to isolate and identify the individual fatty acids in hydrolysates of natural lipids.

4. Chromatographic techniques, which have proved extremely valuable in the separation and identification of the constituent fatty acids of lipids. The free fatty acids present in a complex mixture can be separated by column chromatography with rubber powder as the solid phase.[21] A very important analytical method is the separation of the methyl esters of fatty acids by gas-liquid chromatography; the columns containing a stationary phase are operated at elevated temperatures, vaporizing

[20] H. J. Deuel, Jr., *Ann. Rev. Biochem.*, **19,** 89 (1950); T. P. Hilditch, *ibid.*, **22,** 125 (1953).

[21] J. Boldingh, *Rec. trav. chim. Pays-Bas,* **69,** 247 (1950).

the components of the mixture of methyl esters, and the vapors are forced through the column by a stream of inert gas (nitrogen).[22]

5. The Craig countercurrent distribution technique (p. 139), which has been applied with success to the separation and quantitative estimation of individual fatty acids.

The presence of double bonds in the unsaturated fatty acids provides an additional analytical method for the characterization of a mixture of triglycerides. If such a mixture, or the fatty acids obtained from it upon saponification, is treated with iodine, 2 atoms of iodine are added per double bond. Thus the iodine number of a natural fat or oil is defined

$$
\begin{array}{ccc}
\text{R—CH} & & \text{R—CHI} \\
\| & + \text{I}_2 \rightarrow & | \\
\text{R}'\text{—CH} & & \text{R}'\text{—CHI}
\end{array}
$$

as the number of grams of I_2 that will be bound by 100 grams of the test material. This value serves as a measure of the relative proportion of unsaturated fatty acid units in the triglyceride. In the study of the stereochemical configuration (*cis* or *trans*) of individual unsaturated fatty acids, infrared spectroscopy has been employed to good advantage.

As might be expected from their chemical structure, the unsaturated fatty acids are susceptible to oxidation at their double bonds. In the presence of suitable catalysts (metals, hemin, etc.) or of the enzyme lipoxidase (cf. p. 609), long-chain unsaturated fatty acids may be converted by oxidation to short fatty acid chains. It is currently believed that this cleavage involves the intermediate formation of peroxides. The short-chain fatty acids, because of their characteristic odor, are primarily responsible for the rancidity of fats that have been exposed to oxygen. Because of the industrial importance of this aspect of fat chemistry, much attention has been given to the search for antioxidants which will prevent such oxidation. Among the many substances that will act as antioxidants are a number of phenols (hydroquinone, pyrogallol, etc.) and naturally occurring substances such as glutathione, ascorbic acid, and the tocopherols (vitamin E; Chapter 39).

Like other unsaturated compounds, fats containing unsaturated fatty acids may be hydrogenated at their double bonds, in the presence of a suitable catalyst (palladium or platinum), with the conversion of the unsaturated acid to the corresponding saturated fatty acid. Thus oleic, linoleic, and linolenic acids give stearic acid upon hydrogenation. When cottonseed oil is subjected to hydrogenation, it is converted to a solid fat. This procedure, known as "the hardening of oils," is important in

---

[22] A. T. James and A. J. P. Martin, *Biochem. J.*, **63**, 144 (1956); A. T. James and J. Webb, *ibid.*, **66**, 515 (1957).

the manufacture of butter substitutes such as margarine. In general, the greater the proportion of saturated fatty acid units in a mixture of triglycerides, the higher is the melting point of the mixture.

As noted previously, it has proved difficult to establish unequivocally the nature and position of each of the fatty acids present in the individual triglycerides found in a natural mixture. From the relative proportion of the fatty acids formed upon hydrolysis, however, it would appear that natural fats do not contain appreciable quantities of symmetrical triglycerides in which all three fatty acid units are the same. Such symmetrical neutral fats have been synthesized in the laboratory; triglycerides containing three units of stearic acid or of oleic acid are termed tristearin or triolein, respectively. The more abundant constituents of natural fats and oils are mixed triglycerides, in which two or three different fatty acid units are present. Representatives of such mixed triglycerides are oleodipalmitin (1 oleic acid and 2 palmitic acid units) and oleopalmitostearin (oleic, palmitic, and stearic acid units). To designate the position of individual fatty acid units in a mixed triglyceride, it is customary to use the symbols α and β as shown. It will

$$\alpha \quad CH_2O\text{—}OCC_{17}H_{35}$$
$$\beta \quad CHO\text{—}OCC_{17}H_{33}$$
$$\alpha' \quad CH_2O\text{—}OCC_{15}H_{31}$$
$$\alpha\text{-Stearo-}\beta\text{-oleo-}\alpha'\text{-palmitin}$$

be obvious that mixed triglycerides with different fatty acid residues at the α and α' positions should exhibit optical activity due to the asymmetry about the β-carbon atom.

Waxes and Related Substances. The simple lipids discussed in the foregoing have in common the presence of glycerol as the alcohol which is bound in ester linkage to fatty acid residues. These fats and oils are differentiated from the waxes, in which glycerol is replaced by a long-chain alcohol. Thus, beeswax consists largely of the ester of palmitic acid with the straight-chain alcohol myricyl alcohol $CH_3(CH_2)_{29}OH$. Cuticle waxes (flower petals, fruit skins, vegetable leaves) contain long-chain fatty acids (C_{24} to C_{36}), both as the free acids and as esters, together with long-chain primary and secondary alcohols, ketones, and paraffin hydrocarbons. The wax of *Mycobacterium tuberculosis* has very complex fatty acids that contain as many as 90 carbon atoms. In animal tissues and in blood plasma, fatty acids are present, not only in the form of triglycerides, but also as esters of the important alcohol cholesterol ($C_{27}H_{45}OH$), which will be discussed in Chapter 26. Alcohols that are long-chain alkyl ethers of glycerol occur as major components in the lipids of marine organisms such as starfish, squid, and sharks. The alkyl groups represent the carbon chains of alcohols corresponding to C_{16} and C_{18} fatty acids, as shown. The biosynthesis of these ethers appears to follow pathways similar to those for the fatty acids and glycerol, from which the ethers are probably derived.

	Glycerol Ether	R Group	Related Fatty Acid
CH_2OH	Batyl alcohol	$CH_3(CH_2)_{16}CH_2—$	Stearic acid
$\vert$			
$CHOH$	Chimyl alcohol	$CH_3(CH_2)_{14}CH_2—$	Palmitic acid
$\vert$			
CH_2OR	Selachyl alcohol	$CH_3(CH_2)_7CH\!=\!CH(CH_2)_7CH_2—$	Oleic acid

Phospholipids [23]

A large variety of natural lipids are distinguished from the simple lipids by virtue of the fact that they contain, in addition to carbon, oxygen, and hydrogen, other elements, notably nitrogen and phosphorus. This group has been referred to as "compound lipids" or "heterolipids" (the term "lipins" has also been used). These compounds initially attracted considerable attention because of their presence in the nerve tissues of animals. The pioneer studies in this field were performed during the latter half of the nineteenth century by Thudichum, who summarized his work in a classical monograph entitled *A Treatise on the Chemical Constitution of the Brain* (London, 1884).

The most thoroughly investigated of the complex lipids are the so-called phosphatides. These include the phosphatides known as the lecithins and cephalins, which are widespread in animal and plant tissues, where they frequently represent the major portion of the cell lipids. The early literature on these substances has been reviewed by MacLean,[24] and the more recent advances in this field have been discussed by Witcoff[25] and Baer.[26] The lecithins from various sources (brain, liver, egg yolk, soybean, wheat germ, and yeast) have the same general structure; in these phosphatides, the distinguishing feature is the participation of one of the hydroxyl groups of glycerol in an ester linkage with phosphoric acid, which is in turn esterified by means of the simple nitrogenous base choline. The other two alcohol groups of glycerol are involved in ester linkages with long-chain fatty acids (indicated R and R' in the formula), similar to those that predominate in natural fats (oleic, palmitic, stearic,

[23] W. D. Celmer and H. E. Carter, *Physiol. Revs.*, **32**, 167 (1952); R. M. C. Dawson, *Biol. Revs.*, **32**, 188 (1957).

[24] H. MacLean and J. Smedley-MacLean, *Lecithin and Allied Substances*, Longmans, Green and Co., London, 1927.

[25] H. Witcoff, *The Phosphatides*, Reinhold Publishing Co., New York, 1951.

[26] E. Baer, *Ann. Rev. Biochem.*, **24**, 135 (1955).

linoleic, etc.). In addition, lecithins may contain the tetraethenoid fatty acid arachidonic acid. The glycerophosphatides of brain appear to differ from those of other organs in their greater content of highly unsaturated fatty acids of the C_{22} series. Most of the lecithins contain both a

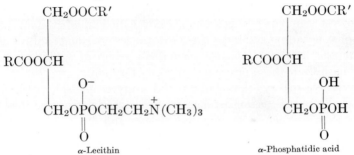

saturated and an unsaturated fatty acyl group, although some are known which contain either two saturated or two unsaturated groups. In the lecithins (from liver and egg yolk) that contain both types of fatty acid, the unsaturated acid appears to be linked solely at the α-position of glycerol, and the saturated acid only at the β-position.[27] Therefore, in the formula shown for α-lecithin, R' represents an unsaturated alkyl group, and R a saturated group.

Phosphatides in which two acidic groups of the phosphoric acid residues are unsubstituted are termed phosphatidic acids; their salts have been isolated from plant and animal tissues. It is uncertain, however, whether these acids exist as such in biological systems, or whether they arise during the isolation procedure by the degradation of more complex phospholipids (cf. pp. 580, 615). If lecithin is considered a derivative of a phosphatidic acid, it may be named phosphatidylcholine. The formula of an α-phosphatidic acid is shown; like α-lecithin, it is a derivative of α-glycerophosphate (α-glycerylphosphoric acid). It is extremely doubtful that β-lecithins (derived from β-glycerophosphate) occur in nature.[28]

α-Lecithins and α-phosphatidic acids have a center of asymmetry about the β-carbon of glycerol (cf. p. 565). As indicated in the formulae, it is now known that naturally occurring α-lecithins, as well as other related phospholipids, are derivatives of L-α-glycerophosphoric acid.[29] It will be noted that lecithin is a dipolar ion in which a negative charge on the phosphoric acid residue is neutralized by a positive charge on the quaternary nitrogen of choline.

Another group of phosphatides, the cephalins, may be separated from the lecithins by taking advantage of the greater solubility of the latter

[27] D. J. Hanahan, *J. Biol. Chem.*, **211**, 313, 321 (1954).
[28] E. Baer and M. Kates, *J. Biol. Chem.*, **185**, 615 (1950).
[29] E. Baer and J. Maurukas, *J. Biol. Chem.*, **212**, 25, 39 (1955).

substances in alcohol. It was originally believed that all the natural materials classified as cephalins were analogous in structure to α-lecithin except for the substitution of the choline residue by that of ethanolamine (aminoethanol, $HOCH_2CH_2NH_2$). However, it was later found that the "cephalin fraction" of the phospholipids is heterogeneous in nature. The simplest members of this group are now called aminoethanol cephalins or phosphatidylaminoethanols; these substances are somewhat more acidic than are the lecithins, because the amino group of ethanolamine is a weaker base than the quaternary nitrogen of choline.

α-Glycerophosphorylethanolamine and α-glycerophosphorylcholine not only occur in nature as constituents of the phosphatides described above, but also exist as such in mammalian tissues and fluids.[30]

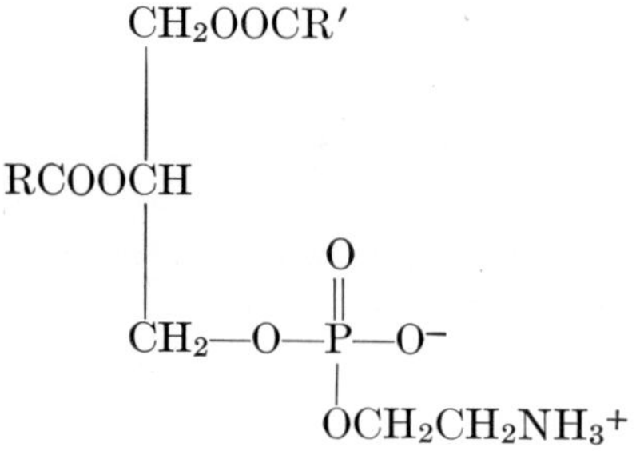

$$CH_2OOCR'$$

$$RCOOCH$$

$$\underset{\underset{OCH_2CH_2NH_3{}^+}{}}{CH_2-O-\overset{\overset{O}{\|}}{P}-O^-}$$

Phosphatidylaminoethanol

$$CH_2OOCR'$$

$$RCOOCH$$

$$\underset{\underset{\underset{COO^-}{}}{OCH_2CHNH_3{}^+}}{CH_2-O-\overset{\overset{O}{\|}}{P}-O^-}$$

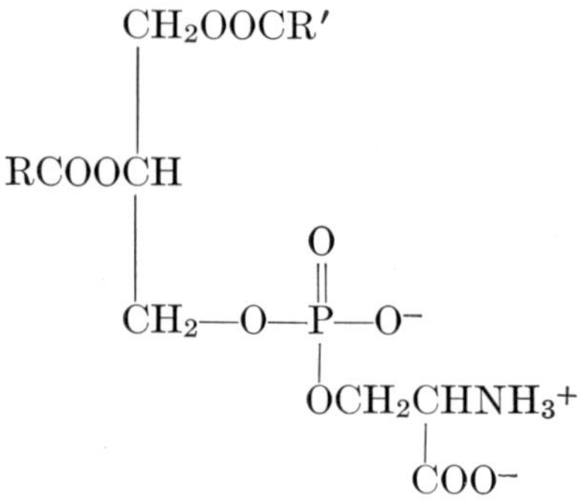

Phosphatidyl-L-serine

A second type of cephalin, which has been obtained from brain and other animal tissues, was assigned the name "phosphatidylserine," since it contains serine in place of aminoethanol. The amino acid has the L-configuration, and the fatty acid residues have been shown to be those of oleic and stearic acid.[31] Phosphatidylserine, as well as various phosphatidylaminoethanols and phosphatidylcholines, has been synthesized by Baer and his associates.[29, 32]

It has been suggested[2] that the three types of phosphatides discussed above be termed "phosphoglycerides," to distinguish them from still another group of phospholipids, the acetal phospholipids or "phosphoglyceracetals" (formerly called plasmalogens). These substances, which constitute an appreciable proportion (ca. 10 per cent) of brain and muscle phospholipids, were discovered by Feulgen in 1924 by means of the "plasmal" reaction, i.e., a histochemical test for aldehydes. In this test Schiff's reagent (fuchsin sulfurous acid) gives a red color after pretreat-

[30] G. Schmidt et al., *J. Biol. Chem.*, **212**, 887 (1955); R. M. C. Dawson et al., *Biochem. J.*, **65**, 627 (1957).

[31] J. Folch, *J. Biol. Chem.*, **174**, 439 (1948).

[32] E. Baer et al., *J. Am. Chem. Soc.*, **78**, 232 (1956).

ment of the phosphatide with $HgCl_2$. Thannhauser et al.[33] have prepared in crystalline form an acetal phosphatide from beef brain. In the formula

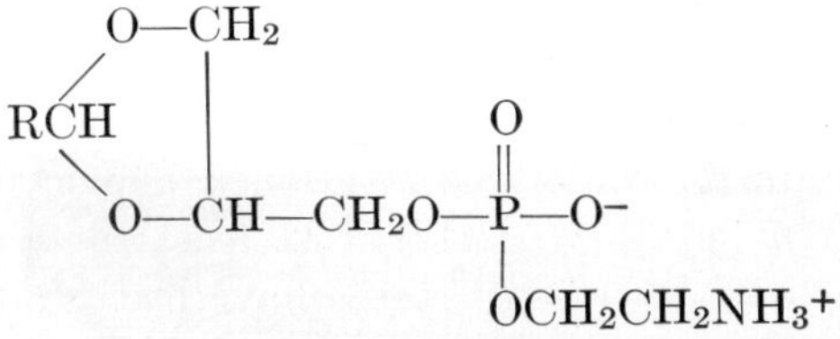

$$
\begin{array}{l}
\text{O—CH}_2 \\
\text{RCH} \qquad\qquad \text{O} \\
\text{O—CH—CH}_2\text{O—P—O}^- \\
\qquad\qquad\qquad \text{OCH}_2\text{CH}_2\text{NH}_3^+
\end{array}
$$

Acetal phosphatide

shown, R is the remainder of a long-chain aliphatic aldehyde; the alde-hydes corresponding to stearic and palmitic acids have been obtained from the crystalline phosphatide. It will be noted that two of the hydroxyls of glycerylphosphorylethanolamine are bound in acetal linkage. However, more recent work indicates that the acetal structure suggested by Thannhauser et al. may arise in the procedure used for the isolation of the compound. It has been found[34] that the "cephalin fraction" and the "lecithin fraction" of beef brain and heart contain appreciable amounts of material that gives aldehyde reactions. Analysis of partially purified preparations of the aldehyde-containing material has shown that, unlike the crystalline acetal phospholipid, they have two long-chain

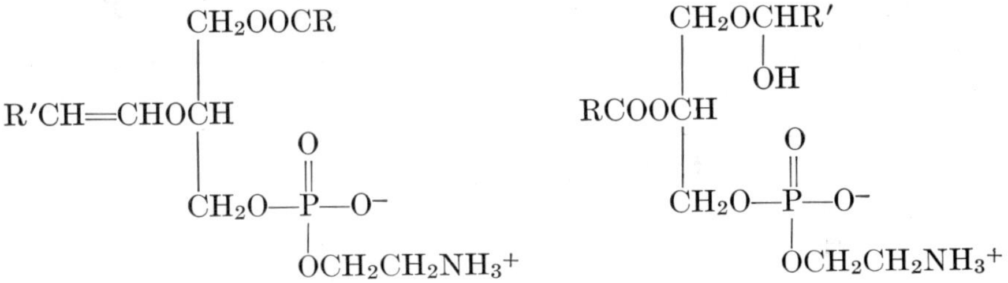

$$
\begin{array}{ll}
\text{CH}_2\text{OOCR} & \text{CH}_2\text{OCHR}' \\
& \qquad\quad \text{OH} \\
\text{R}'\text{CH}{=}\text{CHOCH} & \text{RCOOCH} \\
\qquad\qquad \text{O} & \qquad\qquad \text{O} \\
\text{CH}_2\text{O—P—O}^- & \text{CH}_2\text{O—P—O}^- \\
\quad \text{OCH}_2\text{CH}_2\text{NH}_3^+ & \quad \text{OCH}_2\text{CH}_2\text{NH}_3^+
\end{array}
$$

Proposed structures for phosphatidalaminoethanol

alkyl groups, one of which is present in a fatty acyl group linked as an ester. The available evidence indicates that the other alkyl group is pres-ent as part of an α,β-unsaturated ether (Rapport) rather than a hemi-acetal (Klenk), as shown in the formulae. Since the base can be choline, ethanolamine, or serine, the names phosphatidalcholine, phosphatidal-aminoethanol, and phosphatidalserine have been suggested for these substances. In contrast to the lecithins, phosphatidalcholine from beef heart muscle contains only a small proportion of saturated fatty acids; linoleic acid predominates among the unsaturated fatty acids present.[35]

[33] S. J. Thannhauser et al., *J. Biol. Chem.*, **188**, 417 (1951).

[34] E. Klenk and H. Debuch, *Z. physiol. Chem.*, **296**, 179 (1954); **299**, 66 (1955); M. M. Rapport and N. Alonzo, *J. Biol. Chem.*, **217**, 199 (1955); M. M. Rapport et al., *ibid.*, **225**, 851, 859 (1957); *J. Neurochem.*, **1**, 303 (1957).

[35] E. Klenk and G. Krickau, *Z. physiol. Chem.*, **308**, 98 (1957).

It is of interest that palmitaldehyde, which may be obtained by hydrolysis of acetal phosphatides, is essential for the luminescence of extracts of the luminous bacteria *Achromobacter fischerii*. Presumably, the production of light by the bacterial preparations depends on the initial oxidation of the aldehyde to palmitic acid (cf. p. 346).

In addition to the phosphatides mentioned above, phospholipids are known that contain inositol (p. 412). At least three distinct types of "inositides" have been described;[36] these have been differentiated on the basis of the inositol derivatives obtained by hydrolysis of the phosphatide. One type of inositol-containing phosphatide (found in liver, heart, wheat germ, soybean) yields inositol monophosphate,[37] and is analogous in structure to the other known glycerophosphatides; the members of this group may be termed phosphatidylinositols. Another type, found in brain,[38] yields diphosphoinositol, and may have the structure shown. A third group (found in soybean, peanut, and bacteria) yields on hydrolysis inositol monophosphates that contain in addition galactose or arabinose bound in glycosidic linkage.[39]

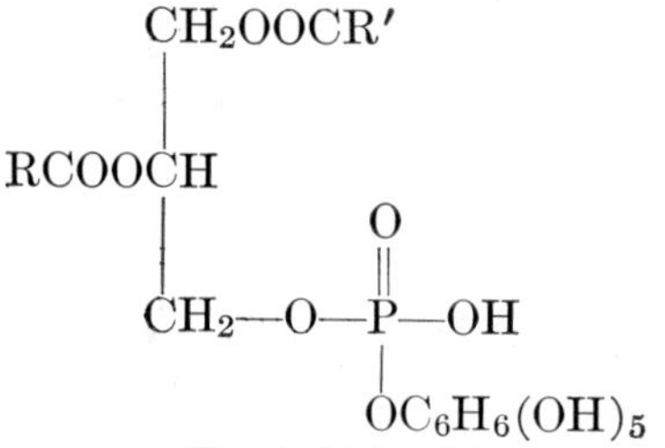

$$CH_2OOCR'$$
$$|$$
$$RCOOCH$$
$$|\qquad O$$
$$|\qquad \|$$
$$CH_2{-}O{-}P{-}OH$$
$$|$$
$$OC_6H_6(OH)_5$$

Phosphatidylinositol

$$\qquad\qquad O$$
$$\qquad\qquad \|$$
$$CH_2O{-}P{-}O$$
$$|\qquad\quad |$$
$$\qquad\quad OH \quad |$$
$$RCOOCH \qquad C_6H_6(OH)_4$$
$$|\qquad O \qquad |$$
$$|\qquad \| \qquad |$$
$$CH_2O{-}P{-}O$$
$$\qquad\quad |$$
$$\qquad\quad OH$$

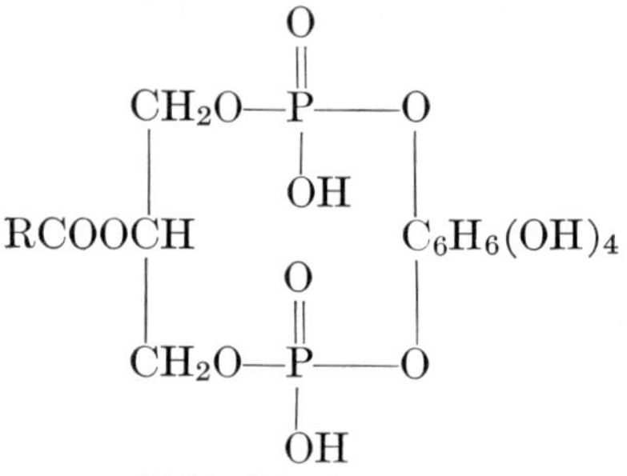

Diphosphoinositide
(possible structure)

Other naturally occurring carbohydrate derivatives that may be classified as lipids because of their solubility in organic solvents are α-D-galactopyranosyl-2-glycerol (isolated from the red marine alga *Irideae laminarioides*[40]) and β-D-galactopyranosyl-1-glycerol (found in wheat flour[41]), and a substance composed of 2 molecules of L-rhamnose and 2 molecules of β-hydroxy-*n*-decanoic acid.[42]

[36] J. Folch and F. W. LeBaron, *Canad. J. Biochem. Physiol.*, **34**, 305 (1956).

[37] J. M. McKibbin, *J. Biol. Chem.*, **220**, 537 (1956); E. Okuhara and T. Nakayama, *ibid.*, **215**, 295 (1955).

[38] J. Folch, *J. Biol. Chem.*, **177**, 505 (1949); J. N. Hawthorne, *Biochim. et Biophys. Acta*, **18**, 389 (1955).

[39] J. N. Hawthorne and E. Chargaff, *J. Biol. Chem.*, **206**, 27 (1954).

[40] E. W. Putnam and W. Z. Hassid, *J. Am. Chem. Soc.*, **76**, 2221 (1954).

[41] H. E. Carter et al., *J. Am. Chem. Soc.*, **78**, 3735 (1956).

[42] G. Hauser and M. L. Karnovsky, *J. Biol. Chem.*, **224**, 91 (1957).

Sphingolipids [23, 43]

In his pioneer work Thudichum obtained from brain tissue a lipid material which differed from the lecithins and cephalins in that it did not contain glycerol. This material was named sphingomyelin; upon hydrolysis it yields, in addition to fatty acids and phosphoric acid, the two nitrogenous bases, choline and sphingosine.[44] As may be seen from the formula of sphingosine, the configuration about the carbon atom with the amino group is that found in L-serine; the configuration about the double bond is *trans*. Sphingosine may be named 1,3-dihydroxy-2-amino-octadec-4-ene. Sphingomyelins have been prepared not only from brain, but also from other animal tissues such as lung and spleen. A probable formula[45] for sphingomyelin is shown; in the formula, R is a lignoceric acid residue ($C_{23}H_{47}CO$).

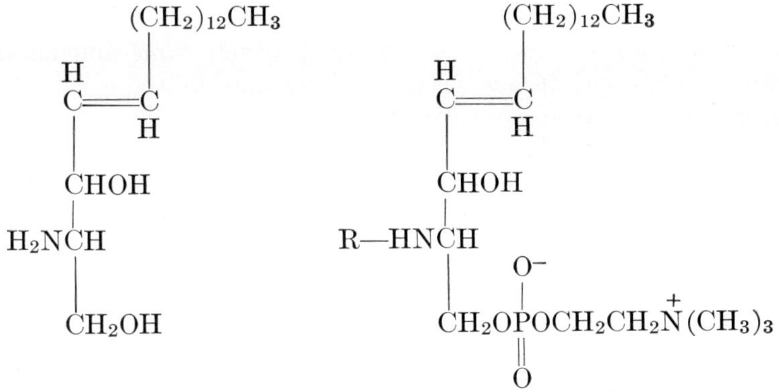

$(CH_2)_{12}CH_3$

$$H—C=C—H$$

$CHOH$

H_2NCH

CH_2OH

Sphingosine

$(CH_2)_{12}CH_3$

$$H—C=C—H$$

$CHOH$

$R—HNCH$

$CH_2OPOCH_2CH_2\overset{+}{N}(CH_3)_3$ with O^- and O

Sphingomyelin

The base sphingosine is also found as a constituent of the brain lipids known as cerebrosides (or galactolipins) and gangliosides. Some sphingomyelins and cerebrosides may contain dihydrosphingosine (the octadecane compound corresponding to sphingosine),[46] and a 4-hydroxy derivative of dihydrosphingosine (1,3,4-trihydroxy-2-amino-octadecane, "phytosphingosine")[47] has been isolated from higher plants, yeasts, and fungi. It has been suggested therefore that all lipids that contain

[43] H. E. Carter et al., *Canad. J. Biochem. Physiol.*, **34**, 320 (1956).

[44] H. E. Carter et al., *J. Biol. Chem.*, **170**, 285 (1947); **191**, 727 (1951); *J. Am. Chem. Soc.*, **75**, 1007 (1953).

[45] S. J. Thannhauser et al., *J. Biol. Chem.*, **135**, 1 (1940); **166**, 669, 677 (1946); **172**, 135, 141 (1948); G. Rouser et al., *J. Am. Chem. Soc.*, **75**, 310 (1953); G. Marinetti et al., *ibid.*, **75**, 313 (1953).

[46] H. E. Carter et al., *J. Biol. Chem.*, **170**, 269 (1947).

[47] H. E. Carter et al., *J. Biol. Chem.*, **206**, 613 (1954).

sphingosine, dihydrosphingosine, or phytosphingosine be designated sphingolipids.

The cerebrosides were studied first by Thudichum and later by Thierfelder and Klenk.[48] Mention will be found in the literature of several types of cerebrosides; these are named kerasin, phrenosin (or cerebron), nervon, and oxynervon, and are differentiated on the basis of their constituent fatty acids.

Kerasin: Lignoceric acid $(CH_3(CH_2)_{22}COOH)$

Phrenosin: Cerebronic acid $(CH_3(CH_2)_{21}(CHOH)COOH)$

Nervon: Nervonic acid $(CH_3(CH_2)_7CH{=}CH(CH_2)_{13}COOH)$

Oxynervon: Oxynervonic acid
$$(CH_3(CH_2)_7CH{=}CH(CH_2)_{12}(CHOH)COOH)$$

Acid hydrolysis of most cerebrosides yields only a fatty acid, sphingosine, and D-galactose. Cerebrosides may occur in tissues other than brain. In Gaucher's disease, cerebrosides appear in relatively large amount in the liver and the spleen; it has been reported that in these cerebrosides the sugar is glucose instead of galactose.

A probable structure for a cerebroside (phrenosin[49]) is shown (R is the cerebronic acid residue); it has not been established whether the glycosi-

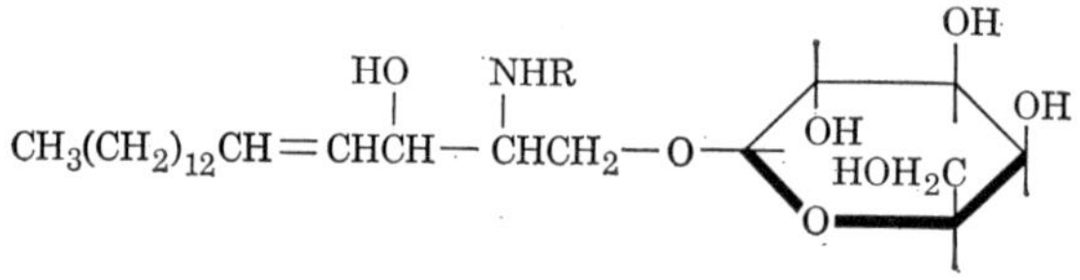

Phrenosin

dic linkage is α or β. Beef brain also contains a cerebroside sulfuric ester that yields, on hydrolysis, cerebronic acid, sphingosine, D-galactose, and sulfuric acid; its structure is similar to that of phrenosin, with the sulfate residue linked to the hydroxyl at carbon 6 of galactose.[50]

The gangliosides, which appear to be closely related to the cerebrosides, occur in the ganglion cells of nervous tissue and in most parenchymatous tissues (e.g., spleen, erythrocytes). They are complex substances, and are believed to contain sphingosine, long-chain fatty acids, hexoses (mainly galactose, but some glucose), and a polyhydroxy amino acid named neuraminic acid.[51] The structure of N-acetylneuraminic acid

[48] H. Thierfelder and E. Klenk, *Chemie der Cerebroside und Phosphatide,* Springer Verlag, Berlin, 1930.

[49] H. E. Carter and F. L. Greenwood, *J. Biol. Chem.,* **199,** 283 (1952).

[50] S. J. Thannhauser et al., *J. Biol. Chem.,* **215,** 211 (1955).

[51] E. Klenk et al., *Z. physiol. Chem.,* **295,** 164 (1953); **304,** 35 (1956).

(sialic acid), a characteristic constituent of some mucoproteins, is shown on p. 426.

Analytical procedures for the determination of phospholipids and sphingolipids in tissues have been developed by Schmidt et al.,[52] and improved methods for the isolation of purified cerebrosides and gangliosides have been described.[53]

Lipoproteins [54]

Much of the lipid material of mammalian plasma is bound to protein in the form of lipoproteins,[55] which migrate electrophoretically with the α_1- and β_1-globulin fractions (p. 106) of plasma and are therefore termed α_1- and β_1-lipoproteins. The lipid constituents of these conjugated proteins are largely cholesterol esters (p. 621) and phospholipids. The major fatty acid components are stearic, palmitic, and oleic acids; some lipoprotein fractions of plasma also contain palmitoleic, linoleic, or arachidonic acid.[56] Although in the plasma of mammals (man, dog, beef, pig) nearly all the phospholipid contains choline, and is therefore largely composed of lecithins and sphingomyelins, bird plasma contains a much larger proportion of cephalins. The total plasma phospholipid of various species is about 150 to 200 mg per 100 cc.

Intracellular lipoproteins are probably extremely important in the maintenance of the structural and functional integrity of multienzyme systems in particulate elements of cells (e.g., mitochondria of liver cells and the grana of chloroplasts). Among the lipoproteins may be included the lipovitellin of egg yolk; this conjugated protein contains approximately 18 per cent of phospholipid.[57] It may be noted also that brain tissue contains, in addition to diphosphoinositide (p. 570), inositol bound to protein.[58]

[52] G. Schmidt et al., *J. Biol. Chem.*, **166**, 505 (1946).

[53] N. S. Radin et al., *J. Biol. Chem.*, **217**, 789 (1955); **219**, 977 (1956); L. Svennerholm, *Acta Chem. Scand.*, **8**, 1108 (1954).

[54] E. Chargaff, *Advances in Protein Chem.*, **1**, 1 (1944).

[55] J. L. Oncley, *Harvey Lectures*, **50**, 71 (1956).

[56] G. A. Gillies et al., *J. Am. Chem. Soc.*, **78**, 4103 (1956).

[57] G. Alderton and H. L. Fevold, *Arch. Biochem.*, **8**, 415 (1945).

[58] F. N. LeBaron and J. Folch, *J. Neurochem.*, **1**, 101, (1956).

Enzymic Hydrolysis of Triglycerides

In higher animals, ingested triglycerides are largely broken down in the small intestine through the hydrolytic action of a lipase present in the pancreatic secretion. Lipase activity has also been demonstrated in gastric juice. Partially purified preparations of pancreatic lipase cause the hydrolysis of the ester linkages of triglycerides with the resulting formation of glycerol and fatty acids. Such lipase preparations hydrolyze symmetrical triglycerides of short- or long-chain fatty acids[1] and ethyl esters of long-chain fatty acids.[2] When the substrate is a mixed triglyceride of long-chain fatty acids similar to those found in natural fats or oils, the hydrolysis proceeds in a stepwise manner (Fig. 1), with the rapid formation of di- and monoglycerides, followed by slow hydrolysis of the monoglyceride.[3] A similar sequence of reactions occurs in the human gastrointestinal tract.[4] The enzyme designated pancreatic lipase appears to be specific for the removal of fatty acid residues linked to the primary hydroxyl groups (at the α- and α'-positions) of glycerol. It is probable that another enzyme effects the cleavage of the 2-monoglycerides to complete the sequence shown in Fig. 1.

Evidence has been presented for the occurrence of lipases in various animal tissues (lung, placenta, etc.), in seeds (castor bean, soybean),[5]

---

[1] S. S. Weinstein and A. M. Wynne, *J. Biol. Chem.*, **112**, 641 (1936); F. Schønheyder and K. Volqvartz, *Enzymologia*, **11**, 178 (1944).

[2] A. K. Balls and M. B. Matlack, *J. Biol. Chem.*, **123**, 679 (1938).

[3] F. H. Mattson and L. W. Beck, *J. Biol. Chem.*, **214**, 115 (1955); **219**, 735 (1956); P. Savary and P. Desnuelle, *Biochim. et Biophys. Acta*, **21**, 349 (1956).

[4] D. H. Blankenhorn and E. H. Ahrens, Jr., *J. Biol. Chem.*, **212**, 69 (1955); R. S. Harris et al., *J. Clin. Invest.*, **34**, 685 (1955).

[5] T. P. Singer and B. H. J. Hofstee, *Arch. Biochem.*, **18**, 229, 245 (1948); E. Bamann et al., *Biochem. Z.*, **325**, 170 (1954).

and in fungi. At alkaline pH values, the rate of lipase action is increased by the addition of proteins (albumins), soaps (sodium salts of long-chain fatty acids), or bile salts (sodium salts of glycocholic and taurocholic acids; p. 633). These substances serve to disperse (emulsify) the triglycerides in aqueous solutions, and therefore are presumed to favor

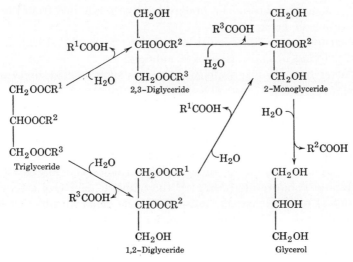

Fig. 1. Probable reaction sequence in the complete hydrolysis of triglycerides by pancreatic lipases.

enzyme-substrate combination.[6] It has also been suggested that one function of the bile salts secreted into the small intestine is to lower the pH optimum of pancreatic lipase to a value more nearly equal to the pH of the intestinal contents.[7] Calcium ions activate lipase, presumably by removal of the strongly inhibitory fatty acids as insoluble calcium salts.

Some animal tissues appear to contain an enzyme ("lipoprotein lipase") that acts on triglycerides only when they are associated with proteins. A substrate for this enzyme may be prepared by combining natural triglycerides (e.g., coconut oil) with the α_1-lipoprotein (p. 573) of human plasma. Treatment of such a lipid-protein complex with a lipoprotein lipase preparation (from rat heart) causes the liberation of free fatty acids; presumably the α_1-lipoprotein is regenerated.[8] Similar lipid-protein complexes occur in blood as "chylomicrons" (tiny droplets or particles with a diameter of about 1 μ) after the ingestion and absorption of fats. The triglycerides of chylomicrons are hydrolyzed by the heart

[6] F. Schønheyder and K. Volqvartz, *Acta Physiol. Scand.,* **9,** 57 (1945).

[7] B. Borgström, *Biochim. et Biophys. Acta,* **13,** 149 (1954).

[8] E. D. Korn, *J. Biol. Chem.,* **215,** 1, 15 (1955).

lipoprotein lipase, and by a similar enzyme present in the plasma of animals treated with heparin (p. 425).[9] Indeed, this enzyme was detected in blood in the course of a search for the "clearing factor" that appears after the intravenous injection of heparin, and that is responsible for the disappearance of the plasma turbidity associated with fat absorption (alimentary lipemia).[10] It has been concluded, therefore, that the clearing factor found in plasma is a lipoprotein lipase released from the tissues by the action of heparin.

It is customary to distinguish the lipases from the so-called simple esterases (found in many tissues of animals) on the basis of the ability of the latter to hydrolyze rapidly substrates such as ethyl butyrate, but to act slowly, if at all, on triglycerides. Partially purified esterase preparations have been obtained from liver by numerous investigators.[11] Such liver esterase preparations (and those from pancreas and intestinal mucosa) have a broad specificity in respect to the nature of the fatty acid and the alcohol from which the ester is derived.[12] In particular, esterase preparations from these animal tissues hydrolyze the fatty acid esters of cholesterol (p. 621);[13] the name "cholesterol esterase" has been applied to this enzymic activity, but its separate identity has not been established. The characterization of the specificity of many esterase preparations described in the literature must await their further purification. The action of such purified esterases on thiol esters (RCO—SR′) will be of special interest in relation to the thiol esterase ("deacylase") activity found in many tissues.

Although the action of the lipases and esterases results in extensive hydrolysis of ester linkages, reversal of hydrolysis may readily be demonstrated with the appropriate fatty acid and alcohol as starting materials. This synthetic action of the ester-hydrolyzing enzymes was first shown by Kastle and Loevenhart in 1900, and has been extensively studied by a number of investigators.[14] Esterases also can catalyze the replacement of a component of an ester linkage in a "transesterification"

[9] G. A. Overbeek and J. Van der Vies, *Biochem. J.*, **60**, 665 (1955).

[10] P. F. Hahn, *Science*, **98**, 19 (1943); D. S. Robinson and J. E. French, *Quart. J. Exptl. Physiol.*, **38**, 233 (1953); H. Engelberg, *J. Biol. Chem.*, **222**, 601 (1956).

[11] J. S. Falconer and D. B. Taylor, *Biochem. J.*, **40**, 831 (1946); W. M. Connors et al., *J. Biol. Chem.*, **184**, 29 (1950); J. Burch, *Biochem. J.*, **58**, 415 (1954); **59**, 97 (1955).

[12] B. H. J. Hofstee, *J. Biol. Chem.*, **199**, 357, 365 (1952); **207**, 219 (1954); W. N. Aldridge, *Biochem. J.*, **57**, 692 (1954).

[13] J. E. Byron et al., *J. Biol. Chem.*, **205**, 483 (1953); H. H. Hernandez and I. L. Chaikoff, *ibid.*, **228**, 447 (1957).

[14] P. Rona and R. Ammon, *Biochem. Z.*, **249**, 446 (1932); E. A. Sym, *Biochem. J.*, **30**, 609 (1936); E. Schreiber, *Z. physiol. Chem.*, **276**, 56 (1942).

reaction;[15] replacement reactions of this type are analogous to those catalyzed by other hydrolases (p. 273).

$$RCOOR' + R''OH \rightleftharpoons RCOOR'' + R'OH$$

Application of the isotope technique to the study of the digestion of triglycerides in the rat and the human[16] has shown that this process includes both the hydrolysis of glycerides and the formation of new glycerol esters. The newly formed ester bonds may arise by synthesis (e.g., the condensation of a C^{14}-labeled fatty acid with a diglyceride to yield a triglyceride) and by transesterification (e.g., a labeled fatty acid replaces an unlabeled acid in a preformed glyceride). It may be added that, during digestion, not only 2-monoglycerides (cf. Fig. 1), but also 1-monoglycerides appear in the intestinal tract; the mechanism for the formation of the latter compounds is uncertain. It is unlikely that significant amounts of either type of monoglyceride arise by direct condensation of a free fatty acid and free glycerol, since glycerol is not incorporated into glycerides under conditions simulating those within the digestive tract.[17]

Acetylcholinesterase. Mention may be made at this point of the ability of the extracts of many animal tissues to hydrolyze the ester acetylcholine.

$$CH_3CO-OCH_2CH_2\overset{+}{N}(CH_3)_3 + H_2O \rightarrow$$
$$CH_3COOH + HOCH_2CH_2\overset{+}{N}(CH_3)_3$$

Interest in the esterases responsible for this action arises from the role of acetylcholine as a chemical transmitter of nerve stimuli;[18] nerve tissue contains an enzyme acetylcholinesterase (or choline esterase) which catalyzes the hydrolysis of acetylcholine.[19] Acetylcholinesterase also hydrolyzes propionylcholine but has little if any activity toward substrates containing larger fatty acyl groups or alcohols other than choline. The enzyme occurs in all conductive tissues examined and also in erythrocytes. These and other animal tissues (serum, liver, pancreas) contain enzymes that hydrolyze esters of choline more rapidly than esters

[15] C. A. Weast and G. MacKinney, *J. Biol. Chem.*, **133**, 551 (1940); B. Borgström, *Arch. Biochem. and Biophys.*, **49**, 268 (1954).

[16] B. Borgström, *Biochim. et Biophys. Acta*, **13**, 491 (1954); E. H. Ahrens, Jr., and B. Borgström, *J. Biol. Chem.*, **219**, 665 (1956).

[17] K. Bernhard et al., *Helv. Chim. Acta*, **35**, 1404 (1952); R. Reiser et al., *J. Biol. Chem.*, **194**, 131 (1952).

[18] D. Nachmansohn, *Harvey Lectures*, **49**, 57 (1955); C. O. Hebb, *Physiol. Revs.*, **37**, 196 (1957).

[19] K-B. Augustinsson, in J. B. Sumner and K. Myrbäck, *The Enzymes*, Chapter 10, Academic Press, New York, 1950; D. Nachmansohn et al., *J. Biol. Chem.*, **174**, 247 (1948); **186**, 693 (1950).

of other alcohols, but, in contrast to the behavior of acetylcholinesterase, the hydrolytic activity increases as the fatty acid chain is lengthened. This type of enzyme has been termed "pseudocholine esterase."

Both acetylcholinesterase and pseudocholine esterase are strongly inhibited by the alkaloids eserine (also termed physostigmine), prostigmine, and atropine (p. 860) at levels of 10^{-6} M with respect to the inhibitor. Both esterases are inhibited noncompetitively by diisopropylfluorophosphate (p. 261), but they differ in their sensitivity to other inhibitors.[20]

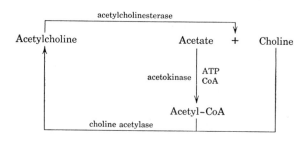

The biosynthesis of acetylcholine in nerve tissues probably occurs by the reaction of acetyl-coenzyme A (p. 482) with choline, and is catalyzed by the enzyme choline acetylase, as shown in the accompanying scheme.

Enzymic Hydrolysis of Phospholipids[21]

In the course of the digestion of lecithin in the gastrointestinal tract of higher animals, the two fatty acid residues apparently can be removed through the enzymic action of pancreatic juice. The pancreatic enzymes responsible for this action have not been purified appreciably, but it appears likely that the same enzymes act on phosphatidylcholine (α-lecithin) and on the phospholipids containing aminoethanol or serine. For this reason, the name "phospholipase" is more descriptive of the action of such enzymes than is the older term "lecithinase." The specific removal of the fatty acid linked to the primary hydroxyl group of glycerol results in the formation of a product (lysolecithin) that is strongly hemolytic; this hydrolytic action is attributed to the enzyme phospholipase A (lecithinase A),[22] which is found not only in animal and plant tissues, but also in microorganisms, snake venom, bee stings, and scorpion venom. The harmful physiological effects of these venoms

[20] F. Bergmann and R. Segal, *Biochim. et Biophys. Acta,* **16,** 513 (1955).

[21] I. L. Chaikoff and G. W. Brown, Jr., in D. M. Greenberg, *Chemical Pathways of Metabolism,* Vol. I, Chapter 7, Academic Press, New York, 1954.

[22] D. J. Hanahan, *J. Biol. Chem.,* **207,** 879 (1954).

is thought to be caused by the action of phospholipase A. The hydrolytic removal of the fatty acid residue of lysolecithin destroys its hemolytic power; this hydrolysis is attributed to the enzyme lysolecithinase (lysolecithinase B, phospholipase B),[23] found in many animal and plant tissues and in microorganisms. Snake venom phospholipase A has been used for the preparation, from lecithins of known structure, of specific lysolecithins; these may be converted to L-α-glycerylphosphorylcholine by the lysolecithinase of the mold *Penicillium notatum*.[24]

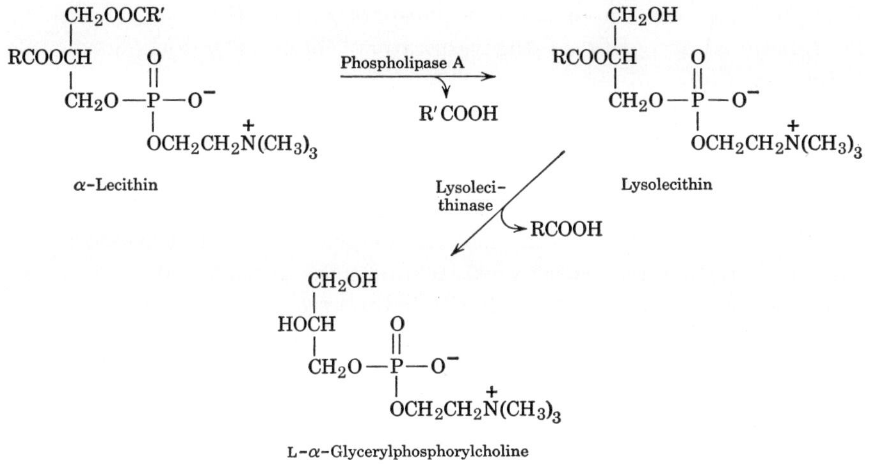

$$\text{L-}\alpha\text{-Glycerylphosphorylcholine}$$

Reference will be found in the older literature to a "lecithinase B"; later work showed that the preparations so designated contained both phospholipase A and lysolecithinase. However, another phospholipase occurs in mammalian brain, snake venoms, and in the toxin of the anaerobic microorganism *Clostridium welchii* (the gas gangrene bacillus).[25] This enzyme hydrolyzes phosphatidylcholine to phosphorylcholine and a diglyceride, and also acts on sphingomyelin (p. 571) to produce phosphorylcholine, but does not attack other phospholipids ("cephalins," lysolecithins, glycerylphosphorylcholine, cerebrosides).[26] It may be termed phospholipase C, but it has been referred to by a variety of other names (*Cl. welchii* lecithinase or α-toxin, glycerophosphatase, lecithinase D); the enzyme appears to be active in ether-ethanol solutions. Apparently, mammalian liver does not contain a

[23] D. J. Hanahan et al., *J. Biol. Chem.*, **206**, 431 (1954); R. M. C. Dawson, *Biochem. J.*, **64**, 192 (1956).

[24] M. Uziel and D. J. Hanahan, *J. Biol. Chem.*, **220**, 1 (1956).

[25] M. G. Macfarlane and B. C. J. G. Knight, *Biochem. J.*, **35**, 884 (1941).

[26] M. G. Macfarlane, *Biochem. J.*, **42**, 587 (1948); D. J. Hanahan and R. Vercamer, *J. Am. Chem. Soc.*, **76**, 1804 (1954).

phospholipase C, although phosphorylcholine is a normal constituent of this tissue.[27]

Another type of phospholipase, found in the tissues of higher plants[28] (carrot, cabbage, cottonseed), hydrolyzes phosphatidylcholine, phosphatidylaminoethanol, and phosphatidylserine to yield an α-phosphatidic acid (p. 567) and a free base. It has been termed phospholipase D (or phosphatidase C).

The phospholipases A, C, and D inhibit electron transport from succinate to cytochrome c if added to a succinoxidase preparation;[29] this effect indicates the importance of phospholipids in the maintenance of the functional integrity of the respiratory chain in mitochondria (cf. p. 359).

As indicated above, the action of lysolecithinase leads to the formation of glycerylphosphorylcholine, as well as the analogous compounds containing aminoethanol or serine. Little is known about the mechanisms whereby these substances are metabolized further in the intestinal tract of higher animals. However, they are cleaved to L-α-glycerophosphate and the corresponding base by extracts of some animal tissues (e.g., rat liver); this hydrolysis has been attributed to an enzyme named "glycerylphosphorylcholine diesterase."[30] A similar enzyme is present in the bacterium *Serratia plymuthicum*, which also contains a phospholipase A and a lysolecithinase, thus enabling the organism to form glycerophosphate and choline or aminoethanol from lecithins and cephalins.[31]

Phosphatases

α-Glycerophosphate is a substrate for several of the phosphatases, and it may be appropriate to discuss these enzymes in this chapter, although they are also important participants in the metabolism of carbohydrates, nucleic acids and nucleotides, and phosphoproteins. The phosphatases represent a very large group of enzymes that act on a variety of phosphate esters;[32] they are usually separated into the following general groups: (1) phosphomonoesterases hydrolyze monoesters of phosphoric

[27] R. M. C. Dawson, *Biochem. J.,* **60,** 325 (1955).

[28] D. J. Hanahan and I. L. Chaikoff, *J. Biol. Chem.,* **172,** 191 (1948); H. L. Tookey and A. K. Balls, *ibid.,* **218,** 213 (1956); M. Kates, *Canad. J. Biochem. Physiol.,* **34,** 967 (1956).

[29] S. W. Edwards and E. G. Ball, *J. Biol. Chem.,* **209,** 619 (1954); H. L. Tookey and A. K. Balls, *ibid.,* **220,** 15 (1956).

[30] R. M. C. Dawson, *Biochem. J.,* **62,** 689 (1956).

[31] O. Hayaishi and A. Kornberg, *J. Biol. Chem.,* **206,** 647 (1954).

[32] J. Roche, in J. B. Sumner and K. Myrbäck, *The Enzymes,* Chapter 11, Academic Press, New York, 1950.

acid,

$$RO—PO_3H_2 + H_2O \rightarrow ROH + H_3PO_4$$

(2) phosphodiesterases hydrolyze diesters of phosphoric acid at one of the ester linkages,

$$RO—P(O)(OH)—OR' + H_2O \rightarrow ROH + R'O—PO_3H_2$$

(3) pyrophosphatases hydrolyze the pyrophosphate linkage of salts of pyrophosphoric acid and of pyrophosphate esters,

$$RO—P(O)(OH)—O—P(O)(OH)—OR' + H_2O \rightarrow$$
$$RO—PO_3H_2 + R'O—PO_3H_2$$

and (4) metaphosphatases hydrolyze metaphosphates $[(HPO_3)_n]$.

The phosphomonoesterases have been studied extensively, and a number of distinct enzymes of this group are known. The best-characterized phosphomonoesterases are those found in blood plasma, milk, intestinal mucosa, and bone; these enzymes act optimally at pH values near 9 and are therefore termed "alkaline phosphatases."[33] The work of Robison and others during the period 1922 to 1930 provided strong evidence for the participation of alkaline phosphatase in bone formation; the enzymic hydrolysis of organic phosphates in the presence of calcium ions is generally believed to cause the deposition of the calcium phosphate in the bones of growing animals.[34] Extensive purification of the alkaline phosphatases of intestinal mucosa and of milk has been reported.[35] Most of the known alkaline phosphatases, after partial purification, require the presence of divalent cations such as Mg^{2+} for enzymic activity, and are inhibited by phosphate. The purified preparations from milk and intestinal mucosa hydrolyze not only a variety of monoesters of phosphoric acid (e.g., β-glycerophosphate, p-nitrophenylphosphate, glucose-6-phosphate, etc.) but also phosphoenolpyruvate (p. 378) and phosphoamides such as creatine phosphate (p. 379).[36]

A number of alkaline phosphomonoesterases appear to be extremely specific in their action. Among these is the enzyme 5'-nucleotidase,[37] which is found in seminal fluid and in snake venom, and which hydrolyzes various nucleoside-5'-phosphates to the corresponding nucleosides (p. 187). Another is the 3'-nucleotidase (from rye grass), which is specific

[33] J. Roche and N.-v. Thoai, *Advances in Enzymol.*, **10**, 83 (1950).

[34] F. Moog, *Biol. Revs.*, **21**, 41 (1946).

[35] G. Schmidt and S. J. Thannhauser, *J. Biol. Chem.*, **149**, 369 (1943); R. K. Morton, *Biochem. J.*, **55**, 795 (1953); **57**, 595 (1954).

[36] R. K. Morton, *Biochem. J.*, **61**, 232, 240 (1955).

[37] L. A. Heppel and R. J. Hilmoe, *J. Biol. Chem.*, **188**, 665 (1951); R. O. Hurst and G. C. Butler, *ibid.*, **193**, 91 (1951).

for nucleoside-3'-phosphates.[38]   A third is fructose-1,6-diphosphatase (p. 461), which hydrolyzes fructose-1,6-diphosphate to fructose-6-phosphate. None of these enzymes appears to act to an appreciable extent on phosphomonoesters such as β-glycerophosphate.

In addition to the "alkaline phosphatases," a number of enzymes, found in animal and plant tissues, act optimally on monoesters of phosphoric acid at pH values near 5. These are usually termed "acid phosphatases." An especially rich source of acid phosphatase is the human prostate gland, from which the enzyme has been purified.[39] It is also abundant in seminal fluid.[40] Phosphorylcholine is an important natural substrate of this enzyme, but it hydrolyzes many other phosphomonoesters, including nucleoside-3'-phosphates and O-phosphoserine. In contrast to the alkaline phosphomonoesterases, the enzymes having an acid pH optimum do not appear to be dependent on Mg^{2+} for their activity. An enzyme that has been considered to be an acid phosphomonoesterase is "phosphoprotein phosphatase" (present in animal tissues),[41] which effects the liberation of inorganic phosphate from phosphoproteins such as casein or phosvitin (p. 56); however, partially purified preparations of this enzyme do not hydrolyze glycerophosphate or O-phosphoserine. It is of interest that such preparations are active toward phosphoamides (e.g., creatine phosphate, amidophosphate), but the interpretation of this finding in relation to the specificity of phosphoprotein phosphatase must await its further purification.

Several of the phosphomonoesterases catalyze condensation reactions in which ester linkages are synthesized. Thus Kay[42] has shown that at high glycerol concentrations appreciable amounts of inorganic phosphate are esterified in the presence of intestinal phosphatase.

Acid and alkaline phosphomonoesterases catalyze replacement reactions in which a phosphate group is transferred from one alcohol to another, or from a phosphoamide to an alcohol.[43] Thus the enzyme preparation that hydrolyzes phenylphosphate can also catalyze the transfer of the phosphate to the 6-hydroxyl of glucose. Such enzyme-catalyzed transphosphorylations by enzymes, usually classified as "hydrolases," are comparable to the transglycosidation (p. 454) and transesterification (p. 576) reactions discussed previously, and to trans-

[38] L. Shuster and N. O. Kaplan, *J. Biol. Chem.*, **201**, 535 (1953).

[39] M. London et al., *J. Biol. Chem.*, **216**, 81 (1955).

[40] F. Lundquist, *Acta Physiol. Scand.*, **14**, 263 (1947).

[41] T. A. Sundararajan and P. S. Sarma, *Biochem. J.*, **56**, 125 (1954); M. F. Singer and J. S. Fruton, *J. Biol. Chem.*, **229**, 111 (1957).

[42] H. D. Kay, *Physiol. Revs.*, **12**, 384 (1932).

[43] B. Axelrod, *J. Biol. Chem.*, **172**, 1 (1948); *Advances in Enzymol.*, **17**, 159 (1956); H. Green and O. Meyerhof, *J. Biol. Chem.*, **197**, 347 (1952); R. K. Morton, *Nature* **172**, 65 (1953).

amidation reactions, involving CO—NH bonds, to be considered in Chapter 29.

$$RO—PO_3H_2 + R'OH \rightleftharpoons R'O—PO_3H_2 + ROH$$

The phosphodiesterases include the liver glycerylphosphorylcholine diesterase mentioned above; similar enzymes that liberate L-α-glycerophosphate and a base from their substrates have been identified in many animal and plant tissues and in some microorganisms. Other phosphodiesterases are the snake venom diesterase that acts on synthetic substrates such as diphenylphosphate $[(C_6H_5O)_2PO_2H]$ or on oligonucleotides,[44] ribonuclease and related enzymes from animal tissues,[45] and the phospholipases C and D. The liberation of an inositol monophosphate from diphosphoinositide (p. 570) by extracts of brain is probably effected by a phosphodiesterase.[46]

Among the enzymes that hydrolyze pyrophosphates is a yeast pyrophosphatase specific for inorganic pyrophosphate; this enzyme has been crystallized by Kunitz.[47] Mention was made previously of the various enzymes that hydrolyze the pyrophosphate linkages of ATP (cf. p. 489), and of the pyrophosphatase that cleaves dinucleotides such as DPN and FAD (cf. p. 336); the latter enzyme may also be responsible for the cleavage of UDPG[48] (p. 205) and of coenzyme A[49] (p. 206) at the pyrophosphate bond.

Metaphosphatases have been found in molds, yeasts, and some bacteria, as well as in various animal tissues.[50] A yeast trimetaphosphatase

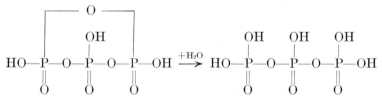

hydrolyzes cyclic trimetaphosphate (which has been isolated from yeast) to the linear triphosphate, which is degraded by yeast pyrophosphatases to three molecules of orthophosphate.[51] The action of other metaphos-

[44] M. Privat de Garilhe and M. Laskowski, Biochim. et Biophys. Acta, 18, 370 (1955).

[45] L. A. Heppel and P. R. Whitfeld, Biochem. J., 60, 1 (1955).

[46] R. Rodnight, Biochem. J., 63, 223 (1956).

[47] M. Kunitz, J. Gen. Physiol., 35, 423 (1952).

[48] J. T. Park, J. Biol. Chem., 194, 885 (1952).

[49] G. D. Novelli et al., J. Biol. Chem., 206, 533 (1954).

[50] B. Ingelman, in J. B. Sumner and K. Myrbäck, The Enzymes, Chapter 12, Academic Press, New York, 1950.

[51] H. Mattenheimer, Z. physiol. Chem., 303, 107, 115, 125 (1956); S. R. Kornberg, J. Biol. Chem., 218, 23 (1956).

phatases is less well characterized. It should be added that the term "metaphosphate," as applied to inorganic polyphosphates obtained from microorganisms and insects, frequently refers not only to cyclic compounds, but also to linear polyphosphates in which three or more phosphoryl groups are joined. A variety of such linear compounds, ranging from triphosphate to heptaphosphate, as well as more highly polymerized polyphosphates, are present in yeast.[52] A possible route for the biosynthesis of such polyphosphates is suggested by the finding that *Escherichia coli* contains an enzyme system that catalyzes the synthesis of a long-chain metaphosphate from ATP; the latter is converted to ADP.[53]

The Intestinal Absorption of Fats and Phospholipids

According to the view offered by Verzar and earlier workers,[54] the absorption of the fatty acids follows the intestinal hydrolysis of fats, and this absorption is aided by the bile salts. In the intestinal wall the fatty acids are recombined with glycerol to form neutral fats, and in this synthetic reaction the phospholipids are believed to serve as intermediates. Doubt about the role of phospholipids in absorption comes from the work of Zilversmit et al.,[55] who showed that in the dog neither the amount nor the rate of turnover of isotopically (P^{32}) labeled phospholipid in the intestinal walls was influenced by the absorption of neutral fats (cream, corn oil) or fatty acids (from corn oil).

An alternative view, proposed by Frazer,[56] arose from the observation that the detergent sodium cetyl sulfonate [$CH_3(CH_2)_{14}CH_2OSO_3Na$] forms a fine emulsion of neutral fats in water but also inhibits lipase action. Since the introduction of an emulsion of a fat with the detergent into the duodenum led to intestinal absorption of the fat, Frazer advanced the hypothesis that, if neutral fat is present in a highly emulsified state, appreciable quantities may be absorbed without prior hydrolysis. According to this view, the bile salts are the natural detergents and facilitate the entrance of the fats into the lymph vessels (lacteals). Estimates of the fat content of human lymph (in the thoracic duct) have been made, and they suggest that perhaps one half of the ingested fat enters the lymphatic system; the rest is presumed to go directly to the liver via the portal blood.

[52] K. Lohmann and P. Langen, *Biochem. Z.*, **328**, 1 (1956).

[53] A. Kornberg et al., *Biochim. et Biophys. Acta*, **20**, 215 (1956).

[54] F. Verzar and E. J. McDougall, *Absorption from the Intestine*, Longmans, Green and Co., London, 1936.

[55] D. B. Zilversmit et al., *J. Biol. Chem.*, **172**, 637 (1948).

[56] A. C. Frazer, *Physiol. Revs.*, **26**, 103 (1946).

The development of a relatively simple procedure for the collection of intestinal or thoracic lymph,[57] combined with the use of isotopic compounds, has provided improved methods for the study of the absorption of lipids. Studies performed by several investigators have shown that complete hydrolysis of glycerides is not essential for the absorption of their constituent fatty acids (see Frazer[58]); some glycerides (tri-, di-, and monoglycerides), as well as glycerol and some free fatty acids, are absorbed. Free fatty acids with fewer than 10 carbon atoms appear in the portal blood, and are transported to the liver.[59] The fatty acids having longer chains are absorbed into the lymph, with concomitant conversion to triglycerides and, to a lesser extent, to phospholipids;[60] these are transported by the lymph to the blood. All the higher fatty acids (both saturated and unsaturated) that have been examined are absorbed in the same manner, whether they enter the gastrointestinal tract as free fatty acids or as triglycerides.[61] The incorporation of fatty acids into glycerides by condensation or by transfer reactions occurs during their passage through the intestinal wall, as well as in the course of digestion in the intestine.[62] The mechanism whereby the esterification observed during absorption is effected has not been elucidated, and the possibility exists that enzymes other than lipases may be involved.

Like the triglycerides, phospholipids need not be hydrolyzed completely prior to absorption, and significant amounts of ingested phospholipids enter the lymph without hydrolysis of the bonds between glycerol and fatty acids or phosphate.[63] When higher fatty acids are fed in the form of phospholipid, they are found in the thoracic lymph in glycerides and in phospholipids, indicating that in part the same mechanism applies as in the digestion and absorption of free fatty acids or of triglycerides. However, there appears to be a preferential absorption of the phospholipid fatty acids in the form of intact phospholipid.

Deposition of Fats in Animal Tissues

It will be clear from the above that in higher animals the absorbed lipids either enter the portal circulation directly or find their way into the systemic circulation by way of the lymphatics and the subclavian veins. In the blood the lipids appear to be transported in large part as

[57] J. L. Bollman et al., *J. Lab. Clin. Med.*, **33**, 1349 (1948).

[58] A. C. Frazer, *Nature*, **175**, 491 (1955).

[59] B. Bloom et al., *Am. J. Physiol.*, **166**, 451 (1951).

[60] B. Borgström, *Acta Chem. Scand.*, **5**, 643 (1951).

[61] S. Bergström et al., *Biochem. J.*, **58**, 600, 604 (1954).

[62] B. Borgström, *J. Biol. Chem.*, **214**, 671 (1955).

[63] B. Bloom et al., *Am. J. Physiol.*, **177**, 84 (1954); R. Blomstrand, *Acta Physiol. Scand.*, **34**, 147, 158 (1955).

chylomicrons, whose formation by the interaction of absorbed triglycerides with the plasma proteins is thought to be spontaneous. Fatty
acids derived from dietary lipids may also be present in the circulation
as components of phospholipids, of cholesterol esters, and of lipoproteins.
A portion of the dietary fatty acids which enter the blood via the
lymphatic system may first reach tissues other than the liver, and be
deposited in the internal organs or in adipose tissues in the form of
"depot fat."[64] Nevertheless, the liver appears to represent a major site
of the transformation of fatty acids in higher animals. It must be emphasized, however, that, both in the adipose tissues and in the liver, the fats
are in a state of continuous flux, with the fatty acids moving from fat
depots to the liver, and vice versa. A portion of the total body fat is
oxidized to CO_2 and water, with the liberation of energy. When the
amount of fat in the diet exceeds the amount degraded, it is stored in
the tissues, and the composition of the body fat is a reflection of the
nature of the dietary fat. Thus the administration of fats or oils rich
in unsaturated fatty acids (soybean oil, peanut oil) leads to the deposition of depot fat which has a relatively high iodine number. However,
only the long-chain fatty acids (C_{16} and higher) appear to be deposited
in the adipose tissues; the shorter fatty acids (e.g., butyric acid) are
oxidized.[65]

Direct evidence for the incorporation of fatty acids into body fats was
provided by the classical experiments of Stetten and Schoenheimer,[66] who

Table I. Incorporation of Isotopic Fatty Acid into Body Fats [66]

	Fatty Acid	Deuterium, atom per cent
Fed:	Palmitic	5.7
Isolated:	Palmitic	1.38
	Stearic	0.53
	Myristic + lauric	0.32
	Palmitoleic	0.36
	Oleic	0.06
	Linoleic	0.02

fed to rats palmitic acid (in the form of its ethyl ester) which had been
labeled with deuterium. After 8 days the animals were sacrificed, and
several of the fatty acids were isolated from the fats of the carcass.
From the data given in Table 1, it will be noted that the isolated
palmitic acid contained much more isotope than any of the other fatty

[64] E. Wertheimer and B. Shapiro, *Physiol. Revs.*, **28**, 451 (1948).

[65] H. C. Eckstein, *J. Biol. Chem.*, **84**, 353 (1929).

[66] D. Stetten, Jr., and R. Schoenheimer, *J. Biol. Chem.*, **133**, 329 (1940).

acids examined. This finding indicates that a significant proportion of the dietary palmitic acid was incorporated into the body fats. Moreover, the appearance of an appreciable amount of deuterium in stearic acid indicates that a direct elongation of a 16-carbon chain to an 18-carbon chain had occurred. Furthermore, the isolation of labeled palmitoleic acid gave proof of the view, long in the literature, that saturated fatty acids can in part be converted to unsaturated fatty acids.

Stearic acid $\rightleftharpoons$ Palmitic acid $\rightarrow$ Shorter-chain acids
(myristic, lauric)

$\Updownarrow$ $\Updownarrow$

Oleic acid   Palmitoleic acid

In connection with the desaturation of stearic and palmitic acids to the corresponding 9-enoic compounds, it may be mentioned that a "fatty acid dehydrogenase" appears to be present in liver and in other tissues.[67]

It will be evident from the data in Table 1 that the linoleic acid, whose isotope concentration was negligible, could not have arisen from the dietary palmitic acid. Therefore, the introduction of a second ethenoid group required for the production of linoleic acid from oleic acid did not occur; this is in agreement with the data of other investigators that linoleic acid and other highly unsaturated fatty acids cannot be readily synthesized by the rat and must be supplied in the diet (cf. p. 560).

In normal animals the lipid content of the liver is approximately 5 per cent of the wet weight; about one half of this is in the form of neutral fat. Under certain conditions, however, the fat content of the liver may rise considerably, to a point where the organ is characterized as being a "fatty liver." Thus, during starvation, large amounts of fat are mobilized from the depots and transferred to the liver. When an excess of fat is present in a diet low in carbohydrate, a fatty liver will result. This effect appears to be induced by fats rich in long-chain saturated fatty acids, but not by those rich in the corresponding unsaturated acids.[68] The feeding of cholesterol also can induce the deposition of abnormal amounts of fat in the liver.[69] Fatty livers may appear as a consequence of liver damage caused by poisoning with carbon tetrachloride or phosphorus, or by one of a number of pathological conditions. Of special interest is the induction of fatty livers in dogs by the surgical removal of the pancreas. The work of Best and his associates during the period 1932 to 1935 indicated that a fatty liver does not appear if choline is added to the diet of a depancreatized animal. This observation

[67] K. Lang and H. Mayer, Z. physiol. Chem., **262**, 120 (1939); A. Jacob, Compt. rend. soc. biol., **147**, 1044 (1953); Compt. rend. acad. sci., **242**, 2180 (1956).

[68] H. J. Channon et al., Biochem. J., **31**, 41 (1937); D. A. Benton et al., J. Biol. Chem., **218**, 693 (1956).

[69] J. H. Ridout et al., Biochem. J., **58**, 297, 301, 306 (1954).

focused attention on choline as a substance which prevents fatty infiltration of the liver; such substances were termed "lipotropic" materials. Subsequent studies showed that methionine, or proteins relatively rich in methionine, also exerted a lipotropic action. It has been found that normal animals maintained on diets deficient in choline and methionine may develop fatty livers. As will be seen from the later discussion dealing with the metabolic interrelationship of choline and methionine (Chapter 32), the lipotropic action of the amino acid is probably due to its role in the synthesis of choline. Other compounds which may bear a close metabolic relationship to choline (e.g., betaine), or may be related

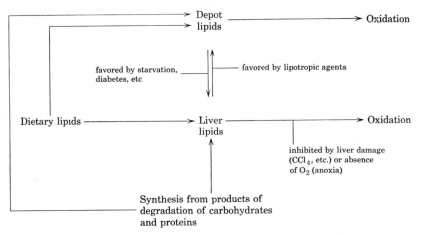

Fig. 2.   Interrelationships in fat metabolism of higher animals.

only through a complex series of metabolic reactions (e.g., various protein amino acids, vitamin B_{12}), also exhibit lipotropic properties. It will be evident that fatty infiltration of the liver can have a number of apparently unrelated causes, and that the prevention or cure of this abnormality probably involves a variety of biochemical processes.[70]

In connection with the role of choline in lipid metabolism, it is of interest that the rate of formation and breakdown of phospholipids (labeled with P^{32}) in the liver of the rat appears to be markedly increased by the administration of choline.[71] The metabolism of phospholipids in rat brain is considerably slower than in the liver or in tissues such as the small intestine or the kidney. In the dog and rat, the liver is the principal site of phospholipid metabolism.[72] The biosynthesis of

[70] C. H. Best, *Federation Proc.*, **9**, 506 (1950); *Proc. Roy. Soc.*, **145B**, 151 (1956).
[71] I. Perlman and I. L. Chaikoff, *J. Biol. Chem.*, **127**, 211 (1939).
[72] D. S. Goldman et al., *J. Biol. Chem.*, **184**, 727 (1950); D. B. Zilversmit and J. L. Bollman, *Arch. Biochem. and Biophys.*, **63**, 64 (1956).

the phospholipids will be considered in the following chapter, together with the intermediate metabolism of free fatty acids and other constituents of lipids.

A summary of the interrelationships of the processes in the fat metabolism of higher animals (and several of the factors that may influence these processes) is shown schematically in Fig. 2. As will be seen later (Chapter 38), the rates of these processes are under the control of hormones elaborated by the organs of internal secretion.

25 · Intermediate Metabolism of Fatty Acids

Oxidation of Fatty Acids[1]

It has long been known that in many living systems fatty acids are oxidized to CO_2 and water. Examination of the stoichiometric relationships in the complete oxidation of a fatty acid such as palmitic acid by molecular oxygen shows a respiratory quotient of 16/23 or approximately 0.7.

$$C_{16}H_{32}O_2 + 23O_2 \rightarrow 16CO_2 + 16H_2O$$

In fact, when an animal is fed a diet consisting predominantly of neutral fats, the observed R.Q. is near 0.7. It will be recalled that the metabolic oxidation of carbohydrate is characterized by an R.Q. of approximately 1.0. The combustion of palmitic acid is accompanied by a $\Delta F°$ of -2338 kcal per mole. Clearly, the oxidation of the long-chain fatty acids can provide considerable energy.

Acetoacetic acid (CH_3COCH_2COOH) had been recognized for many years as a product of the incomplete oxidation of fatty acids in the mammalian organism, since, as shown by Embden in 1906, the perfusion of liver with even-numbered straight-chain fatty acids led to the appearance of acetoacetic acid and its decarboxylation product, acetone. These two ketones, together with l-β-hydroxybutyric acid (D-β-hydroxybutyric acid), are usually termed ketone (or "acetone") bodies; they are found in appreciable amounts in the blood and urine of diabetic animals, including diabetic human subjects. In normal animals, ketone bodies do not accumulate to an appreciable extent; however, the administration of diets abnormally high in fat may result in the excretion

[1] W. C. Stadie, *Physiol. Revs.*, **25**, 395 (1945); I. L. Chaikoff and G. W. Brown, Jr., in D. M. Greenberg, *Chemical Pathways of Metabolism*, Vol. I, Chapter 7, Academic Press, New York, 1954; F. Lynen. *Ann. Rev. Biochem.*, **24**, 653 (1955).

of these compounds in the urine and, in some cases, of acetone in the expired air.

It was also reported by Embden that the perfusion of liver with fatty acids containing an odd number of carbon atoms did not lead to the appearance of ketone bodies (for a further discussion of this finding, see p. 601). The data from the perfusion experiments were explained on the basis of the important work done by Knoop in 1904. Knoop showed that, if one fed to dogs a series of straight-chain fatty acids with a phenyl group at the carbon farthest from the carboxyl, the phenyl derivatives of the even-numbered fatty acids (phenylbutyric acid, etc.) led to the excretion in the urine of phenylacetic acid, whereas the phenyl derivatives of the odd-numbered fatty acids (phenylpropionic acid, phenylvaleric acid) gave rise to benzoic acid. The phenylacetic acid and benzoic acid were present in the urine in the form of phenylacetylglycine (phenaceturic acid) and of benzoylglycine (hippuric acid), respectively. Knoop interpreted this result as evidence for the occurrence, during the oxidation of fatty acids, of the successive removal of 2-carbon units after the oxidation of the β-methylene group to a β-keto group. The Knoop theory is illustrated schematically for two phenylalkyl carboxylic acids.

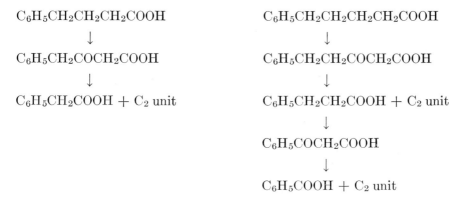

$$C_6H_5CH_2CH_2CH_2COOH$$
$$\downarrow$$
$$C_6H_5CH_2COCH_2COOH$$
$$\downarrow$$
$$C_6H_5CH_2COOH + C_2 \text{ unit}$$

$$C_6H_5CH_2CH_2CH_2CH_2COOH$$
$$\downarrow$$
$$C_6H_5CH_2CH_2COCH_2COOH$$
$$\downarrow$$
$$C_6H_5CH_2CH_2COOH + C_2 \text{ unit}$$
$$\downarrow$$
$$C_6H_5COCH_2COOH$$
$$\downarrow$$
$$C_6H_5COOH + C_2 \text{ unit}$$

As noted above, the Knoop theory, usually termed the β-oxidation theory, was applied by Embden in an attempt to explain the appearance of ketone bodies from even-numbered fatty acids. He supposed that the successive removal of two-carbon fragments by the β-oxidation of such fatty acids would result in the formation of a residual 4-carbon unit; this residual unit would then appear in the form of acetoacetic acid or one of its conversion products (β-hydroxybutyric acid or acetone). On the other hand, the β-oxidation of an odd-numbered fatty acid would, according to Embden's view, give a 3-carbon unit (e.g., propionic acid) as the residual product. An important consequence of this hypothesis was the conclusion that only 1 molecule of acetoacetic acid should be formed per molecule of an even-numbered fatty acid.

In 1915 Hurtley suggested that fatty acids tend to fragment into 4-carbon units; this hypothesis is frequently termed the "multiple-alternate-oxidation" theory. On the basis of this theory, a fatty acid such as octanoic acid would be subject to β-oxidation but would be cleaved only between carbons 4 and 5 of the fatty acid molecule.

$$CH_3CH_2CH_2CH_2 \vdots CH_2CH_2CH_2COOH \rightarrow 2CH_3COCH_2COOH$$

Neither of the theories outlined above proved to be adequate to explain the experimental data of later investigators. Of special importance in the development of new concepts about the oxidation of fatty acids were the studies of Jowett and Quastel[2] with liver slices. They showed that the oxidation of fatty acids with 6, 8, or 10 carbon atoms gave rise to more acetoacetic acid than would be expected on the basis of the β-oxidation theory, and that fatty acids with 5, 7, or 9 carbon atoms also were oxidized with the production of ketone bodies. However, since the C_5 acid valeric acid is a glycogenic substance (p. 493), it must contribute a portion of its molecule to pyruvic acid. To explain these results, MacKay et al.[3] suggested that fatty acids are cleaved into 2-carbon fragments by β-oxidation, and that these fragments condense to form acetoacetic acid. Thus hexanoic acid would give rise to 3 C_2 units, with the formation of 3 equivalents of acetoacetic acid from 2 equivalents of the fatty acid.[4] Similarly, 2 equivalents of valeric acid would be cleaved to give 2 C_2 units, which would condense to form 1 equivalent of acetoacetic acid, and 2 equivalents of pyruvic acid; the pyruvic acid would be available for glycogen synthesis. This hypothesis, which has been amply supported by recent experimental data, is termed the "β-oxidation-condensation" theory.

$$2CH_3CH_2 \vdots CH_2CH_2 \vdots CH_2COOH \rightarrow 6[C_2] \rightarrow 3CH_3COCH_2COOH$$
$$2CH_3CH_2CH_2 \vdots CH_2COOH \rightarrow 2[C_2] + 2CH_3COCOOH$$
$$\downarrow$$
$$CH_3COCH_2COOH$$

Another important contribution was that of Weinhouse et al.,[5] who performed experiments in which isotopic octanoic acid ($C_7H_{15}C^{13}OOH$) was incubated with rat liver slices, and acetoacetic acid was isolated from the incubation mixture and analyzed for C^{13}. From the isotope content of the carboxyl carbon of the octanoic acid (4.4 atom per cent excess C^{13}),

[2] M. Jowett and J. H. Quastel, *Biochem. J.*, **29**, 2159 (1935).

[3] E. M. MacKay et al., *J. Biol. Chem.*, **135**, 157; **136**, 503 (1940).

[4] R. F. Witter et al., *J. Biol. Chem.*, **185**, 537 (1950).

[5] S. Weinhouse et al., *J. Biol. Chem.*, **155**, 143 (1944).

calculations could be made of the isotope contents of the carbonyl and carboxyl carbons (of the acetoacetic acid) to be expected on the basis of each of the three hypotheses discussed above. These values, together with the experimental data, are given in Table 1. The results clearly

Table I. C^{13} Content of Carbonyl and Carboxyl Groups of Acetoacetic Acid Derived from Carboxyl-Labeled Octanoic Acid [5]

	Atom per cent Excess C^{13}	
	Carbonyl C	Carboxyl C
Calculated		
β-Oxidation-condensation	1.1	1.1
Multiple alternate oxidation	0	2.2
β-Oxidation (Knoop-Embden)	0	0
Found	0.84	0.83

favor the β-oxidation-condensation hypothesis, and the observation that the C^{13} values are somewhat lower than those expected was attributed to the presence, in the liver slices, of nonisotopic materials which contributed 2-carbon fragments to the formation of acetoacetate. This would cause a dilution of the isotope and a consequent lowering of the C^{13} content of the acetoacetic acid.

The above experiment of Weinhouse et al. occupies an important place in the sequence of studies of fatty acid oxidation; it must be stressed, however, that the equivalence of isotope content for the carbonyl and carboxyl carbons of acetoacetic acid (cf. Table 1) has not been confirmed. Later studies by Gurin and Crandall[6] showed that the ratio of C^{13} in the CO and COOH groups was less than unity (C^{13}O:C^{13}OOH = about 0.7). This result, together with other evidence that will be considered later (p. 603), has been interpreted to indicate a nonrandom association of the C$_2$ units formed by the oxidation of carboxyl-labeled fatty acids.

It is generally agreed that in higher animals the formation of acetoacetic acid from fatty acids proceeds mainly via a preliminary cleavage into C$_2$ units, followed by a condensation of two of these units to give the 4-carbon compound. However, there is no conclusive evidence to eliminate the possibility that a terminal C$_4$ unit may be directly converted, in small part, to acetoacetic acid. Enzymes that are able to perform such a metabolic conversion are known to be present in liver (see p. 605).

Reference will be found in the literature to the theory proposed by Verkade[7] that fatty acids might be degraded by a mechanism involving an initial ω-oxidation (omega oxidation), i.e., oxidation of the terminal

[6] S. Gurin and D. I. Crandall, Cold Spring Harbor Symposia Quant. Biol., **13**, 118 (1948).

[7] P. E. Verkade, Chemistry and Industry, **57**, 704 (1938).

CH$_3$ group to a COOH, thus forming a long-chain dicarboxylic acid which is then subjected to β-oxidation from both ends of the fatty acid molecule. Strong evidence against this hypothesis has come from more recent studies, and at present it appears doubtful whether ω-oxidation plays a significant role in the metabolic oxidation of fatty acids.[8] However, fatty acids whose structure renders them resistant to oxidative degradation from the carboxyl end of the fatty acid chain probably are oxidized by a process akin to ω-oxidation. Thus, when 2,2-dimethylstearic acid-1-C^{14} was given to rats, about 90 per cent of the absorbed C^{14} was recovered in the urine as dimethyladipic acid.[9]

$$CH_3(CH_2)_{15}[C(CH_3)_2]C^{14}OOH \xrightarrow{-12C} HOOC(CH_2)_3[C(CH_3)_2]C^{14}OOH$$

Enzymic Conversion of Fatty Acids to Acetoacetic Acid [10]

A serious difficulty in the early studies of the enzymic mechanisms involved in the oxidation of fatty acids in a tissue such as liver was the failure to obtain active cell-free preparations. Thus, although the oxidation of fatty acids to CO$_2$ and to acetoacetic acid by liver tissue was observed by Embden in perfusion experiments (1907), little progress was made in the elucidation of the mechanism of this oxidation until 1943, when Muñoz and Leloir[11] showed that homogenized guinea pig liver could oxidize butyric acid, provided that certain accessory materials were added. These were adenosine-5'-phosphate, inorganic phosphate, Mg^{2+}, cytochrome c, and one of the substrates of the citric acid cycle (e.g., succinic acid). The homogenates obtained by these investigators were extremely unstable and did not cause the oxidation of the higher fatty acids (e.g., stearic, oleic, and palmitic acids). Subsequently, Lehninger[12] was able to separate from homogenized rat liver particulate matter (largely mitochondria) which effected the oxidation of saturated fatty acids ranging from butyric acid (C$_4$) to stearic acid (C$_{18}$). With this system, in the presence of ATP, Mg^{2+}, and inorganic phosphate (pH 7.4), 1 equivalent of octanoic acid was oxidized quantitatively to 2 equivalents of acetoacetic acid. The first demonstration that the

$$CH_3(CH_2)_6COOH + 3O_2 \rightarrow 2CH_3COCH_2COOH + 2H_2O$$
Octanoic acid   Acetoacetic acid

oxidation of fatty acids to acetoacetic acid can be catalyzed by soluble

[8] K. Bernhard, *Helv. Chim. Acta*, **24**, 1412 (1941).

[9] S. Bergström et al., *Biochem. J.*, **58**, 604 (1954).

[10] F. Lynen, *Federation Proc.*, **12**, 683 (1953); *Harvey Lectures*, **48**, 210 (1954); F. Lynen and S. Ochoa, *Biochim. et Biophys. Acta*, **12**, 299 (1953); D. E. Green, *Biol. Revs.*, **29**, 330 (1954).

[11] J. M. Muñoz and L. F. Leloir, *J. Biol. Chem.*, **147**, 355 (1943).

[12] A. L. Lehninger, *J. Biol. Chem.*, **161**, 413, 437 (1945); **185**, 275 (1950).

enzyme preparations from liver mitochondria was presented by Drysdale and Lardy,[13] who showed also that coenzyme A (CoA) is an essential cofactor in this process. With either the soluble enzyme system or the particulate mitochondrial preparation, the addition of oxaloacetic acid (and malonic acid) led to the accumulation of citric acid. These findings, coupled with the observation[14] that acetoacetic acid is formed from acetyl phosphate and CoA in the presence of phosphotransacetylase (p. 483) and of an enzyme preparation from pigeon liver, provided evidence that the C_2 unit produced during the oxidation of fatty acids is acetyl-CoA. The formation of citric acid results from the entrance of acetyl-CoA into the citric acid cycle (p. 508).

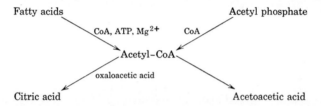

The elucidation of the intermediate steps in the conversion of fatty acids to acetyl-CoA and to acetoacetic acid was accomplished during the period 1950–1955. The sequence of enzymic reactions by which a molecule of acetyl-CoA is formed from the α and carboxyl carbon atoms of a fatty acid has been termed the "fatty acid cycle." In what follows, the constituent reactions of the cycle will be considered in order, and attention will be given to the enzymes of higher plants and micro-organisms, as well as to those of animal tissues.

Just as acetic acid must be "activated" by conversion to acetyl-CoA (see p. 484) before it can enter the citric acid cycle, so also must higher fatty acids be converted to thiol esters of CoA before they are oxidized via the fatty acid cycle. In animal tissues, at least three enzyme systems (termed thiokinases or fatty acid activating enzymes) are known to catalyze the activation of saturated fatty acids by the reaction

$$\text{RCOOH} + \text{ATP} + \text{CoA} \overset{\text{Mg}^{2+}}{\rightleftharpoons} \text{RCO-CoA} + \text{AMP} + \text{pyrophosphate}$$

These thiokinases have been differentiated on the basis of their substrate specificity (Table 2). It will be noted that not only saturated fatty acids, but also unsaturated and hydroxy fatty acids, are activated by these enzyme systems; they do not appear to act on keto acids. A separate thiokinase is known, however, which specifically activates acetoacetic acid. It is of special importance in the over-all metabolism

[13] G. R. Drysdale and H. A. Lardy, *J. Biol. Chem.*, **202**, 119 (1953).
[14] E. R. Stadtman et al., *J. Biol. Chem.*, **191**, 377 (1951).

of ketone bodies (p. 605) that liver apparently contains little of this (or any other) acetoacetic acid activating system.[15]

Several strains of bacteria (*Clostridia, Lactobacilli, Escherichia coli*) lack thiokinases for acetic acid, and appear to form acetyl-CoA by the coupled action of acetokinase and phosphotransacetylase.[16] In organisms

Table 2. Some Enzyme Systems that Catalyze the Formation of Acyl-CoA Derivatives

Enzyme System	Substrates (RCOOH)	Some Sources
Thiokinases		
Aceto-CoA-kinase	Acetic, propionic, and acrylic acids	Heart, yeast, higher plants, *Rhodospirillum rubrum*
Short-chain fatty acid activating enzyme	C_4 to C_{12} saturated fatty acids; α,β- and β,γ-ethenoic derivatives and β-hydroxy derivatives of C_4 and C_6 acids; branched-chain C_4 and C_5 acids	Liver, heart, higher plants
Long-chain fatty acid activating enzyme	C_5 to C_{22} saturated fatty acids; mono-, di-, and trienoic C_{18} acids	Liver
Acetoacetate activating enzyme	Acetoacetic acid	Kidney, heart, brain, yeast
Thiophorases		
Acetyl-CoA thiophorase	C_2 to C_8 saturated fatty acids, vinylacetic acid	*Clostridium kluyverii*
Succinyl-CoA thiophorase	C_4 to C_6 β-keto acids	Heart, skeletal muscle, kidney, adrenal

such as *Clostridium kluyverii*, the formation of other fatty acyl-CoA derivatives involves the transfer of CoA from acetyl-CoA to the fatty acid.[17] The enzymes that catalyze such reactions have been termed

$$\text{Acetyl-CoA} + \text{RCOOH} \rightleftharpoons \text{CH}_3\text{COOH} + \text{RCO-CoA}$$

"thiophorases"; the preparation from *Cl. kluyverii* was named "CoA transphorase" (the name acetyl-CoA thiophorase is given in Table 2).

An analogous reaction occurs in animal tissues, where succinyl-CoA (p. 505) donates CoA preferentially to β-keto acids such as acetoacetic

[15] J. R. Stern et al., *Nature,* **171,** 28 (1953).

[16] E. R. Stadtman, *J. Biol. Chem.,* **196,** 535 (1952).

[17] E. R. Stadtman, *J. Biol. Chem.,* **203,** 501 (1953).

Succinyl-CoA + $CH_3COCH_2COOH \rightleftharpoons$
$$HOOCCH_2CH_2COOH + CH_3COCH_2CO\text{-}CoA$$

acid.[18] The enzyme that catalyzes this reaction is specific for succinyl-CoA; it has been named "CoA transferase" (the name succinyl-CoA thiophorase is used in Table 2) and has been purified appreciably from swine heart.

From the foregoing discussion it is evident that biological systems possess enzymic mechanisms for the activation of saturated fatty acids of all chain lengths up to 22 carbon atoms. Once the CoA derivative of a saturated fatty acid is formed, it is susceptible to oxidation by one or more of the catalytic flavoproteins termed acyl-CoA dehydrogenases or acyl dehydrogenases (p. 344). The first such enzyme to be described was obtained from sheep liver by Lynen, who named it ethylene reductase and showed that it catalyzes the reversible dehydrogenation of butyryl-CoA to form the corresponding α,β-unsaturated compound crotonyl-CoA (*trans*-but-2-enoyl-CoA). Several different acyl-CoA dehydrogenases

$$CH_3CH_2CH_2CO\text{-}CoA + FAD \rightleftharpoons CH_3CH{=}CHCO\text{-}CoA + FADH_2$$

have been found in liver. One of these appears to act most rapidly on CoA derivatives of C_8 to C_{12} fatty acids, but also dehydrogenates acyl-CoA derivatives of fatty acids with as few as 4 carbon atoms and as many as 16 carbon atoms.[19] Another enzyme of this group is a green copper-flavoprotein that acts preferentially on acyl-CoA derivatives of C_4 to C_8 acids,[20] and a third (named palmityl dehydrogenase) acts on CoA derivatives of C_6 to C_{16} (and possibly up to C_{20}) fatty acids.[21]

In the next step of the fatty acid cycle, the α,β-unsaturated compounds produced by the action of the acyl-CoA dehydrogenases are converted to the corresponding β-hydroxy compounds by the addition of the elements of water across the double bond. The enzyme that catalyzes this hydration has been termed "crotonase" or "enoyl hydrase."

$$
\begin{array}{ccc}
\text{CO—CoA} & & \text{CO—CoA} \\
| & & | \\
\text{CH} & & \text{CH}_2 \\
\| & +\,H_2O \rightleftharpoons & | \\
\text{HC} & & \text{HOCH} \\
| & & | \\
\text{CH}_3 & & \text{CH}_3 \\
\text{Crotonyl-CoA} & & \text{L-}\beta\text{-Hydroxybutyryl-CoA}
\end{array}
$$

In the enzymic conversion of crotonyl-CoA to β-hydroxybutyryl-CoA by crotonase, an asymmetric center is introduced (note analogy to the

[18] J. R. Stern et al., *J. Biol. Chem.*, **221**, 1, 15 (1956).
[19] F. L. Crane et al., *J. Biol. Chem.*, **218**, 701 (1956).
[20] D. E. Green et al., *J. Biol. Chem.*, **206**, 1, 13 (1954).
[21] J. G. Hauge et al., *J. Biol. Chem.*, **219**, 727 (1956).

stereospecific hydration of fumarate to L-malate; cf. p. 234). The β-hydroxybutyryl-CoA produced is derived from dextrorotatory β-hydroxybutyric acid (d-β-hydroxybutyric acid). Its enantiomorph, l-β-hydroxybutyric acid, has been shown to be configurationally related to D-lactic acid (cf. p. 80), and may therefore be named D-β-hydroxybutyric acid. In the literature dealing with the enzymes that act on the two β-hydroxybutyric acids and their CoA derivatives, there has been some inconsistency because of the failure to distinguish between their sign of optical rotation (d or l) and their configuration (D or L) as related to glyceraldehyde or lactic acid. In what follows, d-β-hydroxybutyric acid will be denoted L-β-hydroxybutyric acid, and l-β-hydroxybutyric acid will be denoted D-β-hydroxybutyric acid.

Crotonase has been identified in several animal tissues (liver, kidney, brain, skeletal muscle) and in various microorganisms. It has been crystallized from ox liver, and found to have a turnover number of 1,400,000 based on a molecular weight of 210,000.[22] Crystalline crotonase catalyzes the reversible hydration of CoA derivatives of α,β-unsaturated fatty acids having from 4 to 9 carbon atoms, and probably acts on longer fatty acids as well. These substrates may have the *trans* configuration (as shown for crotonyl-CoA in the equation on p. 597) or the *cis* configuration; however, the hydration of the *cis* isomers is slower than that of the *trans* isomers.[23] The crystalline enzyme also acts on branched chain acyl-CoA compounds that are intermediates in the oxidative degradation of the amino acids isoleucine, leucine, and valine (Chapter 32). In addition, the enzyme catalyzes relatively slowly the hydration of β,γ-unsaturated fatty acyl residues (e.g., vinylacetyl-CoA and *trans*-hex-3-enoyl-CoA) to form the same β-hydroxy compounds that arise from the analogous α,β-ethenoid substrates.

The L-β-hydroxyacyl-CoA compounds formed by crotonase are substrates in the next enzymic reaction of the fatty acid cycle: a reversible DPN-linked dehydrogenation leading to the formation of the corresponding β-ketoacyl-CoA compound, as shown. The enzyme that catalyzes this reaction has been identified in liver and heart, and has

$$\text{L-}\beta\text{-Hydroxybutyryl-CoA} + \text{DPN}^+ \rightleftharpoons$$
$$\text{Acetoacetyl-CoA} + \text{DPNH} + \text{H}^+$$

been named β-hydroxyacyl-CoA dehydrogenase or β-oxyacyl dehydrogenase; it has also been termed β-ketoreductase by Lynen, who first observed its action. Purified preparations from beef or sheep liver act on CoA derivatives of β-hydroxy acids of 4 to 12 carbon atoms, and are

[22] J. R. Stern et al., *J. Biol. Chem.*, **218**, 971, 985 (1956).
[23] S. J. Wakil, *Biochim. et Biophys. Acta*, **19**, 497 (1956).

specific for the L-isomers.[24] In addition to this enzyme, liver (and other animal tissues) contains a DPN-linked dehydrogenase that is specific for D-β-hydroxybutyryl-CoA, thus accounting for the interconversion of this compound and its L isomer. As was mentioned previously, D-β-hydroxybutyric acid is one of the ketone bodies; it is oxidized to acetoacetic acid by a DPN-specific dehydrogenase (p. 316) present in liver, and restricted in its action to the D-isomer.[25] The enzymic inter-

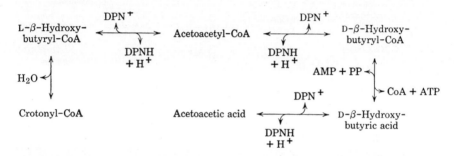

conversions of these C_4 acids and their CoA derivatives are summarized in the accompanying scheme.

The β-ketoacyl-CoA derivatives formed in the reaction catalyzed by the β-hydroxyacyl-CoA dehydrogenase serve as the substrates in the final step of the fatty acid cycle: the enzymic cleavage ("thiolysis") of the β-ketoacyl-CoA compound in the presence of CoA to liberate

$$RCH_2COCH_2CO\text{-}CoA + CoA \rightleftharpoons RCH_2CO\text{-}CoA + CH_3CO\text{-}CoA$$

acetyl-CoA. Lynen demonstrated the presence in liver of an enzyme that mediates this reaction and named it "β-ketothiolase" or "thiolase." Similar enzymes have been found in other animal tissues (heart, kidney, brain), and it appears that more than one β-ketothiolase exists. The enzyme purified from swine heart is specific for acetoacetyl-CoA, whereas cruder preparations from the same source have a broader specificity. On the other hand, purified liver β-ketothiolase acts on β-keto derivatives of C_4 to C_{12} fatty acids;[26] thus this enzyme can effect the cleavage of β-ketooctanoyl-CoA to yield acetyl-CoA and hexanoyl-CoA, which could serve as a substrate for an acyl-CoA dehydrogenase and pass through the fatty acid cycle for a second time (Fig. 1).

It will be seen from Fig. 1 that the fatty acid cycle consists of 4 enzymic reactions involving CoA derivatives. Initially, the fatty acid chain of a saturated acyl-CoA is subjected to dehydrogenation, which is

[24] S. J. Wakil et al., *J. Biol. Chem.*, **207**, 631 (1954).

[25] D. E. Green et al., *Biochem. J.*, **31**, 934 (1937); A. L. Lehninger and G. D. Greville, *Biochim. et Biophys. Acta,* **12**, 188 (1953).

[26] D. S. Goldman, *J. Biol. Chem.*, **208**, 345 (1954).

followed in turn by hydration, a second dehydrogenation, and thiolysis. Although enoyl hydrases, β-hydroxyacyl-CoA dehydrogenases, and thiolases that act on CoA derivatives of long-chain fatty acids (more than C_{12}) have not been isolated, it is assumed that such enzymes exist

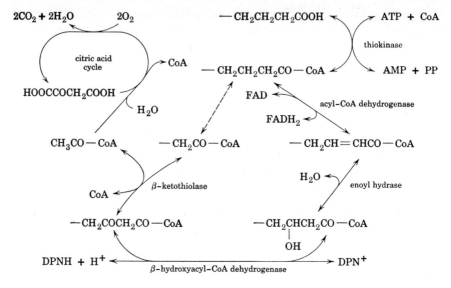

Fig. 1. Pathway of fatty acid oxidation in mammalian liver.

because the higher fatty acids are oxidized by liver preparations. For example, it may be expected that stearyl-CoA is converted quantitatively to acetyl-CoA and palmityl-CoA by reactions analogous to the conversion of octanoyl-CoA to acetyl-CoA and hexanoyl-CoA, for which all the enzymic catalysts have been identified.

It will also be seen from Fig. 1 that only catalytic amounts of CoA are required for the complete oxidation of a fatty acid to CO_2 and H_2O, since the CoA required for the initial activation of the free fatty acid and for the thiolysis of the β-ketoacyl-CoA compounds is regenerated when acetyl-CoA enters the citric acid cycle. As noted earlier, the oxidative degradation of a fatty acid in liver can lead to its quantitative conversion to acetoacetic acid (p. 594). This β-keto acid arises from acetyl-CoA by a stepwise process: 2 molecules of acetyl-CoA condense, in presence of β-ketothiolase, to give acetoacetyl-CoA, which reacts with a molecule of acetyl-CoA to form β-hydroxy-β-methylglutaryl-CoA (p. 630); in liver, this compound is cleaved to acetoacetic acid and acetyl-CoA (p. 788). The over-all process is an apparent hydrolysis:

$$\text{Acetoacetyl-CoA} + H_2O \rightarrow \text{Acetoacetic acid} + \text{CoA}$$

In this manner, all the CoA required for the complete oxidation of a fatty acid to acetyl-CoA is regenerated by the formation of acetoacetic acid.

The reactions discussed above focus attention anew on the important metabolic role of substances closely related to acetic acid. It was seen earlier that acetic acid itself may be converted to acetyl-CoA, which is an intermediate in the incorporation of both carbons of acetic acid into citric acid; this provides a means for the complete oxidation of acetic acid to CO_2 and water via the citric acid cycle. The conversion of pyruvic acid to acetyl-CoA by oxidative decarboxylation represents the mode of entry of this product of glycolysis (or fermentation) into the citric acid cycle. In addition, as will be seen in Chapter 32, the carbon skeleton of certain amino acids (e.g., leucine, valine, phenylalanine) can also contribute to the "acetyl" pool in the course of their metabolic degradation. In later sections of this book, references will also be made to the role of 2-carbon fragments, related to acetic acid, in the metabolic synthesis of fatty acids, of cholesterol, and of porphyrins.

Oxidation of Odd-Numbered Fatty Acids. Acetyl-CoA and acetoacetic acid are formed by the oxidation of odd-numbered fatty acids as well as of the even-numbered compounds (p. 592). Indeed, all the odd-numbered fatty acids tested have been found to serve as substrates for enzymes that act on even-numbered compounds of approximately the same chain length. The removal of C_2 units from an odd-numbered acyl-CoA ultimately leads to the formation of propionyl-CoA (CH_3CH_2CO-CoA); this can be converted to propionic acid, which has been identified as a product of the oxidation of CoA derivatives of odd-numbered fatty acids by kidney and heart preparations. With liver mitochondria, propionic acid does not accumulate, since this system is known to oxidize the C_3 acid.[27] It should be added, however, that a liver preparation which converts even-numbered fatty acids quantitatively to acetoacetic acid forms only slightly more than one equivalent of the keto acid from odd-numbered substrates (C_5 to C_{17}).[28] It would appear therefore that the over-all oxidation of the two types of fatty acids by liver mitochondria must differ significantly.

The oxidation of propionic acid by animal tissues involves the addition of CO_2 to the 3-carbon compound and the intermediate formation of succinic acid, which is oxidized via the citric acid cycle to CO_2 and H_2O.[29] In the presence of a purified preparation from swine heart, the fixation of CO_2 occurs only after propionic acid has been converted to propionyl-

[27] F. M. Huennekens et al., *Arch. Biochem.*, **30**, 66 (1951); *Biochim. et Biophys. Acta*, **11**, 575 (1953).

[28] R. F. Witter et al., *J. Biol. Chem.*, **207**, 671 (1954).

[29] J. Katz and I. L. Chaikoff, *J. Am. Chem. Soc.*, **77**, 2659 (1955); M. Flavin et al., *Nature*, **176**, 823 (1955); H. A. Lardy et al., *J. Biol. Chem.*, **219**, 933, 943 (1956).

CoA by aceto-CoA-kinase (Table 2). ATP is an essential cofactor in the fixation reaction, and the product is methylmalonyl-CoA, which can also arise from methylmalonic acid and CoA by an ATP-dependent activation reaction. Methylmalonyl-CoA is then converted to succinic acid in an interesting isomerization reaction whose mechanism has not been elucidated, but in which succinyl-CoA may be an intermediate.

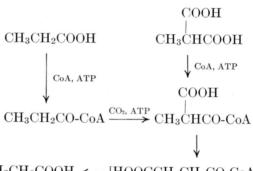

In liver mitochondria, an alternative route for the formation of succinate from propionate and CO_2 may be operative, and it is believed that succinyl-CoA arises by the addition of CO_2 to the terminal carbon atom of a C_3 compound. Still other pathways of propionate metabolism are present in some animal and plant tissues.[30] For example, in cow udder, propionic acid-1-C^{14} is converted to acetic acid-1-C^{14}; this process cannot involve the reactions discussed above, since these would yield unlabeled acetate (cf. p. 515). In peanut mitochondria, propionate appears to be oxidized to β-hydroxypropionic acid, presumably via the CoA derivatives of propionic, acrylic, and β-hydroxypropionic acids; the free β-hydroxy acid is decarboxylated to yield acetate.

Interest in the metabolism of propionyl-CoA stems not only from its relation to the oxidation of straight-chain fatty acids, but also from the fact that it is a product of the oxidative degradation (in animals) of the branched-chain amino acids isoleucine and valine (Chapter 32).

From the foregoing discussion it will be clear that propionyl-CoA, like acetyl-CoA, can be oxidized to CO_2 by way of the citric acid cycle. Consequently, propionic acid will accumulate only under conditions where the operation of this cycle is inhibited. These are also the conditions under which the oxidation of acetyl-CoA is prevented, and acetoacetic acid accumulates.

[30] A. T. James et al., *Biochem. J.*, **64**, 726 (1956); J. Giovanelli and P. K. Stumpf, *J. Am. Chem. Soc.*, **79**, 2652 (1957).

Metabolism of Ketone Bodies

It was mentioned earlier that acetoacetic acid results from a nonrandom association of the active acetate units derived from a carboxyl-labeled fatty acid. Crandall and Gurin[31] have presented evidence (from experiments with octanoic acid labeled with C^{14} in the COOH carbon or in carbon 7) that, in the production of acetoacetic acid from the C_8 acid by

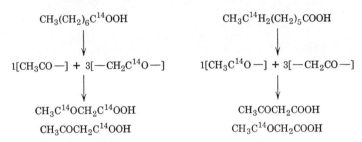

Fig. 2. Formation of acetoacetic acid by nonrandom condensation of two types of active acetyl groups. Observed distribution of C^{14} in acetoacetic acid: from carboxyl-labeled octanoic acid, $CO—C^{14}:COOH—C^{14}=0.75$; from ς-labeled octanoic acid, $CO—C^{14}:COOH—C^{14}=3.3$. (After D. I. Crandall and S. Gurin.[31])

washed homogenates of rat liver, two types of active acetyl groups may arise. One of these may be considered to serve as an acetylating agent via its carbonyl group, which combines with the methyl group of another acetyl unit to form acetoacetic acid (Fig. 2). It would appear that the terminal $CH_3CH_2—$ unit of a fatty acid chain serves predominantly as a source of "carbonyl-activated" C_2 units, whereas the other C_2 fragments ($—CH_2CO—$) can also act as "methyl-activated" units.

From the data of Crandall and Gurin, it follows that the magnitude of the ratio of isotope in the carbonyl and carboxyl groups of acetoacetic acid derived from carboxyl-labeled fatty acids should depend on the length of the fatty acid chain, since, as the chain length increases, the proportion of $—CH_2CO—$ units to $CH_3CO—$ units rises. Experimental evidence for this view was presented by Geyer et al.,[32] who studied the formation of acetoacetic acid from a series of $C^{14}OOH$-labeled fatty acids; for the oxidation of hexanoic acid (C_6) the ratio $CO—C^{14}:COOH—C^{14}$ in acetoacetic acid is 0.47, whereas the degradation of dodecanoic acid (C_{12}) gives a ratio of 0.96. Geyer et al. also showed that, under the conditions of their experiments, only the $—CH_2CO—$

31 D. I. Crandall and S. Gurin, *J. Biol. Chem.*, **181**, 829, 845 (1949).
32 R. P. Geyer et al.. *J. Biol. Chem.*, **185**, 461 (1950); **188**, 185 (1951).

fragments can readily enter the citric acid cycle and be oxidized to CO_2 and water. Since the short-chain fatty acids (hexanoic, octanoic) contain proportionately more terminal CH_3CH_2— units than do the long-chain acids (palmitic, oleic), the former should give rise to more acetoacetic acid, and the latter should be more extensively oxidized by liver preparations to CO_2 and water. This was shown by Kennedy and Lehninger;[33] some of their data are given in Table 3. Subsequent experiments of Brown et al.[34] on the oxidation by liver slices of palmitic acid labeled with C^{14} in the 1, 2, 3, 6, 11, 13, or 15 position confirmed the fact that the terminal C_2 unit (containing carbon 15) of such a long-chain fatty acid is less readily converted to CO_2 than are the other carbon atoms in the chain. These investigators also found complete mixing of all the C_2 units derived from carbon atoms 1 through 14 during the formation of acetoacetic acid, whereas the terminal C_2 unit of palmitic acid was used preferentially as a precursor of the CH_3CO— group of the keto acid.

Table 3. Products of Fatty Acid Oxidation by Washed Liver Mitochondria [33]

The oxidation system contained ATP, cytochrome c, magnesium ions, inorganic phosphate, and succinate or malate.

Substrate	O_2 Uptake, micromoles	Acetoacetic Acid Formed, micromoles	CO_2 Formed, micromoles	R.Q.
Hexanoic acid (0.001 M)	9.1	3.1	0.5	0.06
Octanoic acid (0.001 M)	7.3	3.1	0.9	0.12
Decanoic acid (0.001 M)	4.5	2.3	1.1	0.24
Palmitic acid (0.00025 M)	6.4	0.70	3.8	0.59
Oleic acid (0.00025 M)	6.6	0.17	4.5	0.68

Lynen has explained the observed isotope distribution in acetoacetic acid on the assumption that in the action of β-ketothiolase an intermediate "acyl-enzyme" (p. 281) is formed. Thus, during the formation

(1) $RCH_2COCH_2CO\text{-}CoA$ + Enzyme $\rightleftharpoons$

$$RCH_2CO\text{-enzyme} + CH_3CO\text{-}CoA$$

(2) $RCH_2CO\text{-enzyme} + CoA \rightleftharpoons RCH_2CO\text{-}CoA$ + Enzyme

of acetoacetic acid from a fatty acid such as octanoic acid-7-C^{14}, the operation of the fatty acid cycle would produce 3 equivalents of unlabeled $CH_3CO\text{-}CoA$ and 1 of $CH_3C^{14}O$-enzyme. The isotopic acetyl-enzyme could undergo cleavage in the presence of CoA to yield $CH_3C^{14}O\text{-}CoA$ (reaction 2); in this case the labeled acetyl-CoA would mix with the un-

[33] E. P. Kennedy and A. L. Lehninger, *J. Biol. Chem.*, **185**, 275 (1950).
[34] G. W. Brown, Jr. et al., *J. Biol. Chem.*, **209**, 537 (1954).

labeled compound, and any acetoacetic acid formed from the resultant "acetyl-CoA pool" would be equally labeled in its carbonyl and carboxyl carbons. However, the $CH_3C^{14}O$-enzyme could be used directly, together with unlabeled acetyl-CoA from the pool, for the synthesis of acetoacetyl-CoA (reversal of reaction 1); here the product would contain C^{14} only in its carbonyl carbon. The over-all result of these two processes would be the formation of keto acid labeled predominantly in the carbonyl group.

The conversion of acetoacetyl-CoA to acetoacetic acid follows different pathways in the liver and in extrahepatic tissues. In the liver, this conversion is mediated principally, if not solely, by the sequence of reactions described at the bottom of p. 600. This tissue has only a weakly active acetoacetate-activating system and is devoid of succinyl-CoA thiophorase (p. 596). Extrahepatic tissues (kidney, brain, heart), in contrast to liver, contain either the acetoacetate thiokinase system or the thiophorase. Consequently, acetoacetic acid produced in the liver may be transported in the blood to other tissues, where it can be converted to acetoacetyl-CoA and metabolized further. Thus, studies with

$$CH_3COCH_2C^*OOH \longrightarrow 2[CH_3C^*O] \xrightarrow[\substack{\text{acetic} \\ \text{acid}}]{+\,oxalo-} HOCCOOH \longrightarrow \begin{array}{c} CH_2COOH \\ | \\ CH_2C^*OOH \end{array}$$

isotopic acetoacetic acid showed that, in the presence of oxaloacetic acid, kidney minces can cause the appearance of isotope in intermediates of the citric acid cycle. Acetic acid labeled in the carboxyl carbon will likewise be converted to isotopic succinic acid. If one reisolates acetoacetic acid after the incubation with kidney mince, the isotopic label initially present only in the carboxyl carbon of acetoacetic acid is now found in both the carbonyl and the carboxyl groups.

Apparently, acetoacetic acid is formed in large amounts only when the oxidation of the C_2 units is prevented. In the liver of higher animals acetoacetic acid is not broken down to an appreciable extent to 2-carbon

$$\begin{array}{c} OH \\ | \\ CH_3CHCH_2COOH \end{array} \underset{}{\overset{2H}{\longleftrightarrow}} CH_3COCH_2COOH \xrightarrow{CO_2} CH_3COCH_3$$

fragments. In this tissue, acetoacetic acid may either be reduced to D-β-hydroxybutyric acid by β-hydroxybutyric acid dehydrogenase in the presence of DPNH or be decarboxylated to acetone and CO_2. Acetone may be subjected to metabolic transformations in vivo; in the intact rat acetone is cleaved to form a 2-carbon fragment, which enters the "acetyl" pool.[35] The residual C_1 unit may be used by rat tissues for the synthesis

[35] T. D. Price and D. Rittenberg, J. Biol. Chem., **185**, 449 (1950).

of the methyl groups of methionine and of choline or of the β-carbon of L-serine (cf. p. 774).[36] Propane-1,2-diol (or its 1-phosphate) appears to be an intermediate in the cleavage of acetone to C_2 and C_1 units, and also in the utilization of all 3 carbons of acetone for the synthesis of carbohydrates.[37]

$$CH_3COCH_3 \longrightarrow \underset{\substack{| \quad | \\ HO \quad OH}}{CH_3CHCH_2} \longrightarrow C_2\text{-unit} \quad + \quad C_1\text{-unit}$$

"Acetyl pool"   "Formate pool"

$$C_3\text{-unit} \longrightarrow \text{Carbohydrate}$$

On the basis of the available data, it is possible, therefore, to summarize the course of oxidation of fatty acids to CO_2 and water in the mammalian organism by stating that liver represents a major site of this process, which involves the oxidation of 2-carbon fragments via the citric acid cycle. Under certain circumstances, the liver can also condense the 2-carbon fragments to form ketone bodies which it cannot oxidize at an appreciable rate; if malonate is added to liver slices, thus blocking the citric acid cycle, the oxidation of fatty acids to CO_2 and water is decreased and the formation of ketone bodies is increased.[38] In the intact animal the ketone bodies are carried by the circulation to the tissues (e.g., muscle) and there oxidized to a considerable extent. The oxidation of ketone bodies by the extrahepatic tissues thus provides a major portion of the energy derived from the breakdown of fatty acids in animals. Drury and Wick[39] have shown that ketone bodies compete effectively with substances derived from glucose in the processes of terminal oxidation to CO_2, since the administration of β-hydroxybutyric acid to rabbits receiving C^{14}-labeled glucose markedly reduces the amount of radioactive CO_2 exhaled.

Since animal tissues can convert the carbon atoms of both carbohydrates and fatty acids to CO_2, the question arises whether preference is shown when both types of substrates are available for oxidation. Studies with intact rats[40] and with various tissue preparations[41] have shown that the formation of $C^{14}O_2$ from the carboxyl group of labeled short-chain fatty acids (e.g., butyric or octanoic) is not affected by the simultaneous

[36] W. Sakami, *J. Biol. Chem.*, **187**, 369 (1950).

[37] H. Rudney, *J. Biol. Chem.*, **210**, 361 (1954).

[38] R. P. Geyer and M. Cunningham, *J. Biol. Chem.*, **184**, 641 (1950).

[39] D. R. Drury and A. N. Wick, *J. Biol. Chem.*, **196**, 129 (1952).

[40] W. J. Lossow and I. L. Chaikoff, *Arch. Biochem. and Biophys.*, **57**, 23 (1955).

[41] E. Wertheimer and V. Ben-Tor, *Biochem. J.*, **50**, 573 (1952); A. Allen et al., *J. Biol. Chem.*, **212**, 921 (1955).

presence of carbohydrates (e.g., glucose or pyruvic acid). However, the data on the effect of carbohydrate on the oxidation of long-chain acids (palmitic acid-1-C^{14}) are contradictory, and an unequivocal conclusion is not possible at present.

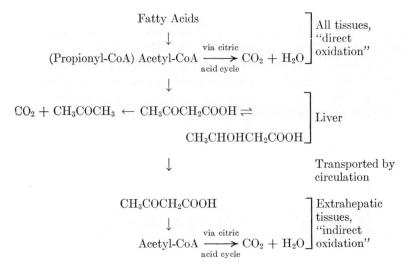

$$\text{Fatty Acids} \quad \left.\begin{array}{l} \\ \end{array}\right] \text{All tissues,}$$

Fatty Acids ↓

(Propionyl-CoA) Acetyl-CoA $\xrightarrow[\text{acid cycle}]{\text{via citric}}$ $CO_2 + H_2O$] All tissues, "direct oxidation"

↓

$CO_2 + CH_3COCH_3 \leftarrow CH_3COCH_2COOH \rightleftharpoons$

$CH_3CHOHCH_2COOH$] Liver

↓ Transported by circulation

CH_3COCH_2COOH

↓

Acetyl-CoA $\xrightarrow[\text{acid cycle}]{\text{via citric}}$ $CO_2 + H_2O$] Extrahepatic tissues, "indirect oxidation"

The close relationship between the oxidation of fatty acids to CO_2 and the formation of ketone bodies has been emphasized further by studies on the mechanism whereby ammonium ions enhance ketone body formation in rat liver slices.[42] In the presence of an excess of ammonium ions, α-ketoglutaric acid is removed by a reductive amination to form glutamic acid. This interrupts the citric acid cycle at the stage leading to succinic acid, and the level of oxaloacetic acid is consequently decreased. Since the preferred pathway of oxidation of the C_2 units to CO_2 and H_2O is blocked, the metabolism of the C_2 units appears to be shunted in the direction of ketone body formation.

Under conditions of physiological dysfunction (e.g., starvation or diabetes), ketone bodies accumulate in the circulation, and a condition of "ketosis" results. This may be due either to (*a*) a decreased rate of decomposition of ketone bodies in the tissues or to (*b*) an elevated rate of production of ketone bodies. It appears likely that the latter process is more important in ketosis. When a substance such as carbohydrate is fed, the level of ketone bodies in a normal individual drops; such substances are termed "antiketogenic." For a stimulating discussion of the possible mechanism of the action of antiketogenic substances, see Krebs.[43]

[42] R. O. Recknagel and V. R. Potter, *J. Biol. Chem.*, **191**, 263 (1951).

[43] H. A. Krebs, *Harvey Lectures*, **44**, 165 (1950).

Oxidation of Fatty Acids in Microorganisms and Plants

Although the experimental data on the metabolic oxidation of fatty acids were largely obtained in studies with animal tissues, many of the conclusions drawn from these studies appear to apply to other biological forms. For example, the degradation of saturated fatty acids by microorganisms such as *Neisseria catarrhalis, Nocardia opaca,* and *Pseudomonas fluorescens*[44] seems to proceed by the β-oxidation of the substrate. The appropriate enzymes of these microorganisms have not been examined, but preparations of enzymes from the anaerobe *Clostridium kluyverii* have been used in extensive studies on the mechanism of fatty acid oxidation in bacteria.[45] The proposed pathway for the β-oxidation of butyric acid by *Cl. kluyverii* is shown in Fig. 3. This pathway differs

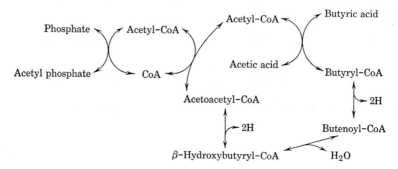

Fig. 3. Proposed pathway of fatty acid metabolism in *Clostridium kluyverii.*

in several respects from the fatty acid cycle of animal tissues (cf. p. 600); the initial activation of butyric acid is catalyzed by acetyl-CoA thiophorase ("CoA transphorase") rather than by a thiokinase, and the acetyl-CoA arising from the thiolysis of acetoacetyl-CoA is converted to acetyl phosphate by the action of phosphotransacetylase (p. 483). Like mammalian liver, *Cl. kluyverii* contains a thiol esterase ("deacylase") that hydrolyzes acetoacetyl-CoA to acetoacetic acid.

It will be seen from Fig. 3 that the over-all reaction effected by the complete circuit of the cycle is as follows:

Butyric acid + phosphate + H_2O $\rightleftharpoons$

Acetyl phosphate + acetic acid + 4H

The evolution of methane (the principal constituent of marsh gas) in

[44] C. I. Randles, *J. Bact.,* **60,** 627 (1950); D. M. Webley et al., *J. Gen. Microbiol.,* **13,** 361 (1955); D. Ivler et al., *J. Bact.,* **70,** 99 (1955).

[45] E. R. Stadtman, *Federation Proc.,* **12,** 692 (1953); J. L. Peel and H. A. Barker, *Biochem. J.,* **62,** 323 (1956).

swamps is a consequence of the fermentation of organic matter by "methane bacteria," a group of anaerobes. The methane fermentation of fatty acids by these bacteria is believed to involve the intermediate formation of acetic acid.[46]

In some higher plants (e.g., peanut) the oxidation of long-chain fatty acids is effected not only by β-oxidation, but also by other pathways.[47] Studies on a complex enzyme system extracted from peanut cotyledons indicate the existence of a specific fatty acid peroxidase which forms $C^{14}O_2$ from only the carboxyl carbon of labeled long-chain saturated fatty acids (palmitic, stearic, myristic) in the presence of H_2O_2 generated by the action of glycolic acid oxidase (p. 338). In the peroxidase-catalyzed decarboxylation, a long-chain fatty aldehyde is thought to be formed.

In connection with the oxidation of fatty acids by plant tissues, it may be added that the enzyme lipoxidase,[48] found in many higher plants, acts on long-chain fatty acids containing 2 or more double bonds (e.g., linoleic, linolenic, arachidonic acids) in the presence of oxygen to form short-chain fatty acids. It is currently believed that this oxidative cleavage involves the intermediate formation of peroxides. Lipoxidase has been crystallized from soybeans.[49] Enzymes of this group are believed to be present in animal tissues, but have not been characterized.

Biosynthesis of Fatty Acids

Fatty acids, with the exception of the highly unsaturated members of this group of compounds, appear to be synthesized readily in animals and in other organisms. All the reactions given in Fig. 1 for the formation of acetyl-CoA from higher fatty acids are reversible. Consequently, a biological system that can oxidize fatty acids to C_2 units should be able to synthesize long-chain fatty acids by the successive addition of C_2 units to the carboxyl carbon of a growing fatty acid chain. Numerous experimental studies with animals, plants, and microorganisms have provided data in support of this hypothesis.

Before the elucidation of the enzymic mechanisms in the oxidation of fatty acids, considerable information had been gathered about the biosynthesis of fatty acids in vivo. It will be recalled (see p. 586) that

[46] H. A. Barker, *Bacterial Fermentations,* John Wiley & Sons, New York, 1957.

[47] T. E. Humphreys et al., *J. Biol. Chem.,* **210**, 941 (1954); **213**, 941 (1955); P. K. Stumpf and G. A. Barber, *Plant Physiol.,* **31**, 304 (1956); P. Castelfranco et al., *J. Biol. Chem.,* **214**, 567 (1955); P. K. Stumpf, *ibid.,* **223**, 643 (1956).

[48] R. T. Holman and S. Bergström, in J. B. Sumner and K. Myrbäck, *The Enzymes,* Vol. II, Chapter 60, Academic Press, New York, 1951.

[49] H. Theorell et al., *Arch. Biochem.,* **14**, 250 (1947).

the administration, to an animal, of palmitic acid labeled with deuterium led to the appearance of the isotope in several other fatty acids (stearic and palmitoleic acids in particular). The appearance of deuterium in these fatty acids may also be induced by bringing the D_2O concentration of the body water to a level of ca. 2 per cent. If the D_2O content of the body water is maintained at this level by the continuous administration

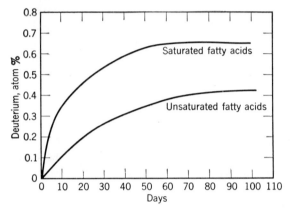

Fig. 4. Deuterium content of fatty acids of mice given heavy water to raise the body water to 1.5 per cent D_2O. [From D. Rittenberg and R. Schoenheimer, *J. Biol. Chem.*, **121**, 235 (1937).]

of "heavy water" and the test animals are sacrificed after varying periods of time, it is found that the rates at which the isotope appears in the saturated and unsaturated fatty acids are different (Fig. 4).[50] Of special importance is the observation that the final isotope level attained in the saturated fatty acids was approximately half that of the body water. Thus, in the course of fatty acid synthesis, approximately one half of the hydrogen atoms was derived from the hydrogen of the body water. Also, since the unsaturated fatty acids contain less isotope than the saturated fatty acids, the former cannot be intermediates in the biosynthesis of the saturated acids.

The early experiments of Schoenheimer and Rittenberg with animals whose body water had been enriched with respect to its D_2O content also provided information about the probable pathway of fatty acid biosynthesis. The oleic acid isolated from such animals was cleaved by chemical oxidation to pelargonic and azelaic acids; upon isotope analysis, these two C_9 acids were found to contain the same concentration of deuterium. These data suggested that the isotopic hydrogen had been

[50] R. Schoenheimer, *The Dynamic State of Body Constituents,* Harvard University Press, Cambridge, 1942.

distributed fairly evenly along the oleic acid chain, and that the synthesis of long-chain fatty acids involves the condensation of smaller units.

$$CH_3(CH_2)_7CH{=}CH(CH_2)_7COOH$$

$$\downarrow$$

$$CH_3(CH_2)_7COOH + HOOC(CH_2)_7COOH$$

Pelargonic acid   Azelaic acid

It has long been known that fat may be formed after the administration of carbohydrate or of protein to an animal. Definitive proof of this *in vivo* synthesis came from the studies of Schoenheimer and Rittenberg,[51] of Stetten and Grail,[52] and of Masoro et al.,[53] and subsequent investigators have confirmed and extended their findings. Evidence is also at hand to show that the increase in the fat content of the seeds of higher plants is accompanied by a decrease in the amount of carbohydrate. Various microorganisms have been found to convert carbohydrates to fat, and some of these organisms can accumulate as much as 50 per cent of their dry weight in fat. For example, Kleinzeller[54] showed that, in the presence of glucose, the yeast *Torulopsis lipofera* forms fat at a rate of 4 to 11 per cent of its dry weight in 5 hr.

In the metabolic conversion of the carbon atoms of glucose to fatty acids, acetyl-CoA is known to be an essential intermediate. Among the earlier experiments that led to the recognition of the role of acetyl-CoA, perhaps the most informative were those with microorganisms. Of special importance was the work of Barker, Stadtman, and their associates[55] with *Clostridium kluyverii,* which can form short-chain fatty acids (butyric and caproic acids) from ethanol. These investigators showed that 2 C_2 units condense to form a C_4 compound, which condenses with another C_2 unit to form the C_6 acid. Moreover, they succeeded in preparing a cell-free extract of the organism capable of effecting the series of reactions shown in the accompanying scheme. It will be noted that ethanol is dehydrogenated to acetaldehyde which, in the presence

$$CH_3CH_2OH \rightarrow CH_3CHO \rightarrow [\text{Acetyl-CoA}]$$
$$+$$
$$[C_2 \text{ Compound}]$$
$$CH_3(CH_2)_2COOH \leftarrow [C_4 \text{ Compound}] \leftarrow\!\!\rule{0pt}{1.5em}$$

of coenzyme A and DPN$^+$, is converted to acetyl-coenzyme A. Subse-

[51] R. Schoenheimer and D. Rittenberg, *J. Biol. Chem.,* **114,** 381 (1936).

[52] D. Stetten, Jr., and G. F. Grail, *J. Biol. Chem.,* **148,** 509 (1943).

[53] E. J. Masoro et al., *J. Biol. Chem.,* **179,** 1117 (1949).

[54] A. Kleinzeller, *Biochem. J.,* **38,** 480 (1944).

[55] E. R. Stadtman and H. A. Barker, *J. Biol. Chem.,* **180,** 1085, 1095, 1117, 1169 (1949); **184,** 769 (1950); **191,** 365 (1951).

quent work led to the recognition of acetoacetyl-CoA and butyryl-CoA as intermediates in the formation of butyric acid; the reaction sequence shown in Fig. 3 summarizes the current knowledge of fatty acid synthesis in *Cl. kluyverii.*

It would also appear that the fatty acids synthesized by yeast can be quantitatively derived from acetic acid[56] and that the conversion of carbohydrate to fatty acids in the mold *Neurospora* proceeds via C_2 units.[57]

Evidence for the role of C_2 units in the biosynthesis of the higher fatty acids of animal fats came from the experiments of Rittenberg and Bloch,[58] who fed to mice and rats doubly labeled acetic acid ($CD_3C^{13}OOH$), and showed that both carbon atoms can be utilized for the synthesis of the fatty acids of the body fats. Subsequent work by Bloch[59] and Gurin[60] demonstrated the incorporation of isotopic carbon atoms of labeled acetic acid into fatty acids in the presence of liver slices and extracts. Preparations of other mammalian tissues (mammary gland, intestinal mucosa, lung, heart, spleen, etc.) have been shown to effect similar incorporation. Furthermore, the formation of odd-numbered fatty acids by the addition of C_2 units to propionate-1-C^{14} also has been observed by James et al.[30]

As may be expected from the present knowledge of the fatty acid cycle, the conversion of acetate to long-chain fatty acids requires the participation of ATP and CoA for the aceto-CoA-kinase reaction, and a source of hydrogen atoms for the reduction of β-ketoacyl-CoA and of α,β-unsaturated acyl-CoA compounds (cf. p. 600).[61] Since the generation of ATP and the formation of DPNH (required for the β-hydroxyacyl-CoA dehydrogenase reaction) and of reduced flavin (required for the acyl-CoA dehydrogenase reaction) are endergonic processes, it is clear that the synthesis of fatty acids must be coupled to exergonic processes that occur in the oxidative breakdown of other tissue constituents, especially carbohydrates. The reduction of the flavin involved in the acyl-CoA dehydrogenase reaction appears to be effected (in the liver) by TPNH, which is formed in reactions such as the oxidation of isocitric

[56] A. G. C. White and C. H. Werkman, *Arch. Biochem.,* **13**, 27 (1947).

[57] R. C. Ottke et al., *J. Biol. Chem.,* **189**, 429 (1951).

[58] D. Rittenberg and K. Bloch, *J. Biol. Chem.,* **160**, 417 (1945).

[59] K. Bloch, *Cold Spring Harbor Symposia Quant. Biol.,* **13**, 29 (1948).

[60] R. O. Brady and S. Gurin, *J. Biol. Chem.,* **199**, 421 (1952); J. Van Baalen and S. Gurin, *ibid.,* **205**, 303 (1953).

[61] A. Tietz and G. Popjak, *Biochem. J.,* **60**, 155 (1955); R. G. Langdon, *J. Biol. Chem.,* **226**, 615 (1957); P. Hele et al., *Biochem. J.,* **65**, 348 (1957); J. W. Porter et al., *Biochim. et Biophys. Acta,* **25**, 35, 41 (1957); W. Seubert et al., *Angew. Chem.,* **69**, 359 (1957).

acid (p. 504). In this connection it is of interest that the synthesis of labeled fatty acids from acetate-1-C[14] by liver extracts is stimulated by the addition of citric or isocitric acid, possibly because TPNH is produced in the isocitric acid dehydrogenase reaction.[62]

The coupling of carbohydrate oxidation with fatty acid synthesis is strikingly illustrated by the fact that liver preparations from diabetic animals, although able to oxidize fatty acids to ketone bodies, cannot effect fatty acid synthesis from C_2 compounds.[63] However, when such a liver preparation is supplemented with a carbohydrate that it can oxidize (glycogen, fructose, fructose-1,6-diphosphate, glucose-6-phosphate), its ability to synthesize fatty acids is regained. In this connection it is of interest that liver slices from diabetic animals pretreated with insulin or given fructose also exhibit fatty acid synthesis.[64] In the diabetic animal, the conversion of glucose to glucose-6-phosphate is markedly depressed, but fructose can still enter the sequence of glycolytic reactions (Chapter 38).

The formation of long-chain fatty acids from acetyl-CoA (from whatever source) may be termed "lipogenesis," and represents a *de novo* synthesis. Presumably, the intermediate short-chain fatty acids are not released in appreciable amounts by the multienzyme system involved in the elongation of the fatty acid chain. However, the very long-chain fatty acids (C_{16} to C_{20}) characteristic of animal tissues can also be built up by the addition of a C_2 unit to a preformed fatty acid of shorter chain length. For example, when labeled acetate was given to mice and the fatty acids of the liver lipids were isolated, it was found that the stearic acid arose not only by *de novo* synthesis from 9 equivalents of acetate, but also by the addition of a C_2 unit to a pre-existing C_{16} chain.[65] Furthermore, ingested myristic acid (tetradecanoic acid) has been found to serve as an important precursor of fatty acids containing more than 14 carbon atoms.[66] The available evidence has led to the view that the conversion of the short-chain fatty acids (less than C_{10}) into the longer chains proceeds mainly via an initial oxidation to C_2 units,[67] and the greater the length of an ingested higher fatty acid, the more probable is its elongation and storage in the tissues.

[62] R. O. Brady et al., *J. Biol. Chem.*, **222**, 795 (1956); F. Dituri et al., *ibid.*, **226**, 407 (1957); A. Tietz, *Biochim. et Biophys. Acta*, **25**, 303 (1957).

[63] W. Shaw and S. Gurin, *Arch. Biochem. and Biophys.*, **47**, 220 (1953); W. N. Shaw et al., *J. Biol. Chem.*, **226**, 417 (1957).

[64] S. S. Chernick and I. L. Chaikoff, *J. Biol. Chem.*, **186**, 535 (1950); N. Baker et al., *ibid.*, **194**, 435 (1952).

[65] W. G. Dauben et al., *J. Am. Chem. Soc.*, **75**, 2347 (1953).

[66] H. S. Anker, *J. Biol. Chem.*, **194**, 177 (1952).

[67] R. O. Brady and S. Gurin, *J. Biol. Chem.*, **187**, 589 (1950).

It will be recalled that some of the highly unsaturated fatty acids (p. 560) serve as essential dietary factors for the normal growth and development of animals, since these compounds are not synthesized readily by animal tissues. Linoleic acid (a C_{18} diethenoid acid) and linolenic acid (a C_{18} triethenoid acid) are synthesized *de novo* in higher plants and molds[68] by mechanisms that have not been elucidated. Arachidonic acid (a C_{20} tetraethenoid acid) can arise in animals by the addition of a C_2 unit to a C_{18} compound derived from dietary linoleic acid.[69] The biosynthesis of arachidonic acid by the elongation of the linoleic acid carbon chain also involves the introduction of 2 new double bonds, but it is not known how the dehydrogenation is effected, and whether it occurs before or after the formation of the C_{20} chain. Linolenic acid, which is less effective than linoleic acid in the prevention or cure of fatty acid deficiency,[70] is also converted to a longer highly unsaturated fatty acid.

It will be clear from the foregoing discussion of the oxidation and synthesis of fatty acids in animal tissues that these substances are constantly being renewed; i.e., they are in a dynamic state. However, as shown by long-term experiments[71] (300 to 360 days), at least 60 per cent of the total fatty acids in a rat represents relatively inert material; for one half of this inert fraction to be replaced by new fatty acids requires 70 days or more, i.e., the half-life is about 70 days. From shorter experiments, which measure essentially only the more dynamic fraction of the total tissue constituents, it has been estimated[72] that in adult rats the saturated fatty acids of the depot fat have a half-life of 16 to 17 days. Similarly, the half-life of the unsaturated fatty acids of the depot fat is approximately 20 days. As might be expected, the half-life of the liver fatty acids is much less; experiments in which the deposition of long-chain saturated and unsaturated fatty acids in liver triglycerides and phospholipids was measured after the administration of $CH_3C^{14}OOH$ have shown that the half-life of the fatty acids is probably about a few hours.[73] These figures cannot be taken as an index solely of the relative rate of synthesis and breakdown of fatty acids in the individual tissues concerned; clearly, in the intact animal, fatty acids are transported from one tissue to another. The figures mentioned above do serve, however, to re-emphasize the central role of the liver in the intermediate metabolism of the fatty acids.

[68] K. Bernhard, *Cold Spring Harbor Symposia Quant. Biol.*, **13**, 26 (1948).

[69] J. F. Mead et al., *J. Biol. Chem.*, **205**, 683 (1953); **218**, 401; **219**, 705; **220**, 257 (1956); G. Steinberg et al., *ibid.*, **224**, 841 (1957).

[70] H. J. Deuel, Jr., and R. Reiser, *Vitamins and Hormones*, **13**, 29 (1955).

[71] R. C. Thompson and J. E. Ballou, *J. Biol. Chem.*, **223**, 795 (1956).

[72] A. Pihl et al., *J. Biol. Chem.*, **183**, 441 (1950).

[73] S. B. Tove et al., *J. Biol. Chem.*, **218**, 275 (1956).

Biosynthesis of Phospholipids and Triglycerides [74]

Earlier studies on phospholipid turnover in intact rats indicated that plasma phospholipids are removed from the circulation as a unit and completely resynthesized in the tissues.[75] Although there is no evidence for the interconversion of phosphoglycerides containing choline, ethanolamine, and inositol,[76] data on the incorporation of C^{14}-labeled fatty acids into the phosphatidylcholine fraction of rat liver suggest that there may be a significant difference in the rate of replacement of the fatty acyl groups at the α and β positions.[77] Moreover, studies on the incorporation of labeled precursors into phospholipids by slices of animal tissues (liver, pancreas, brain) have shown that one constituent of a phospholipid may be incorporated independently of the others. For example, it is possible to alter the rate at which labeled fatty acids are incorporated without causing a corresponding change in the turnover rate of the phosphorus, the bases, or glycerol.[78] The available knowledge about the metabolic pathways of phospholipid synthesis in tissues such as liver is insufficient to explain completely such observations relating to the turnover of phospholipids. However, significant progress has been made in defining some of the enzymic reactions that are involved.

Most of the experimental work on phospholipid synthesis *in vitro* has dealt with the formation of choline-containing compounds; it is probable that analogous pathways leading to aminoethanol-containing phosphatides are present. The metabolic origin of the nitrogenous components of phospholipids (choline, aminoethanol, L-serine) will be considered in Chapter 32. The glycerol portion can arise as a consequence of the anaerobic breakdown of carbohydrate (p. 477) or from triglycerides ingested in the diet; free glycerol has been shown to be a precursor of both phospholipids and of triglycerides *in vivo*.[79]

Although it is uncertain whether phosphatidic acids exist as such in animal tissues (p. 567), they can be synthesized from fatty acids, glycerol, and inorganic phosphate (via ATP) by cell-free preparations from liver.[80] The initial step in this process is the formation of L-α-

[74] E. P. Kennedy, *Federation Proc.*, **16**, 847 (1957).

[75] E. O. Weinman et al., *J. Biol. Chem.*, **187**, 643 (1950); M. E. Tolbert and R. Okey, *ibid.*, **194**, 755 (1952).

[76] R. M. C. Dawson, *Biochem. J.*, **61**, 552 (1955).

[77] D. J. Hanahan and R. Blomstrand, *J. Biol. Chem.*, **222**, 677 (1956).

[78] R. J. Rossiter, *Canad. J. Biochem. Physiol.*, **34**, 358 (1956).

[79] A. P. Doerschuk, *J. Biol. Chem.*, **193**, 39 (1951); L. I. Gidez and M. I. Karnovsky, *ibid.*, **206**, 229 (1954).

[80] A. Kornberg and W. E. Pricer, Jr., *J. Biol. Chem.*, **204**, 329, 345 (1953); C. Bublitz and E. P. Kennedy, *ibid.*, **211**, 951 (1954).

glycerophosphate from glycerol and ATP in a reaction catalyzed by "glycerokinase"; a partially purified preparation of this enzyme from rat liver also converts dihydroxyacetone and glyceraldehyde to the corresponding phosphates. The glycerophosphate can then react with 2

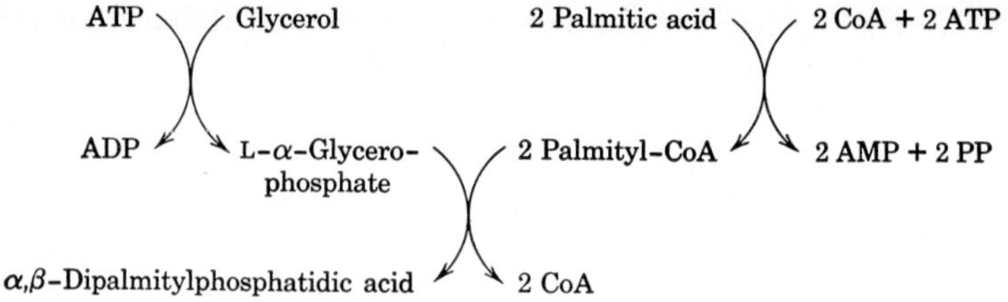

ATP ⟍ ⟋ Glycerol 　　　2 Palmitic acid ⟍ ⟋ 2 CoA + 2 ATP

ADP ⟋ ⟍ L–α–Glycero-　　　2 Palmityl–CoA ⟋ ⟍ 2 AMP + 2 PP
　　　　　phosphate

α,β–Dipalmitylphosphatidic acid ⟋ ⟍ 2 CoA

molecules of a fatty acyl-CoA compound (formed by the action of a thiokinase) to yield an α,β-diacylphosphatidic acid, as shown in the accompanying scheme for the synthesis of dipalmitylphosphatidic acid.

The enzyme-catalyzed reaction of fatty acyl-CoA compounds with the hydroxyl groups of glycerol probably represents an important process in the biosynthesis of neutral fats such as the triglycerides. Thus, Weiss and Kennedy[81] have shown that an enzyme preparation from chicken liver catalyzes the formation of a triglyceride from a D-α,β-diglyceride and palmityl-CoA. It will be recalled that pancreatic lipase can mediate glyceride formation by direct condensation of free fatty acids with glycerol hydroxyl groups (p. 577), so that two enzymic pathways appear to be present in animals for the biosynthesis of triglycerides.[82] The lipase-catalyzed condensation may be more important in the intestinal digestion and absorption of glycerides, and the CoA-linked reaction may be the predominant route in the liver and other internal tissues.

In the scheme shown for the biosynthesis of a phosphatidic acid, inorganic phosphate is introduced by the oxidative generation of ATP (p. 381), and transferred to glycerol. A different mode of entry of phosphate appears to be operative in the biosynthesis of phosphatidylcholine (or phosphatidylaminoethanol). In this metabolic pathway, phosphorylcholine is formed from choline and ATP by "choline phosphokinase"; this enzyme has been found in many animal tissues, and has been purified from yeast.[83] The incorporation of phosphorylcholine into phospholipids by liver preparations is preceded by its reaction with cytidine triphosphate to form cytidine diphosphate choline (CDP-choline) and pyrophosphate.[84] This reaction is analogous to the forma-

[81] S. B. Weiss and E. P. Kennedy, *J. Am. Chem. Soc.,* **78**, 3550 (1956).

[82] L. A. Jedeiken and S. Weinhouse, *Arch. Biochem. and Biophys.,* **50**, 134 (1954); A. Tietz and B. Shapiro, *Biochim. et Biophys. Acta,* **19**, 374 (1956).

[83] J. Wittenberg and A. Kornberg, *J. Biol. Chem.,* **202**, 431 (1953).

[84] E. P. Kennedy et al., *J. Biol. Chem.,* **222**, 193 (1956); **227**, 951 (1957).

tion of UDPG from UTP and glucose-1-phosphate (cf. p. 451). "PC-cytidyl transferases" that catalyze the formation of CDP-choline have been identified in liver, yeast, and higher plants, and the compound has been isolated in crystalline form from yeast.[85] Another enzyme system

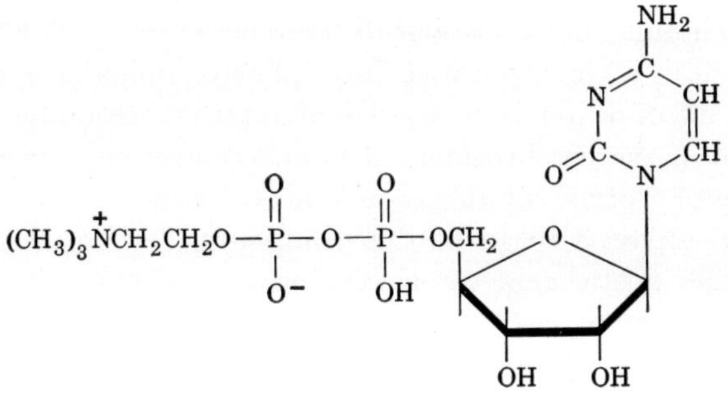

$$(CH_3)_3 \overset{+}{N}CH_2CH_2O-\overset{\overset{O}{\parallel}}{\underset{\underset{O^-}{|}}{P}}-O-\overset{\overset{O}{\parallel}}{\underset{\underset{OH}{|}}{P}}-OCH_2$$

Cytidine diphosphate choline

present in liver catalyzes the reversible pyrophosphorolysis of CDP-choline and concomitant transfer of the phosphorylcholine portion to an α,β-diglyceride to form a phosphatidylcholine and cytidine-5′-phosphate. It is probable that the same sequence of reactions is involved in the incorporation of aminoethanol into phosphatidylaminoethanols, and that enzyme systems specific for aminoethanol derivatives serve as catalysts.

The formation of labeled phospholipids from isotopic phosphoryl-choline by liver mitochondria is stimulated not only by α,β-diglycerides, but also by phosphatidic acids.[86] This effect is a consequence of the

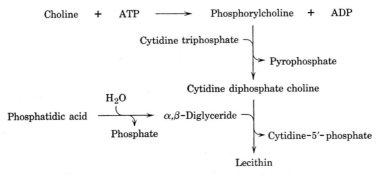

enzymic hydrolysis of the phosphatidic acid to form an α,β-diglyceride, which is utilized, together with CDP-choline, for the net synthesis of a phosphatidylcholine.[87] A proposed pathway of the biosynthesis of phosphatidylcholine (lecithin) is shown in the accompanying diagram.

[85] I. Lieberman et al., *Science*, **124**, 81 (1956).
[86] M. Rodbell and D. J. Hanahan, *J. Biol. Chem.*, **214**, 607 (1955).
[87] S. W. Smith et al., *J. Biol. Chem.*, **228**, 915 (1957).

Although the enzyme studies described above provide a pathway whereby phosphorylcholine may be incorporated into lecithin, it should be added that data obtained from isotope studies suggest that phosphorylcholine may not be the sole precursor of the phosphate of liver lecithin.[88]

Little is known about the biosynthesis of phospholipids other than phosphatidylcholine or phosphatidylaminoethanol. The mechanisms whereby inositol is incorporated into phospholipids are obscure, and fragmentary information is available about the metabolic pathways in the formation of the cerebrosides. In this connection, however, mention may be made of isotope studies on the biosynthesis of the base sphingosine. Carbon atoms 3 to 18 of this compound (cf. formula) appear to be derived from acetic acid by a condensation of C_2 units leading to a C_{16} fatty acid derivative.[89] Carbon atoms 1 and 2 (the aminoethanol portion of sphingosine) do not arise directly from acetic acid or from

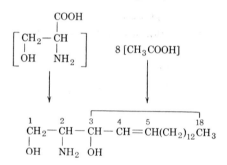

preformed aminoethanol; they are derived from the β and α carbons of serine, which also provides the amino group.[90] The carboxyl group of serine is lost during the utilization of the amino acid for the synthesis of sphingosine. It is probable that the conversion of sphingosine to sphingomyelin involves the interaction of an N-acylsphingosine (a "ceramide") with CDP-choline in a manner that is analogous to the mode of lecithin formation from an α,β-diglyceride and CDP-choline.[91]

[88] R. M. C. Dawson, *Biochem. J.*, **59**, 5 (1955); **62**, 693 (1955).

[89] I. Zabin and J. F. Mead, *J. Biol. Chem.*, **205**, 271 (1953); **211**, 87 (1954).

[90] D. B. Sprinson and A. Coulon, *J. Biol. Chem.*, **207**, 585 (1954); R. O. Brady et al., *J. Biol. Chem.*, **233**, 26, 1072 (1958).

[91] M. Sribney and E. P. Kennedy, *J. Biol. Chem.*, **233**, 1315 (1958).

26 ·

Chemistry
and Metabolism
of Steroids

Chemistry of Sterols

The group of lipids discussed in Chapter 23 are usually classed together as saponifiable lipids, i.e., substances that are soluble in organic solvents and are converted to water-soluble substances upon hydrolysis with alkali. However, the extraction of a plant or animal tissue with organic solvents may yield an appreciable quantity of lipid material that is resistant to saponification. Such unsaponifiable lipids may include one or more of a variety of organic substances belonging to a group of crystalline alcohols known as sterols (Greek, *stereos*, solid). In the tissues of vertebrates, the principal sterol is the C_{27} alcohol cholesterol (Greek *chole*, bile) which is especially abundant in nerve tissues and in gall stones. The classical work of Wieland, Windaus, Diels, Rosenheim, and King led to the formulation of the structure of cholesterol; the fundamental carbon skeleton is the cyclopentanoperhydrophenanthrene ring. In accordance with the suggestion of Callow and Young,[1] compounds chemically related to cholesterol are designated steroids. The extensive literature dealing with steroids is summarized in the important monograph of Fieser and Fieser.[2]

It will be noted from the formula shown on p. 620 that cholesterol has a double bond in the 5,6 position. In animal tissues, cholesterol is accompanied by small amounts (ca. 2 per cent) of the dihydro derivative cholestanol, sometimes termed "dihydrocholesterol." Clearly, hydrogenation of the 5,6 double bond can lead to the formation of 2 isomers, which differ in their configuration about carbon 5 at the juncture of rings A and B. In cholestanol the two rings are so joined that the hydrogen

[1] R. K. Callow and F. G. Young, *Proc. Roy. Soc.*, **157A**, 194 (1936).
[2] L. F. Fieser and M. Fieser, *The Natural Products Related to Phenanthrene*, 3rd Ed., Reinhold Publishing Corp., New York, 1949.

atom on carbon 5 and the methyl group on carbon 10 are *trans* to each other; to indicate this, the bond linking the CH_3 to carbon 10 is drawn as a solid line and that linking the H to carbon 5 as a dotted line. By convention, substituents connected by solid lines (β-orientation) are

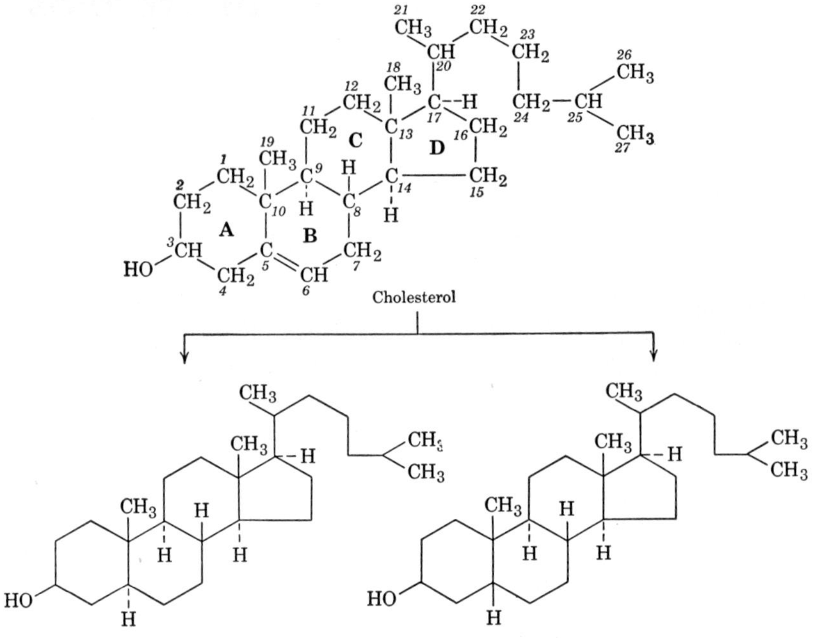

Cholesterol

Cholestanol
(A/B *trans*, or *allo*)

Coprostanol
(A/B *cis*, or *normal*)

regarded as projecting in front of the plane of the steroid ring system, and those connected by dotted lines (α-orientation) as lying behind the plane. The dihydrocholesterol isomeric with cholestanol, but differing from it with respect to the configuration about carbon 5, is a constituent of animal feces, and is named coprostanol (earlier name, coprosterol). In the accompanying formulae for the isomeric dihydrocholesterols a simplified formulation of the steroids is used.

In cholestanol, the spatial relationship of the rings to one another may be described as follows: A:B, *trans;* B:C, *trans;* C:D, *trans.* On the other hand, in coprostanol, rings A and B are *cis*, while B:C and C:D are *trans.* The configuration characteristic of the hydrocarbon skeleton of cholestanol is termed the *allo* configuration, to distinguish it from the "normal" configuration of the coprostanol series. Occasionally, the configuration of steroids of the *allo* series is designated by the term 5α (i.e., the linkage between the H and carbon 5 has the α-orientation), and for compounds of the *normal* series the term 5β is used. For a discussion of the configuration of steroids, see Shoppee.[3]

Examination of the formulae of the three sterols will show the possibility of isomerism with respect to the configuration about carbon 3, which bears the hydroxyl group. Since the orientation of the hydroxyl group in these naturally occurring sterols is *cis* with respect to the methyl group at carbon 10, the bond at carbon 3 is drawn as a solid line (β-orientation). In the carbon 3 epimer of cholestanol (epicholestanol) the hydroxyl group has the α-orientation (i.e., the formula is drawn with a dotted line between OH and carbon 3). In natural sterols, the hydrogen at carbon 8, the methyl group at carbon 13, and the side chain at carbon 17 have the same orientation as the methyl group at carbon 10 (β-orientation), while the hydrogen atoms at carbons 9, 14, and 17 have the opposite orientation (α-orientation). Since the hydrocarbon portion of the cholestanols is named cholestane, cholestanol may be termed cholestan-3β-ol or 3β-hydroxycholestane (epicholestanol is cholestan-3α-ol). In partially unsaturated sterols (e.g., cholesterol), the presence of a double bond is indicated by the usual systematic suffix "ene"; the position of nuclear unsaturation may be designated either by the symbol Δ with a superscript denoting the lower-numbered carbon atom involved in the double bond, or by placing the carbon number immediately before the function term "ene." Since cholesterol is a derivative of $Δ^5$-cholestene (or cholest-5-ene), its systematic name is $Δ^5$-cholesten-3β-ol (or cholest-5-en-3β-ol). The hydrocarbon portion of coprostanol is named coprostane (or 5β-cholestane); coprostanol is therefore coprostan-3β-ol (or 5β-cholestan-3β-ol). The terms cholestane and coprostane may be used to designate the appropriate steroids related to the parent compounds.

An important method for the separation of the 3β-hydroxysteroids from the epi forms involves their selective precipitation by digitonin, a glycoside in which the aglycone is the steroid sapogenin digitogenin (p. 636). The relative insolubility of digitonides of the 3-hydroxysteroids not only depends on the orientation of the 3-hydroxy group, but is influenced by the configuration of rings A and B and by the presence of substituents on ring D.[4] Digitonin is extremely useful for the separation of free cholesterol from natural sources, since it will not precipitate cholesterol esters (e.g., cholesteryl palmitate) such as those found in blood plasma. Human blood plasma has a total cholesterol content of approximately 200 mg per 100 cc; of this amount, roughly one fourth is present as free cholesterol.

Almost all the cholesterol (free and esterified) of human plasma is

[3] C. W. Shoppee, *Ann. Reps.,* **43,** 200 (1947); *Vitamins and Hormones,* **8,** 255 (1950).

[4] R. M. Haslam and W. Klyne, *Biochem. J.,* **55,** 340 (1953).

associated with lipoproteins; this is also true of the plasma phospho-lipids (p. 573).[5] Over 50 per cent of the total plasma cholesterol is found in the β_1-lipoprotein fraction, and the remainder of the cholesterol is associated with the α_1- and α_2-lipoprotein fractions.[6] A correlation has been reported between the relative concentrations of human plasma lipoproteins and the incidence of arteriosclerosis, but the status of this problem is uncertain at present.[7]

A number of color reactions are available for the identification of cholesterol. In the Liebermann-Burchard reaction, a green color is produced when a chloroform solution of acetic anhydride is added to a solution of cholesterol in concentrated sulfuric acid; no reaction is given by cholestanol or coprostanol. For a discussion of this and other color reactions given by the sterols see Schoenheimer et al.[8] and Bergmann.[9] Steroids may be separated by chromatography on filter paper or on columns of adsorbents such as alumina.[10]

Other Natural Sterols. In higher plants, the principal sterols are compounds having 29 carbon atoms. Representatives of these are stigma-

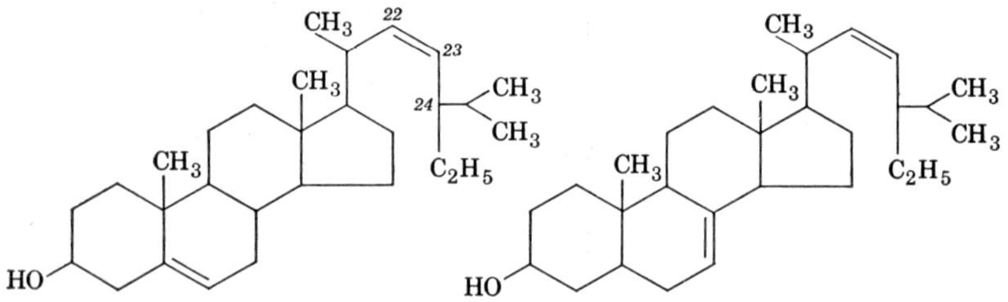

Stigmasterol α–Spinasterol

sterol (from soybean oil), Δ^7-stigmasterol (from wheat germ oil), several spinasterols (from spinach and cabbage), and the sitosterols (from many plants). β-Sitosterol is 22,23-dihydrostigmasterol, and γ-sitosterol is the 24-epimer of β-sitosterol.

An important sterol found in yeast, ergot, and the mold *Neurospora* is the C_{28} compound ergosterol, which contains 3 double bonds. Another important, though minor, constituent of the sterol fraction of yeast lipids is the C_{27} compound zymosterol ($\Delta^{8,24}$-cholestadien-3β-ol). In-terest in ergosterol derives from the discovery that, upon irradiation with ultraviolet light, it gives rise to vitamin D_2 (calciferol). It may be added

[5] R. J. Havel et al., *J. Clin. Invest.*, **34**, 1345 (1955).

[6] H. G. Kunkel and R. Trautman, *J. Clin. Invest.*, **35**, 641 (1956).

[7] J. W. Gofman et al., *Physiol. Revs.*, **34**, 589 (1954).

[8] R. Schoenheimer et al., *J. Biol. Chem.*, **110**, 659 (1935).

[9] W. Bergmann, *Progress in the Chemistry of Fats and Oils*, **1**, 18 (1952).

[10] I. E. Bush, *Brit. Med. Bull.*, **10**, 229 (1954).

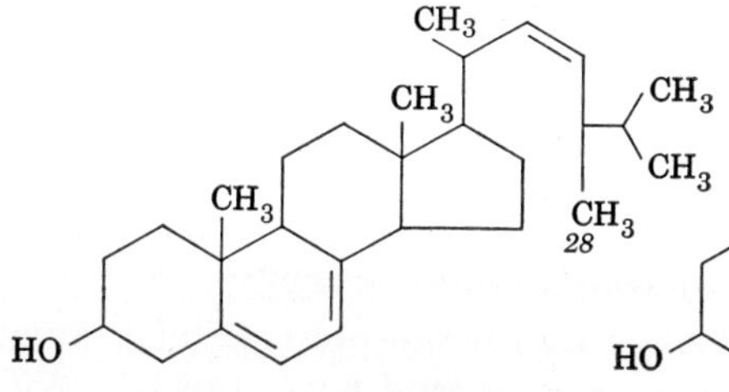

Ergosterol

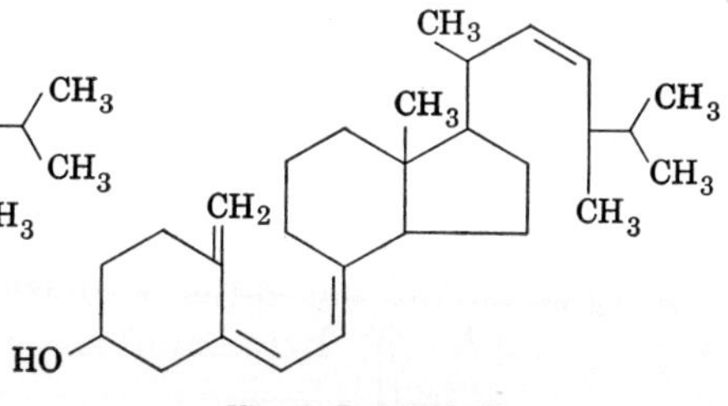

Vitamin D₂ (calciferol)

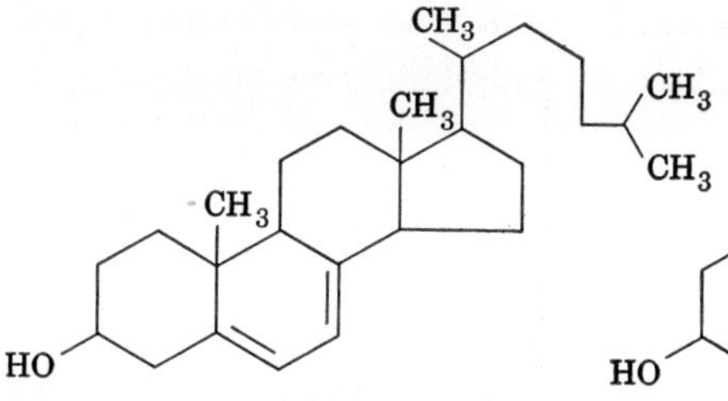

7–Dehydrocholesterol

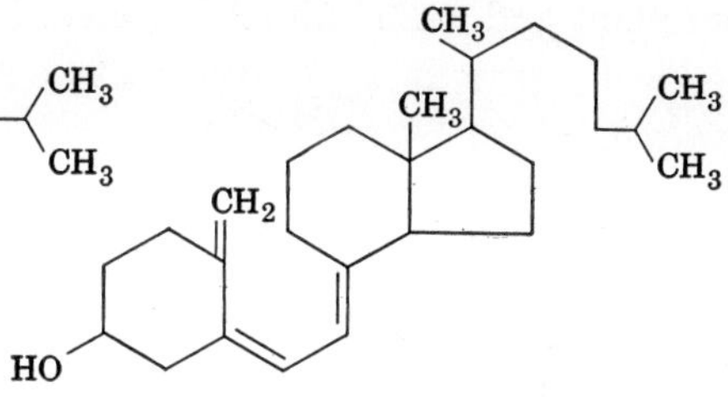

Vitamin D₃

that some animal tissues contain, in addition to cholesterol and cholestanol, small amounts of 7-dehydrocholesterol which, on irradiation with ultraviolet light, is converted to another member of the vitamin D group (vitamin D_3); vitamin D_3 is present in fish liver oils. The names ergocalciferol and cholecalciferol have been assigned to vitamins D_2 and D_3, respectively. The role of this group of vitamins in metabolism will be discussed in Chapter 39.

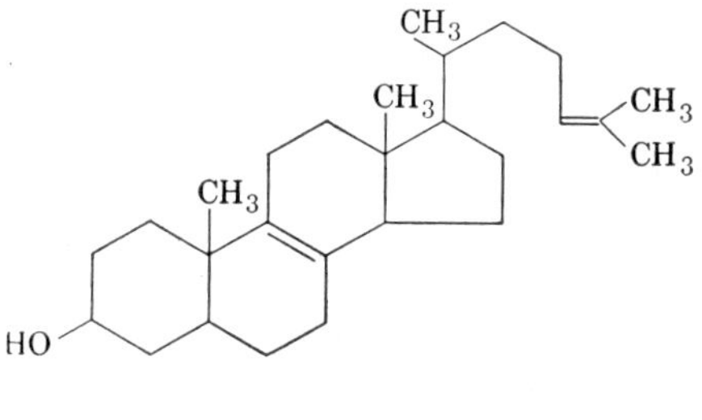

Zymosterol

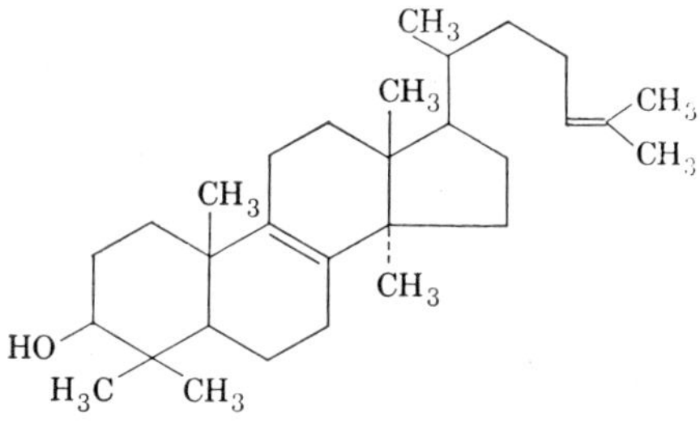

Lanosterol

7-Dehydrocholesterol ($\Delta^{5,7}$-cholestadien-3β-ol) contains 2 double bonds, one of which is also present in cholesterol (Δ^5-cholestenol). In addition to these two sterols, animal tissues and excreta contain an isomer of cholesterol, Δ^7-cholestenol (lathosterol), which represents about 30 per cent of the total steroids of rat skin.[11]

[11] D. R. Idler and C. A. Baumann, *J. Biol. Chem.*, **195**, 623 (1952); W. W. Wells and C. A. Baumann, *Arch. Biochem. and Biophys.*, **53**, 471 (1954).

An important animal sterol, shown by Ruzicka to be the major constituent of the sterols of wool fat, is the C_{30} compound lanosterol
(lanastadienol, cryptosterol); it is 4,4',14α-trimethyl-$\Delta^{8,24}$-cholestadien-
3β-ol, and hence is related to zymosterol (p. 623). Lanosterol is present
in very small amounts in liver and yeast, and has been shown to be an
intermediate in the biosynthesis of cholesterol[12] (p. 628).

The studies by W. Bergmann[9] have shown the presence of a number
of other sterols in the tissues of invertebrates, and have drawn attention
to the fact that no sharp line of demarcation separates the sterols obtained
from plant and from animal sources. For example, γ-sitosterol is present

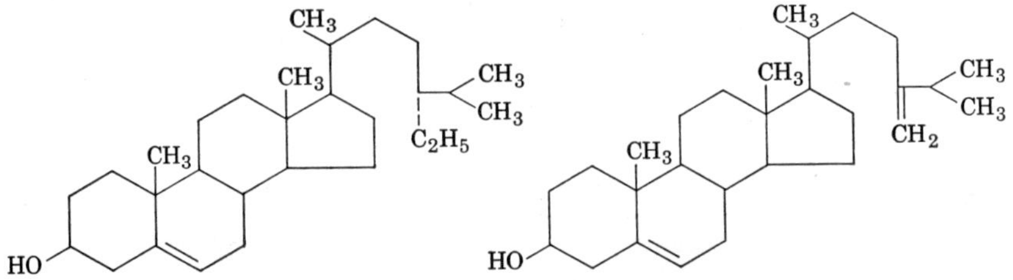

γ-Sitosterol   Ostreasterol

not only in higher plants but also in several invertebrates; it is probably
identical with the "clionasterol" first isolated from sponges. Brassicasterol (7,8-dihydroergosterol) is found in higher plants and in bivalves,
and the compound ostreasterol (or chalinasterol) is the principal sterol in
oysters and clams. Chondrillasterol, the 24-epimer of the plant sterol
α-spinasterol (p. 622), has been isolated from fresh water algae and from
marine sponges. It may be added that cholesterol is also found in many
invertebrates, including protozoa and sponges.

Metabolism of Cholesterol [13]

Despite the wide variety of sterols that occur in nature, and that may
be ingested by higher animals, only a very few are absorbed by the
intestinal mucosa and transferred to the circulation. Cholesterol is
absorbed readily, but cholestanol and coprostanol are not; ergosterol and
closely related sterols also are absorbed, but apparently this is not true
of any other plant sterol tested. Cholesterol absorption proceeds via the
lymph, and about 50 per cent of the absorbed cholesterol is esterified;
the major portion of the cholesterol in plasma is in the form of fatty
acid esters. The substrate specificity of the intestinal esterases (cf. p.

[12] R. B. Clayton and K. Bloch, *J. Biol. Chem.*, **218**, 305 (1956).
[13] D. K. Fukushima and R. S. Rosenfeld, in D. M. Greenberg, *Chemical Pathways of Metabolism*, Vol. I, Chapter 8, Academic Press, New York, 1954.

576) may play an important role in determining the ability of an animal to absorb hydroxylated steroids.[14] Intestinal mucosa also contains a "sterol dehydrogenase" that catalyzes the conversion of cholesterol to 7-dehydrocholesterol.[15]

Although the total plasma cholesterol is higher in human subjects than in other animals (e.g., rat), cholesterol is absorbed relatively poorly in man, and much of it is excreted in the feces. Some of the fecal cholesterol is derived from material secreted into the intestinal tract in the bile. The

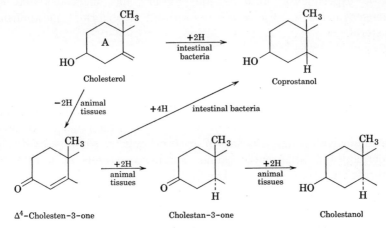

Fig. 1. Postulated pathways of coprostanol and cholestanol formation.

other major steroid of animal feces is coprostanol, which arises from the action of intestinal bacteria on cholesterol. Schoenheimer et al.[16] demonstrated the intestinal conversion of dietary deuterium-labeled cholesterol and Δ^4-cholesten-3-one to fecal coprostanol, and suggested that intestinal bacteria form coprostanol from cholesterol via Δ^4-cholestenone (Fig. 1). Fecal microorganisms that convert cholesterol and Δ^4-cholestenone to coprostanol have been identified; however, the ketone is not an obligatory intermediate, and cholesterol probably is directly reduced in a stereospecific manner to coprostanol.[17] Other fecal sterols (in addition to unabsorbed dietary sterols) include 7-dehydrocholesterol and Δ^7-cholestenol (probably derived from the intestinal mucosa) and cholestanol. It is probable that cholestanol is formed in the tissues by the stereospecific reduction of absorbed Δ^4-cholestenone; this ketone is

[14] H. H. Hernandez et al., *J. Biol. Chem.*, **206**, 757 (1954).

[15] G. N. Festenstein and R. A. Morton, *Biochem. J.*, **60**, 22 (1955).

[16] R. Schoenheimer et al., *J. Biol. Chem.*, **111**, 183 (1935); M. Anchel and R. Schoenheimer, *ibid.*, **125**, 23 (1938).

[17] R. S. Rosenfeld et al., *J. Biol. Chem.*, **211**, 301 (1954); **222**, 321 (1956); A. Snog-Kjaer et al., *J. Gen. Microbiol.*, **14**, 256 (1956).

not converted to cholesterol.[18]　The conversion of Δ^4-cholestenone to cholestanol has been observed in rat liver homogenates; such preparations also convert Δ^4-cholestenone to cholestanone, and reduce the latter to cholestanol. The saturated ketone may therefore be an intermediate in the formation of cholestanol, as shown in Fig. 1.

Other important products of the metabolic conversion of cholesterol are the bile acids (p. 633) and the steroid hormones (p. 637). Several substances arising from the chemical oxidation of cholesterol are carcinogenic in experimental animals, and Fieser[19] has suggested that such carcinogens can also arise *in vivo* as a result of abnormal metabolism of cholesterol.

Biosynthesis of Cholesterol

Although dietary cholesterol is readily absorbed by higher animals, it is not an essential component of their diet. On the other hand, several lower biological forms (larvae of certain insects, some parasites and microorganisms) apparently cannot synthesize sterols at a rate commensurate with their needs.[20]　The fact that most animals can make their sterols from smaller carbon compounds has long been known, and the use of isotopic methods has provided important information about the metabolic pathways in sterol synthesis.

Of special significance have been the studies of Bloch and his associates.[21]　Their earlier experiments[22] had shown that acetic acid is an effective precursor of cholesterol in the rat. Accordingly, each of two types of doubly labeled acetic acid ($C^{13}H_3C^{14}OOH$ and $C^{14}H_3C^{13}OOH$) was incubated with liver slices, and cholesterol was isolated and subjected to systematic chemical degradation to determine the nature and concentration of the isotope in the carbon atoms of the sterol.[23]　The results showed clearly that all the carbon atoms of cholesterol were labeled and that both carbons of acetic acid are used for cholesterol synthesis; of the 27 carbon atoms of the sterol, 15 are derived from the methyl carbon of acetic acid and 12 are derived from the carboxyl carbon. The data

[18] H. S. Anker and K. Bloch, *J. Biol. Chem.,* **178**, 971 (1949); W. M. Stokes et al., *ibid.,* **213**, 325 (1955); F. M. Harold et al., *ibid.,* **221**, 435 (1956).

[19] L. F. Fieser, *Science,* **119**, 710 (1954); L. F. Fieser et al., *J. Am. Chem Soc.,* **77**, 3928 (1955).

[20] P. H. Silverman and Z. H. Levinson, *Biochem. J.,* **58**, 291 (1954); R. L. Conner and W. J. van Wagtendonk, *J. Gen. Microbiol.,* **12**, 31 (1955).

[21] K. Bloch, *Harvey Lectures,* **48**, 68 (1954).

[22] K. Bloch and D. Rittenberg, *J. Biol. Chem.,* **155**, 243 (1944).

[23] H. N. Little and K. Bloch, *J. Biol. Chem.,* **183**, 33 (1950); J. Wuersch et al., *ibid.,* **195**, 439 (1952).

obtained by Bloch,[24] together with those of Cornforth et al.,[25] have given the metabolic origin of all the **27** carbon atoms of cholesterol from the carbon atoms of acetate (Fig. 2). It may be added that the incorporation of labeled acetate into cholesterol is not limited to rat liver slices, but is also effected by homogenates and cell-free extracts of this tissue.[26]

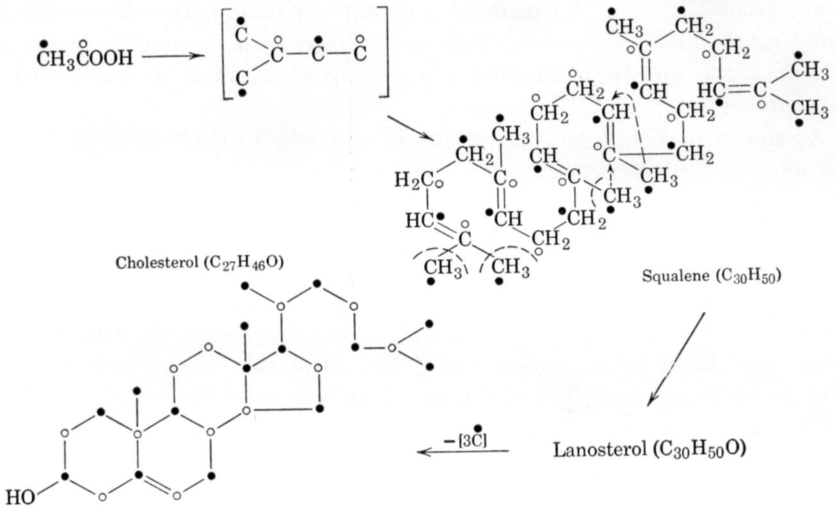

Fig. 2. Utilization of carbon atoms of acetic acid in the biosynthesis of squalene and cholesterol.

Of the compounds tested by Bloch and Rittenberg[22] as precursors of cholesterol, acetate was the most effective; however, later work[27] showed that the isopropyl group of isovaleric acid is an even better precursor of cholesterol in the rat. It was also found that liver slices can synthesize cholesterol from acetoacetic acid, without apparent degradation of the β-keto acid to C_2 units.[28] These facts, and the pattern of labeling in the experiments with labeled acetate, led to the suggestion that a 5-carbon isoprenoid compound (p. 653) may be an intermediate in the biosynthesis of cholesterol. They also drew attention to the suggestion made in 1934 by Robinson that the isoprenoid compound squalene could provide the carbon skeleton of the cholesterol molecule. The experi-

[24] R. B. Woodward and K. Bloch, *J. Am. Chem. Soc.*, **75**, 2023 (1955).

[25] J. W. Cornforth et al., *Biochem. J.*, **54**, 597 (1953); **65**, 94 (1957).

[26] I. D. Frantz, Jr. and N. L. R. Bucher, *J. Biol. Chem.*, **206**, 471 (1954); N. L. R. Bucher and K. McGarrahan, *ibid.*, **222**, 1 (1956).

[27] I. Zabin and K. Bloch, *J. Biol. Chem.*, **185**, 131 (1950); **192**, 267 (1951).

[28] G. L. Curran, *J. Biol. Chem.*, **191**, 775 (1951); R. O. Brady et al., *ibid.*, **193**, 137 (1951).

mental demonstration of the metabolic conversion of acetate to squalene, and of squalene to cholesterol, soon followed;[29] the role of squalene as an intermediate in the biosynthesis of cholesterol became more probable when it was shown[30] that the C^{14}-labeling of biosynthetic squalene is in complete accord with that of biosynthetic cholesterol (Fig. 2).

The best known source of squalene is the unsaponifiable fraction of shark liver oil; it occurs in small amounts in mammalian liver and in some plant oils. Human scalp skin is relatively rich in squalene, and C^{14}-squalene has been isolated from scalp skin slices incubated with labeled acetate.[31]

As shown in Fig. 2, the conversion of squalene to cholesterol probably involves an initial cyclization and oxidation to yield lanosterol (p. 623); in this process, the squalene molecule is "folded" in a specific manner before ring formation occurs, and two methyl groups of squalene are shifted to provide the methyl groups at the 13 and 14 positions of lanosterol (indicated by the dotted line arrows in Fig. 2). The role of lanosterol as a precursor of cholesterol was suggested by Ruzicka in 1953, and later work demonstrated the formation of lanosterol from acetate in intact rats,[32] the conversion of squalene to lanosterol by a soluble multienzyme system from rat liver,[33] and the transformation of lanosterol to cholesterol by rat liver preparations.[34] The over-all reaction whereby squalene is converted to cholesterol requires the participation of O_2,[26] and involves the removal (by oxidation to CO_2) of 3 methyl groups (indicated by curved dash lines in Fig. 2). These methyl groups represent the 4, 4', and 14 substituents in lanosterol; the 14-methyl group appears to be the first to be removed, with the formation of a 4,4'-dimethylcholestadienol.[35] The loss of these 3 methyl groups may be expected to give zymosterol (p. 623), which serves as a precursor of cholesterol in rat liver homogenates and in the intact rat.[36] For the formation of cholesterol from either lanosterol or zymosterol, the double bond in the side chain (between carbon atoms 24 and 25) must be reduced, and the Δ^8-ene function must be changed to a Δ^5-ene function. The mechanisms in these changes are unknown, but it is of interest that a sterol believed to be $\Delta^{5,24}$-cholestadien-3β-ol has been found in animal

[29] R. G. Langdon and K. Bloch, *J. Biol. Chem.*, **200**, 129, 135 (1953).

[30] J. W. Cornforth and G. Popjak, *Biochem. J.*, **58**, 403 (1954).

[31] N. Nicolaides et al., *J. Am. Chem. Soc.*, **77**, 1535 (1955).

[32] P. B. Schneider et al., *J. Biol. Chem.*, **224**, 175 (1957).

[33] T. T. Tchen and K. Bloch, *J. Biol. Chem.*, **226**, 921, 931 (1957).

[34] R. B. Clayton and K. Bloch, *J. Biol. Chem.*, **218**, 319 (1956).

[35] F. Gautschi and K. Bloch, *J. Am. Chem. Soc.*, **79**, 684 (1957); J. A. Olson, Jr., et al., *J. Biol. Chem.*, **226**, 941 (1957).

[36] J. D. Johnston and K. Bloch, *J. Am. Chem. Soc.*, **79**, 1145 (1957); E. Schwenk et al., *Arch. Biochem. and Biophys.*, **55**, 274 (1955); **66**, 381 (1957).

tissues, and appears to be a biological precursor of cholesterol.[37] Thus, zymosterol (the $\Delta^{8,24}$-diene) may be converted to the $\Delta^{5,24}$-diene (desmosterol) prior to the reduction of the side chain.

The utilization of acetate for sterol synthesis is not limited to higher animals; yeast and the mold *Neurospora* use acetate as a precursor of ergosterol.[38] Experiments with a strain of *Neurospora* grown in the presence of $C^{14}H_3C^{13}OOH$ indicate that over 90 per cent of the carbon of the sterol can be derived from acetate. However, as shown by studies with yeast, carbon 28 of ergosterol (p. 623) is derived from "C_1 units" rather than from acetate.[39] As in the rat, squalene and zymosterol may be intermediates in ergosterol synthesis by intact yeast cells.[40] In larvae of the beetle *Dermestes vulpinus*, which require an exogenous source of cholesterol (or 7-dehydrocholesterol), the conversion of squalene to lanosterol appears to be blocked; in this insect, acetate-1-C^{14} is converted to labeled squalene, but not to lanosterol or to cholesterol.[41]

Although the formation of squalene from acetate is well established, the metabolic pathway of this conversion is not completely known. From the isotopic labeling of squalene derived from isotopic acetate (cf. Fig. 2), it may be concluded that squalene is derived from 6 identical isoprenoid units. Until recently, the isoprenoid compound found to be most active as a biological precursor of cholesterol was the C_5 acid dimethylacrylic acid (also termed β-methylcrotonic acid or senecioic acid). However, as shown by isotope experiments, the C_6 compound mevalonic acid (β,δ-dihydroxy-β-methylvaleric acid) is a much better precursor of

$$\underset{\text{Mevalonic acid}}{HOOC\overset{\bullet}{C}H_2-\underset{\underset{OH}{|}}{\overset{\overset{CH_3}{|}}{C}}-CH_2\overset{*}{C}H_2OH} \xrightarrow{\overset{\overset{O}{\parallel}}{CO_2}} \underset{\text{Squalene}}{\left[\overset{\overset{CH_3}{|}}{CH_3\overset{\bullet}{C}}=CH\overset{*}{C}H_2CH_2\overset{\overset{CH_3}{|}}{C}=CH\overset{*}{C}H_2CH_2\overset{\overset{CH_3}{|}}{C}=CH\overset{*}{C}H_2- \right]_2}$$

cholesterol than is dimethylacrylic acid.[42] The δ-lactone of mevalonic acid has been isolated from natural sources in the course of efforts to identify an acetate-replacing growth factor for some *Lactobacilli*. Mevalonic acid also is used readily for the synthesis of squalene by yeast or

[37] W. M. Stokes et al., *J. Biol. Chem.*, **220**, 415 (1956); **232**, 347 (1958).

[38] R. Sonderhoff and H. Thomas, *Ann. Chem.*, **530**, 195 (1937); R. C. Ottke et al., *J. Biol. Chem.*, **186**, 581 (1950); **189**, 429 (1951).

[39] H. Danielson and K. Bloch, *J. Am. Chem. Soc.*, **79**, 500 (1957); G. J. Alexander and E. Schwenk, *J. Biol. Chem.*, **232**, 599, 611 (1958).

[40] L. M. Corwin et al., *J. Am. Chem. Soc.*, **78**, 1372 (1956); W. G. Dauben and T. W. Hutton, *ibid.*, **78**, 2647 (1956).

[41] K. Bloch et al., *Biochim. et Biophys. Acta*, **21**, 176 (1956).

[42] P. A. Tavormina et al., *J. Am. Chem. Soc.*, **78**, 4498, 6210 (1956).

liver preparations.[43] This conversion appears to involve the condensation of units of mevalonic acid (or a derivative), with the loss of the carboxyl carbon as CO_2; experiments with labeled mevalonic acid (containing C^{14} and tritium) have excluded dimethylacrylic acid as an intermediate between mevalonic acid and squalene (see scheme on p. 629).

Because of the supposed role of dimethylacrylic acid as a precursor of cholesterol, considerable attention was devoted to the biosynthesis of this C_5 compound by rat liver preparations (Fig. 3). In addition, studies on the formation, in higher plants, of the polyisoprenoid rubber (p. 664) have contributed important information about the biosynthesis of dimethylacrylic acid and of related branched-chain compounds.

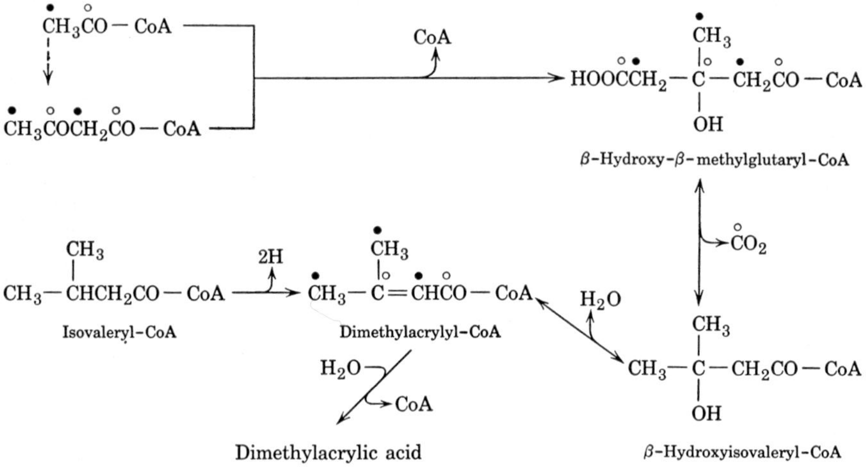

Fig. 3. Postulated pathways for the biosynthesis of dimethylacrylic acid in higher animals.

The formulation of the reactions shown in Fig. 3 is based largely on studies with C^{14}-labeled compounds. Such studies have shown that dimethylacrylic acid, β-hydroxyisovaleric acid, and isovaleric acid are formed from acetate by homogenates or by particle-free extracts of rat liver.[44] Of special importance is the fact that acetate-2-C^{14} gives rise to dimethylacrylic acid that is labeled in accord with the labeling found in the isoprenoid units of squalene and of cholesterol formed from acetate-2-C^{14} (cf. Figs. 2 and 3).

As shown in Fig. 3, the initial branched-chain compound formed from acetyl-CoA and acetoacetyl-CoA is a mono-CoA derivative of β-hydroxy-

[43] B. H. Amdur et al., *J. Am. Chem. Soc.*, **79**, 2646 (1957); F. Dituri et al., *ibid.*, **79**, 2650 (1957); J. W. Cornforth et al., *Biochem. J.*, **69**, 146 (1958).

[44] J. L. Rabinowitz and S. Gurin, *J. Biol. Chem.*, **208**, 307 (1954); J. L. Rabinowitz et al., *Federation Proc.*, **14**, 760 (1955); H. Rudney and T. G. Farkas, *ibid.*, **14**, 757 (1955); H. Rudney, *J. Biol. Chem.*, **227**, 363 (1957).

β-methylglutaric acid. (This acid does not appear to serve as a precursor in cholesterol synthesis, presumably because it is not converted readily to the acyl-CoA derivative.) Decarboxylation of the acyl-CoA compound is believed to yield β-hydroxyisovaleryl-CoA; the reversal of this reaction, i.e., the fixation of CO_2 by β-hydroxyisovaleryl-CoA to form β-hydroxy-β-methylglutaryl-CoA, is effected by liver preparations (p. 788).

The dehydration of β-hydroxyisovaleryl-CoA to dimethylacrylyl-CoA is catalyzed by crystalline crotonase (p. 598). Dimethylacrylyl-CoA can also arise by the dehydrogenation of isovaleryl-CoA;[45] this reaction, which is analogous to the dehydrogenation of fatty acyl-CoA compounds in the β-oxidation of straight-chain fatty acids (p. 597), is also effected by an enzyme system present in liver extracts. The enzymic conversion of isovaleryl-CoA to dimethylacrylyl-CoA explains the observation that isovaleric acid is an effective precursor of cholesterol. It is of interest that isovaleric acid is present in relatively large amounts in the skin excretions of dogs and of other animals.[46] This C_5 acid may arise not only from acetate, as described above, but also by the degradation of L-leucine (Chapter 32).

The conversion of C^{14}-labeled β-hydroxyisovaleric acid and dimethylacrylic acid to squalene and cholesterol has been demonstrated in rats and with rat liver preparations,[47] and the isotope distribution in the labeled cholesterol is consistent with the view that the acids were converted to cholesterol without prior degradation to acetate. The chemical events in the conversion of dimethylacrylic acid and mevalonic acid to squalene have not been elucidated. It may be surmised that dimethylacrylic acid is converted (via its acyl-CoA derivative) to β-hydroxy-β-methylglutaryl-CoA (Fig. 3), from which mevalonic acid could arise by reduction. The possibility exists that the biosynthesis of squalene involves the intermediate formation of a C_{15} unit, and that 2 such units combine to form squalene (note that squalene is composed of 2 identical $C_{15}H_{25}$ units; p. 627). A known C_{15} compound that might be a precursor of squalene is the isoprenoid farnesenic acid, which can be prepared by the chemical oxidation of the widely distributed plant alcohol farnesol (p. 663). It is uncertain at present whether rat liver extracts can convert farnesenic acid to squalene.

$$\underset{\text{Farnesenic acid}}{CH_3\overset{\overset{\textstyle CH_3}{|}}{C}=CHCH_2CH_2\overset{\overset{\textstyle CH_3}{|}}{C}=CHCH_2CH_2\overset{\overset{\textstyle CH_3}{|}}{C}=CHCOOH}$$

[45] B. K. Bachhawat et al., *J. Biol. Chem.*, **219**, 539 (1956).

[46] E. Brouwer and N. J. Nijkamp, *Biochem. J.*, **55**, 444 (1953).

[47] K. Bloch et al., *J. Biol. Chem.*, **211**, 687 (1954); F. Dituri et al., *ibid.*, **221**, 181 (1956).

Although the liver is of major importance in cholesterol synthesis, other animal tissues are also capable of performing this process.[31, 48] As judged by isotope data, the half-life of cholesterol in the liver of the intact rat is about 6 days; in the extrahepatic tissues the half-life is about 32 days.

The Bile Acids [49]

The bile acids are quantitatively the most important end products of cholesterol metabolism in higher animals. It will be noted from the formulae of the bile acids shown that the ring structure is identical to

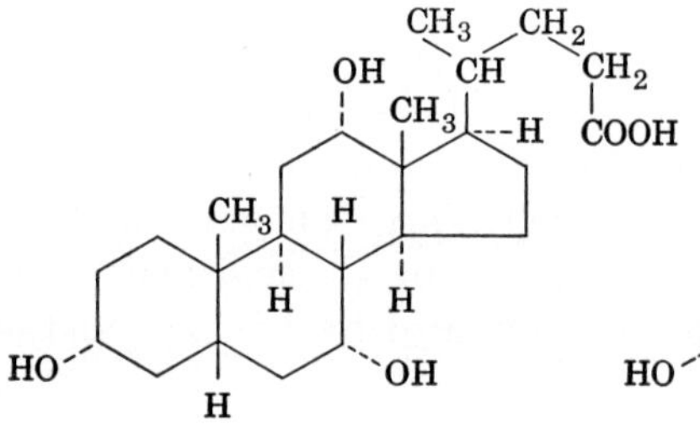

Cholic acid

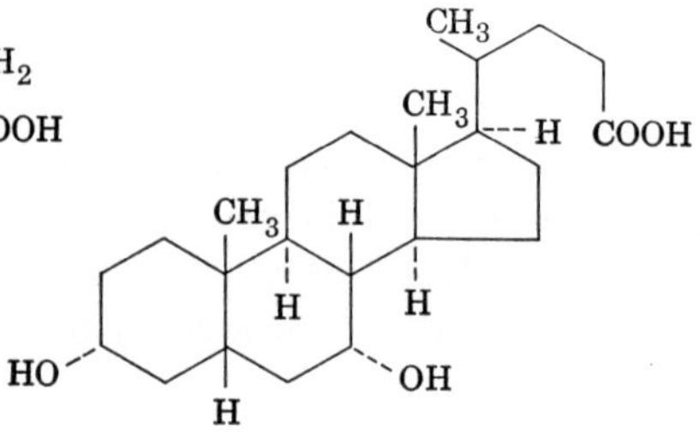

Chenodeoxycholic acid

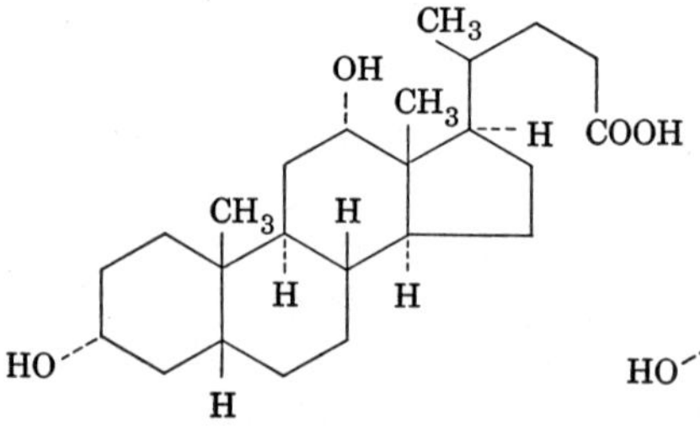

Deoxycholic acid

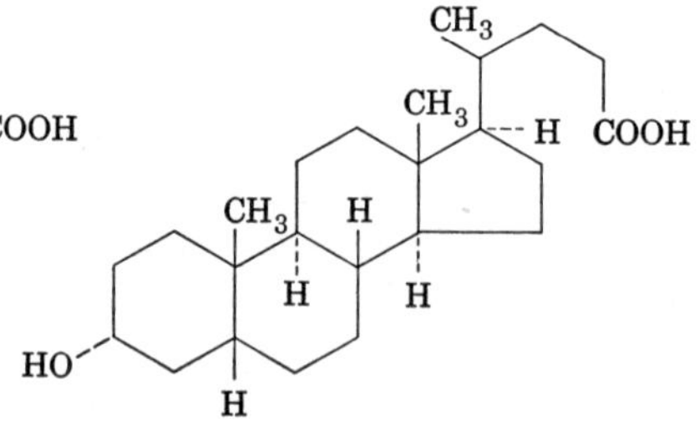

Lithocholic acid

that of coprostanol (rings A and B are *cis*); the parent steroid is the C_{24} compound termed cholanic acid. All of the hydroxyl groups have an α-orientation, and these bile acids do not form precipitates with digitonin (p. 621). In human bile, the principal bile acids are cholic acid ($3\alpha,7\alpha,12\alpha$-trihydroxycholanic acid), chenodeoxycholic acid ($3\alpha,7\alpha$-dihydroxycholanic acid), and deoxycholic acid ($3\alpha,12\alpha$-dihydroxycholanic acid); lithocholic acid (3α-hydroxycholanic acid) occurs only in traces. Other bile acids also have been found in the bile of vertebrates. For example, pig bile contains bile acids with a 6-hydroxyl group, such as

---

[48] P. A. Srere et al., *J. Biol. Chem.*, **182**, 629 (1950).
[49] G. A. D. Haslewood, *Physiol. Revs.*, **35**, 178 (1955).

hyocholic acid ($3\alpha,6\alpha,7\alpha$-trihydroxycholanic acid), and python bile contains pythocholic acid (probably $3\alpha,12\alpha,16\alpha$-trihydroxycholanic acid).[50]

The bile acids occur in bile as "conjugates" of the amino acids glycine and taurine, to which they are bound by an amide linkage as shown.

Side chain of glycocholic acid   Side chain of taurocholic acid

Thus, cholic acid is linked to a glycine residue in glycocholic acid, and to a taurine residue in taurocholic acid. These conjugates are present as anions ($-COO^-$ and $-SO_3^-$) at physiological pH values, and their water-soluble salts (bile salts) are effective in emulsifying fats and other water-insoluble substances. Because of this high surface activity, the bile salts promote the intestinal absorption of lipids such as cholesterol. Bile acids conjugated with taurine are found in the bile of all higher animals examined, but glycine conjugates appear to be limited to some mammals (e.g., rabbit, guinea pig, man). Although bile secreted into the intestinal tract contains little, if any, free bile acids, they are found in the feces; it is probable that the amide bond of the conjugates is cleaved by microorganisms present in the large intestine.

Metabolism of Bile Acids.[51] The metabolic conversion of isotopic cholesterol to labeled cholic acid has been demonstrated in several mammals (rat, rabbit, man). The liver is the principal site of this conversion, and the bile acids (as conjugates) are secreted into the intestine via the bile ducts and gall bladder. Since the bile acids are not oxidized to CO_2 in animal tissues, they represent true end products of cholesterol metabolism. However, only a small fraction of the bile acid conjugates that enter the intestinal tract is directly excreted in the feces; they are largely reabsorbed and returned to the liver via the portal circulation.

In studies on the metabolic pathways in the biosynthesis of bile acids, isotopic precursors have been injected into animals with a bile fistula, and the bile was collected and analyzed before it entered the intestinal tract. For the separation of the component bile acids, chromatographic and countercurrent distribution techniques have been of decisive value. Such studies have led to the formulation of the metabolic pathways shown in Fig. 4.

[50] G. A. D. Haslewood and V. Wootton, *Biochem. J.*, **47**, 584 (1950); G. A. D. Haslewood, *ibid.*, **62**, 637 (1956).

[51] M. D. Siperstein and I. L. Chaikoff, *Federation Proc.*, **14**, 767 (1955); S. Bergström and B. Borgström, *Ann. Rev. Biochem.*, **25**, 177 (1956).

Comparison of the formulae of cholesterol (cf. p. 620) with those of the bile acids shows that the metabolic conversion involves the reduction of ring B, the introduction of α-oriented hydroxyl groups, and the transformation of the 8-carbon side chain to a 5-carbon chain. The formation of the 5-carbon side chain of the bile acids involves the oxidative removal of carbons 25, 26, and 27 of cholesterol.[52] It appears that the hydroxyla-

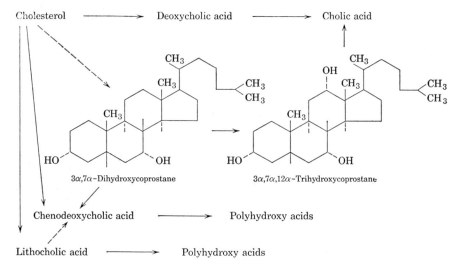

Fig. 4. Postulated pathways of bile acid formation in the intact rat. Transformations that have been demonstrated experimentally are indicated by solid line arrows; postulated transformations are denoted by dash line arrows.

tion of the ring system is largely completed before the formation of the 5-carbon side chain; thus 7α-hydroxycholesterol can be a precursor of cholic acid in the rat, and both 3α,7α-dihydroxycoprostane and 3α,7α,12α-trihydroxycoprostane are readily converted to cholic acid. The dihydroxycoprostane also serves as a precursor of chenodeoxycholic acid, which, in the rat, is not a precursor of cholic acid but is converted to bile acids with hydroxyl groups at the 3, 6, and 7 positions.[53] On the other hand, deoxycholic acid is readily transformed to cholic acid, and is an intermediate in the conversion of cholesterol to cholic acid.[54] The hydroxylation of deoxycholic acid has been effected with rat liver extracts, and the substrate is the taurine conjugate (taurodeoxycholic acid), which is converted to taurocholic acid.

[52] I. Zabin and W. F. Barker, *J. Biol. Chem.*, **205**, 633 (1953); W. S. Lynn, Jr. et al., *Federation Proc.*, **14**, 783 (1955).

[53] S. Bergström et al., *Acta Chem. Scand.*, **8**, 1109 (1954); *Biochim. et Biophys. Acta*, **19**, 556 (1956); T. A. Mahowald et al., *J. Biol. Chem.*, **225**, 781, 811 (1957); S. Lindstedt, *Acta Chem. Scand.*, **11**, 417 (1957).

[54] S. Bergström and U. Gloor, *Acta Chem. Scand.*, **8**, 1373 (1954); **9**, 1545 (1955).

The conversion of a hydroxylated C_{27} sterol to a bile acid presumably proceeds by initial oxidation of one of the 2 methyl groups at carbon 25 to a carboxyl group, yielding a hydroxylated coprostanic acid. $3\alpha,7\alpha,12\alpha$-trihydroxycoprostanic acid has been isolated from alligator bile; on injection into rats, it is degraded to cholic acid.[55]

Lithocholic acid is also formed from cholesterol in the intact rat, and its conversion to chenodeoxycholic acid has been postulated. Lithocholic acid is metabolized further to hitherto unidentified acids.

It should be emphasized that the reactions indicated in Fig. 4 are based on experiments with rats, especially since it has been shown[56] that deoxycholic acid is not converted to cholic acid in the rabbit.

Although only the conversion of deoxycholic acid to cholic acid by rat liver has been shown to involve the conjugates, prior conjugation with glycine or taurine may also be necessary for the hydroxylation of lithocholic acid and of chenodeoxycholic acid. The formation of the bile acid conjugates is catalyzed by enzymes present in liver;[57] in this process, the bile acid is "activated" by enzymic conversion to an acyl-CoA compound (e.g., cholyl-CoA) in a manner analogous to the activation of fatty acids (p. 595).[58] The reaction of cholyl-CoA with glycine

$$\text{Cholic acid} \xrightarrow[\text{ATP, Mg}^{2+}]{\text{CoA}} \text{Cholyl-CoA} \begin{cases} \xrightarrow{\text{taurine}} \text{Taurocholic acid} \\ \xrightarrow{\text{glycine}} \text{Glycocholic acid} \end{cases}$$

or taurine is catalyzed by a "transferase" distinct from the "activating enzyme." It was mentioned before that the type of conjugate found in bile may differ in various animal species. It is significant, therefore, that enzyme preparations from rabbit liver have been found to form only glycocholic acid, whereas those from chicken liver form only taurocholic acid. With preparations from rat and human liver, both types of conjugates are formed from cholic acid; presumably, the reaction of cholyl-CoA with glycine and with taurine is catalyzed by different "transferases."

Steroid Glycosides

Among the naturally occurring derivatives of the steroids are a large number of glycosides found widely distributed in the plant kingdom. Mention may be made first of the "neutral saponins" which, in solution,

[55] R. J. Bridgwater and S. Lindstedt, *Acta Chem. Scand.*, **11**, 409 (1957).

[56] P. H. Ekdahl and J. Sjövall, *Acta Physiol. Scand.*, **34**, 287, 329 (1955).

[57] J. Bremer, *Acta Chem. Scand.*, **10**, 56 (1956); *Biochem. J.*, **63**, 507 (1956); W. H. Elliott, *ibid.*, **62**, 427, 433 (1956); M. D. Siperstein and A. W. Murray, *Science*, **123**, 377 (1956).

[58] W. H. Elliott, *Biochem. J.*, **65**, 315 (1957).

are extremely effective as surface-active agents (detergents). Associated with this property is their ability to hemolyze erythrocytes. Hydrolysis of the steroid saponins produces aglycones (sapogenins), the best studied

Tigogenin

Digitoxigenin

Strophanthidin

Periplogenin

Sarmentogenin

Gamabufotalin

$$NH{=}C(NH_2)\text{—}NH(CH_2)_3CH(COOH)NH\text{—}CO(CH_2)_6COOH$$

Suberylarginine

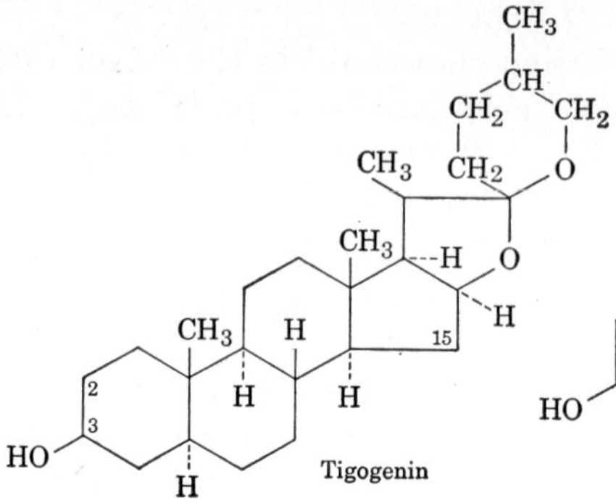

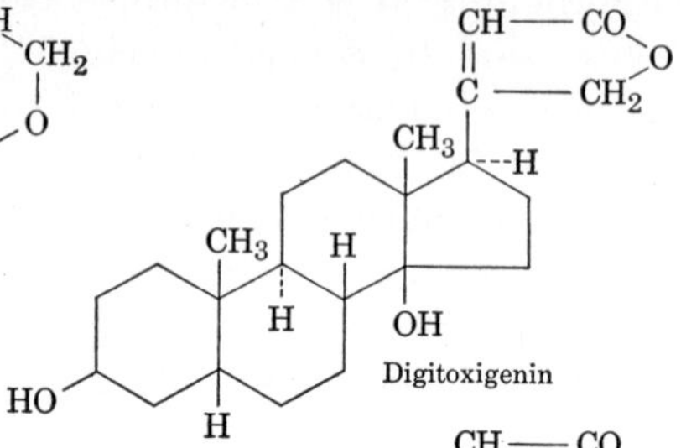

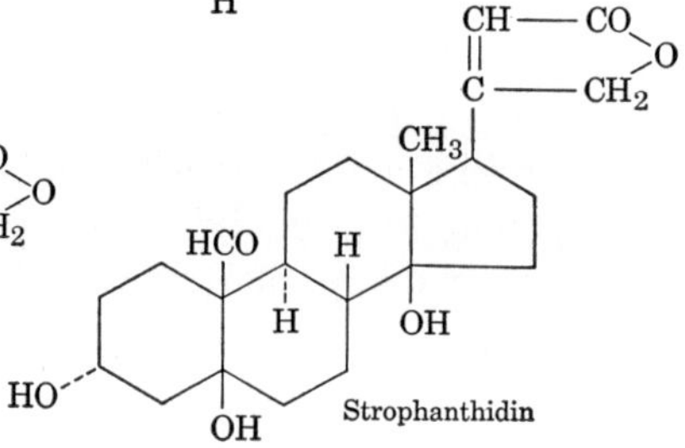

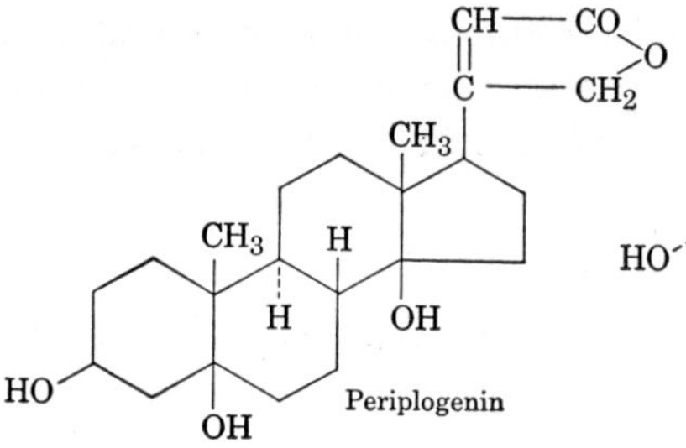

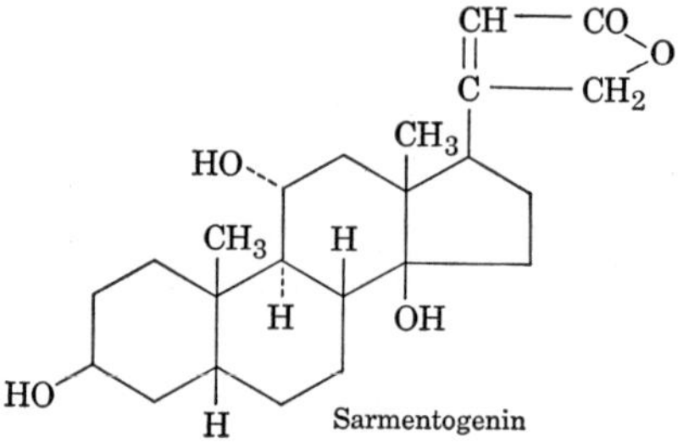

of which are the following (obtained from the saponins of *Digitalis purpurea*): digitogenin (from digitonin), gitogenin (from gitonin), and tigogenin (from tigonin). The formula of tigogenin is shown; gitogenin is the corresponding $2\alpha,3\beta$-diol, and digitogenin is the $2\alpha,3\beta,15\beta$-triol.[59]

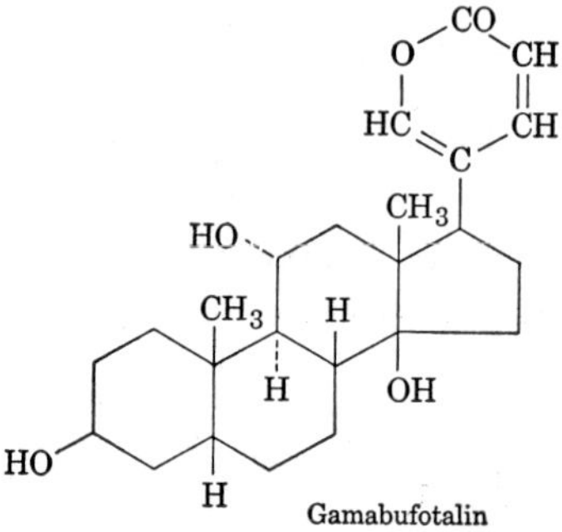

[59] C. Djerassi et al., *J. Am. Chem. Soc.*, **78**, 3166 (1956).

Another large group of steroid glycosides, usually found associated with the saponins, are the compounds that exhibit a characteristic stimulatory action on the activity of mammalian heart. Overdosage with these cardiac glycosides leads to the stoppage of heart action, and some of these substances have been used by aborigines as arrow poisons. A few of the more thoroughly investigated cardiac aglycones are: digitoxigenin (from *Digitalis purpurea*), periplogenin (from *Periploca graeca*), and strophanthidin (from *Strophanthus kombe*).[60] The cardiac aglycone sarmentogenin (from *Strophanthus sarmentosus*) is of special interest because of the presence of an 11-hydroxyl group, as in some adrenal steroids (p. 639).

The venom secreted by the parotid glands of various toads contains steroids that are structurally related to the aglycones of the cardiac glycosides from plants. Among these toad steroids is gamabufotalin, whose formula is shown; all the known members of this group have a 6-membered unsaturated lactone group. In the venom, these steroids are not linked to sugars, but rather to suberylarginine by an ester linkage involving one of the hydroxyl groups of the steroid nucleus and the free carboxyl group of suberic acid.

It will be noted that cardiac aglycones mentioned above contain a pentenolactone group at carbon 17 of the steroid nucleus. This group has also been found in the vesicant (blister-inducing) agent protoanemonin, which occurs naturally in the buttercup and in related plants.[61] Protoanemonin is readily converted to the dimeric product, anemonin.

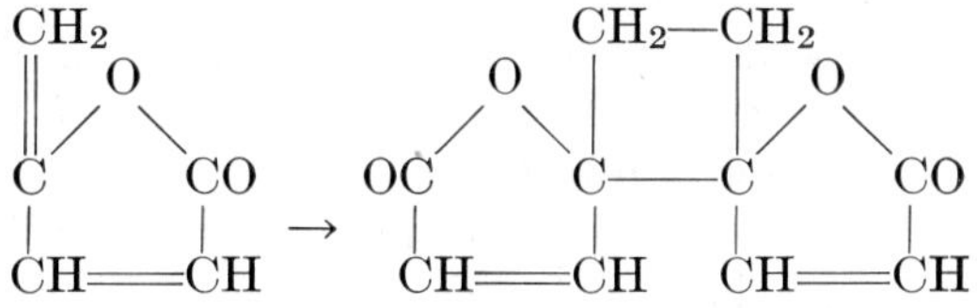

Protoanemonin → Anemonin

The Steroid Hormones

Like the bile acids, a number of steroid hormones of animal origin may be described as products of cholesterol metabolism. In this chapter, the chemical structure of these hormones and their metabolic synthesis and degradation are considered; their physiological effects will be discussed in Chapter 38 in relation to the hormonal control of metabolism.

The steroid hormones are usually classified into several groups (adrenocortical hormones, estrogens, androgens) on the basis of their physiological

[60] R. C. Elderfield, *Chem. Revs.*, **17**, 187 (1935); A. Stoll, *The Cardiac Glycosides*, Pharmaceutical Press, London, 1937; T. Reichstein, *Angew. Chem.*, **63**, 412 (1951).
[61] R. Hill and R. van Heyningen, *Biochem. J.*, **49**, 332 (1951).

effects, but these depend on their chemical structure. Thus the adreno-cortical hormones (elaborated by the cortex of the adrenal gland) are all derivatives of the C_{21} hydrocarbons pregnane and allopregnane (Table 1). Largely as a result of the work of Reichstein and his associates[62] and of Kendall, Wintersteiner, and Simpson, twenty-four different

Table I. Parent Hydrocarbons of the Steroid Hormones

Total Number of Carbon Atoms	Hydrocarbon-5β-series	R	R'	Hydrocarbon-5α-series
21	5β-Pregnane (pregnane)	CH_3	C_2H_5	5α-Pregnane (allopregnane)
19	5β-Androstane (etio-cholane)	CH_3	H	5α-Androstane (androstane)
18	Estrane	H	H	

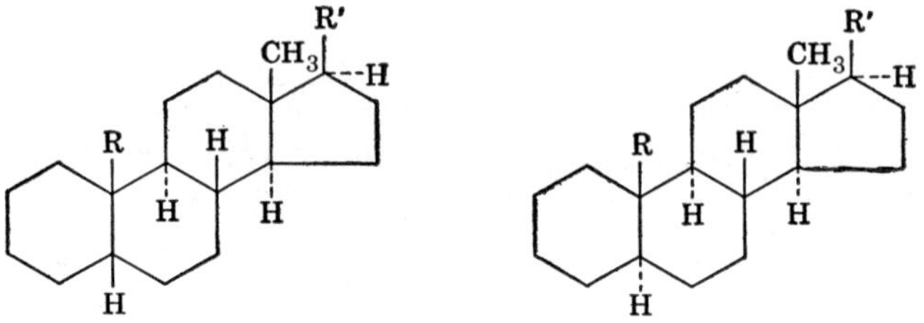

5β-Series (rings A/B *cis*)   5α-Series (rings A/B *trans*)

steroids of this type have been isolated from extracts of the adrenal cortex. Of these, seven compounds are of special interest, since their administration can cause many of the physiological effects produced by the unfractionated tissue extract (Chapter 38). The formulae of these "corticosteroids" are shown on p. 639.

Corticosterone and cortisol are the major corticosteroids secreted by the adrenal gland into the circulation; the others (deoxycorticosterone, 17-hydroxydeoxycorticosterone, 11-dehydrocorticosterone, cortisone, aldosterone) are secreted in much smaller amounts. It will be noted from the formulae that all these corticosteroids have at carbon 17 a ketol side chain ($—CO—CH_2OH$); this is a strongly reducing group, as in the keto sugars (cf. p. 409).

Another pregnane derivative in the adrenal gland is progesterone (p. 640), which lacks the ketol group, and differs from the adrenal cortical hormones in its physiological effects. The function of progesterone is to promote the proliferation of uterine mucosa and thus to prepare this tissue to receive the fertilized ovum. This "progestational" hormone is elaborated in relatively large amounts by the corpus luteum of the

[62] T. Reichstein and C. W. Shoppee, *Vitamins and Hormones,* **1,** 345 (1943); S. A. Simpson et al., *Experientia,* **10,** 132 (1954).

ovary; its presence in adrenal tissue is a consequence of its role as an intermediate in the biosynthesis of the typical adrenocortical hormones

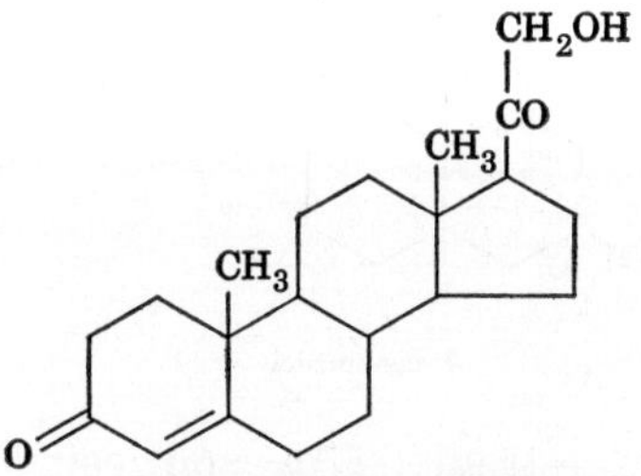

Deoxycorticosterone (DOC)

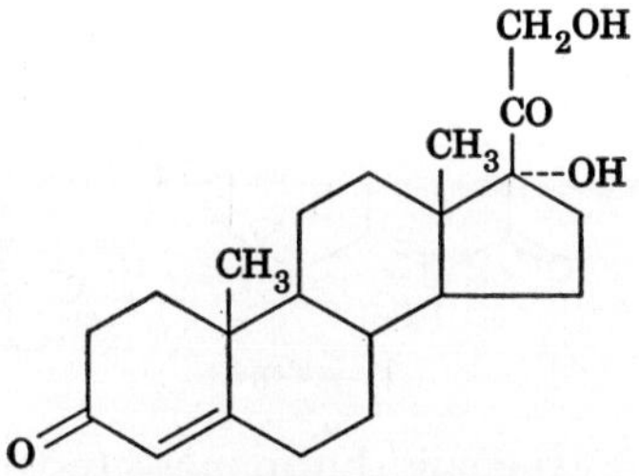

17-Hydroxydeoxycorticosterone
(Deoxycortisol, Reichstein's compound S)

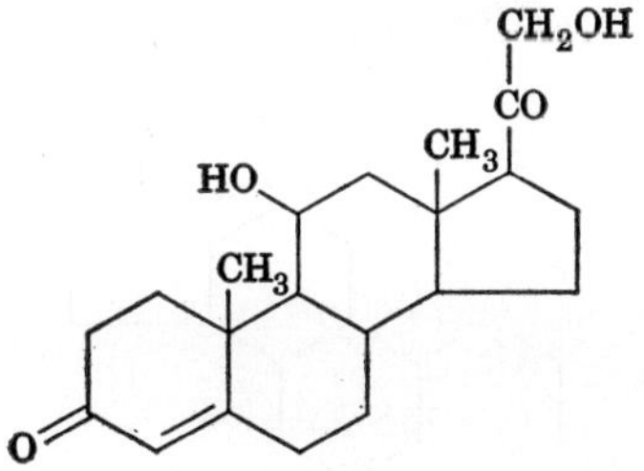

Corticosterone

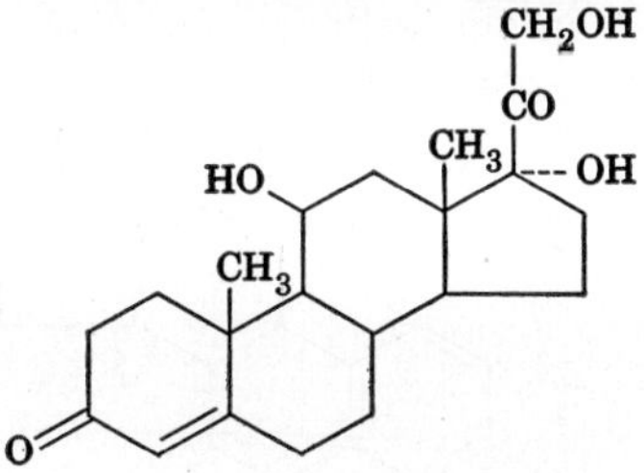

17-Hydroxycorticosterone
(Cortisol, hydrocortisone, Kendall's compound F)

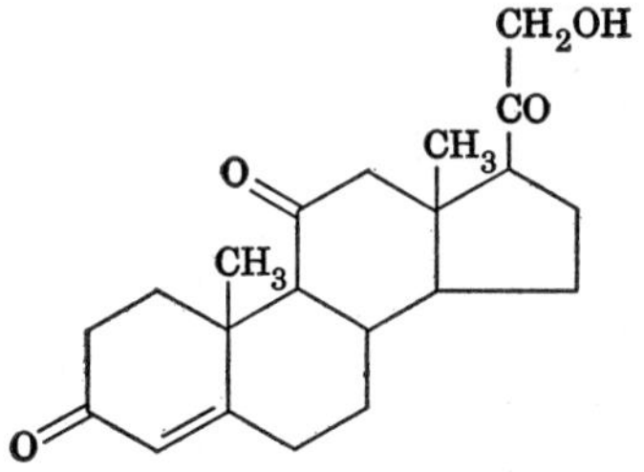

11-Dehydrocorticosterone

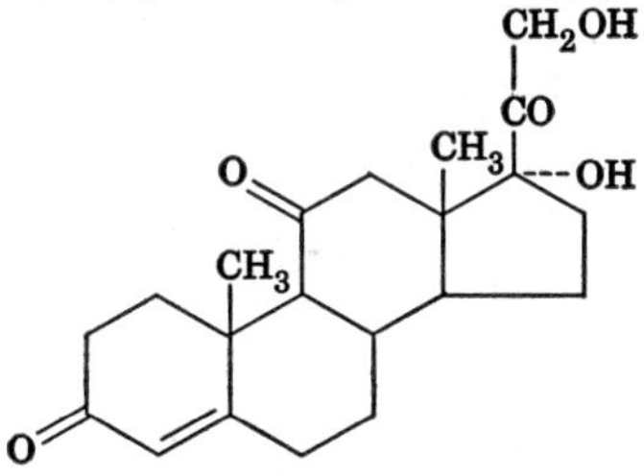

17-Hydroxy-11-dehydrocorticosterone
(Cortisone, Kendall's compound E)

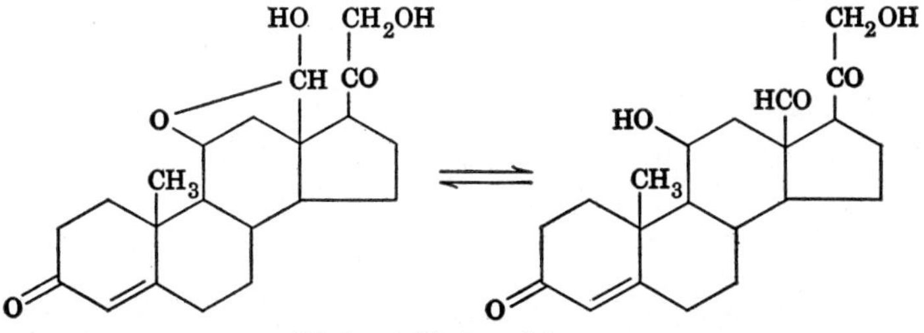

Aldosterone (Electrocortin)

(p. 643). A closely related steroid, pregnanediol, is present in human and rabbit urine, and is a major product of progesterone metabolism in these species (p. 648).

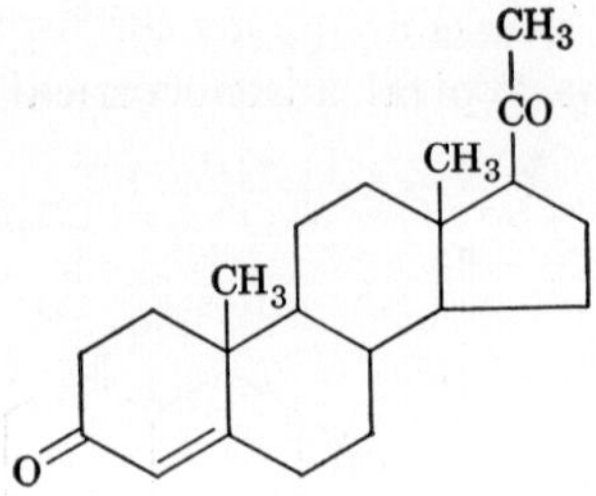

Progesterone 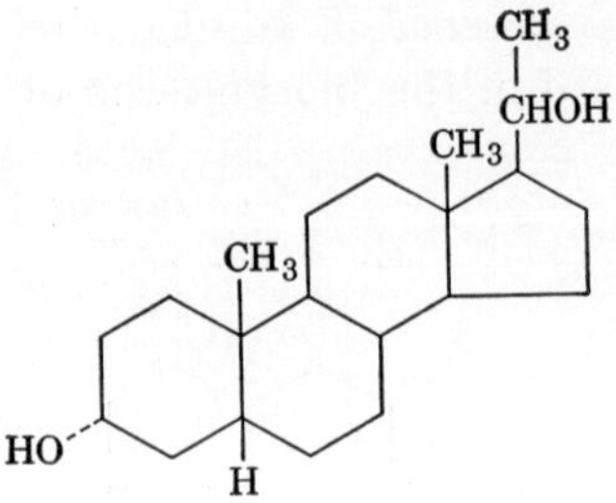   Pregnanediol

The estrogenic hormones (estrone, estradiol-17β, and estriol) are derivatives of the C_{18} hydrocarbon estrane (cf. Table 1). Estrone is produced in the follicle of the ovary, and its name is derived from its

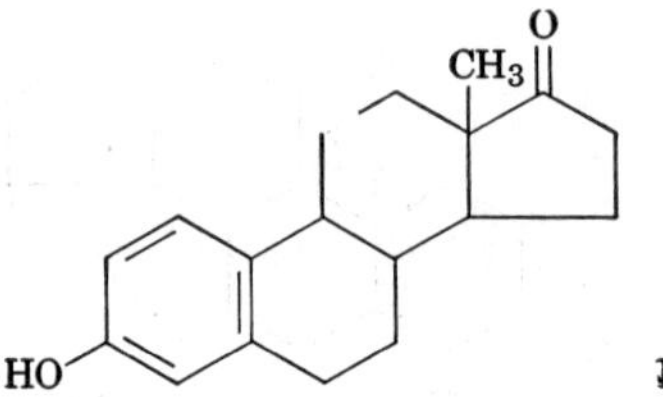

Estrone 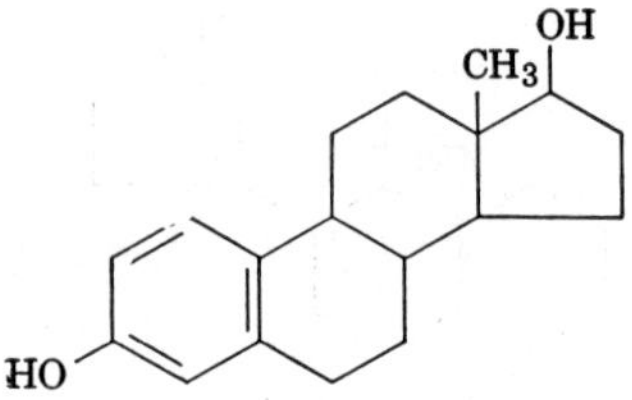   Estradiol-17β

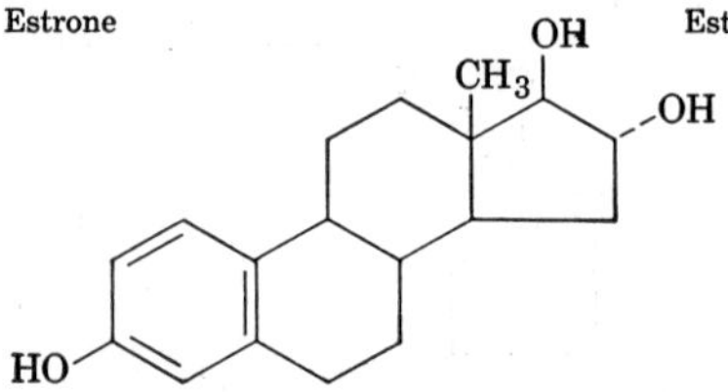

Estriol

ability to induce estrus (sexual heat) in immature female rats. It was first isolated in 1929 (Doisy, Butenandt[63]) from the urine of pregnant women, and has also been obtained from adrenal extracts, as well as from ovaries, mare urine, the urine of stallions, and palm kernel extracts. Human pregnancy urine also contains estriol, and mare urine and ovaries also contain estradiol. These estrogens (or follicular hormones) are concerned with the development of the secondary sex characters (mammary glands, female form). Estradiol is the most potent physiologically, and estriol is the least active.

Comparison of the structure of the estrogens mentioned above with that of the other steroids discussed in this chapter shows the estrogens to be characterized by the absence of a methyl group at carbon 10 and by the aromatic nature of ring A. Mare urine contains two other steroids,

[63] A. Butenandt, *Chemistry and Industry*, **55**, 990 (1936).

equilin and equilenin, in which ring B is either partially or totally converted to the aromatic form. These two compounds are only weakly estrogenic.

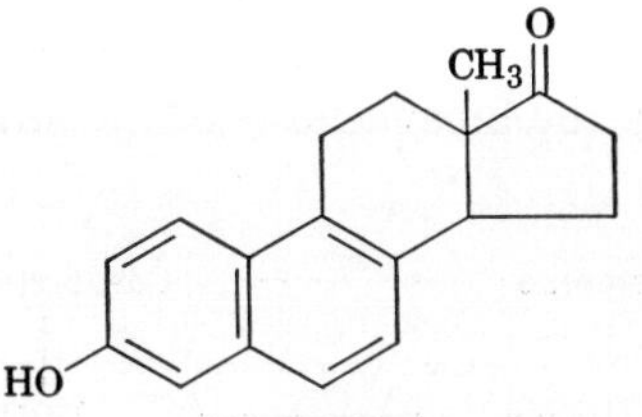

Equilenin

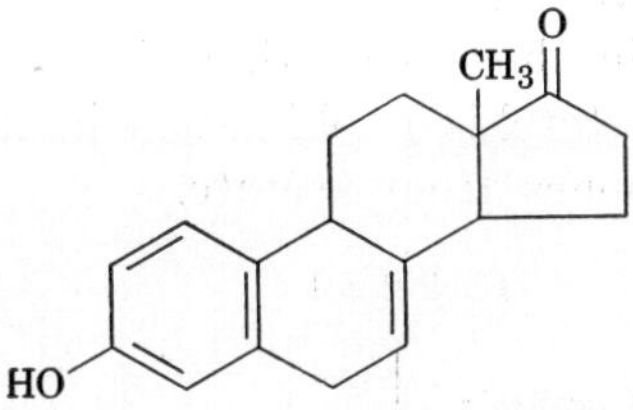

Equilin

Just as the ovarian follicular hormones cause the development of the typical female characteristics, so the principal steroid hormone of the testis (testosterone) exerts a profound influence on the male genital

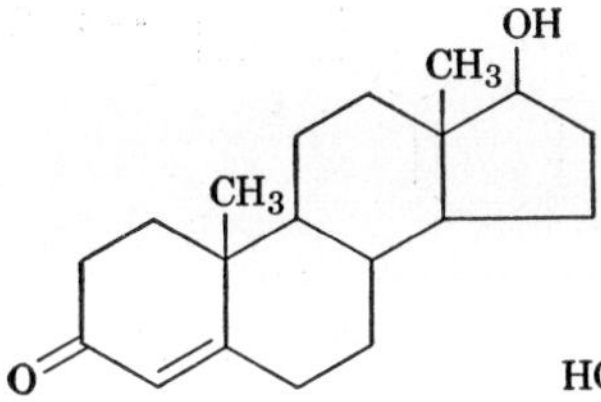

Testosterone

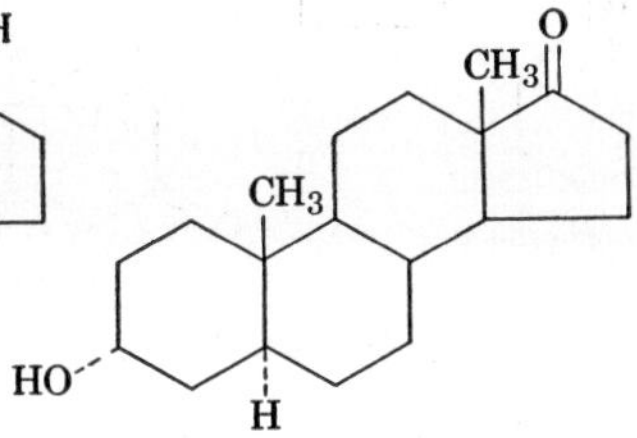

Androsterone

tract and is concerned with the appearance of the secondary male characteristics (e.g., the growth of the cock's comb, or the horns of a stag). Androsterone, a major product of the metabolism of testosterone, is excreted in the urine; it is an androgen, but is less active than testosterone.[64] These androgenic hormones are derivatives of the C_{19} hydrocarbon androstane (Table 1).

Biosynthesis of the Adrenal Hormones.[65] The view that cholesterol is a precursor of the adrenal steroid hormones received support from the observation[66] that the amount of cholesterol in adrenal glands is markedly decreased when the production and release of hormones is stimulated. It had also been shown that the administration of deuterium-labeled cholesterol to a pregnant woman gave rise to labeled pregnanediol in the urine;[67] presumably, the administered cholesterol was converted in

[64] R. I. Dorfman and R. A. Shipley, *Androgens,* John Wiley and Sons, New York, 1956.

[65] O. Hechter and G. Pincus, *Physiol. Revs.,* **34,** 459 (1954); N. Saba and O. Hechter, *Federation Proc.,* **14,** 775 (1955).

[66] C. N. H. Long, *Recent Progress in Hormone Research,* **1,** 99 (1947).

[67] K. Bloch, *J. Biol. Chem.,* **157,** 661 (1945).

the placenta to progesterone, from which pregnanediol was then formed (p. 648). Subsequent work demonstrated that adrenal tissue can convert C^{14}-labeled cholesterol to labeled progesterone,[68] as well as to corticosterone and cortisol,[69] and that cholesterol is a more efficient precursor of the hormones than is acetate. It is not certain, however, that cholesterol is an obligatory intermediate in the biosynthesis of the adrenal hormones from acetate.

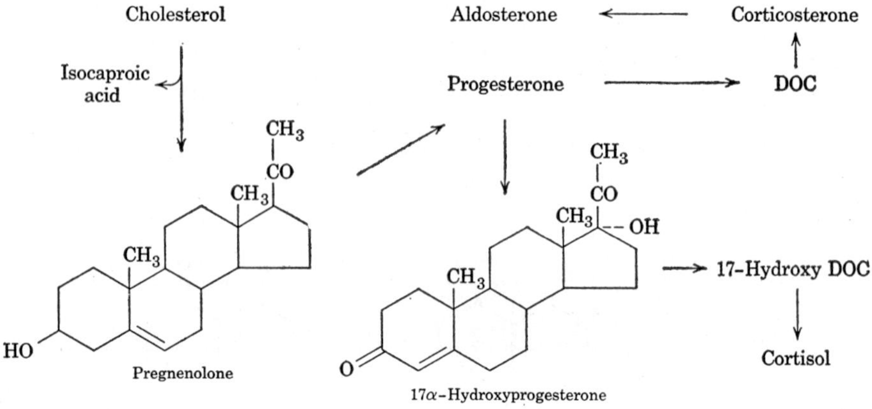

Fig. 5. Proposed pathways in the biosynthesis of the adrenal cortical hormones.

The current views about the pathways in the biosynthesis of the adrenal corticosteroids are largely based on the identification of labeled products formed by perfusion of isolated adrenal glands with C^{14}-labeled precursors, or by incubation of such precursors with homogenates or extracts of the gland. The known metabolic reactions leading from cholesterol to several of the adrenal steroids are given in Fig. 5. Comparison of the formula of cholesterol (p. 620) with those of corticosterone and cortisol (the major steroids of the adrenal secretion) shows that four important structural changes must occur in the formation of these corticosteroids: (1) scission of the isooctyl side chain of cholesterol to convert the C_{27} steroid to a C_{21} compound; (2) formation of the Δ^4-3-keto group characteristic of ring A; (3) introduction of a hydroxyl group at carbon 21 (in the synthesis of cortisol, this may be preceded by the addition of the α-hydroxyl group at carbon 17); (4) introduction of a β-hydroxyl group at carbon 11. All these transformations are effected by an adrenal preparation that performs the net synthesis of corticosterone and cortisol from cholesterol under conditions where neither the hormones nor cholesterol is formed from acetate.[70]

[68] E. G. Bligh et al., *Arch. Biochem. and Biophys.*, **58**, 249 (1955).

[69] O. Hechter et al., *Arch. Biochem. and Biophys.*, **46**, 201 (1953).

[70] E. Reich and A. L. Lehninger, *Biochim. et Biophys. Acta,* **17**, 136 (1955).

The first recognized products of cholesterol metabolism in adrenal tissue are the C_{21} steroid pregnenolone (Fig. 5) and the C_6 fatty acid isocaproic acid. Enzyme systems that effect their formation have been identified in particle-free adrenal extracts; for maximal activity, DPN and ATP are required.[71] The conversion of cholesterol to pregnenolone appears to be the rate-determining step in the formation of the cortical hormones, and it has been reported that the pituitary adrenotrophic hormone (which stimulates adrenal cortical secretion *in vivo;* Chapter 38) regulates the rate of this step.[72]

Pregnenolone is converted to progesterone by the action of a DPN-dependent 3β-hydroxysteroid dehydrogenase system found in the microsomal fraction of adrenal tissue.[73] The dehydrogenation reaction results in the removal of 2 hydrogen atoms from the CHOH group at position 3 and the simultaneous shift of the double bond from the Δ^5 position to the Δ^4 position (see formulae of pregnenolone and progesterone). The conversion of pregnenolone to progesterone also is catalyzed by preparations from placenta and from corpus luteum,[74] and thus appears to be involved in the formation of progesterone from cholesterol in these tissues. This conversion of cholesterol to pregnenolone and progesterone is also effected by the testis and the ovary, and probably represents the initial steps in the biosynthesis of the C_{19} and C_{18} steroid hormones produced in these organs.

In the adrenal gland, progesterone serves as a precursor of cortisol and of corticosterone (cf. Fig. 5). On the pathway leading to cortisol, a hydroxyl group is introduced in the 17 position by an enzyme system ("17-hydroxylase"); the product is 17α-hydroxyprogesterone.[75] A different enzyme system catalyzes the introduction of a hydroxyl group in 21 position to form 17-hydroxydeoxycorticosterone from 17α-hydroxyprogesterone; this enzyme system, which requires both TPNH and O_2 for its activity, can also convert progesterone to deoxycorticosterone.[76] It is probable that both a reduced pyridine nucleotide and O_2 are essential for the action of the 17-hydroxylase as well as of the "21-hydroxylase" (p. 644).

The final steps in the formation of corticosterone and of cortisol involve the introduction of the 11β-hydroxyl group by an enzyme system ("11β-hydroxylase") present in the mitochondrial fraction of adrenal tissue,

[71] E. Staple et al., *J. Biol. Chem.,* **219,** 845 (1956).

[72] D. Stone and O. Hechter, *Arch. Biochem. and Biophys.,* **51,** 457 (1954).

[73] K. F. Beyer and L. T. Samuels, *J. Biol. Chem.,* **219,** 69 (1956).

[74] W. H. Pearlman et al., *J. Biol. Chem.,* **208,** 231 (1954).

[75] J. E. Plager and L. T. Samuels, *J. Biol. Chem.,* **211,** 21 (1954); H. Levy et al., *ibid.,* **211,** 867 (1954).

[76] K. J. Ryan and L. L. Engel, *J. Biol. Chem.,* **225,** 103 (1957).

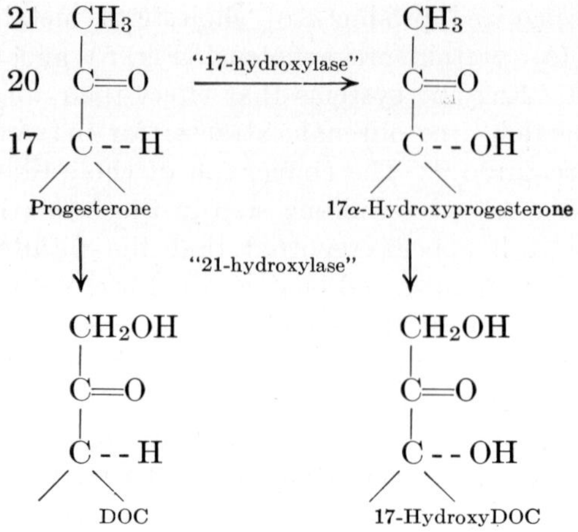

21　CH₃　　　　　　　　　　　　　CH₃
　　|　　　　　　　　　　　　　　|
20　C=O　　"17-hydroxylase"　　　C=O
　　|　　　————————→　　　　　|
17　C - - H　　　　　　　　　　　C - - OH
　　/　\　　　　　　　　　　　　/　\
　Progesterone　　　　　　17α-Hydroxyprogesterone

↓　　　　"21-hydroxylase"　　↓

CH₂OH　　　　　　　　　　　CH₂OH
|　　　　　　　　　　　　　　|
C=O　　　　　　　　　　　　　C=O
|　　　　　　　　　　　　　　|
C - - H　　　　　　　　　　　C - - OH
/　\　　　　　　　　　　　　/　\
　DOC　　　　　　　　　17-HydroxyDOC

and which requires TPNH and O_2 for its activity.[77]　The oxygen of the newly introduced hydroxyl group is derived from O_2 and not from water, indicating that an oxidase (or peroxidase; cf. p. 363) is involved in the reaction.　It will be seen from the formulae on p. 639 that 11β-hydroxylation of DOC and of 17-hydroxyDOC yields corticosterone and cortisol respectively.

Little is known at present about the biosynthesis of the other adrenal cortical hormones.　Aldosterone (which contains an aldehyde group at carbon 18) may arise from DOC, since adrenal preparations can effect this transformation.[78]　The conversion of cortisol to cortisone occurs *in vivo,* and it has been assumed that cortisone and dehydrocorticosterone arise by the oxidation of the 11β-hydroxyl group of cortisol and corticosterone respectively.

Biosynthesis of the Androgens.[64]　Cholesterol and acetate serve as precursors in the biosynthesis of testosterone by the testis, and the postulated metabolic pathway (Fig. 6) involves the same steps leading from cholesterol to 17α-hydroxyprogesterone as in the biosynthesis of the adrenal cortical hormones.[79]　Oxidative degradation of 17α-hydroxyprogesterone (loss of carbons 20 and 21 as acetic acid) produces Δ^4-androstene-3,17-dione, which is reduced to testosterone.

Several androgens other than testosterone are present in adrenal extracts.　These probably arise from dehydroepiandrosterone, which is

[77] M. Hayano and R. I. Dorfman, *J. Biol. Chem.,* **211**, 227 (1954); *Arch. Biochem. and Biophys.,* **59**, 529 (1955); A. C. Brownie et al., *Biochem. J.,* **58**, 218 (1954); **62**, 29 (1956); J. K. Grant, *ibid.,* **64**, 559 (1956).

[78] P. J. Ayres et al., *Biochem. J.,* **65**, 22p (1957).

[79] R. O. Brady, *J. Biol. Chem.,* **193**, 145 (1951); H. H. Wotiz et al., *ibid.,* **216**, 677 (1955); W. R. Slaunwhite, Jr. and L. T. Samuels, *ibid.,* **220**, 341 (1956); W. S. Lynn and R. Brown, *Biochim. et Biophys. Acta,* **21**, 403 (1956).

thought to be the initial C_{19} steroid formed in the adrenal gland[80] (Fig. 6).

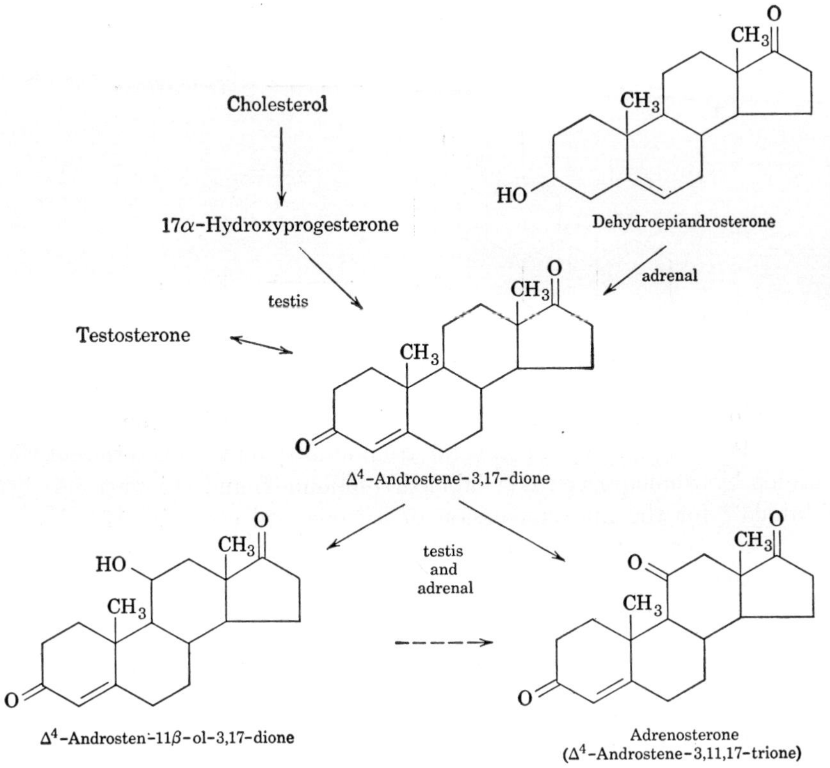

Fig. 6. Postulated pathways in the biosynthesis of testicular and adrenal androgens.

Biosynthesis of the Estrogens.[81] Although the ovary and placenta are the major sites of estrogen formation, both the adrenal gland and the testis also produce estrone. Relatively little is known about the mechanism of estrone synthesis in any endocrine tissue, but the possibility that progesterone and testosterone serve as intermediates is suggested by the finding that placental tissue can convert testosterone to Δ^4-androstene-3,17-dione and thence to estrone.[82] Similar synthesis of estrogens from testosterone is effected by ovarian tissue, which also forms androstene-

[80] A. S. Meyer et al., *Acta Endocrinologica,* **18,** 148 (1955); E. Bloch et al., *J. Biol. Chem.,* **224,** 737 (1957).

[81] R. I. Dorfman, in G. Pincus and K. V. Thimann, *The Hormones,* Vol. III, Chapter 12, Academic Press, New York, 1955.

[82] A. S. Meyer, *Biochim. et Biophys. Acta,* **17,** 441 (1955); *Experientia,* **11,** 99 (1955).

3,17-dione from progesterone.[83] The degradation of androgens may involve hydroxylation at carbon 19, followed by oxidative removal of the entire CH_2OH group to yield a C_{18} steroid with the characteristic aromatic ring A of the estrogens (cf. accompanying scheme).

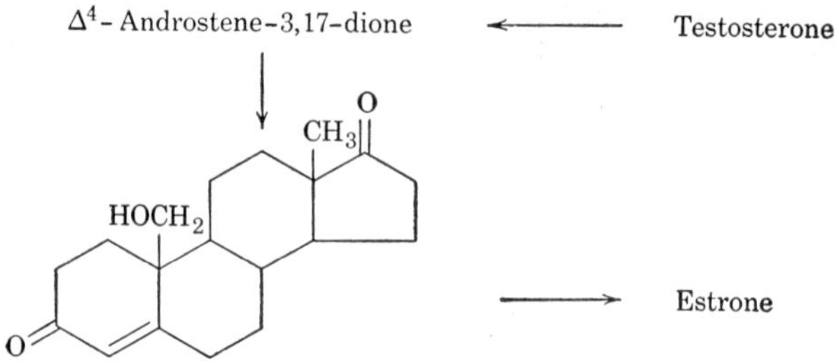

Δ^4-Androstene-3,17-dione ←———— Testosterone

————→ Estrone

Δ^4-Androsten-19-ol-3,17-dione

Most of the available data on the interrelation of estrone, estradiol-17β, and estriol (p. 640) have come from studies on the excretion of these steroids by women given C^{14}-labeled compounds, and evidence has been obtained[84] for the interconversion of estrone and estradiol-17β, both of which are converted to estriol. A DPN-dependent "estradiol-17β dehydrogenase" is present in human placenta, and it catalyzes the interconversion of estrone and estradiol-17β; the enzyme system does not act on estradiol-17α, an estrogen isolated from mare urine.[85] It is uncertain, however, whether estradiol-17β is an obligatory intermediate in the formation of estriol from estrone.[86]

Catabolism of the Steroid Hormones.[81] The breakdown of steroid hormones in human beings leads to the excretion of catabolic products in the urine, largely as conjugates of glucuronic acid or (in the case of androgens) of sulfuric acid.[87] The conjugation of steroids with glucuronic acid is catalyzed by an enzyme system in liver, and involves the transfer of a glucuronic acid residue from UDP-glucuronic acid (p. 537) to a steroid hydroxyl group.[88] The liver also contains an enzyme system that catalyzes the formation of steroid sulfates[89] by the interaction of

[83] B. Baggett et al., *J. Biol. Chem.*, **221**, 931 (1956); H. H. Wotiz et al., *ibid.*, **222**, 487 (1956); S. Solomon et al., *J. Am. Chem. Soc.*, **78**, 5453 (1956).

[84] C. T. Beer and T. F. Gallagher, *J. Biol. Chem.*, **214**, 335, 351 (1955).

[85] L. Langer and L. L. Engel, *J. Biol. Chem.*, **233**, 583 (1958).

[86] M. Levitz et al., *J. Biol. Chem.*, **222**, 981 (1956); G. F. Marrian et al., *Biochem. J.*, **66**, 60 (1957); J. B. Brown and G. F. Marrian, *J. Endocrinol.*, **15**, 307 (1957).

[87] S. Lieberman and S. Teich, *Pharmacol. Revs.*, **5**, 285 (1953).

[88] K. J. Isselbacher and J. Axelrod, *J. Am. Chem. Soc.*, **77**, 1070 (1955); G. J. Dutton, *Biochem. J.*, **64**, 693 (1956).

[89] R. H. DeMeio and C. Lewycka, *Endocrinology*, **56**, 489 (1955); A. B. Roy, *Biochem. J.*, **63**, 294 (1956).

the steroid with an "activated" form of sulfuric acid (adenosine-3'-phosphate-5'-phosphosulfate; p. 795). For the isolation of the free steroids from urine, the glucuronides and sulfates are hydrolyzed by treatment of the urine with a preparation of β-glucuronidase (p. 432) or steroid sulfatase (p. 796).

The liver is probably the major site of the mammalian catabolism of all the steroid hormones, which are converted to a large variety of physiologically inactive compounds. Similar "inactivation" reactions also occur in the kidney,[90] and the products may be directly excreted in the urine. The steroid metabolites formed in the liver can enter the intestinal tract via the bile, or be carried in the circulation to the kidney and excreted in the urine.

Many of the urinary products arising from the catabolism of steroid hormones are formed upon perfusion of the liver (rat, dog) with C^{14}-labeled corticosteroids or testosterone,[91] and several of the enzyme systems that are involved in these transformations have been studied in liver extracts. At least five distinct types of enzymic reaction are known to be catalyzed by rat liver preparations; these types are denoted by means of Roman numerals in Fig. 7. Similar reactions occur in the liver of other species (dog, guinea pig, rabbit), but the products formed may be stereoisomers of those shown for the rat.

As may be seen from Fig. 7, reactions of type I involve the reduction of the Δ^4-double bond (TPNH is the reductant), and may be followed by a reaction of type II, the reduction of the 3-keto group to a 3α-hydroxyl group (DPNH is the reductant).[92] The products tetrahydrocortisone and tetrahydrocortisol are derivatives of pregnane; however, on perfusion of rat liver with cortisone or cortisol the 5-epimers, i.e., allopregnane (p. 638) derivatives, are formed, and both 3α- and 3β-hydroxy compounds may be identified. Similarly, progesterone gives rise to allopregnane-3,20-dione and allopregan-3α-ol-20-one.[93] Consequently, rat liver contains enzymes that effect type I reactions with the formation of pregnane and allopregnane derivatives,[94] and enzymes for type II reactions yielding 3α- and 3β-hydroxy compounds.

In reactions of type III, the 11-keto group is reduced to a 11β-hydroxyl group. It appears that substrates of this enzyme system must contain the Δ^4-3-keto function, since cortisone is reduced to cortisol but tetrahydrocortisone is not reduced to the corresponding tetrahydrocortisol.[95]

[90] F. M. Ganis et al., *J. Biol. Chem.*, **218**, 841 (1956).

[91] E. Caspi and O. Hechter, *Arch. Biochem. and Biophys.*, **52**, 478 (1954); **61**, 299 (1956); L. R. Axelrod et al., *J. Biol. Chem.*, **219**, 455 (1956).

[92] G. M. Tomkins, *J. Biol. Chem.*, **218**, 437 (1956); **225**, 13 (1957).

[93] W. Taylor, *Biochem. J.*, **56**, 463 (1954).

[94] E. Forchielli and R. I. Dorfman, *J. Biol. Chem.*, **223**, 443 (1956).

[95] H. J. Hubener et al., *J. Biol. Chem.*, **220**, 499 (1956).

Such substrate specificity is not displayed by liver enzymes that catalyze reactions of type IV, the reduction of the 20-keto group; both unsaturated steroids (cortisone, cortisol) and saturated steroids (tetrahydrocortisone,

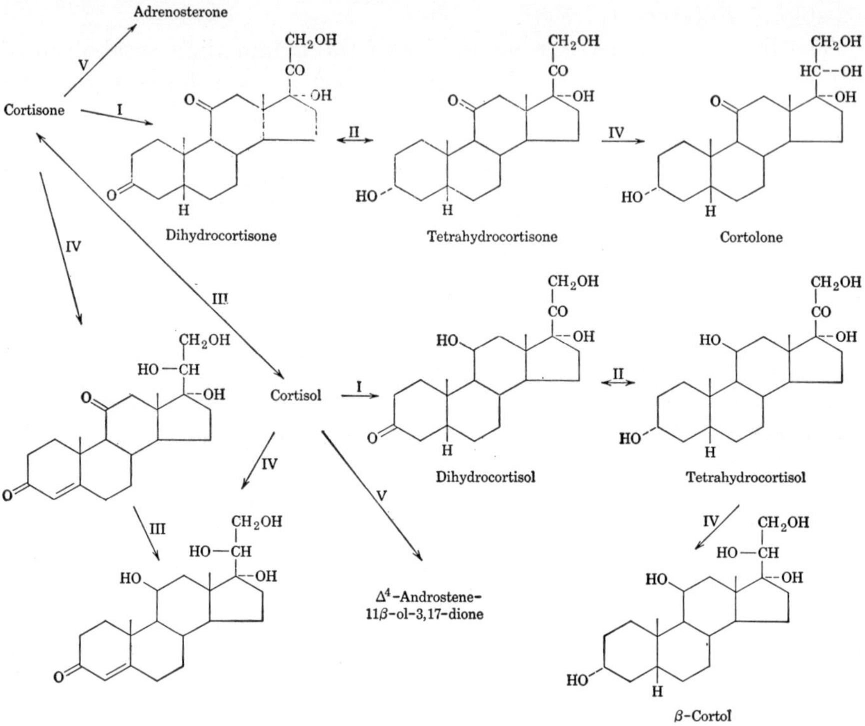

Fig. 7. Catabolic reactions of adrenal steroids catalyzed by rat liver enzymes. Roman numerals correspond to the reaction types discussed in the text.

tetrahydrocortisol) are reduced. However, the products formed may be either 20α-hydroxy compounds (cortolone) or 20β-hydroxy compounds (β-cortol).[96] Highly hydroxylated steroids such as cortolone and cortol represent the major urinary end products of the catabolism of the adrenal cortical hormones in humans.[97]

Although the 20-hydroxy compound pregnanediol (p. 640) is the main urinary product of progesterone metabolism in human subjects and rabbits, it is not excreted by rats. Rabbit liver can convert progesterone to pregnanediol; pregnane-3,20-dione and pregnan-3α-ol-20-one (products of reaction types I and II) are also formed. On the other hand, rat liver appears to be unable to reduce the 20-keto group of progesterone,

[96] C. de Courcy and J. J. Schneider, *J. Biol. Chem.*, **223**, 865 (1956).
[97] D. K. Fukushima et al., *J. Biol. Chem.*, **212**, 449 (1953).

but this reaction can occur in some other rat tissues, since eviscerated rats convert progesterone to Δ^4-pregnen-20α-ol-3-one.[98]

Reactions of type V produce C_{19} steroids from C_{21} steroids;[99] presumably, the degradation is similar to that by which testicular androgens are formed (p. 644).

Androstane derivatives formed in the liver or brought to it by the circulation are subjected to catabolic reactions. For example, adreno-

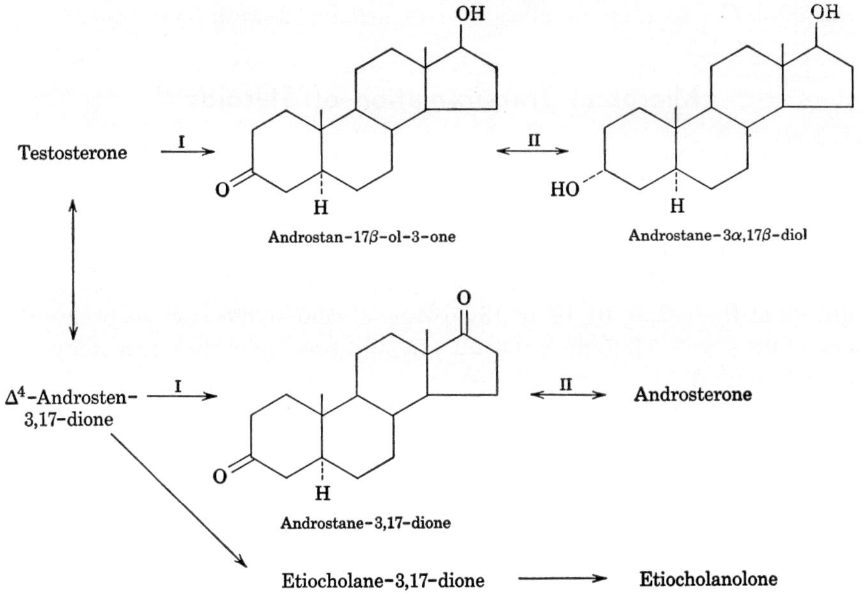

Testosterone $\xrightarrow{\text{I}}$

Androstan-17β-ol-3-one

$\xleftarrow{\text{II}}$ Androstane-3α,17β-diol

Δ^4-Androsten-3,17-dione $\xrightarrow{\text{I}}$

Androstane-3,17-dione

$\xleftrightarrow{\text{II}}$ Androsterone

Etiocholane-3,17-dione $\longrightarrow$ Etiocholanolone

sterone (cf. Fig. 6), Δ^4-androsten-11β-ol-3,17-dione, and testosterone are reduced to the corresponding 3α-hydroxyandrostane derivatives by reactions of types I and II. In addition, testosterone is converted to androsterone (p. 641) by a series of enzymic reactions in which the first step is the oxidation of testosterone by DPN$^+$ to form Δ^4-androsten-3,17-dione; subsequent reduction of the Δ^4-3-keto group yields androsterone,[100] as shown in the accompanying scheme. The 5β-epimer of androsterone, etiocholanolone (etiocholan-3α-ol-17-one), is another urinary constituent derived from testosterone.[101] Etiocholanolone is formed *in vivo* after the administration of Δ^4-androstene-3,17-dione, which may be converted

[98] W. G. Wiest, *J. Biol. Chem.*, **221**, 461 (1956).

[99] E. Forchielli et al., *J. Biol. Chem.*, **215**, 713 (1955); L. R. Axelrod and L. L. Miller, *Arch. Biochem. and Biophys.*, **60**, 373 (1956).

[100] C. D. West and L. T. Samuels, *J. Biol. Chem.*, **190**, 827 (1951); P. Ofner, *Biochem. J.*, **61**, 287 (1955).

[101] D. K. Fukushima et al., *J. Biol. Chem.*, **206**, 863 (1954).

to the urinary product via etiocholane-3,17-dione (the 5β-epimer of androstane-3,17-dione; p. 649).

The variety of reactions described above are not the only ones known to occur in mammalian liver, or postulated on the basis of urinary steroid metabolites. For example, it has been found that hydroxyl groups of either the α- or β-orientation can be introduced into the 2 and 6 positions of C_{21} and C_{19} steroids, and the formation of 16α-hydroxy-testosterone has been reported. Furthermore, the administration of estradiol-17β to humans gives rise to urinary 2-methoxyestrone.[102]

Microbial Transformation of Steroids [103]

Essentially all the reactions in the catabolism of steroid hormones by mammalian tissues are duplicated in microbial cultures supplemented with an exogenous source of steroids. Furthermore, microorganisms (molds, fungi, and bacteria) are able to effect transformations that have not been observed in animals. For example, they can introduce hydroxyl groups at the 1, 7, 8, 10, 14, or 15 position of compounds such as progesterone, DOC, and 17-hydroxyDOC. In addition, microbes can dehydrogenate ring A of several Δ^4-3-keto steroids to form the corresponding $\Delta^{1,4}$-dien-3-one compounds; among the substances prepared in this

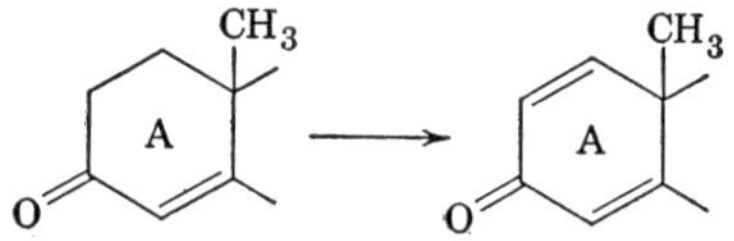

manner are 1-dehydrocortisone and 1-dehydrocortisol, which are more active physiologically than are the parent adrenal hormones.[104] Of special importance in the development of improved methods for the synthesis of corticosteroids was the discovery[105] that some microorganisms can introduce 11α- and 11β-hydroxyl groups, a reaction that is difficult to effect by the available techniques of organic synthesis. A significant characteristic of the hydroxylation reactions leading to the formation of 6β-, 11α-, 11β-, 17α-, or 21-hydroxysteroids is that O_2, rather than water, serves as the source of the hydroxyl oxygen atom[106] (cf. p. 644).

[102] S. Kraychy and T. F. Gallagher, *J. Am. Chem. Soc.,* **79,** 754 (1957).

[103] A. Wettstein, *Experientia,* **11,** 465 (1955); J. Fried et al., *Recent Progress in Hormone Research,* **11,** 149 (1955); S. H. Eppstein et al., *Vitamins and Hormones,* **14,** 359 (1956).

[104] H. L. Herzog et al., *Science,* **121,** 176 (1955).

[105] D. H. Peterson and H. C. Murray, *J. Am. Chem. Soc.,* **74,** 1871 (1952); D. R. Colingsworth et al., *J. Biol. Chem.,* **203,** 807 (1953).

[106] M. Hayano et al., *Biochim. et. Biophys. Acta,* **21,** 380 (1956).

Most of the known microbial enzyme systems that act on steroids catalyze the oxidation of ring A. For example, extracts of a soil bacterium convert cholesterol to Δ^4-cholesten-3-one[107] (p. 625), and *Escherichia freundii* (adapted to grow on cholic acid) contains a DPN-dependent dehydrogenase that oxidizes 3α-hydroxy bile acids to the corresponding 3-keto compounds.[108] Steroid hormones are substrates for several enzymes obtained from *Pseudomonas testosteroni* adapted to grow on testosterone. This organism contains both α- and β-hydroxysteroid dehydrogenases that are DPN-dependent.[109] The "α-enzyme" catalyzes the reversible dehydrogenation of 3α-hydroxy steroids in the androstane, pregnane, and cholane series to the corresponding ketones, and its action resembles that of the 3α-hydroxysteroid dehydrogenase of rat liver (p. 647). The "β-enzyme" effects analogous reactions of the

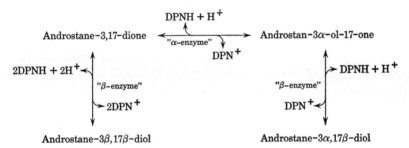

3β-hydroxy compounds, and in addition catalyzes the dehydrogenation of 17β-hydroxy steroids in the androstane and estrane series. The action of the two enzymes is shown in the accompanying scheme, with androstane-3,17-dione as the initial substrate. *Pseudomonas testosteroni* also contains an isomerase that catalyzes the conversion of Δ^5-3-ketosteroids to Δ^4-3-ketosteroids,[110] and a Δ^1-dehydrogenase (possibly a flavoprotein) that catalyzes the conversion of C_{19} steroids such as Δ^4-androstene-3,17-dione to the corresponding $\Delta^{1,4}$-diene.[111] For a discussion of the enzymic mechanisms in the metabolism of steroids by microorganisms and animals, see Talalay.[112]

[107] T. C. Stadtman et al., *J. Biol. Chem.*, **206**, 511 (1954).

[108] O. Hayaishi et al., *Arch. Biochem. and Biophys.*, **56**, 554 (1955).

[109] P. Talalay et al., *J. Biol. Chem.*, **212**, 801 (1955); P. I. Marcus and P. Talalay, *ibid.*, **218**, 661, 675 (1956).

[110] P. Talalay and V. S. Wang, *Biochim. et Biophys. Acta*, **18**, 300 (1955).

[111] H. R. Levy and P. Talalay, *J. Am. Chem. Soc.*, **79**, 2658 (1957).

[112] P. Talalay, *Physiol. Revs.*, **37**, 362 (1957).

Chemistry and Metabolism of Carotenoids, Anthocyanins, and Related Compounds

27 ·

Carotenoids[1]

Among the unsaponifiable lipids of plants and animals are found representatives of a group of pigments (light yellow to purple) known as the carotenoids. These substances are present in small amounts in nearly all higher plants and in many microorganisms (e.g., red and green algae, fungi, and photosynthetic bacteria); they are probably also present in all animals. Although the nature of these pigments has interested chemists since the substance named "carotene" was isolated from carrots in 1831, the structure of some of the carotenoids was definitely established only after 1925, and the structure of many others is still unknown. The

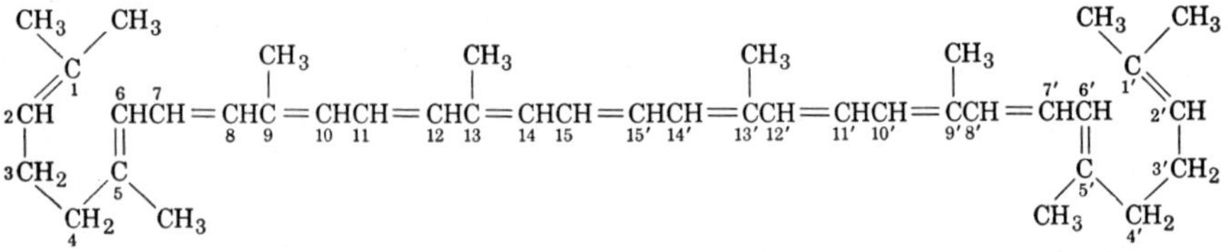

Lycopene

advances in the elucidation of the nature of the carotenoids have come primarily from the application of the chromatographic techniques invented by Tswett in 1906 (p. 115). By this method, several investigators, notably Karrer, Kuhn, Lederer, and Zechmeister, were able to separate the various carotenoids from one another and chemical studies of the individual carotenoids permitted the determination of their structure.

The carotenoids found in nature may be considered derivatives of the red pigment lycopene, found in tomatoes and many other fruits and

[1] P. Karrer and E. Jucker, *Carotenoids*, translated by E. A. Braude, Elsevier Publishing Co., Inc., New York, 1950; T. W. Goodwin, *Carotenoids, Their Comparative Biochemistry*, Chemical Publishing Co., New York, 1954; *Ann. Rev. Biochem.*, **24**, 497 (1955).

flowers, as well as in some microorganisms. Lycopene has the empirical formula $C_{40}H_{56}$ and is a highly unsaturated straight-chain hydrocarbon (a polyene) composed of two identical units joined by a double bond between carbon atoms 15 and 15'. Each of these $C_{20}H_{28}$ units may be considered to be derived from 4 isoprene units; the formula of isoprene is $CH_2{=}C(CH_3){-}CH{=}CH_2$. As will be seen in a subsequent section dealing with the terpenes, the carotenoids represent only one group of plant materials which may be related structurally to isoprene.

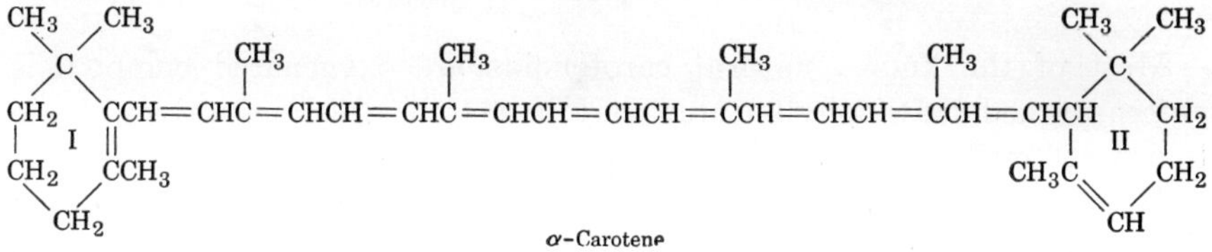

α-Carotene

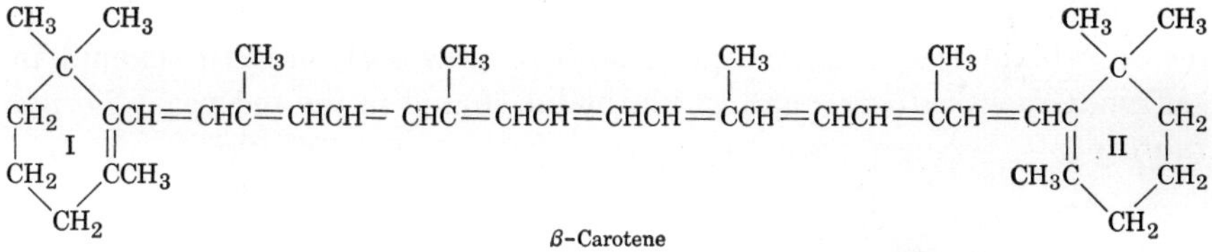

$$\underset{\text{I}}{\overset{\displaystyle\text{CH}_3\ \ \text{CH}_3}{\underset{\text{CH}_2}{\overset{\text{C}}{\underset{\text{CH}_2}{\underset{\text{CH}_2}{\big|}}}}}\ \ \text{CCH}{=}\overset{\text{CH}_3}{\text{CHC}}{=}\text{CHCH}{=}\overset{\text{CH}_3}{\text{CHC}}{=}\text{CHCH}{=}\overset{\text{CH}_3}{\text{CCH}}{=}\text{CHCH}{=}\overset{\text{CH}_3}{\text{CCH}}{=}\text{CHCH}\ \ \overset{\text{CH}_3\ \ \text{CH}_3}{\underset{\text{II}}{\text{C}}}$$

β-Carotene

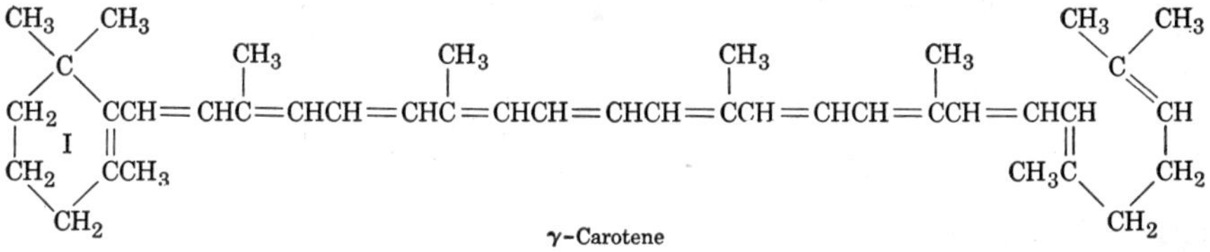

γ-Carotene

Three other important naturally occurring carotenoid hydrocarbons having the composition $C_{40}H_{56}$ are named α-, β-, and γ-carotene. One or more of these carotenes is commonly found in all higher plants and in many unicellular organisms. A characteristic feature of the carotenes is the presence of a ring at one or both ends of the hydrocarbon chain. This ring is structurally related to the substances termed α- and β-ionone; ring I of α-, β-, and γ-carotene and ring II of β-carotene correspond to a β-ionone residue, while ring II of α-carotene corresponds to an α-ionone residue (see p. 654).

Carotenoids that are more saturated than the $C_{40}H_{56}$ compounds described above also are widespread in nature. Among this group are the colored compounds neurosporene ("tetrahydrolycopene," probably $C_{40}H_{60}$) and ζ-carotene (an octahydrolycopene, $C_{40}H_{64}$). In addition, colorless carotenoids are present in plants and microorganisms;

e.g., phytoene $(7,8,11,12,12',11',8',7'$-octahydrolycopene[2]) and phytofluene (believed to be either $C_{40}H_{64}$ or $C_{40}H_{68}$).

$$
\begin{array}{cc}
\underset{\text{CH}_2}{\overset{\displaystyle \overset{\text{CH}_3 \quad \text{CH}_3}{\diagdown\diagup}}{\underset{\displaystyle \underset{\text{CH}_2}{\diagdown\diagup}}{\overset{\text{C}}{\underset{\text{CH}_2 \quad \text{CCH}_3}{\diagup}}}} \text{CCH=CHCOCH}_3 & \underset{\text{CH}}{\overset{\displaystyle \overset{\text{CH}_3 \quad \text{CH}_3}{\diagdown\diagup}}{\underset{\displaystyle \underset{\text{CH}_2 \quad \text{CCH}_3}{}}{\overset{\text{C}}{\underset{\text{CH}_2 \quad \text{CHCH}}{\diagup}}}} \text{CHCH=CHCOCH}_3
\end{array}
$$

β-Ionone $\qquad\qquad\qquad$ α-Ionone

Most of the known natural carotenoids are oxygenated compounds (often termed xanthophylls), and may be classified as derivatives of the hydrocarbons lycopene or α-, β-, or γ-carotene (Table 1).

A few of the naturally occurring carotenoids contain carboxyl groups; these compounds have fewer than 40 carbon atoms and are believed to arise in the plant by oxidative cleavage of the longer carotenoids. Examples are bixin (found in the pods of *Bixa orellana*), crocetin (found in saffron, *Crocus sativus*), and torularhodin (found in the red yeast *Torula rubra*).

$$
\underset{\text{CH}_3}{\text{HOOCCH}} = \text{CHC} = \text{CHCH} = \text{CH}\underset{\text{CH}_3}{\text{C}} = \text{CHCH} = \text{CHCH} = \underset{\text{CH}_3}{\text{CCH}} = \text{CHCH} = \underset{\text{CH}_3}{\text{CCH}} = \text{CHCOOCH}_3
$$

Bixin

$$
\underset{\text{CH}_3}{\text{HOOCC}} = \text{CHCH} = \underset{\text{CH}_3}{\text{CHC}} = \text{CHCH} = \text{CHCH} = \underset{\text{CH}_3}{\text{CCH}} = \text{CHCH} = \underset{\text{CH}_3}{\text{CCOOH}}
$$

Crocetin

$$
\underset{\underset{\text{CH}_2}{\overset{\overset{\text{CH}_3 \quad \text{CH}_3}{\diagdown\diagup}}{\overset{\text{C}}{\underset{\text{CH}_2 \quad \text{CCH}_3}{\diagup}}}}{}}{\text{CH}_2} \quad \text{CCH} = \underset{\text{CH}_3}{\text{CHC}} = \text{CHCH} = \underset{\text{CH}_3}{\text{CHC}} = \text{CHCH} = \text{CHCH} = \underset{\text{CH}_3}{\text{CCH}} = \text{CHCH} = \underset{\text{CH}_3}{\text{CCH}} = \text{CHCH} \quad \overset{\text{COOH}}{\underset{\underset{\text{CH}}{\text{CH}_3\text{C}\diagdown\diagup\text{CH}}}{|}}
$$

Torularhodin

Carotenoids are found in the tissues of many animals (vertebrates and invertebrates). These pigments may occur in the fat globules of ovaries and eggs of many species, in the fat depots, in milk, in eye tissue, and in epidermal outgrowths (feathers, shells, wings) of birds, crustaceans, and butterflies. Carotenoids are frequently responsible for the pigmentation in tissues of marine invertebrates and in fishes.[3]

[2] W. J. Rabourn and F. W. Quackenbush, *Arch. Biochem. and Biophys.*, **61**, 111 (1956).

[3] D. L. Fox, *Animal Biochromes and Structural Colors*, Cambridge University Press, Cambridge. 1953.

Table I. Some Naturally Occurring Carotenoids

Parent Carotenoid	Oxygenated Derivative Name	Source
Lycopene	Lycoxanthin (3-oxylycopene)	Tomato, *Rhodospirillum*
	Lycophyll or Lycoxanthophyll (3,3'-dioxylycopene)	Berries of *Solanum dulcamara*
α-Carotene	Lutein or Xanthophyll (3,3'-dioxy-α-carotene)	Green leaves, flowers, fruits
β-Carotene	Cryptoxanthin (3-oxy-β-carotene)	Fruits, berries, yellow corn (*Zea mays*)
	Zeaxanthin (3,3'-dioxy-β-carotene)	Yellow *Zea mays*
	Violaxanthin (zeaxanthin-5,6,6',5'-diepoxide)	Green leaves, flowers
	Echinenone (4-keto-β-carotene)	Marine invertebrates
	Canthaxanthin (4,4'-diketo-β-carotene)	Mushroom, *Corynebacterium*
	Astacin (3,4,4',3'-tetraketo-β-carotene)	Lobster shells
	Astaxanthin (3,3'-dioxy-4,4'-diketo-β-carotene)	Green algae
γ-Carotene	Rubixanthin (3-oxy-γ-carotene)	Flowers, green sulfur bacteria

The carotenoids present in the tissues of higher animals probably are derived solely from dietary sources. Thus, an important derivative of β-carotene, vitamin A_1 ($C_{20}H_{29}OH$), is essentially an oxidation product of one half of the β-carotene molecule. Obviously, the $C_{20}H_{28}$ units of the α- and γ-carotenes and of cryptoxanthin which contain the β-ionone residue could also give rise to vitamin A_1. β-Carotene is converted in the animal organism to vitamin A_1, which is found in large amounts in the livers of salt water fish, e.g., the cod. The closely related vitamin A_2 is found in the livers of fresh water fish; vitamin A_2 contains one double bond more than does vitamin A_1 (p. 656). Both vitamins may be present in animal eyes, where they play an essential role in vision (p. 658).

Compounds like β-carotene that are converted *in vivo* to vitamin A_1 are termed provitamins A_1 (Chapter 39). In higher animals, the major site of the oxidative degradation of the provitamin to vitamin A_1 is the small intestine.[4] No carotenoid provitamin is known that serves as a

[4] F. H. Mattson et al., *Arch. Biochem.*, **15**, 65 (1947); *J. Biol. Chem.*, **176**, 1467 (1948); S. Y. Thompson et al., *Brit. J. Nutrition*, **3**, 50 (1949); A. Rosenberg and A. E. Sobel, *Arch. Biochem. and Biophys.*, **44**, 320 (1953).

direct precursor of vitamin A_2. Since both vitamins A_1 and A_2 often are present in animals fed either β-carotene or vitamin A_1, it has been assumed that vitamin A_1 is dehydrogenated *in vivo* to vitamin A_2.

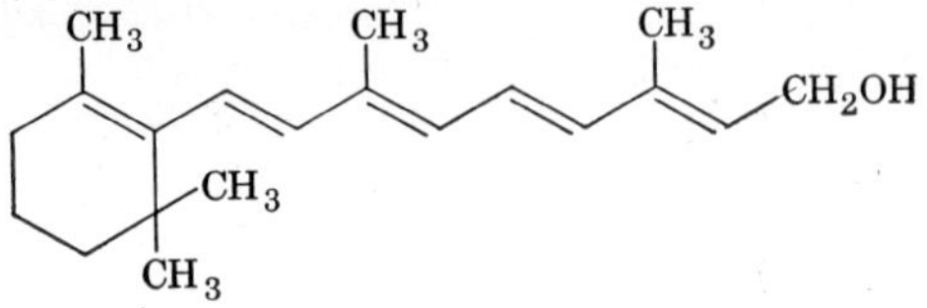

Vitamin A_1
(all-*trans*)

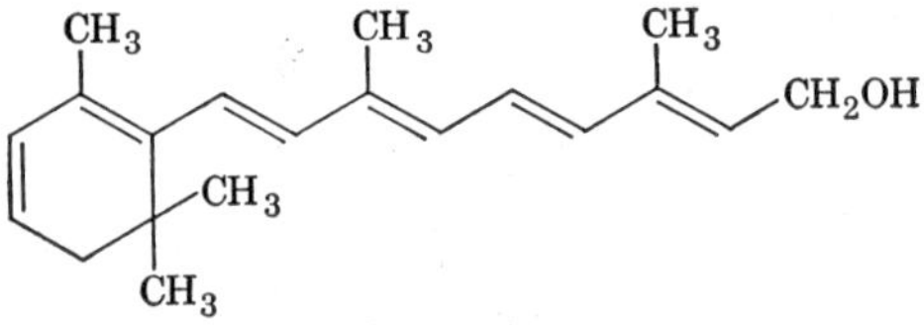

Vitamin A_2

The assay of natural materials for vitamin A activity is facilitated by the application of the reaction, discovered by Carr and Price,[5] in which a distinctive blue color develops when the carotenes and vitamin A are treated with a solution of antimony trichloride ($SbCl_3$) in chloroform. Like other highly unsaturated compounds, the carotenoids exhibit characteristic absorption maxima in the ultraviolet and visible regions of the spectrum.

It may be anticipated that *cis-trans* isomerism should be possible about the many double bonds of the carotenoids. The studies of Zechmeister[6] and of others have shown that by far the major proportion of the naturally occurring carotenoid molecules have their double bonds in the all-*trans* configuration, as shown above for vitamins A_1 and A_2; however, extensive isomerization, with the formation of a series of compounds having *cis* double bonds, may be effected by irradiation of the natural carotenoids with ultraviolet light or with visible light in the presence of iodine. These products differ from the parent material in their absorption spectra and chromatographic behavior. Such isomerization is reversible, and *cis* compounds may be converted, by similar treatment, into the more stable *trans* forms. Small amounts of carotenoids containing a few *cis* double bonds occur in nature, and animal tissues can also isomerize carotenoids. Thus the crystalline vitamin A_1 isolated from natural sources is the all-*trans* isomer, but both this form and the so-called neo-a (13-*cis*) form are always present in rat liver,[7] whereas the neo-b (11-*cis*)

[5] F. H. Carr and E. A. Price, *Biochem. J.*, **20**, 497 (1926).

[6] L. Zechmeister, *Ann. N. Y. Acad. Sci.*, **49**, 220 (1948); *Experientia*, **10**, 1 (1954).

[7] C. D. Robeson and J. G. Baxter, *J. Am. Chem. Soc.*, **69**, 136 (1947).

form[8] is found only in the eye (p. 659). The stereoisomers of vitamin A_1 differ widely in their effectiveness in curing the symptoms of vitamin A deficiency (Chapter 39), the all-*trans* isomer being the most active in this regard. The structure of several geometrical isomers[9] of vitamin A_1 is shown in Fig. 1.

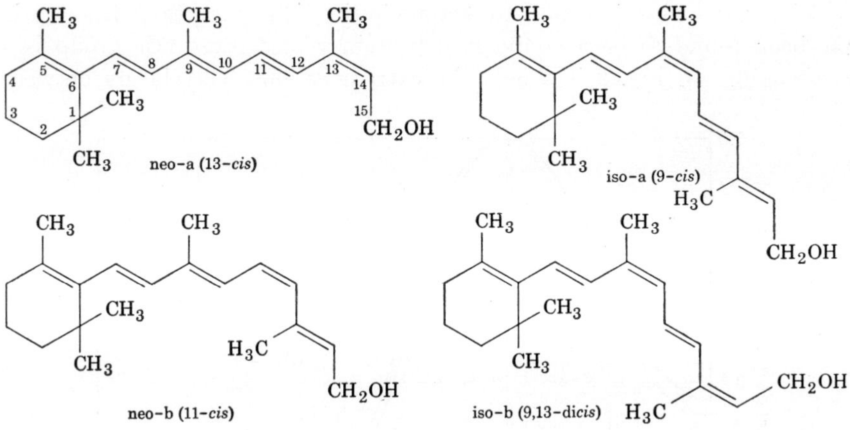

Fig. 1. Geometrical isomers of vitamin A_1.

Physiological Role of the Carotenoids

Although the most extensive investigation of the biochemical role of the carotenoids has dealt with their relationship to vitamin A activity in the nutrition of animals, considerable attention has also been given to

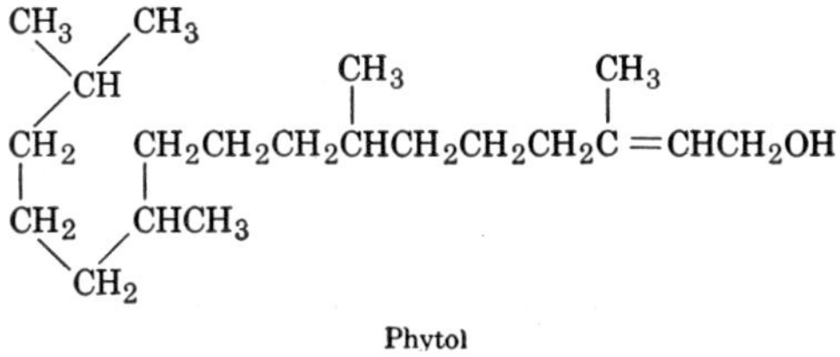

Phytol

the role played by these substances in plants and microorganisms. In green plants, carotenoids occur together with chlorophyll in the chloroplasts; the phytol residue of the chlorophylls (p. 182) may be formed from carotenoids, to which it is closely related chemically. The possible role of carotenoids in photosynthesis has been mentioned previously

[8] W. Oroshnik, *J. Am. Chem. Soc.*, **78**, 2651 (1956); W. Oroshnik et al., *Proc. Natl. Acad. Sci.*, **42**, 578 (1956); P. K. Brown and G. Wald, *J. Biol. Chem.*, **222**, 865 (1956).

[9] C. D. Robeson et al., *J. Am. Chem. Soc.*, **77**, 4111, 4120 (1955).

(p. 548) ; they also participate in determining the phototropic responses (movements in response to light) of higher plants, fungi, and bacteria.[10]

Studies by Wald, Morton, and others[11] have provided impressive evidence for the central role of the carotenoids in the photochemical processes associated with vision. In 1877 Boll discovered a photosensitive pigment in the retina of the frog, and this pigment was named rhodopsin or *Sehpurpur* (visual purple) by Kühne in the following year. Rhodopsin has been found to be a conjugated protein whose prosthetic group is a carotenoid. In Fig. 2 is shown the extremely close correlation between

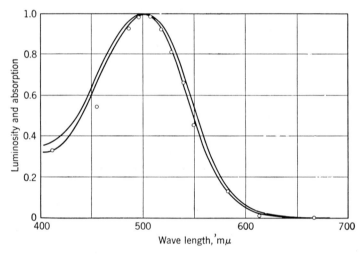

Fig. 2. Comparison of absorption spectra of rhodopsin (curves) with photochemical effectiveness of light for scotopic vision (points). [From S. Hecht, *J. Opt. Soc. Am.,* **32**, 42 (1942).]

the absorption spectrum of a solution of rhodopsin and the photochemical effectiveness of light for scotopic vision, i.e., the quanta of light required, at various wave lengths, for the production of a constant and very low brightness in the eye.

On illumination with white light, rhodopsin is converted to a mixture of the carotenoid retinene$_1$ and the rhodopsin protein (opsin). Retinene$_1$ is the aldehyde corresponding to vitamin A_1, and it may be prepared from the latter by oxidation with manganese dioxide. The visual impulse is associated with the initial photochemical transformation of rhodopsin into the orange-red "lumi-rhodopsin." This "light reaction" can be

[10] C. B. van Niel, *Ann. Rev. Microbiol.,* **8,** 105 (1954); C. B. van Niel et al., *Biochem. J.,* **63,** 408 (1956).

[11] G. Wald, *Ann. Rev. Biochem.,* **22,** 497 (1953); in O. H. Gaebler, *Enzymes: Units of Biological Structure and Function,* Academic Press, New York, 1956; H. J. A. Dartnall, *The Visual Pigments,* Methuen and Co., London, 1957.

demonstrated by chilling a solution of rhodopsin (e.g., an extract of frog retina prepared in red light, to which rhodopsin is insensitive) to $-40°$ C, and then exposing it to white light. The succeeding steps in the bleaching of rhodopsin to retinene$_1$ plus opsin are nonphotochemical. Thus, when the temperature of the lumi-rhodopsin solution is raised to about $-15°$ C, a somewhat more purple pigment ("meta-rhodopsin") is formed, and at about $20°$ C this yields the mixture of retinene$_1$ and opsin ("indicator yellow").[12]

Retinal tissue has a high content of DPN (p. 308), and this substance plays an important role in the metabolism of retinene$_1$. Thus the retinene released by the bleaching of rhodopsin is reduced to vitamin A$_1$ by DPNH in the presence of a retinal "retinene$_1$ reductase."[13] This enzyme is probably identical with alcohol dehydrogenase (p. 319), since it oxidizes ethanol to acetaldehyde; furthermore, retinene$_1$ can be reduced to vitamin A$_1$ by DPNH in the presence of crystalline horse liver alcohol dehydrogenase.

To effect the oxidation, *in vitro*, of vitamin A$_1$ to retinene$_1$ by DPN$^+$ in the presence of retinene reductase, the aldehyde must be removed from the equilibrium

$$\text{Vitamin A}_1 + \text{DPN}^+ \rightleftharpoons \text{Retinene}_1 + \text{DPNH} + \text{H}^+$$

which is far to the left. For example, the retinene$_1$ may be trapped by the addition of an aldehyde reagent such as hydroxylamine. However, a more physiological "aldehyde-trapping reagent" is opsin, which, in the dark, spontaneously reacts with retinene$_1$ to form rhodopsin. Thus the formation of rhodopsin from vitamin A$_1$ and opsin has been accomplished by coupling the enzymic oxidation of the carotenoid alcohol by DPN$^+$ with the spontaneous condensation of the carotenoid aldehyde with a purified preparation of opsin. This series of reactions leading from vitamin A$_1$ to rhodopsin constitutes the major biochemical events in "dark adaptation."

It is important to note, however, that rhodopsin is formed only by the combination of opsin with neo-b retinene$_1$ (the aldehyde corresponding to neo-b vitamin A$_1$; p. 657). On the other hand, the bleaching of rhodopsin yields all-*trans* retinene$_1$, which may be reduced to all-*trans* vitamin A$_1$. Consequently, before rhodopsin can be regenerated either the all-*trans* retinene must be isomerized to the neo-b aldehyde, or all-*trans* vitamin A$_1$ must be isomerized to neo-b vitamin A$_1$, which is reduced to neo-b retinene$_1$.[14] As noted earlier (p. 656), all-*trans* caroten-

[12] R. A. Morton and G. A. J. Pitt, *Biochem. J.,* **59,** 128 (1955).

[13] G. Wald and R. Hubbard, *J. Gen. Physiol.,* **32,** 367 (1949).

[14] R. Hubbard, *J. Gen. Physiol.,* **39,** 935 (1956); F. D. Collins et al., *Biochem. J.,* **56,** 493 (1954).

oids are isomerized by light to a mixture of *trans* and *cis* compounds. Although some rhodopsin can be formed from the all-*trans* isomers of vitamin A_1 or retinene$_1$ if they are isomerized by light, the yield of rhodopsin is poor because the isomerization is nonspecific.[15] However, eye tissue contains a "retinene isomerase" that specifically catalyzes the interconversion of the all-*trans* and neo-b isomers of retinene$_1$; the

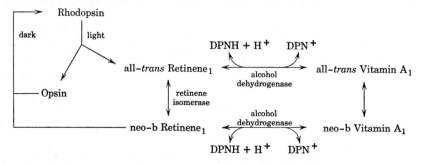

Fig. 3. Chemical events in the visual cycle.

isomerization occurs slowly in the dark, but is rapid in light. The sequence of chemical events in the visual cycle is summarized in Fig. 3.

In addition to rhodopsin, found in the retinal rods of frogs, birds, and mammals, other related visual pigments have also been found in these and other species (cf. Table 2). All these pigments are conjugated

Table 2. Visual Pigments of Vertebrates

Carotenoid	Protein	Visual Pigment		Source
		Name	Absorption Maximum	
Retinene$_1$	Rod opsin	Rhodopsin	500 mμ	Land and marine animals
Retinene$_1$	Cone opsin	Iodopsin	562 mμ	Land animals
Retinene$_2$	Rod opsin	Porphyropsin	522 mμ	Fresh water animals
Retinene$_2$	Cone opsin	Cyanopsin	620 mμ	Fresh water fish

proteins that differ with respect to their carotenoid—retinene$_1$ or retinene$_2$ (vitamin A_2 aldehyde)—or their protein (rod opsin or cone opsin). Thus rhodopsin and porphyropsin[16] are associated with the retinal rods (responsible for vision at low illumination), and iodopsin and cyanopsin[17] with the retinal cones (responsible for color vision). Each

[15] R. Hubbard and G. Wald, *J. Gen. Physiol.*, **36**, 269 (1952–1953); R. Hubbard, *J. Am. Chem. Soc.*, **78**, 4662 (1956).

[16] G. Wald, *Nature*, **175**, 390 (1955).

[17] G. Wald et al., *Science*, **118**, 505 (1953); *J. Gen. Physiol.*, **38**, 623 (1954–1955).

of these visual pigments and the related vitamin A are believed to participate in a visual cycle like that described above for rhodopsin and vitamin A_1.

In addition to the substances listed in Table 2, a "violet receptor" with an absorption maximum near 440 mμ has been found in the human eye.[18] The combined action of several visual pigments whose sensitivity to light spans the visible spectrum (ca. 400 to 660 mμ) may thus provide the basis for color vision. It is of interest that another group of visual pigments, which appear to contain retinine$_1$, has been detected in the retinas of deep sea fishes; these pigments appear to be specifically adapted for the utilization of light that penetrates into deep sea waters (wave length, ca. 480 mμ).[19]

For a comprehensive review of work on the physiological aspects of vision, and their relation to the quantum nature of light, see Pirenne.[20]

Terpenes [21]

As mentioned previously, the carotenoids are not the only naturally occurring products that may be considered to be composed of isoprene units. Among the unsaponifiable substances found in plants are many hydrocarbons known as terpenes. In general, these hydrocarbons, and their oxygenated derivatives, have fewer than 40 carbon atoms. The terpene hydrocarbons of the elementary composition $C_{10}H_{16}$ (corresponding to 2 isoprene units) are named monoterpenes; the compounds having the composition $C_{15}H_{24}$ are named sesquiterpenes; and members of the $C_{20}H_{32}$ and $C_{30}H_{48}$ groups are named di- and triterpenes, respectively. The group of terpenes with 40 carbon atoms, or tetraterpenes, include the carotenoids discussed earlier in this chapter.

The mono- and sesquiterpenes and their oxygenated derivatives occur as components of the essential oils obtained by steam distillation of the tissues of many plants; some of these terpenes are useful in the perfumery industry. Among the monoterpenes of interest are the hydrocarbon myrcene (from oil of bay) and the alcohol geraniol (from rose oil). Citral, the aldehyde corresponding to geraniol, is the major constituent of the oil of lemon grass. Other monoterpenes, which contain a monocyclic structure, are limonene (present in citrus and other oils), menthol (from mint oil), carvone (from caraway). In addition, a variety of bi- and tricyclic monoterpenes and their derivatives occur naturally.

[18] E. Auerbach and G. Wald, *Science,* **120**, 401 (1954).

[19] E. J. Denton and F. J. Warren, *Nature,* **178**, 1059 (1956); F. W. Munz, *Science,* **125**, 1142 (1957).

[20] M. H. Pirenne, *Biol. Revs.,* **31**, 194 (1956).

[21] R. H. Eastman and C. R. Noller, in H. Gilman, *Organic Chemistry,* Vol. IV, John Wiley and Sons, New York, 1953; J. L. Simonsen et al., *The Terpenes,* 2nd Ed., 5 vols., Cambridge University Press, Cambridge, 1947–1957.

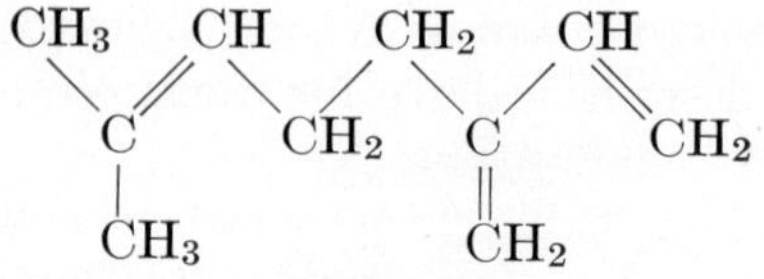

CH₃   CH   CH₂   CH   CH₃   CH   CH₂   CH₃
  \ / \   / \ /   \ / \   / \ /
   C   CH₂   C   CH₂   C   CH₂   C
   | ‖ | ‖
   CH₃   CH₂   CH₃   HCCH₂OH
        Myrcene 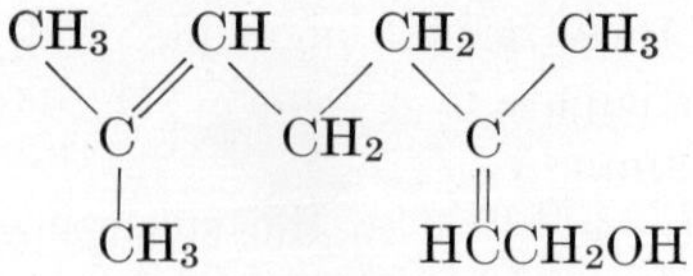   Geraniol

Examples of these are α-pinene (the principal constituent of oil of turpentine, obtained from pine trees), d-camphor (from *Cinnamomum camphora*), d-borneol (from hemlock oil), d-tanacetone or β-thujone (from tansy oil), and d-Δ³-carene (from pine needle oil).

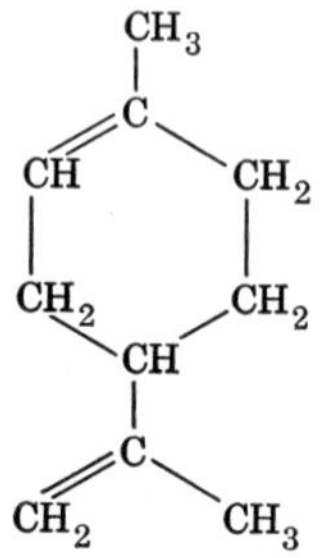

Limonene 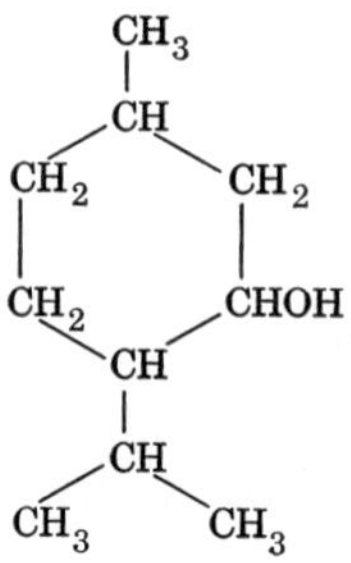   Menthol 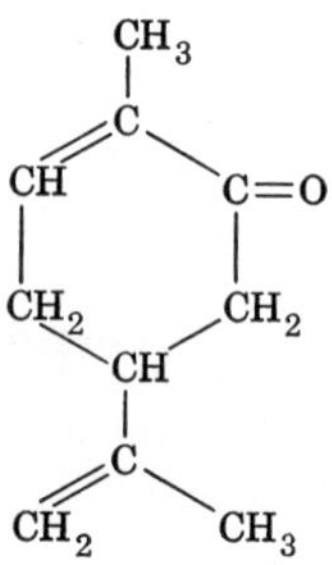   Carvone 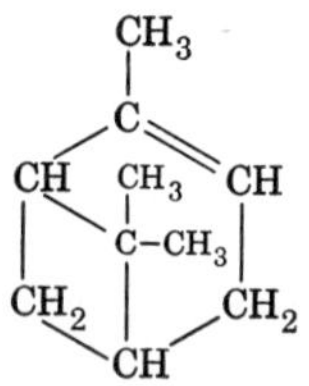   α-Pinene

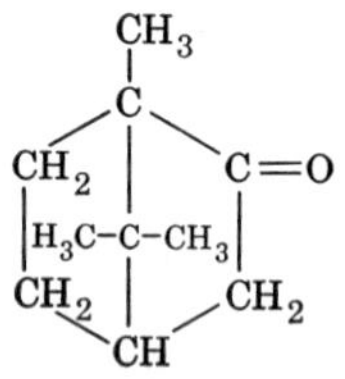

d-Camphor 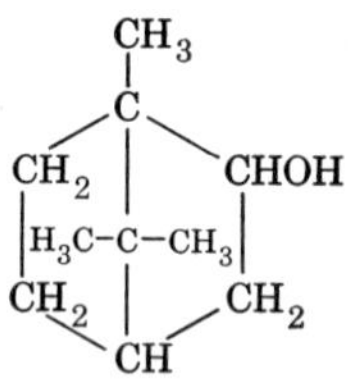   d-Borneol 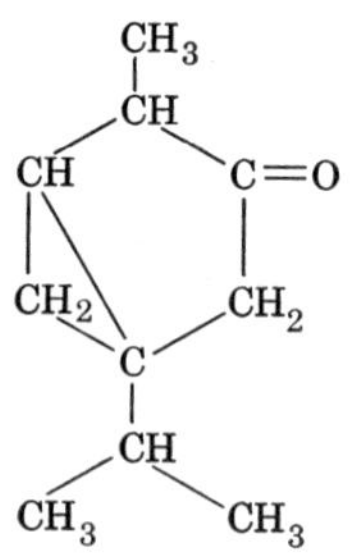   Thujone 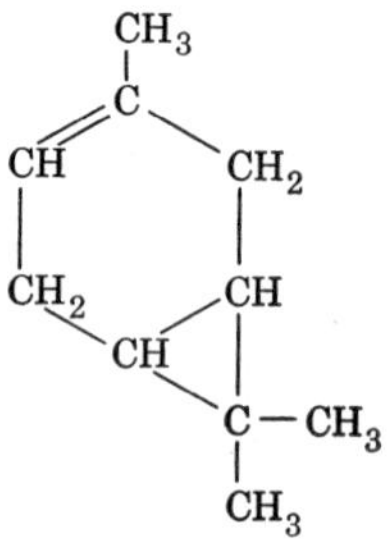   d-Δ³-Carene

An interesting monoterpene carboxylic acid, chrysanthemum monocarboxylic acid, is found in the form of an ester in the insecticidal oils obtained from pyrethrum flowers (*Chrysanthemum cineraii folium*). The formula of one of the esters (pyrethrin I) is shown; the alcohol formed from this compound is named pyrethrolone.

Of the sesquiterpenes, farnesol (cf. p. 631) appears to be widely distributed, but is found in the essential oils of plants in small amounts. Other members of this group are γ-bisabolene (from oil of bergamot), and cadinene (from oil of guayule and other plants).[22]

[22] A. J. Haagen-Smit, *Fortschritte der Chemie organischer Naturstoffe*, **12**, 1 (1955).

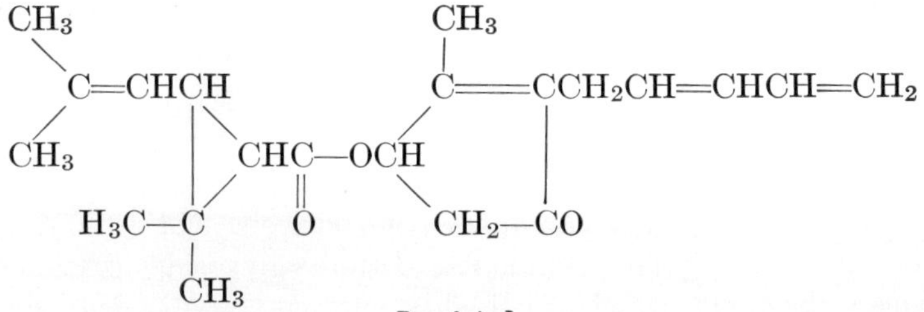

Pyrethrin I

The diterpenes[22] present in plants are, in general, not distillable with steam, and are found as constituents of the resins and balsams. The best known derivatives of this group of compounds are the resin acids abietic acid and sapietic acid (*l*-pimaric acid), obtained from the nonvolatile residue of pine oil. Vitamins A_1 and A_2 and their aldehydes (the retinenes) are monocyclic derivatives of diterpenes, and phytol (p. 657) is derived from an acyclic diterpene.

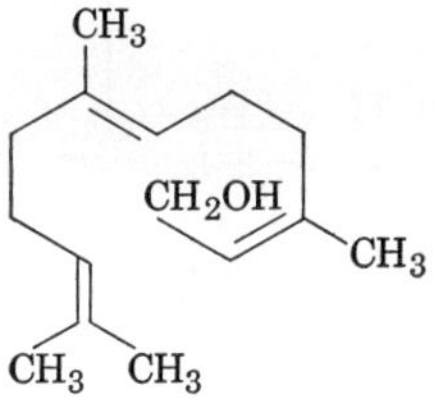

Farnesol

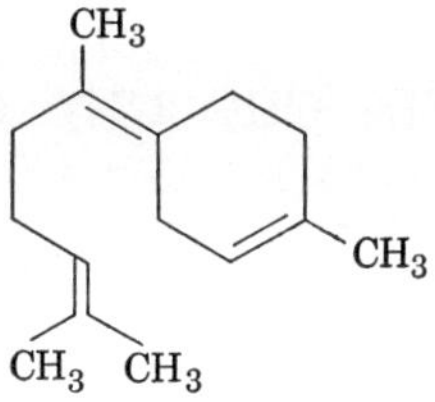

γ-Bisabolene

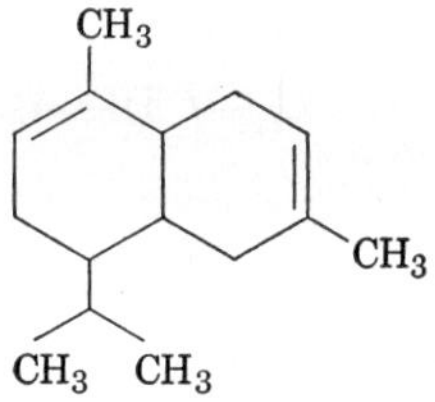

Cadinene

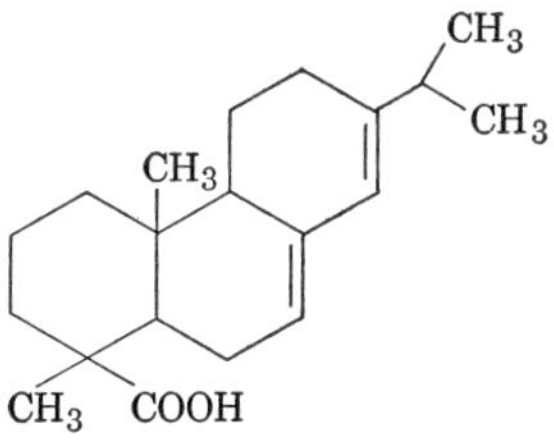

Abietic acid

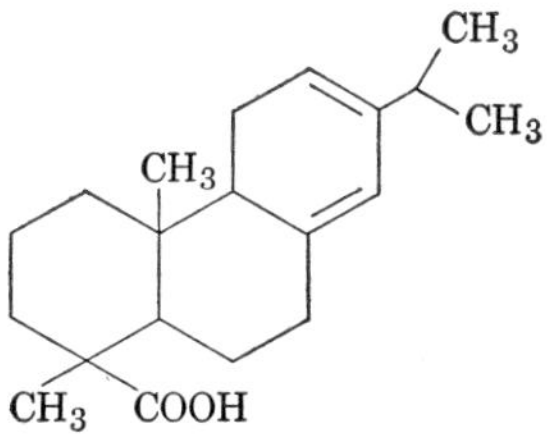

Sapietic acid

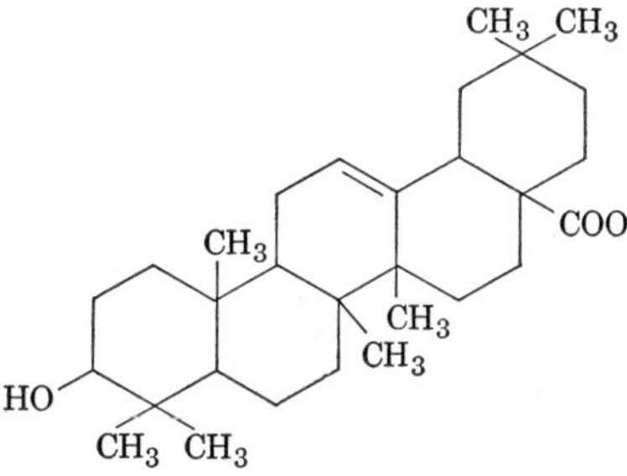

Oleanolic acid

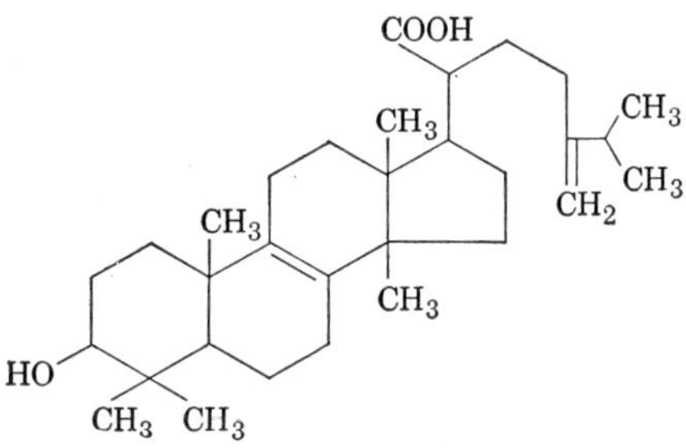

Eburicoic acid

The triterpenes,[23] although not widely distributed in nature, are of special interest, since they include the acyclic hydrocarbon squalene (p. 627) and the tetracyclic alcohol lanosterol (p. 623), which are important intermediates in the biosynthesis of cholesterol. A triterpene derivative found in higher plants is oleanolic acid; another, isolated from the fungus *Polyporus sulphureus*, is eburicoic acid (p. 663).[24]

Some of these triterpenoid compounds occur as glycosides (e.g., aesculin, from horse chestnut) which are highly surface-active agents and can hemolyze erythrocytes. Such glycosides are classed with certain steroid glycosides (p. 635) as saponins. The sapogenin oleanolic acid occurs as the free triterpenoid acid in olive leaves and as a saponin in sugar beet.

Mention should also be made of terpene rubber, found as the principal component in the latex of several tropical plant species. Rubber is a polyterpene composed of long chains of 500 to 5000 isoprene units, joined in linear array.

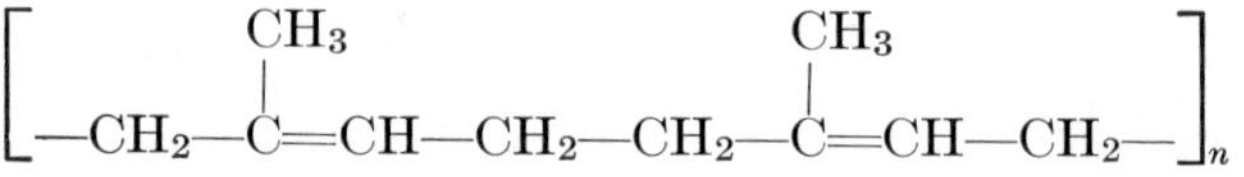

$$\left[-CH_2-\underset{\underset{CH_3}{|}}{C}=CH-CH_2-CH_2-\underset{\underset{CH_3}{|}}{C}=CH-CH_2- \right]_n$$

Biosynthesis of Isoprenoid Compounds

Ruzicka[25] drew attention to the fact that the carbon skeleton of geraniol, farnesol, or rubber is composed of isoprene units linked in a "regular" (or "head to tail") arrangement, whereas in some other terpenes an irregular linkage of isoprene units is found (e.g., the central linkage between the two $C_{15}H_{25}$ units of squalene, or that between the two $C_{20}H_{28}$ units of lycopene and the carotenes). Furthermore, he

Regular arrangement: $C-\underset{\underset{C}{|}}{C}-C-C-\!\!-\!\!-C-\underset{\underset{C}{|}}{C}-C-C$

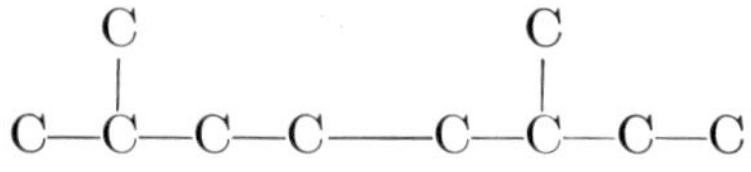

Irregular arrangement: $C-\underset{\underset{C}{|}}{C}-C-C-\!\!-\!\!-C-C-\underset{\underset{C}{|}}{C}-C$

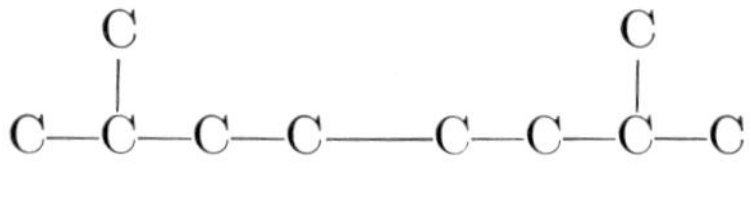

postulated that terpenes are formed in nature by the condensation of isoprenoid compounds in either of these sequences, and that the cyclic terpenes result from intramolecular rearrangements by known chemical mechanisms. This "isoprene rule" has been valuable in the determination

[23] E. R. H. Jones and T. G. Halsall, *Fortschritte der Chemie organischer Naturstoffe*, **12**, 44 (1955).

[24] J. S. E. Holker et al., *J. Chem. Soc.*, **1953**, 2422.

[25] L. Ruzicka, *Experientia*, **9**, 357 (1953).

of the structure of terpenes, and in the study of their biosynthesis. The fruitful application of the isoprene rule to the study of the biosynthesis of squalene, lanosterol, and cholesterol from acetate has been discussed on p. 627. The available data about the biosynthesis of rubber offer further support for this hypothesis. Thus acetic acid is a major precursor for the formation of rubber by seedlings or excised tissues of the guayule plant, and it is probable that dimethylacrylic, β-hydroxyisovaleric, and β-hydroxy-β-methylglutaric acids (or their CoA derivatives) are intermediates in the process.[26] The *in vivo* synthesis of rubber appears to be closely related to the synthesis of simpler terpenes; for example, a high concentration of the essential oil (main component, α-pinene) is found in the leaves of the guayule only during those periods when the formation of rubber is proceeding at a minimum rate.

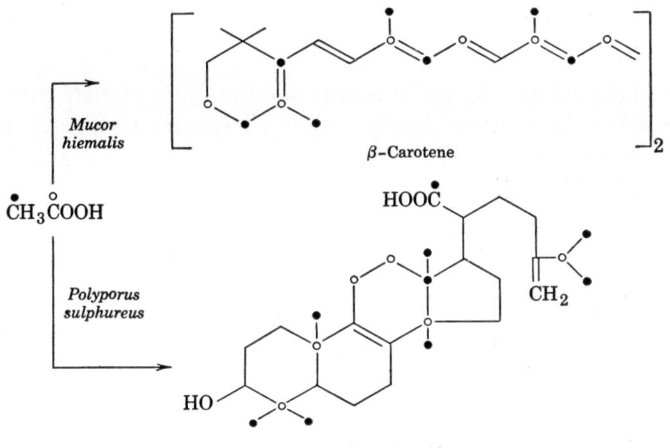

Fig. 4. Origin of some of the carbon atoms of β-carotene and of eburicoic acid formed from labeled acetic acid by fungi.

The biosynthesis of β-carotene[27] and of eburicoic acid[28] by fungi also appears to involve the initial conversion of C_2 units derived from acetic acid (probably acetyl-CoA) to a compound such as mevalonic acid, followed by the formation of larger isoprenoid compounds (Fig. 4). It is

[26] J. A. Johnston et al., *Proc. Natl. Acad. Sci.*, **40**, 1031 (1954); J. Bonner, *Federation Proc.*, **14**, 765 (1955); H. J. Teas and R. S. Bandurski, *J. Am. Chem. Soc.*, **78**, 3549 (1956).

[27] E. C. Grob and R. Bütler, *Helv. Chim. Acta,* **37**, 1908 (1954); **38**, 1313 (1955); **39**, 1975 (1956).

[28] W. G. Dauben and J. H. Richards, *J. Am. Chem. Soc.*, **78**, 5329 (1956); **79**, 968 (1957).

of special interest that the isotope distribution in biosynthetic eburicoic acid from a fungus given labeled acetate is strictly analogous to that in biosynthetic lanosterol and cholesterol from animal tissues (cf. p. 627), suggesting that eburicoic acid, like lanosterol, arises by a cyclization of squalene. In addition, the biosynthesis of eburicoic acid resembles that of ergosterol in the fact that the carbon of the $=CH_2$ group (C_{28}) is derived from "C_1 units."[29]

Although the biosynthesis of carotenoids probably is analogous to the biosynthesis of squalene (Fig. 4), little is known about the metabolic interrelations among the various carotenoids. It has been suggested that the first C_{40} compound formed is a colorless, highly saturated polyene (e.g., a tetrahydrophytoene), which then undergoes successive dehydrogenation reactions to yield colored carotenoids (e.g., lycopene). Some support for this view has come from studies with mutant strains of microorganisms (*Torula rubra*, *Neurospora crassa*, and *Rhodopseudomonas spheroides*).[30] However, the results of other studies[31] on the biosynthesis of carotenoids in many organisms, including higher plants, do not accord with this hypothesis, and the possibility exists that colorless polyenes and colored carotenoids are synthesized by separate pathways from a common precursor, and that each C_{40} compound is formed independently of all the others.

Other Fat-Soluble Vitamins

Among the fat-soluble components of many plant tissues are two groups of compounds designated by the collective terms vitamin E (or the antisterility factor) and vitamin K (or the antihemorrhagic factor). As may be seen from their formulae, each of these vitamins contains a number of isoprene units.

The Vitamin E Group.[32] The presence in vegetable oils of material essential for normal reproduction in rats was demonstrated independently by Evans and by Mattill in the early 1920's; the active principle was called vitamin E or the antisterility factor. When in 1936 two compounds with vitamin E activity were isolated from wheat germ oil, they were named α- and β-tocopherol (Greek *tokos*, birth; *phero*, to bear). Subsequently, five other tocopherols were obtained from cereal grains (wheat

---

[29] W. G. Dauben et al., *J. Am. Chem. Soc.*, **79**, 1000 (1957).

[30] J. Bonner et al., *Arch. Biochem.*, **10**, 113 (1946); F. T. Haxo, *Fortschritte der Chemie organischer Naturstoffe*, **12**, 169 (1955); M. Griffiths and R. Stanier, *J. Gen Microbiol.*, **14**, 698 (1956).

[31] G. Mackinney et al., *Proc. Natl. Acad. Sci.*, **42**, 404 (1956); *J. Biol. Chem.*, **220**, 759 (1956); E. A. Shneour and I. Zabin, *ibid.*, **226**, 861 (1957).

[32] R. S. Harris et al., in W. H. Sebrell, Jr., and R. S. Harris, *The Vitamins*, Vol. III, Chapter 17, Academic Press, New York, 1954.

germ, corn oil, soybean oil, rice).[33]   All the tocopherols are derivatives of a 6-hydroxychroman bearing an isoprenoid side chain at position 2, and they differ only in the substituents on carbon atoms, 5, 7, and 8. At the suggestion of Karrer, the term "tocol" is used to designate this general class of chromans and refers specifically to the compound in which hydrogen atoms are present at the 5, 7, and 8 positions; hence, α-tocopherol could also be designated 5,7,8-trimethyltocol.

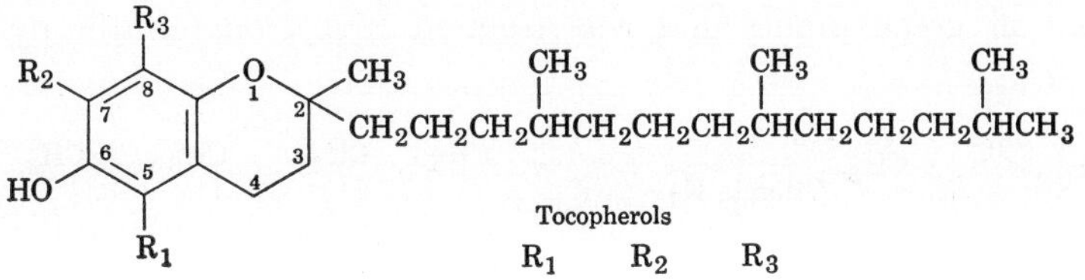

Tocopherols	R_1	R_2	R_3
α:	CH_3	CH_3	CH_3
β:	CH_3	H	CH_3
γ:	H	CH_3	CH_3
δ:	H	H	CH_3
ϵ:	CH_3	H	H
ζ:	CH_3	CH_3	H
η:	H	CH_3	H

Little information is available about the metabolism of the tocopherols. Much of the tocopherol content of blood plasma seems to be associated with a tocopherol-protein conjugate, and the formation *in vitro* of such a conjugate has been reported.   Possibly this substance represents the principal means by which vitamin E is transported by the circulatory system.   Apparently the tocopherols are rapidly catabolized since they are found in animal urine only after the administration of massive doses of the vitamins.   Studies on the fate of C^{14}-labeled α-tocopherol in animals indicate that the vitamin is excreted as such in the feces, and that it is degraded in the tissues to products that appear in the urine as glucuronides.   The catabolism of α-tocopherol appears to involve both the oxidative cleavage of the chroman ring to yield quinone- or hydro-quinone-like compounds (Chapter 39) and the degradation of the aliphatic side chain.[34]

The Group of K Vitamins.[35]   The name vitamin K (for *Koagulations-*

[33] J. Green and S. Marcinkiewicz, *Nature*, **177**, 86 (1956).
[34] E. J. Simon et al., *J. Biol. Chem.*, **221**, 807 (1956).
[35] R. S. Harris et al., in W. H. Sebrell, Jr., and R. S. Harris, *The Vitamins*, Vol. II, Chapter 9, Academic Press, New York, 1954.

Vitamin) was proposed in 1934 by Dam for the natural material which cured or prevented the fatal hemorrhagic conditions he had observed some years earlier in newly hatched chicks maintained on artificial diets. This hemorrhagic tendency was associated with a decrease in the prothrombin (p. 703) content of the blood and, as has been demonstrated for higher animals in general, the antihemorrhagic activity of the K vitamins is due to their essential role in the biosynthesis of prothrombin.

Vitamin K_1 or phylloquinone (2-methyl-3-phytyl-1,4-naphthoquinone) is found in green plants and was isolated first from alfalfa by Dam,

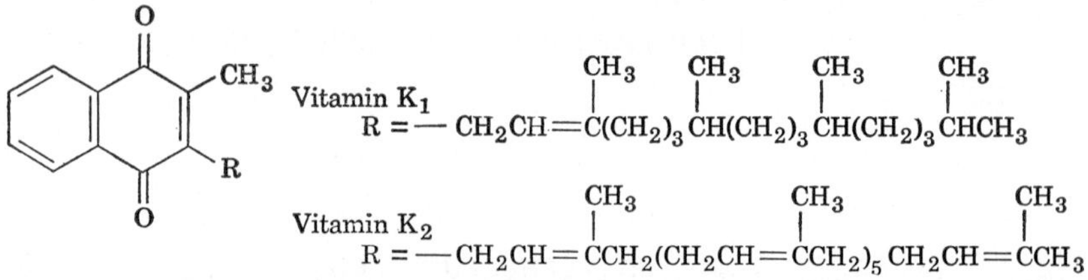

Karrer, and their associates. Vitamin K_2 (2-methyl-3-farnesyldigeranyl-1,4-naphthoquinone), which is formed by bacteria and was isolated first from putrefied fish meal by Doisy and coworkers, differs from phylloquinone only in the substituent in the 3 position of the naphthoquinone ring. These are the only naturally occurring forms of vitamin K that have been completely characterized. However, many synthetic compounds have been shown to have vitamin K activity for animals; the most active of these is the compound 2-methyl-1,4-naphthoquinone (also called menadione or vitamin K_3), which, on a molar basis, is as active as vitamin K_1. In this connection, it may be mentioned that phthiocol (2-methyl-3-hydroxy-1,4-naphthoquinone), first obtained from an alkaline hydrolysate of the lipid fraction of tubercle bacilli, has a slight antihemorrhagic action in chicks. Most of the other "synthetic vitamins" are derivatives of 1,4-naphthoquinone or of the corresponding naphthohydroquinone (e.g., 2-methyl-1,4-dihydroxynaphthalene). In addition, naphthol derivatives such as 2-methyl-4-amino-1-naphthol will replace the natural vitamin in the promotion of prothrombin formation. Thus the specificity requirements for vitamin K activity are quite broad, and it is not possible to decide on the functional form of the vitamin *in vivo*.

Vitamin K deficiency is encountered infrequently in higher animals since vitamin K_2 is synthesized by the intestinal bacteria. This source of vitamin K may be eliminated by the administration of sulfonamides that inhibit the growth of the requisite intestinal organisms.[36] In newborn human infants the absence of intestinal bacteria coupled with

[36] S. Black et al., *J. Biol. Chem.*, **145**, 137 (1942).

the absence of a store of the vitamin K_1 in the tissues may result in a characteristic hemorrhagic condition which can readily be cured by the administration of any of the active compounds.

There are no experimental data on the mode of synthesis of either vitamin K_1 or K_2. Nor are any data available about their metabolic fate in animals or plants. Animal tissues contain relatively small amounts of material with demonstrable vitamin K activity, and vitamin K_1 is known to be rapidly metabolized *in vivo*.

The Anthocyanins and Related Compounds[37]

Although the anthocyanins and their chemical relatives are not lipids, they are frequently considered together with the carotenoids since these two groups of substances, together with chlorophyll, represent the principal pigments of plants. In green plants chlorophyll is localized in the grana of chloroplasts, which also contain carotenoids. The other pigments, which are freely soluble in water, are found primarily in the vacuolar sap of plant cells.

Most of our knowledge of the chemistry of the anthocyanins stems from the classical work of Willstätter and of Robinson. These red, blue, and violet pigments are glycosides containing 1 or 2 carbohydrate units and an aglycone known as an anthocyanidin. The anthocyanidins are derivatives of 3,5,7-trihydroxyflavylium hydroxide (2-phenyl-3,5,7-tri-hydroxybenzopyrylium hydroxide). The assignment of the positive charge to the oxygen atom in the oxonium salt shown in Fig. 5 is arbitrary, since the flavylium ion is a resonance hybrid.

Three main groups of anthocyanidins are differentiated on the basis of the extent of substitution in ring B (Table 3). Obviously, a great variety of anthocyanins may exist, since, in the anthocyanidin moiety, the number of hydroxyl groups may vary from 4 to 6, and any number of these hydroxyls may be methylated. The number of carbohydrate units in the glycosides may be either 1 (in which case it is generally linked to the 3-hydroxyl of the aglycone) or 2 (linked to the hydroxyls at the 3 and 5 positions of the anthocyanidin). The color of the pigments depends both on the number of hydroxyl groups and on the extent to which the hydroxyl groups are replaced by methoxyl groups. The color of a solution of an anthocyanidin also depends on the pH, since these pigments are indicators that are generally red in acid solution, violet or purple at neutral pH values, and blue in alkaline solution (Fig. 5).

[37] K. P. Link, in H. Gilman, *Organic Chemistry*, 2nd Ed., Vol. II, John Wiley and Sons, New York, 1943; S. Wawzonek, in R. C. Elderfield, *Heterocyclic Compounds*, Vol. II, John Wiley and Sons, New York, 1951.

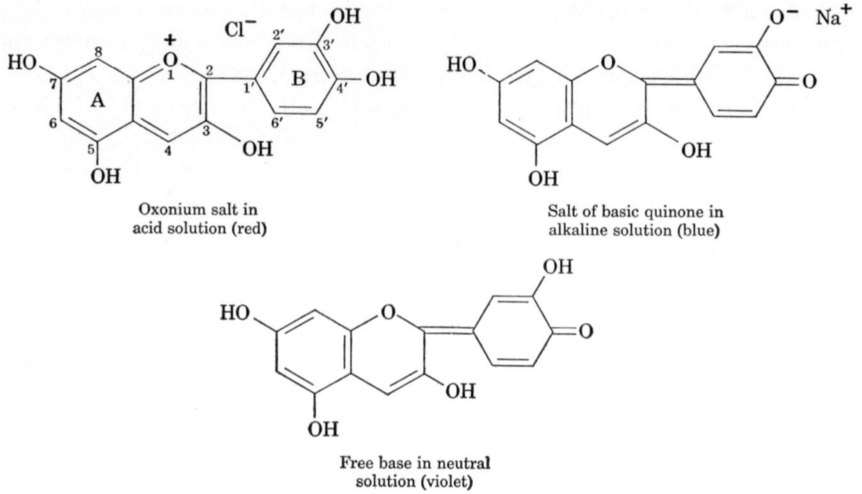

Oxonium salt in
acid solution (red)

Salt of basic quinone in
alkaline solution (blue)

Free base in neutral
solution (violet)

Fig. 5. Structural changes responsible for color variation of cyanidin (3,5,7,3′,4′-pentahydroxyflavylium hydroxide).

Another widely distributed group of water-soluble plant pigments, related structurally to the anthocyanins, are derivatives of 2-phenyl-1,4-benzopyrone (flavone). Flavone has been isolated from the primrose

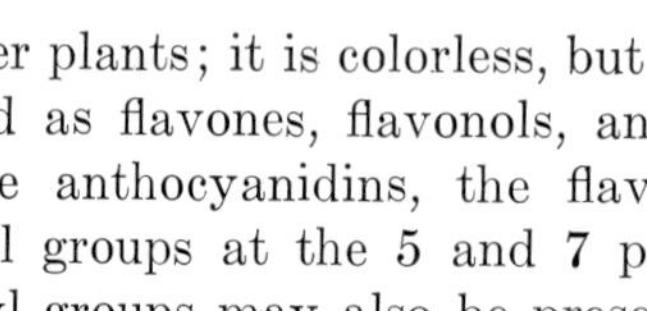

2-Phenyl-1,4-benzopyrone
(flavone)

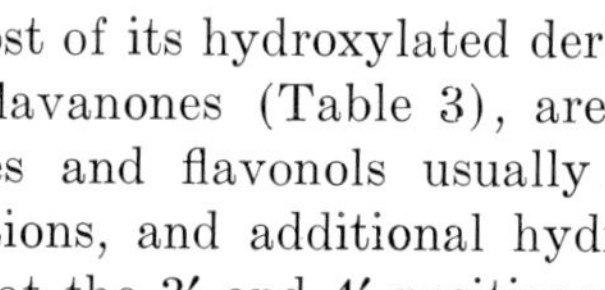

Flavonol

and other plants; it is colorless, but most of its hydroxylated derivatives, classified as flavones, flavonols, and flavanones (Table 3), are yellow. Like the anthocyanidins, the flavones and flavonols usually contain hydroxyl groups at the 5 and 7 positions, and additional hydroxyl or methoxyl groups may also be present at the 3′ and 4′ positions. These pigments occur both in the free form and as glycosides.

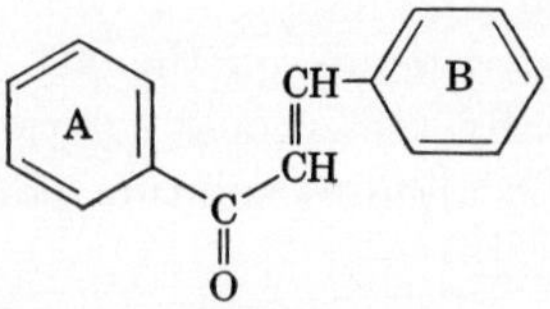

Chalcone

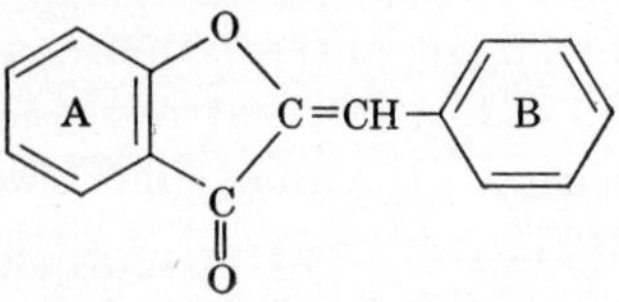

Aurone

Higher plants may contain two additional groups of yellow pigments, the chalcones (derivatives of benzalacetophenone or chalcone) and the aurones (derivatives of benzalcoumaran-3-one or aurone). These pigments (Table 3) occur in the free form or as glycosides.

Table 3. Some Water-Soluble Plant Pigments

Anthocyanidins

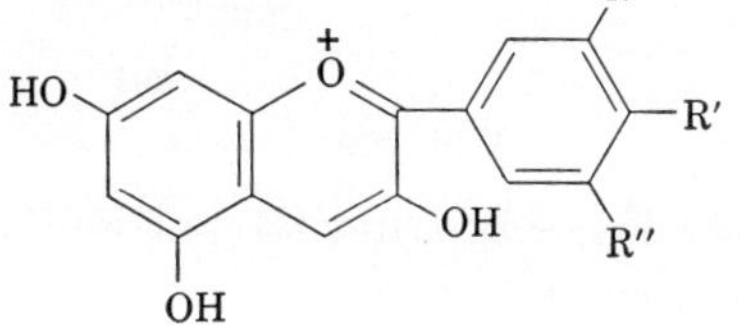

	R	R′	R″
Pelargonidin	H	OH	OH
Cyanidin	OH	OH	H
Delphinidin	OH	OH	OH
Peonidin	OCH_3	OH	H
Malvidin	OCH_3	OH	OCH_3

Flavones and flavonols

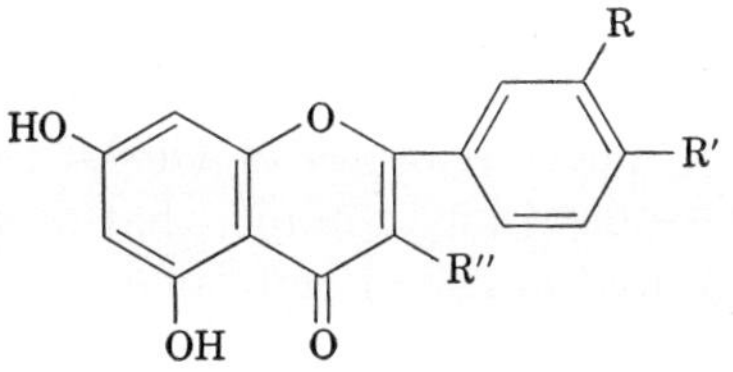

	R	R′	R″
Chrysin	H	H	H
Apigenin	H	OH	H
Luteolin	OH	OH	H
Kaempferol	H	OH	OH
Quercetin	OH	OH	OH

Flavanones

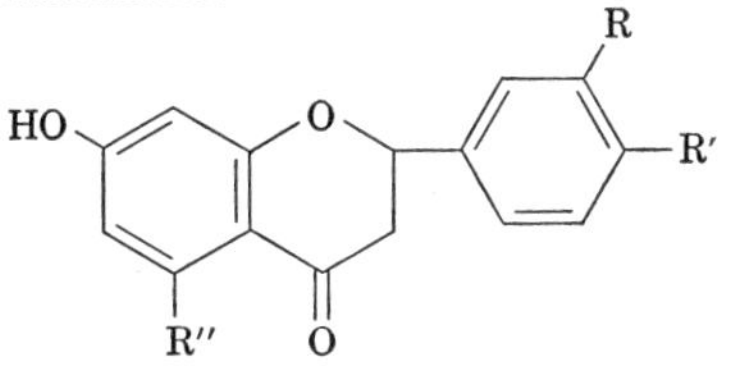

	R	R′	R″
Naringenin	H	OH	OH
Eriodictyol	OH	OH	OH
Liquiritigenin	H	OH	H

Chalcones

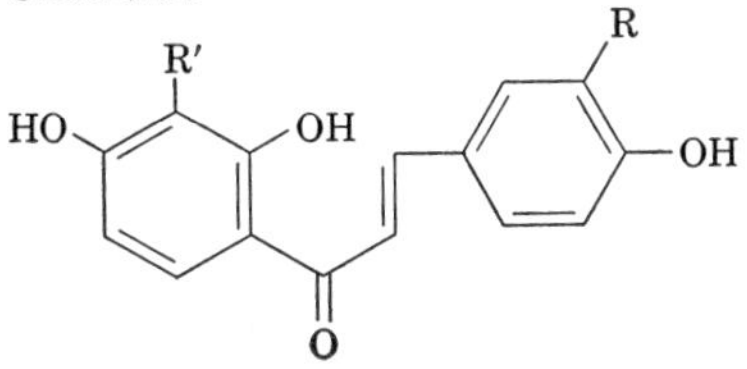

	R	R′
Dahlia chalcone	H	H
Butein	H	OH
Okanin	OH	OH

Aurones

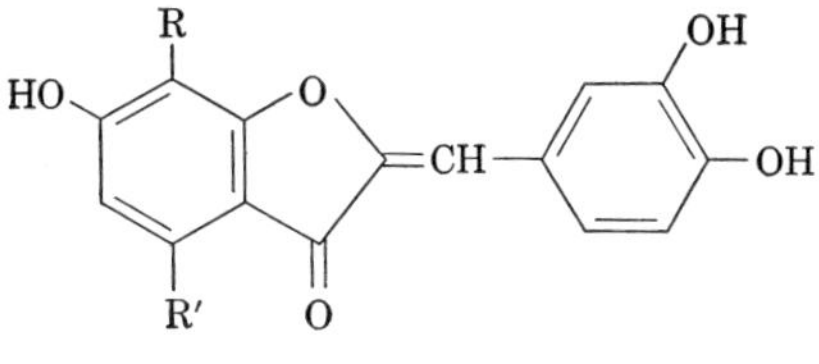

	R	R′
Aureusidin	H	OH
Sulfuretin	H	H
Maritimetin	OH	H

It will be noted from Table 3 that all the aglycones of the water-soluble plant pigments are variants of the same basic carbon skeleton C_6—C_3—C_6. The fact that several species of plants contain esters of p-coumaric and caffeic acids suggests that these C_3—C_6 acids have a

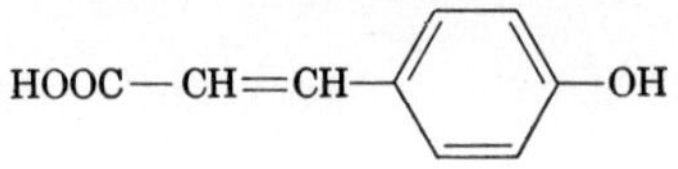

HOOC — CH=CH-⟨ ⟩-OH   HOOC — CH=CH-⟨ ⟩-OH
                                                              |
                                                              OH

   p-Coumaric acid 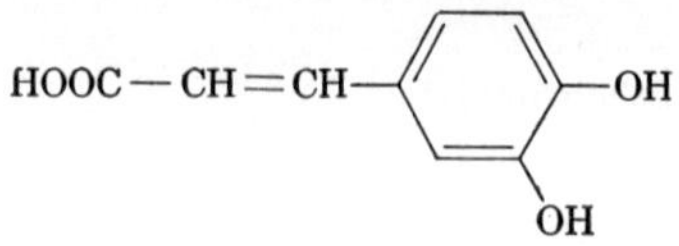   Caffeic acid

biosynthetic relation to the corresponding C_3—C_6 (ring B) portions of the various aglycones. Presumably, a phenylpropane derivative condenses with a polyphenol to yield the C_6—C_3—C_6 structure. For discussions of the proposed pathways of biosynthesis of these pigments, see Seshadri and Paech.[38]

Color production is one of the most thoroughly explored areas in the study of the genetics of higher plants.[39] The researches of Onslow, of Scott-Moncrieff, and of Geissman[40] have shown, for example, that separate genes control the production of 4'-hydroxylated aglycones (e.g., pelargonidin, apigenin, kaempferol) and of 3',4'-dihydroxylated aglycones (e.g., cyanidin, luteolin, quercetin). The number and position of hydroxyl groups attached to ring A are also controlled by different genes, and the nature and position of the carbohydrate units in the glycosides are determined by still other genetic factors.

[38] T. R. Seshadri, *Ann. Rev. Biochem.*, **20**, 487 (1951); K. Paech, *Ann. Rev. Plant Physiol.*, **6**, 273 (1955).

[39] W. J. C. Lawrence and J. R. Price, *Biol. Revs.*, **15**, 35 (1940).

[40] E. G. Jorgensen and T. A. Geissman, *Ach. Biochem. and Biophys.*, **55**, 389 (1955); T. A. Geissman and J. B. Harborne, *ibid.*, **55**, 447 (1955).

28 · Metabolic Utilization of Inorganic Nitrogen Compounds

The proteins are of vital importance in the maintenance of the structural and functional integrity of all biological forms. In living organisms, however, proteins are continuously being broken down to smaller fragments (peptides and amino acids), and some of the nitrogen is transferred to end products of protein metabolism (e.g., ammonia, urea, uric acid, alkaloids). This degradation of proteins is counteracted by metabolic mechanisms for the synthesis of proteins. All the available data on protein formation in biological systems indicate that amino acids and their derivatives serve as precursors of proteins; as noted earlier, protein synthesis from amino acids is an endergonic process and must be coupled to energy-yielding steps in the oxidative breakdown of carbohydrates and fats.

As will be seen from the succeeding chapters, a variety of metabolic reactions are available for the degradation, synthesis, and interconversion of the protein amino acids. Consequently, the capacity of an organism to synthesize a protein does not depend upon an external source of all the constituent amino acids. However, many organisms must receive, from the external environment, one or more amino acids which either are not formed *in vivo* or are synthesized too slowly to permit normal protein synthesis. Such amino acids are termed "indispensable" (p. 724), and, when the requirements for such indispensable amino acids have been met, the remainder of the nitrogen needed for protein synthesis can be supplied in the form of ammonium salts. The generalization may be made that ammonia forms the key intermediate in nitrogen metabolism, and most organisms, when supplied with an adequate source of utilizable carbon compounds, other essential elements (e.g., sulfur, phosphorus), and indispensable dietary nutrients, can readily use ammonia as the principal metabolic source of protein nitrogen. Many microorganisms belonging to the group of Gram-negative bacteria (e.g., *Escherichia coli*) can grow, i.e., synthesize protein, in a culture medium in which ammonium salts are the sole nitrogen compounds. Higher animals (e.g., the rat) can also derive a major proportion of their protein nitrogen from dietary ammonium salts, but these organisms must be supplied, in addition, with a dietary source of certain indispensable amino acids. Among the microorganisms, the lactic acid bacteria also require certain preformed amino acids; advantage has been taken of this property for the amino acid analysis of protein hydrolysates (p. 126).

Ammonia is not the only inorganic substance, however, that can serve as a source of nitrogen for metabolism. It will be recalled that higher plants readily utilize inorganic nitrate, which represents the principal form of nitrogen supplied to plants by soil. In addition, numerous microorganisms can use as nitrogen sources not only nitrates or ammonia but also nitrites. These aspects of the metabolism of inorganic nitrogen compounds will be considered later in this chapter. Attention will be given first to the important group of microorganisms that transform atmospheric nitrogen (N_2) into inorganic or organic nitrogen compounds and therefore can use the nitrogen of the air for metabolic purposes. The process of converting free nitrogen gas to bound (or fixed) nitrogen is termed "nitrogen fixation."

Nitrogen Fixation [1]

The best known representatives of the nitrogen-fixing organisms are the heterotrophic bacteria which can grow in the complete absence of bound nitrogen, so long as a source of carbon (e.g., mannitol) and atmospheric nitrogen are present. Among these bacteria are members of the genus *Azotobacter* (isolated by Beijerinck in 1901), a group of aerobic organisms found free living in soil. *Azotobacter* is remarkably efficient in the fixation of nitrogen, since the uptake of 1 millimole of O_2 leads to the fixation of as much as 0.1 millimole of N_2. *Azotobacter* and other nitrogen-fixing organisms require trace quantities of molybdenum or vanadium salts for nitrogen fixation and for growth; approximately 1 part per million of one of these metals is sufficient to exert an optimal effect.

Biochemical studies indicate strongly that, in *Azotobacter*, ammonia is the product of nitrogen fixation which is incorporated into organic substances.[2] The major points of evidence in favor of this view are the following:

[1] P. W. Wilson and R. H. Burris, *Bact. Revs.*, **11**, 41 (1947); *Ann. Rev. Microbiol.*, **7**, 415 (1953); P. W. Wilson, *Advances in Enzymol.*, **13**, 345 (1952); R. H. Burris, in W. D. McElroy and B. Glass, *Inorganic Nitrogen Metabolism*, Johns Hopkins Press, Baltimore, 1956.

[2] R. M. Allison and R. H. Burris, *J. Biol. Chem.*, **224**, 351 (1957).

1. If *Azotobacter vinelandii* is exposed for a short time (3 to 15 min) to N_2 labeled with N^{15}, most of the isotopic nitrogen is recovered in the bacterial glutamic acid, glutamine, and aspartic acid. An exactly analogous result is obtained if the isotopic N_2 is replaced by ammonium salts containing $N^{15}H_4{}^+$. As will be seen later, when higher plants and animals are given isotopic ammonium ions, the greatest accumulation of N^{15} also is found in the glutamic and aspartic acid residues of the proteins.

2. When both N_2 and ammonium ions, or compounds that can readily give rise to ammonia (e.g., urea), are present, *Azotobacter* preferentially uses ammonia as the sole source of nitrogen; thus, in the presence of ammonia, nitrogen fixation is suppressed.[3]

3. On the other hand, compounds such as nitrate or nitrite that are not readily converted to ammonia by *Azotobacter* do not inhibit nitrogen fixation so effectively as urea; the organism must be cultivated on these substances (i.e., it must be adapted) before it will be able to use them in place of atmospheric nitrogen.

Significant evidence for the view that ammonia is the key intermediate in nitrogen fixation has come from studies with another soil microorganism, *Clostridium pasteurianum*, first isolated by Winogradsky in 1893. In contrast to *Azotobacter*, this organism is an anaerobe, and it derives energy from the fermentative degradation of glucose and related compounds. Also, unlike *Azotobacter* and other aerobic nitrogen-fixing bacteria that rapidly utilize any available ammonia for the synthesis of amino acids, *Cl. pasteurianum* excretes into the culture medium considerable quantities of ammonia and other nitrogen compounds. Consequently, it has been possible to show that N^{15}-labeled N_2 is directly converted into isotopic ammonia by *Cl. pasteurianum*.[4] For example, when growing cells were exposed for 45 min to N_2 containing 31.3 atom per cent excess N^{15}, the ammonia isolated from the medium contained 14 atom per cent excess N^{15}; the latter isotope concentration was approximately ten times as great as that of the total nitrogen of the medium. Since the amide-N of glutamine and of asparagine contained 8 and 2 atom per cent excess N^{15}, respectively, the isotopic ammonia in the medium could not have been derived primarily from the deamidation of these two amides.

Although the evidence is strong for the conversion of N_2 to NH_3 prior to incorporation of the nitrogen into organic compounds, the chemical events in this conversion are not known. Some of the inorganic nitrogen

[3] J. W. Newton et al., *J. Biol. Chem.*, **204**, 445 (1953).
[4] I. Zelitch et al., *J. Biol. Chem.*, **191**, 295 (1951).

compounds that may be derived by oxidation or reduction of N_2 are shown in the accompanying scheme; it cannot be stated at present which of these intermediates between N_2 and NH_3 are involved in nitrogen fixation. In this connection, it is of interest that labeled nitrous oxide (N^{15}_2O) is slowly assimilated by *Azotobacter vinelandii*, and that N_2O competitively inhibits fixation of N_2.[5] The other possible intermedi-

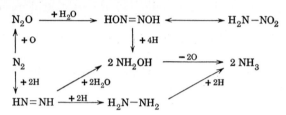

ates—hyponitrous acid[6] ($HON{=}NOH$), nitramide ($H_2N{-}NO_2$), hydroxylamine (NH_2OH), and hydrazine ($H_2N{-}NH_2$)—are too toxic or insufficiently stable (or both) to be tested adequately with the nitrogen fixing bacteria; diimide ($HN{=}NH$) is too unstable to be isolated as such. The possibility exists that the free inorganic compounds shown in the scheme do not represent the true intermediates between N_2 and NH_3 in the cell, and that these intermediates are organic substances to which the inorganic nitrogen compounds are bound.

The enzyme system thought to perform the over-all hydrogenation of N_2 to NH_3 has been termed "nitrogenase," but little is known about its properties, because considerable difficulties have been encountered in the preparation of cell-free extracts that can effect nitrogen fixation.[7] In particular, the immediate metabolic source of protons and electrons for the reduction of N_2 to NH_3 is unknown. It has been suggested that "nitrogenase" is closely related to the enzyme hydrogenase, which catalyzes the reaction $2H^+ + 2e \rightleftharpoons H_2$, and which is present in many microorganisms, including bacteria that do not fix N_2.

The relationship between nitrogen fixation and the action of hydrogenase has been brought out especially clearly by work with a photosynthetic purple bacterium (*Rhodospirillum rubrum*) which produces molecular hydrogen upon illumination.[8] This photosynthetic production of hydrogen is abolished, however, when N_2 is present. Gest and Kamen have shown that under these conditions nitrogen fixation occurs. Aside from providing further evidence for the view that an essential photochemical reaction in photosynthesis is a reduction, this important finding

[5] M. M. Mozen and R. H. Burris, *Biochim. et Biophys. Acta,* **14,** 577 (1954).

[6] M. T. Chaudhary et al., *Biochim. et Biophys. Acta,* **14,** 507 (1954).

[7] W. E. Magee and R. H. Burris, *J. Bact.,* **71,** 635 (1956).

[8] H. Gest and M. D. Kamen, *Science,* **109,** 558, 560 (1949).

also indicates a direct link between the "nitrogenase" system and the reaction catalyzed by hydrogenase. It would appear that in *Rhodospirillum rubrum* nitrogen fixation is coupled to the utilization of electrons and protons arising from the photolysis of water by activated chlorophyll (p. 549), and that these electrons and protons can either be converted to H_2 by hydrogenase, or utilized for the reduction of N_2.[9] It may be added that a variety of other photosynthetic organisms (bacteria, algae) also can fix atmospheric nitrogen.[10]

A close relation between nitrogen fixation and hydrogenase is further indicated by the finding that H_2 inhibits the utilization of N_2 by *Azotobacter*, and studies with a cell-free preparation of *Clostridium pasteurianum* also show a link between hydrogenase and the reduction of N_2. Partially purified hydrogenase preparations from *Cl. pasteurianum* contain a molybdoflavoprotein (cf. p. 339) which participates in electron transfer from H_2 to a variety of oxidants.[11]

The fixation of N_2 by *Azotobacter* is favored by reduced oxygen tension,[12] suggesting that, in this aerobic organism, O_2 and N_2 compete for electrons and protons derived from the oxidation of metabolites. This observation is consistent with the finding that anaerobes such as *Clostridia* fix N_2 more efficiently than does *Azotobacter*.

Symbiotic Nitrogen Fixation.[13] *Azotobacter vinelandii* and *Clostridium pasteurianum* are only two of the many nitrogen-fixing organisms found in nature. As noted before, they are free-living organisms, and, when soil is allowed to lie fallow, such organisms contribute to its natural fertilization. Soil may also be fertilized by the cultivation of one of the leguminous plants (alfalfa, clover, lupins, beans, etc.). The roots of these legumes have nodules formed by the action of the group of bacteria of the *Rhizobium* family; *Rhizobia*, in association with the root cells of the plant, can effect the fixation of atmospheric nitrogen. Since neither the root cells nor the bacteria separately can fix nitrogen, the process is usually termed "symbiotic nitrogen fixation." Among the numerous students of the biochemistry of this process has been Virtanen,[14] who suggested that the key intermediate in nitrogen fixation is hydroxylamine. The detection of hydroxylamine in root nodules and the finding that small, but significant, amounts of oximinosuccinic acid were released

[9] H. Gest et al., in W. D. McElroy and B. Glass, *Inorganic Nitrogen Metabolism,* Johns Hopkins Press, Baltimore, 1956.

[10] G. E. Fogg, *Ann. Rev. Plant Physiol.,* **7,** 51 (1956).

[11] A. L. Shug et al., *J. Am. Chem. Soc.,* **76,** 3355 (1954); in W. D. McElroy and B. Glass, *Inorganic Nitrogen Metabolism,* Johns Hopkins Press, Baltimore, 1956.

[12] C. A. Parker, *Nature,* **173,** 780 (1954).

[13] P. W. Wilson, *The Biochemistry of Symbiotic Nitrogen Fixation,* University of Wisconsin Press, Madison, 1940.

[14] A. I. Virtanen, *Biol. Revs.,* **22,** 239 (1947).

into the soil led Virtanen to suggest that this compound, as well as hydroxylamine, functions in the fixation of N_2 into amino acids, as shown in the accompanying scheme. However, hydroxylamine is a

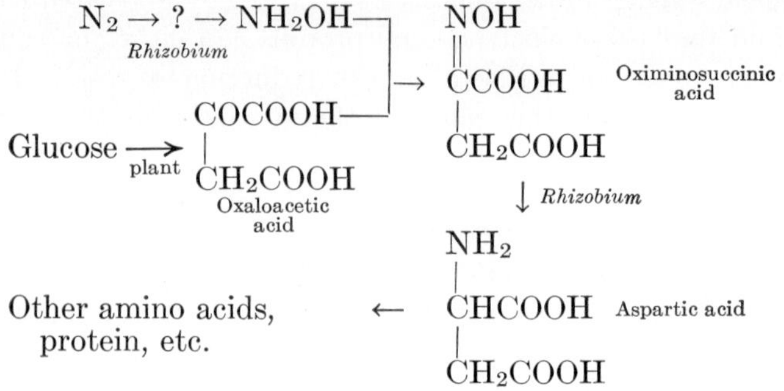

$$N_2 \rightarrow ? \rightarrow NH_2OH \longrightarrow$$
$$\underset{Rhizobium}{}$$

$$\begin{array}{l} NOH \\ \| \\ CCOOH \qquad \text{Oximinosuccinic} \\ | \qquad\qquad\qquad \text{acid} \\ CH_2COOH \end{array}$$

$$\text{Glucose} \underset{plant}{\longrightarrow} \begin{array}{l} COCOOH \\ | \\ CH_2COOH \\ \text{Oxaloacetic} \\ \text{acid} \end{array}$$

$$\downarrow Rhizobium$$

Other amino acids, $\leftarrow$
protein, etc.

$$\begin{array}{l} NH_2 \\ | \\ CHCOOH \qquad \text{Aspartic acid} \\ | \\ CH_2COOH \end{array}$$

relatively toxic substance, and it is possible that oximes may arise by reactions other than the direct interaction of free NH_2OH with keto acids. The enzymic reduction of oximes to amino acids, as well as the enzymic transfer of oximino ($=NOH$) groups from one keto acid to another, has been demonstrated with microorganisms and with a variety of other biological systems.[15]

A significant advance in the study of symbiotic nitrogen fixation has been the demonstration of this phenomenon with excised root nodules from several leguminous plants.[16] Such preparations exhibit optimum nitrogen fixation at an oxygen tension of about 0.5 atmosphere, and little fixation is observed under anaerobic conditions or at high oxygen pressure.

In connection with the requirement of O_2 for symbiotic nitrogen fixation, it will be recalled from the discussion of the heme proteins that a hemoglobin-like pigment has been found in root nodules (p. 164). Free-living *Rhizobia* do not produce this pigment, and root cells produce it only when they are in symbiosis with the bacteria. The pigment appears to be absent in aerobic nitrogen-fixing organisms such as *Azotobacter*. The heme protein of root nodules combines reversibly with oxygen or carbon monoxide in a manner similar to the behavior of the oxygen-transporting pigments of animals (hemoglobin, myoglobin, hemocyanin),[17] and CO inhibits nitrogen fixation at very low concentrations. Although no definite function can be assigned to this heme protein in symbiotic nitrogen fixation, it is reasonable to suppose that the pigment acts to speed up the transfer of oxygen to the nitrogen-fixing system.

[15] K. Yamafugi et al., *Enzymologia*, **17**, 110 (1954).

[16] M. H. Aprison et al., *J. Biol. Chem.*, **208**, 29 (1954); W. E. Magee and R. H. Burris, *Plant Physiol.*, **29**, 199 (1954).

[17] H. N. Little and R. H. Burris, *J. Am. Chem. Soc.*, **69**, 838 (1947).

Metabolism of Nitrite and Nitrate

Soil nitrate represents the principal source of nitrogen for higher plants, and the natural accumulation of nitrate in soil ("soil nitrification") is the consequence of the microbial oxidation of ammonia continually formed from nitrogen compounds by degradative processes in all organisms.[18] In 1890 Winogradsky isolated from soil the organisms named *Nitrosomonas,* which rapidly converts ammonia to nitrite, and *Nitrobacter,* which oxidizes nitrite to nitrate.

$$NH_4^+ + 1.5O_2 \rightarrow NO_2^- + H_2O + 2H^+ \quad (\Delta F° = \text{ca.} -75 \text{ kcal})$$

$$NO_2^- + 0.5O_2 \rightarrow NO_3^- \quad (\Delta F° = \text{ca.} -20 \text{ kcal})$$

These two organisms exhibit remarkable specificity; *Nitrobacter* is inactive toward ammonia, and *Nitrosomonas* does not oxidize nitrite. They are autotrophic bacteria and therefore do not require the presence of organic substances for growth; however, the occasional statement that such compounds (e.g., glucose) are inhibitory is erroneous. Whatever carbon compounds are required are synthesized by the cells from CO_2 and water; the energy for these endergonic syntheses is derived from the oxidation of ammonia or nitrite. Approximately 6 to 8 per cent of the maximally available energy released in the two oxidative reactions is utilized for chemosynthesis; the remainder is largely dissipated as heat.[19]

The oxidation of ammonia to nitrite by *Nitrosomonas* may involve hydroxylamine as an intermediate, since this organism can convert NH_2OH (at low concentrations) to nitrite; furthermore, in the presence of hydrazine as an inhibitor, ammonia is converted to hydroxylamine.[20] In relation to the possibility that bound hydroxylamine is an intermediate, it may be added that a variety of organisms are capable of oxidizing oximes.[21] Little is known about the role of other possible intermediates (hyponitrite, nitramide, etc.) in the conversion of ammonia to nitrite by *Nitrosomonas.* The oxidation of nitrite to nitrate by *Nitrobacter* has not been studied extensively; this process appears to involve the participation of a cytochrome.[22]

The reverse of the nitrification reactions, the reduction of nitrate to nitrite, hydroxylamine, ammonia, or N_2, has been demonstrated in many

[18] C. C. Delwiche, in W. D. McElroy and B. Glass, *Inorganic Nitrogen Metabolism,* Johns Hopkins Press, Baltimore, 1956; H. Lees, in Society for General Microbiology, *Autotrophic Micro-organisms,* Cambridge University Press, London, 1954.

[19] L. G. M. Baas-Becking and G. S. Parks, *Physiol. Revs.,* **7,** 85 (1927).

[20] H. Lees, *Nature,* **169,** 156 (1952); T. Hofman and H. Lees, *Biochem. J.,* **54,** 579 (1953).

[21] J. H. Quastel et al., *Nature,* **166,** 940 (1950).

[22] H. Lees and J. R. Simpson, *Biochem. J.,* **65,** 297 (1957).

heterotrophic microorganisms (e.g., *Escherichia coli, Clostridium welchii, Proteus vulgaris,* and *Pseudomonas aeruginosa*). When volatile products (N_2, N_2O) are formed from nitrate by soil bacteria, nitrogen is lost from the soil ("denitrification").

The first step in the utilization of nitrate by organisms that can metabolize it is a reduction to nitrite, catalyzed by the enzyme "nitrate reductase." This enzyme has been found in higher plants, and in microorganisms adapted to grow on nitrate; it appears to be a molybdoflavoprotein.[23] As noted earlier (p. 339), it catalyzes electron transfer from TPNH or DPNH to nitrate, and molybdenum probably participates in this process, thus providing an explanation for the long-known requirement of trace amounts of this metal in the metabolism of various plant and microbial cells. The equilibrium in the reaction

$$\text{TPNH} + \text{H}^+ + \text{NO}_3^- \rightarrow \text{TPN}^+ + \text{NO}_2^- + \text{H}_2\text{O}$$

is far to the right, and a reversal of the reaction leading to the reduction of TPN^+ has not been effected. In the reduction of NO_3^- to NO_2^-, the gain of 2 electrons is accompanied by a change in the oxidation number of the nitrogen atom from $+5$ to $+3$.

For organisms containing nitrate reductase, nitrate can serve as the terminal electron acceptor for the oxidation of metabolites (e.g., succinic acid, lactic acid, and formic acid) under anaerobic conditions; this utilization of nitrate as the terminal oxidant is inhibited by O_2. Thus the reduced pyridine nucleotide needed for the nitrate reductase reaction is generated by dehydrogenase-catalyzed hydrogen transfer from a metabolite. In photosynthetic organisms, reduced pyridine nucleotide may be generated by photoreduction (p. 554); the reduction of nitrate is promoted by illumination, and nitrate serves as an alternative electron acceptor in photosynthesis.[24] In some bacteria (e.g., *Micrococcus denitrificans*), the reduction of nitrate can be coupled to the oxidation of H_2. Clearly, nitrate can be used by many organisms for the exergonic oxidation of metabolites, and it has been reported that such electron transfer is accompanied by the generation of ATP, in a manner comparable to respiratory chain phosphorylation[25] (p. 381).

Since nitrate can be used by many organisms not only as a participant in energy-yielding reactions, but also as a source of nitrogen for cellular proteins, enzymic mechanisms must be available for the further reduction

[23] D. J. D. Nicholas and A. Nason, *J. Biol. Chem.,* **211**, 183 (1954); *Plant Physiol.,* **30**, 135 (1955); *J. Bact.,* **69**, 580 (1955).

[24] H. J. Evans and A. Nason, *Plant Physiol.,* **28**, 273 (1954); C. B. van Niel et al., *Biochim. et Biophys. Acta,* **12**, 67 (1953).

[25] S. Taniguchi et al., in W. D. McElroy and B. Glass, *Inorganic Nitrogen Metabolism,* Johns Hopkins Press, Baltimore, 1956.

of the nitrite produced in the nitrate reductase reaction. Bacterial and plant enzyme preparations have been obtained which catalyze the reduction of nitrite by TPNH to hydroxylamine; in this conversion, catalyzed by "nitrite reductase," a transfer of 4 electrons occurs (oxidation number of nitrogen in NH_2OH is -1). It has been assumed that two successive 2-electron steps are involved, with a substance at the oxidation level of the nitroxyl radical (NOH) or the dimeric hyponitrite (oxidation number of nitrogen, $+1$) as an intermediate. The evidence for the formation of such an intermediate in the reduction of nitrite to hydroxylamine is largely circumstantial. In addition to the nitrite reductase system, an enzyme preparation that catalyzes the reduction of hydroxylamine by DPNH to ammonia has been obtained from *Neurospora;* both the nitrite reductase and the "hydroxylamine reductase" systems appear to involve the participation of flavin components.[26] It may be concluded, therefore, that an enzymic pathway is available for the conversion of nitrate to ammonia in microbes and plants. Although the utilization of nitrate-nitrogen for amino acid synthesis may proceed by this pathway, the possibility is not excluded that NH_2OH may be used in form of oximes, which are then reduced to amino acids. For example, oximinosuccinic acid (p. 678) and the homologous oximinoglutaric acid have been shown to serve as excellent nitrogen sources for oat plants.[27]

Under usual agricultural or natural conditions, many plants (apple tree, asparagus, etc.) obtain so little nitrate from the soil that notable amounts of this compound are found only in the roots. The ammonia formed in this tissue is then used for amino acid synthesis or is translocated to the stems and leaves. However, some plants (tomato, tobacco, etc.) are usually grown with an abundant supply of nitrogenous fertilizer; in these, nitrate may be present in large quantities in the leaves, where reduction to ammonia also occurs. It is of interest that under normal conditions the reduction of nitrate does not appear to be reversible in plants, since the administration of N^{15}-labeled ammonium salts to tobacco leaves did not lead to the appearance of N^{15} in the nitrate fraction.[28]

It will be clear from the previous discussion that the conversions of nitrate to nitrite, hydroxylamine, and ammonia are endergonic processes and must be coupled to the breakdown of carbohydrate. This has been demonstrated experimentally with tomato plants which had been depleted of nitrogen; the administration of nitrate leads not only to the appearance

[26] A. Nason, in W. D. McElroy and B. Glass, *Inorganic Nitrogen Metabolism,* Johns Hopkins Press, Baltimore, 1956; A. Medina and D. J. D. Nicholas, *Biochim. et Biophys. Acta,* **25,** 138 (1957).

[27] J. G. Wood, *Ann. Rev. Plant Physiol.,* **4,** 1 (1953).

[28] C. C. Delwiche, *J. Biol. Chem.,* **189,** 167 (1951).

of nitrite but also to a parallel decrease in the carbohydrate stores of the plant and a marked increase in the rate of respiration.[29]

As mentioned earlier, some soil bacteria produce N_2O from nitrate. Since N_2O is at the oxidation level of hyponitrous acid, it has been suggested that N_2O arises by the transfer of 2 electrons to nitrite and the intermediate formation of the nitroxyl radical (NOH) or some

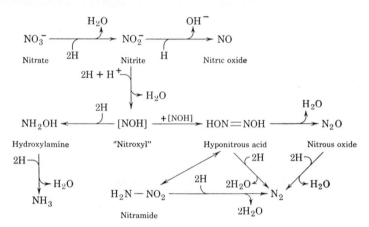

Fig. 1. Postulated pathways in the metabolic reduction of nitrate to NH_3, N_2, N_2O, and NO in microorganisms and higher plants.

organic derivative of this radical. In addition to N_2O, nitrogen gas is a normal product of denitrification by several bacteria (e.g., *Denitrobacillus lichenoformis*) and may arise by the reduction of N_2O or of hyponitrite (or an organic derivative).[30] Furthermore, cell-free extracts of some bacteria (*Pseudomonas stutzeri, Bacillus subtilis*) have been obtained which convert nitrate not only to N_2O and N_2, but also to NO.[31] In considering the possible mechanisms of these denitrification reactions, it is of interest that DPNH and ascorbic acid react nonenzymically with nitrite at acid pH values to form N_2O, N_2, and NO.[32] Such nonenzymic reactions between nitrous acid and organic substances have also been observed with amino acids and peptides (p. 49), and with a derivative of p-hydroxycinnamic acid, which is oxidized to the corresponding

[29] K. C. Hamner, *Botan. Gaz.*, **97**, 744 (1936).

[30] W. Verhoeven, in W. D. McElroy and B. Glass, *Inorganic Nitrogen Metabolism,* Johns Hopkins Press, Baltimore, 1956.

[31] V. A. Najjar and M. B. Allen, *J. Biol. Chem.*, **206**, 209 (1954); C. W. Chung and V. A. Najjar, *ibid.*, **218**, 617, 627 (1956).

[32] H. J. Evans and C. McAuliffe, in W. D. McElroy and B. Glass, *Inorganic Nitrogen Metabolism,* Johns Hopkins Press, Baltimore, 1956.

p-hydroxymandelic acid derivative.[33]   The possibility exists, therefore, that the gases formed in denitrification may arise at least in part from nonenzymic reactions of nitrous acid with oxidizable cell constituents.

The postulated pathways in the reduction of nitrate are summarized in Fig. 1.   It will be noted that several of the steps are the reverse of the reactions thought to occur in nitrogen fixation and in nitrification. As in these processes, it is likely that some of the postulated intermediates in nitrate reduction are actually bound to organic compounds, but no conclusive evidence on this question is available at present.

[33] G. Taborsky et al., *J. Biol. Chem.*, **226**, 103 (1957); C. Zioudrou et al., *J. Am. Chem. Soc.*, **79**, 4114, 5951 (1957).

29 ·

Enzymic Cleavage
and
Synthesis of Peptide Bonds

In most microorganisms and higher plants, the nitrogen for protein synthesis is assimilated in the form of simple compounds such as nitrate, ammonia, or amino acids. In higher animals, however, most of the nitrogen used for metabolic purposes is derived from the ingestion of the tissue proteins of other organisms (plant and animal). Before this dietary nitrogen can be made available for the synthesis of new proteins, the ingested proteins must first be degraded to amino acids or other simple nitrogen compounds (ammonia, peptides). All organisms that can use proteins as sources of nitrogen are equipped with enzymes (proteolytic enzymes, proteases) which catalyze the hydrolytic cleavage of peptide bonds. Some aspects of the specificity of the proteolytic enzymes were discussed on p. 274, but, because of their importance in the intermediate metabolism of proteins and of peptides, these enzymes will be considered more fully in what follows. Valuable surveys of this field have been prepared by Northrop et al.,[1] Smith,[2] Neurath and Schwert,[3] and Green and Neurath.[4]

Hydrolysis of Proteins and Peptides in Mammalian Digestion

In higher animals, the enzymic degradation of dietary proteins to amino acids takes place in a physiological apparatus which performs the process of digestion. Since the digestion of proteins, and of other food-

[1] J. H. Northrop, M. Kunitz, and R. M. Herriott, *Crystalline Enzymes*, 2nd Ed., Columbia University Press, New York, 1948.

[2] E. L. Smith, in J. B. Sumner and K. Myrbäck, *The Enzymes*, Academic Press, New York, 1951.

[3] H. Neurath and G. W. Schwert, *Chem. Revs.*, **46**, 69 (1950).

[4] N. M. Green and H. Neurath, in H. Neurath and K. Bailey, *The Proteins*, Vol. IIB, Chapter 25, Academic Press, New York, 1954.

stuffs, has been studied primarily in mammals, most of the available information relates to the enzymes of the gastrointestinal tract (Table 1) of these organisms; this knowledge has, however, proved to be of value for the understanding of analogous metabolic reactions in other biological forms, such as the invertebrates and the insectivorous plants.

Table I. Proteolytic Enzymes in Mammalian Gastrointestinal Tract

Secretion	Enzyme	Comments
Gastric	Pepsin	A proteinase also found in the gastric juice of birds, reptiles, and fish
	Rennin	A milk-coagulating enzyme present in the juice of the fourth stomach of the calf
Pancreatic	Trypsin	A proteinase
	Chymotrypsin	A proteinase
	Carboxypeptidase	A peptidase
Intestinal	Aminopeptidases Prolidase Tripeptidase Dipeptidases	Peptidases

Pepsin. In the course of the gastrointestinal digestion of proteins, the enzymic attack is initiated in the stomach, at a pH of ca. 1.0, by pepsin. This substance occupies an important place in the development of enzyme chemistry since, as was noted earlier (p. 209), the demonstration of the chemical nature of the process of gastric digestion by Réaumur and Spallanzani during the eighteenth century marked a new chapter in the history of physiology. However, the real foundations of modern gastric physiology were not laid until 1833, when William Beaumont, an American army surgeon, described his studies on Alexis St. Martin. An accidental discharge of a shotgun that caused a permanent opening (fistula) connecting the stomach and abdominal surface made St. Martin one of the most famous patients in the history of experimental medicine. Thus the possibility of obtaining gastric juice through the fistula enabled Beaumont to perform, for the first time, studies of the influence of dietary and emotional factors on the secretion of the gastric juice. In the course of these experiments, Beaumont established conclusively the solvent power and acidity of the gastric secretion.

The name "pepsin" was assigned by Schwann in 1836, and during the latter part of that century Pekelharing (1896) reported some progress in the purification of the enzyme. The most decisive advance was made in 1930 when Northrop described the preparation of pepsin from swine

gastric mucosa in the form of striking hexahedral crystals (cf. p. 23);
subsequent work has led to the numerous improvements in the original
method of crystallization.[1] Crystalline pepsin preparations have also
been obtained from other animal species (beef, salmon, tuna[5]).

Crystalline swine pepsin is a protein (particle size approximately
35,000) characterized by an unusually low isoelectric point (less than
pH 1) and by the fact that it is readily denatured at pH values higher
than 6. The enzyme contains, per unit of 35,000, 1 equivalent of bound
phosphate which can be removed by means of potato phosphomonoesterase (p. 581) without loss of pepsin activity. Pepsin contains 1
N-terminal isoleucine residue per unit of about 35,000.[6] Partial hydrolysis of crystalline pepsin gives peptides of phospho-L-serine (p. 55).[7]

Pepsin is classified as a proteinase, since it causes the degradation of
nearly all proteins. It does not hydrolyze the protamines or the keratins
to a measurable extent. The pH optimum of its action on proteins varies
somewhat with the nature of the protein substrate, but is in all cases
near 2.[8] The action of crystalline swine pepsin on bovine serum albumin
leads to the formation of fragments that contain, on the average, seven
amino acid residues;[9] however, the limits of variation in the size of the
individual fragments have not been ascertained. Because of the complex
nature of the protein substrate, it is difficult to determine the site of
enzymic action and the chemical structure of the split products that are
formed. For this reason, the discovery in 1938 of simple peptide derivatives that are hydrolyzed by crystalline pepsin made possible the first
systematic examination of the specificity of the enzyme.[10] Thus crystalline swine pepsin was found to catalyze the hydrolysis of the peptide
bond between the glutamic acid and tyrosine residues in the compound
carbobenzoxy-L-glutamyl-L-tyrosine. In this substrate, the carbobenzoxy group merely serves as an acyl substituent at the amino group
of the glutamic acid residue; the tripeptide glycyl-L-glutamyl-L-tyrosine
is also hydrolyzed. Subsequent studies showed that even simple peptides such as L-cystinyl-bis-L-tyrosine and L-methionyl-L-tyrosine are
hydrolyzed by crystalline pepsin.[11] These findings with synthetic
substrates demonstrated that pepsin acts at peptide linkages, and provided additional support for the peptide theory of protein structure
(p. 130).

[5] E. R. Norris and J. C. Mathies, *J. Biol. Chem.,* **204,** 673 (1953).

[6] K. Heirwegh and P. Edman, *Biochim. et Biophys. Acta,* **24,** 219 (1957).

[7] M. Flavin, *J. Biol. Chem.,* **210,** 771 (1954).

[8] L. K. Christensen, *Arch. Biochem. and Biophys.,* **57,** 163 (1955).

[9] A. Beloff and C. B. Anfinsen, *J. Biol. Chem.,* **176,** 863 (1948).

[10] J. S. Fruton and M. Bergmann, *J. Biol. Chem.,* **127,** 627 (1939).

[11] C. R. Harington and R. V. Pitt-Rivers, *Biochem. J.,* **38,** 417 (1944); C. A.
Dekker et al., *J. Biol. Chem.,* **180,** 155 (1949).

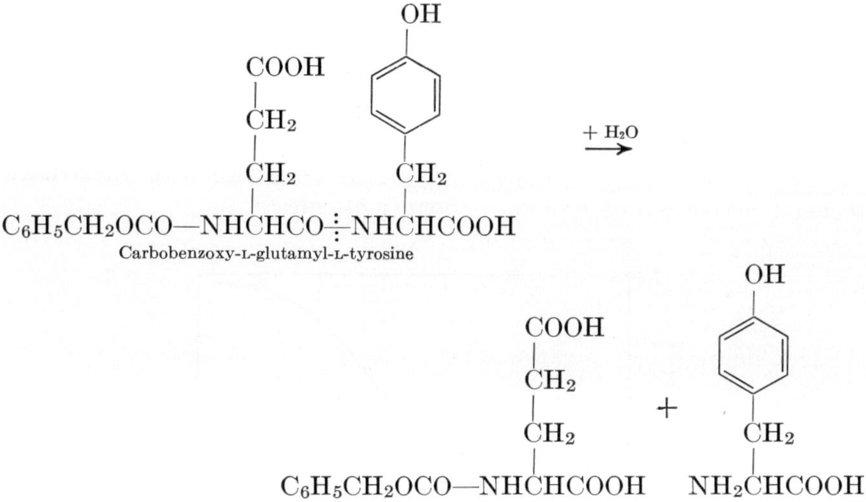

$$
\begin{array}{c}
\text{COOH} \\
| \\
\text{CH}_2 \\
| \\
\text{CH}_2 \\
| \\
\text{C}_6\text{H}_5\text{CH}_2\text{OCO—NHCHCO} \div \text{NHCHCOOH}
\end{array}
\qquad
\overset{+ \text{H}_2\text{O}}{\longrightarrow}
$$

Carbobenzoxy-L-glutamyl-L-tyrosine

$$
\begin{array}{c}
\text{COOH} \\
| \\
\text{CH}_2 \\
| \\
\text{CH}_2 \\
| \\
\text{C}_6\text{H}_5\text{CH}_2\text{OCO—NHCHCOOH}
\end{array}
\quad + \quad
\begin{array}{c}
\text{OH} \\
\\
\\
\text{CH}_2 \\
| \\
\text{NH}_2\text{CHCOOH}
\end{array}
$$

Carbobenzoxy-L-glutamic acid   L-Tyrosine

It will be noted that the synthetic substrates mentioned above all contain an L-tyrosine residue, which participates in the sensitive peptide bond through its amino group. Of a variety of amino acid residues examined, only that of L-phenylalanine served as a suitable replacement for the tyrosine residue in synthetic substrates hydrolyzed by pepsin. More recent studies[12] have shown that acyl dipeptides in which both amino acids are either tyrosine or phenylalanine (e.g., acetyl-L-phenyl-alanyl-L-tyrosine) are hydrolyzed more rapidly than carbobenzoxy-L-glutamyl-L-tyrosine. It would appear, therefore, that the specificity of pepsin favors the hydrolysis of peptide linkages in which an aromatic amino acid provides the amino group for the sensitive peptide bond. This bond need not be adjacent to a free α-carboxyl group, as in carbo-benzoxy-L-glutamyl-L-tyrosine, since substitution of the COOH of the tyrosine residue does not abolish pepsin action. Consequently, pepsin is an enzyme which can attack peptide bonds in the interior of peptide chains; such enzymes have been termed "endopeptidases." The endo-peptidases are differentiated from the "exopeptidases," which are re-stricted in their action to the hydrolysis of peptide bonds adjacent to terminal α-amino or α-carboxyl groups. Clearly, since there are rela-tively few terminal α-amino or α-carboxyl groups in intact proteins, the proteinases must attack peptide bonds that are centrally located in peptide chains; i.e., they must be endopeptidases.

Although studies of the action of pepsin on synthetic substrates and proteins indicate a preference for peptide bonds involving aromatic amino acid residues, pepsin preparations have been shown[13] also to

[12] L. E. Baker, *J. Biol. Chem.*, **193**, 809 (1951).
[13] F. Sanger and H. Tuppy, *Biochem. J.*, **49**, 481 (1951).

hydrolyze proteins at other types of peptide bonds (e.g., leucyl-valyl).

Pepsin can digest itself, with the liberation of dialyzable peptides that retain enzymic activity toward synthetic substrates.[14] This important finding focuses attention on the possibility discussed earlier (p. 260) that the catalytic action of some enzymes is associated with a restricted region ("active center") of the protein molecule.

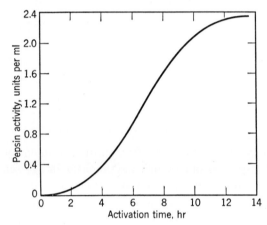

Fig. 1. Autocatalytic conversion of pepsinogen to pepsin at pH 4.6 and 25° C. Initial concentration of pepsinogen, 1 mg per ml. The pepsin activity was tested with hemoglobin as the substrate. [From R. M. Herriott, *J. Gen. Physiol.*, **21**, 501 (1938).]

In the cells of the gastric mucosa, pepsin does not occur as such, but as the inactive precursor pepsinogen, first isolated in crystalline form by Herriott.[1] Pepsinogen is a protein having a particle size of approximately 42,000; its isoelectric point is pH 3.7, and it is fairly stable in alkaline solution. The potential enzymic activity of pepsinogen is realized merely by making its solution slightly acid. At pH values less than 6, pepsinogen is converted to pepsin by an autocatalytic reaction (Fig. 1). The conversion of pepsinogen to pepsin involves pepsin itself as the catalytic agent; the addition of pepsin increases the rate of the conversion, and the pH optimum for the activation is approximately 2. This process thus provides an example of a proteinase (pepsin) acting on another protein (pepsinogen) to produce a structural change which leads to the formation of more of the proteinase. During this activation, approximately 22 per cent of the pepsinogen nitrogen appears in the form of nonprotein nitrogen; about 9 peptide bonds are cleaved per unit

[14] G. E. Perlmann, *Nature*, **173**, 406 (1954).

of 42,000, with the concomitant "unmasking" of the active center of the enzyme.[15] Among the products of the conversion of pepsinogen to pepsin is a peptide (molecular weight, ca. 3000) that inhibits pepsin.[16]

Rennin.[17] For many years, there was discussion about the possible identity of rennin, the enzyme found in the fourth stomach of the calf, with calf pepsin. Like many proteinases (pepsin, chymotrypsin, etc.), rennin causes the coagulation of casein in the presence of calcium ions; the pH optimum for this action is near 5. The enzymic individuality of rennin was established through its crystallization,[18] and by the demonstration that the properties of the crystalline material are quite different from those of pepsin. Crystalline rennin is not limited in its action to the clotting of milk, since it also hydrolyzes hemoglobin (pH optimum, 3.7); however, the nature of the linkages broken by rennin is not known.

Trypsin. The process of protein digestion in the mammalian gastrointestinal tract is continued in the upper loop of the small intestine (duodenum) at pH values near 6 by enzymic constituents derived from the pancreatic secretion. Until the demonstration of the multiple nature of the proteinase activity of pancreatic juice, it was believed that this secretion contained only one proteinase, named trypsin. The mixture of proteolytic enzymes in pancreatic juice may be designated more appropriately by the term pancreatin; the term trypsin has been retained for one of the proteinases, and the term chymotrypsin has been assigned to another. The presence of an additional proteinase in the pancreas is indicated by the finding of an enzyme (elastase) that appears to be relatively specific for the degradation of elastin (p. 53), although other proteins also are hydrolyzed by the enzyme.[19] Furthermore, evidence is available for the existence of a pancreatic "protaminase."

Trypsin was obtained in crystalline form by Kunitz and Northrop;[1] its molecular weight is about 24,000, and its isoelectric point is near pH 10.5.[20] The enzymic attack on proteins such as casein is optimal near pH 8, although some proteolytic activity may be demonstrated at pH values as low as 6. Like pepsin, trypsin has been found to be an endopeptidase which acts at CO—NH linkages in synthetic substrates of simple structure. From the studies of Bergmann and his associates,[21]

[15] R. M. Herriott, in W. D. McElroy and B. Glass, *The Mechanism of Enzyme Action,* Johns Hopkins Press, Baltimore, 1954; H. Van Vunakis and R. M. Herriott, *Biochim. et Biophys. Acta,* **23,** 600 (1957).

[16] H. Van Vunakis and R. M. Herriott, *Biochim. et Biophys. Acta,* **22,** 537 (1956).

[17] N. J. Berridge, *Advances in Enzymol.,* **15,** 423 (1954).

[18] N. J. Berridge and C. Woodward, *J. Dairy Research,* **20,** 255 (1953).

[19] I. Banga and J. Boló, *Nature,* **178,** 310 (1956); U. J. Lewis et al., *J. Biol. Chem.,* **222,** 705 (1956).

[20] L. W. Cunningham, *J. Biol. Chem.,* **211,** 13 (1954).

[21] K. Hofmann and M. Bergmann, *J. Biol. Chem.,* **130,** 81 (1939); **138,** 243 (1941).

it has been concluded that the specificity of trypsin is directed to the hydrolysis of peptide bonds to which an L-arginine or L-lysine residue contributes the carbonyl group. Suitable synthetic substrates for crystalline trypsin are, therefore, benzoyl-L-argininamide or benzoyl-L-lysinamide; these are deamidated to benzoyl-L-arginine and benzoyl-L-lysine, respectively. The replacement of either of these amino acid

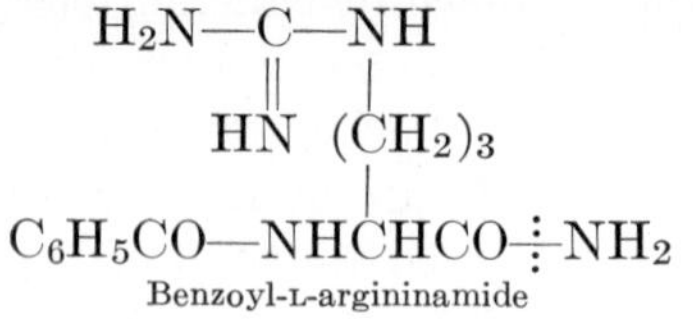

$$
\begin{array}{cc}
H_2N-C-NH & NH_2 \\
\parallel \quad | & | \\
HN \quad (CH_2)_3 & (CH_2)_4 \\
| & | \\
C_6H_5CO-NHCHCO\dot{-}NH_2 & C_6H_5CO-NHCHCO\dot{-}NH_2 \\
\text{Benzoyl-L-argininamide} & \text{Benzoyl-L-lysinamide}
\end{array}
$$

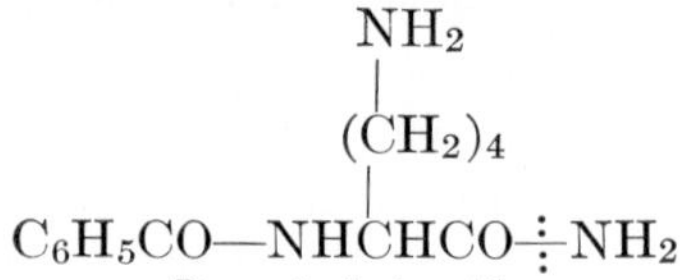

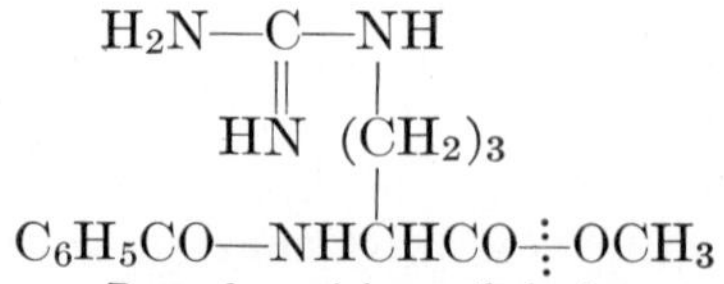

$$
\begin{array}{c}
H_2N-C-NH \\
\parallel \quad | \\
HN \quad (CH_2)_3 \\
| \\
C_6H_5CO-NHCHCO\dot{-}OCH_3 \\
\text{Benzoyl-L-arginine methyl ester}
\end{array}
$$

residues by a variety of others renders the compound resistant to the action of trypsin. Crystalline trypsin also hydrolyzes protamines and synthetic lysine peptides prepared by polymerization reactions (cf. p. 136).[22] Crystalline trypsin can act at ester linkages as well as at amide bonds, provided that the other specificity requirements of the enzyme are met.[3] Thus trypsin hydrolyzes benzoyl-L-arginine methyl ester, but not benzoyl-L-leucine methyl ester. This important finding and the discovery that chymotrypsin also hydrolyzes ester linkages (p. 693) raise the possibility that such linkages may be present in intact proteins (cf. p. 131).

The specificity of trypsin for bonds involving an arginine or lysine residue applies not only to synthetic substrates, but also to proteins, thus making this enzyme a valuable reagent in the study of the amino acid sequence in complex polypeptide chains (cf. p. 145).

Trypsin is derived from an inactive precursor, named trypsinogen, present in the acinar cells of the pancreas. This precursor was obtained in crystalline form by Kunitz and Northrop,[1] who showed that the formation of trypsin occurs rapidly when trypsinogen is dissolved in neutral solution. The transformation of trypsinogen to trypsin is most rapid at pH values of 7 to 8, and the activation is catalyzed by trypsin; the reaction, therefore, is autocatalytic. In the course of this activation, enzymically inert protein is also formed as a by-product; this side reaction may be prevented by conducting the activation in the presence of Ca^{2+}. It has long been known that alkaline earth ions such as Ca^{2+}

promote the conversion of trypsinogen to trypsin, and it is probable that this effect is a consequence of the inhibition by Ca^{2+} of the enzymic formation of inert protein from denatured trypsin.[23]

The conversion of trypsinogen to trypsin can be effected by proteolytic enzymes other than trypsin. Thus the duodenal mucosa elaborates an enzyme named enterokinase which can perform this process. Also, Kunitz has shown that a mold of the *Penicillium* group forms an enzyme which acts optimally at pH 3.4 in the activation of trypsinogen; the trypsin produced is indistinguishable from that formed by the autocatalytic conversion of trypsinogen or by the action of enterokinase.

The molecular weight of trypsinogen as determined by sedimentation-diffusion is similar to that of trypsin, but it is known that trypsinogen is a slightly larger protein. In the conversion of the precursor to trypsin (either by trypsin or by enterokinase), only one peptide bond appears to be hydrolyzed, with the liberation of the acidic hexapeptide valyl-(aspartyl)$_4$-lysine.[24] Since the N-terminal amino acid sequence of trypsin is isoleucyl-valyl-glycyl-, the transformation of inactive trypsinogen to active trypsin is caused by the cleavage of a lysyl-isoleucyl bond in the precursor protein.

In pancreatic extracts, trypsinogen is accompanied by a large basic peptide (molecular weight, ca. 9000) which has been obtained in crystalline form. This peptide combines with trypsin in a 1:1 ratio to form an inactive trypsin-inhibitor compound.[25] Inhibitors of trypsin activity have been prepared from a variety of natural sources;[26] of special interest is the isolation from soybean extracts of a crystalline protein of molecular weight ca. 24,000 which forms an inactive addition compound with crystalline trypsin.[27] Egg white contains a water-soluble mucoprotein which is a powerful inhibitor of trypsin, and trypsin inhibitors have also been found in lung tissue, in blood, and in human and bovine colostrum (the milk formed immediately after delivery of the young).

A striking inhibition of trypsin is effected by diisopropylfluorophosphate[28] (DFP; p. 261), which also inhibits chymotrypsin and various esterases. In the reaction with trypsin, 1 molecule of DFP combines with 1 molecule of the protein (molecular weight, 24,000)

[23] L. Gorini and F. Felix, *Biochim. et Biophys. Acta,* **11,** 535 (1953); N. M. Green and H. Neurath, *J. Biol. Chem.,* **204,** 379 (1953).

[24] E. W. Davie and H. Neurath, *J. Biol. Chem.,* **212,** 515 (1955); P. Desnuelle and C. Fabre, *Biochim. et Biophys. Acta,* **18,** 49 (1955); I. Yamashina, *Acta Chem. Scand.,* **10,** 739 (1956).

[25] N. M. Green and E. Work, *Biochem. J.,* **54,** 257, 347 (1953).

[26] M. Laskowski and M. Laskowski, Jr., *Advances in Protein Chem.,* **9,** 203 (1954).

[27] M. Kunitz, *J. Gen. Physiol.,* **30,** 291, 311 (1947); **32,** 241 (1948); E. W. Davie and H. Neurath, *J. Biol. Chem.,* **212,** 507 (1955).

[28] E. F. Jansen and A. K. Balls, *J. Biol. Chem.,* **194,** 721 (1952).

with the liberation of HF, and the formation of an inactive diisopropyl-phosphoryl trypsin (DIP-trypsin). The site of attachment of the DIP-group is not known, but it may be the β-hydroxyl group of a serine residue.

Chymotrypsin. As noted earlier, the pancreatic secretion contains, in addition to trypsin, another proteinase, named chymotrypsin. These two enzymes were first distinguished from each other by virtue of the fact that trypsin decreases the clotting time of blood but does not clot milk, whereas chymotrypsin clots milk but not blood. Chymotrypsin is a term applied to the members of a closely related group of enzymic proteins (α-, β-, γ-, δ-, and π-chymotrypsins) all having the same proteolytic activity, and all derived from an inactive precursor (chymotrypsinogen) present in the pancreatic acinar tissue. Chymotrypsinogen was first crystallized by Kunitz and Northrop, and it may be considered one of the most homogeneous protein preparations yet described because of the extremely satisfactory nature of its solubility curves (cf. p. 26). This protein has a molecular weight of about 25,000, a frictional ratio of 1.12, and an isoelectric point near pH 9.5. Chymotrypsinogen contains, per unit of 25,000, one free α-amino group, which belongs to a cystine residue; the other amino group of this residue is linked in the peptide chain.[29] The protein appears to contain a C-terminal tyrosine residue.[30]

The addition of catalytic amounts of trypsin to solutions (pH ca. 8) of chymotrypsinogen causes the activation of the precursor; other proteinases (e.g., subtilisin; p. 708) also can activate chymotrypsinogen. Rapid activation is effected by relatively large amounts of trypsin (ca. 1 mg per 30 mg of chymotrypsinogen), with the initial formation of π-chymotrypsin, which is then converted to δ-chymotrypsin.[31] Studies by Desnuelle, Neurath, and their associates[32] have shown that in the conversion of chymotrypsinogen to π-chymotrypsin a single peptide bond (arginyl-isoleucyl) is cleaved by trypsin. The formation of δ-chymotrypsin is caused by the action of π-chymotrypsin on itself, with the liberation of the dipeptide serylarginine, and the appearance of a C-terminal leucine. Thus the conversion of chymotrypsinogen to δ-chymotrypsin involves the successive action of trypsin and chymotrypsin on the peptide sequence -leucyl-seryl-arginyl-isoleucyl-.

If smaller amounts of trypsin are used (ca. 1 mg per 10 gm of chymotrypsinogen), the major products are α-, β-, and γ-chymotrypsin,

[29] F. R. Bettelheim, *J. Biol. Chem.*, **212**, 235 (1955).

[30] B. Meedom, *Acta Chem. Scand.*, **10**, 881 (1956).

[31] C. F. Jacobsen, *Compt. rend. trav. lab. Carlsberg, Sér. chim.*, **25**, 325 (1947).

[32] M. Rovery et al., *Biochim. et Biophys. Acta*, **17**, 565 (1955); W. J. Dreyer and H. Neurath, *J. Biol. Chem.*, **217**, 527 (1955); H. Neurath and G. H. Dixon, *Federation Proc.*, **16**, 791 (1957).

which appear to have essentially the same molecular weight as chymotrypsinogen and π- and δ-chymotrypsin. α-Chymotrypsin is the active enzyme first crystallized by Kunitz and Northrop; its isoelectric point is near pH 8, and its particle weight is about 43,000, which corresponds to a dimeric form of the protein. α-Chymotrypsin arises by autolytic cleavage of π-chymotrypsin not only at the leucyl-seryl linkage, but also at a tyrosyl-alanyl bond located in a different part of the protein molecule. Since no fragmentation of the protein occurs in the formation of α-chymotrypsin, it is assumed that the separate peptide chains having isoleucyl and alanyl N-terminal residues are held together by disulfide bridges (cf. p. 132). The nature of the structural differences among α-, β-, and γ-chymotrypsin (other than in their crystal form) is unclear; it is possible that additional peptide bonds may have been cleaved by autolysis.[33] Brown et al.[34] have described still another crystalline form of chymotrypsin named chymotrypsin B.

The chymotrypsins cause the hydrolysis of peptide bonds not only in proteins but also in suitable synthetic substrates (pH optimum ca. 8). α-Chymotrypsin is an endopeptidase and readily hydrolyzes CO—NH linkages in which the carbonyl group is supplied by L-tyrosine, as in the simple compound benzoyl-L-tyrosylglycinamide. Other synthetic substrates of chymotrypsin are acetyl-L-tyrosinamide and glycyl-L-tyrosinamide. If the tyrosine residue of acetyl-L-tyrosinamide is replaced by

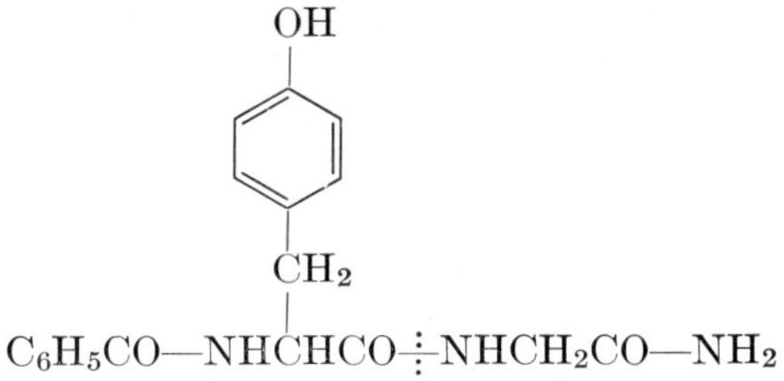

$$C_6H_5CO—NHCHCO \dotplus NHCH_2CO—NH_2$$
Benzoyl-L-tyrosylglycinamide

that of L-phenylalanine, of L-tryptophan, of L-methionine, or of L-leucine, hydrolysis of the amide bond is observed; replacement by other protein amino acids prevents enzyme action. α-Chymotrypsin hydrolyzes the ester bond of acetyl-L-tyrosine ethyl ester much faster than it acts on the corresponding amide. Of special interest is the finding[35] that 5-(p-hydroxyphenyl)-3-ketovaleric acid is hydrolyzed by chymotrypsin at the bond shown in the formula on page 694. It will be seen from the foregoing that the enzyme readily interacts with derivatives of

[33] J. A. Gladner and H. Neurath, *J. Biol. Chem.*, **206**, 911 (1954); M. Rovery et al., *Biochim. et Biophys. Acta*, **23**, 608 (1957).

[34] K. D. Brown et al., *J. Biol. Chem.*, **173**, 99 (1948).

[35] D. G. Doherty, *J. Am. Chem. Soc.*, **77**, 4887 (1955).

β-phenylpropionic acid; if the CO group of the acid participates in an amide, ester, or even a C—C bond, such a linkage is hydrolyzed under

$$HO-\langle\ \rangle-CH_2CH_2CO\dot{-}CH_2COOH \qquad O_2N-\langle\ \rangle-O\dot{-}COCH_3$$

5-(p-Hydroxyphenyl)-3-ketovaleric acid   O-Acetyl-p-nitrophenol

suitable conditions. In accord with this conclusion is the fact that β-phenylpropionic acid itself is an effective competitive inhibitor of chymotrypsin.

α-Chymotrypsin also catalyzes the hydrolysis of O-acetyl-p-nitro-phenol; in this reaction, p-nitrophenol is liberated more rapidly than acetate, and an intermediate acetyl-chymotrypsin is formed.[36] If the reaction is conducted at pH 6, the intermediate may be isolated in crystalline form. This "acyl-enzyme" is inactive toward chymotrypsin substrates, but at alkaline pH values the acetyl group is hydrolyzed off, and the enzymic activity is restored. The acetyl group of acetyl-chymotrypsin can also be transferred to acceptors other than water; with ethanol, ethyl acetate is formed.[37] It has been suggested that an imidazolyl group of chymotrypsin is acetylated by O-acetyl-p-nitro-phenol, and that this group is part of the "active center" of the enzyme.[38]

The inhibition of α-chymotrypsin by DFP (p. 261) leads to the intro-duction of 1 diisopropylphosphoryl (DIP) group per unit of about 25,000. Although acid hydrolysis of the inactive DIP-chymotrypsin gives phospho-L-serine, it is possible that an imidazolyl group of the protein is the site of attack by DFP, and that the DIP group is trans-ferred to the hydroxyl group of serine in the course of acid hydrolysis.[39]

Digestion of Proteins. Pepsin, trypsin, and chymotrypsin represent the principal protein-splitting enzymes of the mammalian gastrointestinal tract. They cause the breakdown of large protein molecules to small peptides and free amino acids, and they will in general attack different peptide bonds, thus leading to an extensive cleavage of dietary proteins. It should be added, however, that, despite the manifold capacities of these protein-splitting enzymes, not all proteins are readily digestible. For example, most vertebrates do not digest the insoluble fibrous protein keratin. On the other hand, the clothes moth has, in its digestive system,

[36] B. S. Hartley and B. A. Kilby, *Biochem. J.*, **50**, 672 (1952); **56**, 288 (1954); A. K. Balls and F. L. Aldrich, *Proc. Natl. Acad. Sci.*, **41**, 190 (1955).

[37] A. K. Balls and H. N. Wood, *J. Biol. Chem.*, **219**, 245 (1956); C. E. McDonald and A. K. Balls, *ibid.*, **221**, 993 (1956).

[38] B. S. Hartley, *Ann. Reps.*, **51**, 303 (1955); H. Gutfreund and J. M. Sturtevant, *Biochem. J.*, **63**, 656 (1956); M. L. Bender and B. W. Turnquest, *J. Am. Chem. Soc.*, **79**, 1652, 1656 (1957).

[39] N. K. Schaffer et al., *J. Biol. Chem.*, **214**, 799 (1955).

a relatively high concentration of sulfhydryl compounds, which effect the reduction of the disulfide groups of keratin (cf. p. 132); the resulting product (keratein) is readily attacked by the proteinase of the moth intestinal tract.[40]

The difference in the behavior of keratin and keratein as substrates for proteinases calls attention to the importance of linkages other than peptide bonds in determining the structure of proteins. Striking illustrations of this fact have come from the studies of Linderstrøm-Lang and his associates[41] on the hydrolysis of native and denatured β-lactoglobulin by trypsin or chymotrypsin. Thus, in the initial stages of the enzymic hydrolysis of the native protein, the observed electrostriction (p. 709) is abnormally large; with a denatured protein as the substrate, the initial electrostriction is within the range observed in the hydrolysis of simple peptides. These results can be explained by the assumption that the initial cleavage of the peptide bonds of the native protein is accompanied by the spontaneous rupture of linkages other than peptide bonds. It has been suggested that these labile linkages are related to those broken in the denaturation of proteins (p. 154). It is a general phenomenon that the denatured form of corpuscular proteins are attacked more readily by proteinases than the corresponding native proteins.

The digestibility of dietary proteins will be impaired if the foodstuffs include a substance that inhibits the action of one or more of the gastrointestinal proteinases. This has been shown to occur when a diet contains a large proportion of soybeans which, it will be recalled, contain a powerful inhibitor of pancreatic trypsin.

It is of interest that living animal tissues are more resistant to digestion by proteinases than dead tissues; this has proved to be of some clinical value in the use of trypsin to dissolve dead human tissue which accumulates in several diseases. Northrop has conducted studies on the action of pepsin, trypsin, and other proteinases on living organisms (tadpoles, eggs of *Arbacia*, etc.).[42]

In the digestive tract, the action of the proteinases leads to the formation of peptides (and amino acids) and is followed by that of a series of enzymes able to hydrolyze peptides but inactive toward proteins or larger peptide fragments. These are the exopeptidases (also termed peptidases), whose specificity is such that they act only at peptide bonds adjacent to free terminal α-carboxyl or α-amino groups. The peptidases thus complete the conversion of dietary proteins to amino acids by cleavage of amino acids from the ends of the smaller peptide chains. The possibility

---

[40] K. Linderstrøm-Lang and F. Duspiva, *Z. physiol. Chem.*, **237**, 131 (1935).

[41] K. Linderstrøm-Lang, *Cold Spring Harbor Symposia Quant. Biol.*, **14**, 117 (1949).

[42] J. H. Northrop, *J. Gen. Physiol.*, **9**, 497 (1926); **30**, 375 (1947).

is not excluded, however, that some peptides escape hydrolysis in the intestine and are absorbed into the portal circulation.

Carboxypeptidase. The best known of the peptidases is one that attacks peptides from the carboxyl end of the chain, and is, therefore, termed carboxypeptidase. It accompanies trypsin and chymotrypsin in the pancreatic secretion and has been crystallized from beef pancreas by Anson,[1] who also has shown that in fresh pancreas carboxypeptidase is present in the form of an inactive precursor (procarboxypeptidase) which is readily converted to the active enzyme by catalytic amounts of trypsin. Procarboxypeptidase has a particle weight of about 90,000, whereas that of the active enzyme is only about 34,000; thus in the activation by trypsin nearly two thirds of the precursor is split off.[43] Crystalline carboxypeptidase contains 1 atom of zinc per unit of 34,000, and the metal ion appears to be essential for enzymic activity.[44]

As noted previously (p. 276), carboxypeptidase does not exhibit absolute specificity with respect to the side chain (R') of the terminal amino acid at the carboxyl end of the peptide chain. However, the rate of carboxypeptidase action is most rapid when the terminal amino acid

$$\underset{\text{RCO}\dot{-}\text{NHCHCOOH}}{\overset{\overset{\displaystyle \text{R}'}{|}}{}} \qquad \underset{\text{RCO}\dot{-}\text{OCHCOOH}}{\overset{\overset{\displaystyle \text{CH}_2\text{C}_6\text{H}_5}{|}}{}}$$

residue is that of L-phenylalanine. Replacement of phenylalanine by other L-amino acids gives the following decreasing order in the rate of hydrolysis: tyrosine, tryptophan, leucine, methionine, isoleucine, alanine. glycine. In addition, the enzyme hydrolyzes ester linkages of suitable substrates, e.g., acyl derivatives of β-phenyllactic acid (cf. formula).

Carboxypeptidase can also hydrolyze some peptide linkages adjacent to free α-carboxyl groups in the peptide chains of proteins; this property has been employed for the determination of C-terminal amino acids in proteins (cf. p. 144).

Intestinal Exopeptidases.[45] The intestinal mucosa contains a number of peptidases which complement the action of pancreatic carboxypeptidase in effecting the cleavage of peptides formed by the partial breakdown of the dietary proteins. Among these intestinal enzymes are several aminopeptidases, i.e., enzymes that catalyze the hydrolysis of peptide linkages adjacent to the free α-amino group of a peptide. One aminopeptidase acts preferentially on peptides in which the free amino group is that of an L-leucine residue; it is therefore named leucine aminopeptidase. A convenient substrate for this enzyme is L-leucinamide.

[43] P. J. Keller et al., *J. Biol. Chem.*, **223**, 457 (1956).
[44] B. L. Vallee and H. Neurath, *J. Biol. Chem.*, **217**, 253 (1955).
[45] E. L. Smith, *Advances in Enzymol.*, **12**, 191 (1951).

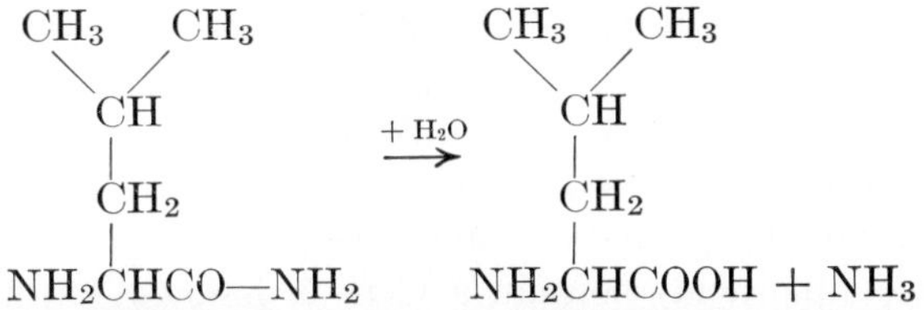

$$\begin{array}{ccc}
CH_3 \quad CH_3 & & CH_3 \quad CH_3 \\
\diagdown\diagup & & \diagdown\diagup \\
CH & \xrightarrow{+ H_2O} & CH \\
| & & | \\
CH_2 & & CH_2 \\
| & & | \\
NH_2CHCO{-}NH_2 & & NH_2CHCOOH + NH_3
\end{array}$$

L-Leucinamide   L-Leucine

Highly purified preparations of leucine aminopeptidase also hydrolyze CO—NH bonds involving N-terminal amino acid residues other than leucine,[46] and this enzyme has proved to be a valuable reagent in studies on the structure of proteins and natural polypeptides.

Smith has provided evidence for the view that the aminopeptidases,[47] and some of the other known peptidases, are metal enzymes. It has long been known that the addition of metal ions such as Mn^{2+}, Mg^{2+}, Co^{2+}, and Zn^{2+} activates certain peptidases. Smith has proposed that these

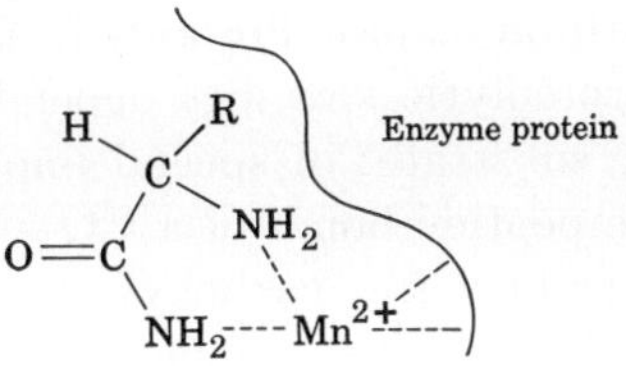

$$\begin{array}{c}
H \diagdown \diagup R \\
C \qquad \text{Enzyme protein} \\
O{=}C \diagdown NH_2 \\
NH_2{-}{-}{-}Mn^{2+}{-}{-}{-}
\end{array}$$

metal-activated peptidases function by forming an enzyme-substrate complex in which the metal ion serves as one of the combining groups. For example, the catalytic action of leucine aminopeptidase, which is stimulated by Mn^{2+}, is thought to involve the formation of an intermediate compound of the type shown in the accompanying diagram.

Some aminopeptidases can attack peptides of varying chain length, but there are several that appear to be confined in their action to dipeptides and tripeptides. Thus a number of specific dipeptidases have been identified; one of these, which is activated by Co^{2+}, appears to be limited in its action to the hydrolysis of glycylglycine.[48] Another aminopeptidase is restricted in its action to the hydrolysis of tripeptides, but it will hydrolyze a large variety of these; the activity of this enzyme (tripeptidase[49]) does not appear, however, to depend on the presence

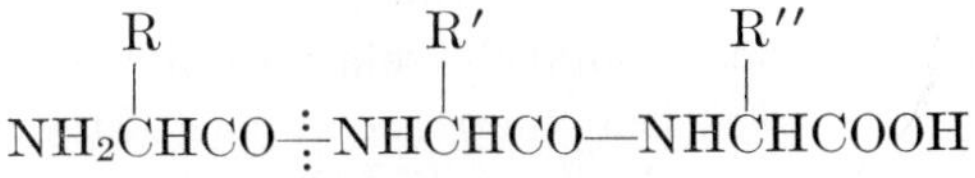

$$\begin{array}{ccc}
R & R' & R'' \\
| & | & | \\
NH_2CHCO\dot{-}NHCHCO{-}NHCHCOOH
\end{array}$$

[46] E. L. Smith and D. H. Spackman, *J. Biol. Chem.*, **212**, 271 (1955).

[47] E. L. Smith, *Federation Proc.*, **8**, 581 (1949).

[48] E. L. Smith, *J. Biol. Chem.*, **173**, 571 (1948).

[49] E. L. Smith and M. Bergmann, *J. Biol. Chem.*, **153**, 627 (1944); J. S. Fruton et al., *ibid.*, **173**, 457 (1948); **191**, 153 (1951); E. Adams et al., *ibid.*, **199**, 845 (1952).

of metal ions for its activity. Tripeptidases also are present in blood and in lymphoid tissues (thymus, mesenteric node, etc.), but their physiological role in these tissues is unknown.

All the peptidases discussed above catalyze the hydrolysis only of amide bonds involving primary amines: i.e., CO—NH bonds. Peptides of proline (an imino acid) contain a CO—N linkage; the hydrolysis of

$$\text{NH}_2\text{CH}_2\text{CO}-\text{N} \underset{\diagdown}{\overset{\diagup}{}} \begin{array}{c} \text{CH}_2\text{—CH}_2 \\ | \\ \text{CH—CH}_2 \\ | \\ \text{COOH} \end{array}$$

Glycyl-L-proline

peptides such as glycyl-L-proline requires the action of a specific intestinal peptidase, named prolidase, which is activated by Mn^{2+}.

Specificity of the Gastrointestinal Proteolytic Enzymes.[50]   In general, the specificity of the proteolytic enzymes depends on the nature of the peptide backbone in the substrate; of special importance is the presence, adjacent to the sensitive peptide bond, of a CO—NH group (as for some of the endopeptidases) or of a free carboxyl or amino group (as for the exopeptidases).   In addition, the endopeptidases and several of the exopeptidases exhibit more or less specific requirements for the presence of the side chains of particular amino acid residues in a definite structural relationship to the sensitive peptide bond (Table 2).

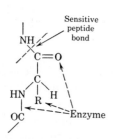

All of the enzymes listed in Table 2 are stereochemically specific for the L-form of the amino acid residue bearing the characteristic side-chain group. Thus pepsin does not hydrolyze acetyl-L-phenylalanyl-D-tyrosine at a measurable rate, leucine aminopeptidase does not act on D-leucylglycylglycine, and chymotrypsin does not split benzoyl-D-tyrosinamide. To explain this stereochemical specificity, it has been assumed that a mutual adjustment of enzyme and substrate (a "polyaffinity" relationship) occurs in such a way that there are at least three points of specific interaction (cf. p. 277). As shown in Fig. 2, proteinases such as trypsin and chymotrypsin are believed to combine with their substrates by specific interaction with the side-chain group (R), with some element

Fig. 2. Postulated polyaffinity relationship between a proteinase and its substrate. [From J. S. Fruton, *Yale J. Biol. and Med.*, **22**, 263 (1950).]

[50] M. Bergmann and J. S. Fruton, *Advances in Enzymol.*, **1**, 63 (1941); M. Bergmann, *ibid.*, **2**, 49 (1942).

Table 2. Specificity of Proteolytic Enzymes

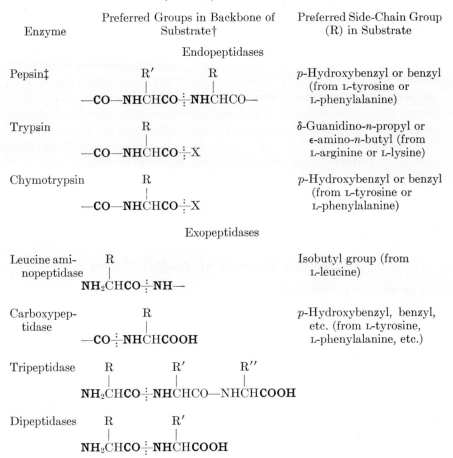

Enzyme	Preferred Groups in Backbone of Substrate†	Preferred Side-Chain Group (R) in Substrate
	Endopeptidases	
Pepsin‡	R′ R —CO—NHCHCO⋮NHCHCO—	*p*-Hydroxybenzyl or benzyl (from L-tyrosine or L-phenylalanine)
Trypsin	R —CO—NHCHCO⋮X	δ-Guanidino-*n*-propyl or ε-amino-*n*-butyl (from L-arginine or L-lysine)
Chymotrypsin	R —CO—NHCHCO⋮X	*p*-Hydroxybenzyl or benzyl (from L-tyrosine or L-phenylalanine)
	Exopeptidases	
Leucine aminopeptidase	R NH₂CHCO⋮NH—	Isobutyl group (from L-leucine)
Carboxypeptidase	R —CO⋮NHCHCOOH	*p*-Hydroxybenzyl, benzyl, etc. (from L-tyrosine, L-phenylalanine, etc.)
Tripeptidase	R R′ R″ NH₂CHCO⋮NHCHCO—NHCHCOOH	
Dipeptidases	R R′ NH₂CHCO⋮NHCHCOOH	

† The requisite groups in the peptide backbone are indicated in bold-faced letters.
‡ The specificity of pepsin is incompletely established.

of the sensitive peptide bond, and probably with some element of the peptide bond adjacent to the sensitive linkage. In suggesting that the carbonyl group is a point of attachment of the enzyme to the sensitive peptide bond, it is also assumed that the enzyme acts to effect an electronic shift analogous to that postulated for the nonenzymic catalysis of the hydrolysis of amides and esters (cf. p. 280). Strong support for this view comes from the fact, cited earlier, that crystalline proteinases such as trypsin or chymotrypsin hydrolyze ester linkages in compounds exactly analogous in structure to the peptide substrates but containing a CO—OR group in place of the sensitive peptide bond (CO—NH). Thus the other specificity requirements, especially with regard to the nature of the side chain, appear to be similar for the enzymic hydrolysis of the amides (or peptides) and of the esters.

From the preceding discussion it is clear that, despite the extraordinary specificity and variety of action exhibited by the proteolytic enzymes of the gastrointestinal tract, the presence of so large a number of enzymes permits the hydrolysis of dietary proteins of the most varied amino acid composition. The extensive enzymic apparatus present in the gastrointestinal tract thus ensures the breakdown of dietary proteins to amino acids; these products enter the portal circulation and are carried to the liver and other tissues, where they may be used for the synthesis of tissue proteins (Chapter 30) or may participate in reactions that lead to their degradation (Chapter 31).

The intestinal absorption of amino acids does not occur by free diffusion, but rather by a metabolic process that is specific for L-amino acids, and which appears to be coupled to oxidative phosphorylation.[51]

Proteolytic Enzymes of Animal Tissues

The studies of the gastrointestinal proteinases and peptidases have provided a groundwork for the examination of the properties of the proteolytic enzymes derived from other animal tissues, as well as from plants and microorganisms. It has long been known that animal tissues (e.g., liver, spleen, kidney) contain proteolytic enzymes, since tissues can undergo a process of "autolysis," which includes the extensive degradation of tissue proteins to amino acids and peptides. Among these intracellular enzymes are several proteinases named "cathepsins." The term "cathepsin" was originally employed to designate what was thought to be a single proteinase of animal tissues, but several members of this group of enzymes are now known. Thus far, three separate proteinases of animal tissues have been characterized; these are termed cathepsin A, cathepsin B, and cathepsin C (Table 3). Although none of the cathepsins has been prepared in crystalline form, the use of simple synthetic substrates of known structure has permitted the identification, partial purification, and study of the properties of these enzymes. Of the three cathepsins listed in Table 3, only cathepsins B and C (from beef spleen) have been purified extensively.[52]

It is of interest that in their specificity the known cathepsins A, B, and

[51] W. T. Agar et al., *Biochim. et Biophys. Acta,* **14,** 80 (1954); **22,** 21 (1956); G. Wiseman, *J. Physiol.,* **120,** 63 (1953); **127,** 414 (1955); L. Fridhandler and J. H. Quastel, *Arch. Biochem. and Biophys.,* **56,** 424 (1955).

[52] H. H. Tallan et al., *J. Biol. Chem.,* **194,** 793 (1952); L. M. Greenbaum and J. S. Fruton, *ibid.,* **226,** 173 (1957).

C are counterparts of pepsin, trypsin, and chymotrypsin, respectively. Thus cathepsin A, which acts on carbobenzoxy-L-glutamyl-L-tyrosine, is comparable in its specificity to pepsin; cathepsin B has a specificity simi-

Table 3. Some Intracellular Proteolytic Enzymes of Animal Tissues

Current Name†	Former Name	Typical Synthetic Substrate
Cathepsin A‡	Cathepsin I	Carbobenzoxy-L-glutamyl-L-tyrosine
Cathepsin B	Cathepsin II	Benzoyl-L-argininamide
Cathepsin C		Glycyl-L-phenylalaninamide
Leucine aminopeptidase	Cathepsin III	L-Leucinamide
Carboxypeptidase	Cathepsin IV	Carbobenzoxyglycyl-L-phenylalanine
Tripeptidase		Glycylglycylglycine

† Each of the names given in this column may be considered to represent a class of enzymes; these terms may be prefaced by the site of origin of a particular enzyme (e.g., beef spleen cathepsin B, swine kidney carboxypeptidase).

‡ The designation of this enzyme as an endopeptidase is based solely on its apparent similarity in specificity to crystalline swine pepsin, and must be considered provisional. The specificity of pepsin is incompletely defined, and cathepsin A has not yet been purified extensively.

lar to that of trypsin, and acts on benzoyl-L-argininamide; and cathepsin C has a specificity similar to that of chymotrypsin, and acts on glycyl-L-phenylalaninamide. However, the specificity of cathepsin C is more sharply restricted than that of chymotrypsin, and the intracellular enzyme appears to be limited in its action to CO—NH (or CO—OR) bonds of dipeptide derivatives having a free α-amino group.[53]

$$\overset{\text{R}}{\underset{|}{\ }} \quad \overset{\text{R}'}{\underset{|}{\ }}$$
$$\text{NH}_2\text{CHCO—NHCHCO}\overset{:}{\underset{:}{-}}\text{NH—}$$

These cathepsins attack proteins and are endopeptidases; they differ from the digestive proteinases in the pH optima of their hydrolytic action (near pH 6) and in the fact that cathepsins B and C are maximally active in the presence of sulfhydryl compounds such as cysteine or glutathione.[54] When a tissue dies the pH becomes slightly acid, and the autolytic action of the intracellular enzymes is favored. In the process of autolysis, the tissue proteinases are aided by a variety of tissue exopeptidases, which are counterparts of the carboxypeptidase, amino-

[53] N. Izumiya and J. S. Fruton, *J. Biol. Chem.*, **218**, 59 (1956).
[54] J. S. Fruton and M. J. Mycek, *Arch. Biochem. and Biophys.*, **65**, 11 (1956).

peptidases, dipeptidases, tripeptidase, and prolidase found in the pancreatic secretion and in the gastrointestinal tract. The intracellular carboxypeptidase has a pH optimum near 5 and is activated by sulfhydryl compounds. With the exception of tripeptidase, the other known exopeptidases of animal tissues are activated by metal ions. The aminopeptidase of swine kidney has been purified appreciably.[55]

It should be emphasized that the above listing of the intracellular proteolytic enzymes of animal tissues is not a complete one; other cathepsins[56] and exopeptidases are present, but the specificity of most of these has not been adequately characterized. The physiological role of the intracellular proteolytic enzymes in the living cell is not clear at the present time; it is believed, however, that they may play a role in the biosynthesis of the peptide bonds of proteins and of naturally occurring peptides (cf. p. 717).

Blood Coagulation.[57] Although the addition of crystalline trypsin to mammalian blood accelerates the rate of blood coagulation (cf. p. 692), pancreatic trypsin is not concerned with the phenomenon of blood clotting in normal mammals. This process, under the control of a complex system whose details are far from clear, involves the participation of proteolytic enzymes present in blood. The formation of the clot is caused by the enzymic conversion, by the plasma proteinase thrombin, of the plasma protein fibrinogen to the insoluble protein fibrin. Partially purified preparations of thrombin hydrolyze p-toluenesulfonyl-L-arginine methyl ester,[58] which is also a synthetic substrate for crystalline trypsin, and, like trypsin, thrombin preparations are inhibited by DFP (p. 691). In the conversion of fibrinogen to fibrin, peptide material is released,[59] thus indicating that peptide bonds have been cleaved. It is probable that the association of fibrin particles to form a clot depends on the unmasking of reactive sites by the proteolytic removal of the peptide material.[60]

Purified fibrinogen may also be clotted by proteinases such as the plant enzyme papain (p. 704) and by various snake venoms which contain proteolytic enzymes. It is probable that some of the toxic action of such venoms is due to their proteolytic activity.

In normal plasma the level of thrombin is negligible; as needed, it

[55] D. Spackman et al., *J. Biol. Chem.*, **212**, 255 (1955).

[56] A. Schäffner and M. Truelle, *Biochem. Z.*, **315**, 391 (1943); K. Lang and E. Wegner, *ibid.*, **318**, 462 (1948).

[57] T. Astrup, *Advances in Enzymol.*, **10**, 1 (1950); W. H. Seegers, *ibid.*, **16**, 23 (1955).

[58] S. Sherry and W. Troll, *J. Biol. Chem.*, **208**, 95 (1954).

[59] L. Lorand and W. R. Middlebrook, *Biochem. J.*, **52**, 196 (1952); *Science*, **118**, 515 (1953); F. R. Bettelheim, *Biochim. et Biophys. Acta*, **19**, 121 (1956).

[60] T. H. Donnelly et al., *Arch. Biochem. and Biophys.*, **56**, 369 (1955); M. Laskowski, Jr., et al., *J. Biol. Chem.*, **222**, 815 (1956).

arises from an enzymically inactive precursor named prothrombin. Human plasma contains 10 to 15 mg of prothrombin per 100 ml. The conversion of prothrombin to thrombin requires the presence of Ca^{2+} ions and may be effected by substances of unknown nature derived from many animal tissues, especially lung and brain.[61] These tissue substances have been given the names thromboplastin (by Howell) and thrombokinase (by Morawitz). It is of interest that crystalline trypsin does not clot fibrinogen directly but accelerates blood coagulation by converting prothrombin to thrombin.

In addition to the thromboplastin derived from tissues, other natural activators of prothrombin are derived from the blood platelets and from a plasma protein (plasma Ac-globulin); the latter is converted by thrombin into an activator of prothrombin. The available data suggest the following sequence of chemical events in blood coagulation. A small amount of prothrombin is activated by thromboplastic factors from tissues and from platelets. The thrombin thus formed activates plasma Ac-globulin, which causes the conversion of more prothrombin to thrombin; this increases the amount of thrombin to a level sufficient to cause the clotting of fibrinogen.

The factors that promote blood coagulation are counteracted by several that promote the maintenance of the fluidity of the blood. One of these anticoagulant substances is heparin (p. 425), which, in the presence of serum, blocks the conversion of prothrombin to thrombin. Normal blood contains only small amounts of heparin, but its concentration is markedly increased in anaphylactic shock. In addition to heparin, normal blood contains substances of unknown nature which inactivate thrombin (antithrombin) and thromboplastin (antithromboplastin). Thrombin also is inhibited by hirudin (present in the glandular secretion of leeches), which is a protein of molecular weight about 16,000.

Another factor present in plasma which contributes to the prevention of the accumulation of fibrin clots is a precursor of an enzyme (or enzymes) that dissolves fibrin and hydrolyzes casein, and therefore is assumed to be a proteolytic enzyme. The enzyme is variously named plasmin, fibrinolysin, plasma tryptase; the mechanism of its formation from its precursor (plasminogen, profibrinolysin) is unknown, but this conversion may be effected by shaking plasma with an organic solvent (e.g., chloroform) or by the addition of an enzyme preparation from streptococci (streptokinase).[62] Plasmin preparations hydrolyze synthetic substrates of pancreatic trypsin.[63] An inhibitor of plasmin (antiplasmin, antifibrinolysin) is present in normal plasma.

[61] R. G. Macfarlane, *Physiol. Revs.*, **36**, 479 (1956).

[62] L. R. Christensen, *J. Clin. Invest.*, **28**, 163 (1949); W. Troll and S. Sherry, *J. Biol. Chem.*, **213**, 881 (1955).

[63] W. Troll et al., *J. Biol. Chem.*, **208**, 85 (1954).

Brief mention may be made at this point of the fact that both fibrinogen and prothrombin are synthesized in the liver and that vitamin K
(p. 668) is essential for the synthesis of prothrombin; a deficiency in this
vitamin therefore leads to an impairment of the blood-clotting mechanism.
The action of vitamin K is counteracted by the drug dicumarol [3,3'-
methylene-bis(4-hydroxycoumarin)].[64]

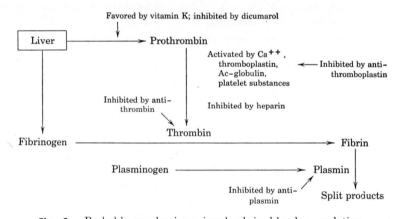

Dicumarol

It is obvious from the foregoing that, despite the extensive studies in
this field, much remains to be learned about the enzymic mechanisms
involved in blood coagulation. The scheme shown in Fig. 3 may be
useful in summarizing the present status of the problem.

Favored by vitamin K; inhibited by dicumarol

Liver ⟶ Prothrombin

Activated by Ca^{++},
thromboplastin,
Ac–globulin,
platelet substances

◀— Inhibited by anti–
thromboplastin

Inhibited by anti–
thrombin

Inhibited by heparin

Thrombin

Fibrinogen ⟶ Fibrin

Plasminogen ⟶ Plasmin

Inhibited by anti–
plasmin

Split products

Fig. 3. Probable mechanisms involved in blood coagulation.

Proteolytic Enzymes of Higher Plants

Proteolytic enzymes are widely distributed in many kinds of plant
tissue, but most of the available information deals with the proteinases
present in the latex of several plant species. For example, the latex of
the papaya (*Carica papaya*) contains active proteinases; two of these
(papain and chymopapain) have been obtained in crystalline form.[65]

[64] K. P. Link, *Federation Proc.*, **4**, 176 (1945); *Harvey Lectures*, **39**, 162 (1944).
[65] A. K. Balls and H. Lineweaver, *J. Biol. Chem.*, **130**, 669 (1939); E. F. Jansen
and A. K. Balls, *ibid.*, **137**, 459 (1941); J. Kimmel and E. L. Smith, *ibid.*, **207**,
515 (1954); *Advances in Enzymol.*, **19**, 267 (1957).

Crystalline papain has a molecular weight of about 20,500, and an apparent isoelectric point at pH 8.8. It readily forms a mercuric complex which contains 1 gram atom of Hg per 43,000 grams of protein. Approximately two thirds of the 180 amino acid residues of crystalline mercuripapain can be removed by means of purified aminopeptidase (p. 702) without loss of potential enzymic activity.[66]

Other intracellular plant proteinases, which have properties similar to those of papain and are therefore named "papainases," are ficin (from the latex of the fig, *Ficus carica*) and bromelin (from the pineapple). These enzymes act over a wide pH range (optima near pH 6) on proteins and on synthetic peptide derivatives of suitable structure. Papain and ficin hydrolyze the amide bonds of benzoyl-L-argininamide and of carbobenzoxy-L-methioninamide, and papain hydrolyzes carbobenzoxy-L-glutamic acid-α-amide (carbobenzoxy-L-isoglutamine) and benzoylglycinamide; the backbone specificity requirements of these enzymes resemble those of trypsin and chymotrypsin (cf. Table 2). Papain hydrolyzes not only amide and peptide bonds, but also ester linkages (e.g., in benzoylglycine ethyl ester) and thiol esters (e.g., benzoylglycyl ethane thiol, $C_6H_5CONHCH_2CO$—SC_2H_5).[67]

In order to exhibit maximal proteolytic activity toward proteins or toward synthetic substrates, papain, ficin, and bromelin require activation by one of a variety of substances (glutathione, cysteine, H_2S, HCN, etc.). Crude preparations of these enzymes are always accompanied by sufficient natural activator (probably glutathione) to permit some proteolytic activity; the further addition of one of the substances listed above increases the rate of enzymic action. In addition to their role in binding inhibitory metal ions (e.g., Cu^{2+}, Hg^{2+}), these substances appear to react directly with inactive papain; however, the mechanism of this direct activation has not been elucidated. One opinion is that the activators serve as reducing agents for the conversion of disulfide groups in the inactive enzyme protein to sulfhydryl groups which are believed to be essential for enzymic activity.[68]

$$R\text{—}S\text{—}S\text{—}R + 2 \text{ cysteine} \rightarrow 2 \text{ } R\text{—}S\text{—}H + \text{cystine}$$
Inactive   Active
papain   papain

Another view has emerged from studies with volatile activators (HCN, H_2S); when these were removed from an enzyme solution under anaerobic conditions, the enzymic activity was lost. This finding was interpreted

[66] E. L. Smith et al., *J. Biol. Chem.*, **207**, 533, 551 (1954); *Federation Proc.*, **16**, 801 (1957); R. L. Hill and E. L. Smith, *J. Biol. Chem.*, **231**, 117 (1958).

[67] R. B. Johnston, *J. Biol. Chem.*, **221**, 1037 (1956).

[68] T. Bersin and W. Logemann, *Z. physiol. Chem.*, **220**, 209 (1933).

as indicating a reversible addition of the activator to the enzyme protein.[69]

$$\text{Papain} + H_2S \rightarrow \text{Papain}—H_2S$$
(Inactive)   (Active)

In order to effect maximal activation of an extensively dialyzed preparation of papain with 0.2 M HCN, traces of cysteine (4×10^{-5} M) were required; this may mean that the combination of HCN or of another activator (cysteine, H_2S) with the inactive proenzyme must be preceded by a reduction of the disulfide groups in the inactive protein. It has been suggested that the reversible addition of an activator involves a reaction with a carbonyl group in the enzyme to form a hemimercaptal (with cysteine or H_2S) or a cyanohydrin (with HCN), since carbonyl reagents (hydroxylamine, phenylhydrazine) inhibit papain; this inhibition may be counteracted by an increase in the concentration of the activator.

Although the mechanism of the activation of the intracellular plant proteinases is not yet clearly established, the process itself appears to be of some importance in the regulation of the intracellular activity of these enzymes by the natural activators, the most important of which is glutathione. Some of the intracellular proteinases of animal tissues (e.g., cathepsin B, tissue carboxypeptidase) also require activation by sulfhydryl compounds; probably, similar mechanisms are involved in the activation of both the animal and plant enzymes.

The proteinases which require activation by cysteine, glutathione, HCN, etc., are completely inhibited by small concentrations (ca. 1×10^{-4} M) of iodoacetate. Mention was made on p. 325 of the inhibition of glyceraldehyde-3-phosphate dehydrogenase by this reagent. Many other enzymes are also inhibited irreversibly by iodoacetate, and it is assumed that the inhibition involves a combination of the reagent with essential sulfhydryl groups on the enzyme protein.[70]

$$\text{Protein}—SH + ICH_2COO^- \rightarrow \text{Protein}—S—CH_2COO^- + HI$$

Of special importance in the nitrogen metabolism of plants are the proteolytic enzymes of seeds and seedlings. When a seed germinates, the reserve seed proteins are rapidly hydrolyzed to smaller fragments (presumably amino acids and small peptides), which are then used by the embryonic plant for protein synthesis. Mounfield[71] and others have shown that the proteolytic activity of the dormant wheat seed is small, but increases enormously on germination. Of the seed proteinases, only

[69] G. W. Irving, Jr. et al., *J. Biol. Chem.*, **139**, 569 (1941); *J. Gen. Physiol.*, **25**, 669 (1942); *J. Biol. Chem.*, **144**, 161 (1942).

[70] L. Hellerman, *Physiol. Revs.*, **17**, 454 (1937).

[71] J. D. Mounfield, *Biochem. J.*, **30**, 549, 1778 (1936); **32**, 1675 (1938).

arachain (from the peanut) has been studied carefully thus far; it has a pH optimum near pH 7 and does not require activation by sulfhydryl compounds. In the latter respect arachain resembles several other plant proteinases such as solanain (from the fruit of the horsenettle, *Solanum elaeagnifolium*).

In addition to the various proteinases mentioned above, several exopeptidases have also been found in higher plants. Thus malt and extracts of spinach and cabbage contain a leucine aminopeptidase which is activated by Mn^{2+}. It is of interest that, in the sprouting of oat seedlings, the peptidase activity is concentrated near the growing point of the coleoptile.[72]

Proteolytic Enzymes of Microorganisms

Bacteria, yeasts, and fungi contain a large variety of proteinases and peptidases, but, with few exceptions, these enzymes have not been purified extensively.[73] Numerous anaerobic organisms liberate into the culture medium proteinases which can hydrolyze gelatin and collagen; these enzymes are frequently termed collagenases. The collagenase of *Clostridium welchii* has been shown to be identical with its "K-toxin," which disintegrates the collagen network in infected human wounds (gas gangrene).[74] This enzyme acts optimally near pH 7 and does not require activation by sulfhydryl compounds. A collagenase has also been obtained in partially purified form from the pathogenic anaerobe *Clostridium histolyticum*.[75] *Micrococcus lysodeikticus* elaborates a proteinase which is inactive and unstable in the absence of Ca^{2+}, and the addition of anions which bind calcium (oxalate, phosphate, citrate) abolishes the enzyme action.[76] A variety of aerobic bacteria (e.g., *Bacillus pyocyaneus*, *Serratia marcescens*) also elaborate extracellular proteinases.

The liberation, into the culture medium, of protein-splitting enzymes permits an organism to use proteins as sources of nitrogen for growth. Gorini and Crevier[77] have shown that, when a protein (serum albumin) serves as the sole nitrogen source for the growth of *Bacterium megatherium*, Ca^{2+} is essential for growth; this is apparently due to the metal activation of the bacterial proteinase. In general, the more readily

[72] K. Linderstrøm-Lang and H. Holter, *Z. physiol. Chem.*, **204**, 15 (1932).

[73] E. Maschmann, *Ergebn. Enzymforsch.*, **9**, 155 (1943).

[74] W. E. van Heyningen, *Bacterial Toxins*, Blackwell Scientific Publications, Oxford, 1950.

[75] I. Mandl et al., *J. Clin. Invest.*, **32**, 1323 (1953); R. deBellis et al., *Nature*, **174**, 1191 (1954).

[76] L. Gorini and C. Fromageot, *Compt. rend.*, **229**, 559 (1949).

[77] L. Gorini and M. Crevier, *Biochim. et Biophys. Acta*, **7**, 291 (1951).

diffusible peptides present in partial hydrolysates of proteins are better than pure proteins as sources of nitrogen for bacterial growth. Commercial peptone preparations (e.g., pepsin digest of fibrin) are commonly used in bacteriological media. It may be added that many bacteria do not liberate extracellular proteinases into the culture medium; these "nonproteolytic" organisms therefore require readily diffusible nitrogen sources (ammonia, amino acids, small peptides) for growth. Examination of the ability of organisms to liquefy gelatin provides a routine method widely used to distinguish the "proteolytic" from the "nonproteolytic" bacteria.

The proteinase subtilisin, elaborated by *Bacillus subtilis,* has been crystallized.[78] This enzyme was discovered because of its action in converting egg albumin (which crystallizes in needles) into a new protein (plakalbumin) which crystallizes in plates. In this conversion, a hexapeptide (L-alanyl-glycyl-L-valyl-L-aspartyl-L-alanyl-L-alanine) is split off, apparently from the interior of a peptide chain of egg albumin, and the enzyme cleaves the hexapeptide further at the aspartyl-alanyl bond.[79] Subtilisin attacks many proteins, including ribonuclease, which is cleaved to fragments that still retain enzymic activity (Chapter 35).

Some group A streptococci elaborate a proteinase which has been obtained in crystalline form. At pH 7, and in the presence of cysteine (which is required as an activator), this enzyme attacks many proteins and also hydrolyzes benzoyl-L-argininamide.[80]

In addition to the above proteinases, a variety of peptidases which hydrolyze di- and tripeptides have been found in microorganisms. Most of these enzymes are not liberated into the medium, and must be extracted from the disintegrated cells. Several of the enzymes which act on dipeptides are maximally activated by Fe^{2+} plus cysteine. Although the peptidases of most organisms exhibit specificity for the L-form of the peptide substrates, extracts of *Leuconostoc mesenteroides* hydrolyze D-peptides such as D-leucylglycylglycine.[81] This ability of some bacterial peptidases to act at peptide bonds involving D-amino acid residues is of interest in view of the fact that most of the naturally occurring D-peptides described thus far are elaborated by microorganisms (cf. p. 137).

The proteolytic enzymes of bacteria are important in the digestion of dietary proteins in the rumen of animals such as the sheep.[82]

[78] A. V. Güntelberg and M. Ottesen, *Compt. rend. trav. lab. Carlsberg, Sér. chim.,* **29,** 36 (1954).

[79] M. Ottesen and A. Wollenberger, *Nature,* **170,** 801 (1952); M. Ottesen, *Arch. Biochem. and Biophys.,* **65,** 70 (1956).

[80] S. D. Elliott, *J. Exptl. Med.,* **92,** 201 (1950); M. J. Mycek et al., *J. Biol. Chem.,* **197,** 637 (1952).

[81] M. J. Johnson and J. Berger, *Advances in Enzymol.,* **2,** 69 (1942).

[82] M. I. Chalmers and R. L. M. Synge, *Advances in Protein Chem.,* **9,** 93 (1954); E. F. Annison, *Biochem. J.,* **64,** 705 (1956).

Analytical Methods for Determination of Proteolysis

A variety of analytical procedures are available for the determination of the extent of hydrolysis of proteins and peptides by proteolytic enzymes. With protein substrates, it is convenient to add, at various time intervals, trichloroacetic acid to aliquots of the enzyme digest; this reagent precipitates the undigested protein and the larger peptide fragments, as well as the enzyme protein. As the enzymic hydrolysis proceeds, the proportion of material (nonprotein nitrogen) soluble in the trichloroacetic acid solution increases. If a protein substrate contains tyrosine and tryptophan residues (e.g., hemoglobin, casein, serum albumin), the increase in nonprotein material in the trichloroacetic acid filtrate may be followed spectrophotometrically by measurement of the optical density at 280 mμ (cf. p. 74);[83] alternatively, use may be made of the Folin-Ciocalteu phosphomolybdotungstic acid reagent, which gives a blue color with tyrosine.[84]

The enzymic scission of peptide bonds in proteins and peptides may be followed by one of several titrimetric methods. In the pH range 5 to 7 the cleavage of a peptide bond may be represented as:

$$RCO-NHR' + H_2O \rightarrow RCOO^- + R'NH_3^+$$

Mention was made on p. 91 of the formol and alcohol methods for the alkalimetric titration of the charged ammonium group of amino acids and peptides; since the hydrolysis of a peptide bond leads to the appearance of equivalent amounts of carboxylate and ammonium ions, alkalimetric titration gives a measure of the extent of hydrolysis. Another method involves titration with standard hydrochloric acid in aqueous acetone as the solvent and naphthyl red as the indicator; here the increase in carboxylate ions is determined directly.

Other analytical procedures for following proteolysis are the use of the nitrous acid method for the determination of α-amino groups (p. 49), the colorimetric ninhydrin method for amino groups (p. 51), and the gasometric ninhydrin method for α-amino acids (p. 51). In addition, the appearance of new charged groups (when peptide bonds are broken) leads to a volume contraction (electrostriction) which may be measured in a dilatometer.[85]

When the action of a proteolytic enzyme leads to the cleavage of an amide ($-CO-NH_2$) bond, the ammonia liberated may be determined by the Conway procedure (p. 63).

[83] M. Kunitz, *J. Gen. Physiol.,* **30,** 291 (1947).

[84] M. L. Anson, *J. Gen. Physiol.,* **20,** 565 (1937); K. Wallenfels, *Biochem. Z.,* **321,** 189 (1950).

[85] K. Linderstrøm-Lang and C. F. Jacobsen, *Compt. rend. trav. lab. Carlsberg. Sér. chim.,* **24,** 1 (1941).

Enzymic Hydrolysis of Amides Derived from Amino Acids

From the previous discussion of the specificity of proteolytic enzymes, it is clear that these enzymes are not limited in their action to peptide bonds between two amino acid residues but can also hydrolyze amide bonds in which only one amino acid residue is involved. Thus, trypsin splits benzoyl-L-argininamide, leucine aminopeptidase hydrolyzes L-leucinamide, and carboxypeptidase acts on benzoyl-L-tyrosine. For this reason it is impossible to establish a sharp line of demarcation between these enzymes and the so-called "amidases." For example, the discovery by Schmiedeberg in 1881 that extracts of animal tissues hydrolyze hippuric acid to benzoic acid and glycine led to the introduction of the term "histozyme," and later "hippuricase," for the enzyme responsible for this cleavage. Since hippuricase has not been purified, and crude preparations also attack the N-benzoyl derivatives of various L-amino acids, it is not possible to decide at present whether this enzyme is identical with an intracellular carboxypeptidase, and whether all the benzoylamino acids are hydrolyzed by the same enzyme. Similar uncertainty applies to the enzymes responsible for the known metabolic cleavage of N-acetylamino acids,[86] and of N-formylamino acids. Although the tissue enzymes ("acylases") that hydrolyze such acylamino acids have not been purified extensively, they are known to be specific for the L-forms of their substrates, and kidney acylase preparations have proved to be extremely valuable for the enzymic resolution of racemic amino acids.[87]

Two amino acid amides, however, appear to be substrates for specific enzymes, distinct from the known peptidases. These are L-asparagine and L-glutamine (p. 62), which are hydrolyzed by asparaginase and glutaminase, respectively. Asparaginase, which acts optimally near pH 8, is widely distributed in animal and plant tissues, and in microorganisms; the glutaminase of animal tissues has its optimum between pH 8 and 9.[88] In most animal species, the kidney represents the richest store of glutaminase activity, which is presumably responsible for the formation of urinary ammonia from blood glutamine (see Chapter 33). Glutaminases have been found not only in animal tissues but also in plant tissues and in microorganisms. The possibility exists that one of the glutaminases may be identical with an enzyme, found in animal tissues, which hydrolyzes the tripeptide glutathione (p. 136) to L-glutamic acid

[86] K. Bloch and D. Rittenberg, *J. Biol. Chem.*, **169**, 467 (1947); B. C. Whaler, *J. Physiol.*, **130**, 278 (1955).

[87] J. P. Greenstein, *Advances in Protein Chem.*, **9**, 121 (1954).

[88] A. Meister, *Physiol. Revs.*, **36**, 103 (1956).

and L-cysteinylglycine; in this reaction the peptide bond involving the γ-carboxyl group of the glutamic acid residue is broken.

It may be added that a variety of amides which do not contain amino acid residues are also subject to enzymic hydrolysis in biological systems. Thus extracts of the yeast *Torula utilis* hydrolyze acetamide, propion-amide, and lactic acid amide, while extracts of animal tissues hydrolyze amides of aromatic acids (benzoic acid, *p*-nitrobenzoic acid) and acetyl derivatives of aromatic amines (aniline).

Among the bacterial amidases should be included penicillinase, which catalyzes the hydrolysis of penicillin at the CO—NH linkage of the 4-membered β-lactam ring (cf. p. 60) to form a penicilloic acid. The formation of penicillinase by bacteria requires the presence, in the culture medium, of an inducer (p. 746).

Enzymic Synthesis of Peptide Bonds [89]

In the hydrolytic action of all the proteolytic enzymes examined thus far, the cleavage of the sensitive bonds is nearly complete (ca. 99 per cent) when the reactions proceed in a homogeneous medium. For example, an estimate has been made of the equilibrium constant for the hydrolysis of benzoyl-L-tyrosylglycinamide by crystalline chymotrypsin at pH 7.9 and 25° C by incubating benzoyl-L-tyrosine (0.025 M), in the presence of the enzyme, with glycinamide (0.05 M) that had been labeled with N^{15} in the glycine nitrogen ($N^{15}H_2CH_2CO—NH_2$).[90] After a

$$\underset{\substack{\text{Benzoyl-L-tyrosylglycinamide}\\\text{(BTGA)}}}{C_6H_5CO—NH\overset{\overset{\displaystyle CH_2C_6H_4OH}{|}}{C}HCO—NHCH_2CO—NH_2} + H_2O \ \rightleftharpoons$$

$$\underset{\substack{\text{Benzoyl-L-tyrosine}\\\text{(BT}^-)}}{C_6H_5CO—NH\overset{\overset{\displaystyle CH_2C_6H_4OH}{|}}{C}HCOO^-} + \underset{\substack{\text{Glycinamide}\\\text{(GA}^+)}}{^+NH_3CH_2CO—NH_2}$$

suitable time, the chymotrypsin was inactivated, and a known amount of unlabeled benzoyl-L-tyrosylglycinamide was added as a carrier. This substance was then reisolated in analytically pure form, and recrystallized to constant N^{15} concentration. By means of the equation for isotope dilution (p. 127), it was possible to calculate, from the N^{15}

[89] H. Borsook, *Advances in Protein Chem.*, **8**, 127 (1953); J. S. Fruton, *Harvey Lectures*, **51**, 64 (1957); in D. Rudnick, *Aspects of Synthesis and Order in Growth*, Princeton University Press, Princeton, 1954.

[90] J. S. Fruton et al., *J. Biol. Chem.*, **190**, 39 (1951); A. Dobry et al., *ibid.*, **195**, 149 (1952).

content of the isolated material, the concentration of the benzoyl-L-tyrosylglycinamide that had been synthesized under the conditions of the enzyme experiment; this was found to be 3.2×10^{-4} M. Thus approximately 99 per cent of the initial benzoyl-L-tyrosine and of the total initial glycinamide is in equilibrium with about 1 per cent of the synthetic product. At pH 7.9 approximately half of the glycinamide is present in the form of the conjugate base ($pK' = 7.93$); hence the total concentration of charged and uncharged glycinamide is twice that of the protonated form shown in the equation. Since the pK' of benzoyl-L-tyrosine is near pH 3, this compound is predominantly in the carboxylate form. On the assumption that the activity coefficients of the components in the above reaction are all equal to unity, the equilibrium constant for the condensation is

$$K = \frac{[BTGA][H_2O]}{[BT^-][GA^+]} = \frac{0.00032 \times 1}{0.025 \times 0.025} = 0.51$$

From this equilibrium constant one may calculate that $\Delta F^\circ_{298} = -1365$ log $0.51 = +0.4$ kcal (cf. p. 232). Hence the hydrolysis of the substrate has a ΔF°_{298} of -0.4 kcal. It may be added that calorimetric measurement of the heat of hydrolysis of benzoyl-L-tyrosylglycinamide by chymotrypsin at pH 7.9 gave a value of $\Delta H_{298} = -1.55$ kcal. Similarly, in the partial hydrolysis of polymeric lysine peptides by trypsin (cf. p. 690), $\Delta H_{298} = -1.25$ kcal per mole per bond hydrolyzed.

The above data apply to the energy changes in the hydrolysis or synthesis of peptide bonds not adjacent to α-NH_3^+ or α-COO^- groups; such bonds correspond to the interior peptide linkages of proteins. When a CO—NH bond links two amino acids in a dipeptide (e.g., L-alanylglycine), the hydrolytic reaction near pH 7 may be written:

$$\begin{array}{c} CH_3 \\ | \\ {}^+NH_3CHCO-NHCH_2COO^- + H_2O \rightleftharpoons \end{array}$$

$$\begin{array}{c} CH_3 \\ | \\ {}^+NH_3CHCOO^- + {}^+NH_3CH_2COO^- \end{array}$$

Most of the thermodynamic values for the hydrolysis of dipeptides have been obtained by calculation of ΔF° from data on the enthalpy and entropy of the products and reactants[91] (cf. p. 236); in this manner, the free-energy change in the hydrolysis of alanylglycine at pH 7 (all reactants at unit activity) has been calculated to be about -4 kcal per mole. The difference between this value (and similar values for the hydrolysis of other dipeptides) and that for the hydrolysis of interior peptide bonds is a consequence of the fact that the pK' of the ammonium

[91] H. M. Huffman, *J. Physical Chem.*, **46**, 885 (1942).

group in amino acids is much higher than that for the ammonium group of amino acid amides and peptides (e.g., glycine, $pK_2' = 9.6$; glycinamide, $pK' = 7.93$; L-alanylglycine, $pK_2' = 8.2$), as first suggested by Linderstrøm-Lang.[92]

The hydrolysis of CO—NH$_2$ bonds (as in benzoyl-L-tyrosinamide) may be accompanied by $\Delta F'$ (pH 7) values of the same order of magnitude as those for the hydrolysis of dipeptides. Since the equilibria are so far in the direction of hydrolysis, reliable data for $\Delta F'$ are not available from measurements of the equilibrium constant; however, calorimetric determinations of the enthalpy change in the enzyme-catalyzed hydrolysis of such amide bonds have given values for ΔH_{298} near —6 kcal per mole[93] (cf. p. 378).

Enzymic Synthesis of Peptide Bonds by Condensation Reactions. From the data cited above it is clear that the synthesis of CO—NH bonds is an endergonic process, and that negligibly small amounts of the condensation product are present at equilibrium in a homogeneous system. In order to increase the amount of synthetic product formed in a condensation reaction, it is necessary to couple the endergonic peptide synthesis to a process that provides energy to the system. The simplest known example of such a coupled reaction is the experiment in which the reactants are so chosen that the synthetic product has a solubility lower than its equilibrium concentration. For example, if, in the chymotrypsin-catalyzed synthesis mentioned above, glycinamide is replaced by glycinanilide, benzoyl-L-tyrosylglycinanilide crystallizes from the solution, and, under conditions where about 1 per cent of the corresponding amide is formed, the yield of the anilide may be 65 per cent.[94] It is reasonable to assume that the free-energy changes for the synthesis of the amide and the anilide, in homogeneous solution, are similar; the energy-yielding process that drives the synthesis of the anilide is the removal of the product from solution, because, unlike the amide, benzoyl-L-tyrosylglycinanilide has a solubility lower than the theoretical equilibrium concentration. Similar proteinase-catalyzed synthesis of amide and peptide bonds, in which the product is sparingly soluble, has been shown with intracellular proteinases such as papain, ficin, and cathepsin C.[95]

Since the function of the proteinase is to catalyze the attainment of equilibrium, it is not surprising that the specificity requirements found

[92] K. Linderstrøm-Lang, *Lane Medical Lectures: Proteins and Enzymes*, Stanford University Press, Stanford, 1952.

[93] J. M. Sturtevant, *J. Am. Chem. Soc.*, **75**, 2016 (1953); W. W. Forrest et al., *ibid.*, **78**, 1349 (1956).

[94] M. Bergmann and J. S. Fruton, *J. Biol. Chem.*, **124**, 321 (1938).

[95] M. Bergmann and J. S. Fruton, *Ann. N. Y. Acad. Sci.*, **45**, 409 (1944).

earlier for the catalysis of the hydrolytic process also apply to the synthetic process. In particular, the stereochemical specificity is the same, and this has been used for the enzymic resolution of racemic amino acids; an example is the resolution of DL-methionine by means of papain.[96]

The demonstration that proteinases can effect the synthesis of peptide bonds by condensation reactions in which these enzymes exhibit specificity of action is important in considering the enzymic mechanisms whereby peptide chains of proteins are made in living cells. Although the extent of such synthesis is negligible in homogeneous systems *in vitro*, it is obvious that, with living matter, one is dealing not with an invariant set of components in a homogeneous system but with a polyphasic system in a highly dynamic state. As will be seen from the discussion in the succeeding chapter, in animals there is an extremely rapid exchange of nitrogen between the tissue proteins and the "metabolic pool" of nonprotein nitrogen compounds. The possibility cannot be excluded, therefore, that proteinases may effect peptide synthesis by condensation reactions coupled to the removal of the synthetic products from the equilibrium mixture by their relative insolubility, by their participation in other chemical reactions, or by their entrance into the circulating fluids of the organism. However, it has not been possible as yet to demonstrate the occurrence of such coupled reactions in biological systems, and it is not known whether proteinases effect the intracellular condensation of peptide units with the elimination of the elements of water. If such condensation reactions do occur *in vivo*, it is likely that they are more important in the formation of interior CO—NH bonds of peptide chains than in the synthesis of terminal peptide bonds (adjacent to free α-NH$_3$+ or α-COO$^-$ groups) or of CO—NH$_2$ bonds, since more work must be done to "pull" such syntheses by removal of the product (cf. p. 239). As will be seen later in this chapter, several endergonic syntheses of peptides and amides are known to be driven by coupling to the enzymic cleavage of ATP.

Catalysis of Transamidation Reactions by Proteolytic Enzymes. Like other "hydrolases," proteolytic enzymes catalyze not only the hydrolysis of CO—NH bonds and the reversal of such hydrolysis, but also replacement reactions (cf. p. 273):

$$RCO—NHR' + NH_2X \rightleftharpoons RCO—NHX + NH_2R'$$

In the equation shown the first of the two reactants is a typical substrate for a proteinase, and the second is a replacement agent. Such reactions may be termed transamidation or transpeptidation reactions and are strictly analogous to the processes by which one component of a gly-

[96] C. A. Dekker and J. S. Fruton, *J. Biol. Chem.,* **173,** 471 (1948).

cosidic or ester linkage is replaced by another closely related substance in a transglycosidation or transesterification reaction. Transamidation reactions have been demonstrated with several of the known proteinases[97] (chymotrypsin, trypsin, papain, ficin, cathepsin B, cathepsin C), and it has been shown that the specificity of each enzyme toward the reactant having the CO—NH group is the same for replacement as for hydrolysis. It has been concluded that in both types of reaction the same activated enzyme-substrate complex is formed, and that the replacement agent competes with water for this reactive intermediate. The possibility exists that a common intermediate in hydrolysis and transamidation is an "acyl-enzyme" in which the reactive carbonyl group of the substrate is linked to the catalytic center of the proteinase (cf. p. 282).

$$RCO-NHR' + EnzH \rightleftharpoons RCO-Enz + NH_2R'$$

$$RCO-Enz + NH_2X \rightleftharpoons RCO-NHX + EnzH$$

$$RCO-Enz + H_2O \rightarrow RCOOH + EnzH$$

From the effect of pH on the relative extent of hydrolysis and replacement by proteinases such as papain or cathepsin C, it appears that the replacement agent (NH_2X) reacts in the unprotonated form. For example, hydroxylamine ($pK' = 6.0$) does not react extensively at pH 5, but at pH values more alkaline than 6 the transamidation reaction yielding a hydroxamic acid is readily demonstrable. Furthermore, dipeptides

$$RCO-NH_2 + NH_2OH \rightleftharpoons RCO-NHOH + NH_3$$

such as L-leucylglycine ($pK_2' = $ ca. 8.0) are more effective replacement agents at pH values near 7.5 than are free amino acids ($pK_2' = $ ca. 9.6). Thus the rate of a replacement reaction is a function of the concentration of the unprotonated amine serving as replacement agent, and it depends both on the pK' of the corresponding acid and on the pH of the solution.

It must be added, however, that pH is not the only determining factor in the effectiveness of a replacement agent in competing with water for reaction with the enzyme-substrate complex, since two amines having the same pK' values, but of unlike chemical structure, may differ greatly in reactivity. For example, at pH 7.5, papain catalyzes the reaction of 0.05 M carbobenzoxyglycinamide with 0.05 M L-leucylglycine, and the extent of replacement to form carbobenzoxyglycyl-L-leucylglycine exceeds the extent of hydrolysis to carbobenzoxyglycine. On the other hand, 0.05 M glycylglycine or D-leucylglycine, whose pK_2' values are also near 8.0, are much less effective as replacement agents if used instead

[97] R. B. Johnston et al., *J. Biol. Chem.*, **185**, 629; **187**, 205 (1950); S. G. Waley and J. Watson, *Biochem. J.*, **57**, 529 (1954); K. Blau and S. G. Waley, *ibid.*, **57**, 538 (1954).

of L-leucylglycine in the papain-catalyzed reaction, and the extent of hydrolysis is much greater than the transamidation to form the carbo-benzoxytripeptide.[98] Such results show that, in transamidation reactions, the proteinases exhibit specificity toward the replacement agent as well as toward the substrate containing the sensitive CO—NH bond. A further indication of enzymic specificity toward replacement agents is the fact that in the catalysis of a given transamidation reaction (e.g., the reaction of benzoyl-L-argininamide with NH_2OH) papain is a more effective catalyst than is trypsin.[99] In general, the intracellular protein-ases appear to be excellent catalysts of replacement reactions, and several instances are known in which the extent of transamidation far exceeds that of hydrolysis, despite the vastly greater molar concentration of water.[100] It has been suggested therefore that, at physiological pH values, a major physiological role of the intracellular proteinases may be to catalyze transamidation reactions.

The energy change in a transamidation reaction may be estimated in a manner similar to that described on p. 375 for transphosphorylation reactions. An example is the following reaction, catalyzed by chymo-trypsin:

$$\text{Benzoyl-L-tyrosinamide} + {}^+\text{glycinamide} \rightleftharpoons$$
$$\text{Benzoyl-L-tyrosylglycinamide} + NH_4{}^+$$

If the free-energy change in the hydrolysis of the amide bond in benzoyl-L-tyrosinamide is designated $\Delta F'_1$ and the free-energy change in the hydrolysis of the peptide bond in benzoyl-L-tyrosylglycinamide is de-noted as $\Delta F'_2$, then the $\Delta F'$ for the replacement reaction will be given by the difference between $\Delta F'_1$ and $\Delta F'_2$. A value for $\Delta F'_1$ is not avail-able, but calorimetric measurements have given a ΔH_{298} of -5.8 kcal per mole for the hydrolysis of benzoyl-L-tyrosinamide. Since the enthalpy change in the hydrolysis of benzoyl-L-tyrosylglycinamide is -1.5 kcal (p. 712), the over-all enthalpy change in the replacement reaction is -4.3 kcal per mole. If it is assumed that the entropy changes in the two hydrolytic reactions are of a similar order of magnitude, the transamidation reaction is seen to be exergonic.

Examination of the above replacement reaction shows it to be an enzyme-catalyzed transamidation in which a small group (ammonia) is replaced by a larger group (glycinamide), thus effecting the elongation of the peptide chain. Another model reaction in which the lengthening of a peptide chain is catalyzed by a proteinase is the exergonic conver-

[98] Y. P. Dowmont and J. S. Fruton, *J. Biol. Chem.*, **197**, 271 (1952); M. J. Mycek and J. S. Fruton, *ibid.*, **226**, 165 (1957).

[99] J. Durell and J. S. Fruton, *J. Biol. Chem.*, **207**, 487 (1954).

[100] M. E. Jones et al., *J. Biol. Chem.*, **195**, 645 (1952).

sion of L-alanyl-L-phenylalaninamide (L-ala-L-pheam) at pH 7.5 to a hexapeptide amide, as shown in the accompanying scheme. In this reaction, catalyzed by cathepsin C, the activated dipeptide unit derived from L-ala-L-pheam first reacts with another molecule of the dipeptide

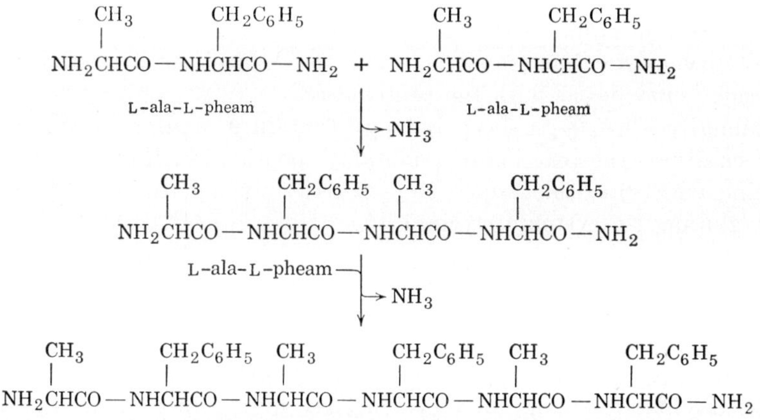

$$
\underset{\text{L-ala-L-pheam}}{NH_2CHCO-NHCHCO-NH_2} + \underset{\text{L-ala-L-pheam}}{NH_2CHCO-NHCHCO-NH_2}
$$

with CH₃, CH₂C₆H₅ substituents

$$
\downarrow{-NH_3}
$$

$$
\underset{\text{L-ala-L-pheam}}{NH_2CHCO-NHCHCO-NHCHCO-NHCHCO-NH_2}
$$

$$
\downarrow{-NH_3}
$$

$$
NH_2CHCO-NHCHCO-NHCHCO-NHCHCO-NHCHCO-NHCHCO-NH_2
$$

amide to form an intermediate tetrapeptide amide, which then serves as the replacement agent in a second step leading to the hexapeptide amide.[101] This type of polymerization has been demonstrated with other dipeptide amides that are substrates for cathepsin C, and is analogous to the reaction catalyzed by crystalline muscle phosphorylase (cf. p. 442) or by polynucleotide phosphorylase (cf. Chapter 35).

Although these findings indicate the ability of proteinases to catalyze the elongation of peptide chains in a specific manner under physiological conditions, it must be emphasized that, in the catalysis of replacement reactions, a proteinase acts at a preformed CO—NH bond. If a biological system is provided only with free amino acids from which it must make its proteins, some CO—NH bonds must be formed *de novo* in endergonic reactions coupled with energy-yielding processes before the elongation of peptide chains by transpeptidation can occur.

Other Enzymic Transamidation Reactions. It was noted previously that glutamine is hydrolyzed to glutamic acid and ammonia by enzymes present in a variety of biological systems. Waelsch[102] and others have shown the existence of bacterial enzymes that catalyze the reaction of glutamine with hydroxylamine to form γ-glutamylhydroxamic acid. Of special interest is the transamidation reaction of glutamine, catalyzed by an enzyme preparation from *Bacillus subtilis;* this organism, like the anthrax bacillus, produces a capsular polypeptide composed of D-glutamyl

[101] J. S. Fruton et al., *J. Biol. Chem.*, **204**, 891 (1953).
[102] H. Waelsch, *Advances in Enzymol.*, **13**, 237 (1952).

residues linked by γ-peptide bonds (p. 138). Williams and Thorne[103] have shown that at pH 9 the *B. subtilis* enzyme forms γ-glutamyl peptides from glutamine, thus suggesting that the capsular polypeptide is formed from glutamine by successive transamidation reactions. The partially purified enzyme preparations that catalyze replacement reactions with glutamine as the substrate also hydrolyze the amide, and the possibility exists that transamidation and hydrolysis are catalyzed by the same enzyme, as with the proteinases.

Animal tissues (e.g., sheep kidney) contain a similar enzyme system that catalyzes the reaction of γ-glutamyl peptides such as γ-L-glutamylglycine with dipeptides such as L-cysteinylglycine to form glutathione (γ-L-glutamyl-L-cysteinylglycine).[104]

$$\text{γ-L-Glutamylglycine} + \text{L-cysteinylglycine} \rightleftharpoons \text{Glutathione} + \text{glycine}$$

Glutathione is known to participate in other transamidation reactions catalyzed by enzymes present in animal tissues.[105] For example, the tripeptide reacts with L-phenylalanine at pH values near 8 to form γ-glutamylphenylalanine and cysteinylglycine; at pH 6, the hydrolysis of glutathione predominates (cf. p. 710). It has been suggested that in the various transamidation reactions of glutamine, of γ-glutamyl peptides, and of glutathione, a "γ-glutamyl-enzyme" is formed and reacts either with a replacement agent or with water. Like glutamine, asparagine can undergo transamidation reactions in the presence of bacterial enzyme preparations, and it is probable that a "β-aspartyl-enzyme" is an intermediate in such reactions.

In addition to the above enzyme systems that catalyze transamidation reactions of glutamine, preparations have been obtained from animal tissues (brain, liver)[106] and from plants[107] that catalyze the reaction of glutamine with NH_2OH in the presence of Mn^{2+} (or Mg^{2+}) and of trace amounts of ADP and phosphate. This enzymic activity appears to be closely related to the ability of these preparations to catalyze the synthesis of glutamine from glutamic acid and ammonia in the presence of ATP (cf. p. 721). Although the formation of an intermediate γ-glutamyl-enzyme is a possibility, the role of ADP and of phosphate in the transamidation reaction remains to be elucidated.

Role of ATP in the Enzymic Synthesis of CO—NH Bonds. The earlier discussion of the oxidative degradation of carbohydrates has shown that

[103] W. J. Williams and C. B. Thorne, *J. Biol. Chem.,* **210,** 203; **211,** 631 (1954); **212,** 427 (1955).

[104] P. J. Fodor et al., *J. Biol. Chem.,* **203,** 991 (1953).

[105] C. S. Hanes et al., *Nature,* **166,** 288 (1950); *Biochem. J.,* **51,** 25 (1952); F. J. R. Hird and P. H. Springell, *Biochim. et Biophys. Acta,* **15,** 31 (1954).

[106] A. Lajtha et al., *J. Biol. Chem.,* **205,** 553 (1953).

[107] P. K. Stumpf et al., *Arch. Biochem. and Biophys.,* **30,** 126; **33,** 333 (1951).

much of the energy liberated in this process is made available for a variety of endergonic processes by the synthesis of the pyrophosphate bonds of ATP, and the participation of ATP in an exergonic transphosphorylation reaction. Lipmann[108] was among the first to suggest that the biosynthesis of CO—NH bonds is coupled to the cleavage of pyrophosphate bonds of ATP. The experimental examination of this proposal has largely involved the study of the synthesis of certain amides or of glutathione in the presence of slices, homogenates, or crude extracts of animal tissues. Thus liver slices form hippuric acid (or p-aminohippuric acid) from benzoic acid (or p-aminobenzoic acid) and glycine; in the intact animal, the liver is the site of this "detoxication" reaction, and the product is excreted in the urine. Other examples of the biosynthesis of amides involving aromatic acids are the formation and urinary excretion of dibenzoyl-L-ornithine by birds and of phenylacetyl-L-glutamine in man and the chimpanzee, when benzoic acid or phenylacetic acid is administered in the diet of the appropriate species.

$$\begin{array}{cc}
\text{C}_6\text{H}_5\text{CO—NHCH}_2 & \text{CO—NH}_2 \\
| & | \\
(\text{CH}_2)_2 & (\text{CH}_2)_2 \\
| & | \\
\text{C}_6\text{H}_5\text{CO—NHCHCOOH} & \text{C}_6\text{H}_5\text{CH}_2\text{CO—NHCHCOOH} \\
\text{Dibenzoyl-L-ornithine} & \text{Phenylacetyl-L-glutamine}
\end{array}$$

Another model system employed is the acetylation of aromatic amines (e.g., sulfanilamide) by acetic acid in the presence of pigeon liver homogenates. As noted earlier (p. 482), studies on this system led to the discovery of coenzyme A, and to the demonstration that the formation of the acetylating agent (acetyl-CoA) is coupled to the cleavage of ATP. The acetylation of an amine then occurs as follows:

$$\text{CH}_3\text{CO-CoA} + \text{NH}_2\text{R} \rightarrow \text{CH}_3\text{CO—NHR} + \text{CoA}$$

A similar mechanism is involved in the formation of hippuric acid by liver and kidney preparations; benzoyl-CoA is formed from benzoate and coenzyme A in the presence of ATP, and reacts with glycine in an enzyme-catalyzed reaction that appears to be specific for this amino acid. Moreover, the formation of phenylacetylglutamine by human tissues involves the conversion of phenylacetic acid to a CoA derivative, which reacts with glutamine.[109]

In these reactions, the carbonyl group of acetic acid or of benzoic acid is made reactive by conversion of the free acid into a thiol ester, as in

[108] F. Lipmann, *Federation Proc.*, **8**, 597 (1949).

[109] D. Schachter and J. V. Taggart, *J. Biol. Chem.*, **203**, 925 (1953); **208**, 263 (1954); K. Moldave and A. Meister, *Biochim. et Biophys. Acta*, **24**, 654; **25**, 434 (1957).

the "activation" of fatty acids (cf. p. 595); this is an endergonic process, and is coupled to the cleavage of ATP to AMP and pyrophosphate. Evidence has been presented for the view that in the "activation" of acetate, an acetyl-AMP (p. 484) is formed, and is bound to the enzyme:

$$RCOO^- + ATP + Enz \rightleftharpoons RCO\text{-}AMP\text{-}Enz + pyrophosphate$$

It will be noted that the postulated reaction is reversible; therefore, if radioactive (P^{32}) pyrophosphate is added to a mixture containing a suitable enzyme preparation, the acid, and ATP, the isotope should appear in the ATP (cf. p. 282). Such an effect has been demonstrated not only with acetate as $RCOO^-$, but also with a variety of L-amino acids,[110] and it has been suggested that α-aminoacyl-AMP compounds are the activated forms of amino acids in the biosynthesis of proteins. It appears that crude enzyme preparations from rat liver contain a group of catalysts which differ in their specificity toward individual L-amino acids. Thus, a liver fraction was obtained that catalyzes pyrophosphate exchange only in the presence of L-methionine. An enzyme preparation with a similar specificity toward L-methionine has been obtained from yeast.[111] Furthermore, a highly purified enzyme preparation from beef pancreas "activates" L-tryptophan and, to a much lesser extent, L-tyrosine and L-phenylalanine.[112]

The formation of peptide bonds by the reaction of activated amino acids with other amino acids has not yet been demonstrated unequivocally in the enzyme systems discussed above; however, in the presence of high concentrations of hydroxylamine, hydroxamic acids are produced, and the pyrophosphate exchange is inhibited. Although these findings are consistent with the formation of α-aminoacyl-AMP compounds as intermediates, it must be added that such compounds have not been identified in incubation mixtures. Synthetic materials, obtained by the chemical interaction of L-amino acid chlorides or anhydrides with AMP, react readily with hydroxylamine, and are effective acylating agents in reactions with amino groups of proteins. An enzyme preparation obtained from *Escherichia coli* catalyzes the reaction of synthetic L-leucyl-AMP with hydroxylamine.[113] Such synthetic materials also promote pyrophosphate exchange in the presence of the enzyme preparations, ATP, and labeled pyrophosphate.

It is of interest that the biosynthesis of pantothenic acid (Chapter 39) from pantoic acid and β-alanine (in *Escherichia coli*) appears to resemble

[110] M. B. Hoagland et al., *J. Biol. Chem.*, **218**, 345 (1956); J. A. deMoss and G. D. Novelli, *Biochim. et Biophys. Acta*, **22**, 49 (1956).

[111] P. Berg, *J. Biol. Chem.*, **222**, 1025 (1956); **233**, 601 (1958).

[112] E. W. Davie et al., *Arch. Biochem. and Biophys.*, **65**, 21 (1956).

[113] J. A. deMoss et al., *Proc. Natl. Acad. Sci.*, **42**, 325 (1956).

the reactions described above. Maas[114] has shown that the reaction of pantoic acid with ATP gives a pantoyl-AMP compound, which reacts with β-alanine to form pantothenic acid.

The enzymic synthesis of glutamine and of glutathione also is coupled to the cleavage of ATP, but, in contrast to the reactions discussed above, the nucleotide is cleaved to ADP and phosphate. Thus, in the formation of L-glutamine from L-glutamic acid and ammonia by enzyme preparations from pigeon liver, sheep brain, and green peas,[115] the reaction is:

$$\text{Glutamic acid} + NH_3 + ATP \rightleftharpoons \text{Glutamine} + ADP + \text{phosphate}$$

The studies of Bloch and his associates[116] have shown that the enzymic synthesis of glutathione by preparations from pigeon liver and from yeast involves two successive reactions, in each of which ATP is cleaved to ADP and phosphate:

Glutamic acid + cysteine + ATP →
$$\gamma\text{-Glutamylcysteine} + ADP + \text{phosphate}$$

γ-Glutamylcysteine + glycine + ATP →
$$\text{Glutathione} + ADP + \text{phosphate}$$

The enzymic mechanisms in the biosynthesis of glutamine and of glutathione have not been elucidated, but phosphorylated enzymes appear to be formed as intermediates.[117]

The metabolic turnover of glutathione in animal tissues and in yeast is extremely rapid,[118] and it has been suggested that this widely distributed tripeptide may play a role in the biosynthesis of proteins.

Plastein Formation

When a concentrated peptic digest of a protein is incubated with pepsin at pH 4, an insoluble precipitate, termed "plastein," is formed.[119] Similar insoluble products have been obtained from concentrated peptic digests by treatment with papain or chymotrypsin.[120] In view of the complexity of the mixture of peptides that serve as reactants in plastein

[114] W. K. Maas, *Federation Proc.*, **15**, 305 (1956).

[115] W. H. Elliott, *J. Biol. Chem.*, **201**, 661 (1953).

[116] J. E. Snoke and K. Bloch, *J. Biol. Chem.*, **199**, 407 (1952); **213**, 825 (1955); S. Mandeles and K. Bloch, *ibid.*, **214**, 639 (1955).

[117] A. Kowalsky et al., *J. Biol. Chem.*, **219**, 719 (1956).

[118] H. Waelsch and D. Rittenberg, *J. Biol. Chem.*, **144**, 53 (1942); F. Turba et al., *Biochem. Z.*, **327**, 410 (1956).

[119] H. Wasteneys and H. Borsook, *Physiol. Revs.*, **10**, 110 (1930).

[120] H. B. Collier, *Can. J. Research*, **18B**, 255, 272, 305 (1940); H. Tauber, *J. Am. Chem. Soc.*, **73**, 1288 (1951).

formation, little can be said at present concerning the nature of the reactions in this process. From the preceding discussion in this chapter, it will be clear that both condensation reactions (leading to peptide bond formation) and transpeptidation reactions are possible.[121] Obviously, the appearance of a precipitate is, in itself, an unsatisfactory indication of the enzymic synthesis of peptide bonds. This was emphasized by Strain and Linderstrøm-Lang,[122] who showed that the oxidative formation of disulfide bridges between cysteine-containing peptides, present in a partial hydrolysate of fibrin, also leads to the formation of an insoluble precipitate. Although many investigators[119] considered plastein formation to simulate protein synthesis and believed that there occurred a reversal of the hydrolytic action of a proteinase, later studies showed that the average molecular weight of the plasteins was relatively low (ca. 1000).[123]

[121] F. Haurowitz and J. Horowitz, *J. Am. Chem. Soc.,* **77,** 3138 (1955).

[122] H. H. Strain and K. Linderstrøm-Lang, *Enzymologia,* **5,** 86 (1938).

[123] A. I. Virtanen and H. K. Kerkkonen, *Acta Chem. Scand.,* **1,** 140 (1947).

30 ·

Metabolic Breakdown and Synthesis of Proteins

Although the nature of the intracellular enzyme-catalyzed reactions involved in the interconversion of proteins and amino acids is obscure, there has been accumulated a considerable body of data about the over-all process of protein metabolism in a wide variety of biological forms. Since most of the available information relates to the breakdown and synthesis of proteins in higher animals, this aspect of the subject will be discussed first; consideration will then be given to the problem of protein metabolism in plants and in microorganisms.

Nitrogen Equilibrium

The over-all metabolism of nitrogen compounds in nongrowing animals may be studied conveniently by relating the amount of nitrogen excreted to the nitrogen content of the diet. The expired air and perspiration contain only a small fraction of the total excretory nitrogen, and one may assume that the urine and feces contain nearly all of the nitrogen compounds derived from the metabolism of proteins and excreted by the organism. When an animal is maintained under conditions such that the total nitrogen content of the urine and feces equals the amount of dietary nitrogen, the animal is said to be in "nitrogen balance" or "nitrogen equilibrium."[1] If the excretory nitrogen is greater than the dietary nitrogen, the animal is in "negative nitrogen balance"; if the excretory nitrogen is less, the animal is in "positive nitrogen balance." Thus, in negative nitrogen balance there is a loss of a quantity of tissue nitrogen which is not replaced by dietary nitrogen; in man this condition is observed as a consequence of fevers, of wasting diseases, or of inadequate dietary protein. An animal in positive nitrogen balance retains in its tissues a greater quantity of dietary nitrogen than it excretes; this

[1] J. B. Allison, *Federation Proc.*, **10**, 676 (1951).

is observed in growing animals where the amount of tissue protein is continually augmented by the synthesis of new protein and in physiological states which require additional protein synthesis (e.g., the synthesis of milk proteins in lactation).

To maintain an adult animal in a state of nitrogen equilibrium, it is clearly essential to provide in the diet a quantity of nitrogen adequate for the metabolic needs of the organism. Since the dietary nitrogen of animals is largely in the form of protein, the minimal quantity of dietary nitrogen required for the maintenance of nitrogen equilibrium in a normal adult animal may be termed the "protein minimum." For man this quantity is approximately 1 gram of protein per kilogram of body weight per day, if the diet contains enough carbon compounds (carbohydrates and fats) to meet the energy needs ("caloric requirement," Chapter 37) of the organism.

Indispensable Amino Acids

The quantity of protein considered to be minimal cannot be taken to apply to all proteins regardless of their amino acid composition. As has been indicated before (p. 54), certain amino acids are indispensable components of the diet of higher animals. Rose[2] has shown that for the maintenance of nitrogen equilibrium in adult men the following amino acids must be supplied in the diet:

L-Lysine	ca. 0.8 gram per day
L-Tryptophan	ca. 0.25 gram per day
L-Phenylalanine	ca. 1.1 grams per day
L-Threonine	ca. 0.5 gram per day
L-Valine	ca. 0.8 gram per day
L-Methionine	ca. 1.1 grams per day
L-Leucine	ca. 1.1 grams per day
L-Isoleucine	ca. 0.7 gram per day

The values on the right represent the minimal amount of each indispensable amino acid that will maintain nitrogen equilibrium in a human subject receiving a dietary supply of nitrogen and carbon compounds sufficient to permit the synthesis of all the dispensable amino acids. The fact that these amino acids are indispensable for the maintenance of nitrogen equilibrium in man was demonstrated by feeding, to adult males, mixtures of pure amino acids. If one of the eight amino acids listed above was omitted from the experimental diet, the subject went into negative nitrogen balance (Fig. 1); nitrogen equilibrium was restored when the complete amino acid mixture was fed once again.

[2] W. C. Rose, *Federation Proc.*, **8**, 546 (1949); W. C. Rose et al., *J. Biol. Chem.*, **217**, 987 (1955).

Before these important studies on human subjects, Rose had established the amino acid requirements of the immature rat for growth[3] (Fig. 2). The foundations for this work lay in the contributions of Osborne and Mendel to the development of highly purified diets which supported the growth of white rats. These investigators demonstrated in 1912 to 1914

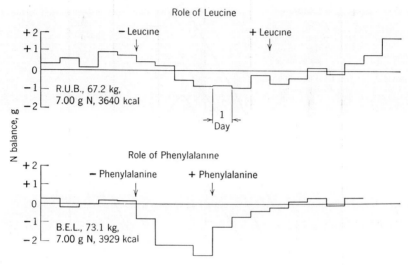

Fig. 1. Effect of leucine and of phenylalanine on the maintenance of nitrogen equilibrium in human subjects. The body weight of the subject and the nitrogen content and caloric value (cf. Chapter 37) of the food consumed daily are indicated for each experiment. [From W. C. Rose et al., *J. Biol. Chem.*, **193**, 605 (1951).]

the necessity for the presence of lysine and tryptophan in the diet of the growing rat. Subsequent studies, largely conducted in Rose's laboratory, showed that other amino acids also were indispensable; the complete list includes the eight amino acids required by human subjects for nitrogen equilibrium and, in addition, L-histidine. For optimal growth, L-arginine must be present as well. Apparently, the growing rat can synthesize arginine to a significant extent, but not at a sufficiently rapid rate to permit normal growth. In these experiments, rats were fed mixtures containing approximately twenty pure amino acids and so prepared as to simulate the amino acid composition of casein. The "dispensable" amino acids in the mixtures are important as sources of nitrogen; however, when the ten indispensable amino acids are fed in sufficient quantity, the nitrogen of the other amino acids may be replaced in the diet by ammonium salts.[4] Similarly, with human subjects, nitrogen equilibrium

[3] W. C. Rose, *Physiol. Revs.*, **18**, 109 (1938).
[4] H. A. Lardy and G. Feldott, *J. Biol. Chem.*, **186**, 85 (1950).

can be maintained by the administration of the eight essential amino acids, if sufficient glycine and urea are added to the diet to meet the total nitrogen requirement of the organism.[5]

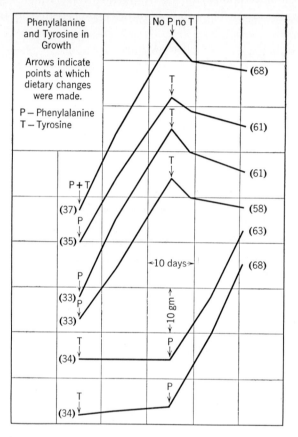

Fig. 2. Growth curves illustrating the dietary requirement of growing rats for phenylalanine but not for tyrosine. The initial and final weights (in grams) of the animals are indicated in parentheses for each growth curve. [From M. Womack and W. C. Rose, *J. Biol. Chem.,* **107,** 449 (1934).]

It must be stressed that the indispensable nature of a given amino acid is defined in terms of the effect, on some physiological response in a particular species, of the omission of that amino acid from an otherwise "complete" diet. Thus glycine, which is not a dietary essential for the growing rat, is required by the growing chick for optimal growth. Further

[5] W. C. Rose and R. L. Wixom, *J. Biol. Chem.,* **217,** 997 (1955).

discussion of the role of amino acids in the diet of animals may be found in the review by Almquist.[6]

From the foregoing it follows that a given dietary protein, in order to serve as the sole nitrogen source for growth or nitrogen equilibrium, must provide a sufficient quantity of the indispensable amino acids. Since proteins differ widely in their amino acid composition (cf. p. 125), they also differ significantly in their "biological value" as sources of those amino acids that the organism cannot make at a sufficiently rapid rate. Furthermore, in the evaluation of the nutritive quality of dietary proteins, the factor of digestibility (cf. p. 694) must be taken into account. If the digestibility of a protein food is defined as the per cent of the protein nitrogen fed that is absorbed by the intestinal wall, egg "protein" has a digestibility of about 96 per cent, whereas cottonseed "protein" is only 78 per cent digestible. The extent to which the absorbed nitrogen is utilized by an animal is related to the "biological value" of the protein from which the nitrogen was derived. Thus a protein such as gliadin may be quite digestible, but, because of its deficiency in lysine, its biological value as a sole source of dietary nitrogen is low. For a discussion of the biological evaluation of dietary proteins, see Allison.[7]

Since the indispensable dietary amino acids are used in the biosynthesis of the characteristic cellular proteins, it may be expected that all of these amino acids (in addition to other protein amino acids) must be available at the same time. Indeed, it has been shown that, if the feeding of only one indispensable amino acid is delayed, the utilization of the others is markedly decreased. Observations of this kind have emphasized the importance of the "time factor" in relation to the availability of indispensable amino acids for protein synthesis in tissues.

Further insight into the role of the indispensable amino acids has been gained from studies with fasted animals. When an animal is subjected to fasting, protein (as well as carbohydrate and fat) is lost from the tissues. Thus, if rats are fasted for 7 days, the liver loses approximately 40 per cent of its protein and decreases markedly in size. On the other hand, the decrease in the proteins of the carcass (largely muscle and connective tissues), although three times that of the liver proteins in absolute amount, represents a smaller per cent loss (approximately 8 per cent).[8] This indicates that the metabolic degradation of liver proteins is much more rapid than is that of the carcass proteins (cf. p. 731).

[6] H. J. Almquist, in D. M. Greenberg, Amino Acids and Proteins, Charles C Thomas, Springfield, 1951.

[7] J. B. Allison, Advances in Protein Chem., 5, 155 (1949); Physiol. Revs., 35, 664 (1955).

[8] T. Addis et al., J. Biol. Chem., 115, 111, 117 (1936).

Among the liver proteins lost by fasted animals are some enzymes (catalase, xanthine oxidase).[9]   After the resumption of feeding and the administration of a high-protein diet, the labile liver proteins are rapidly resynthesized and the liver returns to its normal size. A similar regeneration of liver tissue is observed after surgical removal of a portion of the liver (partial hepatectomy) and administration of a high-protein diet. However, for such regeneration of liver proteins lost either by starvation or by hepatectomy, the diet must contain some, if not all, of the amino acids classified as indispensable. For example, when fasted rats are given a diet deficient in methionine, the rate of liver regeneration is markedly inhibited.[10] It appears probable, therefore, that an important function of the indispensable amino acids is to participate in the synthesis of labile liver proteins, which include many enzymes essential for normal metabolic function.

For the growth and multiplication of animal cells (e.g., mouse fibroblasts, human carcinoma, chick embryo) in tissue culture, not only the eight amino acids listed on p. 724 are required in the medium, but additional amino acids (L-arginine, L-histidine, L-cystine or L-cysteine, L-tyrosine) must also be present.[11]

The Dynamic State of Proteins in Metabolism

Ever since the recognition, during the latter part of the nineteenth century, of the conversion of dietary amino acids to tissue proteins, there have been numerous experimental attempts to clarify the metabolic relationship between the amino acids that enter an organism (either as dietary amino acids or as products of the digestion of dietary proteins) and the amino acid residues in the characteristic tissue proteins. Much of the early history of this field is summarized in the monograph by Cathcart.[12] Perhaps the most decisive advance was made in 1938, when Schoenheimer introduced the use of isotopic amino acids in metabolic studies.[13] Schoenheimer and his associates synthesized a number of amino acids in which the N^{15} content of the amino nitrogen was greatly enriched above the natural abundance of this element (0.37 atom per

[9] L. L. Miller, *J. Biol. Chem.*, **172**, 113 (1948); W. W. Westerfeld and D. A. Richert, *ibid.*, **192**, 35 (1951).

[10] H. C. Harrison and C. N. H. Long, *J. Biol. Chem.*, **161**, 545 (1945).

[11] H. Eagle, *J. Biol. Chem.*, **214**, 839 (1955); *J. Exptl. Med.*, **102**, 37 (1955); J. F. Morgan and H. J. Morton, *J. Biol. Chem.*, **215**, 539 (1955).

[12] E. P. Cathcart, *The Physiology of Protein Metabolism*, Longmans, Green and Co., London, 1912.

[13] R. Schoenheimer, *The Dynamic State of Body Constituents*, Harvard University Press, Cambridge, 1942.

cent N^{15}). In later studies, other workers used amino acids labeled with deuterium, S^{35}, and C^{14}.

Before the application of the isotope technique to the study of protein metabolism, it was widely believed that the major portion of the amino acids entering the body of an animal in nitrogen equilibrium was not used for protein synthesis, but was catabolized and the nitrogen excreted into the urine, largely in the form of urea. This view, formulated by Folin in 1905 on the basis of quantitative studies on the relation between the compounds in the urine and the constituents of the diet, differentiated between two kinds of protein metabolism:

1. One type of metabolism, characterized by the urinary excretion of urea, was thought to be extremely variable and to depend on the composition of the diet; this was termed "exogenous" protein metabolism.

2. The second type of metabolism was thought to be relatively constant and to lead to the urinary excretion of creatinine and, to a lesser extent, of uric acid. According to Folin, this second type of metabolism reflected the "wear and tear" of the tissue proteins, and was termed "endogenous" protein metabolism.

The fact that this picture of protein metabolism required revision became clear from a simple experiment, in which Schoenheimer injected into a rat glycine-N^{15} (1.06 atom per cent excess N^{15}), and at the same time gave the animal benzoic acid. It will be recalled that benzoic acid is excreted by many animals in the form of benzoylglycine (hippuric acid). If the administered glycine-N^{15} were simply conjugated with benzoic acid, the N^{15} concentration of the urinary hippuric acid should have been the same as that of the injected amino acid. Actually, the isotope concentration of the isolated hippuric acid was 0.48 atom per cent excess N^{15}. This result showed that some of the glycine in the isolated hippuric acid came from glycine other than that which had been administered, and the conclusion was inescapable that, from a metabolic point of view, the administered glycine-N^{15} had "mixed" with unlabeled glycine already present in the body of the animal. The large dilution factor (1.06/0.48 = 2.2) indicated that a significant portion of this unlabeled glycine must have been derived from the tissue proteins of the animal, and showed that a strict separation of an "exogenous" and "endogenous" protein metabolism could not be made.

Further evidence for the metabolic interrelation between dietary amino acids and the amino acid residues of tissue proteins came from a classical paper[14] in which Schoenheimer and his associates described experiments

14 R. Schoenheimer et al., *J. Biol. Chem.*, **130,** 703 (1939).

on the administration of labeled leucine to rats. The L-leucine (6.54 atom per cent excess N^{15}) was fed as part of a casein-containing diet to nongrowing rats, the urine and feces were collected, and after 3 days the rats were sacrificed and the N^{15} content of the protein nitrogen and of the nonprotein nitrogen in the tissues was determined. The data in Table 1 describe the results of an experiment in which 4 rats were given a total of 1.261 milliequivalents of N^{15} as isotopic L-leucine (1 milliequivalent of N^{15} equals 15 mg of N^{15} or 132 mg of N^{15}-leucine), and the urine, excreta, and tissues of the 4 rats were pooled before analysis.

Table 1. Distribution of N^{15} after Administration of Isotopic Leucine[14]

	Milliequivalents of N^{15}†	Per Cent of N^{15} Administered
Excreta: Feces	0.026	2.1
Urine	0.348	27.6
Tissues: Nonprotein fraction‡	0.098	7.8
Protein fraction	0.725	57.5
	1.197	95.0

† Milliequivalents of N^{15} in a given sample equals milliequivalents of total $N \times$ atom per cent excess N^{15} divided by 100.

‡ This refers to the fraction of the tissue contents which was soluble in trichloroacetic acid.

This experiment and many others like it were of extreme importance in the historical development of knowledge of protein metabolism, since they definitely disproved the view that, when the nitrogen intake of an animal equals its nitrogen output, i.e., the animal is in a state of "nitrogen equilibrium," the nitrogen that is excreted stems mainly from the dietary amino acids. As may be seen from the data in Table 1, during the 3-day period, a major portion of the labeled nitrogen in the administered leucine had been incorporated into the body proteins and not excreted. Furthermore, the total quantity of protein in the animal could not have changed appreciably in the course of the experiment, because the weight of the rats did not change; the incorporation of the dietary nitrogen into the tissue proteins must have been a consequence, therefore, of the operation of continuous chemical processes which do not produce any net change in the protein composition of the tissues. Clearly, the tissue proteins must be considered to be in a state of metabolic flux, to which the terms "dynamic equilibrium" or "continuing metabolism" have been applied.[15]

[15] H. Borsook and G. L. Keighley, *Proc. Roy. Soc.*, **118B**, 488 (1935).

Some tissue proteins, however, incorporate N^{15} derived from the isotopic leucine to a greater extent than others. This is illustrated by the data in Table 2, which show that, although the absolute amounts of

Table 2. N^{15} Concentration of Protein of Different Tissues (Pooled Tissues from 4 Rats)[14]

	Milli-equivalents of Total N	Milli-equivalents of N^{15}	Atom Per Cent Excess N^{15}
Blood plasma	11.2	0.0121	0.108
Erythrocytes	35.7	0.0068	0.019
Liver	59.5	0.0363	0.061
Carcass (muscle, skin, bones, connective tissues)	1685	0.505	0.030

protein and of N^{15} are very much smaller in the liver than in the carcass, the N^{15} concentration, i.e., atom per cent excess N^{15}, in the liver proteins is twice that of the carcass proteins. It was concluded, therefore, that the series of chemical processes involved in the breakdown and synthesis of protein is more rapid in liver than in the carcass; i.e., the liver proteins are in a "more dynamic state" of metabolic replacement than are the carcass proteins.

Schoenheimer et al.[14] also examined the distribution of N^{15} among some of the amino acids obtained upon hydrolysis of the liver proteins (0.061 atom per cent excess N^{15}) from the experimental animals. The isotope concentrations of pure samples of the isolated amino acids, and of the ammonia liberated from the proteins on alkali treatment (amide nitrogen) are given here in atom per cent excess N^{15}:

Glycine	0.048	Arginine	0.058
Tyrosine	0.033	Lysine	0.004
Glutamic acid	0.121	Leucine	0.518
Aspartic acid	0.076	Amide-N	0.051

Of the isolated amino acids, leucine had the highest isotope content; thus a portion of the administered leucine must have been incorporated into the liver proteins without having been degraded. The appearance of isotope in the other amino acids means that the nitrogen of leucine had been used for the synthesis of these amino acids. The concept that body proteins are in a dynamic state thus entails the view that the protein amino acids are also undergoing constant change and interconversion. An examination of the isotope content of the isolated amino acids shows that glutamic acid has a higher N^{15} concentration than any other amino acid except leucine. This may be taken as evidence for a relatively greater metabolic activity of glutamic acid. On the other hand, the N^{15} concentration of the isolated lysine indicates that little, if any, of its nitrogen was derived from the nitrogen of the isotopic leucine; this points to a slow metabolic turnover of the nitrogen of lysine. These metabolic relationships among the various amino acids will become clearer from Chapter 32, where their intermediate metabolism is discussed.

The experimental results of Schoenheimer and of other investigators have led to the concept that, in the dynamic system involving dietary amino acids, tissue proteins, and urinary nitrogen, there exists a "meta-

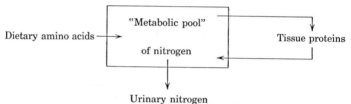

bolic pool" of nitrogen, whose place in metabolism may be indicated by the accompanying diagram. It must be emphasized at once that this highly schematic representation of the dynamic state of proteins in metabolism does not specify the components of the "metabolic pool"; these have been assumed, for convenience, to be largely amino acids, but the presence of peptides in the "pool" has not been excluded. Nor does the scheme specify the nature of the tissue proteins; as shown in Table 2, the mixed proteins of different tissues differ greatly in the rate at which they become labeled with N^{15}. This result has been confirmed by numerous later workers, who have used amino acids labeled with S^{35} or with C^{14}, and it is known that several animal tissues (intestinal mucosa, liver, kidney, spleen, pancreas, bone marrow) are rapidly labeled after injection of an isotopic amino acid, whereas other tissues (skin, muscle, brain, erythrocytes) become labeled much more slowly.[16] Furthermore, different proteins, even from the same tissue, exhibit differences in the rate at which they are labeled.

In view of the extensive morphological differentiation in higher animals, it is an obvious oversimplification to assume that a homogeneous "metabolic pool" of an amino acid exists throughout the organism, and that a labeled amino acid introduced into the blood mixes equally rapidly with unlabeled amino acid in all the tissues. If this were so, the differences in the extent of labeling of the proteins of various tissues could be attributed to differences in the rate of protein "turnover" in these tissues. It is known, however, that most amino acids are transferred rapidly from

[16] F. Friedberg et al., *J. Biol. Chem.*, **173**, 355 (1948); D. M. Greenberg and T. Winnick, *ibid.*, **173**, 199 (1948).

the blood to some tissues (liver, kidney), and relatively slowly to others (muscle, brain). For example, the exchange of plasma glycine-2-C^{14} with glycine in the liver of rabbits is rapid, and is limited only by the rate of blood flow, whereas the exchange with muscle glycine is much slower, probably as a consequence both of a lower rate of blood flow in muscle and of a slow rate of penetration of glycine into muscle cells.[17] Similarly, the slow incorporation of S^{35}-labeled methionine into brain proteins has been attributed to the "blood-brain barrier" which limits the rate of penetration of the amino acid, rather than a low rate of protein metabolism in brain tissue.[18] It follows, therefore, that the "metabolic pool" indicated in the scheme must be considered to represent the summation of many "metabolic pools" present in individual tissues, and perhaps even in individual cells.

Despite these and other uncertainties in the evaluation of results on the labeling of tissue proteins, such data have been used to calculate the rate at which the mixed proteins of a tissue are replaced (turnover rate) in the dynamic state of protein metabolism. For example, it has been estimated that, in man, the time required for one half of the total liver protein to be regenerated ("half-life") is about 10 days, whereas the half-life of the total muscle proteins is believed to be about 180 days. In the rat, the liver proteins appear to have a half-life about 5 days, and the proteins of the rat carcass (muscle tissue, connective tissue, etc.) appear to be regenerated more slowly (half-life, ca. 21 days).[19] The last figure must be considered to represent the average of the turnover of some muscle proteins in a more dynamic state and of other proteins that are relatively inert in their metabolic behavior. Among the proteins of the adult rat that are regenerated at a relatively slow rate are the muscle proteins myosin and actin[20] and the tendon protein collagen.[21]

Although the estimates of the turnover rate of tissue proteins involve simplifying assumptions of uncertain validity, and can be considered only as approximations, they indicate considerable differences in the dynamic state of the various proteins of an animal and also underline the central role of the liver in the dynamics of protein metabolism. It should be added that, although the turnover rate of liver proteins is approximately 10 times that of the muscle proteins, the latter represent the bulk of the protein of the animal body (cf. Table 2). Therefore, in

[17] O. B. Henriques et al., *Biochem. J.*, **60**, 409 (1955).

[18] M. K. Gaitonde and D. Richter, *Biochem. J.*, **59**, 690 (1955); A. Lajtha et al., *J. Neurochem.*, **1**, 289 (1957).

[19] D. Rittenberg, *Harvey Lectures*, **44**, 200 (1950).

[20] L. E. Bidinost, *J. Biol. Chem.*, **190**, 423 (1951).

[21] A. Neuberger et al., *Biochem. J.*, **49**, 199 (1951); R. C. Thompson and J. E. Ballou, *J. Biol. Chem.*, **223**, 795 (1956).

regard to the amount of protein synthesized per unit time, muscle is of equal if not greater importance.

As a consequence of their short half-life, the labile liver proteins not only incorporate isotope at an extremely rapid rate after the administration of an isotopic amino acid, but also lose the isotope rapidly. Since the muscle proteins have a much longer half-life, they acquire the isotope much more slowly and retain it for longer time periods. Thus, in the course of protein metabolism in the intact animal, the N^{15} retained by the organism is gradually accumulated in the muscle proteins. After the administration of an isotopic compound has been discontinued, the total N^{15} in the animal body at first decreases rapidly, with the rapid transfer of N^{15} from the labile tissue proteins to the excretory products; later these changes in N^{15} content occur more slowly, as a consequence of the slower turnover rate of the muscle proteins.

In considering the dynamic state of proteins in animals, it should be noted that the liver manufactures plasma proteins which are released into the circulation (cf. p. 738); in the rabbit, the plasma proteins synthesized by the liver represent about 40 per cent of the total protein (ca. 1.9 grams per day per kg of body weight) made in this tissue.[17] Similarly, the pancreas, whose proteins have been found to become labeled rapidly, secretes proteins (amylase, chymotrypsinogen, etc.) in the pancreatic juice. Furthermore, the intestinal mucosa, which exhibits the highest turnover rate as judged by isotope experiments, undergoes rapid cellular disintegration and replacement. The question has been raised, therefore, whether the apparent dynamic state of body proteins, inferred from isotope studies, is primarily a reflection of such secretion of protein from intact cells, and of cell destruction, rather than of intracellular breakdown of proteins (cf. p. 746). This view implies a return to the concept of endogenous protein metabolism, proposed by Folin (p. 729). Although an unequivocal decision on this question cannot be made at present, it is likely that, in some animal cells, an intracellular turnover of protein occurs,[22] as postulated by Schoenheimer.

Amino Acid Incorporation and Release in Tissue Preparations. Upon incubation with an isotopic amino acid, liver slices and (to a lesser extent) liver homogenates incorporate the isotope into the protein fraction. This incorporation is inhibited by the exclusion of oxygen, or by the addition of dinitrophenol (cf. p. 385), thus suggesting that the generation of ATP is essential for the process.[23] Upon differential centrifugation of a liver homogenate incubated with an isotopic amino acid, it was found that the microsomal fraction becomes labeled more rapidly than the other

[22] K. Moldave, *J. Biol. Chem.*, **221**, 543 (1956); **225**, 709 (1957).

[23] P. C. Zamecnik and I. D. Frantz, Jr., *Cold Spring Harbor Symposia Quant. Biol.*, **14**, 199 (1949); P. Siekevitz, *J. Biol. Chem.*, **195**, 549 (1952).

cellular components examined (mitochondria, nuclei, supernatant fluid).[24] This has led to the view that the microsomes may be the most important site of protein synthesis in the liver cell. It is believed that the amino acids, before their incorporation into microsomal protein, are converted to α-amino acyl-AMP compounds (p. 720) by an enzyme system present in the cytoplasmic fluid. Guanosine diphosphate (or guanosine triphosphate) increases the extent of amino acid incorporation, but its role is not yet understood.[25] Of special interest is the fact that the amino acid incorporation into liver microsomes, which are rich in ribonucleic acid (RNA), is inhibited by the addition of ribonuclease (cf. p. 190), thus suggesting that RNA plays a role in protein synthesis, and that the activated amino acids are incorporated into a ribonucleoprotein fraction of the microsomes.[26] The incorporation of labeled amino acids into ribonucleoprotein particles also has been demonstrated with a cell-free system obtained from the Ehrlich mouse ascites tumor.[27] It has been suggested that such ribonucleoprotein material serves as a precursor in the synthesis of other cellular proteins; however, in the case of mouse pancreas, this ribonucleoprotein fraction is labeled to a lesser extent than are trypsinogen and chymotrypsinogen,[28] thus casting doubt on the general validity of this hypothesis. The possible role of nucleic acids in protein synthesis will be discussed further on p. 746.

In studies such as those described above, it is not always evident whether the labeled protein represents material newly synthesized from its component amino acids, or whether the labeled amino acid had replaced its unlabeled analogue in a preformed peptide chain. However, net synthesis of protein in pigeon pancreas slices has been demonstrated by Hokin,[29] who has shown the formation of amylase, lipase, and ribonuclease from amino acids in the medium. For amylase synthesis, only nine of the ten L-amino acids essential for rat growth (cf. p. 725) were required; the fact that L-methionine could be omitted from the medium is concordant with the absence of this amino acid in pancreatic amylase.

In the incorporation of labeled amino acids into the proteins of rabbit reticulocytes, a stimulation by "fructose-amino acids" [1-deoxy-1-(N-amino acid)-2-ketohexoses] has been observed,[30] but the mode of their action is unknown at present.

24 P. C. Zamecnik and E. B. Keller, *J. Biol. Chem.*, **209**, 337 (1954).

25 E. B. Keller and P. C. Zamecnik, *J. Biol. Chem.*, **221**, 45 (1956).

26 J. W. Littlefield et al., *J. Biol. Chem.*, **217**, 111 (1955).

27 J. W. Littlefield and E. B. Keller, *J. Biol. Chem.*, **224**, 13 (1957).

28 M. M. Daly et al., *J. Gen. Physiol.*, **39**, 207 (1956).

29 L. E. Hokin, *Biochem. J.*, **50**, 216 (1951); R. Schucher and L. E. Hokin, *J. Biol. Chem.*, **210**, 551 (1954); E. S. Younathan and E. Frieden, *ibid.*, **220**, 801 (1956).

30 H. Borsook et al., *J. Biol. Chem.*, **196**, 669 (1952); **215**, 111 (1955); P. H. Lowy and H. Borsook, *J. Am. Chem. Soc.*, **78**, 3175 (1956).

Although significant progress has been made in the study of protein synthesis in animal cells, the enzymic mechanisms involved in the conversion of amino acids to proteins are not known as yet. It is extremely probable that an initial step is the activation of the α-carboxyl groups of free amino acids (cf. p. 720) in reactions coupled to oxidative phosphorylation, thus linking the exergonic breakdown of carbohydrates and fats to the endergonic formation of peptide bonds. The subsequent chemical events leading to the formation of completed protein molecules are largely matters of stimulating conjecture.[31]

It is implicit in the concept of the dynamic state of proteins that the process of protein synthesis is balanced in the intact cell by the degradation of cellular proteins. Efforts to elucidate the enzymic mechanisms in the degradative phase of intracellular protein turnover have involved experiments in which the proteins of rat liver were labeled by injection of an isotopic amino acid (methionine-S^{35}, leucine-C^{14}), and the release of isotope from liver slices was measured.[32] The finding that such release is decreased by exclusion of oxygen or by dinitrophenol has led to the suggestion that the intracellular breakdown of proteins is also an energy-requiring process. It is frequently assumed that the cathepsins (p. 700), which represent the only known proteinases of animal tissues, are responsible for the intracellular hydrolysis of proteins; the role of inhibitors of oxidative phosphorylation is unknown, but it may be related to the need for energy in the transfer of proteins to the site of catheptic activity from other parts of the cell. Evidence has been presented that several of the cathepsins of rat liver are localized in cellular particles associated with the mitochondrial fraction.[33]

Pattern of Labeling in the Biosynthesis of Proteins from Isotopic Amino Acids. Several investigators have shown that, if one or more isotopic amino acids are administered to an animal, and discrete proteins are isolated from the tissues or body fluids, every residue of a given labeled amino acid in the peptide chain of a single protein has the same isotope content. For example, Muir et al.[34] injected into rats valine-C^{14} (labeled in the side-chain methyl groups), and, after suitable time intervals, sacrificed the animals and isolated samples of crystalline hemoglobin. The protein was converted to the DNP-derivative (cf. p. 142), which was then subjected to acid hydrolysis. Since the valine residue is present both as a terminal amino acid and in the interior of the peptide chain,

---

[31] H. Borsook, *J. Cellular and Comparative Physiol.*, **47**, Suppl. 1, 35 (1956); C. E. Dalgliesh, *Science*, **125**, 271 (1957).

[32] M. V. Simpson, *J. Biol. Chem.*, **201**, 143 (1953); D. Steinberg and M. Vaughan, *Biochim. et Biophys. Acta*, **19**, 584 (1956).

[33] C. de Duve et al., *Biochem. J.*, **60**, 604 (1955); J. T. Finkenstaedt, *Proc. Soc. Exptl. Biol. Med.*, **95**, 302 (1957).

[34] H. M. Muir et al., *Biochem. J.*, **52**, 87 (1952).

the acid hydrolysate of DNP-hemoglobin contained both DNP-valine and unsubstituted valine. After the DNP-valine had been removed from the mixture, the free valine was converted to DNP-valine and isolated. Both samples of DNP-valine were found to have the same specific radioactivity. Other experiments, in which radioactive amino acids were injected into a lactating goat, and the pattern of labeling of the milk proteins casein and β-lactoglobulin was examined, also showed uniform distribution of the label within the peptide chains of these proteins.[35] In a striking series of experiments on the biosynthesis of muscle proteins,[36] as many as five different isotopic amino acids were administered simultaneously to rabbits, and highly purified samples of muscle aldolase and glyceraldehyde-3-phosphate dehydrogenase (or phosphorylase) were isolated. Upon analysis of several of the amino acids obtained after hydrolysis of the crystalline proteins, it was found that the ratio of the specific radioactivity of each labeled amino acid in aldolase to the specific radioactivity of the same amino acid in the other muscle enzyme was nearly constant.

These *in vivo* studies indicate that in the synthesis of proteins such as globin, milk proteins, and muscle enzymes, all the residues of a given amino acid are derived from a common "metabolic pool," and make it improbable that free peptides are intermediates in the metabolic conversion of amino acids to these proteins. The above results have been interpreted as demonstrating a rapid "all-at-once" process in which the requisite activated amino acids are aligned along a "template" (cf. p. 748); however, it must be emphasized that the *in vivo* isotope studies do not exclude the rapid successive formation of peptide bonds without the release from the protein-synthesizing system of peptide intermediates, or the existence of small "pools" of intermediate peptides that equilibrate rapidly with the amino acid "pools." Furthermore, it has been reported that the administration of isotopic glycine to rats leads to nonuniform labeling of the glycine residues of muscle collagen.[37] It will be recalled that the "turnover rate" of this protein is slow (p. 733), and the possibility exists that, in the biosynthesis of proteins that are made more rapidly, the formation of labeled peptide intermediates is obscured.

Of special interest in this connection are the *in vitro* experiments of Anfinsen and his associates,[38] who have found nonuniform labeling of ovalbumin (by hen oviduct) and of insulin and ribonuclease (by calf

[35] B. A. Askonas et al., *Biochem. J.*, **58**, 326 (1954); **61**, 105 (1955); C. Godin and T. S. Work, *ibid.*, **63**, 69 (1956).

[36] M. V. Simpson and S. F. Velick, *J. Biol. Chem.*, **208**, 61 (1954); M. Heimberg and S. F. Velick, *ibid.*, **208**, 725 (1954); M. V. Simpson, *ibid.*, **216**, 179 (1955).

[37] G. Gehrmann et al., *Arch. Biochem. and Biophys.*, **62**, 509 (1956).

[38] D. Steinberg and C. B. Anfinsen, *J. Biol. Chem.*, **199**, 25 (1952); M. Vaughan and C. B. Anfinsen, *ibid.*, **211**, 367 (1954); D. Steinberg et al., *Science*, **124**, 389 (1956).

pancreas slices). For example, partial degradation of the insulin synthesized by pancreas slices in the presence of glycine-C^{14} gave peptides
in which the specific radioactivity of the glycine residues was markedly
different. The apparent discrepancy between the results of *in vivo*
labeling experiments and those conducted *in vitro* may perhaps be
ascribed to differences in the rates of metabolic reactions in the two
types of systems. Thus the removal of a tissue from the intact animal
may be expected to lead to profound changes in the rates of those
enzymic processes that are influenced by factors such as hormonal
regulation and normal blood flow.

Biosynthesis of Plasma Proteins

As noted previously, the plasma proteins represent nearly one half
of the proteins synthesized in the liver, and it has been shown that this
organ is the site of formation of serum albumin, fibrinogen, and the
α- and β-globulins.[39] Thus, one of the major physiological functions
of the liver is to convert a portion of the amino acids transported from
the small intestine into plasma proteins. Striking experimental evidence
for the role of the liver in the formation of plasma proteins was provided
by studies on dogs, conducted by Whipple and his associates.[40] One
of the techniques employed (plasmapheresis) involves the reduction of
the plasma protein level by repeated bleeding and simultaneous reinjec-
tion of the washed blood cells suspended in a physiological salt solution.
If a dog then is fed a suitable protein, or given by intravenous injection
a protein (e.g., casein) hydrolysate, the plasma proteins are promptly
regenerated, indicating that the nitrogenous compounds (amino acids and
peptides) derived from the casein were used for the synthesis of the
plasma proteins. Other evidence for the synthesis of plasma proteins
in the liver has come from the observation that, if the blood flow from the
intestine to the liver is diverted surgically or if the liver is damaged, there
results a decrease in the level of the circulating serum proteins of animals.

Numerous experiments have demonstrated the dynamic state of the
plasma proteins. For example, Miller et al.[41] administered lysine-6-C^{14}
to a dog, and, when the C^{14} content of the plasma proteins reached a
sufficiently high value, labeled plasma from this animal was injected
intravenously into another dog from which an equal amount of plasma
had been withdrawn. The specific radioactivity of the plasma proteins
in the second dog was determined at several time intervals and found

[39] L. L. Miller and W. F. Bale, *J. Exptl. Med.*, **99**, 125 (1954).
[40] S. C. Madden and G. H. Whipple, *Physiol. Revs.*, **20**, 194 (1940).
[41] L. L. Miller et al., *J. Exptl. Med.*, **90**, 297 (1949).

to decrease gradually. From these studies, it was calculated that, in the dog, the half-life of serum albumin is about 7 days, and that of the total globulins about 3 days.

The extensive turnover of the plasma proteins is a resultant of their rapid synthesis in the liver and their utilization by the tissues as sources of amino acids, a portion of which is employed for the synthesis of the characteristic tissue proteins.[42] The plasma proteins thus represent a major vehicle for the transport, to the peripheral tissues, of dietary nitrogen, which passes first from the small intestine to the liver and thence to the other tissues. In addition, plasma proteins serve important functions in the maintenance of the osmotic pressure of the blood (p. 31), in the control of the pH of plasma (p. 100), in the transport of lipids and of other substances (p. 573), in blood coagulation (p. 702), and in immune reactions (p. 740). Normal human plasma contains approximately 6.7 grams of protein per 100 ml; of this amount more than one half (3.5 to 4.0 grams) is in the serum albumin fraction. In contrast to the high protein nitrogen content of plasma, only small amounts of free amino acids and of peptides are present;[43] these account for about 7 mg of nitrogen per 100 ml of human plasma. The blood amino acids are readily taken up by the tissues, where the intracellular amino acid concentration is usually much higher than that of plasma. Such uptake of amino acids against a concentration gradient requires the expenditure of energy, and depends on the metabolic activity of the living cell.[44]

Formation of Antibodies. If a suitable animal (e.g., a rabbit) is injected repeatedly with a solution of a foreign protein, after a time the serum contains specific "antibodies" to the protein administered (the "antigen"). In addition to proteins, many polysaccharides (cf. p. 428) are also antigenic.[45] Upon mixing a solution of the antigen with a sample of serum from the immunized animal, the antigen and antibody interact, and under appropriate conditions form a precipitate (the "precipitin reaction").[46] Frequently the specificity of the serological test is so great as to permit a differentiation between preparations of a given protein from different species. For example, the hemoglobin of the horse, sheep, goat, or dog, when injected into rabbits, elicits the formation of antibodies which react readily with the specific hemoglobin used but do not react appreciably with the hemoglobins from the other three species.

[42] H. Walter et al., J. Biol. Chem., **224,** 107 (1957).

[43] W. H. Stein and S. Moore, J. Biol. Chem., **211,** 915 (1954).

[44] H. N. Christensen, in W. D. McElroy and B. Glass, Amino Acid Metabolism, Johns Hopkins Press, Baltimore, 1955.

[45] M. Heidelberger, Ann. Rev. Biochem., **25,** 641 (1956).

[46] W. C. Boyd, in H. Neurath and K. Bailey, The Proteins, Vol. IIB, Chapter 22, Academic Press, New York, 1954.

Such sharp serological specificity is not always observed, however. Thus antisera from rabbits immunized to egg albumin from various species give a precipitin reaction with egg albumins other than the one used as the antigen.

The remarkable specificity of the immune response was demonstrated in the classical studies of Karl Landsteiner (1868–1943).[47] Many organic substances which, when injected alone, do not elicit antibody formation give rise to specific precipitins when combined chemically with a protein. Such organic substances were termed "haptens" by Landsteiner, who prepared artificial conjugated antigens by treatment of various proteins with the diazonium derivatives of an extensive series of aromatic amines (e.g., C_6H_5N=NCl from aniline) to form "azoproteins." Thus the azoprotein prepared by the use of diazotized o-aminobenzoic acid, upon injection into rabbits, elicited the formation of antibodies that gave the precipitin reaction with this antigen, but not with the azoprotein prepared with diazotized p-aminobenzoic acid. Furthermore, azoproteins containing haptenic groups that differ only in stereochemical configuration also were shown to be serologically specific.

Many efforts have been made to discern chemical differences among antibodies specific for different antigens. However, all studies conducted thus far indicate that the antibodies are indistinguishable from the proteins of the γ-globulin fraction of plasma. For example, rabbit antibodies to a series of pneumococcal polysaccharides all have the same particle weight, electrophoretic mobility, amino acid composition, and N-terminal amino acid sequence as normal rabbit γ-globulin.[48] These findings support the hypothesis[49] that normal and immune γ-globulins are formed from the same precursor, and that, in the presence of the antigen, the polypeptide chain of the precursor is folded in a specific manner. It is believed, therefore, that the specific antibodies differ from the normal γ-globulins only in the conformation of their peptide chains.

In contrast to the other major protein fractions of plasma (cf. p. 106), the γ-globulins (and antibodies) are largely synthesized in tissues other than the liver,[50] and are considered by some investigators to be products of the "plasma cells"; these cells, although widely distributed in the animal body, are chiefly localized in tissues such as lymph nodes, bone marrow, and spleen.

[47] K. Landsteiner, *The Specificity of Serological Reactions*, 2nd Ed., Harvard University Press, Cambridge, 1945.

[48] E. L. Smith et al., *J. Biol. Chem.*, **214**, 197 (1955).

[49] F. Breinl and F. Haurowitz, *Z. physiol. Chem.*, **192**, 45 (1930); L. Pauling, *J. Am. Chem. Soc.*, **62**, 2643 (1940).

[50] L. L. Miller et al., *J. Exptl. Med.*, **99**, 133 (1954).

Upon administration of an isotopic amino acid to an animal actively synthesizing antibody in response to an antigen, the label is incorporated into the antibody; however, when antibody obtained from one animal is injected into another animal (passive immunization), the administration of a labeled amino acid to the second animal does not lead to significant labeling of the antibody.[51] This finding is in accord with the view that the biosynthesis of specific antibodies occurs only in the presence of the antigens.

Abnormal Plasma Proteins. In the human disease multiple myeloma (a tumor of the bone marrow), an elevation of the serum globulin fraction is usually observed, and some of the anomalous globulins resemble the γ-globulins in electrophoretic mobility, particle weight, and amino acid composition.[52] It has been suggested that the "myeloma globulins" represent individual normal γ-globulins that are produced in excess by the large number of plasma cells in the tumor.

In many cases of multiple myeloma, the urine contains protein material that is characterized by the property of being precipitated at about 50° C, and of being redissolved upon boiling of the urine. This phenomenon was discovered by Bence-Jones in 1848, and the urinary protein of multiple myeloma patients is termed "Bence-Jones protein."[53] Upon administration of labeled amino acids to patients with multiple myeloma, the Bence-Jones protein becomes labeled very rapidly, and appears to arise directly from the "metabolic pool" of nitrogen, rather than from plasma or tissue proteins.[54]

Metabolism of Phosphoproteins

It will be recalled that several proteins (casein, phosvitin) are characterized by a relatively high content of phosphate, believed to be linked to the β-hydroxyl group of serine and threonine residues (p. 56). Such phosphoproteins[55] appear to be present in a large variety of animal cells, but in most instances have not been isolated in satisfactory form. However, this "phosphoprotein fraction" of animal tissues is of considerable metabolic interest, since the phosphate has an extremely high turnover rate, as shown by the administration of P^{32}-labeled phosphate.[56] Acid

[51] M. Heidelberger et al., *J. Biol. Chem.*, **144**, 555 (1942).

[52] F. W. Putnam and B. Udin, *J. Biol. Chem.*, **202**, 727 (1953); E. L. Smith et al., *ibid.*, **216**, 601 (1955).

[53] F. W. Putnam and P. Stelos, *J. Biol. Chem.*, **203**, 347 (1953); H. F. Deutsch, *ibid.*, **216**, 97 (1955).

[54] F. W. Putnam et al., *J. Biol. Chem.*, **221**, 517 (1956).

[55] G. E. Perlmann, *Advances in Protein Chem.*, **10**, 1 (1955).

[56] J. N. Davidson et al., *Biochem. J.*, **49**, 311 (1951); E. P. Kennedy and S. W. Smith, *J. Biol. Chem.*, **207**, 153 (1954).

hydrolysis of the labeled phosphoprotein fraction yields O-phosphoserine of high specific radioactivity. The enzymic mechanisms in the rapid turnover of phosphoprotein phosphate are unknown; however, rat liver mitochondria can catalyze the transfer of phosphate from ATP to proteins such as casein,[57] and the enzymic liberation of phosphate from phosphoproteins by "phosphoprotein phosphatase" (present in many animal tissues) has also been demonstrated (cf. p. 582). The metabolic role of the phosphoproteins is obscure, but it is of interest that the major part of the phosphoprotein fraction of *Escherichia coli* is localized in the bacterial cell wall, and that the cell walls ("ghosts") of erythrocytes also contain phosphoprotein.[58]

Protein Breakdown and Synthesis in Higher Plants [59,60]

In the germination of seeds, the reserve proteins (e.g., seed globulins, glutelins, prolamines) are rapidly degraded,[61] presumably through the hydrolytic action of proteolytic enzymes (cf. p. 706). Thus, when lupin seedlings are allowed to germinate in the dark, there occurs a marked decrease in the protein content of the seed; this is accompanied by the appearance of a large quantity of asparagine and of a little glutamine. The classical work of Schulze (1876) gave the first quantitative indications of the magnitude of the changes involved; some of his data are given in Table 3. Schulze concluded that, on germination, the reserve

Table 3. Protein Metabolism of Lupin Seedlings Germinated in the Dark [59]

Constituent	Grams per 100 g of Ungerminated Seeds		
	Ungerminated	12-day-old Seedlings	Difference
Protein	45.1	11.7	−33.4
Asparagine	0	18.2	+18.2
Other soluble nitrogen compounds	7.8	20.4	+12.6
Total weight	100.0	81.7	−18.3

proteins of seeds are converted to split products (amino acids and peptides) which contribute a considerable portion of their nitrogen to the

[57] G. Burnett and E. P. Kennedy, *J. Biol. Chem.*, **211**, 969 (1954).

[58] G. Agren, *Acta Chem. Scand.*, **10**, 152, 876 (1956).

[59] A. C. Chibnall, *Protein Metabolism in the Plant*, Yale University Press, New Haven, 1939.

[60] F. C. Steward and J. F. Thompson, in H. Neurath and K. Bailey, *The Proteins*, Vol. IIA, Chapter 19, Academic Press, New York, 1954.

[61] C. E. Danielsson, *Acta Chem. Scand.*, **5**, 541 (1951).

formation of asparagine. Subsequent work by Prianischnikov provided strong support for this hypothesis.

When a lupin seed is germinated in the light, the accumulation of asparagine is as great as it is in darkness until expansion of the green leaf tissue begins. The concentration of asparagine then diminishes as it, together with the breakdown products of the reserve proteins, is utilized for the synthesis of the proteins of the leaves. The subsequent growth of the plant depends on the utilization of nitrogen of the soil (cf. p. 679) for the synthesis of the proteins of stem and leaf tissues. The over-all nitrogen metabolism of higher plants is somewhat difficult to study, since plants do not exhibit a protracted period of nitrogen equilibrium comparable to that of a mature animal. However, data from isotope experiments point to the existence of a "dynamic state" for plant proteins, analogous to that of the labile proteins of animal tissues. Thus, Vickery et al.[62] have shown that, when a mature tobacco plant is transferred into a nutrient medium containing $N^{15}H_4{}^+$ for 72 hr, not only is N^{15} incorporated into the plant proteins, but also the amount of isotope so incorporated is greater than would have been expected had all the N^{15} been used for the synthesis of the additional protein required for the growth of the plant (Table 4). Moreover, Hevesy et al.[63] found that

Table 4.   Effect of Administration of $N^{15}H_4Cl$ to Tobacco Plants[62]

Isotope concentration of NH_4Cl in nutrient solution, 1.21 atom per cent excess N^{15}

| | Leaf | | Stem | |
Fraction	Atom Per Cent Excess	Per Cent Replacement	Atom Per Cent Excess	Per Cent Replacement
Protein N	0.099	8.2	0.184	15.2
Ammonia N	0.260	21.5	0.275	22.7
Amide N	0.217	17.9	0.286	23.6

N^{15} (from $N^{15}H_4{}^+$) is incorporated into the mature leaves of sunflowers in the absence of a change in leaf size. As with animal tissues (cf. p. 733), differences in the turnover rate of the proteins of individual plant tissues have been observed, and a separation may therefore be made between plant proteins undergoing rapid turnover and those that are relatively stable.[64] Efforts to clarify the mechanisms of protein synthesis in plant tissues by the study of excised leaves have shown several factors (oxygen supply, presence of carbohydrate, optimal concentration

[62] H. B. Vickery et al., *J. Biol. Chem.*, **135**, 531 (1940).

[63] G. Hevesy et al., *Compt. rend. trav. lab. Carlsberg. Sér. chim.*, **23**, 213 (1940).

[64] F. C. Steward et al., *Nature*, **178**, 734, 789 (1956).

of potassium ions, high nitrogen level in nutrient solution) to favor protein synthesis or to counteract the tendency of the excised leaves to lose protein.[65] The incorporation of C^{14}-labeled amino acids into excised discs of tobacco leaves is promoted by illumination, and cell-free preparations from such leaves incorporate amino acids into the chloroplasts by a process that is stimulated by light and oxygen.[66]

In tobacco plants infected with tobacco mosaic virus (p. 185) there occurs a rapid multiplication of the virus protein. When infected tobacco leaves are infiltrated with $N^{15}H_4Cl$, isotopic nitrogen appears in the virus protein,[67] which is derived from nitrogen compounds (probably amino acids or peptides) that exchange more rapidly with $NH_4{}^+$ than do the extractable leaf proteins. The virus protein is not in metabolic equilibrium with the "metabolic pool," since N^{15} is only incorporated in the virus protein of leaves which show active virus multiplication. Once the virus infection has run its course, the nitrogen of the virus protein does not exchange with that of the cytoplasmic protein. It would seem, therefore, that the synthesis of the virus protein is essentially irreversible, and, since this process removes products derived from the normal leaf proteins, these intermediates are lost as potential precursors for the synthesis of normal protein by the infected leaf cell.

Protein Synthesis in Microorganisms

The most distinctive evidence of protein synthesis by microorganisms is their multiplication, and the study of the rate and extent of microbial growth has provided an important means of experimental attack on the problem of the mechanism of conversion of amino acids to proteins in unicellular organisms. As in other biological systems, the proteins of microorganisms may be considered to be derived from amino acids supplied by an external source or synthesized from ammonia and suitable carbon compounds. It will be recalled that, among the bacteria, the organisms that can utilize ammonia as the sole source of nitrogen for growth are in general Gram-negative (p. 193), and that most Gram-positive organisms require the presence in the medium of certain preformed amino acids. Some of these indispensable amino acids (e.g., glutamic acid, histidine) do not enter the cell by free diffusion, and energy derived from the carbohydrate metabolism of the cell is required for their assimilation. Other amino acids, such as lysine and tyrosine, appear to enter the cell by a process indistinguishable from a simple diffusion. When nongrowing Gram-positive bacteria (e.g., *Staphylo-*

[65] A. H. K. Petrie, *Biol. Revs.*, **18**, 105 (1943).

[66] M. L. Stephenson et al., *Arch. Biochem. and Biophys.*, **65**, 194 (1956).

[67] M. Meneghini and C. C. Delwiche, *J. Biol. Chem.*, **189**, 177 (1951).

coccus aureus, Streptococcus fecalis) are maintained under conditions such that protein synthesis is prevented, these organisms can establish an appreciable intracellular concentration of free glutamic acid (and of certain other amino acids) and assimilate the amino acid from the culture medium against a concentration gradient.[68] However, if the nongrowing cells are supplied with all the amino acids that are indispensable for growth, the glutamic acid removed from the medium is incorporated into proteins, and free glutamic acid does not accumulate within the cell. Experiments with C^{14}-labeled glutamic acid in the medium indicate that the amino acid can be incorporated into bacterial proteins even when protein synthesis is blocked (e.g., through inhibition of phenylalanine incorporation into protein by *p*-chlorophenylalanine); it appears that glutamic acid may be incorporated by "exchange" with glutamic acid residues in the bacterial protein,[69] or by some other mechanism.

The role of peptides as possible intermediates in the bacterial conversion of amino acids to proteins is uncertain. In many instances, the growth response of a microbial culture to a peptide is equivalent to that observed with mixtures of the component amino acids, suggesting that the peptide is hydrolyzed by bacterial peptidases prior to utilization for growth. Numerous examples are known, however, of better growth in the presence of peptides than with the component amino acids.[70] The greater efficiency of some peptides (e.g., of L-proline or of L-tyrosine) in promoting the growth of appropriate amino acid-requiring mutants of *Escherichia coli* or of lactic acid bacteria has been attributed to the "protection" of the essential amino acid from destruction by bacterial amino acid deaminases or decarboxylases; these enzymes do not act on amino acid residues of peptides. Presumably, the essential amino acids are gradually released by the bacterial peptidases, and utilized for protein synthesis. However, this explanation does not appear to hold in other instances, and the possibility exists that certain peptides may be utilized by some organisms without prior hydrolytic cleavage of the peptide bonds. Of special interest in this connection is the growth-promoting activity toward *Lactobacillus casei* of peptides obtained by partial hydrolysis of some proteins (e.g., insulin). Among the active peptides (grouped under the collective term "strepogenin") is L-seryl-L-histidyl-L-leucyl-L-valyl-L-glutamic acid.[71]

[68] E. F. Gale, *Advances in Protein Chem.*, **8**, 285 (1953).

[69] E. F. Gale and J. P. Folkes, *Biochem. J.*, **55**, 721, 730 (1953).

[70] J. S. Fruton and S. Simmonds, *Cold Spring Harbor Symposia Quant. Biol.*, **14**, 55 (1949); H. Kihara et al., *J. Biol. Chem.*, **197**, 801 (1952); D. Stone and H. Hoberman, *ibid.*, **202**, 203 (1953); V. J. Peters et al., *ibid.*, **202**, 521 (1953); J. O. Meinhart and S. Simmonds, *ibid.*, **216**, 51 (1955).

[71] R. B. Merrifield and D. W. Woolley, *J. Am. Chem. Soc.*, **78**, 358, 4646 (1956).

Induced Formation of Bacterial Enzymes.[72] Many microorganisms are able to "adapt" to the utilization of one of a variety of substances added to the culture medium by forming an enzyme (or enzyme system) that is not evident when the organism is grown in the absence of the added substance. This phenomenon is termed "enzyme induction," and the substance that elicits the response is an "enzyme inducer." For example, the enzyme β-galactosidase (p. 432) appears in *Escherichia coli* when the organism is grown in the presence of β-galactosides such as lactose (a substrate of the enzyme) or methyl-β-D-thiogalactoside (which is not hydrolyzed by the enzyme). Thus an inducer need not be a substrate of the enzyme whose formation it evokes; however, the inducer is taken up by the organism, and participates in some unknown manner in the intracellular process of enzyme formation.[73]

In the induced formation of β-galactosidase during bacterial growth, the enzyme protein appears to arise from the constituents of the medium, rather than by turnover of cell proteins.[74] For example, when *Escherichia coli* was grown in the presence of $S^{35}O_4{}^{2-}$, the labeled sulfur was incorporated into the proteins of the organism. If such labeled cells were transferred to a medium containing unlabeled sulfate and an inducer of β-galactosidase, the enzyme that appeared was found (upon isolation in partially purified form) to contain little or no S^{35}. This indicates that the labeled proteins of the growing cells did not contribute sulfur amino acids to the formation of β-galactosidase. It appears likely that in a rapidly growing cell population a "dynamic state" of proteins is not evident (cf. p. 734), and that the synthesis of proteins from the appropriate nutrients is essentially a unidirectional process, with little or no intracellular protein breakdown.

Role of Nucleic Acids in Protein Synthesis

The pioneer cytochemical studies of Brachet[75] and of Caspersson showed a correlation between the intensity of protein synthesis and the content of pentose nucleic acid (PNA or RNA) in a wide variety of cells. Subsequent work has further documented this correlation. In addition, studies on the induced formation of bacterial enzymes have

[72] J. Monod and M. Cohn, *Advances in Enzymol.,* **13,** 67 (1952); S. Spiegelman et al., in W. D. McElroy and B. Glass, *Amino Acid Metabolism,* Johns Hopkins Press, Baltimore, 1955; M. Cohn, *Bact. Revs.,* **21,** 140 (1957).

[73] J. Monod, in O. H. Gaebler, *Enzymes: Units of Biological Structure and Function,* Academic Press, New York, 1956.

[74] B. Rotman and S. Spiegelman, *J. Bact.,* **68,** 419 (1954); D. S. Hogness et al., *Biochim. et Biophys. Acta,* **16,** 99 (1955).

[75] J. Brachet, in E. Chargaff and J. N. Davidson, *The Nucleic Acids,* Vol. II, Chapter 28, Academic Press, New York, 1955.

provided important evidence in favor of the view that RNA plays a significant role in protein synthesis. Thus Gale and Folkes[76] have shown that cells of *Staphylococcus aureus*, after partial disruption by supersonic vibration, are still able to form inducible β-galactosidase, but lose the capacity to make the enzyme if they are treated with ribonuclease. With *Bacillus megatherium* "protoplasts" (cells deprived of their rigid cell walls), obtained by treatment of the bacteria with lysozyme in hypertonic solution, the addition of ribonuclease also decreases markedly the formation of induced β-galactosidase.[77] It would appear, therefore, that hydrolysis of intracellular RNA by ribonuclease destroys an essential participant in protein synthesis. This conclusion is further suggested by the effect of ribonuclease on the incorporation of amino acids into proteins by the microsomal fractions of liver homogenates (cf. p. 735), by amoebae, and by onion root tips.[78] Although there is considerable evidence to show a close relation between cellular RNA and cytoplasmic protein synthesis, the details of this metabolic interdependence are unknown. The possibility exists that, in some instances, polynucleotides may promote oxidative phosphorylation (cf. p. 384), thus favoring amino acid incorporation by the increased generation of ATP.

It will be recalled that the plant viruses are nucleoproteins containing RNA, and that the nucleic acid portion appears to be responsible for the infectivity (cf. p. 200). These infective RNA molecules induce the cellular replication of their structure, and the increase in amount of the foreign RNA in an infected leaf appears to alter the normal cytoplasmic pathways of protein synthesis, with the formation of abnormal proteins.[79]

Whereas the pentose nucleic acids are largely present in the cytoplasmic components of living cells, the deoxypentose nucleic acids (DNA) are localized in the cell nucleus (p. 193). The incorporation of amino acids into the proteins of isolated calf thymus nuclei appears to depend on the presence of DNA, since treatment of such nuclei with deoxyribonuclease causes a loss of incorporating activity; the addition of DNA preparations to deoxyribonuclease-treated nuclei leads to a recovery of the activity.[80]

The cell nucleus contains the genetic apparatus for the transmission of inherited characteristics. Studies on the transforming principles of pneu-

[76] E. F. Gale and J. P. Folkes, *Biochem. J.,* **59,** 661, 675 (1955); E. F. Gale, *Harvey Lectures,* **51,** 25 (1957).

[77] O. E. Landmann and S. Spiegelman, *Proc. Natl. Acad. Sci.,* **41,** 698 (1955).

[78] J. Brachet, *Nature,* **174,** 876 (1954); **175,** 851 (1955).

[79] R. Jeener, *Advances in Enzymol.,* **17,** 477 (1956); C. Van Rysselberge and R. Jeener, *Biochim. et Biophys. Acta,* **23,** 18 (1957).

[80] V. G. Allfrey et al., *J. Gen. Physiol.,* **40,** 451 (1957); *Proc. Natl. Acad. Sci.,* **43,** 589 (1957).

mococci and on the bacterial viruses have provided significant evidence for the view that DNA represents the nuclear material which determines the inherited capacities of the entire cell, and which is transmitted from parent cell to progeny (cf. Chapter 35). For example, exposure to ultraviolet light of pneumococci unable to utilize mannitol (strain M⁻) gives rise to a mutant (strain M⁺) that can metabolize this substance. When DNA prepared from the M⁺ strain was added to the culture medium (containing mannitol) in which M⁻ cells were growing, the M⁻ cells were transformed into mannitol-utilizing organisms, and acquired a mannitol phosphate dehydrogenase which they had not been able to form previously.[81] Thus a portion of the DNA of the M⁻ strain had been altered by the mutagenic action of ultraviolet light, and this altered DNA could transform M⁻ cells so as to enable them to form an inducible cytoplasmic enzyme essential for the metabolic utilization of mannitol. In the M⁺ strain, the altered DNA is transferred from parent cells to progeny, and thus carries the genetic potentiality for the synthesis of the enzyme.

The mechanism whereby the genetic information in the DNA of the nucleus is transmitted to the cytoplasmic apparatus of protein synthesis is unknown. In view of the association of RNA with this process, the possibility exists that specific RNA molecules are made in the nucleus under the influence of specific DNA molecules, and are then transferred to the cytoplasm.[82]

The recognition of the role of RNA and DNA in the intracellular synthesis of specific proteins has led to stimulating speculations about the role of nucleic acids as "templates" in protein synthesis.[83] In particular, the DNA model proposed by Crick and Watson (p. 200) has been assumed as a basis for further hypotheses about the manner in which the specific structure of a DNA molecule might cause the specific alignment of activated amino acid units in the sequence present in the completed protein. However, much further experimental work is needed on the chemical structure of individual nucleic acids, and on the enzymic mechanisms of protein synthesis, before the status of such hypotheses can be properly assessed. In connection with the possibility that amino acid units may be attached to nucleic acids in the process of protein synthesis, it may be added that the natural occurrence of materials composed of nucleotides and amino acids has been reported;[84] the metabolic role of these compounds remains to be elucidated.

[81] J. Marmur and R. D. Hotchkiss, *J. Biol. Chem.*, **214**, 383 (1955).

[82] D. Mazia, in O. H. Gaebler, *Enzymes: Units of Structure and Function*, Academic Press, New York, 1956.

[83] A. L. Dounce, *Enzymologia*, **15**, 251 (1952); *Nature*, **172**, 541 (1953); L. S. Lockingen and A. G. DeBusk, *Proc. Natl. Acad. Sci.*, **41**, 925 (1955).

[84] J. L. Potter and A. L. Dounce, *J. Am. Chem. Soc.*, **78**, 3078 (1956).

Of special interest is the observation that, when some bacteria (e.g., *Staphylococcus aureus*) are treated with penicillin (p. 60), uridine nucleotides linked to peptides accumulate in the cells.[85] The predominant nucleotide-peptide compound appears to be composed of uridine-5'-pyrophosphate (UDP), an amino sugar (possibly 3-O-carboxyethyl-N-acetylglucosamine), and a peptide containing D-glutamyl, L-lysyl, L-alanyl, and D-alanyl residues (ratio of glutamic acid/lysine/alanine of 1/1/3). Subsequent work demonstrated the presence, in cell walls of *S. aureus*, of a material composed of an aminohexose, glutamic acid, lysine, and alanine in similar proportions.[86] The possibility exists therefore that transglycosidation reactions involving UDP derivatives (cf. p. 464) occur in the biosynthesis of peptide and protein constituents of bacterial cell walls, and that these reactions are blocked by penicillin. By interfering with the formation of cell walls, penicillin induces the formation of bacterial protoplasts.[87]

[85] J. T. Park, *J. Biol. Chem.*, **194**, 877, 885, 897 (1952).

[86] J. T. Park and J. L. Strominger, *Science*, **125**, 99 (1957).

[87] J. Lederberg, *Proc. Natl. Acad. Sci.*, **42**, 574 (1956); F. E. Hahn and J. Clark, *Science*, **125**, 119 (1957).

31 ·

General Metabolism
of
Protein Amino Acids

In the preceding chapter it was noted that, if an amino acid (e.g., leucine) labeled with N^{15} is administered to an animal, a number of the amino acids of the mixed liver proteins are found to contain N^{15}. It must be concluded, therefore, that the mammalian organism can utilize the nitrogen of leucine in the biosynthesis of other amino acids. That this may be true of the nitrogen of amino acids other than leucine is implicit in the concept of indispensable and dispensable amino acids. Clearly, if the growing rat can satisfy its entire dietary requirement for protein nitrogen with just ten amino acids, the nitrogen of some if not all of the essential compounds must serve as the dietary precursor of the amino nitrogen of the dispensable amino acids synthesized *in vivo* during the deposition of new protein in the tissues.

Two general metabolic mechanisms are known for the utilization of the amino nitrogen of one amino acid in the formation of another amino acid. The first mechanism involves the initial separation of the nitrogen from the carbon chain of one amino acid by the process of deamination, and the utilization of the ammonia so formed for the synthesis of other amino acids. In the second general mechanism, free ammonia is not formed, and the nitrogen is transferred directly in a transamination reaction. Both deamination and transamination have been shown to occur not only in animal tissues but also in higher plants and microorganisms. It will be seen from the discussion in Chapter 32 that these two types of reactions play an important role in the metabolism of all the protein amino acids.

A valuable reference work on the metabolism of amino acids has been prepared by Meister.[1]

[1] A. Meister, *Biochemistry of the Amino Acids*, Academic Press, New York, 1957.

Deamination of α-Amino Acids [2]

It has been known since the work of Neubauer (1909) and of Knoop (1910) that mammalian tissues can deaminate amino acids to give rise to keto acids. Perhaps the most decisive contribution to the understanding of the mechanism of this conversion came from the studies of Krebs,[3] who showed that the kidney and liver of many animals contain enzymes which produce ammonia from amino acids with the concomitant uptake of oxygen. In a quantitative study of the oxidative deamination of alanine to pyruvic acid, by preparations of the liver or kidney of a wide variety of animal species, Krebs observed that approximately 1 mole of oxygen was consumed for every 2 moles of ammonia formed:

$$\underset{|}{R} \qquad\qquad \underset{|}{R}$$
$$NH_2CHCOOH + \tfrac{1}{2}O_2 \rightarrow O{=}CCOOH + NH_3$$

This oxidative deamination was postulated by Neubauer and Knoop; as will be seen from the subsequent discussion, the equation describes the summation of several consecutive reactions.

From a comparison of the relative rates at which rat kidney slices deaminated a series of L- and D-amino acids, Krebs concluded that some members of the D-series are attacked more rapidly than are the L-enantiomorphs, and that different enzymes (D-amino acid oxidases and L-amino acid oxidases) are involved in the deamination of the two sets of optical antipodes. These conclusions received support from the observation that the D-amino acid oxidases of kidney or liver could readily be extracted with water, whereas the L-amino acid oxidases remained bound to the tissue. Also, in the crude tissue preparations, the L-amino acid oxidases were inhibited by HCN or octanol, whereas the D-amino acid oxidases were insensitive to these agents. Subsequently, the D-amino acid oxidase of sheep kidney was purified appreciably, and shown to be a flavoprotein containing FAD (p. 335). This enzyme only catalyzes the oxidative deamination of D-amino acids (Table 1); it is inactive toward L-amino acids as well as glycine. D-Amino acid oxidase activity has also been found in microorganisms (bacteria and fungi). Despite the widespread distribution of D-amino acid oxidases, their physiological role is unknown at present.

Although Krebs was unable to separate an enzyme with L-amino acid oxidase activity from the tissue particles, Blanchard et al.[4] obtained,

---

[2] H. A. Krebs, in J. B. Sumner and K. Myrbäck, *The Enzymes,* Academic Press, New York, 1951; A. Meister, in W. D. McElroy and H. B. Glass, *Amino Acid Metabolism,* Johns Hopkins Press, Baltimore, 1955.

[3] H. A. Krebs, *Biochem. J.,* **29,** 1620 (1935).

[4] M. Blanchard et al., *J. Biol. Chem.,* **155,** 421 (1944); **161,** 583 (1945).

from rat liver and kidney, enzyme preparations which act specifically on the L-forms of a variety of amino acids (Table 1); the enzymic activity is associated with a flavoprotein which contains FMN. L-Amino acid oxidase occurs in snake venoms; the enzyme has been purified from

Table I. Specificity of Some Amino Acid Oxidases [7]

	L-Amino Acid Oxidases				D-Amino Acid Oxidases	
L- or D-Amino Acid Used as Substrate	Rat Kidney (Purified Preparation), Relative Velocity	*Proteus vulgaris* (Cell-free Extract), Relative Velocity	*Neurospora crassa,* Q_{O_2}[†]	Cobra Venom, Q_{O_2}[†]	Sheep Kidney, Q_{O_2}[†]	*Neurospora crassa,* Q_{O_2}[†]
Glycine	0	0			0	
Alanine		0	41	0	64	0.8
Valine	28	0	6	0	35	1.2
Leucine	100	91	78	77	13.9	0.5
Isoleucine	71	15	33	0	22	0.2
Serine	0	0	8	0	42	0
Threonine	0	0	2	0	2.1	3
Methionine	81	65	40	94	80	0.0
Cystine	15		56	0	1.9	0
Lysine	0	0	14	0	0.6	0
Arginine	0	30		23		
Ornithine	0	0	51	0	3.1	0
Proline	77	0	0	0	148	0
Glutamic acid	0	0	9	0	0	0.7
Aspartic acid	0	0	5	0	1.4	0.3
Histidine	9	33	75	0	6.2	0.5
Phenylalanine	45	100	52	111	26	1.2
Tyrosine	20	62	34	246	190	0.3
Tryptophan	40	88	27	76	37	0

[†] $Q_{O_2} = \mu l$ of O_2 absorbed per milligram of dry weight enzyme preparation per hour.

moccasin venom,[5] and shown to be a flavoprotein containing FAD. This preparation is the most active of the known amino acid oxidases, having a turnover number (p. 211) of 3100, compared to approximately 2000 for purified mammalian D-amino acid oxidase and 6 for mammalian L-amino acid oxidase. L-Amino acid oxidase preparations also have been obtained from several microorganisms (e.g., *Proteus vulgaris,*[6] *Neurospora crassa*[7]) ; the latter organism contains a D-amino acid oxidase as well (cf. Table 1).

Glycine, which is not attacked by any of the known D- or L-amino acid oxidases, is deaminated by a specific glycine oxidase (found in the liver or kidney of mammals[8]) which catalyzes the degradation of glycine to

[5] T. P. Singer and E. B. Kearney, *Arch. Biochem.,* **27**, 348; **29**, 190 (1950).

[6] P. K. Stumpf and D. E. Green, *J. Biol. Chem.,* **153**, 387 (1944).

[7] A. E. Bender and H. A. Krebs, *Biochem. J.,* **46**, 210 (1950); K. Burton, *ibid.,* **50**, 258 (1951).

[8] S. Ratner et al., *J. Biol. Chem.,* **152**, 119 (1944).

ammonia and glyoxylic acid; this enzyme is also believed to be a flavo-protein and to contain FAD.

$$NH_2CH_2COOH + \tfrac{1}{2}O_2 \rightarrow NH_3 + OHC—COOH$$

Sarcosine (N-methylglycine) is converted, in the presence of glycine oxidase, to methylamine and glyoxylic acid. The oxidative deamination of glycine has also been demonstrated with enzyme preparations from various bacteria.

The several flavoproteins that catalyze the oxidative deamination of amino acids can use as the ultimate electron acceptor molecular oxygen, which is reduced to hydrogen peroxide (cf. p. 338). In anaerobic systems, methylene blue can serve as the electron acceptor, and the oxidative deamination of the amino acid is accompanied by the reduction of the dye to the leuco form. The aerobic deamination of an amino acid to a keto acid may be described by equations 1 through 4 as shown. Accord-

(1) $\quad \underset{\displaystyle NH_2—CH—COOH}{\overset{\displaystyle R}{|}} + \text{flavin} \rightarrow \underset{\displaystyle NH{=}C—COOH}{\overset{\displaystyle R}{|}} + \text{flavinH}_2$

(2) $\quad \underset{\displaystyle NH{=}C—COOH}{\overset{\displaystyle R}{|}} + H_2O \rightarrow \underset{\displaystyle O{=}C—COOH}{\overset{\displaystyle R}{|}} + NH_3$

(3) $\quad \text{FlavinH}_2 + O_2 \rightarrow \text{Flavin} + H_2O_2$

(4) $\quad H_2O_2 \rightarrow H_2O + \tfrac{1}{2}O_2$

$$\underset{\displaystyle NH_2—CH—COOH}{\overset{\displaystyle R}{|}} + \tfrac{1}{2}O_2 \rightarrow \underset{\displaystyle O{=}C—COOH}{\overset{\displaystyle R}{|}} + NH_3$$

ing to this formulation, reaction 1 gives rise to an α-imino acid that is unstable in aqueous solution, and is hydrolyzed spontaneously to the corresponding keto acid and ammonia (reaction 2).[9] In some instances, however, the initial dehydrogenation reaction may yield an unstable α,β-unsaturated amino acid, which undergoes spontaneous hydrolysis.[10]

$$\underset{\displaystyle NH_2—CH—COOH}{\overset{\displaystyle CH_2R}{|}} \xrightarrow{-2H} \underset{\displaystyle NH_2—C—COOH}{\overset{\displaystyle CHR}{\|}} \xrightarrow{+H_2O} \underset{\displaystyle O{=}C—COOH}{\overset{\displaystyle CH_2R}{|}} + NH_3$$

The possibility exists that neither the imino acid nor the α,β-unsaturated amino acid is formed as a free intermediate, and that the hydrolysis occurs while the dehydrogenated substrate is attached to the flavoprotein.

In the oxidative deamination of amino acids, the hydrogen peroxide formed in reaction 3 is decomposed, in the presence of enzyme preparations containing catalase (p. 365), to water and oxygen. In the absence

---

[9] C. Frieden and S. F. Velick, *Biochim. et Biophys. Acta*, **23**, 439 (1957).

[10] G. Taborsky, *Yale J. Biol. and Med.*, **27**, 267 (1955)

of catalase, the hydrogen peroxide oxidizes the keto acid to the next lower fatty acid with the evolution of carbon dioxide, and the over-all reaction is

$$NH_2—(CHR)—COOH + O_2 \rightarrow RCOOH + CO_2 + NH_3$$

In order to isolate the keto acid formed by oxidative deamination, it is necessary to add catalase if it is not already present in the enzyme preparation, or to add a compound such as ethanol which is preferentially oxidized by the hydrogen peroxide.

The D- and L-amino acid oxidases are valuable enzymic reagents for the identification and quantitative estimation of individual optically active amino acids. They are also useful in the preparation of L- or D-amino acids from the corresponding racemates, and of α-keto acids.[11]

Among the compounds that are not deaminated by the L-amino acid oxidases is L-glutamic acid. The oxidative deamination of this amino acid to the corresponding keto acid, α-ketoglutaric acid, is effected by the widely distributed enzyme L-glutamic dehydrogenase, which catalyzes an oxidation-reduction reaction between L-glutamic acid and either DPN

$$\begin{array}{ccc} CH_2COOH & & CH_2COOH \\ | & & | \\ CH_2 & & CH_2 \\ | & & | \\ NH_2—CH—COOH + DPN^+ & \rightleftharpoons & NH{=}C—COOH + DPNH + H^+ \\ \text{\small L-Glutamic acid} & & \text{\small α-Iminoglutaric acid} \end{array}$$

or TPN. The reversible dehydrogenation of L-glutamic acid to the hypothetical α-iminoglutaric acid (cf. p. 753) is followed by the spontaneous hydrolysis of the imino acid to yield ammonia and α-ketoglutaric acid. The enzyme has been crystallized from beef liver[12] and found to contain zinc.[13]

As will become evident from the subsequent discussion of amino acid metabolism, the fact that the reactions between L-glutamic acid and the pyridine nucleotides are readily reversible is probably of prime importance in the nitrogen metabolism of all living systems. Clearly, the reversible conversion of L-glutamic acid to α-ketoglutaric acid, which is a member of the citric acid cycle (p. 508), serves also as a link between the metabolism of this amino acid with the metabolism of carbohydrates. In some organisms, similar considerations apply to the interconversion of L-alanine and pyruvic acid; thus a DPN-specific L-alanine dehydrogenase has been identified in *Bacillus subtilis*.[14]

[11] A. Meister et al., *J. Biol. Chem.*, **192**, 535 (1951); **197**, 309 (1952).
[12] J. A. Olsen and C. B. Anfinsen, *J. Biol. Chem.*, **197**, 67 (1952); **202**, 841 (1953).
[13] B. L. Vallee et al., *J. Am. Chem. Soc.*, **77**, 5196 (1955).
[14] J. M. Wiame and A. Piérard, *Nature*, **176**, 1073 (1955).

All the reactions that have been considered thus far as mechanisms by which the C—N bond in an amino acid may be cleaved are oxidative processes and give rise to ammonia and α-keto acids. There are, however, other reactions whereby such cleavage is effected. For example, the deamination of L-aspartic acid to yield fumaric acid (p. 240) is catalyzed by the enzyme aspartase, found in *Escherichia coli*[15] and other microorganisms,[16] but not in mammalian tissues. Although animal tissues have been observed to form ammonia rapidly from L-aspartic acid, this process apparently is not due to a direct deamination of the amino acid (cf. p. 760). However, an enzyme termed D-aspartic acid oxidase, found in rabbit liver and kidney, catalyzes the oxidation by molecular oxygen of D-aspartic acid to oxaloacetic acid. This enzyme is a flavoprotein and contains FAD. It is almost inactive toward other D-amino acids and appears to be different, therefore, from the D-amino acid oxidase first found by Krebs.

An enzyme analogous in its action to aspartase but specific for the deamination of L-histidine to urocanic acid (so called because it was first isolated from dog urine) is present in bacteria,[17] and has been named histidine-α-deaminase or histidase. Preparations from mam-

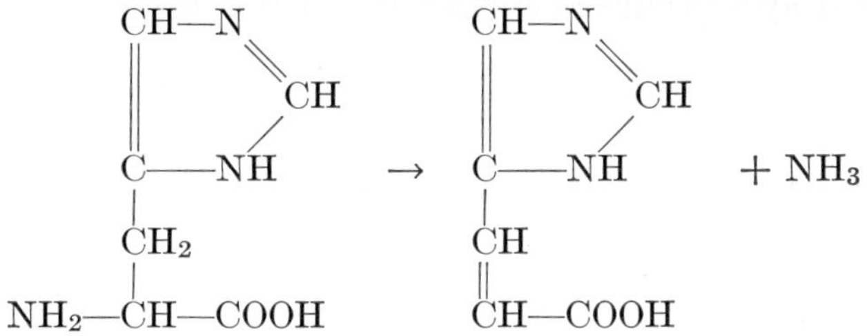

malian (rat, cat, and rabbit) liver also have been shown to form urocanic acid from histidine.[18] Urocanic acid is present in guinea pig epidermis, and urocanylcholine (murexine) occurs in some mollusks. An enzyme analogous to histidine-α-deaminase, but which acts on tyrosine, has been observed in *Bacillus proteus*.[19]

L-Serine is another amino acid whose enzymic deamination can be accomplished by means of a nonoxidative reaction. Here the elements

[15] J. H. Quastel and B. Woolf, *Biochem. J.*, **20**, 545 (1926); E. F. Gale, *ibid.*, **32**, 1583 (1938).

[16] N. Ellfolk, *Acta Chem. Scand.*, **8**, 151 (1954); **9**, 771 (1955); V. R. Williams and R. T. McIntyre, *J. Biol. Chem.*, **217**, 467 (1955).

[17] H. Tabor and O. Hayaishi, *J. Biol. Chem.*, **194**, 171 (1952); R. L. Wickremasinghe and B. A. Fry, *Biochem J.*, **58**, 268 (1954).

[18] D. A. Hall, *Biochem. J.*, **51**, 499 (1952); A. H. Mehler and H. Tabor, *J. Biol. Chem.*, **201**, 775 (1953).

[19] K. Hirai, *Biochem. Z.*, **114**, 71 (1921).

of water are removed in the presence of the enzyme serine dehydrase (found in mammalian liver[20]); the resulting α-aminoacrylic acid is unstable and rearranges to α-iminopropionic acid, which is hydrolyzed in water to yield ammonia and pyruvic acid. L-Threonine is also acted

$$
\underset{\text{L-Serine}}{\overset{\overset{\displaystyle CH_2OH}{|}}{NH_2-CH-COOH}} \xrightarrow{-H_2O} \overset{\overset{\displaystyle CH_2}{\|}}{NH_2-C-COOH} \longrightarrow
$$

$$
\overset{\overset{\displaystyle CH_3}{|}}{NH=C-COOH} \xrightarrow{+H_2O} \overset{\overset{\displaystyle CH_3}{|}}{O=C-COOH} + NH_3
$$

upon by an analogous enzyme, L-threonine dehydrase, and the products of the dehydration of threonine are ammonia and α-ketobutyric acid. Many microorganisms (bacteria, molds, yeast) deaminate L-serine and L-threonine by these nonoxidative reactions, but it is uncertain whether there is a specific dehydrase for each of these amino acids.[21] In addition, E. coli and Neurospora[22] contain a D-serine dehydrase that also acts slowly on D-threonine. As shown initially for the D-serine dehydrase of E. coli,[23] and subsequently confirmed for the other enzymes, the activity of all the dehydrases involves the participation of pyridoxal phosphate (p. 761) as a cofactor.

An enzyme closely related to serine dehydrase is known as cysteine desulfhydrase, and it catalyzes the removal of the elements of hydrogen sulfide from L-cysteine.[24] The distribution of cysteine desulfhydrase in

$$
\underset{\text{L-Cysteine}}{\overset{\overset{\displaystyle CH_2SH}{|}}{NH_2-CH-COOH}} \xrightarrow{-H_2S} \overset{\overset{\displaystyle CH_2}{\|}}{NH_2-C-COOH} \longrightarrow
$$

$$
\overset{\overset{\displaystyle CH_3}{|}}{NH=C-COOH} \xrightarrow{+H_2O} \overset{\overset{\displaystyle CH_3}{|}}{O=C-COOH} + NH_3
$$

nature is similar to that of serine dehydrase; it has been found in animal tissues (chiefly in liver), yeast, and many bacteria.[25] Like the dehydrases, the cysteine desulfhydrases are pyridoxal phosphate-dependent enzymes.

[20] E. Chargaff and D. B. Sprinson, J. Biol. Chem., 151, 273 (1943); F. W. Sayre and D. M. Greenberg, ibid., 220, 787 (1956).

[21] A. B. Pardee and L. S. Prestidge, J. Bact., 70, 667 (1955); H. E. Umbarger and D. Brown, ibid., 71, 443 (1956); 73, 105 (1957).

[22] C. Yanofsky, J. Biol. Chem., 198, 343 (1952).

[23] D. E. Metzler and E. E. Snell, J. Biol. Chem., 198, 363 (1952).

[24] C. V. Smythe, J. Biol. Chem., 142, 387 (1942).

[25] F. Binkley, J. Biol. Chem., 150, 261 (1943); R. E. Kallio, ibid., 192, 371 (1951); M. A. Metaxas and E. A. Delwiche, J. Bact., 70, 735 (1955).

The amino acids L-homoserine (p. 790) and L-homocysteine (p. 794) are also deaminated enzymically by nonoxidative reactions, with the formation of α-ketobutyric acid. The deamination of homoserine has been demonstrated with rat liver preparations, and that of homocysteine with *Proteus morganii;* the bacterial enzyme system is known to require pyridoxal phosphate for maximal activity.

Some of the strictly anaerobic microorganisms such as *Clostridium sporogenes* and *Clostridium botulinum* employ special methods for the deamination of amino acids.[26] Stickland reported in 1934 that, although suspensions of washed bacterial cells do not produce ammonia from any unsupplemented amino acid, some amino acids are deaminated by the cells in the presence of organic dyes that can serve as oxidizing agents, whereas other amino acids are deaminated in the presence of dyes that serve as reducing agents. If one amino acid from each group is added to a cell suspension, there occurs an intermolecular oxidation-reduction reaction with the concomitant production of ammonia. The protein amino acids have been classified into two groups on the basis of their behavior in the so-called "Stickland reaction": those that act as reducing agents (e.g., alanine) and those that act as oxidizing agents (e.g., glycine). For example, when glycine and alanine are incubated together with *Cl. sporogenes* under anaerobic conditions, the over-all reaction is:[27]

$$\text{L-Alanine} + 2 \text{ glycine} \xrightarrow{+\ 2H_2O} 3 \text{ Acetic acid} + 3 \text{ NH}_3 + CO_2$$

Experiments with enzyme preparations from *Cl. sporogenes* indicate that this reaction involves the following steps:[28]

1. A reversible oxidative deamination of L-alanine to pyruvic acid by a dehydrogenase system for which DPN$^+$ and inorganic phosphate are essential. This L-amino acid dehydrogenase system also acts on L-valine, L-leucine, and L-isoleucine to yield the corresponding α-keto acids. Under anaerobic conditions, DPNH accumulates; aerobically, with methylene blue as an electron carrier (cf. p. 334), oxygen is the terminal electron acceptor. In either case, when ADP is added to the incubation mixture, ATP is formed.

2. The oxidative decarboxylation of pyruvic acid to acetic acid by an α-keto acid dehydrogenase system, which requires the presence of DPN$^+$, coenzyme A, thiamine pyrophosphate, and inorganic phosphate. The decarboxylation involves the intermediate formation of acetyl phosphate (via acetyl-CoA) as in other bacterial systems (cf. p. 482).

[26] B. Nisman, *Bact. Revs.,* **18,** 16 (1954).

[27] D. D. Woods, *Biochem. J.,* **30,** 1934 (1936).

[28] R. Mamelak and J. H. Quastel, *Biochim. et Biophys. Acta,* **12,** 103 (1953).

3. The reductive deamination of glycine to acetic acid by DPNH (or by molecular hydrogen in the presence of DPN$^+$). The utilization of H_2 for reductive deamination has been observed with other anaerobes and with facultative aerobes studied under anaerobic conditions;[29] these organisms contain the enzyme hydrogenase (p. 676). Steps 1 and 2 lead to the formation of 2 equivalents of DPNH, which can effect the reduction of 2 equivalents of glycine to acetic acid, thus accounting for the stoichiometry of the over-all reaction written above. In addition to the "glycine reductase" system, preparations of *Cl. sporogenes* contain a "proline reductase" system which converts L-proline (p. 70) to δ-amino-valeric acid ($NH_2CH_2CH_2CH_2CH_2COOH$). When the reduction of proline is coupled to the oxidative deamination of alanine, the over-all Stickland reaction is:

$$\text{L-Alanine} + 2\text{ L-proline} \xrightarrow{\text{+2H}_2\text{O}}$$
$$\text{Acetic acid} + 2\text{ δ-aminovaleric acid} + NH_3 + CO_2$$

Although the oxidative and reductive processes in the Stickland reaction involve the participation of the DPN system, it is not known whether DPN$^+$ is the immediate electron acceptor or whether DPNH is the immediate electron donor in the conversion of the amino acids. Indeed, for the proline reductase system from another *Clostridium* (strain HF), it is probable that a direct reaction between proline and DPNH does not occur.[30] It may be added that this strain also contains a specific glycine reductase system which deaminates glycine to acetic acid only in the presence of inorganic phosphate and of ADP, and that the deamination is accompanied by the formation of ATP.[31] It would appear, therefore, that both the reductive and oxidative processes characteristic of the Stickland reaction can serve as sources of energy for the synthesis of ATP.

Regardless of the enzymic mechanisms involved in the metabolic deamination of protein amino acids, it will be obvious that, since many of the reactions discussed above are readily reversible, they provide metabolic pathways for the addition of ammonia to a number of non-nitrogenous carbon compounds (α-ketoglutaric acid, pyruvic acid, oxalo-acetic acid, fumaric acid, etc.). Thus the ammonia formed by the deamination of one amino acid, or supplied in the diet as an ammonium salt, may be used for the synthesis of other amino acids, provided that the requisite carbon skeleton is available. In fact, Schoenheimer demonstrated that the administration, to adult rats, of N^{15}-ammonium salts leads to the appearance of the isotope in the α-amino groups of many

[29] J. C. Hoogerheide and W. Kocholaty, *Biochem. J.*, **32**, 949 (1938).
[30] T. C. Stadtman, *Biochem. J.*, **62**, 614 (1956).
[31] T. C. Stadtman and P. Elliott, *J. Am. Chem. Soc.*, **78**, 2020 (1956).

protein amino acids, some of which are classified as indispensable. This result is readily understandable in the light of the fact that certain of the indispensable amino acids (e.g., tryptophan, histidine) may be replaced in the diet of the growing rat by the corresponding α-keto acids. In these cases, the indispensable nature of a particular amino acid is a reflection of the inability of the animal to synthesize the carbon skeleton of that amino acid, rather than to introduce the α-amino nitrogen.

Transamination Reactions [1,32]

As noted at the beginning of this chapter, metabolic reactions are known in which the α-amino nitrogen of one amino acid is transferred directly to the carbon skeleton of another amino acid. In such transamination reactions, an amino acid and a keto acid interact, as shown, under the influence of specific enzymes. It now appears probable that

$$
\underset{\text{NH}_2\text{CHCOOH}}{\overset{\text{R}}{|}} + \underset{\text{O=CCOOH}}{\overset{\text{R}'}{|}} \rightleftharpoons \underset{\text{O=CCOOH}}{\overset{\text{R}}{|}} + \underset{\text{NH}_2\text{CHCOOH}}{\overset{\text{R}'}{|}}
$$

this mechanism represents the most important metabolic pathway both in the formation and in the deamination of many amino acids.

A typical transamination was first observed by Herbst and Engel[33] in model systems; thus, when a mixture of α-aminophenylacetic acid and pyruvic acid in water is heated, alanine, benzaldehyde, and CO_2 are formed. Presumably, the latter two products arise from the decomposition of phenylglyoxylic acid. More recently, the nonenzymic trans-

$$
\underset{\text{NH}_2\text{CHCOOH}}{\overset{\text{C}_6\text{H}_5}{|}} + \underset{\text{O=CCOOH}}{\overset{\text{CH}_3}{|}} \rightarrow \underset{\text{CHO}}{\overset{\text{C}_6\text{H}_5}{|}} + CO_2 + \underset{\text{NH}_2\text{CHCOOH}}{\overset{\text{CH}_3}{|}}
$$

amination between glyoxylic acid (p. 772) and several α-amino acids (alanine, aspartic acid, glutamic acid) at pH 7.4 and 25 to 30° C has been shown to yield glycine and the corresponding α-keto acids.[34]

The first definite evidence for the presence in animal tissues of enzymes that catalyze such reactions was provided by Braunstein and Kritzmann,[35] who reported that, in minced preparations of pigeon breast muscle, any α-amino acid, with the exception of glycine, could yield its amino group either to α-ketoglutaric acid to produce L-glutamic acid or to oxaloacetic acid to produce L-aspartic acid. Subsequent work by

[32] A. Meister, *Advances in Enzymol.*, **16**, 185 (1955).

[33] R. M. Herbst and L. L. Engel, *J. Biol. Chem.*, **107**, 505 (1934).

[34] H. I. Nakada and S. Weinhouse, *J. Biol. Chem.*, **204**, 831 (1953).

[35] A. E. Braunstein and M. G. Kritzmann, *Enzymologia*, **2**, 129 (1937).

Cohen[36] provided evidence for the existence of only two transaminating systems in swine heart muscle:

(1) L-Glutamic acid + oxaloacetic acid $\rightleftharpoons$
α-Ketoglutaric acid + L-aspartic acid

(2) L-Glutamic acid + pyruvic acid $\rightleftharpoons$
α-Ketoglutaric acid + L-alanine

The equilibrium constants in reactions 1 and 2 (at 25° C) are about 6.7 and 1.5 respectively.[37] These two transamination reactions are known to occur in a variety of animal tissues, in higher plants, and in many microorganisms.

The enzymes (transaminases) that catalyze reactions 1 and 2 have been studied intensively, first those of mammalian muscle and later those in *Streptococcus fecalis*. Green et al.[38] prepared from swine heart two partially purified enzymes: one catalyzes reaction 1 and may be termed glutamic-aspartic transaminase (also termed glutamic-oxaloacetic transaminase); the other catalyzes reaction 2 and is termed glutamic-alanine transaminase (or glutamic-pyruvic transaminase). The existence of the glutamic-aspartic transaminase helps to explain the deamination of L-aspartic acid by tissues that are devoid of aspartase (p. 755) but contain glutamic dehydrogenase.

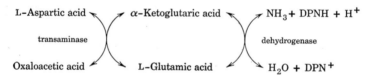

Studies on the purified glutamic-aspartic transaminase of *Streptococcus fecalis* showed it to consist of an enzyme protein and the cofactor pyridoxal phosphate[39] (p. 761), a member of the group of substances designated vitamin B_6 (Chapter 39). Indeed, almost all of the known enzymic transamination reactions have been shown to require the participation of pyridoxal phosphate.

The first indications of the role of vitamin B_6 in transamination came from the observation that the tissues of B_6-deficient rats have low transaminase activity;[40] subsequent work has confirmed and extended these findings.[41] It was also found that, when *S. fecalis* (which normally

[36] P. P. Cohen, *Biochem. J.*, **33**, 1478 (1939); *J. Biol. Chem.*, **136**, 565 (1940).
[37] H. A. Krebs, *Biochem. J.*, **54**, 82 (1953).
[38] D. E. Green et al., *J. Biol. Chem.*, **161**, 559 (1945).
[39] H. C. Lichstein et al., *J. Biol. Chem.*, **161**, 311 (1945).
[40] F. Schlenk and E. E. Snell, *J. Biol. Chem.*, **157**, 425 (1945).
[41] M. Brin et al., *J. Biol. Chem.*, **210**, 435 (1954).

requires an external source of vitamin B_6 for growth) is grown in a medium low in this vitamin, the bacterial cells exhibit only slight transaminase activity; the addition of pyridoxal phosphate to suspensions of such deficient cells produces full enzyme activity.

Braunstein and Kritzmann first suggested that transamination is accomplished by a direct condensation reaction between the amino and keto acids to form a labile intermediate Schiff base which then undergoes rearrangement and hydrolysis. With the discovery of the role of pyridoxal phosphate in enzymic transamination, and the demonstration by Snell (cf. p. 769) that nonenzymic transamination occurs in model systems between pyridoxal and glutamic acid, or between pyridoxamine and α-ketoglutaric acid, it was suggested that pyridoxal phosphate and pyridoxamine phosphate act as intermediates in biological transaminations.[42] The initial reaction between an amino acid substrate and the aldehydic form of the cofactor to yield a keto acid and pyridoxamine

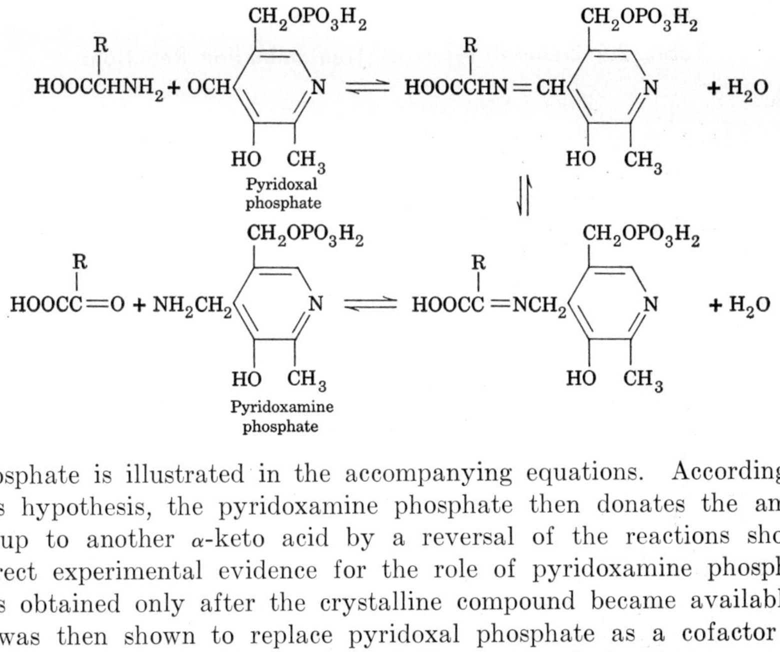

phosphate is illustrated in the accompanying equations. According to this hypothesis, the pyridoxamine phosphate then donates the amino group to another α-keto acid by a reversal of the reactions shown. Direct experimental evidence for the role of pyridoxamine phosphate was obtained only after the crystalline compound became available;[43] it was then shown to replace pyridoxal phosphate as a cofactor for glutamic-aspartic transaminase.[44] Unlike pyridoxal phosphate, pyridoxamine phosphate combines with the enzyme protein slowly, and, once this combination has occurred, it is difficult to remove the pyridoxamine phosphate from the protein.

[42] F. Schlenk and A. Fisher, *Arch. Biochem.*, **12**, 69 (1947).
[43] E. A. Peterson and H. A. Sober, *J. Am. Chem. Soc.*, **76**, 169 (1954).
[44] A. Meister et al., *J. Biol. Chem.*, **206**, 89 (1954).

Although pyridoxine (Chapter 39) has vitamin B_6 activity for many organisms, crystalline pyridoxine phosphate (which contains no aldehyde or amino group) does not serve as a cofactor in transamination. In fact, pyridoxine phosphate and deoxypyridoxine phosphate inhibit transamination, presumably because they combine with the enzyme protein at the site normally occupied by pyridoxal phosphate or pyridoxamine phosphate. The inhibitory action of deoxypyridoxine phosphate on enzymic transamination may account for the "antivitamin" action of deoxypyridoxine *in vivo*.

The development of extremely sensitive analytical methods, involving chromatographic, spectroscopic, manometric, or isotope techniques, has led to the recognition of a wide variety of transamination reactions in biological systems (Table 2). The known reactions may be divided among five general types; many of the specific reactions will be considered in Chapter 32 in relation to their role in the metabolism of individual amino acids.

Table 2. General Types of Transamination Reactions

Type	General Reactions	Occurrence
1	L-α-Amino acid + α-ketoglutaric acid $\rightleftharpoons$ α-Keto acid + L-glutamic acid	Animals, plants, and microorganisms
2	D-α-Amino acid + α-ketoglutaric acid $\rightleftharpoons$ α-Keto acid + D-glutamic acid	*B. subtilis, B. anthracis*
3	γ-Aminobutyric acid + α-ketoglutaric acid $\rightleftharpoons$ Succinic semialdehyde + L-glutamic acid	Brain, microorganisms
	L-Ornithine + α-keto acid $\rightleftharpoons$ L-Glutamic-γ-semialdehyde + L-α-amino acid	Liver, *Neurospora*
4	L-Glutamine + α-keto acid $\rightarrow$ α-Ketoglutaramic acid + L-α-amino acid	Liver
	L-Asparagine + α-keto acid $\rightleftharpoons$ α-Ketosuccinamic acid + L-α-amino acid	Liver, higher plants
5	L-α-Amino monocarboxylic acid$_1$ + α-keto monocarboxylic acid$_2$ $\rightleftharpoons$ α-Keto monocarboxylic acid$_1$ + L-α-amino monocarboxylic acid$_2$	Animals, plants, and microorganisms

It is now known that glutamic-aspartic transaminase and glutamic-alanine transaminase are two members of a much larger group of enzymes that catalyze reactions of type 1. At least two bacterial forms, which contain D-amino acids (cf. p. 769), have transaminases that are specific for such enantiomorphs[45] (type 2). In many transamination reactions, ω-amino acids (rather than α-amino acids) serve as "amino group donors"; here aldehydes are formed[46] (type 3). Specific trans-

[45] C. B. Thorne et al., *J. Bact.*, **69**, 357; **70**, 420 (1955).

[46] S. P. Bessman et al., *J. Biol. Chem.*, **201**, 385 (1953); A. Meister, *ibid.*, **206**, 587 (1954).

aminases for glutamine and asparagine (type 4) also have been described;[47] the α-keto acids corresponding to these amino acid amides are termed α-ketoglutaramic acid and α-ketosuccinamic acid respectively. The latter compounds may be deamidated by enzymes termed ω-amidases; thus the coupling of a specific transaminase and ω-amidase can effect the conversion of glutamine (or asparagine), in the presence of an α-keto acid (e.g., pyruvic acid), to α-ketoglutaric acid (or oxaloacetic acid). In some transamination reactions, neither partner is a derivative of a dicarboxylic amino acid (type 5).

Although a single tissue or microbial culture may contain several transaminases of different specificity, the glutamic-aspartic transaminase appears to be ubiquitous in living organisms, and the majority of the recognized transamination reactions include glutamic acid as one of the participants. These facts point to an important role for both glutamic acid and aspartic acid in nitrogen transfer. This conclusion is in agreement with the data, obtained by the feeding of N^{15}-compounds to rats, which showed that glutamic acid and, to a lesser extent, aspartic acid take up nitrogen entering the animal body in the form of various amino acids (such as glycine or leucine), or even as ammonium ions, much more rapidly than do other protein amino acids. The importance of glutamic and aspartic acids in nitrogen metabolism is not limited to animal tissues. Attention was drawn on p. 742 to the role of glutamine and asparagine in the protein metabolism of the germinating seeds and the tissues of higher plants. These amides are interconvertible, in metabolism, with the corresponding free amino acids (cf. p. 721).

On deamination, glutamic acid, aspartic acid, alanine, serine, and cysteine all give rise to α-keto acids which are also intermediates in carbohydrate metabolism, thus explaining the glycogenic action of these amino acids (cf. p. 493). In addition, several other amino acids also can give rise to carbohydrate in the animal body. Before the development of the isotope technique, the utilization of the carbon atoms of amino acids for the biosynthesis of carbohydrates and fats was studied in experimental animals that had been made sensitive to the influx of new glucogenic or ketogenic materials. For example, use was made of dogs rendered diabetic by the removal of the pancreas or of animals treated with phlorizin (p. 441), which interferes with the reabsorption of glucose by the renal tubules. In such experimental animals, certain amino acids cause the appearance of extra glucose in the urine, i.e., are glucogenic, whereas others induce the excretion of ketone bodies, i.e., are ketogenic. Another method for the detection of glucogenic amino acids involves the study of the deposition of liver glycogen after the administration of a

[47] A. Meister and P. E. Fraser, *J. Biol. Chem.,* **210,** 37 (1954).

test compound to previously starved rats. On the basis of such experimental procedures, the protein amino acids have been classified as shown in Table 3. Obviously, this classification refers to the metabolic fate

Table 3. Glucogenic and Ketogenic Amino Acids

Amino Acid	Glucogenic	Ketogenic
Glycine	+	−
Alanine	+	−
Serine	+	−
Threonine	+	−
Valine	+	−
Leucine	−	+
Isoleucine	(+)	(+)
Lysine	−	−
Hydroxylysine	?	?
Glutamic acid	+	−
Aspartic acid	+	−
Phenylalanine	?	+
Tyrosine	(+)	+
Tryptophan	−	−
Histidine	+	−
Arginine	+	−
Methionine	−	−
Cystine	(+)	−
Proline	+	−
Hydroxyproline	+	(+)

of amino acids under the somewhat "unphysiological" conditions of diabetes or starvation. From the discussion in Chapter 32 it will be apparent that the administration of a nonglucogenic amino acid labeled with isotopic carbon may lead to the appearance of the isotope in liver glycogen. Similarly, nonketogenic amino acids may provide carbon for the biosynthesis of ketone bodies and fatty acids when these processes are studied by means of the isotope technique. These apparent discrepancies are analogous to the situation discussed earlier in relation to the conversion of acetate to glucose in the animal body (cf. p. 513).

In the metabolic conversion of the carbon atoms of amino acids to carbohydrate and fatty acids, deamination may represent the first step, and the resultant carbon compound may be metabolized further to give rise to a recognized precursor of carbohydrate or fat. Since the carbon chains of those amino acids designated as dispensable for animals, and the carbon chains of all amino acids in autotrophic plants and microorganisms must be synthesized in vivo, reactions must exist that link the breakdown of carbohydrate and fat with the synthesis of amino acids. Some amino acids are formed from carbohydrate and fat by the reversal of the reactions in the conversion of the nitrogenous compounds to carbohydrate and fat; other amino acids are synthesized and degraded by separate pathways. However, the metabolic deamination of most amino acids, and the amination reactions leading to their synthesis, are effected by means of transamination reactions. The central role of glutamic acid and aspartic acid in these processes is shown in Fig. 1, which summarizes some of the known metabolic relations among amino acids for mammalian liver. Obviously, all the reactions given in Fig. 1 do not

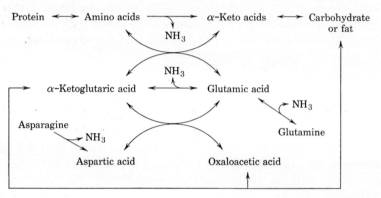

Fig. 1. Some enzymic reactions in the synthesis and degradation of amino acids in mammalian liver.

occur in every biological system, and systems other than liver may effect reactions not observed in this tissue. Thus, in some bacteria, the reactions catalyzed by aspartase or by L-alanine dehydrogenase may represent important metabolic links between ammonia and amino acids.

It has long been known that carbohydrates (and fats) exert a "protein-sparing" effect in higher animals.[48] For example, the transfer of an animal in negative nitrogen balance (p. 723) to a diet rich in carbohydrate may result in a marked decrease in the amount of nitrogen excreted in the urine. Even in animals initially in nitrogen equilibrium an increase in dietary carbohydrate may produce a condition of positive nitrogen balance, i.e., a "retention" of protein in the animal body; upon the removal of the additional carbohydrate from the diet, the "stored" protein nitrogen is excreted in the urine, and nitrogen equilibrium is gradually re-established. Although the mechanism by which carbohydrate "spares" protein is not understood, it has been suggested[49] that the oxidation of excess carbohydrate (or fat) results in an increase of available DPNH, thus enhancing the ability of liver glutamic dehydrogenase to form glutamic acid from ammonia that would otherwise be excreted

[48] H. N. Munro, *Physiol. Revs.*, **31**, 449 (1951).
[49] L. L. Miller et al., *Federation Proc.*, **14**, 707 (1955).

(cf. p. 848); glutamic acid-nitrogen then could be used in transamination reactions, and the resultant α-amino acids "stored" as protein.

Decarboxylation of Amino Acids [1,50]

The foregoing discussion of the general metabolism of amino acids has dealt only with reactions involving α-amino groups. Enzyme systems are also known which attack amino acids at the carboxyl group and catalyze the decarboxylation of amino acids to yield carbon dioxide and an amine; these enzymes are termed amino acid decarboxylases.

$$\underset{NH_2CHCOOH}{\overset{R}{|}} \rightarrow \underset{NH_2CH_2}{\overset{R}{|}} + CO_2$$

A list of the better known amino acid decarboxylases is given in Table 4.

Most of the bacterial decarboxylases are formed in large quantities only when the organisms are grown in an acid medium (pH 2.5 to 5.5, depending on the organism); their formation also depends on the presence in the culture medium of the specific substrate, and the decarboxylases are, therefore, adaptive enzymes whose function appears to be that of protecting the bacterial cells against an acid environment by the production of amines. However, diaminopimelic decarboxylase is a "constitutive" enzyme, always present in bacteria that normally make L-lysine by the decarboxylation of $meso$-α,ϵ-diaminopimelic acid (p. 83); this decarboxylase specifically removes the carboxyl group on the asymmetric carbon atom having the D configuration.[51] Other decarboxylases are specific for L-amino acids, and, in general, each enzyme acts only upon the L-form of a single amino acid. However, the tyrosine decarboxylase from *Streptococcus fecalis* can act on 3,4-dihydroxy-L-phenylalanine (dopa) as well as on tyrosine; it also decarboxylates phenylalanine, but at a much slower rate than that at which it attacks the two other amino acids. Likewise, the decarboxylation of L-leucine and of L-valine by *Proteus vulgaris* is believed to be catalyzed by a single enzyme.[52]

The extreme specificity of most of the bacterial decarboxylases makes them excellent analytical tools for the estimation of the following amino acids: lysine, arginine, histidine, ornithine, tyrosine, glutamic acid, aspartic acid, and diaminopimelic acid. Each of the decarboxylation

[50] E. F. Gale, *Advances in Enzymol.*, **6**, 1 (1946); H. Blaschko, *ibid.*, **5**, 67 (1945); O. Schales, in J. B. Sumner and K. Myrbäck, *The Enzymes*, Chapter 50, Academic Press, New York, 1951.

[51] D. L. Dewey et al., *Biochem. J.*, **58**, 523 (1954); *J. Gen. Microbiol.*, **11**, 307 (1954); R. F. Denman et al., *Biochim. et Biophys. Acta*, **16**, 442 (1955).

[52] L. Ekladius and H. K. King, *Biochem. J.*, **62**, 7p (1956).

reactions proceeds quantitatively, and the CO_2 formed may be measured manometrically (p. 288).

Table 4. Enzymic Decarboxylation of Amino Acids

Amino Acid	Decarboxylation Product	Occurrence
L-Arginine	Agmatine	Microorganisms (e.g., *E. coli*)
L-Aspartic acid	L-Alanine	*Cl. welchii*
L-Aspartic acid	β-Alanine	*Rhizobium leguminosarum*
L-Cysteic acid	Taurine	Liver, spleen, brain
L-Cysteine sulfinic acid	Hypotaurine	Liver, spleen, brain
L-Glutamic acid	γ-Aminobutyric acid	Microorganisms (e.g., *Cl. welchii, E. coli*), animal tissues (brain, liver, muscle), higher plants (barley, spinach, phlox)
γ-Hydroxy-L-glutamic acid	γ-Amino-α-hydroxy-butyric acid	*E. coli*
γ-Methylene-L-glutamic acid	α-Methylene-γ-amino-butyric acid	Barley, red pepper, peanut
L-Histidine	Histamine	Microorganisms (e.g., *Cl. welchii, Lactobacilli*), animal tissues (kidney, liver, duodenum)
L-Lysine	Cadaverine	Microorganisms (e.g., *B. cadaveris, E. coli*)
meso-α,ε-Diaminopimelic acid	L-Lysine	Microorganisms (e.g., *E. coli, A. aerogenes*)
L-Ornithine	Putrescine	Microorganisms (e.g., *Cl. septicum*)
L-Phenylalanine	β-Phenylethylamine	Microorganisms (e.g., *S. fecalis*)
L-Tyrosine	Tyramine	Microorganisms (e.g., *S. fecalis*), animal tissues (e.g., kidney)
3,4-Dihydroxy-L-phenyl-alanine	3,4-Dihydroxy-β-phenyl-ethylamine	Microorganisms (e.g., *S. fecalis*), animal tissues (e.g., kidney)
5-Hydroxy-L-tryptophan	5-Hydroxytryptamine	Animal tissues (e.g., kidney, brain, stomach)
L-Valine	Isobutylamine	*Proteus vulgaris*
L-Leucine	Isoamylamine	*Proteus vulgaris*

Some of the amines produced from amino acids by bacteria have pharmacological activity in animals. For example, histamine causes a fall in blood pressure, whereas tyramine and 3,4-dihydroxyphenylethyl-amine are pressor substances similar in action to, though less potent than, adrenalin. The production of such toxic compounds by intestinal bacteria obviously can have a deleterious effect upon the host if large quantities of the amines are absorbed into the blood stream. Histidine decarboxylase is also present in animal tissues (liver, kidney, intestine, lung) rich in histamine.[53]

The action of mammalian 5-hydroxytryptophan decarboxylase produces another pressor substance, 5-hydroxytryptamine (serotonin; p. 844).[54] This amine is found together with adrenalin in the parotid gland secretion (i.e., venom) of certain toads, and is identical with the invertebrate hormone enteramine. Several other decarboxylases have been found in mammalian tissues, mainly in liver, kidney, and brain. Of special interest are "dopa" decarboxylase[55] and glutamic decarboxylase.[56] The product of the decarboxylation of glutamic acid is γ-aminobutyric acid, which has been identified as a constituent of brain tissue in a variety of mammals as well as in frogs and pigeons. Glutamic decarboxylase is also present in higher plants,[57] and γ-aminobutyric acid is found in plant tissues; for example, in potato tubers this substance is the third most abundant of the soluble nitrogen compounds.[58] Some plant extracts that exhibit glutamic decarboxylase activity also decarboxylate γ-methyleneglutamic acid (p. 63).[59]

All of the well-defined amino acid decarboxylases have been shown to require pyridoxal phosphate for activity; histidine decarboxylase requires, in addition, a metal ion (Fe^{3+}, Al^{3+}).[60] Only pyridoxal phosphate has coenzyme activity; neither pyridoxamine phosphate nor pyridoxine phosphate (Chapter 39) will replace the aldehydic compound. The postulated mechanism of the decarboxylation reaction is shown in the scheme at the top of p. 769.

The dependence of decarboxylases on pyridoxal phosphate has been demonstrated by means of enzyme preparations from animals or bacteria deficient in vitamin B_6 (pyridoxine). For example, brain tissue of vitamin B_6-deficient rats contains the normal amount of glutamic decarboxylase protein, but is notably poor in the cofactor. Consequently, a decreased activity toward glutamic acid is observed unless pyridoxal phosphate is added to the tissue preparations. Similarly, *Streptococcus fecalis* contains active tyrosine decarboxylase only if the cells are cultured in the presence of vitamin B_6, but the presence of the specific

[53] H. T. Graham et al., *Biochim. et Biophys. Acta,* **20,** 243 (1956).

[54] C. T. Clarke et al., *J. Biol. Chem.,* **210,** 139 (1954).

[55] O. Schales and S. S. Schales, *Arch. Biochem.,* **24,** 83 (1949); W. J. Hartman et al., *J. Biol. Chem.,* **216,** 507 (1955).

[56] W. J. Wingo and J. Awapara, *J. Biol. Chem.,* **187,** 267 (1950); E. Roberts and S. Frankel, *ibid.,* **190,** 505 (1951).

[57] O. Schales et al., *Arch. Biochem.,* **10,** 455; **11,** 155 (1946).

[58] J. F. Thompson et al., *Plant Physiol.,* **28,** 401 (1953).

[59] L. Fowden and J. Done, *Biochem. J.,* **55,** 548 (1953).

[60] B. M. Guirard and E. E. Snell, *J. Am. Chem. Soc.,* **76,** 4745 (1955).

$$\underset{\substack{R \\ |}}{HOOCCHNH_2} + OCH\langle \text{ring} \rangle \xrightarrow{-H_2O} \underset{\substack{R \\ |}}{HOOCCHN} = CH\langle \text{ring} \rangle$$

with $CH_2OPO_3H_2$ and HO CH_3 on the pyridine rings, then $-CO_2 \downarrow$

$$\underset{\substack{R \\ |}}{CH_2NH_2} + OCH\langle \text{ring} \rangle \xleftarrow{+H_2O} \underset{\substack{R \\ |}}{CH_2N} = CH\langle \text{ring} \rangle$$

decarboxylase protein can be demonstrated by the restoration of enzymic activity when pyridoxal phosphate is added to a suspension of the inactive cell material. *S. fecalis* requires for growth a variety of protein amino acids supplemented with either pyridoxine or D-alanine. The latter compound can be formed by the bacteria from L-alanine in an enzymic reaction catalyzed by "alanine racemase," which also requires pyridoxal phosphate for activity.[61] A similar alanine racemase is present in the anthrax bacillus and in *B. subtilis,* and probably acts together with transaminases to form the D-glutamic acid of the capsular polypeptides of these organisms (p. 138).

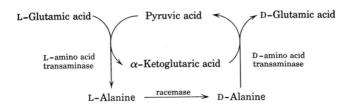

Alanine racemase, the decarboxylases, the transaminases, and the dehydrases and desulfhydrases (p. 756) represent four types of enzyme systems in which pyridoxal phosphate is involved as a cofactor. The fact that the four types of chemical reaction catalyzed by these enzymes are very different, although the same cofactor is required, emphasizes the important role of the enzyme protein in determining the mode of action of a given enzyme system.

Each of these four types of reaction (including stereospecific trans-aminations) has been duplicated in nonenzymic model systems consisting of an aqueous solution of the appropriate substrates, pyridoxal, and a

[61] J. Olivard and E. E. Snell, *J. Biol. Chem.,* **213,** 203 (1955).

metal ion (e.g., Cu^{2+}, Fe^{2+}, Fe^{3+}, Al^{3+}).[62] From their studies of such model systems, Snell and his associates have suggested that the Schiff bases[63] (p. 51) derived from amino acids and pyridoxal are stabilized by chelation, as shown in the accompanying formula. Subsequent intramolecular reactions (i.e., expulsion of H^+, CO_2, OH^-, or SH^-, coupled with a shift of electrons) produce chelates that are spontaneously

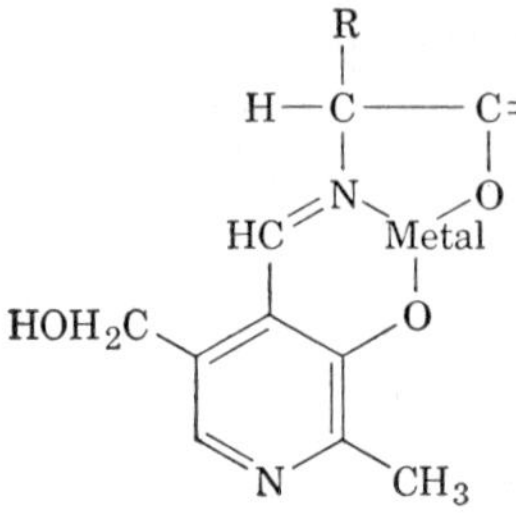

hydrolyzed to the expected reaction products. Thus the metal ion appears to perform the catalytic function of the specific protein in the enzymic reaction; the phosphate group of pyridoxal phosphate is thought to be involved in binding the Schiff base to the enzyme protein.

Other reactions catalyzed by pyridoxal phosphate-dependent enzyme systems are important in the metabolism of serine (p. 775), of threonine (p. 791), of methionine (p. 793), and of tryptophan (p. 841); these reactions have also been reproduced in model systems.[64] The presence of pyridoxal phosphate in crystalline muscle phosphorylase was mentioned previously (p. 440).

[62] D. Metzler et al., *J. Am. Chem. Soc.*, **76**, 648 (1954); J. B. Longenecker and E. E. Snell, *ibid.*, **79**, 142 (1957).

[63] D. E. Meltzer, *J. Am. Chem. Soc.*, **79**, 485 (1957).

[64] J. B. Longenecker and E. E. Snell, *J. Biol. Chem.*, **213**, 229 (1955).

32 ·
Special Aspects
of
Amino Acid Metabolism

In the preceding chapter, consideration was given to the metabolic fate of the α-amino and α-carboxyl groups of protein amino acids. Since the metabolism of individual amino acids includes not only the general processes of deamination, transamination, and decarboxylation, but also enzymic action at the characteristic side chains, the metabolic fate of each protein amino acid must be considered separately.[1]

Metabolism of Glycine [2]

Biosynthesis of Glycine. Glycine appears to be readily synthesized by most organisms. Isotope experiments[3] have demonstrated the formation *in vivo* of glycine from nitrogen that enters the animal body as ammonium ions or in the amino groups of amino acids such as leucine or tyrosine. A possible pathway of glycine synthesis is the amination of glyoxylic acid either by a reversal of oxidative deamination or by transamination, and the direct conversion of glyoxylic acid to glycine has been demonstrated in the intact rat.[4] Other C_2 compounds converted to glycine *in vivo* are glycolic acid, glycolaldehyde, and ethanolamine (aminoethanol); studies with labeled compounds have given evidence for the interconversions shown in Fig. 1.

Clearly, glyoxylic acid can be both a precursor and a degradation product of glycine. In rat liver slices, glycine and glyoxylic acid are

[1] W. D. McElroy and B. Glass, *Amino Acid Metabolism,* Johns Hopkins Press, Baltimore, 1955; A. Meister, *Biochemistry of the Amino Acids,* Academic Press, New York, 1957.

[2] H. R. V. Arnstein, *Advances in Protein Chem.,* **9,** 1 (1954).

[3] R. Schoenheimer, *The Dynamic State of Body Constituents,* Harvard University Press, Cambridge, 1942.

[4] S. Weinhouse and B. Friedmann, *J. Biol. Chem.,* **191,** 707 (1951); **221,** 665 (1956); A. Weissbach and D. B. Sprinson, *ibid.,* **203,** 1023, 1031 (1953).

rapidly oxidized to CO_2 by an apparent oxidative decarboxylation of glyoxylic acid to formic acid;[5] the mechanism whereby formic acid is formed has not been elucidated, but this reaction may be of importance in glycine metabolism, since the α-carbon of glycine is used in many biosynthetic processes in which formic acid can also serve as a carbon precursor (cf. p. 774).

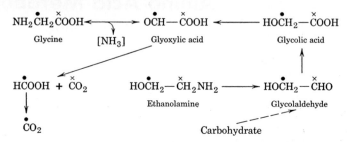

Fig. 1. Metabolism of glycine and of glyoxylic acid in the rat. The fate of the individual carbon atoms is indicated by the dots and crosses.

The pathway leading from glycolic acid to glycine is operative in higher plants.[6] Furthermore, glyoxylic acid participates in transamination reactions to yield glycine in microbial systems (e.g., *Pseudomonas*, *Neurospora*);[7] several strains of *Pseudomonas* form glyoxylic acid from isocitric acid (p. 518). In animals and higher plants, the C_2 precursor of glycine could arise from carbohydrates by transketolase-catalyzed reactions (p. 529), since carbons 1 and 2 of ribose are known to be precursors of the α- and carboxyl carbons of glycine, respectively.

Although the formation of glycine from C_2 compounds undoubtedly occurs in biological systems, it represents a minor pathway for glycine synthesis in animal tissues. As first shown by Shemin,[8] the principal source of glycine in the animal body is the amino acid serine. For his investigations, Shemin took advantage of the fact that the administration of benzoic acids to animals leads to the excretion in the urine of hippuric acid (cf. p. 729); any compound that can serve as a source of protein glycine will likewise serve as a precursor of the glycine portion of hippuric acid. The conversion of serine to glycine without rupture of the carbon—nitrogen bond was proved by the use of doubly labeled serine $HOCH_2CHN^{15}H_2C^{13}OOH$; the $COOH$—C^{13}/N^{15} ratio was the same in the glycine formed as in the serine administered. Shemin suggested, therefore, that serine is degraded to glycine and formate. Subsequent

[5] H. I. Nakada et al., *J. Biol. Chem.*, **216**, 583 (1955); **233**, 8 (1958).

[6] N. E. Tolbert and M. S. Cohan, *J. Biol. Chem.*, **204**, 649 (1953).

[7] L. L. Campbell, Jr., *J. Bact.*, **71**, 81 (1956).

[8] D. Shemin, *J. Biol. Chem.*, **162**, 297 (1946).

work has shown that the major portion of tissue glycine arises from serine, which is formed from carbohydrates or fats via an intermediate C_3 compound.[9]

The metabolic conversion of serine to glycine and a C_1 unit is reversible.[10] Formic acid can serve as a precursor of the C_1 unit; if isotopic formate and isotopic glycine are fed to fasted rats, doubly labeled serine is formed.[11] It is clear that, in the intact animal, the

$$HC^{14}OOH + NH_2CH_2C^{13}OOH \rightarrow NH_2\underset{|}{\overset{C^{14}H_2OH}{CH}}\!-\!C^{13}OOH$$

over-all process serine $\rightleftharpoons$ glycine + C_1 unit is in constant operation. The C_1 unit derived from serine enters into a variety of metabolic transformations (Fig. 2) which will be discussed later. This interconversion of serine and glycine also occurs in microorganisms; its probable occurrence in higher plants is indicated by the utilization of formic acid as a source of the β-carbon atom of serine.[12]

Studies with bacteria[13] and rats[14] showed that the vitamin pteroyl-L-glutamic acid (folic acid; p. 207) is involved in the serine-glycine interconversion. Although the role of derivatives of pteroylglutamic acid (PGA) as carriers of C_1 units has been studied extensively with extracts of animal tissues and of bacteria, the nature of the functional form of the vitamin is uncertain.[15] The available evidence indicates, however, that tetrahydroPGA (Fig. 3), rather than PGA itself, is the precursor of the active cofactor. The characterization of the compounds formed in biological systems is made difficult by the spontaneous oxidation by air of tetrahydroPGA derivatives to the corresponding PGA compounds; furthermore, N^{10}-formyltetrahydroPGA and anhydroleucovorin ($N^{5,10}$-methenyltetrahydroPGA) are readily converted to the more stable N^5-formyl compound leucovorin[16] (Fig. 3). Enzyme-catalyzed reactions leading to the formation of N^5-formyl- or N^{10}-

[9] H. R. V. Arnstein and D. Keglevic, *Biochem. J.,* **62,** 199 (1956).

[10] R. L. Kisliuk and W. Sakami, *J. Biol. Chem.,* **214,** 47 (1955).

[11] W. Sakami, *J. Biol. Chem.,* **176,** 995 (1948).

[12] N. E. Tolbert, *J. Biol. Chem.,* **215,** 27 (1955).

[13] J. Lascelles and D. D. Woods, *Biochem. J.,* **58,** 486 (1954); J. Lascelles et al., *J. Gen. Microbiol.,* **10,** 267 (1954).

[14] J. R. Totter et al., *J. Biol. Chem.,* **178,** 847 (1949); **186,** 145 (1950); D. Elwyn and D. B. Sprinson, *ibid.,* **184,** 475 (1950).

[15] N. Alexander and D. M. Greenberg, *J. Biol. Chem.,* **220,** 775 (1956); B. Wright, *ibid.,* **219,** 873 (1956); F. M. Huennekens et al., *ibid.,* **224,** 435 (1957); J. M. Peters and D. M. Greenberg, *ibid.,* **226,** 329 (1957); R. L. Blakley, *Biochem. J.,* **65,** 342 (1957).

[16] M. May et al., *J. Am. Chem. Soc.,* **73,** 3067 (1951); C. A. Nichol et al., *Science,* **121,** 275 (1955).

formyltetrahydroPGA from tetrahydroPGA (or PGA) and formate, formaldehyde, or the β-carbon of serine have been shown to occur in

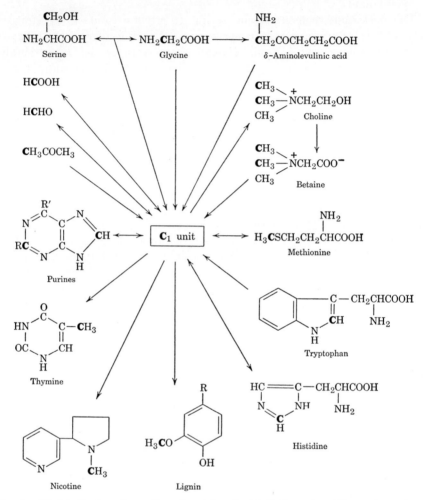

Fig. 2. Metabolic transformations involving "active" C_1 units. The carbon atoms shown in boldface type are formed from or converted to a metabolically active C_1 unit.

bacteria and in liver preparations.[17] Such formyl derivatives are probably directly involved in purine metabolism (Chapter 35) but not in the biosynthesis or degradation of serine; here the tetrahydroPGA

[17] S. F. Zakrzewski and C. A. Nichol, *J. Biol. Chem.*, **213**, 697 (1955); V. M. Doctor and J. Awapara, *ibid.*, **220**, 161 (1956); L. Jaenicke, *Biochim. et Biophys. Acta*, **17**, 588 (1955).

cofactor probably transfers a C_1 unit at the oxidation level of a hydroxymethyl group $(—CH_2OH)$.[10]

In addition to the cofactor derived from PGA, pyridoxal phosphate is also required in the enzymic interconversion of serine and glycine.[18] The reversible cleavage of serine to glycine and formaldehyde is catalyzed in nonenzymic systems by pyridoxal and metal ions; it has been sug-

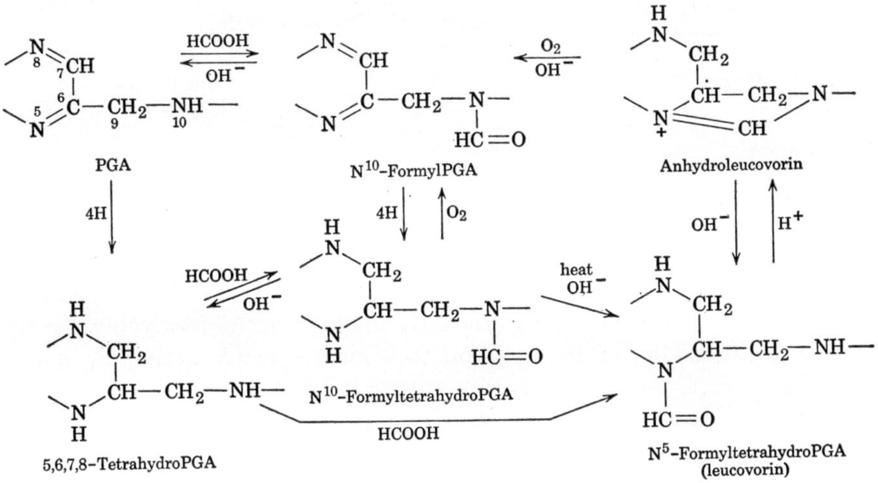

Fig. 3. Chemical interconversions of pteroylglutamic acid (PGA) and some of its derivatives. Only the part of the PGA molecule involved in the reactions is shown.

gested, therefore, that Schiff bases, composed of pyridoxal phosphate and glycine or serine (cf. p. 770), interact with a tetrahydroPGA cofactor in the enzymic transfer of C_1 units. The enzyme system that catalyzes this transfer has been termed "serine aldolase" or "serine hydroxymethylase." A postulated mechanism for the metabolic interrelation of serine, glycine, formaldehyde, and formate is shown in Fig. 4. As indicated in Fig. 4, the enzymic synthesis of serine from glycine and formate in the presence of PGA and pyridoxal phosphate requires DPNH (or TPNH). A reduced pyridine nucleotide is essential for the reduction of PGA to tetrahydroPGA and for the reduction of the formylated tetrahydroPGA to the corresponding hydroxymethyl derivative; hydroxymethyltetrahydroPGA also appears to be formed by the nonenzymic interaction of formaldehyde and tetrahydroPGA.[19]

It was mentioned before that formate may arise in animal tissues

[18] R. L. Blakley, *Biochem. J.*, **61**, 315 (1955).

[19] Y. Hatefi et al., *J. Biol. Chem.*, **227**, 637 (1957); R. L. Kisliuk, *ibid.*, **227**, 805 (1957); F. M. Huennekens et al., *Science*, **128**, 120 (1958).

from the α-carbon of glycine by the intermediate formation of glyoxylic acid (p. 772). An alternative pathway leading from the α-carbon of glycine to formate involves the intermediate formation of δ-amino-

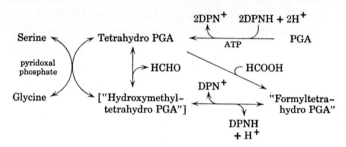

Fig. 4. Postulated mechanism of the synthesis and degradation of serine. The C_1 unit of the tetrahydroPGA derivatives is present at the N^5 or the N^{10} position.

levulinic acid, which may be used directly for porphyrin synthesis (Chapter 34), or may be metabolized via a "succinate-glycine" cycle with the conversion of its δ-carbon to a metabolically active C_1 unit[20] (Fig. 2).

Formate also is derived from the N-methyl groups of betaine[21] (Fig. 2), which is formed in animal tissues by the oxidation of choline (cf. p. 802). Apparently, betaine is initially demethylated to form N-dimethyl-glycine, which is oxidized by an enzyme system in liver to formaldehyde

$$\text{Betaine} \xrightarrow{[CH_3]} \underset{\text{Dimethylglycine}}{(CH_3)_2NCH_2COOH} \xrightarrow{HCHO \longrightarrow HCOOH \longleftarrow HCHO} \underset{\text{Sarcosine}}{CH_3NHCH_2COOH} \longrightarrow \text{Glycine}$$

and sarcosine (N-methylglycine); the N-methyl group of sarcosine is converted to formate through the action of another liver enzyme which cleaves sarcosine to glycine and formaldehyde. Presumably, the formaldehyde is oxidized to formate by liver formaldehyde dehydrogenase (p. 316). It should be added that the conversion of betaine and sarcosine to glycine had been demonstrated by *in vivo* isotope experiments, before the discovery of the oxidases mentioned above.[22]

It is of interest that rabbit kidney contains an enzyme system ("demethylase") that is inactive toward sarcosine, but acts on N-methyl derivatives of various L-amino acids to give formaldehyde and the free

[20] D. Shemin et al., *J. Biol. Chem.,* **215,** 613 (1955).

[21] C. G. Mackenzie et al., *J. Biol. Chem.,* **203,** 743 (1953); **222,** 145 (1956).

[22] K. Bloch and R. Schoenheimer, *J. Biol. Chem.,* **135,** 99 (1940); D. Stetten, Jr., *ibid.,* **140,** 143 (1941)

amino acid.[23] The catalytic action involves the participation of a flavoprotein, and it is believed that the dehydrogenation of the methyl-amino group is followed by hydrolysis of the resulting $CH_2{=}N-$ group.

In addition to the metabolic pathways of the biosynthesis of glycine discussed above, this amino acid is also formed in the breakdown of threonine (cf. p. 792) and of purines (cf. p. 895); these processes do not involve either a C_2 compound or serine as an obligatory intermediate.

Metabolic Transformations of Glycine. The carbon atoms of glycine are utilized for the synthesis of a number of tissue constituents; in many instances, serine appears to be an intermediate.[24] The ready deamination of serine to pyruvic acid (p. 756), and the known metabolic conversions of the keto acid explain the observed incorporation of glycine-carbon into other protein amino acids, into carbohydrates, and into fatty acids.

The formation of ethanolamine from glycine *in vivo* also involves the intermediate formation of serine, which is then decarboxylated.[25] It was noted before that ethanolamine is converted to glycine with the intermediate formation of glycolaldehyde, glycolic acid, and glyoxylic acid (cf. p. 772). Consequently, the over-all process shown in the accompanying scheme effects the oxidation of the carboxyl carbon of a glycine

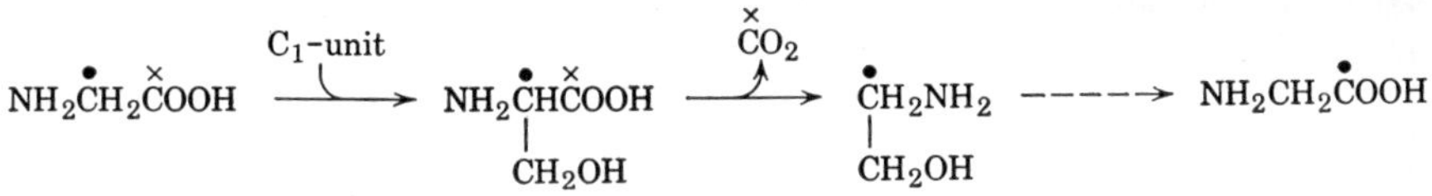

$$NH_2\overset{\bullet}{C}H_2\overset{x}{C}OOH \xrightarrow{\quad C_1\text{-unit}\quad} \underset{CH_2OH}{NH_2\overset{\bullet}{C}H\overset{x}{C}OOH} \xrightarrow{\quad \overset{x}{C}O_2\quad} \underset{CH_2OH}{\overset{\bullet}{C}H_2NH_2} \dashrightarrow NH_2CH_2\overset{\bullet}{C}OOH$$

molecule to CO_2, as well as the transformation of its α-carbon to the carboxyl carbon of the glycine molecule formed from ethanolamine. Repeated operation of this "glycine-ethanolamine" cycle thus results in the complete oxidation of glycine.

In animal tissues, glycine enters into many metabolic reactions that do not involve serine as an intermediate. These include the formation of hippuric acid (p. 719), glutathione (p. 721), creatine (p. 803), porphyrins (p. 864), purines (p. 890), and conjugated bile acids (p. 635).

In some anaerobic bacteria, glycine is converted to acetic acid. The direct reductive deamination of glycine by various *Clostridia* was discussed on p. 757. In *Diplococcus glycinophilus*, which can ferment glycine but does not attack other amino acids or a variety of non-nitrogenous compounds, isotopic glycine is metabolized anaerobically as shown on p. 778.[26] The inability of this organism to attack formic and

[23] M. Moritani et al., *J. Biol. Chem.*, **209**, 485 (1954).

[24] D. B. Sprinson, *J. Biol. Chem.*, **178**, 529 (1949); H. N. Barnet and A. N. Wick, *ibid.*, **185**, 657 (1950).

[25] D. Elwyn et al., *J. Biol. Chem.*, **213**, 281 (1955).

[26] H. A. Barker et al., *J. Biol. Chem.*, **173**, 803 (1948).

pyruvic acids makes it improbable that either acid is an intermediate in glycine fermentation. It appears likely that the glyoxylate cycle (p. 519) is involved, with the intermediate formation of a 4-carbon dicarboxylic

$$\overset{\bullet}{NH_2CH_2}\overset{\times}{COOH} \rightarrow NH_3 + \overset{\bullet}{CH_3}\overset{\bullet}{COOH} + \overset{\times}{CO_2}$$

acid labeled in the 2 centrally located carbon atoms. The metabolism of glycine by aerobic organisms (*Achromobacter, Pseudomonas*) appears to proceed via glyoxylic acid, which is converted to CO_2 and formic acid or formaldehyde.[27]

Metabolism of Alanine

Alanine may be omitted without deleterious effect from the diet of higher animals and from the culture media of most microorganisms. The fact that pyruvic acid is readily formed from carbohydrates and that the glutamic-alanine transaminase is very widely distributed in nature provides a simple explanation for the ability of most living organisms to dispense with an exogenous source of alanine. In some microorganisms, however, L-alanine dehydrogenase (p. 754) may serve as the principal catalyst for the direct synthesis of L-alanine from pyruvic acid and ammonia.

In view of the ease with which alanine may be converted to pyruvic acid (either by deamination or by transamination), the pathway by which alanine can give rise to carbohydrate is obvious. Furthermore, pyruvic acid is an intermediate between alanine and acetyl-CoA (cf. p. 508). The latter conversion has been studied by taking advantage of the fact that the rat acetylates compounds such as *p*-aminobenzoic acid and γ-phenyl-α-aminobutyric acid and excretes the N-acetyl derivatives in the urine.[28] Consequently, although alanine has usually been listed among the glucogenic amino acids (cf. p. 764), it is obvious that the α- and β-carbon atoms may also serve as precursors of fatty acids.

Many microorganisms use alanine, in place of carbohydrates, as a source of energy and of the carbon atoms required for growth and multiplication. In bacterial cultures alanine has been observed to undergo the various types of deamination reactions described in Chapter 31. The fermentation of DL-alanine by an anaerobic organism (*Clostridium propionicum*) may be described by the over-all equation:[29]

$$\overset{CH_3}{\underset{|}{3NH_2CHCOOH}} + 2H_2O \rightarrow$$
$$3NH_3 + 2CH_3CH_2COOH + CH_3COOH + CO_2$$

[27] L. L. Campbell, Jr., *J. Biol. Chem.*, **217**, 669 (1955).

[28] H. S. Anker, *J. Biol. Chem.*, **187**, 167 (1950).

[29] B. P. Cardon and H. A. Barker, *Arch. Biochem.*, **12**, 165 (1947).

This anaerobe also ferments DL-serine and DL-threonine (cf. p. 791) and lactic, pyruvic, and acrylic acids; it does not attack glucose. Of special interest is the fact that all the 3-carbon compounds mentioned give rise to propionic and acetic acids. Thus a portion of each substrate is oxidized to acetic acid with the liberation of carbon dioxide, while another portion is reduced to propionic acid.[30] Dried cells of *Cl. propionicum* (like higher animals and plants; cf. p. 601) metabolize propionic acid further; in the presence of ammonium salts, β-alanine is formed.[31] Since cell-free extracts form β-alanyl-CoA from ammonium ions and propionyl-CoA or acrylyl-CoA ($CH_2{=}CHCO\text{-}CoA$), it has been concluded that the latter two compounds are intermediates in the conversion of propionic acid to β-alanine. In higher animals, β-alanine arises primarily as a product of the degradation of pyrimidines (Chapter 35), but also may be formed from propionic acid (p. 781). It will be recalled that this amino acid is a constituent of coenzyme A (p. 206) and of the dipeptides carnosine and anserine (pp. 137, 824).

α-Alanine is one of the several amino acids whose D-isomer is found in nature, and alanine is unique in that, under certain conditions, an exogenous source of the D-form is essential for the growth of some bacteria. For example, *Streptococcus fecalis* R and *Lactobacillus casei*, which are reported to contain as much D-alanine as L-alanine, must be supplied with D-alanine if their culture media are devoid of vitamin B$_6$. As noted earlier (p. 769), these organisms contain a pyridoxal phosphate-dependent alanine racemase, and B$_6$-deficient cells lack the cofactor essential for the biosynthesis of the D-amino acid.[32] It is of interest that D-α-amino-n-butyric acid has some growth-promoting action for several D-alanine-requiring bacteria, and organisms grown in the presence of D-aminobutyric acid incorporate it in place of D-alanine. Normally, the bacteria contain D-alanine in amounts equal to 1 to 2 per cent of their dry weight. About 60 per cent of the bacterial D-alanine is present in the cell wall in the form of a polypeptide;[33] this is analogous to the presence of D-glutamic acid in the capsular polypeptide of the anthrax bacillus (p. 138).

Metabolism of Valine

L-Valine is classified among the indispensable amino acids for higher animals and is also an essential constituent of the culture media of a number of microorganisms. Isotope experiments have shown that the

[30] F. W. Leaver et al., *J. Bact.*, **70**, 521 (1955).

[31] E. R. Stadtman, *J. Am. Chem. Soc.*, **77**, 5765 (1955).

[32] J. T. Holden and E. E. Snell, *J. Biol. Chem.*, **178**, 799 (1949); J. Olivard and E. E. Snell, *ibid.*, **213**, 203 (1955).

[33] E. E. Snell et al., *J. Biol. Chem.*, **217**, 803 (1955).

carbon skeleton of D-valine also can be used for the biosynthesis of the L-amino acid, and D-valine can replace the L-isomer in rat growth tests.[34]

D-Valine is used by a variety of microorganisms in place of L-valine, although some bacteria are more exacting and grow only when the medium contains the L-form. The conversion of α-ketoisovaleric acid to valine, presumably as the result of a transamination reaction, also has been observed in microorganisms. Further discussion of the microbial synthesis of valine will be found in the section dealing with the metabolism of isoleucine (p. 782) since the biosynthesis of the two amino acids has much in common.

Several compounds have been identified among the products of the action of microorganisms on valine: isobutyric and formic acids (formed by *Proteus vulgaris*), isobutyl amine (produced by putrefactive bacteria), and isobutyl alcohol (produced by yeasts).[35] In those organisms that produce penicillin, L- or D-valine serves as a direct precursor of a portion of the carbon skeleton of the antibiotic (cf. p. 798).

Early studies on valine metabolism in higher animals (e.g., with phlorizinized dogs; p. 763) indicated that 3 of the 5 carbon atoms of D- or L-valine are used for glucose synthesis;[36] subsequent isotope experiments showed that these 3 carbons arise from the isopropyl group of the amino acid.[37] Further work with intact rats and with tissue preparations (liver, heart, kidney)[38] has provided evidence for the pathway of valine degradation shown in Fig. 5. The initial deamination of valine (probably by transamination) gives rise to α-ketoisovaleric acid, which then would be converted to isobutyryl-CoA by a process analogous to the conversion of pyruvic acid to acetyl-CoA (cf. p. 481). The dehydrogenation and hydration reactions are catalyzed by enzymes present in liver and heart extracts, and correspond to steps in the oxidation of straight-chain fatty acids (cf. p. 600). The β-hydroxyisobutyryl-CoA formed by hydration of methylacrylyl-CoA is readily hydrolyzed by a "deacylase," and free β-hydroxyisobutyric acid is oxidized by a DPN-dependent dehydrogenase to methylmalonic semialdehyde (α-formyl-propionic acid). It is thought that the semialdehyde is oxidized to yield methylmalonyl-CoA, and that this product is decarboxylated to

[34] J. White et al., *J. Biol. Chem.*, **199**, 505 (1952); A. Wretlind, *Acta Physiol. Scand.*, **36**, 119 (1956); M. Womack et al., *J. Biol. Chem.*, **224**, 793 (1957).

[35] M. Stephenson, *Bacterial Metabolism*, 3rd Ed., Longmans, Green and Co., London, 1949.

[36] W. C. Rose et al., *J. Biol. Chem.*, **145**, 679 (1942).

[37] W. S. Fones et al., *Arch. Biochem. and Biophys.*, **32**, 89 (1951); E. A. Peterson et al., *ibid.*, **36**, 323 (1952).

[38] D. S. Kinnory et al., *J. Biol. Chem.*, **212**, 385 (1955); W. G. Robinson et al., *ibid.*, **224**, 1; **225**, 511 (1957); G. Rendina and M. J. Coon, *ibid.*, **225**, 523 (1957).

propionyl-CoA, possibly by the reversal of the condensation reaction discussed on p. 602. Clearly, the formation of propionyl-CoA from the isopropyl group of valine provides a source of a recognized precursor of

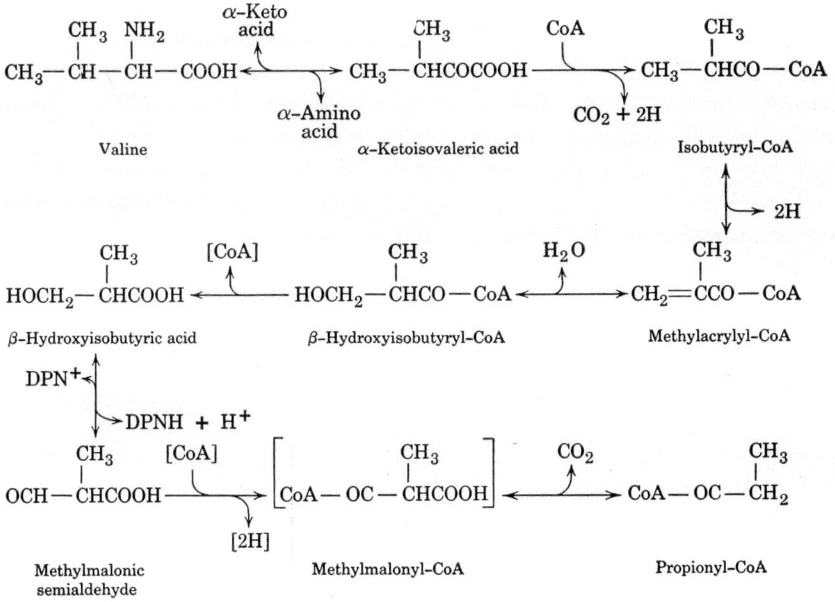

Fig. 5. Proposed pathway for the degradation of valine in animal tissues

glucose. It has been suggested[38] that propionyl-CoA also may be converted to malonic semialdehyde (cf. Fig. 5), which may be aminated to form β-alanine, thus providing an alternative pathway for the biosynthesis of this amino acid in higher animals.

Metabolism of Isoleucine

L-Isoleucine, like L-valine, is an indispensable amino acid for all higher animals, and the corresponding α-keto acid (d-α-keto-β-methylvaleric acid) can replace the amino acid in the diet of the growing rat. Although the diastereoisomers of D- and L-isoleucine (D- and L-alloisoleucine) are inactive in rat growth tests, l-α-keto-β-methylvaleric acid (the α-keto acid derived from D-isoleucine and from L-alloisoleucine) permits the slow growth of young rats on diets devoid of L-isoleucine.[39] This finding suggests that the animal organism is able to effect a change

[39] J. P. Greenstein et al., *J. Biol. Chem.*, **188**, 647 (1951); A. Meister and J. White, *ibid.*, **191**, 211 (1951).

in the configuration about the β-carbon atom of the l-keto acid in order to synthesize L-isoleucine. Apparently, certain bacteria are also able to perform such an inversion. For example, *Lactobacillus arabinosus* can grow in media containing L-alloisoleucine as a potential source of L-isoleucine if an exogenous source of vitamin B_6 is also supplied. Presumably, isoleucine and alloisoleucine are converted to α-keto acids which can tautomerize to form the same enol; the asymmetric synthesis of L-isoleucine would then proceed by the conversion of the enolic compound to d-α-keto-β-methylvaleric acid, and a transamination reaction between this keto acid and glutamic acid.[40] Enzyme preparations from *L. arabinosus* and from hog heart muscle catalyze these conversions,[41] which are summarized in the accompanying scheme.

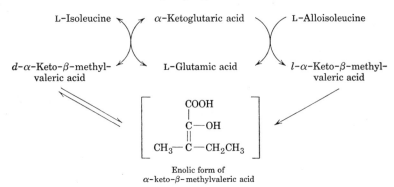

Important experiments on the biosynthesis of isoleucine and valine have been conducted with artificially induced mutant strains of the mold *Neurospora crassa* and of the bacterium *Escherichia coli*, which require for growth an exogenous supply of both isoleucine and valine. During growth in the presence of these amino acids, some of the "double" mutants accumulate α-keto-β-methylvaleric acid and α-keto-isovaleric acid. Such organisms appear to lack a "branched-chain amino acid transaminase" found in the normal (prototrophic) strains; this enzyme catalyzes transamination reactions between L-glutamic acid and the α-keto acids corresponding to L-isoleucine, L-valine, and L-leucine.[42] The mutants (auxotrophs) are therefore unable to form isoleucine and valine, although they can make leucine, since they contain a specific glutamic-leucine transaminase. Another type of "double" mutant accumulates the compounds α,β-dihydroxy-β-ethylbutyric acid (i.e., α,β-dihydroxy-β-methylvaleric acid) and α,β-dihydroxy-β-methylbutyric

[40] D. W. Hood and C. M. Lyman, *J. Biol. Chem.*, **186**, 195 (1950).

[41] A. Meister, *J. Biol. Chem.*, **195**, 813 (1952).

[42] D. Rudman and A. Meister, *J. Biol. Chem.*, **200**, 591 (1953); E. A. Adelberg and H. E. Umbarger, *ibid.*, **205**, 475 (1953).

acid, the dihydroxy analogues of isoleucine and valine, respectively. Mutants of this type are deficient in the enzyme "dihydroxy acid dehydrase" that catalyzes the conversion of the above dihydroxy acids to the corresponding α-keto acids[43] (see the accompanying scheme).

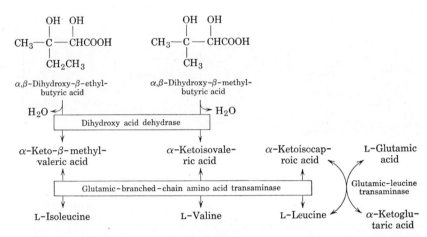

Isotope experiments on the formation of the dihydroxybutyric acids by the "double" mutant of *Neurospora* have provided information about the mode of synthesis of these substances,[44] and similar studies with other microorganisms[45] (yeasts, *E. coli*) have shown that the carbon skeletons of isoleucine and of valine are made by similar pathways in all these biological forms (Fig. 6). All the carbon atoms of valine are derived by a fairly direct route from pyruvic acid. On the other hand, only 2 carbon atoms of isoleucine come directly from pyruvic acid, the remainder of the isoleucine skeleton being derived from α-ketobutyric acid, which is formed from threonine (cf. p. 791). In this connection, it is of interest that threonine appears to be an obligatory intermediate in the synthesis of isoleucine by some microorganisms.

As shown in Fig. 6, the observed distribution of isotopic carbon in valine and isoleucine appears to result from the ketol condensation of an "active acetaldehyde" and the appropriate α-keto acid to form an "acetolactic acid," followed by an intramolecular rearrangement whereby the RCH_2— group migrates from the α-carbon of lactic acid to the carbonyl carbon of the acetyl group.[45]

Since many microorganisms, as well as higher animals, exhibit a

[43] J. W. Meyers and E. A. Adelberg, *Proc. Natl. Acad. Sci.*, **40**, 493 (1954).

[44] E. A. Adelberg, *J. Am. Chem. Soc.*, **76**, 4241 (1954); *J. Biol. Chem.*, **216**, 431 (1956); R. P. Wagner et al., *Proc. Natl. Acad. Sci.*, **44**, 1047 (1958).

[45] M. Strassman et al., *J. Am. Chem. Soc.*, **77**, 1261 (1955); **78**, 228 (1956); H. E. Umbarger and B. Brown, *J. Biol. Chem.*, **233**, 1156 (1958).

requirement for L-isoleucine, L-leucine, and L-valine and, in most instances, can satisfy this requirement with the corresponding α-keto acids,
it is evident that the biosynthesis of the branched chains which characterize the carbon skeletons of all three amino acids presents difficulties
to many forms of living matter. In organisms able to synthesize the

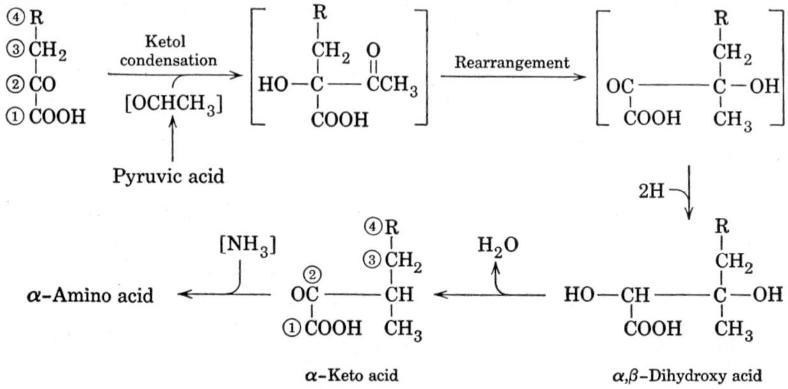

Fig. 6. Postulated mechanism for the formation of isoleucine (R = CH₃) and of
valine (R = H) in microorganisms. The fate of the carbon atoms supplied in
RCH₂COCOOH is indicated by the circled numerals.

branched-chain amino acids, identical intermediates and the same
enzyme systems are used in some steps in the formation of all three
amino acids. For example, an organism that cannot make α-ketoiso-
valeric acid would be unable to synthesize not only valine but also leucine
(cf. p. 786), and an organism lacking dihydroxy acid dehydrase would
be unable to form valine and isoleucine. The normal growth and metabolism of several microbial species depends, therefore, on the maintenance
of a delicate balance in the amounts of branched-chain compounds to
which they are exposed.[46]

In higher animals, isoleucine is weakly ketogenic and also shows slight
glucogenic properties. This metabolic behavior may be explained by the
sequence of reactions leading from isoleucine to propionyl-CoA and
acetyl-CoA, shown in Fig. 7. The origin of the carbon atoms of propionate and of acetate has been determined by supplying C^{14}-labeled
α-methylbutyric acid to rat liver slices,[47] and the individual enzyme
systems that catalyze the degradative reactions have been found in rat

[46] H. E. Umbarger and B. Brown, *J. Bact.*, **70**, 241 (1955).

[47] M. J. Coon and N. S. B. Abrahamsen, *J. Biol. Chem.*, **195**, 805 (1952); M. J.
Coon et al., *ibid.*, **199**, 75 (1952).

liver and in pig heart.[48] It will be seen from Fig. 7 that the steps by which α-methyl-β-hydroxybutyryl-CoA is formed are similar to the initial reactions in the degradation of valine (p. 781) and of leucine (p. 788). The further oxidation of α-methyl-β-hydroxybutyryl-CoA is analogous

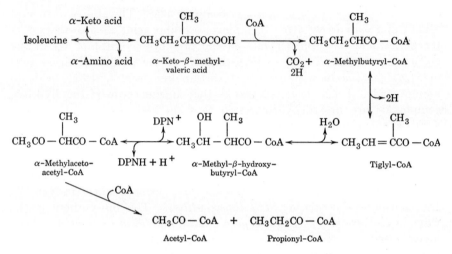

Fig. 7. Degradation of isoleucine in animal tissues.

to the corresponding reactions in the oxidation of straight-chain fatty acids (cf. p. 600). Isoleucine appears to be the only branched-chain amino acid whose carbon skeleton can be oxidized via the "fatty acid cycle."

Metabolism of Leucine

L-Leucine, like L-valine and L-isoleucine, is an essential constituent of the diet of higher animals and of the culture media of a number of microorganisms. The young rat can use α-ketoisocaproic acid in place of L-leucine, and therefore must be able to aminate the keto acid at a rate commensurate with the demands of normal growth. Proof of the conversion *in vivo* of the D- to the L-form was obtained by the isolation of deuteroleucine from the proteins of rats fed D-leucine containing deuterium bound to the β-, γ-, and methyl carbon atoms. The D-leucine used in this experiment contained N[15], as well as deuterium, and the leucine isolated from the tissue proteins also contained some N[15]. Since the D/N[15] ratio in the protein leucine was much higher than the ratio in the D-leucine fed, the conversion of the D- to the L-form must have

[48] W. G. Robinson et al., *J. Biol. Chem.*, **218**, 391 (1956).

involved cleavage of the bond between the amino-N and the α-carbon atom.[49]

Among microorganisms the requirement for leucine may be a completely specific one for the L-amino acid or it may be so unspecific that the organism will grow if supplied with either the L- or the D-isomer, α-ketoisocaproic acid, or α-hydroxyisocaproic acid. The ability of several α-keto and α-hydroxy acids to replace α-amino acids as growth factors for lactic acid bacteria depends on the presence of vitamin B_6 in the culture medium.[50] From an investigation of the ability of dried cells of *Streptococcus fecalis* to convert certain keto and hydroxy acids to amino acids, it has been suggested that during growth the hydroxy compounds are first dehydrogenated to yield keto acids, and these in turn are converted to amino acids by a transamination reaction in which pyridoxal phosphate is an indispensable cofactor and glutamic acid may serve as the amino group donor (cf. p. 762).

The biosynthesis of leucine from labeled precursors (C^{14}-labeled acetate, lactate, pyruvate, or glucose) has been studied in yeasts[51] (*Saccharomyces cerevisiae, Torulopsis utilis*). The biosynthetic pathways in *Escherichia coli, Neurospora crassa,* and *T. utilis* have also been investigated by means of a less direct procedure, the "isotope-competition" technique;[52] here, the ability of an unlabeled compound to decrease the extent of the normal incorporation of C^{14} supplied as glucose (or CO_2) into leucine is taken as evidence that the compound is an intermediate in the pathway leading from glucose (or CO_2) to the amino acid. The data obtained by the direct and indirect methods are concordant, and they indicate that before glucose or acetate is utilized for the formation of leucine, the precursor is converted to pyruvate. Of the 6 carbon atoms in leucine, only the carboxyl and α-carbons arise directly from the carbon atoms of pyruvate; the remainder of the leucine skeleton is probably derived from the isobutyl group of α-ketoisovaleric acid, which also provides the entire carbon chain of valine (cf. p. 783). The postulated mechanism for the formation of α-ketoisocaproic acid from pyruvic acid and α-ketoisovaleric acid (Fig. 8) may involve a series of reactions analogous to those of the citric acid cycle by which α-ketoglutaric acid is formed from pyruvic acid and oxaloacetic acid (cf. p. 508). Further studies are needed to define the enzymic reactions involved in the synthesis of α-ketoisocaproic acid.

[49] S. Ratner et al., *J. Biol. Chem.,* **134,** 653 (1940).

[50] J. T. Holden et al., *J. Biol. Chem.,* **191,** 559 (1951).

[51] O. Reiss and K. Bloch, *J. Biol. Chem.,* **216,** 703 (1955); M. Strassman et al., *J. Am. Chem. Soc.,* **78,** 1599 (1956).

[52] P. H. Abelson, *J. Biol. Chem.,* **206,** 335 (1954); P. H. Abelson and H. J. Vogel, *ibid.,* **213,** 355 (1955).

Little is known about the breakdown of leucine in microorganisms. Among the compounds that have been reported to be products of the catabolism of leucine are: α-ketoisocaproic acid (*Proteus vulgaris*), α-hydroxyisocaproic acid (*Clostridium acetobutylicum*), isoamyl amine (yeasts), and β-methylbutyl alcohol (yeasts).[35]

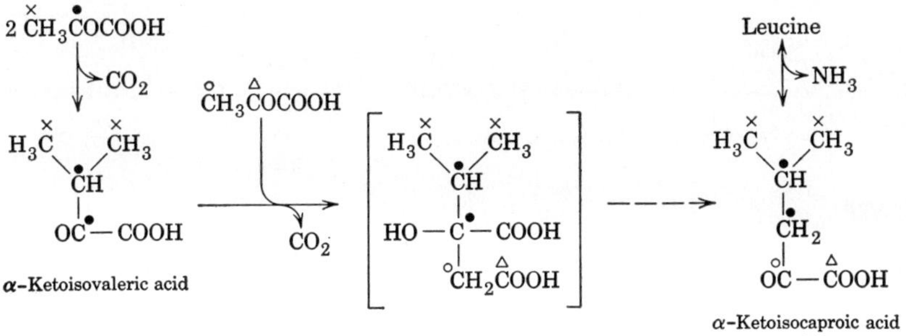

Fig. 8. Postulated mechanism for the biosynthesis of leucine in microorganisms, showing the utilization of carbon atoms of pyruvic acid for the formation of α-ketoisocaproic acid. For the formation of α-ketoisovaleric acid from pyruvic acid, see p. 784.

The pathway of leucine catabolism in animal tissues is now fairly completely established. Leucine has long been known as one of the most strongly ketogenic amino acids; in liver slices the oxidation of 1 mole of leucine produces approximately 1.5 moles of ketone bodies (cf. p. 592). The current views concerning the mechanism of the formation of acetoacetic acid from leucine in animal tissues (liver, kidney, heart muscle) are summarized in Fig. 9. Experiments with intact rats and with liver slices given labeled leucine or isovaleric acid established the fate of each of the carbon atoms of these compounds.[53] For example, the isopropyl group of leucine is converted as a unit to the α-, β-, and γ-carbon atoms of acetoacetic acid, with the addition of CO_2 carbon, which provides the carboxyl carbon of acetoacetic acid. The α- and β-carbon atoms of leucine are converted to an acetyl group before they are incorporated into acetoacetic acid. As shown in Fig. 9, the reactions leading to the production of β-hydroxyisovaleryl-CoA are the same as those in the degradation of valine to β-hydroxyisobutyryl-CoA (cf. p. 781) and of isoleucine to α-methyl-β-hydroxybutyryl-CoA (cf. p. 785). The further breakdown of β-hydroxyisovaleryl-CoA depends upon its carboxylation to yield β-hydroxy-β-methylglutaryl-CoA; this is a reversible two-step process in which CO_2 is first "activated" in an enzyme-catalyzed reaction

[53] M. J. Coon and S. Gurin, *J. Biol. Chem.*, **180**, 1159 (1949); M. J. Coon, *ibid.*, **187**, 71 (1950); R. O. Brady and S. Gurin, *ibid.*, **189**, 371 (1951).

with ATP, and the "active CO_2" (possibly adenosine-5'-phosphoryl carbonate) participates in a second enzyme-catalyzed reaction with the formation of the glutaric acid derivative and AMP.[54] β-Hydroxy-β-methylglutaryl-CoA is cleaved directly to acetoacetic acid and acetyl-CoA, 2 molecules of which can give rise to an additional molecule of acetoacetic acid.

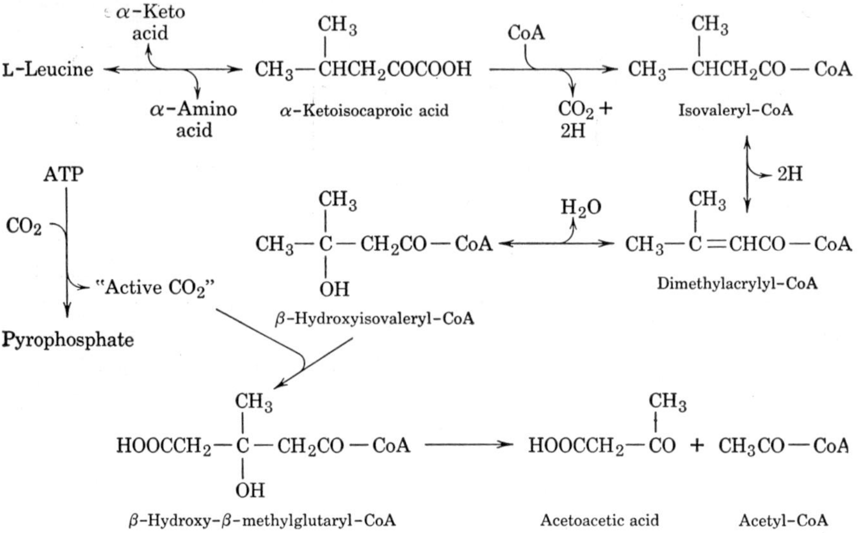

Fig. 9. Degradation of leucine in animal tissues.

Although enzyme studies have shown that acetoacetic acid and acetyl-CoA are formed from isovaleryl-CoA, in the whole animal these products of the breakdown of leucine are metabolized together with the ketone bodies and acetyl-CoA formed from fat or any other source. For example, the formation *in vivo* of C_2 units for the acetylation of amines and for the formation of fatty acids from the isopropyl carbons of isovaleric acid was found to be completely analogous to the formation of those compounds from acetone or acetic acid. However, the metabolism of this isopropyl group in the intact rat has one unique feature: the methyl carbons are used for cholesterol synthesis approximately five times as efficiently as is acetic acid (cf. p. 627). This phenomenon probably reflects the relative ease with which dietary isovaleric acid is converted to compounds that are efficient precursors of the isoprene unit of cholesterol; presumably, the formation of these compounds from dietary acetic acid occurs at a much slower rate.

[54] B. K. Bachhawat et al., *J. Biol. Chem.*, **216**, 727 (1955); **219**, 539 (1956); B. K. Bachhawat and M. J. Coon, *ibid.*, **231**, 625 (1958).

Metabolism of Serine

Like higher animals, most microorganisms can synthesize serine readily. As noted earlier (p. 773), the major pathway by which serine is formed in higher animals involves the utilization of a 3-carbon precursor that can be derived from carbohydrates or fats. Thus the administration of glucose-1-C^{14} to rats leads to the biosynthesis of serine labeled mainly in the β-carbon atom. Although pyruvate-3-C^{14} would also arise from glucose-1-C^{14}, its administration gives rise to serine labeled equally in the α- and β-carbons.[9,55] Hence pyruvic acid is not a direct precursor of serine *in vivo*, and, before pyruvate carbon is utilized for serine synthesis, it must undergo reactions whereby its α- and β-carbons are "randomized."

A possible pathway for the formation of serine in animal tissues is suggested by the finding of a transaminase that catalyzes the transfer of an amino group from L-alanine to hydroxypyruvic acid.[56] According to

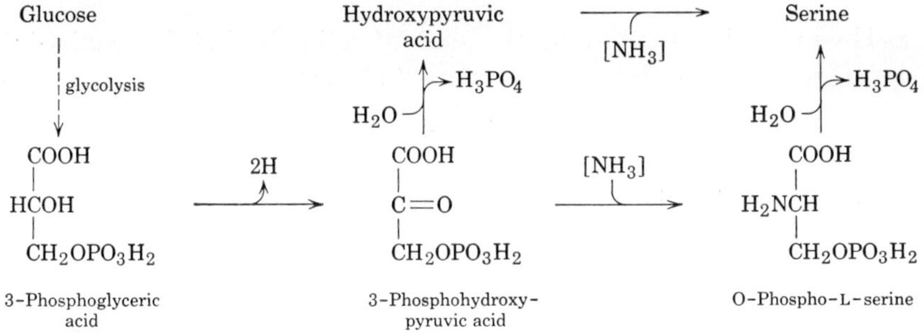

the hypothesis first proposed by Sallach, hydroxypyruvic acid (or phosphohydroxypyruvic acid) is an immediate precursor of serine (or phosphoserine), and is formed from glucose via 3-phosphoglyceric acid (p. 471). Support for this possibility has come from the demonstration that an extract of rat liver can effect the synthesis of serine from glucose, 3-phosphoglyceric acid, hydroxypyruvic acid, or 3-phosphohydroxypyruvic acid.[57] The formation of phosphoserine, either by the reactions shown in the accompanying scheme or by some other enzymic mechanism, is an important metabolic process, since much of the serine in phosphoproteins appears to be present in the form of O-phosphoserine, and since phosphatidylserine (p. 568) is a common constituent of the phospholipids.

The interconversion of serine and glycine, and the conversion of serine

[55] J. F. Nyc and I. Zabin, *J. Biol. Chem.,* **215,** 35 (1955).

[56] H. J. Sallach, *J. Biol. Chem.,* **223,** 1101 (1956).

[57] A. Ichihara and D. M. Greenberg, *J. Biol. Chem.,* **224,** 331 (1957); C. E. Ballou and R. Hesse, *J. Am. Chem. Soc.,* **78,** 3718 (1956).

to ethanolamine, have already been discussed earlier in this chapter. The metabolism of serine is also linked to that of cystine and of tryptophan, as will be seen from the later discussion of the metabolism of these two amino acids.

The production of pyruvic acid by the action of serine dehydrase (cf. p. 756) explains the glycogenic action of serine. Obviously, if serine gives rise, *in vivo*, to pyruvic acid, the α- and β-carbon atoms of the amino acid can also be considered a source of C_2 units and thus of fatty acids and cholesterol. As noted earlier (p. 779), propionic acid and acetic acid are produced in the fermentation of serine by *Clostridium propionicum*. The fact that the same fatty acids are produced from alanine and from pyruvic and lactic acids points to the existence of a close relationship in the bacterial metabolism of all the α-substituted 3-carbon compounds. In higher animals there is a similar convergence of metabolic pathways.

Metabolism of Threonine

L-Threonine is essential in the diet of animals, but is required by only a few microorganisms. From studies with mutant strains of *Neurospora crassa*,[58] it was recognized that homoserine (α-amino-

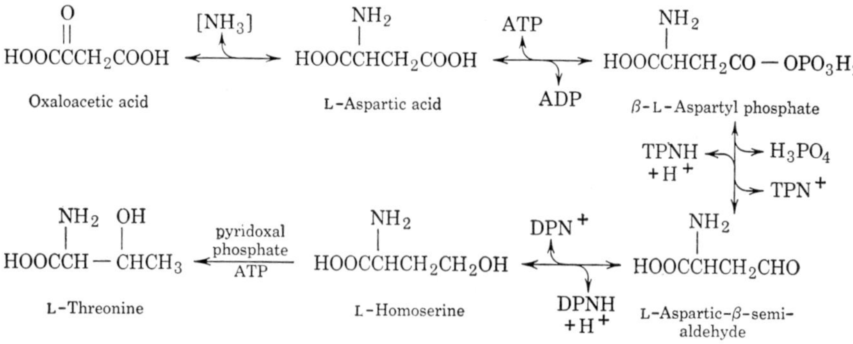

Fig. 10. Microbial synthesis of threonine from oxaloacetic acid.

γ-hydroxybutyric acid) is an important precursor of threonine. Application of the direct labeling and the isotope-competition techniques (p. 786) provided evidence for a biosynthetic pathway in *Neurospora* and other organisms whereby the carbon skeleton of oxaloacetic acid is used, via aspartic acid, for the formation of homoserine and threonine[52] (Fig. 10). Enzymes that catalyze the phosphorylation of aspartic acid by

[58] S. Emerson, *Cold Spring Harbor Symposia Quant. Biol.*, **14**, 40 (1949)

ATP ("β-aspartokinase"), the reduction of aspartyl phosphate ("aspartic semialdehyde dehydrogenase"), and the reduction of aspartic semialdehyde to homoserine ("homoserine dehydrogenase") have been obtained in partially purified form from yeast.[59] The conversion of homoserine to threonine has been demonstrated with extracts of *Escherichia coli* and of yeast,[60] and requires the presence of pyridoxal phosphate and of ATP; the process is believed to involve the initial conversion of homoserine to a phosphate-containing intermediate from which threonine is formed.

Threonine is a precursor of the α-ketobutyric acid used in the microbial biosynthesis of isoleucine (cf. p. 783). In this connection, it may be added that *E. coli* contains not only dehydrases (cf. p. 756) for L-threonine and D-threonine, but also a threonine racemase.[61] In this organism, therefore, α-ketobutyric acid can arise from D-threonine either by direct dehydration (and deamination) or by racemization of the D-amino acid, followed by dehydration.

Just as threonine is the next higher homolog of serine, so the fatty acids formed by the fermentation of threonine by several anaerobic bacteria are the next higher homologs of the acids formed from serine.[29,62] The fermentations by *Clostridium propionicum* are shown in the accompanying equations. The carbon chain of butyric acid arises directly

$$3 \text{ Serine} + H_2O \rightarrow 3 \text{ NH}_3 + \text{propionic acid} + 2 \text{ acetic acid} + 2 \text{ CO}_2$$

$$3 \text{ Threonine} + H_2O \rightarrow 3 \text{ NH}_3 + \text{butyric acid} + 2 \text{ propionic acid} + 2 \text{ CO}_2$$

from that of threonine;[63] unlike the formation of butyric acid by other *Clostridia,* this process does not appear to involve the intermediate formation of C_2 units (cf. p. 608).

In some respects, the metabolic fate of the two hydroxy amino acids is also similar in higher animals. As noted previously (p. 756), the deamination of threonine follows a pathway like that of serine. However, the deamination of threonine *in vivo* apparently is irreversible, since the carbon and nitrogen of protein threonine are derived solely from dietary threonine.[64] Except for lysine, threonine is the only amino acid known to be unable to derive its nitrogen from other amino acids.

In higher animals, threonine (like serine) can be degraded by rupture

[59] S. Black and N. G. Wright, *J. Biol. Chem.,* **213**, 27, 39, 51 (1955).

[60] Y. Watanabe et al., *J. Biochem.* (*Japan*), **42**, 837 (1955); **43**, 283 (1956).

[61] H. E. Umbarger and B. Brown, *J. Bact.,* **71**, 443 (1956); **73**, 105 (1957); H. Amos, *J. Am. Chem. Soc.,* **76**, 3858 (1954).

[62] D. Lewis and S. R. Elsden, *Biochem. J.,* **60**, 683 (1955).

[63] H. A. Barker and T. Wiken, *Arch. Biochem.,* **17**, 149 (1948).

[64] D. F. Elliott and A. Neuberger, *Biochem. J.,* **46**, 207 (1950); H. L. Meltzer and D. B. Sprinson, *J. Biol. Chem.,* **197**, 461 (1952).

of the bond between the α- and β-carbon atoms to yield glycine; the C_2 unit arising from the β- and γ-carbon atoms is convertible *in vivo* to acetate, higher fatty acids, and cholesterol. Different liver enzymes are involved in the formation of glycine from L-threonine and from L-serine.[65] The enzyme which acts on L-threonine (threonine aldolase) catalyzes the formation of glycine and acetaldehyde. Some microorganisms also convert threonine to glycine, but the mechanism of this process is not known.

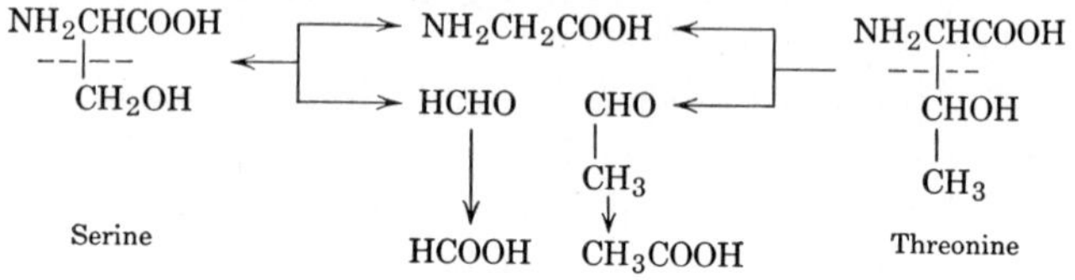

Clearly, the cleavage of threonine to yield glycine permits the metabolic utilization of threonine as a precursor of serine, and hence of carbohydrate. Another mechanism for the utilization of threonine carbon for carbohydrate synthesis involves the dehydration of threonine to α-ketobutyric acid, which is decarboxylated to yield propionic acid (cf. p. 794).

Metabolism of the Sulfur Amino Acids [66,67]

The close interrelationships in the metabolism of the sulfur-containing amino acids (methionine, cystine, and cysteine) make it desirable to discuss these amino acids together. Furthermore, although both cystine and cysteine residues are present in proteins (p. 57), the reversible interconversion of cystine and cysteine is readily accomplished by most organisms, and the two compounds may be considered as a single amino acid in metabolism.

Methionine is an indispensable amino acid for all animals that have been investigated; on the other hand, cystine and cysteine are dispensable. Either L- or D-methionine will satisfy the dietary requirement, and the amino acid may be replaced by the corresponding α-keto acid. In general, both D- and L-methionine have activity as growth factors for those microorganisms known to require the amino acid. It is, however, quite common for an organism to require cystine rather than methionine; here either cystine or cysteine can be used.

Metabolic Relationships between Methionine and Cystine. Since a large part of the dietary requirement of animals for methionine can be

---

[65] S. C. Lin and D. M. Greenberg, *J. Gen. Physiol.,* **38,** 181 (1954); M. A. Karasek and D. M. Greenberg, *J. Biol. Chem.,* **227,** 191 (1957).

[66] V. du Vigneaud, *Harvey Lectures,* **38,** 39 (1943); *A Trail of Research,* Cornell University Press, Ithaca, 1952.

[67] C. Fromageot, *Harvey Lectures,* **49,** 1 (1955).

met by cystine (or cysteine),[68] it was suggested early in the study of the metabolism of the sulfur amino acids that the sulfur of methionine is used in the biosynthesis of cystine; this was proved by the administration (to the rat, dog, and human) of S^{35}-methionine and the isolation of labeled cystine from the test animal. The first step in the conversion of methionine to cystine involves the reversible demethylation of methionine to produce homocysteine (α-amino-γ-thiolbutyric acid). Like L-cystine, both D- and L-homocystine (and homocysteine) exert a sparing action on the dietary requirement of the growing rat for methionine, and they also can completely replace the dietary methionine if the diet is supplemented by appropriate vitamins (cf. p. 807).

The production of cysteine by slices or homogenates of rat liver in the presence of methionine or of homocysteine involves the participation of serine, and as an intermediate there is formed the thioether L-cystathionine, S-(β-amino-β-carboxyethyl)-L-homocysteine (Fig. 11). Cystathionine is also formed from methionine in the intact rat.[69] However, since L-cystathionine replaces cystine but not methionine in the diet of the growing rat, it can be cleaved *in vivo* to form cysteine but not homocysteine.[70] Extracts of rat liver form L-cystathionine from L-homo-

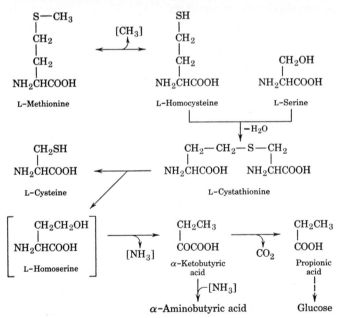

Fig. 11. Metabolic conversion of methionine in higher animals.

[68] W. C. Rose et al., *J. Biol. Chem.*, **215**, 101; **216**, 763 (1955).
[69] M. Tabachnick and H. Tarver, *Arch. Biochem. and Biophys.*, **56**, 115 (1955).
[70] J. R. Rachele et al., *J. Biol. Chem.*, **185**, 817 (1950).

cysteine and L-serine, and cleave the thioether to produce L-cysteine (cf. Fig. 11); pyridoxal phosphate is required for both the enzymic synthesis and cleavage.[71]

There is some uncertainty about the nature of the other product formed from cystathionine. α-Ketobutyric acid has been isolated after incubation of cystathionine with crystalline "cystathionase" (from rat liver). This α-keto acid could arise by deamination of homoserine formed by a hydrolytic cleavage of cystathionine; the enzyme preparation used in these experiments has been shown to produce α-ketobutyric acid from L-homoserine.[72] α-Ketobutyric acid can be aminated to yield α-aminobutyric acid which, like α-ketobutyric acid and homoserine, is a known product of methionine metabolism in higher animals.[73] It should be added that carbon atoms 2, 3 and 4 of methionine and of homoserine are converted as a unit to carbon atoms 1, 2, and 3 of propionic acid, and can be used for the biosynthesis of glucose.[74]

The scheme shown in Fig. 11 represents the major pathway of cysteine synthesis in higher animals, and is essentially an irreversible process.[75] In contrast to the rat, several microorganisms apparently synthesize methionine from cystine; the process by which this synthesis is accomplished is essentially a reversal of the pathway from methionine to cystine in animals. Four types of mutants of *Neurospora crassa* have been classified as sulfur amino acid mutants; each type appears to be unable to perform one of the reactions indicated by the letters *a*, *b*, *c*, and *d* in the biosynthetic pathway shown. The mutant blocked at *b* produces relatively large amounts of L-cystathionine from the sucrose

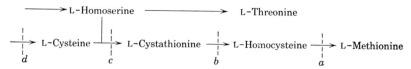

carbon and ammonia nitrogen of the medium, whereas the mutant blocked at *c* synthesizes abnormally large amounts of threonine and of an amino acid that is presumed from its biological activity and chromatographic behavior to be homoserine.[76] L-Homoserine is present in green plants,[77] but its metabolic origin is not known.

[71] F. Binkley et al., *J. Biol. Chem.*, **194**, 109 (1952); D. E. Metzler et al., *J. Am. Chem. Soc.*, **76**, 648 (1954).

[72] Y. Matsuo and D. M. Greenberg, *J. Biol. Chem.*, **230**, 545, 561 (1958).

[73] Y. Matsuo and D. M. Greenberg, *J. Biol. Chem.*, **215**, 547 (1955); **221**, 679 (1956).

[74] R. L. Kisliuk et al., *J. Biol. Chem.*, **221**, 885 (1956).

[75] H. R. V. Arnstein and J. C. Crawhall, *Biochem. J.*, **55**, 280 (1953).

[76] M. Fling and N. H. Horowitz, *J. Biol. Chem.*, **190**, 277 (1951).

[77] A. M. Berg et al., *Acta Chem. Scand.* **8**, 358 (1954).

It has been assumed that *Neurospora* can convert methionine to cystine since no mutant has been found to exhibit a specific requirement for cystine; thus strains that respond to cystine also respond to methionine, homocysteine, or cystathionine. This conclusion does not apply to all microorganisms, however. For example, strains of *Escherichia coli* that make methionine from cystine cannot synthesize, from methionine, all the cystine they require for growth.[78] It is of interest that extracts of *E. coli* convert cystathionine to homocysteine, pyruvic acid, and ammonia by a process that does not appear to involve serine as an intermediate.

The lower homolog of methionine, S-methylcysteine, can arise from serine and methyl mercaptan (CH_3SH) in the presence of an enzyme preparation from yeast.[79] It is probable that the S-methyl-L-cysteine sulfoxide (p. 60) found in plants is formed by oxidation of S-methyl-L-cysteine.

End Products of Metabolism of Sulfur Amino Acids. In normal animals the sulfur of methionine and cystine is excreted mainly as inorganic sulfate, although α-keto-γ-methylthiobutyric acid (the keto acid derived from methionine) and methionine sulfoxide have also been detected as urinary constituents. In addition, approximately 10 per cent of the urinary sulfur is in the form of esters of sulfuric acid (e.g., phenolsulfuric acid). These derivatives ("ethereal sulfates") are formed in the liver

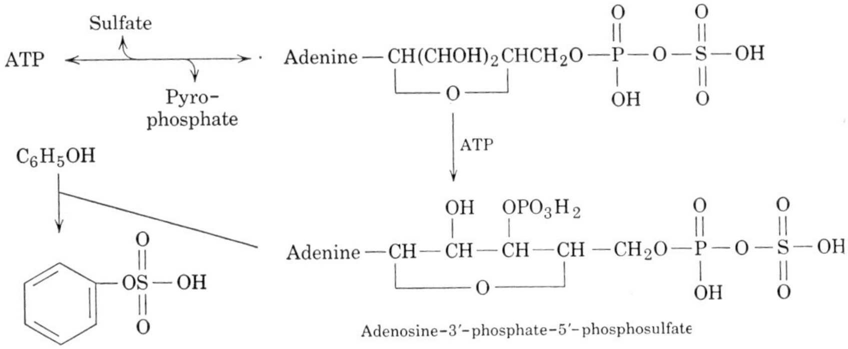

Adenosine-3'-phosphate-5'-phosphosulfate

Phenolsulfuric acid

by conjugation with sulfate of aromatic hydroxy compounds, produced in large part by the bacterial degradation of aromatic amino acids in the intestinal tract (cf. pp. 832, 844). The conjugation involves the initial "activation" of inorganic sulfate, in an enzymic reaction with ATP, and the resulting "active sulfate" (probably the mixed anhydride

[78] S. Simmonds, *J. Biol. Chem.*, **174**, 717 (1948); D. B. Cowie et al., *J. Bact.*, **60**, 233 (1950)

[79] E. C. Wolff et al., *J. Am. Chem. Soc.*, **78**, 5958 (1956).

adenosine-3′-phosphate-5′-phosphosulfate[80]) reacts with the phenol in the presence of a second enzyme.[81] Among the ethereal sulfates are derivatives of hydroxylated steroid hormones (p. 646). Adenosine-3′-phosphate-5′-phosphosulfate may also be a participant in the sulfation reactions that occur in the formation of chondroitin sulfate (p. 424) by chick embryo cartilage.[82]

Animal tissues and some microorganisms (e.g., *Aspergillus*) contain sulfatases[83] which catalyze the hydrolysis of aryl sulfates such as phenolsulfuric acid; marine mollusks are especially rich in these enzymes, and also contain a sulfatase specific for steroid sulfates.

Urine usually contains small amounts of thiosulfate; this substance is formed by enzymes (present in liver and kidney[84]) in a reaction between β-mercaptopyruvic acid and inorganic sulfite, both of which arise from the

$$HSCH_2COCOOH + SO_3{}^{2-} \rightarrow CH_3COCOOH + S_2O_3{}^{2-}$$

metabolism of L-cysteine. The enzyme rhodanese, which has been crystallized from beef liver,[85] catalyzes the "detoxication" reaction between thiosulfate (or organic thiosulfonates) and cyanide, which is converted to thiocyanate:

$$S_2O_3{}^{2-} + CN^- \rightarrow SO_3{}^{2-} + SCN^-$$

In higher animals, the formation of inorganic sulfate from organic sulfur compounds probably occurs by the oxidation of the cysteine-sulfur prior to cleavage of the C—S bond of the amino acid. The existence of this pathway, which was suggested by Pirie in 1934, has been demonstrated in experiments with intact animals given S^{35}-labeled compounds and with the enzyme systems involved.[67,86] As shown in Fig. 12, cysteine is oxidized in the liver to cysteine sulfinic acid, an amino acid first detected as a constituent of brain tissue. The mechanism whereby this oxidation is effected is unclear, but cysteine sulfinic acid is known to be converted to β-sulfinyl pyruvic acid, which is cleaved to pyruvic acid

[80] P. W. Robbins and F. Lipmann, *J. Biol. Chem.*, **229**, 837 (1957); **233**, 681, 686 (1958); F. Lipmann, *Science*, **128**, 575 (1958).

[81] R. H. DeMeio et al., *J. Biol. Chem.*, **213**, 439 (1955); *Biochim. et Biophys. Acta*, **20**, 428 (1956).

[82] F. D'Abramo and F. Lipmann, *Biochim. et Biophys. Acta*, **25**, 211 (1957).

[83] C. Fromageot, in J. B. Sumner and K. Myrbäck, *The Enzymes*, Vol. I, Chapter 13, Academic Press, New York, 1950; K. S. Dodgson et al., *Biochem. J.*, **65**, 131, 668; **66**, 357 (1957); K. S. Dodgson and B. Spencer, *Ann. Reps.*, **53**, 318 (1957).

[84] B. Sörbo, *Biochim. et Biophys. Acta*, **21**, 393 (1956); **24**, 324 (1957).

[85] B. Sörbo, *Acta Chem. Scand.*, **7**, 1129, 1137 (1953); **8**, 694 (1954).

[86] J. Awapara and W. J. Wingo, *J. Biol. Chem.*, **203**, 189 (1953); T. P. Singer and E. B. Kearney, *Arch. Biochem. and Biophys.*, **61**, 397 (1956).

and sulfite. The oxidation of inorganic sulfite to sulfate is catalyzed by a liver enzyme (sulfite oxidase) which appears to require lipoic acid and hypoxanthine as essential cofactors.[87] Although it has been reported that the sequence of reactions by which sulfite is produced from cysteine is

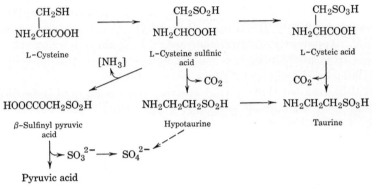

Fig. 12. Catabolism of cysteine in higher animals.

reversible,[88] it is doubtful whether significant amounts of cysteine are formed *in vivo* by such a pathway.

The scheme in Fig. 12 also indicates the routes leading from cysteine to taurine, which occurs in the free state in invertebrates and is a constituent of the taurocholic acids in the bile of mammals (p. 635). The major metabolic pathway of taurine formation appears to involve the enzymic decarboxylation of cysteine sulfinic acid (cf. p. 767) to yield hypotaurine, which is oxidized to taurine; inorganic sulfate also is formed from hypotaurine.[89] The conversion of cysteine sulfinic acid to cysteic acid, and thence to taurine, is probably a minor route, because the decarboxylation of cysteic acid is much slower than that of cysteine sulfinic acid. Taurine itself does not give rise to inorganic sulfate unless it is administered orally; presumably, taurine is degraded by the intestinal microorganisms.[90]

In the intact rat, the carbon atoms of cysteine (and of cystine) are metabolized via pyruvic acid.[75] In addition to the mechanism of pyruvate formation shown in Fig. 12, the liver can effect the desulfhydration of cysteine (cf. p. 756) and also can convert cysteine to β-mercaptopyruvic acid, which is further metabolized in liver to pyruvate and H_2S.[91]

[87] I. Fridovich and P. Handler, *J. Biol. Chem.*, **223**, 321 (1956); **228**, 67 (1957).
[88] P. Chapeville et al., *Biochim. et Biophys. Acta*, **20**, 351 (1956).
[89] L. Eldjarn et al., *J. Biol. Chem.*, **223**, 353 (1956).
[90] G. A. Maw, *Biochem. J.*, **55**, 37 (1953).
[91] A. Meister et al., *J. Biol. Chem.*, **206**, 561 (1954).

The conversion of methionine-sulfur to sulfate may be considered to proceed via the formation of cysteine. This process probably occurs in the liver, which can also effect the breakdown of methionine to yield methyl mercaptan (CH_3SH).[92] In human subjects with severe liver damage, the condition of fetor hepaticus (i.e., a bad odor on the breath) is accompanied by the urinary excretion of methyl mercaptan; the expired air probably contains both methyl mercaptan and dimethyl-sulfide.[93] Apparently, methyl mercaptan is formed in relatively large amounts from methionine that cannot be demethylated to homocysteine (cf. p. 801) by the abnormal liver.

It will be recalled that cystine was the first amino acid to be isolated and that it was obtained originally from urinary calculi (Wollaston, 1806). Such cystine stones are found in the urine of human subjects who have the disease known as cystinuria, a metabolic abnormality that occurs in about 1 out of about 20,000 individuals; this disease has no harmful effects on the subject so long as the urine is kept alkaline to prevent the precipitation of cystine in the kidneys and the concomitant formation of urinary calculi. Chromatographic studies on the amino acid composition of the urine of cystinuric subjects indicate that cystine is not the only amino acid excreted, and that other amino acids (e.g., lysine) are present in even greater quantities than cystine; the earlier detection of the sulfur amino acid was facilitated by its insolu-bility. This important avenue of research on amino acid metabolism shows that the term "cystinuria" may well be a misnomer[94] (cf. p. 858).

In microorganisms the breakdown of cystine can also involve the reduction of cystine to cysteine and the conversion of the latter to ammonia, H_2S, and pyruvic acid. Indeed, the pathways shown in Fig. 12 leading to cysteic acid and pyruvic acid are also followed in the degradation of L-cysteine by *Proteus vulgaris*. Various inorganic sulfur compounds are produced by microorganisms from the sulfur amino acids; these products include sulfate, sulfite, sulfide, thiosulfate, and poly-thionates. In addition, the mold *Scopulariopsis brevicaulis* can cleave S-alkyl derivatives of cysteine to yield the corresponding alkyl mer-captans. This mold and many bacteria (strains of *Pseudomonas*, *Clostridia*, and other soil bacteria) also form methyl mercaptan from methionine.

An important derivative of cysteine produced by *Penicillia* is the antibiotic penicillin (p. 60). Although the mechanisms whereby this dipeptide-like substance is formed are unclear, it is known that an entire L-cysteine residue and the carbon skeleton of L-valine (or D-valine) are

[92] E. S. Canellakis and H. Tarver, *Arch. Biochem. and Biophys.*, **42**, 387 (1953).

[93] F. Challenger and J. M. Walshe, *Biochem. J.*, **59**, 372 (1955).

[94] W. H. Stein, *Proc. Soc. Exptl. Biol. Med.*, **78**, 705 (1951).

incorporated as such into the molecule,[95] as shown in the accompanying formula.

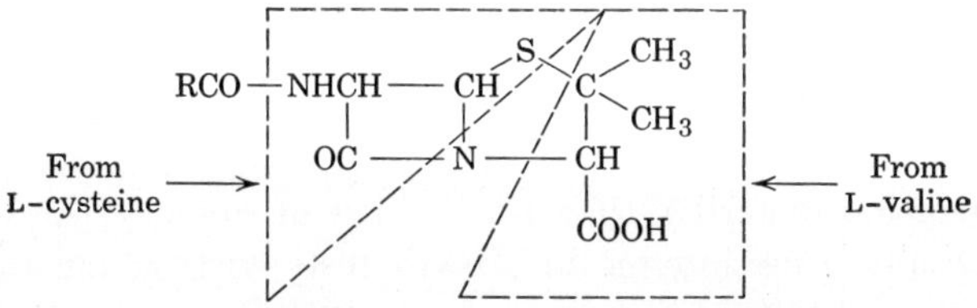

Microbial Utilization of Inorganic Sulfur Compounds. The nutritional requirements of various types of microorganisms for sulfur vary from the ability to use sulfate as the sole source of sulfur to an absolute requirement for cystine and methionine as well as for one or more of the sulfur-containing vitamins. The data available from studies with naturally occurring strains and with artificially produced mutants indicate that sulfate ions are reduced to sulfite ions, and these, in turn, are converted to sulfide ions, which can then be incorporated into cysteine and transferred to methionine. The incorporation of sulfide sulfur may occur by a reversal of the action of cysteine desulfhydrase (cf. p. 756); although this has not been established experimentally with microbial systems, it has been demonstrated with enzyme preparations from rat liver.[96] The direct utilization of sulfite for the synthesis of β-sulfinyl pyruvic acid, and thence of cysteine, may occur in *Aspergillus nidulans* and perhaps in other microorganisms.[97]

A number of autotrophic bacteria are known to be capable of effecting the oxidation of hydrogen sulfide, sulfur, or thiosulfate to sulfate, and to use the energy so liberated for the synthesis of organic substances from CO_2, H_2O, and NH_3. In this regard the "sulfur bacteria"[98] resemble the nitrifying bacteria *Nitrosomonas* and *Nitrobacter* discussed on p. 679. Among the sulfur bacteria is included *Thiobacillus thiooxidans*, which produces sulfuric acid from inorganic sulfur; this organism is capable of withstanding pH values as low as 1.0.

$$S + 1.5O_2 + H_2O \rightarrow H_2SO_4$$

Thiothrix, another member of this group of autotrophic sulfur bacteria, oxidizes H_2S to sulfur, which is deposited intracellularly; as the external supply of H_2S diminishes, the sulfur is oxidized to sulfate. Still other

[95] H. R. V. Arnstein and P. T. Grant, *Biochem. J.,* **57**, 353, 360 (1954); C. M. Stevens et al., *J. Biol. Chem.,* **211**, 297 (1954); **219**, 405 (1956); H. R. V. Arnstein and M. E. Clubb, *Biochem. J.,* **65**, 618 (1957).

[96] C. V. Smythe and D. Halliday, *J. Biol. Chem.,* **144**, 237 (1942).

[97] C. J. Shepherd, *J. Gen. Microbiol.,* **15**, 29 (1956).

[98] K. Baalsrud, in *Autotrophic Micro-organisms,* Cambridge University Press, Cambridge, 1954; W. Vishniac and M. Santer, *Bact. Revs.,* **21**, 195 (1957).

sulfur bacteria are *Thiobacillus thioparus,* which oxidizes thiosulfate to sulfate, and *Thiobacillus denitrificans,* in which the oxidation of sulfur to sulfate is coupled to the reduction of nitrate to N_2.

Transmethylation [66,99]

It was mentioned earlier that the ability of homocystine and homocysteine to replace methionine in growth tests with young rats depends on the vitamin content of the diet. Until 1950 it appeared highly probable that the ingestion of compounds containing "preformed" methyl groups was a prerequisite for the continued growth and health of animals receiving homocystine as the main source of sulfur amino acids. Subsequently, it was recognized that animals, as well as microorganisms and

$$
\begin{array}{cc}
\underset{\substack{\text{CH}_3\\ \diagdown}}{\text{CH}_3}\overset{+}{\text{N}}\text{CH}_2\text{CH}_2\text{OH} \cdot \text{OH}^- & \underset{\substack{\text{CH}_3\\ \diagdown}}{\text{CH}_3}\overset{+}{\text{N}}\text{CH}_2\text{COO}^-\\
\text{Choline} & \text{Betaine}
\end{array}
$$

$$
\begin{array}{cc}
\underset{\substack{\text{CH}_3}}{\overset{\text{CH}_3}{\diagdown}}\overset{+}{\text{S}}\text{CH}_2\text{CH}_2\text{COO}^- & \underset{\substack{\text{CH}_3\text{CH}_2}}{\overset{\text{CH}_3}{\diagdown}}\overset{+}{\text{N}}\text{CH}_2\text{CH}_2\text{OH} \cdot \text{OH}^-\\
\text{Dimethylpropiothetin} & \text{"Monoethylcholine"}
\end{array}
$$

$$
\begin{array}{cc}
\underset{\substack{\text{CH}_3}}{\overset{\text{CH}_3}{\diagdown}}\overset{+}{\text{S}}\text{CH}_2\text{COO}^- & \underset{\substack{\text{CH}_3}}{\overset{\text{CH}_3}{\diagdown}}\overset{+}{\text{S}}\text{CH}_2\text{CH}_2\text{CHCOOH} \cdot \text{OH}^-\\
\text{Dimethylthetin} & \text{S-Methylmethionine}
\end{array}
$$

$$
\begin{array}{cc}
\underset{\substack{\text{CH}_3\text{CH}_2}}{\overset{\text{CH}_3}{\diagdown}}\overset{+}{\text{S}}\text{CH}_2\text{COO}^- & \underset{\substack{\text{CH}_3}}{\overset{\text{CH}_3}{\diagdown}}\overset{+}{\text{As}}\text{CH}_2\text{CH}_2\text{OH} \cdot \text{OH}^-\\
\text{Methylethylthetin} & \text{"Arsenocholine"}
\end{array}
$$

plants, can synthesize the methyl group of methionine from simple 1-carbon compounds, although this process represents a minor pathway of methionine formation in animals that normally ingest adequate amounts of this amino acid. The discussion which follows is concerned with the biological transfer of methyl groups (transmethylation); the synthesis of methyl groups is considered on p. 806.

Several compounds serve as dietary sources of preformed methyl groups

[99] F. Challenger, *Quart. Revs.,* **9,** 255 (1955).

in animal growth tests: the natural products choline (a constituent of the tissues of animals, plants, molds, fungi, and other microorganisms), betaine (found in higher and lower plants as well as in animals), dimethyl-β-propiothetin (found in some marine algae), α-aminodimethyl-γ-butyrothetin (or S-methylmethionine, present in many vegetables), and the compounds "monoethylcholine," dimethylthetin, and methylethylthetin, none of which is known to occur in nature. Since these compounds permit the ready utilization of homocysteine as a precursor of methionine, they have been called "methyl donors," and their methyl groups are referred to as "labile." It will be seen from the structural formulae that the molecules contain either an ammonium or a sulfonium group. However, all compounds in which methyl groups are attached to an "onium" atom are not methyl donors; for example, "arsenocholine" does not act like choline in growth tests. Furthermore, the S-methyl group of methionine also is "labile"; however, this amino acid is converted to a sulfonium compound before the metabolic labilization of its methyl group (cf. p. 804). In general, sulfonium compounds are readily hydrolyzed in water, with the loss of one of the alkyl groups as an alcohol; in the presence of various substances (e.g., amines, thiols), the R' group

$$R_2 \overset{+}{S} R' + OH^- \rightarrow RSR + R'OH$$

may be transferred nonenzymically to such "acceptors." Sulfonium compounds have been included in the group of "energy-rich" substances (cf. p. 380), although reliable data for the free energy of their hydrolysis are not available.

The occurrence of biological transmethylation reactions was suggested to explain the results of growth experiments with rats fed homocysteine and choline. Subsequent studies, in which deuterium-labeled choline, i.e., $(CD_3)_3 N^+ CH_2 CH_2 OH$, was used, demonstrated that the transfer *in vivo* of methyl groups from dietary choline to tissue methionine occurs even when the diet is devoid of all sulfur amino acids. Clearly, the animal organism is able to demethylate the methionine already present in the tissues and can attach a new methyl group to the demethylation product to regenerate the amino acid. By means of isotopically labeled compounds, it has also been shown that a reversible transmethylation reaction involving choline and methionine takes place even if both methyl compounds are supplied in the diet.

Studies with tissue preparations showed that choline does not donate a methyl group directly to homocysteine, but must first be oxidized to betaine. Thus, under aerobic conditions, slices and homogenates of rat liver methylate homocysteine to methionine and use either choline or betaine as a source of methyl groups, but, in the absence of oxygen, only betaine serves as the methyl donor for the conversion of homocysteine to methionine.[100] The enzymic oxidation of choline proceeds in two steps: in the first, choline is oxidized by FAD in the presence of choline oxidase to form betaine aldehyde,[101] which is then oxidized to betaine by a DPN-dependent betaine aldehyde dehydrogenase.[102] A similar

$$(CH_3)_3\overset{+}{N}CH_2CH_2OH \rightarrow (CH_3)_3\overset{+}{N}CH_2CHO \rightarrow (CH_3)_3\overset{+}{N}CH_2COO^-$$

oxidation of choline to betaine probably occurs in green plants and in some bacteria, but the enzymes involved have not been characterized.[103]

In mammalian liver, which contains the enzyme system "betaine-homocysteine transmethylase," betaine donates one of its methyl groups to homocysteine with the formation of methionine and dimethylglycine.[104] As noted previously (p. 776), dimethylglycine can be oxidized in the liver

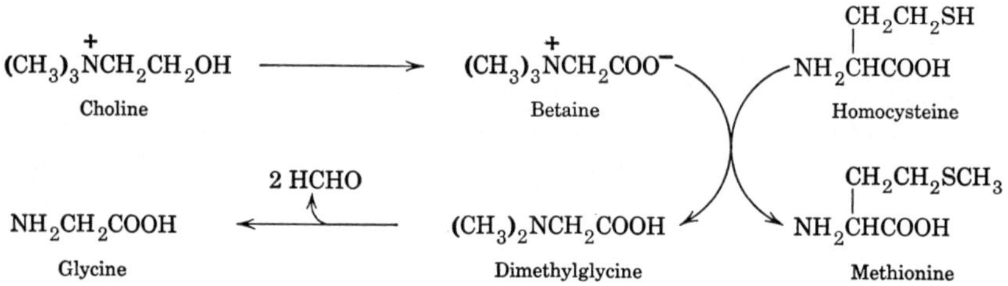

to formaldehyde and glycine. Consequently, in the presence of the requisite oxidative and transmethylating enzymes, choline can give rise to glycine,[105] as shown in the accompanying scheme.

Choline is readily formed from ethanolamine (aminoethanol), and the results of isotope experiments[106] support the view that monomethyl- and dimethylaminoethanol are natural intermediates in the biosynthesis of choline in the rat. The stepwise methylation of ethanolamine to choline also occurs in *Neurospora crassa* and probably in higher plants. Little is known about the enzymic mechanism of this conversion, but the available data suggest that only the synthesis of choline from dimethylamino-ethanol involves a transmethylation reaction in which methionine supplies a preformed methyl group.[107]

The behavior of the thetin derivatives listed on p. 801 as "methyl

[100] J. W. Dubnoff, *Arch. Biochem.*, **24**, 251 (1949).

[101] H. A. Rothschild et al., *J. Biol. Chem.*, **208**, 41; **209**, 511 (1954).

[102] J. R. Klein and P. Handler, *J. Biol. Chem.*, **144**, 537 (1942).

[103] B. T. Cromwell and S. D. Rennie, *Biochem. J.*, **58**, 318, 322 (1954).

[104] J. A. Muntz, *J. Biol. Chem.*, **182**, 489 (1950); L. E. Ericson et al., *Acta Chem. Scand.*, **9**, 859 (1955).

[105] S. Soloway and D. Stetten, Jr., *J. Biol. Chem.*, **204**, 207 (1953).

[106] V. du Vigneaud et al., *J. Biol. Chem.*, **164**, 603 (1946).

[107] J. A. Stekol et al., *J. Am. Chem. Soc.*, **77**, 5192 (1955).

donors" is of interest since none of these sulfonium compounds has been detected in mammalian tissues. Not only do dimethylthetin and dimethyl-β-propiothetin permit the growth of rats on homocystine diets, but both compounds are better methyl donors than betaine for the synthesis of methionine by liver enzyme preparations. It appears that mammalian and avian livers contain a specific "thetin-homocysteine transmethylase"[108] which catalyzes the reaction between dimethylthetin and homocysteine to form S-methylthioglycolic acid (CH_3SCH_2COOH) and methionine.

The metabolism of S-methylmethionine has been studied mainly in microorganisms. Cell-free extracts of *Aerobacter aerogenes* effect methyl transfer from this sulfonium compound to homocysteine; the net reaction is S-methylmethionine + homocysteine $\rightarrow$ 2 methionine.[109] This transmethylation reaction is believed to occur in yeasts, which utilize S-methylmethionine (but not other sulfonium compounds, choline, or betaine) as a source of the methyl group for the conversion of homocysteine to methionine.[110]

In addition to the reactions yielding methionine, a number of other transmethylation reactions are known to occur in animals and plants; one of the most important of these is the reaction by which creatine is formed. In 1935 it was suggested independently by Brand and by Lewis that methionine might serve as the source of the methyl group of creatine. Experimental evidence for the occurrence of this transmethylation reaction has come from studies in which isotopic compounds were fed to animals, and from the elucidation of the enzymic processes involved. In the synthesis of creatine, glycine and arginine participate in a reaction (transamidination) by which the amidine group of arginine is transferred to the nitrogen of glycine to form ornithine and guanidinoacetic acid

$$
\begin{array}{ccc}
\overset{\displaystyle NH}{\underset{\displaystyle ||}{}} & & \\
\overset{\displaystyle NH-C-NH_2}{\underset{\displaystyle |}{}} & \overset{\displaystyle NH_2}{\underset{\displaystyle |}{}} & \overset{\displaystyle NH_2}{\underset{\displaystyle |}{}} \\
\overset{\displaystyle (CH_2)_3}{\underset{\displaystyle |}{}} & \overset{\displaystyle (CH_2)_3}{\underset{\displaystyle |}{}} & \overset{\displaystyle C=NH}{\underset{\displaystyle |}{}} \\
NH_2CHCOOH & + NH_2CH_2COOH \rightleftharpoons NH_2CHCOOH & + NHCH_2COOH \\
\text{Arginine} & \text{Glycine} \qquad\qquad \text{Ornithine} & \text{Guanidinoacetic} \\
& & \text{acid}
\end{array}
$$

(also named glycocyamine); this reaction is discussed further on p. 812. The methylation of guanidinoacetic acid by methionine occurs in liver,[111]

[108] J. W. Dubnoff and H. Borsook, *J. Biol. Chem.*, **176**, 789 (1948); G. A. Maw, *Biochem. J.*, **58**, 665 (1954); **63**, 113 (1956).

[109] S. K. Shapiro, *Biochim. et Biophys. Acta*, **18**, 134 (1955).

[110] F. Schlenk and R. E. DePalma, *Arch. Biochem. and Biophys.*, **57**, 266 (1955).

[111] H. Borsook and J. W. Dubnoff, *J. Biol. Chem.*, **169**, 247; **171**, 363 (1947).

and it involves two distinct enzymic reactions.[112]   In the first reaction, methionine and ATP interact to form S-adenosylmethionine in the presence of the "methionine-activating enzyme"; in the concomitant cleavage of ATP, the terminal phosphoryl group is liberated as inorganic phosphate, and the two internal phosphoryl groups appear as inorganic pyrophosphate.   In the second reaction, which is catalyzed by "guanidinoacetate methylpherase," the methyl group is transferred from

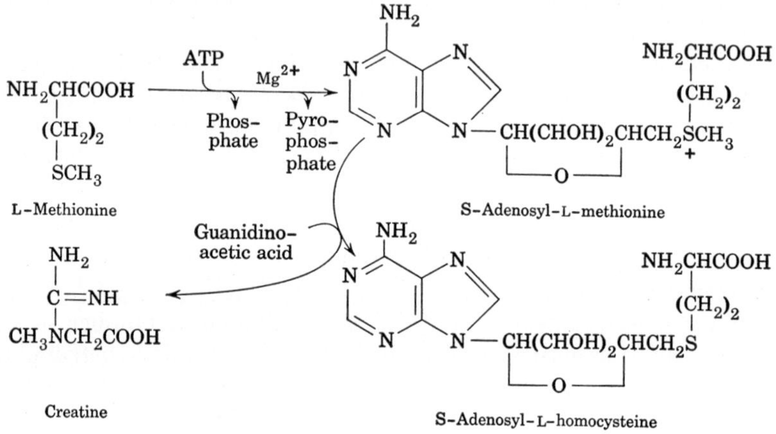

S-adenosylmethionine to guanidinoacetic acid, and S-adenosylhomocysteine and creatine are formed.   The structures of S-adenosylmethionine and of S-adenosylhomocysteine have been established by chemical synthesis.[113]   In liver homogenates, S-adenosylhomocysteine is cleaved to yield free homocysteine; the enzymic mechanism of this process has not been elucidated.

The methyl group of creatine is not labile since it is not transferred *in vivo* to choline. Nor is the nitrogen of creatine used by the animal body as a source of nitrogen for protein synthesis. Creatine may be considered, therefore, to be an end product of the mammalian metabolism of glycine, arginine, and methionine. Normally only small amounts of creatine are excreted in the urine of mammals; before excretion creatine is largely converted to its cyclic anhydride creatinine. Creatine

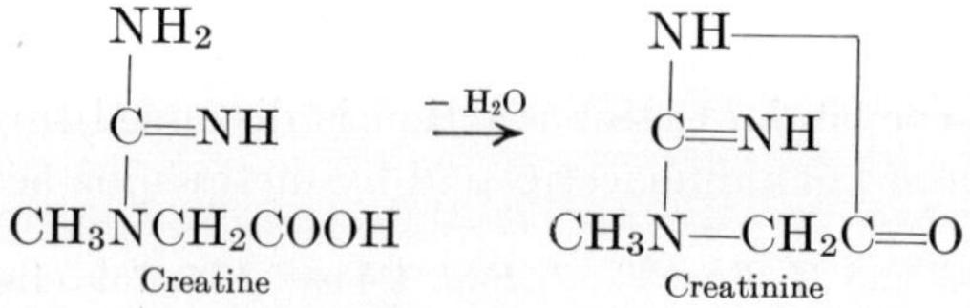

[112] G. L. Cantoni, *J. Biol. Chem.*, **204**, 403 (1953); G. L. Cantoni and P. J. Vignos, *ibid.*, **209**, 647 (1954); G. L. Cantoni and J. Durell, *ibid.*, **225**, 1033 (1957).
[113] J. Baddiley and G. A. Jamieson, *J. Chem. Soc.*, **1954**, 4280; **1955**, 1085.

occurs in relatively large amounts in the tissues of higher animals, especially in muscle, where creatine phosphate plays an important physiological role (cf. p. 486).

A number of microorganisms can utilize creatine as a source of nitrogen for protein synthesis. Among these are several species isolated from soil.[114] One such organism (*Pseudomonas ovalis*) appears to cleave creatine to urea and sarcosine, which is oxidized to CO_2, NH_3, and H_2O after prior conversion to glycine and formaldehyde.

After yeast has grown in the presence of methionine, there may be isolated from the medium 5'-thiomethyladenosine (p. 206), which appears to be formed by the transfer of a thiomethyl group (CH_3S—) from methionine to adenosine.[115] Methyl mercaptan is also used by growing yeasts as a source of the thiomethyl group of thiomethyladenosine; presumably, the CH_3S— group is first incorporated into methionine, and then transferred to adenosine. In some strains of *Aerobacter aerogenes*, thiomethyladenosine can serve as a source of the thiomethyl group of methionine,[116] thus providing an alternative route of methionine formation in this organism.

Among the N-methyl compounds found in animal urine is N^1-methylnicotinamide, the principal excretory product of the vitamin nicotinamide (Chapter 39). The methylation of nicotinamide occurs in the liver,[117] and, as in the formation of creatine, involves a reaction of S-adenosylmethionine, which donates its methyl group to nicotinamide in the presence of the enzyme "nicotinamide methylpherase."[118] Other N-methyl compounds found in mammalian tissues are the dipeptide anserine (p. 137) and the hormone adrenalin (p. 828). Isotope experiments have shown that, *in vivo*, methionine provides the methyl group of each of these substances.

In higher plants, the methyl group of methionine is used as a precursor of the O-methyl groups of lignin (p. 422) and the N-methyl groups of some alkaloids (e.g., nicotine; p. 860). In the molds *Scopulariopsis brevicaulis* and *Aspergillus niger*, methionine provides the methyl groups for the formation of trimethylarsine [$(CH_3)_3As$], dimethyltelluride [$(CH_3)_2Te$], and dimethylselenide [$(CH_3)_2Se$].[119] These methyl compounds are of special interest, since the mode of their formation was

[114] R. Dubos and B. F. Miller, *J. Biol. Chem.*, **121**, 429 (1937); R. H. Nimmo-Smith and G. Appleyard, *J. Gen. Microbiol.*, **14**, 336 (1956); G. Appleyard and D. D. Woods, *ibid.*, **14**, 351 (1956).

[115] F. Schlenk and R. E. dePalma, *J. Biol. Chem.*, **229**, 1037 (1957).

[116] M. Schwartz and S. K. Shapiro, *J. Bact.*, **67**, 98 (1954).

[117] W. A. Perlzweig et al., *J. Biol. Chem.*, **150**, 401 (1943).

[118] G. L. Cantoni, *J. Biol. Chem.*, **189**, 203, 745 (1951).

[119] F. Challenger et al., *J. Chem. Soc.*, **1954**, 1760; P. B. Dransfield and F. Challenger, *ibid.*, **1955**, 1153.

studied early in the history of work on the biosynthesis of methyl groups.[120]

The Biosynthesis and Oxidation of "Labile" Methyl Groups.[121] The formation of methyl groups by living organisms was of interest to investigators long before the discovery of biological transmethylation. It has been known for many years that various molds can convert inorganic compounds of arsenic, tellurium, and selenium into volatile methyl derivatives having distinctive odors. The formation of trimethylarsine, whose garlic-like odor was first reported by Gmelin in 1839, was used by Gosio in 1893 as the basis of a biological test for arsenic. Man and other animals can form dimethyltelluride and dimethylselenide, and preparations of dog liver, lungs, and testicles readily convert inorganic compounds of selenium and tellurium to odorous substances; apparently bacteria are not capable of methylating these metals. The early students of this subject suggested that an indirect methylation reaction is responsible for the formation of compounds such as trimethylarsine, and that formaldehyde serves as the precursor of the methyl groups. As mentioned above, methionine (rather than choline, betaine, or any of the thetins) appears to be the direct source of the methyl groups; however, the methyl group of methionine can be synthesized from formaldehyde in all types of organisms.

It has been shown that both formaldehyde and formate can be converted by animals to "labile" methyl groups present in methionine and choline, and in other methyl compounds derived from methionine.[122] Furthermore, "labile" methyl groups are formed from carbon supplied as any one of the known precursors of "active C_1 units" (cf. p. 774). Such methyl synthesis proceeds within the tissues of rats maintained on diets containing adequate amounts of methionine and choline, i.e., even when there is no obvious need for the formation of methyl groups *de novo*. It must be added, however, that under normal conditions most of the labile methyl compounds in the animal body are probably derived directly from the diet or formed *in vivo* by transmethylation reactions.[123]

Extracts of liver[124] and of *Escherichia coli*[125] have been shown to utilize carbon supplied as formic acid, as formaldehyde, or as the β-carbon of serine for the conversion of homocysteine to methionine.

[120] F. Challenger, *Chem. Revs.*, **36**, 315 (1945).

[121] J. A. Stekol, in W. D. McElroy and B. Glass, *Amino Acid Metabolism*, Johns Hopkins Press, Baltimore, 1955.

[122] V. du Vigneaud et al., *Science*, **112**, 267 (1950); *J. Am. Chem. Soc.*, **72**, 2819 (1950); W. Sakami and A. D. Welch, *J. Biol. Chem.*, **187**, 379 (1950).

[123] V. du Vigneaud et al., *J. Am. Chem. Soc.*, **78**, 5131 (1956).

[124] P. Berg, *J. Biol. Chem.*, **205**, 145 (1953); A. Nakao and D. M. Greenberg, *J. Am. Chem. Soc.*, **77**, 6715 (1955).

[125] C. W. Helleiner and D. D. Woods, *Biochem. J.*, **63**, 26p (1956).

Although the mechanism of this conversion has not been elucidated, it is of interest that, in the intact rat, the β-carbon of serine is more effective than the other known carbon sources for methyl synthesis,[126] and that the β-methylene group of serine [supplied as $HOC^{14}D_2CH(NH_2)COOH$] is utilized intact in the synthetic process. The possibility exists that the $-CH_2OH$ group of serine is transferred as a unit to the sulfur atom of homocysteine to form S-hydroxymethylhomocysteine, which could then be reduced to methionine. As noted before (cf. p. 775), a "hydroxymethyltetrahydroPGA" is presumed to be formed in the cleavage of serine to glycine. Such an intermediate might also serve as a "carrier" of the C_1 unit required for the synthesis of methionine.[127]

In order for a young rat to grow on a homocystine diet devoid of all recognized methyl compounds, an adequate supply of folic acid and of vitamin B_{12} (Chapter 39) must be available to the test animal. The importance of these two vitamins in the synthesis of methyl groups has been suggested by work with both animals and microorganisms.[128] Although the role of folic acid in methyl synthesis is clearly related to its function in the metabolism of C_1 compounds, that of vitamin B_{12} has not been established.

In higher animals, the methyl groups of dimethylaminoethanol (cf. p. 802) appear to be formed from C_1 precursors rather than by transmethylation reactions. Methyl synthesis is also thought to be involved in the formation of dimethylaminoethanol and of choline in higher plants.[129] The compounds that serve as sources of carbon for the formation of methyl groups in animals are also used as precursors of the methyl groups of other plant constituents (e.g., lignin, nicotine). However, in higher plants, formaldehyde and the α-carbon of glycine appear to be more effective sources than is the β-carbon of serine.

In addition to the transmethylation reactions in which they participate, "labile" methyl groups undergo oxidation in the animal body. Thus C^{14}-labeled methyl groups fed to rats as methionine, choline, betaine, dimethylthetin, dimethylpropiothetin, or sarcosine (but not as creatine) are converted to respiratory $C^{14}O_2$ and labeled formate and formaldehyde excreted in the urine.[130] Consequently, any "labile" methyl group must be considered a potential source of C_1 units used in biosynthetic

126 H. R. V. Arnstein and A. Neuberger, *Biochem. J.,* **55,** 259 (1953).

127 D. Elwyn et al., *J. Biol. Chem.,* **213,** 281 (1955); B. A. Lowy et al., *ibid.,* **220,** 325 (1956).

128 M. A. Bennett, *J. Biol. Chem.,* **187,** 751 (1950); W. Shive, *Ann. N. Y. Acad. Sci.,* **52,** 1212 (1950); B. D. Davis and E. S. Mingioli, *J. Bact.,* **60,** 17 (1950); J. A. Stekol et al., *J. Biol. Chem.,* **226,** 95 (1957).

129 H. M. Bregoff and C. C. Delwiche, *J. Biol. Chem.,* **217,** 819 (1955).

130 C. G. Mackenzie et al., *J. Biol. Chem.,* **169,** 757 (1947); **183,** 617 (1950); C. G. Mackenzie and V. du Vigneaud, *ibid.,* **185,** 185 (1950).

GENERAL BIOCHEMISTRY

reactions (cf. p. 774), and its oxidation may depend on its prior incorporation into a folic acid derivative, from which formaldehyde is liberated and then oxidized.[131]

Metabolism of Lysine [132]

L-Lysine is an indispensable constituent of the diet for all animals that have been studied. This nutritional requirement for lysine is extremely specific since only the L-isomer and a few derivatives in which the ϵ-amino group has been substituted (e.g., the ϵ-N-methyl and ϵ-N-acetyl compounds) support the growth of rats.[133] α-N-Acetyllysine is ineffective in this regard, but data from isotope experiments indicate that this derivative can be converted slowly to lysine *in vivo*.[134]

Experiments in which lysine labeled in the α-amino group with N^{15} and in the carbon chain with deuterium have demonstrated conclusively that all the lysine in the body proteins is derived directly from the lysine in the diet; thus lysine does not undergo reversible deamination at the α position *in vivo*, nor is the carbon skeleton of the D-amino acid used for the biosynthesis of the L-form. The L-amino acid oxidases of animal origin do not attack lysine, and only a very small amount of transamination between lysine and α-ketoglutaric acid has been observed; nevertheless, the α-amino nitrogen of lysine has been recovered in other protein amino acids and in the urea and ammonia excreted by rats fed N^{15}-containing lysine. The fact that L-amino acid oxidase deaminates ϵ-N-acetyllysine suggests that the ϵ-amino group of lysine must be masked before the α-amino group is subjected to enzymic attack.[133]

Studies on the metabolism of labeled lysine in homogenates of guinea pig liver,[135] in dogs,[136] and in rats[137] have provided evidence for the pathway of lysine degradation shown in Fig. 13. The feeding of lysine leads to the excretion of pipecolic acid and of L-α-aminoadipic acid, both of which derive their nitrogen from the ϵ-amino group of L-lysine. Another excretory product of lysine metabolism is glutaric acid, which is a source of α-ketoglutaric acid and of glutamic acid. Liver preparations also convert lysine to α-aminoadipic acid; the latter is deaminated slowly to yield an α-keto acid that is decarboxylated rapidly to glutaric

[131] R. L. Herrmann et al., *J. Am. Chem. Soc.*, **77**, 1902 (1955).

[132] E. Work, in W. D. McElroy and B. Glass, *Amino Acid Metabolism*, Johns Hopkins Press, Baltimore, 1955.

[133] A. Neuberger and F. Sanger, *Biochem. J.*, **38**, 119, 125 (1944).

[134] I. Clark and D. Rittenberg, *J. Biol. Chem.*, **189**, 521, 529 (1951).

[135] H. Borsook et al., *J. Biol. Chem.*, **176**, 1383, 1395 (1948).

[136] K. I. Altman et al., *Arch. Biochem.*, **29**, 447 (1950).

[137] M. Rothstein and L. L. Miller, *J. Biol. Chem.*, **206**, 243; **211**, 851 (1954).

acid. It is of interest that the metabolic transformation of lysine to glutaric acid was postulated by Ringer in 1913, on the basis of the observation that neither lysine nor glutaric acid is glucogenic

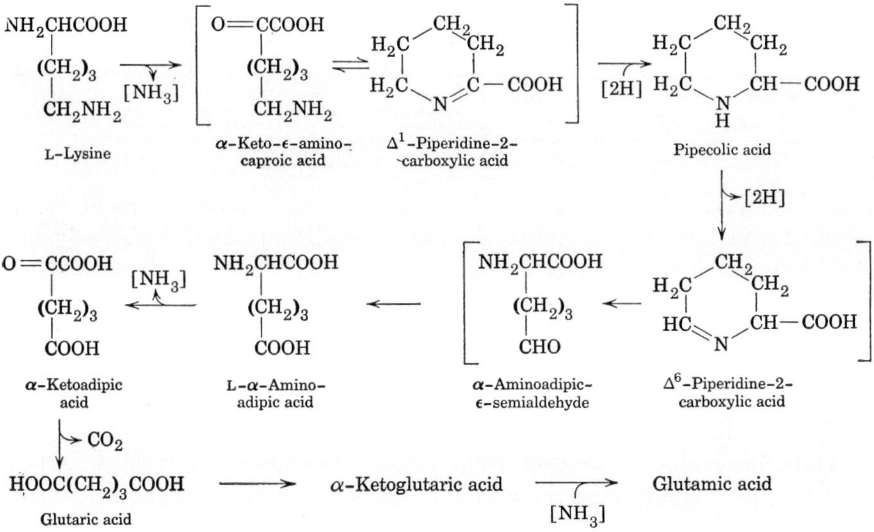

Fig. 13. Degradation of lysine in animal tissues.

As shown in Fig. 13, the loss of the α-amino group of lysine yields an α-keto acid that is known to exist in solution as the cyclic compound Δ^1-piperidine-2-carboxylic acid (Δ^1-dehydropipecolic acid). The reduction of this cyclic compound to pipecolic acid is catalyzed by a pyridine nucleotide-dependent dehydrogenase present in rat and rabbit liver.[138] The further conversion of pipecolic acid to α-aminoadipic acid in animal tissues is assumed to involve the intermediates shown in Fig. 13. It may be added that the breakdown of lysine in *Neurospora* also gives dehydro-pipecolic acid and pipecolic acid;[139] the latter is a product of lysine metabolism in higher plants[140] (cf. p. 71).

A few animal proteins contain the amino acid 5-hydroxy-L-lysine (p. 64); in the rat, L-lysine serves as the sole source of hydroxylysine.[141] Green plants contain 5-hydroxypiperidine-2-carboxylic acid, which may arise from hydroxylysine in a manner similar to the formation of pipecolic acid from lysine.[142] (Cf. reaction on p. 810 and Fig. 13.)

138 A. Meister and S. D. Buckley, *Biochim. et Biophys. Acta,* **23,** 202 (1957).
139 R. S. Schweet et al., *J. Biol. Chem.,* **211,** 517 (1954).
140 N. Grobbelaar and F. C. Steward, *J. Am. Chem. Soc.,* **75,** 4341 (1955).
141 F. M. Sinex and D. D. Van Slyke, *J. Biol. Chem.,* **216,** 245 (1955).
142 A. I. Virtanen and S. Kari, *Acta Chem. Scand.,* **8,** 1290 (1954).

The conversion of lysine to α-aminoadipic acid is not reversible in animals.[143] However, some mutant strains of *Neurospora* that require for growth an exogenous source of lysine can use α-aminoadipic acid in

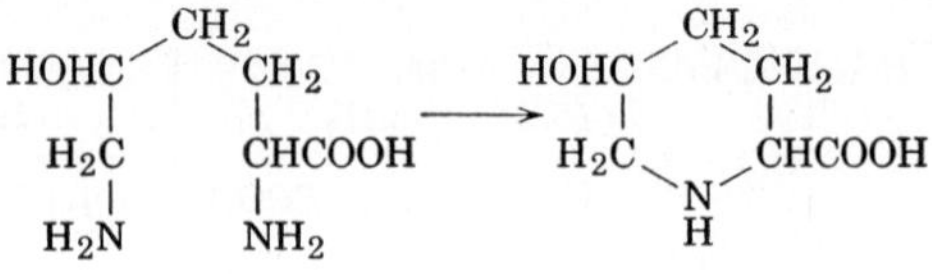

5-Hydroxylysine   5-Hydroxypiperidine-2-carboxylic acid

place of lysine,[144] and some lysine-requiring strains of the mold *Ophiostoma* grow on either α-keto- or α-aminoadipic acid as well as on lysine. In molds, therefore, the biosynthesis of lysine may involve the amination of α-ketoadipic acid to α-aminoadipic acid; the reduction of the latter to α-aminoadipic-ϵ-semialdehyde, followed by an amination reaction, would yield lysine. An analogous series of reactions is believed to occur in the conversion of α-ketoglutaric acid to ornithine both in molds and in higher animals (cf. p. 814).

Data on lysine formation from labeled precursors in yeasts and in *Neurospora* suggest that the carboxyl carbon and the α-carbon of lysine are derived more or less directly from the carboxyl and methyl carbons, respectively, of acetic acid; the remainder of carbon skeleton of lysine is probably derived from α-ketoglutaric acid.[145]

In many bacteria (e.g., *Escherichia coli*) L-lysine arises by the enzymic decarboxylation of α,ϵ-diaminopimelic acid (cf. p. 767), rather than from

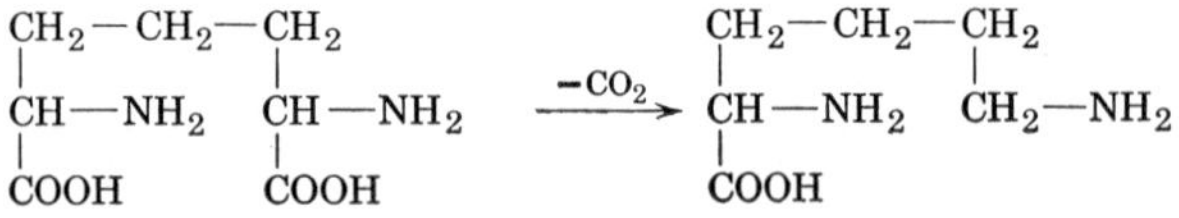

Diaminopimelic acid   L-Lysine

α-aminoadipic acid.[146] In *E. coli*, *meso*-diaminopimelic acid is formed from pyruvic acid and aspartic acid; it is assumed that a 7-carbon intermediate leads to L-diaminopimelic acid,[147] which is converted by a specific racemase to the *meso* compound. Clearly, bacteria differ from

[143] E. Geiger and H. J. Dunn, *J. Biol. Chem.*, **178**, 877 (1949); H. Borsook et al., *ibid.*, **187**, 839 (1950).

[144] H. K. Mitchell and M. B. Houlahan, *J. Biol. Chem.*, **174**, 883 (1948).

[145] C. Gilvarg and K. Bloch, *J. Biol. Chem.*, **193**, 339 (1951); M. Strassman and S. Weinhouse, *J. Am. Chem. Soc.*, **75**, 1680 (1953).

[146] D. L. Dewey et al., *Biochem. J.*, **58**, 523 (1954); D. S. Hoare and E. Work, *ibid.*, **61**, 562 (1955); M. Antia et al., *ibid.*, **65**, 448 (1957).

[147] L. E. Rhuland and B. Bannister, *J. Am. Chem. Soc.*, **78**, 3548 (1956); C. Gilvarg, *Biochim. et Biophys. Acta*, **24**, 216 (1957).

molds and yeasts in the routes by which they synthesize lysine, and it is noteworthy that diaminopimelic acid appears to be absent in yeasts and molds.

It is of interest that diaminopimelic acid has been found in the vegetative cells of several spore-forming bacilli (e.g., *Bacillus cereus*), and that during sporulation this compound is converted to pyridine-2,6-dicarboxylic acid.[148] This conversion appears to resemble the formation of pipecolic acid from lysine.

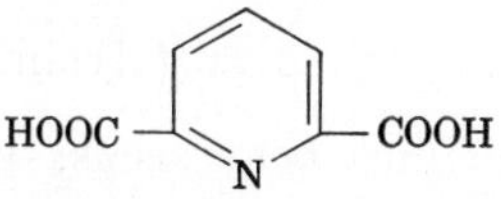

HOOC —⟨ ⟩— COOH

Pyridine-2,6-dicarboxylic acid

Metabolism of Arginine

Arginine occupies a unique position among the indispensable amino acids since it is only required in the diet of the young animal for rapid growth. With young rats, the exclusion from the diet of any indispensable amino acid other than arginine results in loss of weight and eventual death; when arginine is omitted, however, there is a decrease in the rate of growth, but the animal survives.[149] Clearly, arginine can be synthesized *in vivo*, but the rate at which such synthesis can be accomplished is not compatible with the requirements of a rapidly growing animal.

Chemically, the distinguishing feature of the arginine molecule is the amidine group attached to the δ-amino nitrogen, and this group is extremely important in the over-all nitrogen metabolism of animals. For example, the production of urea depends upon the cleavage of arginine, by the enzyme arginase, to yield urea and ornithine (p. 849). The incorporation of carbon dioxide (the final product of the oxidation of carbon compounds) and of ammonia (the end product of the degradation of most nitrogen compounds) into urea involves the intermediate formation of the amino acids citrulline and arginine. The enzymic mechanisms in the biosynthesis of urea will be discussed in Chapter 33. At this point it will suffice to note that the synthesis of arginine from ornithine, CO_2, and NH_3 has been demonstrated in higher animals and in many microorganisms, although it may not occur in some insects (e.g., Drosophila).[150]

Isotope experiments have shown that arginine also provides the amidine group required for the formation of guanidinoacetic acid from

[148] J. J. Perry and J. W. Foster, *J. Bact.*, **69**, 337 (1955); **72**, 295 (1956).
[149] W. C. Rose et al., *J. Biol. Chem.*, **176**, 753 (1948).
[150] T. Hinton, *Arch. Biochem. and Biophys.*, **62**, 78 (1956).

glycine.[151] The transfer of the amidine group of arginine to the nitrogen of glycine (cf. p. 803), catalyzed by kidney transamidinase, is readily reversible, and arginine can be formed from guanidinoacetic acid and ornithine.[152] In addition to this transamidination reaction, the enzyme catalyzes the reversible reaction of arginine or of guanidinoacetic acid with canaline to form canavanine (p. 66), as shown. It is of interest

Arginine + glycine $\rightleftharpoons$ Ornithine + guanidinoacetic acid

Arginine + canaline $\rightleftharpoons$ Ornithine + canavanine

Guanidinoacetic acid + canaline $\rightleftharpoons$ Glycine + canavanine

that, during the germination of jack bean seeds, the initial high concentration of canavanine falls off markedly, and large amounts of homoserine (p. 790) appear in the plant tissue. Presumably, homoserine arises by the cleavage of the O—N bond of canavanine; such a cleavage is effected by various bacteria that degrade canavanine to homoserine and guanidine.[153]

The metabolic reactivity of the amidine group of arginine is shown by the finding that, if N^{15}-glycine is fed to rats, the arginine of the tissue proteins becomes labeled in the amidine-N to a greater extent than in the α- or δ-amino groups of the ornithine derived from the arginine.[154] This experiment also showed that the extent of labeling of the α- and δ-amino-N is almost the same, indicating that the reversible deamination of arginine or ornithine at the α position does not occur to a significant degree *in vivo*.

The metabolic fate of ornithine has been investigated intensively both with intact animals fed labeled compounds and with animal tissue preparations. These studies have shown that the carbon skeleton and the nitrogen atoms of ornithine are used for the synthesis of proline,[155] and that the formation of proline and of arginine (i.e., ornithine) from glutamic acid also occurs *in vivo*.[156] It has been concluded therefore that the following metabolic relations apply to higher animals:

$$\text{Arginine} \rightleftharpoons \text{Ornithine} \rightleftharpoons \text{Proline}$$
$$\uparrow\downarrow \qquad \uparrow\downarrow$$
$$\text{Glutamic acid}$$

[151] K. Bloch and R. Schoenheimer, *J. Biol. Chem.*, **134**, 785 (1940); D. Stetten, Jr., and B. Bloom, *ibid.*, **220**, 723 (1956).

[152] J. B. Walker, *J. Biol. Chem.*, **218**, 549; **221**, 771 (1956); **224**, 57 (1957); S. Ratner and O. Rochovansky, *Arch. Biochem. and Biophys.*, **63**, 277, 296 (1956); W. H. Horner et al., *J. Biol. Chem.*, **220**, 861 (1956).

[153] H. Kihara et al., *J. Biol. Chem.*, **217**, 497 (1955).

[154] D. Shemin and D. Rittenberg, *J. Biol. Chem.*, **158**, 71 (1945).

[155] M. R. Stetten and R. Schoenheimer, *J. Biol. Chem.*, **153**, 113 (1944).

[156] H. J. Sallach et al., *J. Am. Chem. Soc.*, **73**, 4500 (1951).

It should be noted that the conversion of ornithine to glutamic acid is analogous to the conversion of lysine to α-aminoadipic acid discussed on p. 809. The scheme shown was foreshadowed by the work of Dakin,[157] who found that ornithine, proline, and glutamic acid yield approximately equal amounts of glucose when they are administered to a phlorizinized dog.

The demonstration of the ability of animal tissues (kidney slices) to convert proline to glutamic acid antedated the isotope experiments in intact animals.[158] More recently, it has been reported that liver and kidney slices can convert ornithine, as well as proline, to glutamic acid. From results obtained in enzyme experiments on the conversion of proline to glutamic acid, it appears probable that this transformation involves the dehydrogenation of proline to yield a pyrroline carboxylic acid; the latter compound may exist in equilibrium with glutamic acid semialdehyde, and the oxidation of the semialdehyde would yield glutamic acid.[159] Glutamic acid semialdehyde has been isolated as the product of the oxidation of L-proline by preparations of "proline oxidase" from the liver and kidney of several animals.[160] Moreover, liver contains a DPNH-dependent enzyme system that catalyzes the conversion of pyrroline carboxylic acid to proline.[161] The available information about the metabolic relations of the 5-carbon amino acids is summarized in Fig. 14. According to this scheme, the initial step in the metabolic degradation of ornithine is the cleavage of the bond linking the δ-amino nitrogen to the carbon skeleton. This amino group is believed to be transferred to the "pool" of labile nitrogen compounds, of which glutamic acid is the most important member. The subsequent reactions give rise to proline and glutamic acid containing carbon and nitrogen directly derived from glutamic acid semialdehyde. The results obtained on the feeding of N^{15}-glycine cited on p. 812 have been explained by the assumption that the glycine nitrogen is transferred to glutamic acid; the direct conversion of 1 molecule of glutamic acid to the semialdehyde and thence to ornithine by an amination reaction in which a second molecule of glutamic acid serves as the source of the δ-amino group would produce ornithine having the same amount of N^{15} in both amino groups.[162]

A close metabolic relation among the amino acids arginine, glutamic acid, and proline has also been found in microorganisms such as *Peni-*

[157] H. D. Dakin, *J. Biol. Chem.,* **13,** 513; **14,** 321 (1913).

[158] H. Weil-Malherbe and H. A. Krebs, *Biochem. J.,* **29,** 2077 (1935); M. Neber, *Z. physiol. Chem.,* **240,** 70 (1936).

[159] J. V. Taggart and R. B. Krakaur, *J. Biol. Chem.,* **177,** 641 (1949).

[160] K. Lang and G. Schmid, *Biochem. Z.,* **322,** 1 (1951).

[161] M. E. Smith and D. M. Greenberg, *J. Biol. Chem.,* **226,** 317 (1957).

[162] M. R. Stetten, *J. Biol. Chem.,* **189,** 499 (1951).

cillium notatum, Torulopsis utilis, Neurospora crassa, and *Escherichia coli.* In all these microbial species, proline appears to be formed from glutamic acid via glutamic acid semialdehyde and pyrroline carboxylic acid; an enzyme that catalyzes the reduction of the pyrroline compound

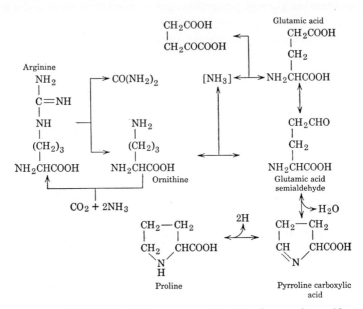

Fig. 14. Metabolic relations among the 5-carbon amino acids.

to proline (cf. Fig. 14) in the presence of TPNH or of DPNH has been identified in *Neurospora* extracts.[163] In microorganisms, as in mammals, proline also can be formed from ornithine by the pathway shown in Fig. 14, but this route is probably of minor significance in the formation of proline from carbon supplied as carbohydrate.[164]

Microorganisms use glutamic acid as a precursor of ornithine and of arginine; the pathway followed in *T. utilis* and in *Neurospora* is like that in animals (cf. Fig. 14). However, in *E. coli* and several other bacteria, glutamic acid is first acetylated, and the resulting N-acetylglutamic acid appears to be reduced to the corresponding γ-semialdehyde; this compound is converted to Nα-acetylornithine by a transamination reaction. As shown in the scheme on page 815, the final step in the synthesis of ornithine is the hydrolytic removal of the acetyl group.[165] Despite the

[163] T. Yura and H. J. Vogel, *Biochim. et Biophys. Acta,* **17,** 582 (1955).

[164] H. J. Vogel and D. M. Bonner, *Proc. Natl. Acad. Sci.,* **40,** 688 (1954); H. J. Vogel, *J. Am. Chem. Soc.,* **78,** 2631 (1956).

[165] W. K. Maas et al., *Proc. Natl. Acad. Sci.,* **39,** 1004 (1953); H. J. Vogel and D. M. Bonner, *J. Biol. Chem.,* **218,** 97 (1956).

different route of ornithine formation in bacteria, as compared to that in higher animals, yeasts, and molds, the role of glutamic acid as the precursor of ornithine explains how this C_5 diamino acid can be formed from carbon supplied as carbohydrate or fat.

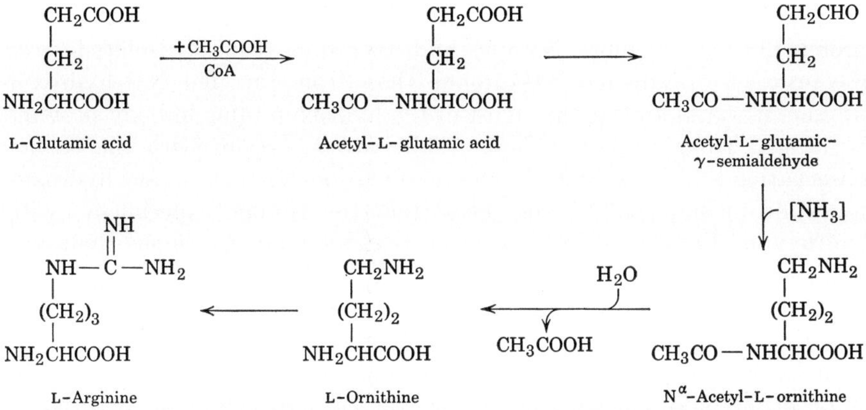

Many microorganisms contain enzymes that degrade arginine to ornithine (cf. p. 853); some can also decarboxylate ornithine to yield putrescine (p. 767). In the latter respect, strains of *Hemophilus para-influenzae* appear to be deficient, since they require trace amounts of putrescine for growth. This diamine may be replaced by agmatine (p. 767), 1,3-propane diamine, or the polyamines spermine and spermidine (p. 66).[166] It is of interest that the microbial synthesis of spermidine appears to be effected by a reaction between putrescine and S-adenosylmethionine (p. 804); in this process, the carboxyl group of methionine is lost as CO_2, and the resulting $-CH_2CH_2CH_2NH_2$ group is transferred to one of the nitrogen atoms of putrescine.[167]

Metabolism of Proline and Hydroxyproline

Both proline and hydroxyproline are among the dispensable dietary amino acids for animals. The current views about the biosynthesis of proline have already been discussed in the section dealing with the metabolism of arginine. Hydroxyproline has been shown, by the isotope technique, to be formed from proline in the intact rat,[155] and by collagen-forming cells such as osteoblasts grown in tissue culture. Although the mechanism of this conversion has not been elucidated as yet, it is known

[166] E. J. Herbst et al., *J. Biol. Chem.*, **214**, 175 (1955).
[167] H. Tabor et al., *J. Am. Chem. Soc.*, **79**, 2978 (1957); R. C. Greene, *ibid.*, **79**, 3929 (1957).

that the over-all oxidation reaction by which kidney slices convert proline to glutamic acid does not involve the intermediate formation of hydroxyproline.

Experiments in which hydroxyproline containing N^{15} was fed to rats have shown that, in contrast to other amino acids, dietary hydroxyproline is not incorporated to an appreciable extent into the body proteins.[168] Since more isotopic hydroxyproline can be isolated from the proteins of rats fed N^{15}-proline than from rats fed N^{15}-hydroxyproline, it would appear that most of the hydroxyproline in body proteins is derived from proline. These results are in accord with the earlier observation that the rabbit excretes a large proportion of dietary hydroxy-L-proline unchanged.[169] The data from the isotope experiments with hydroxyproline also provide evidence that, *in vivo*, exogenous hydroxyproline is not converted directly to proline. The finding that glutamic acid isolated from rats fed N^{15}-labeled hydroxyproline contains N^{15} indicates that the imino nitrogen can enter the metabolic ammonia "pool." It has been known for many years that hydroxyproline, like proline, is glucogenic in the phlorizinized dog. Hence the carbon skeleton of both imino acids can be used in the biosynthesis of glucose. The oxidation by kidney slices of proline to glutamic acid and to α-ketoglutaric acid suggests the metabolic pathway by which the carbon atoms of proline may give rise to carbohydrate. From the results of experiments using kidney and liver preparations, it has been inferred that the reactions involved in the oxidation of hydroxyproline and of proline are analogous. Evidence for the formation of γ-hydroxyglutamic acid semialdehyde from hydroxyproline has been reported, and this transformation probably represents the initial step in the catabolism of hydroxyproline in higher animals. Furthermore, the administration of hydroxyproline-2-C^{14} to rats leads to the appearance of labeled alanine in the liver proteins.[170] It has been suggested that alanine may arise by cleavage of γ-hydroxyglutamic acid in a manner analogous to the cleavage of threonine to glycine (cf. p. 792).

Metabolism of Glutamic Acid

Both glutamic acid and glutamine, the γ-amide of glutamic acid, play central roles in nitrogen metabolism. It will be recalled that glutamic acid, by virtue of its metabolic conversion to α-ketoglutaric acid, serves as an important link between the intermediate metabolism of proteins and of carbohydrates. The deamination, transamination, and decarboxylation reactions involving glutamic acid or glutamine have already been

[168] M. R. Stetten, *J. Biol. Chem.*, **181**, 31 (1949).
[169] S. Pedersen and H. B. Lewis, *J. Biol. Chem.*, **154**, 705 (1944).
[170] G. Wolf et al., *J. Biol. Chem.*, **223**, 95 (1956).

discussed in Chapter 31, and the metabolic relationship of this amino acid to arginine and proline was described earlier in this chapter. Glutamic acid is also related metabolically to histidine (cf. p. 822), and glutamine plays an important role in the metabolism of purines (Chapter 35).

As noted previously, glutamic acid and glutamine are readily interconvertible in a variety of biological systems. These two substances represent a high proportion of the nonprotein nitrogen in animal tissues; for example, one third of the amino acid nitrogen of human blood plasma is in the form of these two amino acids. Glutamine functions both as a storage form of ammonia (ammonium ions), which is toxic to animal tissues, and also as an intermediate in the removal of ammonia from the animal organism[171] (cf. p. 848).

The metabolism of glutamic acid and glutamine appears to be of special significance in nerve tissue.[172] The enzyme systems known to be involved in the deamination, decarboxylation, transamination, and amidation reactions of glutamic acid are all especially active in brain. It has also been found that slices of brain cortex are more efficient than other tissues in their ability to absorb glutamic acid from the medium in which they are suspended. Thus glutamic acid is concentrated within brain cells against a concentration gradient if glucose also is present in the suspension fluid; during this process, the glucose is oxidized and apparently serves as the source of energy required for the uptake of glutamic acid. In the presence of glucose, brain cortex slices absorb potassium ions together with glutamic acid; apparently, the potassium ions are the cationic equivalent for the glutamic acid anions in the assimilation process. This ability of glutamic acid to aid in the transport of potassium ions across cell membranes is highly specific; other amino acids do not replace glutamic acid, and even glutamine is inactive.[173]

Higher plants contain several derivatives of glutamic acid, such as γ-methylglutamic acid and γ-methyleneglutamic acid (cf. p. 63), whose mode of formation is unknown at present. γ-Aminobutyric acid, another plant constituent, probably arises by decarboxylation of glutamic acid. It should be added that, in cultures of carrot tissue, γ-aminobutyric acid is readily converted to glutamic acid, but the enzymic pathway of this conversion has not been established.[174]

The degradation of glutamic acid in most biological systems proceeds by the oxidation of α-ketoglutaric acid in the citric acid cycle. However, in the anaerobe *Clostridium tetanomorphum*, the fermentation of glutamic

171 A. Meister, *Physiol. Revs.*, **36**, 103 (1956).
172 H. Weil-Malherbe, *Physiol. Revs.*, **30**, 549 (1950).
173 H. A. Krebs et al., *Biochem. J.*, **44**, 159, 410 (1949); **47**, 139 (1950).
174 F. C. Steward et al., *Nature*, **178**, 734 (1956).

acid to NH_3, CO_2, acetic acid, and butyric acid involves the intermediate formation of 2-methylfumaric acid (mesaconic acid).[175] From studies with C^{14}-labeled substrates it appears that the fermentation is accom-

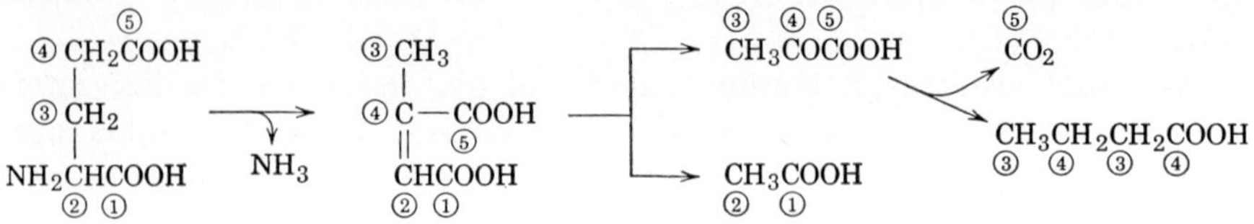

Mesaconic acid

panied by the transformations shown in the accompanying scheme. The mechanism of the interesting rearrangement involved in the conversion of glutamic acid to mesaconic acid remains to be elucidated.

Metabolism of Aspartic Acid

Like glutamic acid, aspartic acid serves to link protein metabolism to carbohydrate metabolism through its reversible conversion to oxaloacetic acid, a member of the citric acid cycle. As noted earlier, aspartic acid is an intermediate in the microbial biosynthesis of homoserine (cf. p. 790), and hence of isoleucine, threonine, and methionine. In some microorganisms, aspartic acid is also directly involved in the formation of lysine (cf. p. 810).

When N^{15}-labeled L-aspartic acid is fed to rats, the amino acid is deaminated at an extremely rapid rate, and the amino nitrogen appears to be metabolized like nitrogen fed in the form of ammonium ions rather than like nitrogen supplied in the α-amino groups of glycine, leucine, or lysine.[176] Thus aspartic acid isolated from the proteins of the test animals contains less N^{15} than does the protein glutamic acid, and the urinary ammonia has less isotope than does the urinary urea. A similar distribution of N^{15} in urinary ammonia and urea is observed after the feeding of N^{15}-labeled ammonium citrate. The rapid conversion of aspartic acid nitrogen to urea is a consequence of the role of aspartic acid as a nitrogen donor in urea synthesis (cf. p. 851).

The extremely rapid transfer of nitrogen from aspartic acid to glutamic acid is believed to occur almost exclusively by a transamination reaction. In the oxidation of L-aspartic acid by washed particles of rat liver, the ammonia liberated is derived from the combined action of the L-glutamic-aspartic transaminase and the L-glutamic acid dehydrogenase; the oxidation of the carbon atoms of aspartic acid to carbon dioxide involves the

[175] J. T. Wachsman and H. A. Barker, *J. Biol. Chem.*, **217**, 695 (1955); J. T. Wachsman, *ibid.*, **223**, 19 (1956).

[176] H. Wu and D. Rittenberg, *J. Biol. Chem.*, **179**, 847 (1949).

entrance of oxaloacetic acid, formed from the amino acid, into the citric acid cycle.

Asparagine (the β-amide of aspartic acid), as well as glutamine, is an important intermediate in the nitrogen metabolism of plants (cf. p. 742). Extracts of lupine seedings and of wheat germ effect the synthesis of asparagine from aspartic acid and ammonia; this process requires the presence of ATP, and resembles the synthesis of glutamine (cf. p. 721).[177] An ATP-dependent synthesis of asparagine has not been found in animal tissues. However, the formation of asparagine from α-ketosuccinamic acid is catalyzed by liver transaminases (cf. p. 762); the biological significance of this reaction is uncertain, since α-ketosuccinamic acid is not known to arise from sources other than asparagine itself.

Metabolism of Histidine [178]

Except for the adult human, all animals whose dietary requirement for histidine has been examined must be supplied with an external source of this amino acid. Although it has been proved unequivocally that the exclusion of histidine from the diet of the human has no demonstrable effect upon the maintenance of nitrogen balance, it is not clear whether histidine is actually synthesized in human tissues or whether the amino acid is made by the intestinal microorganisms and utilized by the host.[179] It appears however that human liver can incorporate carbon supplied as $HC^{14}OOH$ into position 2 of the imidazole ring (see Fig. 15 for numbering of the histidine skeleton), a process characteristic of histidine synthesis in microorganisms; on the other hand, rat liver seems to be unable to effect this incorporation.

Since D-histidine and β-imidazolylpyruvic acid can replace L-histidine in the diet of the rat, it would appear that the requirement of this animal for histidine is a reflection of an inability to synthesize the keto acid.[180] Several microorganisms (*Lactobacilli, Escherichia coli*) also can use β-imidazolylpyruvic acid as a source of histidine.[181] Although animals and bacteria clearly are able to convert β-imidazolylpyruvic acid to histidine by a transamination reaction, the available information indicates that the keto acid is not an intermediate in the microbial synthesis of histidine from carbohydrate carbon and ammonia nitrogen. In all the microorganisms studied (e.g., *Neurospora, E. coli*, yeast), the pathway of histidine synthesis is that shown in Fig. 15.

[177] G. C. Webster and J. E. Varner, *J. Biol. Chem.*, **215**, 91 (1955).

[178] H. Tabor, *Pharmacol. Revs.*, **6**, 299 (1954).

[179] W. C. Rose et al., *J. Biol. Chem.*, **188**, 49 (1951).

[180] R. M. Conrad and C. P. Berg, *J. Biol. Chem.*, **117**, 351 (1937).

[181] H. P. Broquist and E. E. Snell, *J. Biol. Chem.*, **180**, 59 (1949); J. Westley and J. Ceithaml, *Arch. Biochem. and Biophys.*, **60**, 215 (1956).

Mutant strains of *Neurospora* and of *E. coli* that require histidine for growth have been shown to accumulate one or more of the intermediates given in Fig. 15. Subsequent work led to the identification and partial purification of the enzymes that catalyze the component reactions.

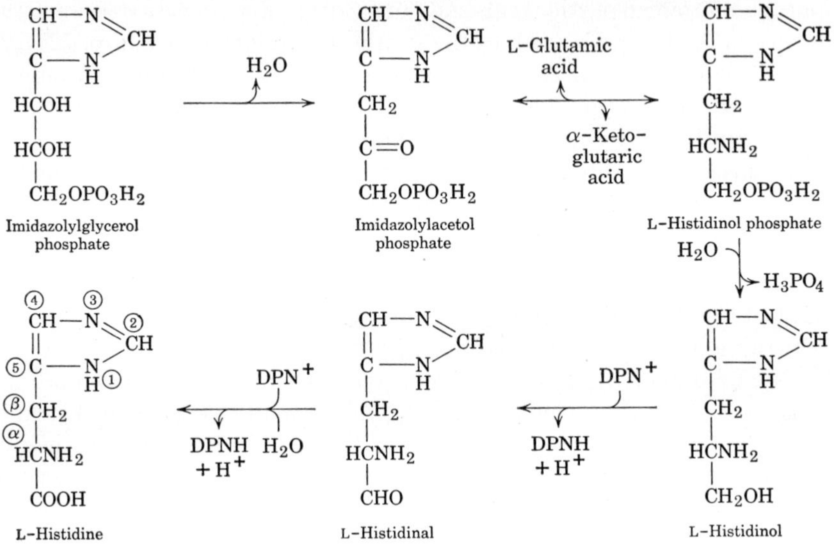

$$
\begin{array}{c}
\text{CH—N} \\
\text{|| } \diagdown \text{CH} \\
\text{C — N} \\
\text{| H} \\
\text{HCOH} \\
\text{|} \\
\text{HCOH} \\
\text{|} \\
\text{CH}_2\text{OPO}_3\text{H}_2
\end{array}
\xrightarrow[\;\;H_2O\;\;]{}
\begin{array}{c}
\text{CH—N} \\
\text{|| } \diagdown \text{CH} \\
\text{C — N} \\
\text{| H} \\
\text{CH}_2 \\
\text{|} \\
\text{C}=\text{O} \\
\text{|} \\
\text{CH}_2\text{OPO}_3\text{H}_2
\end{array}
\underset{\alpha\text{-Keto-glutaric acid}}{\overset{\text{L-Glutamic acid}}{\rightleftharpoons}}
\begin{array}{c}
\text{CH—N} \\
\text{|| } \diagdown \text{CH} \\
\text{C — N} \\
\text{| H} \\
\text{CH}_2 \\
\text{|} \\
\text{HCNH}_2 \\
\text{|} \\
\text{CH}_2\text{OPO}_3\text{H}_2
\end{array}
$$

Imidazolylglycerol phosphate   Imidazolylacetol phosphate   L-Histidinol phosphate

$$H_2O \searrow \qquad \searrow H_3PO_4$$

L-Histidine:

④ CH—N ② ③
‖ ╲CH
⑤ C — N ①
| H
⑧ CH₂
α
HCNH₂
|
COOH

(with DPN⁺, DPNH H₂O + H⁺)

L-Histidinal:

CH—N
‖ ╲CH
C — N
| H
CH₂
|
HCNH₂
|
CHO

(with DPN⁺, DPNH + H⁺)

L-Histidinol:

CH—N
‖ ╲CH
C — N
| H
CH₂
|
HCNH₂
|
CH₂OH

Fig. 15. Biosynthesis of histidine in microorganisms.

These involve the dehydration of imidazolylglycerol phosphate, the transamination reaction between glutamic acid and imidazolylacetol phosphate, and the dephosphorylation of histidinol phosphate, for which enzymes have been obtained from *Neurospora*.[182] The enzyme system that oxidizes histidinol (histidinol dehydrogenase) has been obtained from yeast, *E. coli*, and other bacteria;[183] it catalyzes the following reactions:

(1)   L-Histidinol + 2DPN⁺ → L-Histidine + 2DPNH + 2H⁺

(2)   L-Histidinal + DPN⁺ → L-Histidine + DPNH + H⁺

(3)   L-Histidinal + DPNH + H⁺ → L-Histidinol + DPN⁺

Although histidinal has not been isolated as an intermediate in reaction 1, the aldehyde is assumed to be formed from histidinol by a reversal of reaction 3, and immediately oxidized to histidine by reaction 2.

[182] B. N. Ames et al., *J. Biol. Chem.*, **212**, 687 (1955); **220**, 113 (1956); **226**, 583; **228**, 67 (1957).

[183] E. Adams, *J. Biol. Chem.*, **209**, 829 (1954); **217**, 325 (1955).

Little is known about the metabolic pathways in the biosynthesis of imidazolylglycerol phosphate. Studies with C^{14}-labeled carbon sources suggest that the 5-carbon chain of histidine, consisting of the carbons in the carboxyl group and in the α, β, 5, and 4 positions (cf. Fig. 15), is derived from a pentose.[184] It is probable that, in the microbial synthesis of imidazolylglycerol phosphate, nitrogen 1 and carbon 2 of the purine ring of adenosine-5'-phosphate are transferred as a unit to carbon 1 of ribose-5-phosphate (which presumably enters the reaction in the form of 5-phosphoribosyl-1-pyrophosphate; p. 885), to provide nitrogen 3 and carbon 2 of the imidazole ring.[185] Nitrogen 1 of the imidazole ring is derived from the amide nitrogen of glutamine. The loss of nitrogen 1 and carbon 2 from the purine ring of adenosine-5'-phosphate gives rise to 5-aminoimidazole-4-carboxamide ribotide, a metabolic precursor of inosinic acid (Chapter 35). That carbon 2 of the imidazole ring may be derived from carbon 2 of the purine portion of a nucleotide is concordant with the observation that carbon 2 of the imidazole ring also can be derived from formate (p. 819), provided an adequate supply of folic acid is present; as will be seen in Chapter 35, formate is a metabolic precursor of carbon 2 of the purine ring, and is introduced in a process that involves the participation of a folic acid cofactor.

Metabolic Breakdown of Histidine. Experiments in which rats were given histidine labeled with N^{15} in the imidazole ring showed that the labeled nitrogen was utilized in the same manner as ammonia or as the α-amino nitrogen of dietary amino acids.[186] The degradation of histidine by enzyme preparations from mammalian livers or from various microorganisms (*Pseudomonas fluorescens, Aerobacter aerogenes, Clostridium tetanomorphum*) leads to the production, per mole of histidine, of 1 mole of glutamic acid, 1 mole of a C_1 compound, and 2 moles of ammonia. As shown in Fig. 16, all the biological systems studied degrade histidine to α-formimino-L-glutamic acid[187] (also termed formamidinoglutaric acid or formamidoglutamic acid). This product arises from histidine by the action of histidine-α-deaminase (p. 755) to produce urocanic acid,[188] which is converted to formiminoglutamic acid by the action of the enzyme urocanase. The mechanism of the latter reaction

[184] L. Levy and M. J. Coon, *J. Biol. Chem.*, **208**, 691 (1954); J. Westley and J. Ceithaml, *ibid.*, **219**, 139 (1956).

[185] A. Neidle and H. Waelsch, *J. Am. Chem. Soc.*, **78**, 1767 (1956); H. S. Moyed and B. Magasanik, *ibid.*, **79**, 4812 (1957).

[186] C. Tesar and D. Rittenberg, *J. Biol. Chem.*, **170**, 35 (1947).

[187] B. A. Borek and H. Waelsch, *J. Biol. Chem.*, **205**, 459 (1953); A. Miller and H. Waelsch, *J. Biol. Chem.*, **228**, 365 (1957); H. Tabor and A. H. Mehler, *ibid.*, **210**, 559 (1954).

[188] A. H. Mehler and O. Hayaishi, *Biochem. Preparations*, **4**, 50 (1955).

is not clear, but is believed to involve the intermediate formation of imidazolone propionic acid, as shown in Fig. 16.

The further breakdown of formiminoglutamic acid is different in various biological forms. *Aerobacter aerogenes* contains an enzyme system that converts it to L-glutamic acid and formamide; in intact cells, formamide is oxidized to CO_2 and NH_3.[189] In *Pseudomonas fluorescens*,

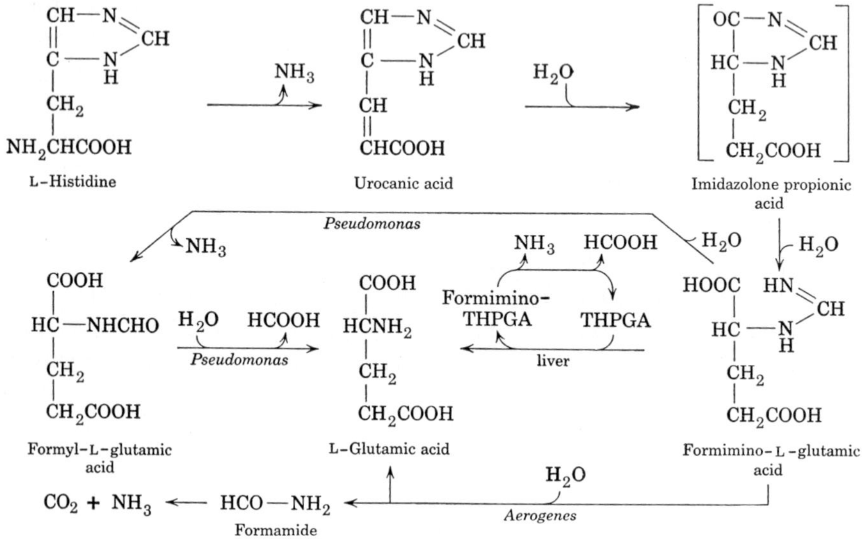

Fig. 16. Degradation of histidine in mammalian liver and in microorganisms. Tetrahydropteroyl-L-glutamic acid is abbreviated THPGA.

formiminoglutamic acid is hydrolyzed to ammonia and N-formyl-L-glutamic acid, which is further degraded by another enzyme to yield glutamic acid and formic acid.

The conversion of formiminoglutamic acid to glutamic acid, formic acid, and ammonia also occurs in mammalian liver, but formylglutamic acid is not an intermediate. Instead, the entire formimino group appears to be transferred to tetrahydroPGA (p. 775),[190] to form N^5-formiminotetrahydroPGA and L-glutamic acid. Ring closure of the folic acid derivative to form $N^{5,10}$-methenyltetrahydroPGA (anhydroleucovorin) results in the liberation of ammonia, and anhydroleucovorin is then converted to N^{10}-formyltetrahydroPGA, from which formic acid is liberated.[191] In this connection, it is significant that formiminoglutamic

[189] B. Magasanik and H. R. Bowser, *J. Biol. Chem.*, **213**, 571 (1955).

[190] A. Miller and H. Waelsch, *J. Biol. Chem.*, **228**, 383, 397 (1957).

[191] H. Tabor and J. C. Rabinowitz, *J. Am. Chem. Soc.*, **78**, 5705 (1956).

acid is excreted in relatively large amounts in the urine of rats deficient in folic acid.[192]

Reference has already been made to several of the derivatives of histidine present in living organisms. One of the most important of these is histamine, formed by the action of histidine decarboxylase. This amine is both a vasodepressor and a stimulator of gastric secretion in higher animals. Mammalian tissues contain an enzyme system, termed histaminase (or diamine oxidase, since it attacks putrescine, cadaverine, and agmatine), which oxidizes histamine. Pyridoxal phosphate appears to be a cofactor for the diamine oxidase of swine kidney.[193] Diamine oxidase activity has also been found in bacteria, higher plants, reptiles, and birds.[194] Although it has not been determined whether enzymes of different specificity are involved, their action on amines is described by the equation

$$RCH_2NH_2 + O_2 + H_2O \rightarrow RCHO + NH_3 + H_2O_2$$

Thus histamine is converted to β-imidazolylacetaldehyde, known to be oxidized by aldehyde oxidase or by xanthine oxidase (p. 339) to imid-

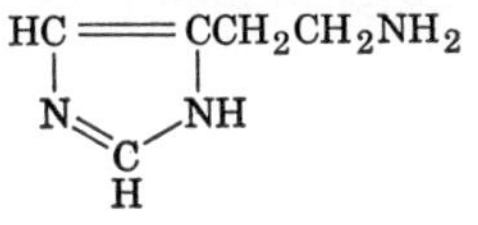

Histamine

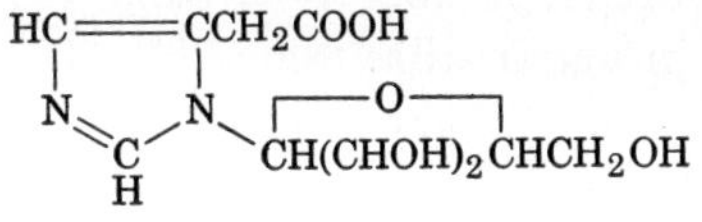

1-Ribosylimidazolylacetic acid

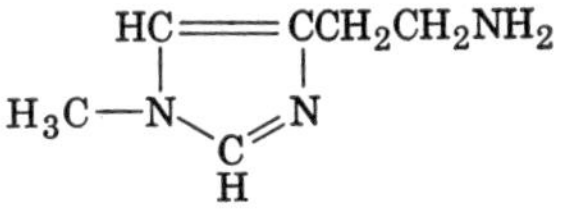

3-Methylhistamine

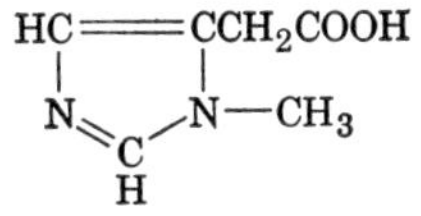

1-Methylimidazolylacetic acid

azolylacetic acid; this product could also arise by oxidative decarboxylation of β-imidazolylpyruvic acid, formed by deamination of histidine. Imidazolylacetic acid and its riboside represent end products of histamine metabolism *in vivo*, and have been found in the urine of higher animals.[195] A major route of histamine catabolism leads to the excretion of 3-methylhistamine and its oxidation product 3-methylimidazolylacetic acid; 1-methylimidazolylacetic acid is also formed in small amounts.[196] The

[192] J. E. Seegmiller et al., *J. Am. Chem. Soc.*, **76**, 6205 (1954).

[193] A. N. Davison, *Biochem. J.*, **64**, 546 (1956).

[194] E. A. Zeller, in J. B. Sumner and K. Myrbäck, *The Enzymes*, Chapter 59, Academic Press, New York, 1951.

[195] S. A. Karjala et al., *J. Biol. Chem.*, **219**, 9 (1956); G. Wolf et al., *ibid.*, **222**, 159 (1956)

[196] R. W. Schayer and S. A. Karjala, *J. Biol. Chem.*, **221**, 307 (1956).

fact that histamine is converted to imidazolylacetic acid derivatives that are methylated at one of the imidazole nitrogens is of interest since the corresponding N-methyl derivatives of histidine also have been found in the urine of some mammals. It appears that the methylation reactions can occur either before or after histidine has been decarboxylated to yield histamine. In higher animals (including man), histamine is also excreted in the urine as α-N-acetylhistamine.

Among the other derivatives of histidine found in animal tissues are the dipeptides carnosine and anserine (p. 137), whose mode of biosynthesis is not known. Methionine appears to serve as a source of the N-methyl group of anserine,[197] but it is uncertain whether the methylation of the imidazole ring occurs before the formation of the peptide bond between the β-alanine and histidine residues. As noted above, the methylhistidine derived from anserine has been isolated from animal urine, and may arise by the hydrolysis of the dipeptide rather than by direct methylation of histidine.

Another naturally occurring histidine derivative is ergothioneine (a betaine of 2-thiolhistidine; p. 67), found in ergot (the fungus *Claviceps purpurea*), molds (*Neurospora, Aspergillus*), higher plants (oats, corn), and in mammalian blood.[198] The ergothioneine in animal tissues appears to be of dietary origin.[199] The available information about its biosynthesis in microorganisms suggests that ergothioneine arises from histidine.[200]

Metabolism of Phenylalanine and Tyrosine [201]

Mammalian Metabolism of Phenylalanine and Tyrosine. The close metabolic relationship of phenylalanine and tyrosine, to be expected from the similarity in their chemical structure, is borne out by a large number of studies on these two amino acids. In 1913 Embden showed, by means of perfusion experiments with dog liver, that this tissue can convert phenylalanine to tyrosine. After the introduction of the isotope technique, evidence was presented for the conversion of phenylalanine to tyrosine by mammals[202] and by invertebrates.[203] This finding was in

[197] I. R. McManus, *J. Biol. Chem.*, **225**, 325 (1957).

[198] D. J. Bell, *Ann. Reps.*, **52**, 285 (1956); D. B. Melville et al., *J. Biol. Chem.*, **223**, 9 (1956).

[199] D. B. Melville et al., *J. Biol. Chem.*, **213**, 61 (1955); **218**, 647 (1956).

[200] H. Heath and J. Wildy, *Biochem. J.*, **64**, 612 (1956); *Nature*, **179**, 196 (1957); D. B. Melville et al., *J. Biol. Chem.*, **224**, 871 (1957).

[201] A. B. Lerner, *Advances in Enzymol.*, **14**, 73 (1953); C. E. Dalgliesh, *Advances in Protein Chem.*, **10**, 31 (1955).

[202] A. R. Moss and R. Schoenheimer, *J. Biol. Chem.*, **135**, 415 (1940); S. Udenfriend and S. P. Bessman, *ibid.*, **203**, 961 (1953).

[203] T. Fukuda, *J. Biochem. (Japan)*, **43**, 137 (1956).

accord with the earlier demonstration that phenylalanine is an indispensable amino acid, but tyrosine is not[204] (cf. p. 726). Moreover, both in the rat and in man, the requirement for phenylalanine is markedly reduced by the inclusion of tyrosine in the diet.[205]

The formation of tyrosine from phenylalanine is catalyzed by a liver enzyme preparation ("phenylalanine hydroxylase") for whose action molecular oxygen, a pyridine nucleotide (probably TPNH), and ferrous

$$\text{L-Phenylalanine} + \text{TPNH} + \text{H}^+ + \text{O}_2 \rightarrow \text{L-Tyrosine} + \text{TPN}^+ + \text{H}_2\text{O}$$

ions are required.[206] It is of interest that the hydroxylation of many aromatic compounds, including phenylalanine, can be effected in nonenzymic systems in the presence of O_2 and ascorbic acid, with Fe^{2+} ions as the catalyst.[207]

Important data on the fate of phenylalanine and tyrosine in mammals were accumulated in the study of several "inborn errors in metabolism" (p. 398). In one of these diseases, known as phenylketonuria (also called phenylpyruvic oligophrenia), phenylalanine, phenylpyruvic acid, phenyllactic acid, and phenylacetic acid are excreted in the urine after the feeding of diets high in phenylalanine or in protein. The largest incidence of this metabolic abnormality is found among inmates of mental hospitals. The phenylketonuric subject cannot convert phenylalanine to tyrosine at the normal rate and therefore forms phenylpyruvic acid in excess of the normal amount. This keto acid is partially excreted unchanged and partially metabolized to phenyllactic and phenylacetic acids, both of which also are excreted. Individuals who are not phenylketonuric, but who carry the genetic factor for the disease (parents of phenylketonuric patients), also appear to have a lowered capacity for the oxidation of phenylalanine.[208] Normal individuals, who readily metabolize phenylpyruvic and phenyllactic acids (probably by conversion to phenylalanine and subsequent oxidation via tyrosine) excrete phenylacetic acid (as phenylacetylglutamine) when this compound is fed. Thus it would appear that phenylacetic acid is not a normal intermediate in the metabolism of phenylalanine. Human urine normally contains a small amount of phenylacetylglutamine, but in phenylketonuria the daily excretion of this substance is about 5 to 10 times that of a normal subject.[209]

Another metabolic abnormality which has given much information

204 M. Womack and W. C. Rose, *J. Biol. Chem.,* **107**, 449 (1934).

205 W. C. Rose and R. L. Wixom, *J. Biol. Chem.,* **217**, 95 (1955).

206 S. Udenfriend and J. R. Cooper, *J. Biol. Chem.,* **194**, 503 (1952); S. Kaufman, *ibid.,* **226**, 511 (1957).

207 S. Udenfriend et al., *J. Biol. Chem.,* **208**, 731, 741 (1954).

208 D. Y. Hsia et al., *Nature,* **178**, 1239 (1956); C. Mitoma et al., *Proc. Soc. Exptl. Biol. Med.,* **94**, 634 (1957).

209 W. H. Stein et al., *J. Am. Chem. Soc.,* **76**, 2848 (1954).

about the metabolism of phenylalanine and tyrosine is the condition known as alcaptonuria, characterized by the excretion of homogentisic acid (2,5-dihydroxyphenylacetic acid). The urine of alcaptonurics rapidly darkens on exposure to air as a result of the oxidation of homogentisic acid to form dark pigments. Since homogentisic acid is readily

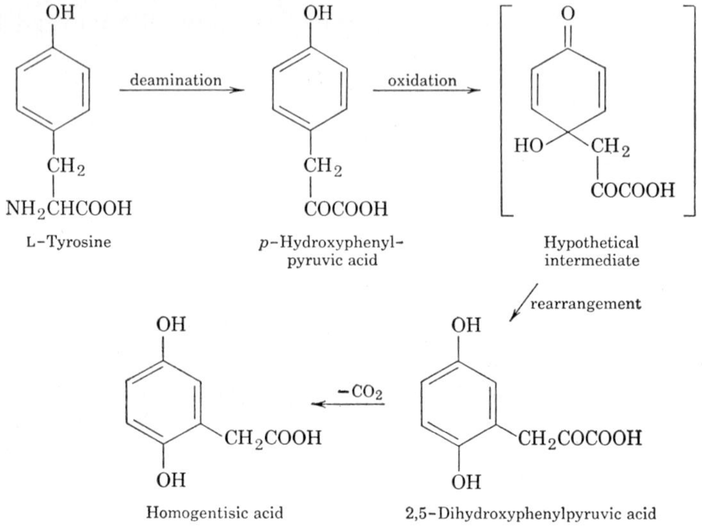

Fig. 17. Possible mode of formation of homogentisic acid.

metabolized by normal animals, it has been assumed to be a normal intermediate in the metabolism of tyrosine; presumably the alcaptonuric is unable to degrade homogentisic acid and therefore excretes it. A possible mechanism for the formation of homogentisic acid, proposed by Neubauer in 1909, is shown in Fig. 17.

The reactions shown in Fig. 17 are effected by enzyme systems present in mammalian liver. The deamination of tyrosine is the result of a transamination reaction involving α-ketoglutaric acid,[210] and the p-hydroxyphenylpyruvic acid is then oxidized to homogentisic acid and CO_2. The mechanism of the oxidative process has not been elucidated, but it appears that molecular oxygen is an essential participant, and that free 2,5-dihydroxyphenylpyruvic acid probably is not an obligatory intermediate.[211] This substance is readily oxidized by crude liver extracts, but not by more highly purified preparations of "p-hydroxyphenylpyruvic oxidase."

[210] B. Schepartz, *J. Biol. Chem.*, **193**, 293 (1951); Z. N. Canellakis and P. P. Cohen, *ibid.*, **222**, 53, 63 (1956).

[211] B. N. La Du and V. G. Zannoni, *J. Biol. Chem.*, **217**, 777 (1955); **219**, 273 (1956); *Nature*, **177**, 574 (1956); S. E. Hager et al., *J. Biol. Chem.*, **225**, 935 (1957).

In the scheme outlined in Fig. 17, it is assumed that the side chain of p-hydroxyphenylpyruvic acid is shifted as a result of the oxidation of the phenol ring, followed by an intramolecular rearrangement and decarboxylation. Although the mechanism by which these reactions are effected is not definitely established, impressive evidence for the intramolecular rearrangement leading to the ultimate formation of homogentisic acid has come from isotope experiments. In these studies,[212] the

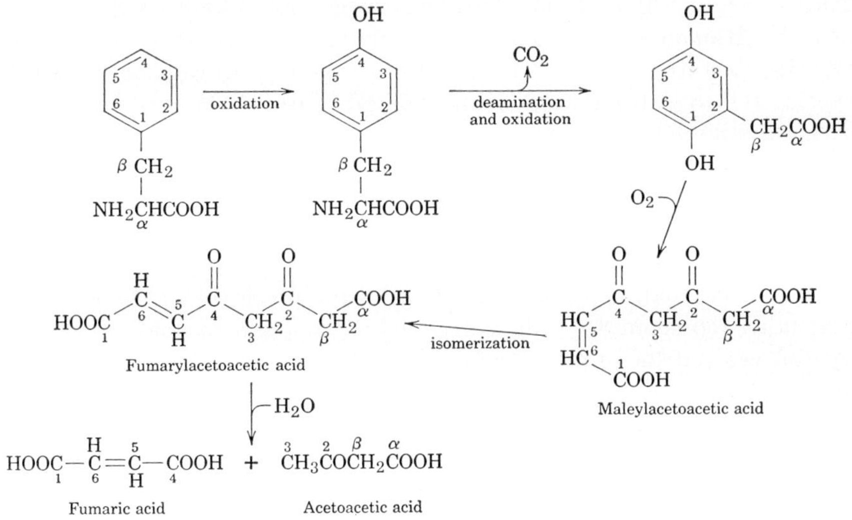

Fig. 18. Oxidative breakdown of phenylalanine and tyrosine. The numbering of the carbon atoms of the benzene ring is intended solely to show their metabolic fate; the numbers do not denote the position of substituents.

oxidation of phenylalanine, of tyrosine, and of homogentisic acid to acetoacetic acid and fumaric acid was examined in phlorizinized rats and with liver slices prepared from normal animals. The results may be summarized by the scheme shown in Fig. 18, where the fate of each of the carbon atoms of phenylalanine is indicated. An enzyme preparation that converts homogentisic acid to acetoacetic acid and fumaric acid has been obtained from liver tissue, and has been fractionated to yield three separate enzyme systems. One of these is an Fe^{2+}-activated enzyme (homogentisic oxidase) which, in the presence of O_2, cleaves homogentisic acid to maleylacetoacetic acid.[213] This is probably the reaction that is

[212] S. Weinhouse and R. H. Millington, J. Biol. Chem., **175**, 995 (1948); **181**, 645 (1949); B. Schepartz and S. Gurin, ibid., **180**, 663 (1949); A. B. Lerner, ibid., **181**, 281 (1949); R. G. Ravdin and D. I. Crandall, ibid., **189**, 137 (1951).

[213] W. E. Knox and S. W. Edwards, J. Biol. Chem., **216**, 479, 489 (1955).

"blocked" in alcaptonuric individuals. By the action of a glutathione-dependent isomerase, maleylacetoacetic acid is transformed to fumaryl-acetoacetic acid,[214] which is then hydrolyzed by "fumarylacetoacetic hydrolase" as shown in Fig. 18.

The vitamin ascorbic acid (Chapter 39) appears to be concerned, in some as yet undetermined manner, with the metabolism of tyrosine in animals. Thus scorbutic guinea pigs (animals suffering from scurvy as a result of the removal of ascorbic acid from the diet) excrete homogentisic acid, p-hydroxyphenylpyruvic acid, and p-hydroxyphenyllactic acid.[215] Human subjects deficient in this vitamin also exhibit abnormal tyrosine metabolism.[216] The administration of ascorbic acid to both species restores the normal utilization of tyrosine. Ascorbic acid also exerts a stimulatory effect on the oxidation of p-hydroxyphenylpyruvic acid and of homogentisic acid by some tissue preparations. However, these effects appear to be nonspecific, and are thought to be related to the strong reducing capacity of the vitamin and to the "protection" of the oxidases from inactivation by molecular oxygen.

In the mammal, tyrosine also serves as the precursor of the hormones adrenalin (epinephrine) and noradrenalin (norepinephrine), elaborated by the adrenal medulla (Chapter 38). Experiments in which phenylalanine labeled with tritium in the benzene ring and with C^{14} in the α-carbon was administered to rats have shown that this amino acid can be converted to adrenalin.[217] The available evidence indicates that the

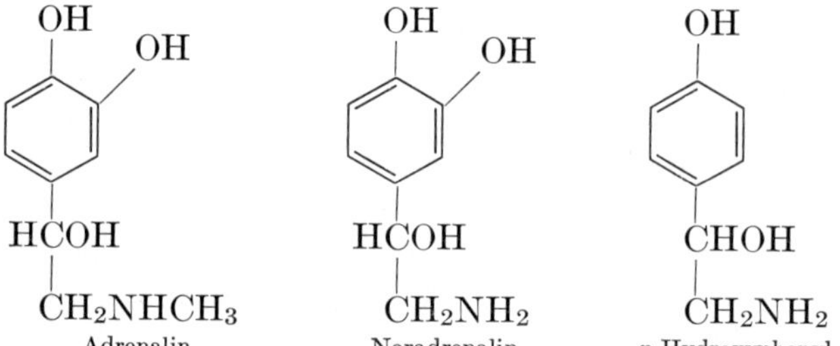

OH   OH
HCOH
CH₂NHCH₃
Adrenalin

OH   OH
HCOH
CH₂NH₂
Noradrenalin

OH
CHOH
CH₂NH₂
p-Hydroxyphenyl-ethanolamine

conversion involves the metabolic pathway shown in Fig. 19.[218] 3,4-Dihydroxy-L-phenylalanine ("dopa") and 3,4-dihydroxyphenylethylamine (hydroxytyramine) have been found in human urine and extracts of the

[214] S. W. Edwards and W. E. Knox, *J. Biol. Chem.*, **220**, 79 (1956).

[215] R. R. Sealock and H. E. Silberstein, *J. Biol. Chem.*, **135**, 251 (1940).

[216] S. Z. Levine et al., *J. Clin. Invest.*, **22**, 551 (1943); L. I. Woolf and M. E. Edmunds, *Biochem. J.*, **47**, 630 (1950).

[217] S. Gurin and A. M. Delluva, *J. Biol. Chem.*, **170**, 545 (1947).

[218] S. Udenfriend and J. B. Wyngaarden, *Biochim. et Biophys. Acta*, **20**, 48 (1956); F. Brücke et al., *Biochem. Z.*, **328**, 56 (1956); M. Goodall and N. Kirshner, *J. Biol. Chem.*, **226**, 213 (1957); *Biochim. et Biophys. Acta*, **24**, 658 (1957).

adrenal gland. "Dopa" may be expected to arise from tyrosine by the action of tyrosinase (p. 367), and is converted to hydroxytyramine by "dopa" decarboxylase, which is present in a variety of mammalian tissues including the adrenal medulla. In the conversion of hydroxytyramine to adrenalin by the adrenal gland, noradrenalin is a probable intermediate.

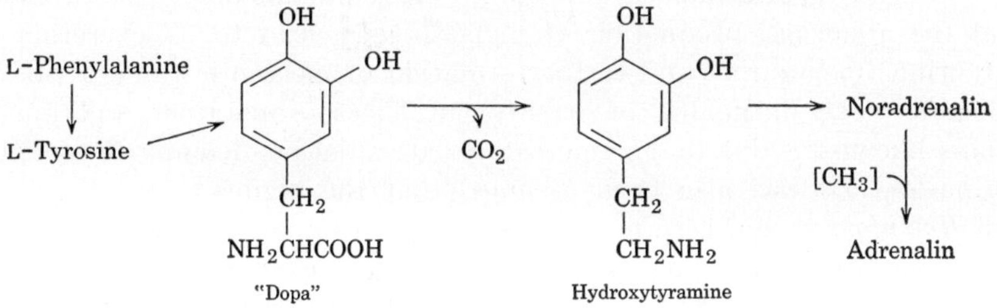

Fig. 19. Probable pathway of adrenalin formation.

Little is known about the process whereby the oxidation of the β-carbon atom of the ethylamine chain is effected; the methylation of noradrenalin to form adrenalin appears to involve an enzymic reaction in which S-adenosylmethionine (p. 804) serves as the methyl donor.

The salivary glands of cephalopods (e.g., the octopus) contain p-hydroxyphenylethanolamine, and it is assumed that this compound arises from tyrosine with the intermediate formation of tyramine. In this connection it is of interest that the saliva of *Octopus macropus* contains as much as 700 mg of free tyrosine per 100 grams of dry weight.

Adrenalin is methylated in the mammalian organism to form the 3-methoxy derivative ("metanephrine"), which is oxidized in a reaction that probably involves "monoamine oxidase"; this enzyme specifically catalyzes the oxidation of many amines according to the equation:[194,219]

$$R'CH_2NR_2 + O_2 + H_2O \rightarrow R'CHO + NHR_2 + H_2O_2$$

The hormone is readily oxidized by ferric compounds to adrenochrome,

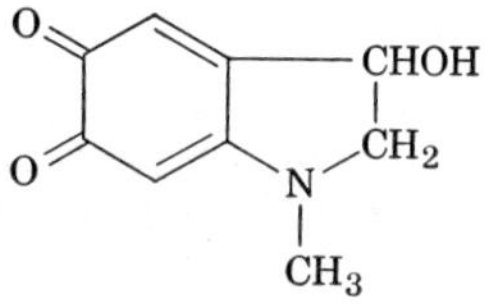

Adrenochrome

[219] H. Blaschko et al., *Biochem. J.,* **31**, 2187 (1937); C. E. M. Pugh and J. H. Quastel, *ibid.,* **31**, 2306 (1937).

which polymerizes to brown melanin-like pigments at alkaline pH values. Some of the iron in ferritin (p. 912) can oxidize adrenalin; this may be of physiological significance, since ferritin may be present in the blood when adrenalin is released into the circulation.[220]

The oxidative metabolism of tyrosine in animals, plants, and bacteria may result in the formation of brown or black pigments called melanins. These pigments are found in the skin of most animals other than albinos, and the abnormal production of melanin may lead to its excretion in the urine (melanuria) and to the formation of melanotic tumors (melanomas). The darkening of freshly cut slices of potatoes and mushrooms likewise is due to enzyme-catalyzed oxidations leading to melanin formation. It has also been assumed that the pigment of colonies of *Bacillus niger* and of certain other bacteria is composed of melanin. The available information on the mechanism of melanin formation from tyrosine is largely based on the work of Raper and of Mason,[221] and is summarized in Fig. 20.

The initial oxidation of tyrosine or of 3,4-dihydroxyphenylalanine is effected by polyphenol oxidases (cf. p. 366). The red pigment indicated in Fig. 20 is formed by the action of potato tyrosinase on 3,4-dihydroxyphenylalanine, and the further steps appear to depend on the pH of the reaction mixture and may not require enzymic catalysis. It is believed that the melanin formed from tyrosine is a polymer of indole-5,6-quinone.[222]

In animals, 3,4-dihydroxyphenylalanine also appears to be degraded to homoprotocatechuic acid (3,4-dihydroxyphenylacetic acid), which can be methylated *in vivo* to homovanillic acid. These two compounds are

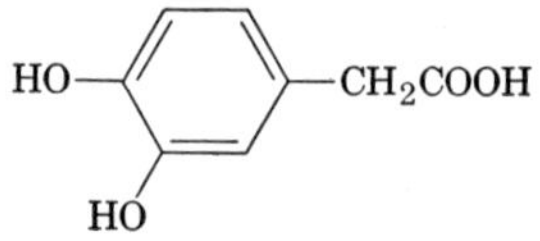

Homoprotocatechuic acid 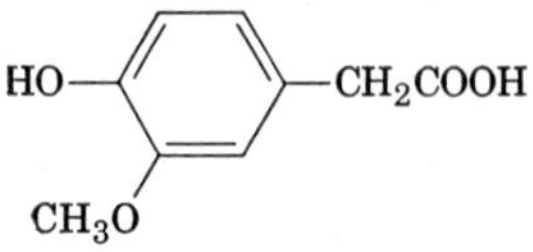   Homovanillic acid

among the many phenolic substances present in human urine; another is 3-methoxy-4-hydroxy-D-mandelic acid, a urinary metabolite of noradrenalin and adrenalin.[223] Although the mechanism of the formation of these various degradation products is not entirely clear, it is probable

[220] S. Green et al., *J. Biol. Chem.*, **220**, 237 (1956).

[221] H. S. Raper, *J. Chem. Soc.*, **1938**, 125; H. S. Mason, *J. Biol. Chem.*, **172**, 83 (1948).

[222] R. J. T. Cromartie and J. Harley-Mason, *Biochem. J.*, **66**, 713 (1957).

[223] M. D. Armstrong et al., *J. Biol. Chem.*, **218**, 293 (1956); K. N. F. Shaw et al., *ibid.*, **226**, 255 (1957); M. D. Armstrong et al., *Biochim. et Biophys. Acta*, **25**, 422 (1957); J. Axelrod et al., *J. Biol. Chem.*, **233**, 697, 702 (1958).

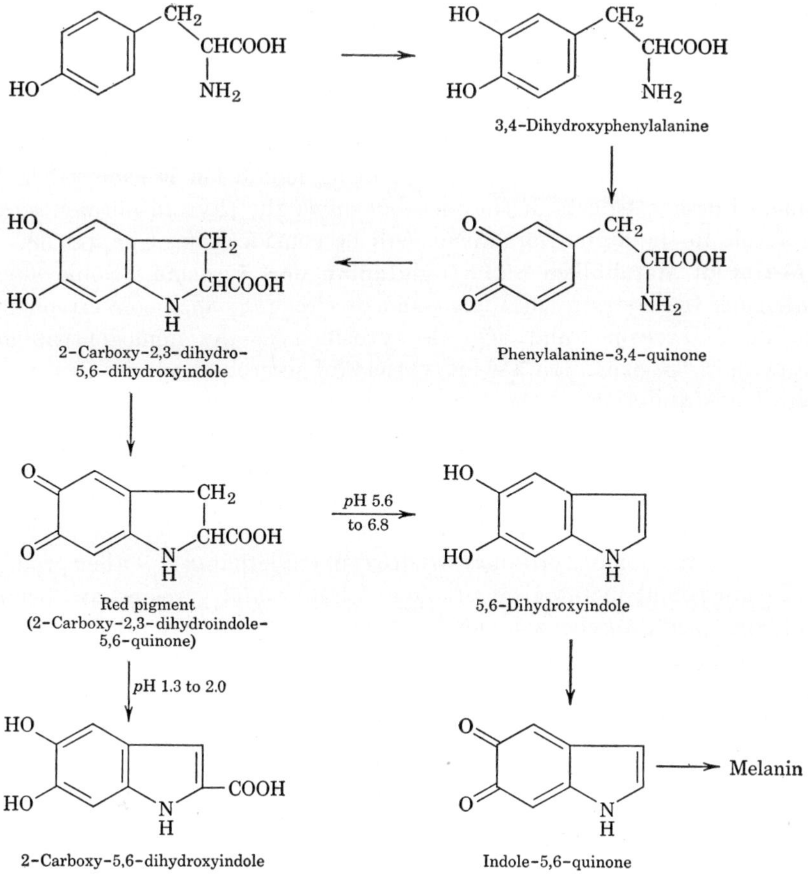

Fig. 20. Proposed mechanism of melanin formation.

that the O-methylation is effected by S-adenosylmethionine.

Among the protein amino acids is the hormone thyroxine (3,5,3′,5′-tetraiodothyronine; p. 69), which is found in the thyroid gland together with 3-iodo-L-tyrosine, 3,3′-diiodothyronine, and the 3,3′,5′- and 3,5,3′-triiodothyronines.[224] Thyroxine can be prepared in the laboratory by the treatment, with iodine, of alkaline solutions of tyrosine-containing proteins (e.g., casein) or of tyrosine peptides.[225] Apparently, the tyrosine residues are iodinated to form 3-iodo- and 3,5-diiodotyrosine, and this process is followed by an oxidative reaction leading to the formation of thyroxine. Although the chemical mechanism of this transformation has not been elucidated, it has been suggested that the formation of the

[224] J. Roche and R. Michel, *Physiol. Revs.*, **35**, 583 (1955).

[225] E. P. Reineke, *Vitamins and Hormones,* **4,** 207 (1946); J. Roche and R. Michel, *Advances in Protein Chem.*, **6,** 253 (1951).

hormone *in vivo* may be similar to this nonenzymic process, and that the iodinated thyronine derivatives arise from mono- and diiodotyrosine in the thyroid gland. These iodinated compounds are removed from the circulation by the liver, where they may be converted to glucuronides, and excreted in the bile. The iodinated thyronines also undergo deiodination reactions in the liver;[226] the resulting iodide ion is excreted in the urine. Further aspects of the metabolism of the thyroid hormones, and their role in the animal organism, will be considered in Chapter 38.

Microbial Metabolism of Phenylalanine and Tyrosine. Some microorganisms (e.g., strains of *Vibrio* and of *Pseudomonas*) convert phenylalanine to tyrosine, and degrade tyrosine via the homogentisic acid pathway[227] (p. 826). In a wide variety of microbial species, the metabolic transformation of the two aromatic amino acids may involve an initial attack at the α-carbon atom. Among the products formed from phenylalanine are phenylpyruvic acid and phenylacetic acid; the corresponding *p*-hydroxy compounds have been identified as metabolic products of tyrosine. The yeast *Saccharomyces cerevisiae* ferments tyrosine with the formation of tyrosol (*p*-hydroxyphenylethanol). Other products of the microbial metabolism of phenylalanine and tyrosine are benzoic acid and *p*-hydroxybenzoic acid, respectively, possibly formed by an initial oxidation at the β-carbon atom. In addition, tyrosine may be degraded to *p*-cresol and to phenol.

Considerable information has been gathered about the oxidative breakdown of phenol, *p*-cresol, benzoic acid, and *p*-hydroxybenzoic acid by a cholera *Vibrio* and by several varieties of *Pseudomonas* (cf. Fig. 21). Much of the evidence for the scheme in Fig. 21 has come from the application of the technique termed "sequential induction" (or "simultaneous adaptation").[228] In this procedure, an organism may be adapted to grow on benzoic acid; then a study is made of the capacity of the organism to metabolize other substances that have been suggested as possible intermediates in the oxidative catabolism of benzoic acid. Thus cells adapted to benzoic acid not only oxidize benzoic acid to β-ketoadipic acid but also form the keto acid from catechol and from *cis,cis*-muconic acid; however, cells adapted to *p*-hydroxybenzoic acid form the β-keto acid only from *p*-hydroxybenzoic and protocatechuic acids, and do not form it from catechol or muconic acid.

Although little is known about the microbial enzymes that form catechol and protocatechuic acid, the enzyme systems that effect the further oxidation of these compounds have been extracted from suitably

---

[226] E. V. Flock and J. L. Bollman, *J. Biol. Chem.*, **214**, 709 (1955).

[227] S. Dagley et al., *J. Gen. Microbiol.*, **8**, 1 (1953).

[228] R. Y. Stanier, in D. Rudnick, *Aspects of Synthesis and Order in Growth*, Princeton University Press, Princeton, 1954.

adapted strains of *Pseudomonas*.[229] As shown in Fig. 21, catechol is oxidized to *cis,cis*-muconic acid by the addition of oxygen atoms supplied by O_2; the reaction is catalyzed by "catechol oxidase" (or "pyrocatechase"), an Fe^{2+}-activated enzyme. It will be recalled that the cleavage

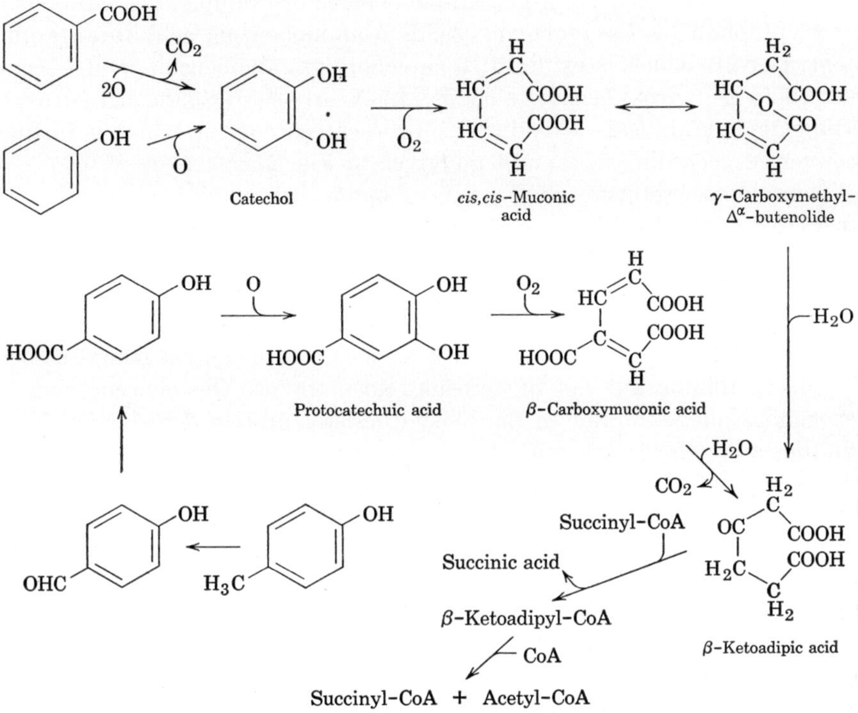

Fig. 21. Oxidative breakdown of aromatic compounds in microorganisms.

of homogentisic acid in animal tissues is also catalyzed by an Fe^{2+}-activated oxidase (cf. p. 827). The reversible conversion of muconic acid to the butenolide (a γ-lactone) is catalyzed by a "lactonizing enzyme," which has been separated from the "delactonizing enzyme" that effects the hydrolysis of the lactone to β-ketoadipic acid. The formation of β-ketoadipic acid from protocatechuic acid involves initial oxidation to β-carboxymuconic acid by "protocatechuic oxidase," but the further steps do not appear to include *cis,cis*-muconic acid or the butenolide as an intermediate. As will be seen from Fig. 21, the catab-

[229] R. Y. Stanier, *Bact. Revs.*, **14**, 179 (1950); B. A. Kilby, *Biochem. J.*, **49**, 671 (1951); R. Y. Stanier et al., *J. Biol. Chem.*, **210**, 799, 809, 821 (1954); M. Katagiri and O. Hayaishi, *ibid.*, **226**, 439 (1957); S. Dagley and M. D. Patel, *Biochem. J.*, **66**, 227 (1957); W. C. Evans, *Ann. Reps.*, **53**, 279 (1957).

olism of β-ketoadipic acid is analogous to that of other β-keto acids (cf. p. 600).

It is to be expected that microorganisms which convert phenylalanine or tyrosine to derivatives of benzoic acid or of phenol may also use the oxidative pathway shown in Fig. 21. Other aromatic compounds are known to be oxidized via β-ketoadipic acid. For example, the catabolism of tryptophan by *Pseudomonas* yields *o*-aminobenzoic acid (anthranilic acid; p. 840) which is oxidized to catechol; *p*-aminobenzoic acid is converted to *p*-hydroxybenzoic acid.[230] In *Neurospora crassa*, dehydroshikimic acid (cf. p. 542) is oxidized to protocatechuic acid, which is further converted according to the scheme given in Fig. 21.[231]

Some microorganisms, such as *Neurospora*, can convert phenylalanine to tyrosine.[232] In addition, several mutant strains of *Escherichia coli* and of *N. crassa* are capable of carrying out a reversible interconversion of phenylalanine and tyrosine, since either amino acid will permit the growth of these mutants on an otherwise amino acid-free medium. On the other hand, one strain of *E. coli*, which requires an exogenous source of phenylalanine but not of tyrosine, does not use the benzene ring of exogenous phenylalanine in the biosynthesis of protein tyrosine.[233] This finding and other work with *E. coli*, *Neurospora*, and *Aerobacter aerogenes* support the view that most of the tyrosine synthesized *in vivo* is not derived from phenylalanine, but that the two amino acids arise from a common precursor by separate pathways. One such precursor has been identified as shikimic acid (p. 542), which can serve as the external source of phenylalanine and tyrosine for certain strains of *E. coli* and of *Neurospora;*[234] shikimic acid also is a precursor of tryptophan and of *p*-aminobenzoic acid in these organisms (p. 842). The utilization of shikimic acid for the microbial biosynthesis of phenylalanine and tyrosine probably involves the sequence of reactions shown in Fig. 22.[235]

Although it has been established that the compound termed "prephenic acid" is an intermediate in this process, its mode of formation from shikimic acid and a C_3 compound is not clear. Prephenic acid is relatively unstable, and at pH values below 6 it undergoes spontaneous decomposition to phenylpyruvic acid. It is probable that *in vivo* the

[230] N. N. Durham, *J. Bact.*, **72**, 333 (1956).

[231] S. R. Gross et al., *J. Biol. Chem.*, **219**, 781 (1956).

[232] R. W. Barratt et al., *J. Bact.*, **71**, 108 (1956).

[233] S. Simmonds, *J. Biol. Chem.*, **185**, 755 (1950).

[234] B. D. Davis, *J. Biol. Chem.*, **191**, 315 (1951); E. L. Tatum et al., *Proc. Natl. Acad. Sci.*, **40**, 271 (1954).

[235] B. D. Davis and E. S. Mingioli, *J. Bact.*, **66**, 129 (1953); U. Weiss et al., *Science*, **119**, 774 (1954); *J. Am. Chem. Soc.*, **78**, 2894 (1956); R. L. Metzenberg and H. K. Mitchell, *Arch. Biochem. and Biophys.*, **64**, 51 (1956).

conversion of prephenic acid to phenylpyruvic acid or to p-hydroxy-phenylpyruvic acid is catalyzed by enzymes. The α-keto acids can readily be converted to the corresponding aromatic amino acids by transamination reactions.

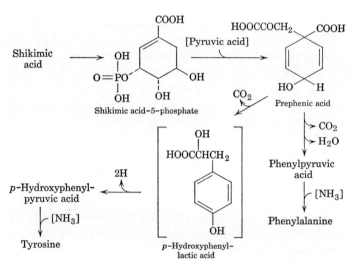

Fig. 22. Postulated pathways in the microbial biosynthesis of aromatic amino acids.

It may be added that, in higher plants, shikimic acid is a precursor of the phenol residues of lignins[236] (p. 422). It is believed that lignin formation involves the conversion of shikimic acid to a substance related to phenylalanine (which is also an efficient precursor of lignin), followed by oxygenation of the benzene ring at the 3, 4, and 5 positions; where methylation of the phenolic hydroxyl groups occurs, the CH_3 group is supplied by methionine.[237] Such substituted aromatic precursors are thought to undergo polymerization reactions to form lignins.[238]

Metabolism of Tryptophan

In the diet of the rat, L-tryptophan may be replaced by the D-isomer or by the corresponding keto acid, indolyl-3-pyruvic acid. Direct evidence for the conversion of the D-amino acid to the L-isomer *in vivo* has been provided by the isolation of tryptophan labeled with N^{15} in the indole nitrogen from the proteins of rats given D-tryptophan similarly

[236] S. A. Brown and A. C. Neish, *Nature,* **175,** 688 (1955); *Canad. J. Biochem. Physiol.,* **34,** 769 (1956); G. Eberhardt and W. J. Schubert, *J. Am. Chem. Soc.,* **78,** 2835 (1956); W. J. Schubert et al., *ibid.,* **79,** 251 (1957).

[237] R. U. Byerrum et al., *J. Biol. Chem.,* **210,** 633 (1954).

[238] S. M. Siegel, *Quart. Rev. Biol.,* **31,** 1 (1956).

labeled.[239] Thus the rat can use nitrogen of the metabolic pool to form tryptophan if the indolylpropionic acid skeleton is provided from an exogenous source. Many microorganisms also can form tryptophan from indolylpyruvic acid; as will be seen from the subsequent discussion, however, the keto acid does appear to be an obligatory intermediate in the microbial biosynthesis of the amino acid.

Both nitrogen atoms of tryptophan can be used in the rat for the synthesis of other amino acids. The α-amino group may be removed by deamination of tryptophan or (more probably) via the formation of alanine (cf. p. 840) derived from the side chain of tryptophan. The mechanism of the conversion of the indole nitrogen to ammonia is uncertain.

The study of the mammalian metabolism of tryptophan may be said to have begun in 1853 when Liebig isolated from dog urine a compound he called kynurenic acid (now known to be 4-hydroxyquinoline-2-carboxylic acid). About 50 years later, after the discovery of tryptophan by Hopkins and Cole, Ellinger observed that kynurenic acid is excreted by animals (e.g., dog, rat, rabbit) after the administration of tryptophan; this directed attention to the metabolic mechanism for the conversion of the amino acid to the quinoline derivative. Subsequent studies showed the presence, in the urine of rats and rabbits maintained on high protein diets, of a yellow compound, xanthurenic acid (4,8-dihydroxyquinoline-2-carboxylic acid). The formation of xanthurenic acid from tryptophan was shown in experiments with rats deficient in pyridoxine (vitamin B_6); such animals excrete xanthurenic acid after the administration of tryptophan.[240] Although xanthurenic acid may be considered an oxidation product of kynurenic acid, it is not formed *in vivo* from the monohydroxy compound. However, both acids share a common precursor, kynurenine, a substance first isolated from rabbit urine. The correct structure of kynurenine was established in 1943 by Butenandt, who had become interested in the compound because of its function as a precursor of eye pigments in insects (p. 839).

In addition to xanthurenic acid, human urine contains the 8-methyl ether of this substance;[241] another urinary metabolite derived from kynurenic acid (in human subjects and rats) is quinoline-2-carboxylic acid (quinaldic acid).[242]

In the mammalian organism, the position of kynurenine as an intermediate in the conversion of tryptophan to kynurenic and xanthurenic acids is indicated in the scheme presented in Fig. 23. The mold *Neuro-*

[239] R. W. Schayer, *J. Biol. Chem.*, **187**, 777 (1950).

[240] S. Lepkovsky et al., *J. Biol. Chem.*, **149**, 195 (1943).

[241] J. M. Price and L. W. Dodge, *J. Biol. Chem.*, **223**, 699 (1956).

[242] H. Takahashi et al., *J. Biol. Chem.*, **223**, 705 (1956).

spora and several bacteria convert tryptophan to kynurenic acid by the same series of reactions.

Direct proof for the scheme in Fig. 23 was obtained by the isolation of isotopic kynurenine and kynurenic acid from the urine of animals given tryptophan labeled in the β-carbon. Later experiments[239,243] with tryptophan containing N^{15} provided evidence that the indole nitrogen

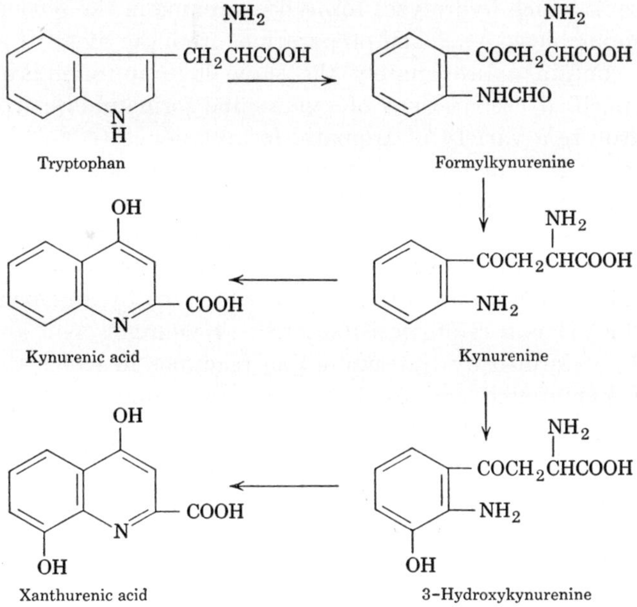

Fig. 23. Formation of kynurenic and xanthurenic acids from tryptophan.

is the precursor of the nitrogen attached to the benzene ring in kynurenine and of the nitrogens of kynurenic and xanthurenic acids.

Mammalian liver (but not other tissues) contain an enzyme system that catalyzes the process[244]

$$\text{L-Tryptophan} \xrightarrow[\text{H}_2\text{O}_2]{\text{O}_2} \text{Formyl-L-kynurenine} \xrightarrow{\text{H}_2\text{O}} \text{L-Kynurenine} + \text{HCOOH}$$

In the first reaction, formylkynurenine is produced in the presence of O_2, catalytic amounts of H_2O_2, and an enzyme system termed tryptophan peroxidase-oxidase. This enzyme system contains iron, and is thought to act as a peroxidase (cf. p. 362) when the iron is in the Fe^{3+} state, and as an oxidase that forms H_2O_2 from O_2 when the iron is in

243 C. Heidelberger et al., *J. Biol. Chem.*, **179**, 143, 151 (1949).

244 W. E. Knox and A. H. Mehler, *J. Biol. Chem.*, **187**, 419, 431 (1950); W. E. Knox, *Biochim. et Biophys. Acta*, **14**, 117 (1954).

the Fe^{2+} state. The activity of the tryptophan peroxidase-oxidase system in liver preparations is markedly and rapidly increased by the administration of tryptophan to animals, and appears to be determined by the level of tryptophan in the blood.[245] In this respect, the oxidation system resembles the "adaptive enzymes" produced by microorganisms in response to the presence of a suitable "inducer" in the culture medium (cf. p. 746). The enzyme "kynurenine formamidase" (also termed "formylase"), which hydrolyzes formylkynurenine in the second reaction, is not an inducible enzyme, and preparations from the livers of all animals examined contain approximately the same high formamidase activity. Partially purified preparations of kynurenine formamidase from *Neurospora* hydrolyze a variety of aromatic formylamines (e.g., *o*-formamidobenzoic acid), but do not cleave aliphatic compounds such as formylglycine or formylglutamic acid.[246] Both a formamidase and a peroxidase-oxidase are present in strains of *Pseudomonas* adapted to tryptophan.[247]

The conversion of kynurenine to 3-hydroxykynurenine involves the participation of molecular oxygen, and is catalyzed by an enzyme system in liver; TPNH is a requisite cofactor.[248] Kynurenic acid and xanthurenic acid are formed by transamination reactions in which the α-amino groups of kynurenine and of 3-hydroxykynurenine are transferred to α-ketoglutaric acid; both reactions are catalyzed by a pyridoxal phosphate-dependent enzyme found in mammalian liver and kidney, in *Neurospora*, and in *Pseudomonas*.[249] The α-keto acids formed from kynurenine and 3-hydroxykynurenine are unstable compounds, and they cyclize spontaneously to form the quinoline carboxylic acids. It is of

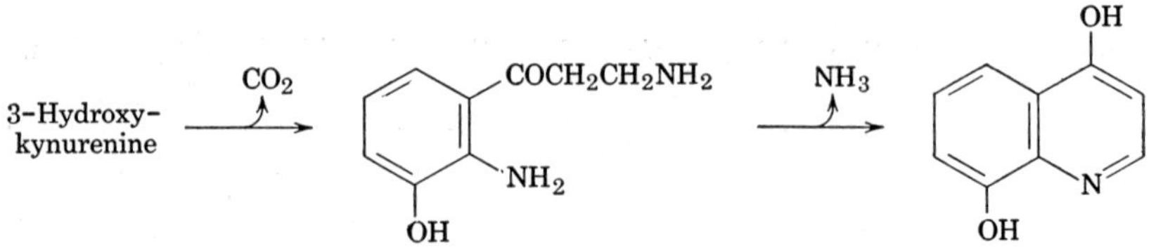

3-Hydroxykynurenamine   4,8-Dihydroxyquinoline

interest that mouse liver homogenates convert 3-hydroxykynurenine not only to xanthurenic acid but also to 4,8-dihydroxyquinoline,[250] probably by the reaction sequence shown.

[245] N. D. Lee, *J. Biol. Chem.*, **219**, 211 (1956).

[246] W. B. Jakoby, *J. Biol. Chem.*, **207**, 657 (1954).

[247] O. Hayaishi and R. Y. Stanier, *J. Bact.*, **62**, 691 (1951).

[248] F. T. deCastro et al., *J. Am. Chem. Soc.*, **78**, 2904 (1956).

[249] M. Mason, *J. Biol. Chem.*, **211**, 839 (1954); **227**, 61 (1957); W. B. Jakoby and D. M. Bonner, *ibid.*, **221**, 689 (1956).

[250] K. Makino and K. Arai, *Science*, **121**, 143 (1955).

In insects, 3-hydroxykynurenine and kynurenine are precursors of eye pigments. The structure of one of these pigments, the yellow xanthommatin from blowflies (*Calliphora erythrocephala*) and other insects, has been elucidated by Butenandt et al.,[251] who have also demonstrated its

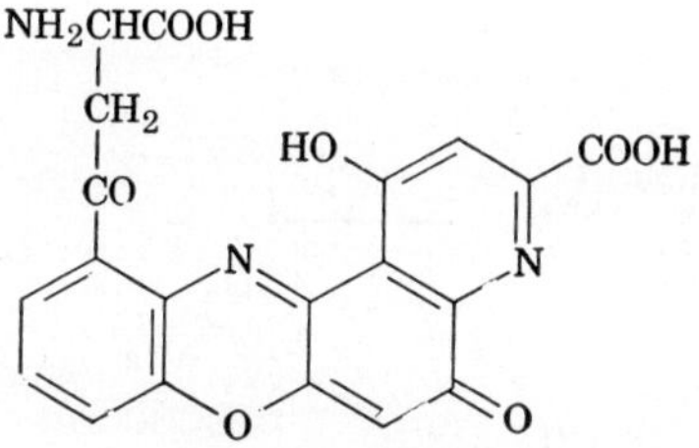

$$NH_2CHCOOH$$
$$|$$
$$CH_2$$
$$|$$
$$CO$$

Xanthommatin

formation *in vivo* from C^{14}-labeled tryptophan or kynurenine. Examination of the structure of xanthommatin will show that it may be considered to be the product of the condensation of 2 molecules of 3-hydroxykynurenine, with the loss of 8 hydrogen atoms and 1 molecule of ammonia. It is of interest therefore that xanthommatin and a red "dopa-melanin" (cf. p. 830) are formed by the action of *Calliphora* tyrosinase on a mixture of 3-hydroxykynurenine and 3,4-dihydroxyphenylalanine ("dopa"). Apparently, dopa is oxidized by the tyrosinase to phenylalanine-3,4-quinone ("dopa quinone"), which then oxidizes 3-hydroxykynurenine to xanthommatin. From biochemical and genetic studies it is known that the production of 3-hydroxykynurenine from kynurenine in the fruit fly (*Drosophila*) is controlled by the so-called cn^+ gene, and the production of kynurenine from tryptophan by the v^+ gene.[252] Mutants of *Drosophila* that lack one of these genes do not have the black eye pigment characteristic of "wild type" insects; however, the pigment is produced if kynurenine or 3-hydroxykynurenine is supplied to the appropriate mutant from an external source. These various findings on eye pigment formation in insects are summarized in the accompanying diagram.

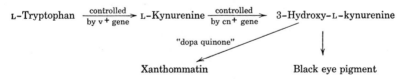

Many higher animals excrete 3-hydroxykynurenine, in addition to

[251] A. Butenandt et al., *Ann. Chem.*, **590**, 75 (1954); *Z. physiol. Chem.*, **301**, 109, 115 (1955); **305**, 284 (1956).

[252] H. Kikkawa, *Advances in Genetics*, **5**, 107 (1953); A. Kühn, *Naturwissenschaften*, **43**, 25 (1956).

kynurenine, kynurenic acid, and xanthurenic acid, but the relative amount of the four compounds in the urine varies with the species studied.[253] In general, the excretion of all these compounds is increased by vitamin B_6 deficiency,[254] a phenomenon that reflects the role of pyridoxal phosphate, both in animals and in microorganisms, in the conversion of

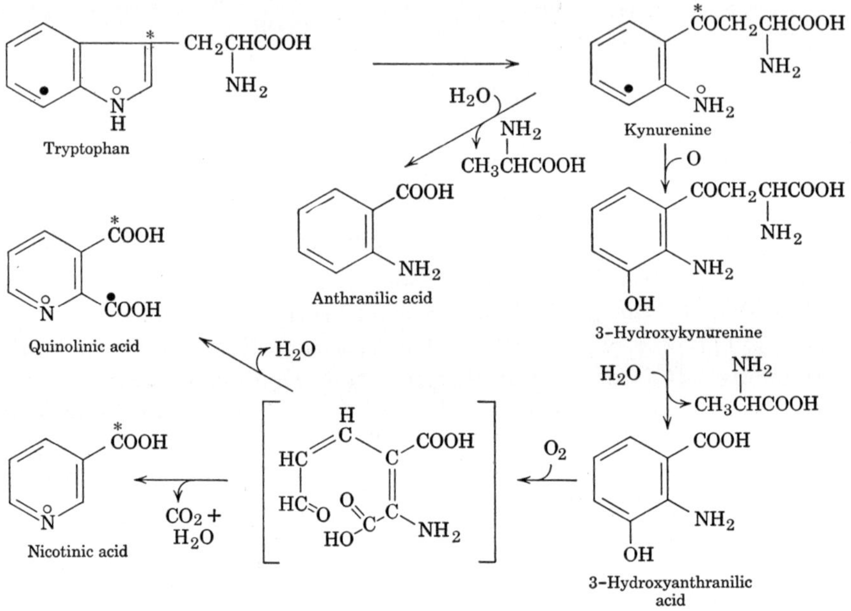

Fig. 24. Postulated mechanism for the synthesis of nicotinic acid. The dots, circles, and stars denote the metabolic fate of 3 atoms of the tryptophan molecule.

kynurenine to compounds other than kynurenic acid and xanthurenic acid. Nutritional studies with rats showed a metabolic relationship between tryptophan and nicotinic acid in mammals,[255] and experiments with mutant strains of *Neurospora* led to the recognition that kynurenine is an intermediate in the conversion of tryptophan to nicotinic acid.[256] Subsequent work with *Neurospora*[257] and with rats showed that 3-hydroxykynurenine and 3-hydroxyanthranilic acid are further intermediates (Fig. 24). The initial reaction in the pathway leading to nicotinic acid is the hydrolysis of 3-hydroxykynurenine to 3-hydroxy-

[253] R. R. Brown and J. M. Price, *J. Biol. Chem.*, **219**, 985 (1956).

[254] C. E. Dalgliesh, *Biochem. J.*, **61**, 328 (1955).

[255] W. A. Krehl et al., *Science*, **101**, 489 (1945); F. Rosen et al., *J. Biol. Chem.*, **163**, 343 (1946).

[256] G. W. Beadle et al., *Proc. Natl. Acad. Sci.*, **33**, 155 (1947).

[257] F. A. Haskins and H. K. Mitchell, *Proc. Natl. Acad. Sci.*, **35**, 500 (1949).

anthranilic acid and L-alanine, catalyzed by a pyridoxal phosphate-dependent enzyme ("kynureninase") present in mammalian liver, *Neurospora,* and *Pseudomonas.*[258] This enzyme appears to be absent from *Escherichia coli* and *Bacillus subtilis;* neither of these bacteria forms nicotinic acid from tryptophan, and the pathway by which they synthesize nicotinic acid is not known.[259] All the enzyme preparations that act on 3-hydroxykynurenine also catalyze the hydrolysis of kynurenine to anthranilic acid and alanine (cf. Fig. 24). For a discussion of the possible role of pyridoxal phosphate in the reactions catalyzed by kynureninase, see Longenecker and Snell.[260]

The scheme presented in Fig. 24 indicates that nicotinic acid may be formed from an intermediate (presumed to be "acroleylaminofumaric acid") which also gives rise to quinolinic acid. Direct proof for the fact that the ring of 3-hydroxyanthranilic acid is opened between carbons 3 and 4 has come from isotope experiments in which suitably labeled tryptophan or 3-hydroxyanthranilic acid was given to rats or to *Neurospora,* and the resulting isotopic nicotinic acid and quinolinic acid were isolated.[261] The results of these experiments are indicated in Fig. 24 by means of symbols to denote the metabolic fate of 3 atoms of the tryptophan molecule. The acyclic intermediate is produced from 3-hydroxyanthranilic acid by rat liver extracts in the presence of O_2, and the oxidase system appears to be activated by Fe^{2+} ions.[262] In this respect, the oxidative cleavage of 3-hydroxyanthranilic acid resembles that of homogentisic acid (cf. p. 827), of catechol, and of protocatechuic acid (cf. p. 833). The formation of quinolinic acid from the intermediate is a spontaneous and rapid reaction. Although liver extracts contain an enzyme that catalyzes the slow decarboxylation of the intermediate to form picolinic acid (pyridine-2-carboxylic acid),[263] the enzyme responsible for the formation of nicotinic acid (pyridine-3-carboxylic acid) has not been identified. Clearly, the production of nicotinic acid also involves a decarboxylation, and experiments with rats and with *Neurospora* indicate that quinolinic acid may be formed from 3-hydroxyanthranilic acid at the expense of nicotinic acid, rather than as an intermediate in

[258] O. Wiss, *Helv. Chim. Acta,* **32,** 1694 (1949); *Z. Naturforsch.,* **7b,** 133 (1952); I. L. Miller and E. A. Adelberg, *J. Biol. Chem.,* **205,** 691 (1953); W. B. Jakoby and D. M. Bonner, *ibid.,* **205,** 699, 709 (1953).

[259] C. Yanofsky, *J. Bact.,* **68,** 577 (1954).

[260] J. B. Longenecker and E. E. Snell, *J. Biol. Chem.,* **213,** 229 (1955).

[261] L. M. Henderson and L. V. Hankes, *J. Biol. Chem.,* **222,** 1069 (1956); C. W. H. Partridge et al., *ibid.,* **194,** 269 (1952).

[262] A. H. Bokman and B. S. Schweigert, *Arch. Biochem. and Biophys.,* **33,** 270 (1951); A. H. Mehler, *J. Biol. Chem.,* **218,** 241 (1956); O. Wiss, *Z. Naturforsch.,* **9b,** 740 (1954); **11b,** 54 (1956).

[263] A. H. Mehler and E. L. May, *J. Biol. Chem.,* **223,** 449 (1956).

the conversion of 3-hydroxyanthranilic acid to nicotinic acid.[264]   Other aspects of the metabolism of nicotinic acid will be discussed in Chapter 39.

It should be noted that a large proportion of the carbon of tryptophan (or 3-hydroxyanthranilic acid) ingested by rats is rapidly oxidized to CO_2.[265]   Since neither nicotinic acid nor quinolinic acid is rapidly degraded *in vivo*, it is likely that 3-hydroxyanthranilic acid is metabolized by some still unidentified pathway which may also involve the entrance of the indole nitrogen of tryptophan into the "metabolic pool" of nitrogen.

Unlike 3-hydroxyanthranilic acid, anthranilic acid is metabolically inert in the mammalian organism.   On the other hand, several microbial

species convert anthranilic acid to catechol and to β-ketoadipic acid (cf. p. 833).   In a number of microorganisms (*Neurospora, Salmonella, E. coli, B. subtilis*), anthranilic acid is formed from shikimic acid (cf. p. 542) and serves as a precursor of tryptophan.   It is believed that in *Neurospora*, at least, there is a "tryptophan cycle," shown in the accompanying scheme.

As indicated in the scheme, the synthesis of tryptophan from anthranilic acid in *Neurospora* involves indole as an intermediate.   This fact was first reported by Tatum and Bonner,[266] who observed that certain mutant strains, which had been classified as "tryptophanless," could be differentiated into three groups: (1) those that showed an absolute requirement for tryptophan, (2) those that would grow on either tryptophan or indole, and (3) those that responded to tryptophan, indole, or anthranilic acid.   Furthermore, the mutants in group 2 produced anthranilic acid, although it was not used as a precursor of tryptophan.

The enzymic conversion of anthranilic acid to indole has been studied with extracts of *E. coli*,[267] and found to involve the intermediate formation of indolyl-3-glycerol phosphate by an enzyme-catalyzed reaction between anthranilic acid and 5-phosphoribosyl-1-pyrophosphate.   A second enzymic reaction causes the cleavage of the intermediate to indole and a triose phosphate.   It will be noted from the scheme on page 843 that the carboxyl group of anthranilic acid is removed, and isotope

264 D. M. Bonner and C. Yanofsky, *J. Nutrition,* **44,** 603 (1951); L. V. Hankes and L. M. Henderson, *J. Biol. Chem.,* **225,** 349 (1957).

265 C. E. Dalgliesh and H. Tabechian, *Biochem. J.,* **62,** 625 (1956).

266 E. L. Tatum and D. M. Bonner, *Proc. Natl. Acad. Sci.,* **30,** 30 (1944).

267 C. Yanofsky, *J. Biol. Chem.,* **217,** 345 (1955); **223,** 171 (1956); **224,** 783 (1957).

experiments have shown that carbons 1 and 2 of the ribose molecule supply carbons 2 and 3, respectively, of the indole ring. The participation of a ribose-5-phosphate derivative in the biosynthesis of indolylglycerol phosphate is analogous to its role in the formation of imidazolylglycerol phosphate (p. 821).

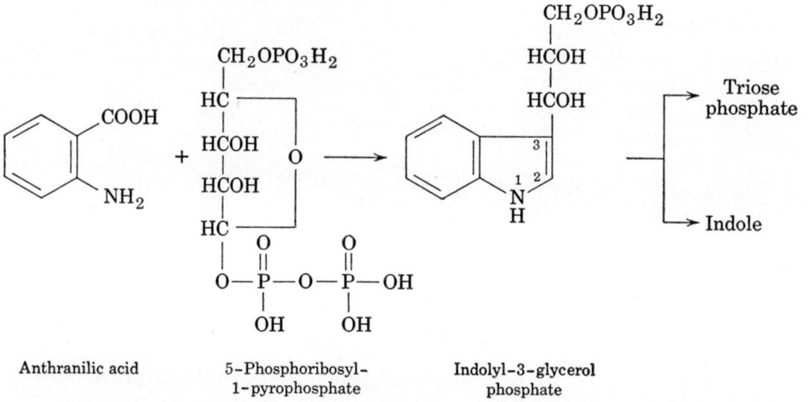

| Anthranilic acid | 5-Phosphoribosyl-1-pyrophosphate | Indolyl-3-glycerol phosphate |

Tryptophan is formed in *Neurospora* by a condensation reaction between indole and L-serine.[266, 268] This reaction is catalyzed by an enzyme system ("tryptophan desmolase" or "tryptophan synthetase") that requires pyridoxal phosphate as a cofactor. Isotope experiments have shown that, during tryptophan synthesis, the hydroxyl group and the α-hydrogen atom of serine are lost.[269] This finding supports the hypothesis that serine first reacts with pyridoxal phosphate to form a

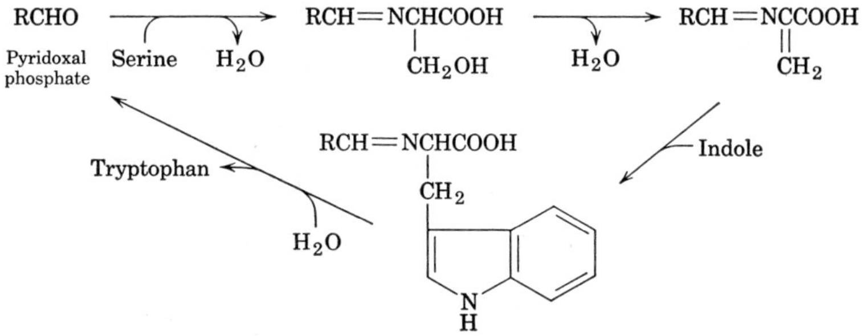

Schiff base from which the elements of water are expelled, and that the resulting aminoacrylic acid derivative then combines with indole to form the Schiff base of tryptophan[270] (see the accompanying scheme).

Mammals apparently cannot form tryptophan by this process, since

[268] W. W. Umbreit, *J. Biol. Chem.*, **165**, 731 (1946).
[269] E. L. Tatum and D. Shemin, *J. Biol. Chem.*, **209**, 671 (1954).
[270] D. E. Metzler et al., *J. Am. Chem. Soc.*, **76**, 648 (1954).

they cannot use indole in place of tryptophan and rapidly excrete almost all of the indole entering the body. There is no conclusive evidence that indole is formed within the tissues of the mammalian organism, although

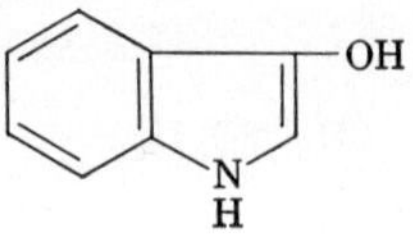

Indoxyl 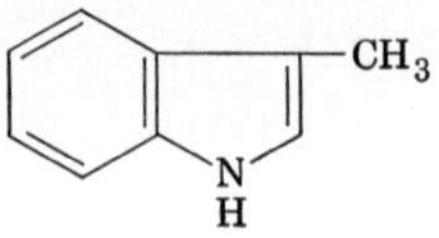   Skatole

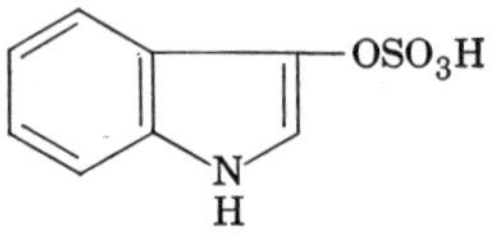

Indoxylsulfuric acid 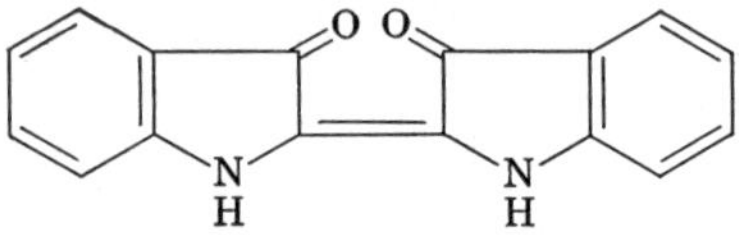   Indigo

urine may contain large quantities of the "detoxication" products of indole, indoxylsulfuric acid (indican) and indoxylglucuronic acid, and of skatole. Presumably, these excretory products have their origin in the indole and skatole formed by the intestinal bacteria; the absorption of indole is followed by its oxidation to indoxyl and conjugation with glucuronic acid, or with sulfuric acid. It may be added that the term indican is also applied to the glucoside of indoxyl which occurs in plants of the *Indigofera* group. This glucoside is split during the extraction of the plants by water or dilute acid, and the indoxyl liberated is spontaneously oxidized to indigo, one of the oldest of the natural dyes.

The bacterial conversion of tryptophan to indole has been known since the work of Hopkins and Cole in 1903. More recently it has been found[271] that extracts of *E. coli* contain the enzyme tryptophanase, which catalyzes the reaction shown; pyridoxal phosphate also serves as

$$\text{L-Tryptophan} \rightarrow \text{Indole} + \text{pyruvic acid} + NH_3$$

the coenzyme for this process. This cleavage of tryptophan occurs under anaerobic conditions and apparently does not involve the intermediate formation of serine (or alanine), since the enzyme preparations do not deaminate serine (or alanine) to yield pyruvic acid and ammonia. Aminoacrylic acid appears to be the immediate precursor of the pyruvic acid and ammonia isolated (cf. p. 756).

The vasoconstrictor substance 5-hydroxytryptamine[272] (also termed serotonin or enteramine) is present in the blood and gastric mucosa of

[271] W. A. Wood et al., *J. Biol. Chem.*, **170**, 313 (1947); H. Gooder and F. C. Happold, *Biochem. J.*, **57**, 369 (1954).

[272] I. H. Page, *Physiol. Revs.*, **34**, 563 (1954).

mammals, in the salivary glands of some cephalopods, and in the secretions of some amphibia. It has also been found in small amounts in the brain of all mammals, birds, and reptiles examined,[273] and in the nerve tissue of invertebrates, and is believed, therefore, to function also as a neurohormonal agent.[274]   Experiments with higher animals and with

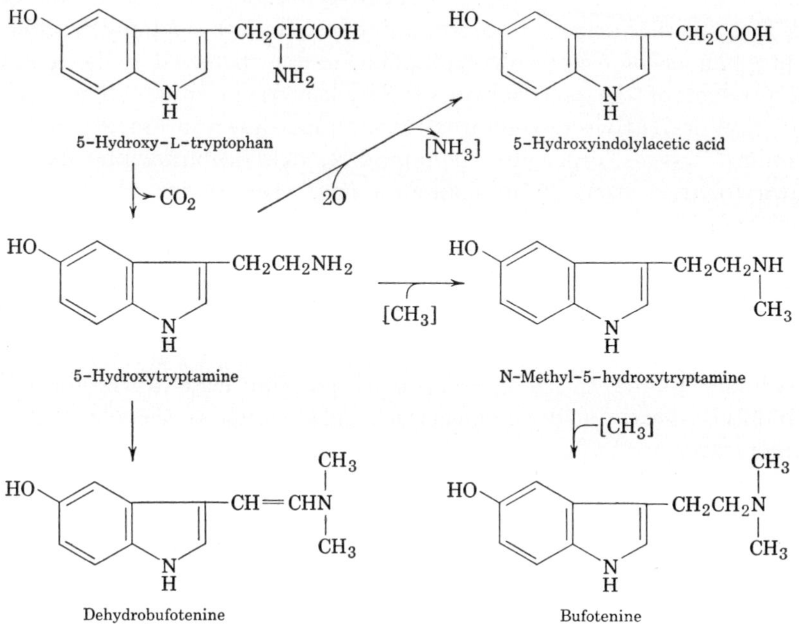

Fig. 25.   Metabolism of 5-hydroxytryptamine in animals.

toads given tryptophan-α-C^{14} have shown that this amino acid is converted to 5-hydroxytryptamine, and that 5-hydroxytryptophan is an intermediate in this process[275] (Fig. 25). The mode of formation of 5-hydroxytryptophan is unclear, but, as noted previously (p. 768), this compound is decarboxylated to 5-hydroxytryptamine by an enzyme of widespread distribution in nature.[276] It may be added that tryptophan is converted to 5-hydroxytryptophan (but not to 5-hydroxytryptamine) by *Chromobacterium violaceum*,[277] which also produces the pigment violacein,[278] a derivative of 5-hydroxyindole. Like some other bacteria

[273] P. Correale, *J. Neurochem.,* **1**, 22 (1956).

[274] B. B. Brodie et al., *Science,* **122**, 968 (1955); **123**, 992 (1956).

[275] S. Udenfriend et al., *J. Biol. Chem.,* **219**, 335 (1956); **224**, 803 (1957).

[276] J. H. Gaddum and N. J. Giarman, *Brit. J. Pharmacol.,* **11**, 88 (1956).

[277] C. Mitoma et al., *Arch. Biochem. and Biophys.,* **63**, 122 (1956).

[278] R. J. S. Beer et al., *J. Chem. Soc.,* **1954**, 2679; J. A. Ballentine et al., *ibid.,* **1957**, 2222.

(cf. p. 841), this organism does not metabolize tryptophan by the "kynurenine pathways" characteristic of *Neurospora* and of higher animals.

In intact animals, and with kidney or liver preparations, 5-hydroxytryptamine is oxidized to 5-hydroxyindolyl-3-acetic acid, presumably with the intermediate formation of the corresponding aldehyde by monoamine oxidase (cf. p. 829). 5-Hydroxyindolylacetic acid has been detected in the urine of many animals after the administration of tryptophan or of 5-hydroxytryptophan, and is believed to be a major end product of the metabolism of 5-hydroxytryptamine. The various N-methyl derivatives of 5-hydroxytryptamine shown in Fig. 25 are found in animal tissues, especially in amphibia; dehydrobufotenine has been shown to arise from tryptophan in toads. Bufotenine also occurs in fungi (mushrooms) and in the seeds of the tropical shrubs of the genus *Piptadenia*. In these seeds, bufotenine is accompanied by its N-oxide, as well as by the closely related N,N-dimethyltryptamine and N,N-dimethyltryptamine-N-oxide;[279] all these plant constituents probably arise from tryptophan.

In higher plants, the metabolism of tryptophan leads to the formation of indolyl-3-acetic acid (indoleacetic acid), which is the plant growth hormone known as auxin[280] (Chapter 38). Large amounts of indoleacetic acid are formed when enzyme preparations from the leaves of certain plants (e.g., pineapple) are incubated under aerobic conditions with tryptophan or with indolyl-3-pyruvic acid.[281] Since the keto acid is present in some plants, and is known to be formed from tryptophan by bacteria,[277, 282] the biosynthesis of indoleacetic acid may follow the reaction sequence

$$\text{Tryptophan} \xrightarrow{-\ [NH_3]} \text{Indolyl-3-pyruvic acid} \xrightarrow{-\ [CO_2]} \text{Indolyl-3-acetic acid}$$

Small amounts of indoleacetic acid are found in normal human urine, but much larger quantities of indoleacetic acid and of N-(3-indolylacetyl)-L-glutamine are excreted by individuals with the syndrome termed "H disease."[283] Although the indoleacetic acid undoubtedly is formed from tryptophan, it is uncertain whether the conversion is effected by the intestinal microorganisms or by the tissues of the patient.

[279] M. S. Fish et al., *J. Am. Chem. Soc.*, **77**, 5892 (1955); **78**, 3668 (1956).
[280] S. G. Wildman et al., *Arch. Biochem.*, **13**, 131 (1947).
[281] S. A. Gordon and F. Sánchez Nieva, *Arch. Biochem.*, **20**, 356, 367 (1949).
[282] B. B. Stowe and K. V. Thimann, *Nature*, **172**, 764 (1953).
[283] J. B. Jepson, *Biochem. J.*, **64**, 14p (1956).

33 ·

End Products
of
Amino Acid Metabolism

In the steady state of nitrogen metabolism in the animal organism, there is a continuous loss of nitrogen from the "metabolic pool" (p. 732) because of the formation of compounds that are excreted from the organism or that are metabolically inert. Such compounds may be termed "end products" of nitrogen metabolism.

From the previous discussion, it will be clear that the metabolism of all amino acids leads to the production of ammonia. In some organisms, ammonia actually is the principal excretory product of nitrogen metabolism; these animals are termed "ammonotelic." In invertebrates, ammonia may represent more than one half of the total excretory nitrogen; the remainder is composed of (a) urea (0 to 20 per cent); (b) uric acid (0 to 10 per cent, except in insects, where it is 50 to 80 per cent); (c) amino acids, creatinine, etc. (3 to 30 per cent). Among the vertebrates, only the *Teleostei* (bony fishes) excrete nitrogen largely in the form of ammonia; the *Elasmobranchii* (cartilaginous fishes), like the amphibious and terrestrial species, excrete only small amounts of ammonia. A stimulating discussion of the possible basis for this difference between the elasmobranch fishes and other aquatic animals may be found in Baldwin's monograph.[1] For most of the terrestrial vertebrates, the principal nitrogenous excretion product is urea; the notable exceptions to this generalization are the reptiles and birds, for which uric acid, instead of urea, serves as the principal vehicle for the excretion of nitrogen. The animals that excrete nitrogen largely in the form of urea are termed "ureotelic" (terrestrial vertebrates except birds and reptiles, the elasmobranch fishes), and those that excrete mainly uric acid "uricotelic" (terrestrial invertebrates, terrestrial vertebrates whose eggs subsist under arid conditions). Baldwin[1] has drawn attention to

[1] E. Baldwin, *Introduction to Comparative Biochemistry,* 2nd Ed., Cambridge University Press, London, 1940.

the direct correlation between the availability of water and the capacity of most aquatic organisms to excrete ammonia, which is quite toxic but extremely soluble; however, amphibious and terrestrial organisms largely excrete urea, which is less toxic but also soluble, or uric acid, a sparingly soluble compound found as the main end product of nitrogen metabolism in animals that do not excrete a highly diluted urine.

Formation of Urea

In ureotelic organisms, the principal site of urea formation is the liver. The primary source of the nitrogen of urinary urea is ammonia derived from amino acids by deamination or by transamination reactions. When there is significant liver damage (e.g., acute yellow atrophy of the liver), or if the liver is removed surgically, the amino acids are not deaminated at the normal rate, and their concentration in the peripheral circulation rises while the level of blood urea falls. Upon administration of N^{15}-labeled ammonium salts to an experimental animal, the isotope is largely excreted in the form of urea, although a portion of the ammonium-N may be utilized for the synthesis of amino acids.[2] Isotope studies have also shown that, in the intact animal, all of the carbon of urinary urea is derived from respiratory CO_2.[3]

As noted previously (p. 817), most of the ammonia (ca. 60 per cent) found in the urine of mammals arises from the hydrolysis of blood glutamine in the kidneys. The remainder of the urinary ammonia is formed by the oxidative deamination of blood amino acids in the kidney. A relationship has been reported between the capacity of amino acids to induce the excretion of ammonia and their deamination *in vitro* by the amino acid oxidases of kidney tissue.[4] The quantity of ammonia excreted is determined in large part by the concentration of acids in the blood. Ammonia excretion increases after the administration of acids to an animal, during exercise (lactic acid production), or in a ketonemia due to starvation or diabetes (acetoacetic acid). Under these conditions, described by the general term "acidosis," some of the ammonia normally converted to urea is used to neutralize the excess acid; this serves to conserve the essential ions: sodium, potassium, calcium, and magnesium (Chapter 36). In acidosis, therefore, the urea excretion is somewhat lower than under normal circumstances. When an animal is given bicarbonate, the reverse condition, that of "alkalosis," is observed. Under these circumstances, the ammonia excretion is diminished, and the urea excretion is correspondingly increased. In general, the sum

---

[2] M. Berenbom and J. White, *J. Biol. Chem.*, **182**, 5 (1950).

[3] C. G. Mackenzie and V. du Vigneaud, *J. Biol. Chem.*, **172**, 353 (1948)

[4] W. D. Lotspeich and R. F. Pitts, *J. Biol. Chem.*, **168**, 611 (1947).

of the urinary ammonia nitrogen and urea nitrogen excreted by an animal on a constant diet remains constant from day to day, but the relative amounts of the two may vary, depending on the electrolyte balance of the blood. It is important to re-emphasize, however, that, although ammonia is a precursor of urinary urea, blood urea is not an important precursor of urinary ammonia.

Clearly, when an animal is transferred from a high-protein diet to a diet low in protein (mostly fat and carbohydrate), the amount of urinary urea decreases appreciably, as shown by the data in Table 1.

Although urea is an end product of nitrogen metabolism in mammalian tissues, the administration of N^{15}- or C^{14}-labeled urea to a suitable animal (rat, cat) leads to the appearance of N^{15} in the tissue proteins[5] or of C^{14} in the respiratory CO_2. This is a consequence of the hydrolytic cleavage of urea to NH_3 and CO_2 by urease (p. 246) present in the bacteria of the gastrointestinal tract.[6] Urease is widely distributed among microorganisms and higher plants; in its action on urea, carbamic acid (NH_2—$COOH$) appears to be formed as an intermediate which then decomposes to NH_3 and CO_2.[7]

Table I. Twenty-Four-Hour Urinary Excretion of a Human Subject[8]

	High-Protein Diet		Low-Protein Diet	
Volume of urine	1170	ml	385	ml
Total nitrogen	16.8	grams	3.6	grams
Urea nitrogen	14.7	grams	2.2	grams
Ammonia nitrogen	0.49	gram	0.42	gram
Uric acid nitrogen	0.18	gram	0.09	gram
Creatinine nitrogen	0.58	gram	0.60	gram
Undetermined nitrogen	0.85	gram	0.29	gram

Mechanism of Urea Formation. Because urea is the major nitrogenous excretion product of man, and most other terrestrial vertebrates, considerable study has been devoted to the biochemical mechanism of its formation from amino acids. Urea was discovered in urine in 1773 by Rouelle, but the first indications of its metabolic source came from the experiments of Kossel and Dakin,[9] who found in animal tissues the enzyme arginase, which causes the hydrolytic cleavage of L-arginine to L-ornithine and urea.

[5] W. C. Rose and E. E. Dekker, *J. Biol. Chem.*, **223**, 107 (1956).

[6] H. L. Kornberg and R. E. Davies, *Physiol. Revs.*, **35**, 169 (1955).

[7] J. H. Wang and D. A. Tarr, *J. Am. Chem. Soc.*, **77**, 6205 (1955).

[8] O. Folin, *J. Am. Med. Assoc.*, **69**, 1209 (1917), according to J. P. Peters and D. D. Van Slyke, *Quantitative Clinical Chemistry*, 2nd Ed., Williams and Wilkins Co., Baltimore, 1946.

[9] A. Kossel and H. D. Dakin, *Z. physiol. Chem.*, **41**, 321 (1904).

Arginase is found in many mammalian tissues, but is especially abundant in the liver. It is present in the livers of all ureotelic vertebrates, but appears to be absent from the livers of uricotelic animals. The enzyme is also found in invertebrates and higher plants. Arginase is activated by Mn^{2+} or Co^{2+}; the pH-dependence curve varies with the metallic activator, but the optimum is, in general, near pH 10. The crystallization of beef liver arginase has been described.[10]

The manner in which arginase participates in urea formation was elucidated in a memorable paper by Krebs and Henseleit,[11] who showed that rat liver slices can convert ammonia to urea. As a part of this study and of an investigation on the deamination of amino acids, various amino acids were tested as substitutes for ammonia in urea formation, and arginine was found to cause the production of much more urea than could be accounted for simply by the action of arginase. From the data obtained, it was clear that arginine was acting catalytically in the production of urea from ammonia; it was subsequently found that L-ornithine and L-citrulline acted in a similar manner. Some of the data obtained by Krebs and Henseleit are shown in Table 2.

Table 2. Urea Synthesis by Rat Liver Slices [11]

Incubation mixture contained, per milliliter, 0.12 mg of NH_3 and 2 mg of DL-lactate; Krebs-Ringer solution, pH 7.4; temperature, 37° C.

Added Substance	Q_{urea}†
None	1.94
L-Ornithine (2 mg per ml)	9.82
L-Citrulline (2 mg per ml)	12.78
L-Citrulline (2 mg per ml), no ammonia	0

† Q_{urea} = cubic millimeters of urea-CO_2 per milligram of dry weight of tissue per hour. The urea-CO_2 was determined manometrically after treatment of the incubation mixture with urease.

In order to explain the catalytic effect of these three substances on urea formation, Krebs proposed a mechanism that has come to be known as the "ornithine cycle" (Fig. 1). It is important to stress that the experiments reported in Table 2 were conducted in the presence of oxygen, and of an oxidizable substrate such as lactic acid. Under these conditions, a small amount of ornithine is sufficient to effect the conversion of an appreciable amount of ammonia to urea.

In subsequent studies, many details of this scheme have been confirmed and extended. Thus the conversion of citrulline to arginine has

[10] S. J. Bach and J. D. Killip, *Biochim. et Biophys. Acta*, **29**, 273 (1958).
[11] H. A. Krebs and K. Henseleit, *Z. physiol. Chem.*, **210**, 33 (1932).

been elucidated by Ratner,[12] who showed that it is effected by liver extracts (ox, rat), and that the nitrogen added to citrulline does not

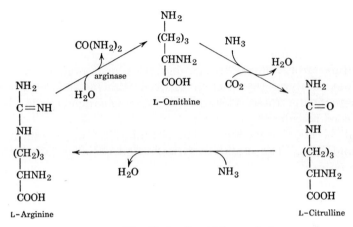

Fig. 1. The Krebs "ornithine cycle."

come directly from ammonia, but from L-aspartic acid. In the metabolic formation of arginine from citrulline and aspartic acid, two enzymic

$$
\begin{array}{cccc}
\text{NH} & \text{COOH} & & \text{NH} & \text{COOH}\\
\parallel & | & & \parallel & |\\
\text{C—OH} & \text{NH}_2\text{CH} & \text{ATP} & \text{C——NH——CH} & \\
| & | & \xrightleftharpoons[\text{AMP}\quad\text{Pyro-}]{\text{Mg}^{2+}} & | & |\\
\text{NH} \;+\; & \text{CH}_2 & & \text{NH} & \text{CH}_2\\
| & | & \text{phosphate} & | & |\\
(\text{CH}_2)_3 & \text{COOH} & & (\text{CH}_2)_3 & \text{COOH}\\
| & & & |\\
\text{NH}_2\text{CHCOOH} & & & \text{NH}_2\text{CHCOOH}
\end{array}
$$

L-Citrulline   L-Aspartic acid   Argininosuccinic acid
(enol form)

$$
\begin{array}{ccc}
\text{NH} & & \text{COOH}\\
\parallel & & |\\
\text{C—NH}_2 & & \text{CH}\\
| & +\; & \parallel\\
\text{NH} & & \text{HC}\\
| & & |\\
(\text{CH}_2)_3 & & \text{COOH}\\
|\\
\text{NH}_2\text{CHCOOH}
\end{array}
$$

L-Arginine   Fumaric acid

steps are involved,[13] as shown in the accompanying scheme. In the first step, citrulline and aspartic acid condense to form argininosuccinic acid; ATP is an obligatory participant in this reaction, and is cleaved

[12] S. Ratner, *Advances in Enzymol.*, **15**, 319 (1954).
[13] S. Ratner et al., *J. Biol. Chem.*, **204**, 95, 115 (1953).

to AMP and inorganic pyrophosphate.[14] L-Aspartic acid cannot be replaced by any other amino acid tested. In the second step, argininosuccinic acid is cleaved by an enzyme whose action resembles that of aspartase (p. 240), with the formation of arginine and fumaric acid. This cleavage is readily reversible, and argininosuccinic acid has been isolated upon incubation of arginine and fumaric acid with enzyme preparations from animal tissues and from microorganisms. The enzyme that catalyzes the reaction between arginine and fumaric acid is fairly specific for these substances, but L-canavanine (p. 66) is active in place of arginine.[15]

It will be noted from Fig. 1 that citrulline is formed from ornithine, NH_3, and CO_2. The studies of Grisolia and Cohen[16] showed that this conversion can be effected by a soluble enzyme system (from rat liver) which requires the presence of ATP, of Mg^{2+}, and of an acyl-L-glutamic acid (e.g., acetyl-L-glutamic acid, carbamyl-L-glutamic acid). They also showed that at least two enzymic reactions occur in the formation of citrulline. In the first step, CO_2, NH_3, and ATP interact, in the presence of Mg^{2+} and an acyl glutamic acid, to form an organic phosphate compound and ADP. In the second step, the phosphate compound reacts with ornithine to form citrulline. The organic phosphate compound (originally termed "compound X") is probably identical with carbamyl phosphate (NH_2—$COOPO_3^{2-}$),[17] since Jones et al. demonstrated that synthetic carbamyl phosphate (prepared by the reaction of KH_2PO_4 with $KCNO$) reacts with ornithine in the presence of liver preparations to form citrulline. The substance phosphorylated by ATP in the first step is assumed to be carbamic acid (NH_2—$COOH$) which is in equilibrium with ammonium bicarbonate (NH_4HCO_3) derived from NH_3 and CO_2. The role of the acyl-L-glutamic acid in the enzymic

$$(1) \quad NH_3 + CO_2 + ATP^{4-} \underset{}{\overset{Mg^{2+}}{\rightleftharpoons}} NH_2\text{—}COOPO_3^{2-} + ADP^{3-} + H^+$$

$$(2) \quad NH_2\text{—}COOPO_3^{2-} + \text{L-ornithine} \rightleftharpoons \text{L-citrulline} + HPO_4^{2-}$$

formation of carbamyl phosphate has not been elucidated. The enzyme that catalyzes the reaction between carbamyl phosphate and ornithine (equation 2) has been purified from rat liver by Reichard,[17] and named "ornithine carbamyl transferase"; the equilibrium constant (pH 7.4, $37°$ C) of the reaction is about 10^5.

[14] S. Ratner and B. Petrack, *Arch. Biochem. and Biophys.,* **65,** 582 (1956).

[15] J. B. Walker, *J. Biol. Chem.,* **204,** 139 (1953).

[16] S. Grisolia and P. P. Cohen, *J. Biol. Chem.,* **191,** 189 (1951); **198,** 561 (1952); **204,** 753 (1953).

[17] M. E. Jones et al., *J. Am. Chem. Soc.,* **77,** 819 (1955); P. Reichard, *Acta Chem. Scand.,* **11,** 523 (1957).

It is clear from the foregoing discussion that ATP is required both for the conversion of citrulline to arginine and for the conversion of ornithine to citrulline. This ATP can be supplied to the urea-synthesizing system of the liver by oxidative phosphorylation coupled to the citric acid cycle, thus explaining the original observation of Krebs and Henseleit that an oxidizable substrate and oxygen were required for urea synthesis (cf. p. 850). In addition, several components of the citric acid cycle are involved, either directly or indirectly, in the transformation of components of the ornithine cycle, as shown in Fig. 2.

The importance of the ornithine cycle in the removal of the toxic ammonium ion from the animal body is illustrated by the observation

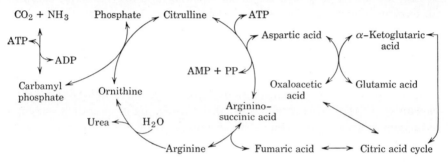

Fig. 2. The ornithine cycle, and its relation to the citric acid cycle.

that prior administration of L-arginine to rats markedly reduces the toxicity of relatively large doses of ammonium salts or of amino acids.[18]

Some reactions of the ornithine cycle have been shown to occur in *Neurospora*. Mutants of this mold have been obtained in which (*a*) the production of ornithine, (*b*) the conversion of ornithine to citrulline, or (*c*) the conversion of citrulline to arginine is blocked.[19] Since *Neurospora* contains not only arginase but also urease, the urea formed in the ornithine cycle can be converted to CO_2 and NH_3. The sequence of reactions in *Neurospora* is shown in the accompanying scheme.

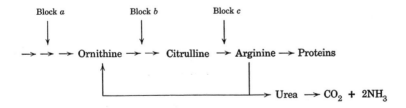

[18] J. P. Greenstein et al., *Arch. Biochem. and Biophys.*, **64**, 342, 355 (1956).
[19] A. M. Srb and N. H. Horowitz, *J. Biol. Chem.*, **154**, 129 (1944).

Various bacteria (e.g., *Streptococcus fecalis*) are known to convert citrulline to ornithine by a process coupled to the phosphorylation of ADP to form ATP.[20] The discovery, by Jones et al.,[17] of the metabolic role of carbamyl phosphate led to the recognition that this microbial process involves the enzymic phosphorolysis of citrulline to form ornithine and carbamyl phosphate, whose phosphate is transferred to ADP with the generation of ATP, and the liberation of CO_2 and NH_3. These two steps clearly represent the reversal of the two reactions in the conversion of ornithine to citrulline in the liver. In contrast to the behavior of the enzyme system from liver, the presence of an acyl-L-glutamic acid is not required for the action of enzyme preparations from *S. fecalis*. It may be added that this organism, as well as other bacteria, contains an enzyme ("arginine desimidase") which converts arginine to citrulline and ammonia.[21] Thus the over-all conversion of arginine to ornithine in *S. fecalis* proceeds by a pathway different from that in mammalian liver, where this process is effected by arginase, with the formation of urea.

The discovery of carbamyl phosphate as a metabolic donor of a carbamyl (NH_2CO—) group has also thrown light on other enzyme-catalyzed reactions in which this group is transferred to an organic compound. For example, enzyme preparations from liver and from bacteria catalyze the reaction of carbamyl phosphate with L-aspartic acid to form carbamyl-L-aspartic acid (ureidosuccinic acid), an intermediate in the biosynthesis and breakdown of pyrimidines (Chapter 35).

Formation of Uric Acid

In uricotelic organisms such as birds, the principal nitrogenous excretion product, uric acid, is formed in the liver and kidneys; the removal of the liver leads to the accumulation of amino acids in the blood. By the administration to pigeons of a variety of compounds labeled with C^{13} or C^{14}, the metabolic origin of the carbon atoms of uric acid has been established.[22] The available evidence indicates that carbon 6 of uric acid is derived from CO_2; carbons 2 and 8 are derived from "formate" (cf. p. 774), known to arise from the β-carbon of serine;[23] carbons 4 and 5 are derived from the carboxyl and methylene groups of glycine, respectively. Studies with isotopic glycine showed that this amino acid contributes nitrogen 7 to the uric acid molecule, and that the N—C—C skeleton of glycine is incorporated as a unit. Nitrogen

---

[20] V. A. Knivett, *Biochem. J.*, **56**, 602, 606; **58**, 480 (1954).

[21] E. L. Oginsky and R. F. Gehrig, *J. Biol. Chem.*, **198**, 791, 799 (1952).

[22] J. C. Sonne et al., *J. Biol. Chem.*, **173**, 69, 81 (1949).

[23] D. Elwyn and D. B. Sprinson, *J. Biol. Chem.*, **184**, 465 (1950).

atom 1 is derived from aspartic acid, and nitrogens 3 and 9 are derived from the amide nitrogen of glutamine;[24] as noted previously, the amino group of aspartic acid (cf. p. 760) and the amide nitrogen of glutamine (cf. p. 721) are readily derived from ammonium ions.

Thus the isotope technique has demonstrated that small fragments serve as precursors in the formation of uric acid in birds (Fig. 3). Other

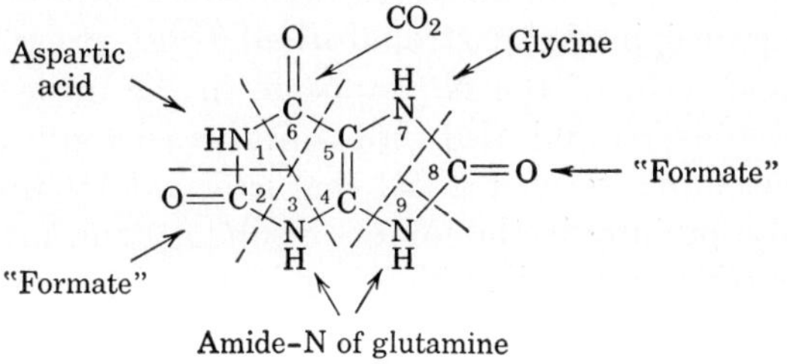

Fig. 3. Metabolic precursors of the carbon and nitrogen atoms of uric acid.

studies have shown that essentially the same conclusions about the sources of carbon and nitrogen for uric acid synthesis apply to mammals (including man). An important difference between birds and mammals, however, is the fact that in the former uric acid is the principal end product of protein metabolism, whereas in man uric acid is primarily an end product of purine metabolism. Since in both kinds of animals similar compounds serve as precursors of the carbon and nitrogen of uric acid, it may be concluded that the similarities apply to the formation of purines at a lower level of oxidation than that of uric acid (e.g., hypoxanthine); consequently, the difference between the species lies in the relative extent to which these precursors, and especially the nitrogen of the metabolic pool, are used for the synthesis of such purines. For example, it has been shown that pigeon liver slices, on incubation with ammonia, give rise to appreciable quantities of hypoxanthine;[25]

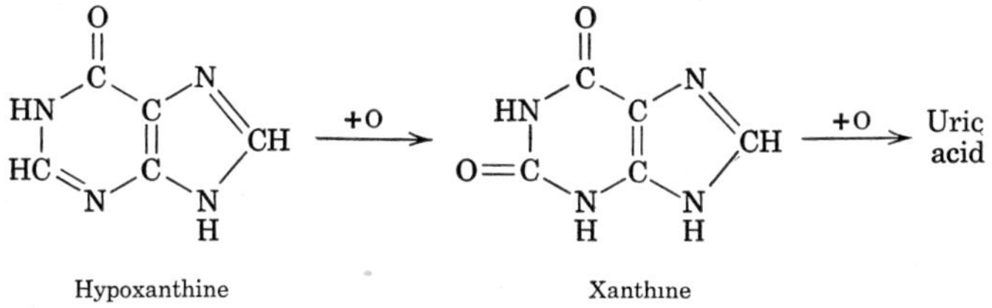

presumably, this is then oxidized, by means of xanthine oxidase (p. 339), to form uric acid. The problem of the mechanism of uric acid formation

[24] J. C. Sonne et al., *J. Biol. Chem.*, **220**, 369 (1956); B. Levenberg et al., *ibid.*, **220**, 379 (1956).

[25] N. L. Edson et al., *Biochem. J.*, **30**, 732, 1380 (1936).

from the small fragments indicated in Fig. 3 thus raises the general question of the biosynthesis of the purines; this will be considered in Chapter 35.

In man, uric acid appears to be a true end product of nitrogen metabolism. If N^{15}-labeled uric acid is administered to human subjects by intravenous injection, about 80 per cent of the isotope is excreted as urinary uric acid.[26] If administered by mouth, isotopic uric acid is extensively degraded in the gastrointestinal tract, presumably by bacterial action, and most of the N^{15} appears in the urine in the form of urea. Human subjects, and also birds, are occasionally afflicted with a metabolic abnormality termed gout, characterized by the deposition in the tissues, and especially in the joints, of solid salts of uric acid (urates) which are extremely insoluble. The immediate cause of this metabolic dysfunction is not entirely clear, but the disease may be the consequence of the overproduction of uric acid.[27]

In most mammals, except man and the higher apes, uric acid is oxidized in the liver to allantoin (discovered by Vauquelin in 1790), which is excreted in the urine. This oxidation is effected by the enzyme uricase, believed to be a copper protein.[28] When uric acid labeled with N^{15} in positions 1 and 3 is subjected to the action of uricase, the allantoin formed is labeled in all of its nitrogen atoms, indicating that a symmetrical intermediate is formed. In the enzymic oxidation, carbon 6 of uric acid is lost as CO_2, whereas carbons 2 and 8 are retained in the

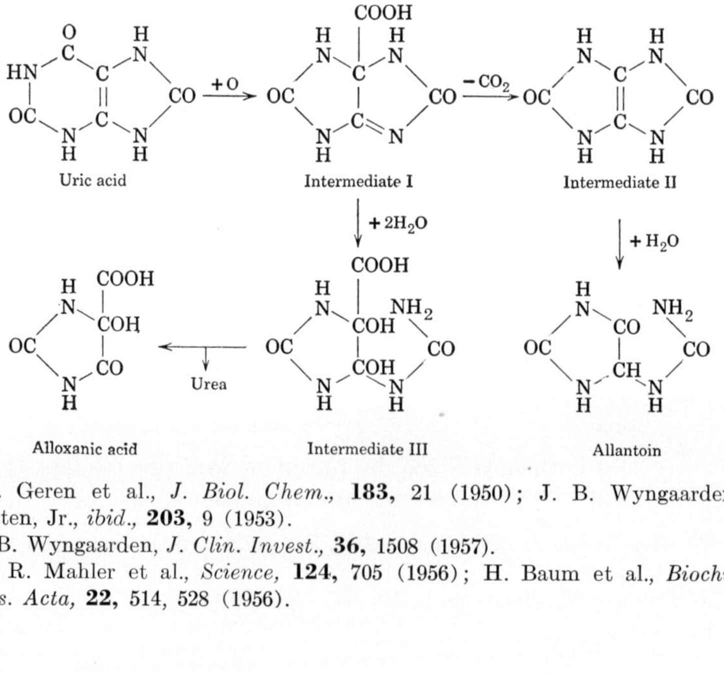

Uric acid   Intermediate I   Intermediate II

Alloxanic acid   Intermediate III   Allantoin

[26] W. Geren et al., *J. Biol. Chem.*, **183**, 21 (1950); J. B. Wyngaarden and D. Stetten, Jr., *ibid.*, **203**, 9 (1953).

[27] J. B. Wyngaarden, *J. Clin. Invest.*, **36**, 1508 (1957).

[28] H. R. Mahler et al., *Science*, **124**, 705 (1956); H. Baum et al., *Biochim. et Biophys. Acta*, **22**, 514, 528 (1956).

allantoin.[29] From the available evidence, it appears that the conversion of uric acid to allantoin proceeds via two intermediates, believed to be compounds I and II shown in the scheme on page 856. It is of interest that, if phosphate buffer is replaced by borate buffer (pH 7.2) in the enzymic incubation mixture, uric acid is mainly oxidized to alloxanic acid and urea, which probably arise from the unstable intermediate III.[30]

In fishes, allantoin may be cleaved to allantoic acid, and thence to urea and glyoxylic acid; the enzymes that catalyze these reactions are termed allantoinase and allantoicase, respectively.[31]

$$
\begin{array}{c}
\text{NH—CO} \\
| \qquad | \\
\text{CO} \qquad | \\
| \qquad | \\
\text{NH—CHNHCONH}_2 \\
\text{Allantoin}
\end{array}
\xrightarrow[\text{inase}]{\text{allanto-}}
\begin{array}{c}
\text{NH}_2 \qquad \text{NH}_2 \\
| \qquad\qquad | \\
\text{CO} \quad \text{COOH} \quad \text{CO} \\
| \qquad | \qquad | \\
\text{NH—CH——NH} \\
\text{Allantoic acid}
\end{array}
\xrightarrow[\text{icase}]{\text{allanto-}}
\begin{array}{c}
2\text{CO(NH}_2)_2 \\
+ \\
\text{COOH} \\
| \\
\text{CHO}
\end{array}
$$

Other End Products of Nitrogen Metabolism in Animals

As noted earlier, in addition to urea, ammonia, and uric acid, animals may excrete varying but small quantities of other nitrogenous end products. One of those excreted in mammalian urine is creatinine, which arises from the creatine in the tissues. Creatine synthesis involves at least two reactions: (a) a transamidination, by which the amidine group of L-arginine is transferred to the nitrogen of glycine to yield guanidino-acetic acid (p. 803); and (b) a transmethylation, by which the S-methyl group of methionine is added to guanidinoacetic acid (p. 804). In vertebrates most of the creatine so formed is found (as creatine phosphate) in the muscle, where a portion of it is continually converted to creatinine (p. 804); this metabolic process is essentially irreversible.

The creatinine excreted in the urine is correlated to the fate of the muscle creatine; diseases that affect muscle are accompanied by an increased excretion of creatinine. Small quantities of creatine also are normally excreted in the urine; the excretion of this compound rises markedly in conditions characterized by the breakdown of muscle tissue. From the data obtained in isotope experiments,[32] it is known that the creatinine (and creatine) in the urine of animals maintained on a diet devoid of these two compounds is derived directly from the creatine of

[29] R. Bentley and A. Neuberger, *Biochem. J.*, **52**, 694 (1952).

[30] E. S. Canellakis and P. P. Cohen, *J. Biol. Chem.*, **213**, 385 (1955).

[31] M. Laskowski, in J. B. Sumner and K. Myrbäck, *The Enzymes*, Chapter 27, Academic Press, New York, 1951.

[32] K. Bloch and R. Schoenheimer, *J. Biol. Chem.*, **133**, 633; **134**, 785 (1940).

the tissues. Creatinine, like uric acid, is a true end product of nitrogen metabolism.

It was noted previously that small amounts of amino acid nitrogen are excreted in the urine. Chromatographic studies have shown that normal adult humans excrete about 1.1 grams of free amino acids per day,[33] corresponding to about 180 mg of nitrogen (ca. 1.2 per cent of the total urinary nitrogen). In addition to the free amino acids, acylated amino acids (e.g., hippuric acid, phenylacetylglutamine) also are present in human urine. In patients suffering from liver disease, such as massive hepatic necrosis or progressive cirrhosis, a marked increase in blood amino acids and in urinary amino acid excretion is frequently observed, probably because of the failure of the liver to metabolize amino acids at a normal rate. In other diseases, such as cystinuria (p. 798) or galactosemia (p. 465), the level of blood amino acids is usually in the normal range, and the increase in urinary amino acids which frequently accompanies these diseases is probably a consequence of the failure of the kidney tubules to reabsorb the amino acids present in the glomerular filtrate. Such abnormal kidney function also appears to be responsible for the amino aciduria observed in Wilson's disease, a rare hereditary condition characterized by progressive degeneration of brain tissue and cirrhosis of the liver, and associated with an abnormal metabolism of copper.[34]

Among the nitrogenous constituents found in living systems is the compound trimethylamine oxide, $(CH_3)_3N{\rightarrow}O$. This substance is present in the tissues and excreta of many marine invertebrates and vertebrates. Although it has been suggested that trimethylamine oxide is an end product of nitrogen metabolism in salt water fish, there is evidence to indicate that the compound is mainly of exogenous origin.[35] This conclusion is in accord with numerous observations that trimethylamine oxide is found only in the tissues of marine fish that feed on zooplankton and crustaceans; in the latter species, the oxide is probably formed from endogenous sources, although no metabolic pathway for its biosynthesis can be defined at present. The unpleasant odor of trimethylamine characteristic of putrefied fish is probably caused by the bacterial reduction of tissue trimethylamine oxide.

Trimethylamine oxide is related to the betaines, of which glycine betaine, $(CH_3)_3N^+CH_2COO^-$, is the simplest example. The relation of this substance to choline in animal metabolism has already been discussed (p. 802). Glycine betaine is present in plants and in the muscle

[33] W. H. Stein, *J. Biol. Chem.*, **201**, 45 (1953).

[34] W. H. Stein et al., *J. Clin. Invest.*, **33**, 410 (1954); G. E. Cartwright et al., *ibid.*, **33**, 1487 (1954).

[35] E. R. Norris and G. J. Benoit, Jr., *J. Biol. Chem.*, **158**, 433, 439, 443 (1945).

tissues of animals. Plant tissues also contain other betaines, such as stachydrine and trigonelline; cyclic betaines of this type are widely

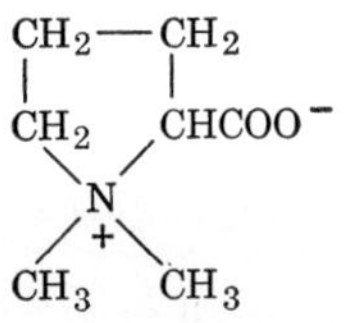

Stachydrine 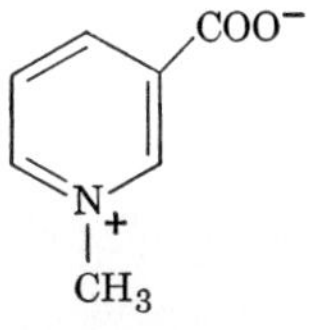   Trigonelline

distributed in plants, and it has been suggested that they may be end products of protein metabolism.

Plant Alkaloids [36]

An important group of substances which may represent end products of nitrogen metabolism in higher plants are the alkaloids, i.e., basic (alkali-like) nitrogen compounds. Most of these compounds exert characteristic physiological effects on animals; some of the oldest pharmacological agents are included in this group. Although the structure of many alkaloids has been established by chemical degradation and ultimate synthesis, relatively little information is available about the metabolic pathways involved in their biogenesis; however, many valuable hypotheses have been based on the structural relationship of various members of this group to known amino acids; in particular, tryptophan, proline, phenylalanine, lysine, and ornithine have been considered as possible precursors.[37]

Nearly all the known alkaloids can be related structurally to amino acids or amino acid derivatives through hypothetical reactions involving, for example, methylation, decarboxylation, or reactions in which formaldehyde or formate participates. The examination of these stimulating hypotheses about the biosynthesis of alkaloids remains a fruitful field of biochemical study by enzymic and isotopic methods. Some of the biological aspects of alkaloid formation in plants have been discussed by Dawson[38] and Mothes.[39]

Several of the hypotheses based on structural similarities have received support from biochemical isotope experiments. For example, studies on

[36] T. A. Henry, *Plant Alkaloids,* 4th Ed., J. and A. Churchill, London, 1949; R. H. F. Manske and H. L. Holmes, *The Alkaloids,* Vols. I–V, Academic Press, New York, 1951–1955.

[37] R. Robinson, *The Structural Relations of Natural Products,* Oxford University Press, London, 1955.

[38] R. F. Dawson, *Advances in Enzymol.,* **8,** 203 (1948).

[39] K. Mothes, *Ann. Rev. Plant Physiol.,* **6,** 393 (1955).

the biosynthesis of nicotine by the tobacco plant have shown that the pyrrolidine ring of this alkaloid is derived from ornithine[40] (as predicted). However, the pyridine ring of nicotine is derived not from lysine, but

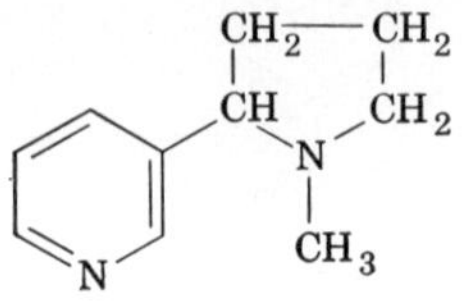

Nicotine 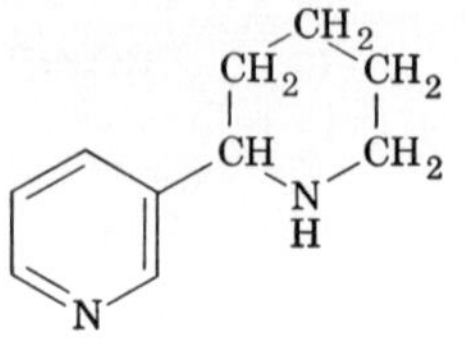   Anabasine

from nicotinic acid,[41] which may arise from tryptophan (cf. p. 840). It is of interest that lysine is utilized for the biosynthesis of the piperidine ring of the tobacco alkaloid anabasine. The formation of the pyrrolidine and piperidine rings of these and other alkaloids may involve the action of diamine oxidase (p. 823) on ornithine and lysine, or on the diamines derived from these amino acids by decarboxylation (p. 767).[42]

Another substance which, like anabasine, contains a piperidine group, and is believed to arise from lysine, is coniine, the chief alkaloid of hemlock. Coniine (2-n-propylpiperidine) was the first alkaloid to be synthesized in the laboratory (Ladenburg, 1886).

Nicotine contains a N-methyl group; the demethylated compound is termed nornicotine. The administration to tobacco plants of methionine labeled in the S-methyl group leads to appreciable incorporation of isotope in the methyl group of nicotine,[43] suggesting that transmethylation from methionine to nornicotine may occur in these plants. However, the possibility also exists that the N-methyl group of nicotine may arise from "active formaldehyde" derived from the α-carbon of glycine or the β-carbon of serine (p. 774).[44]

Among the numerous other alkaloids that contain a pyrrolidine ring is hygrine (p. 861), which is also believed to be derived from ornithine. A group of alkaloids structurally related to hygrine has a condensed pyrrolidine-piperidine ring; an example of this group is the alkaloid tropine, which may arise by ring closure of hygrine. The important alkaloid atropine is the tropine ester of α-phenylglycolic acid.

Among the plant alkaloids is hordenine, which occurs in the roots of germinating barley, and probably arises from phenylalanine via tyrosine,

---

[40] L. J. Dewey et al., *Biochim. et Biophys. Acta,* **18,** 141 (1955).

[41] R. F. Dawson et al., *J. Am. Chem. Soc.,* **78,** 2645 (1956); E. Leete, *ibid.,* **78,** 3520 (1956).

[42] P. J. G. Mann and W. R. Smithies, *Biochem. J.,* **61,** 89 (1955).

[43] L. J. Dewey et al., *J. Am. Chem. Soc.,* **76,** 3997 (1954).

[44] R. U. Byerrum et al., *J. Biol. Chem.,* **216,** 371 (1955).

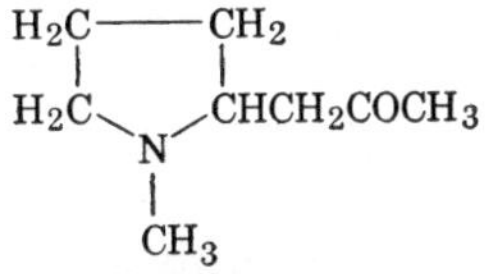

$$H_2C——CH_2$$
$$HC \diagdown \diagup CH$$
$$N$$
$$|$$
$$CH_3$$

H2C———CH2
H2C⟍ ⟋CHCH2COCH3
       N
       |
      CH3

H2C⟍ CH3 ⟋CH2
      CH
      |
      OH

Hygrine 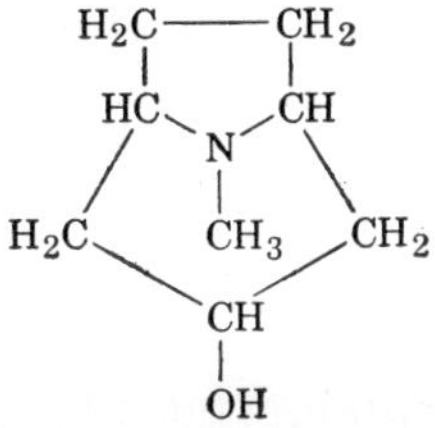   Tropine

tyramine, and N-methyltyramine.[45] The alkaloid ephedrine, which is structurally related to adrenalin, may also be derived from phenylalanine (cf. p. 829).

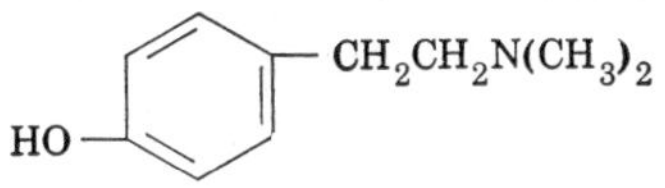

HO— ⟨ring⟩ —CH₂CH₂N(CH₃)₂

⟨ring⟩ —CH — CHNHCH₃
         | |
        OH   CH₃

Hordenine 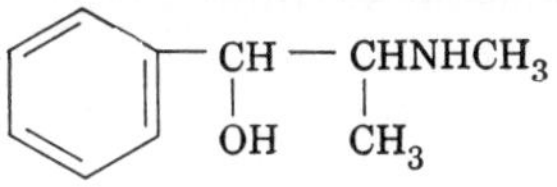   Ephedrine

Another large family of alkaloids contains an indole group; harman is one of the simpler representatives, and eserine (physostigmine) is a more complex member of this family. The biogenesis of harman from tryptophan is suggested by the finding that tryptamine reacts with acetaldehyde under "physiological conditions" (room temperature, pH 5 to 7) to form tetrahydroharman, which also has been isolated from several higher plants.[46] Dehydrogenation of the tetrahydro compound would yield harman.

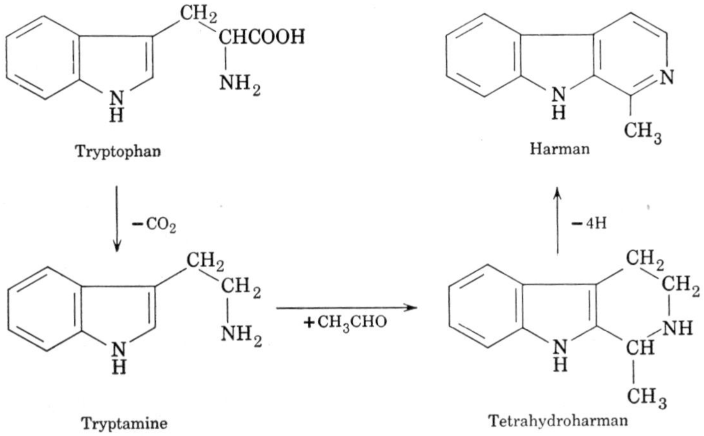

⟨indole ring⟩ CH₂ CHCOOH
                   |
                  NH₂

Tryptophan

⟨indole ring⟩ Harman
              CH₃

↓ −CO₂

⟨indole ring⟩ CH₂ CH₂
                   |
                  NH₂   +CH₃CHO →

Tryptamine

↑ −4H

⟨indole ring⟩ CH₂ CH₂
                    NH
              CH
              |
              CH₃

Tetrahydroharman

[45] J. Massicot and L. Marion, *Canad. J. Chem.*, **35**, 1 (1957).
[46] G. M. Badger and A. F. Beecham, *Nature*, **168**, 517 (1951).

An especially interesting group of indole alkaloids are derived from the drug ergot,[47] which is obtained from the mycelia of the fungus *Claviceps purpurea*. In addition to various products of amino acid decarboxylation (histamine, tyramine, cadaverine, putrescine), ergot contains the pharmacologically active alkaloids ergometrine, ergotamine, and several ergotoxines (ergocristine, ergocornine, ergokryptine). All these alkaloids contain a common structural unit, termed D-lysergic acid. In ergometrine, lysergic acid is linked to L-2-aminopropan-1-ol by an amide bond. In ergotamine, the carboxyl group of lysergic acid is linked to a peptide which, on acid hydrolysis, yields pyruvic acid (derived from α-hydroxyalanine), ammonia, L-phenylalanine, and D-proline; in the intact alkaloid, the proline has the L-configuration, and the D form is an artifact obtained on hydrolysis. The peptide portion of the ergotoxine group yields on hydrolysis dimethylpyruvic acid, ammonia, D-proline, and another amino acid: L-phenylalanine (from ergocristine) or L-valine (from ergocornine) or L-leucine (from ergokryptine).

The structure of ergotamine is shown; it will be seen that a tetracyclic carboxylic acid (lysergic acid) is linked by an amide bond to a cyclic

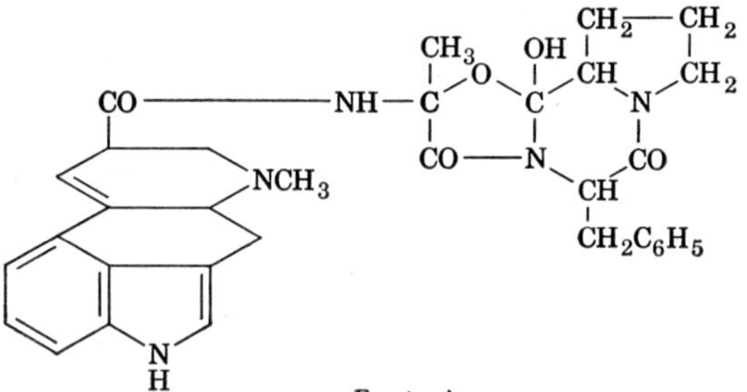

Ergotamine

peptide in which the carboxyl carbon of a proline residue is linked both to the nitrogen of a phenylalanine residue and to an oxygen atom linked to the α-carbon of an alanyl residue. In the ergotoxine group, this alanyl residue is replace by a valyl residue which, on hydrolysis, gives rise to dimethylpyruvic acid. It is noteworthy that this type of cyclic peptide structure ("cyclol") was originally proposed by Wrinch[48] for the polypeptide chains of proteins. There is no experimental evidence at present for the cyclol structure of proteins, and the elucidation of the structure of the ergot alkaloids appears to provide the first indication of the occurrence of cyclol rings in natural products.

It has been reported that the diethylamide of lysergic acid causes

[47] G. Barger, *Ergot and Ergotism*, Gurney and Jackson, London, 1931; A. Stoll, *Chem. Revs.*, **47**, 197 (1950); A. L. Glenn, *Quart. Revs.*, **8**, 192 (1954).
[48] D. M. Wrinch, *Proc. Roy. Soc.*, **160A**, 59 (1937).

hallucinations in human subjects. Because of the possible relation of such induced mental disturbances to naturally occurring psychoses, much experimental study has been devoted to the metabolic effects of this drug,[49] which is believed to act as an antagonist of 5-hydroxytryptamine (serotonin, p. 844) in the brain.

A group of alkaloids, derived from plants of the genus *Rauwolfia*, have assumed considerable clinical importance because of their use as tranquilizing agents in the treatment of nervous and mental disorders.

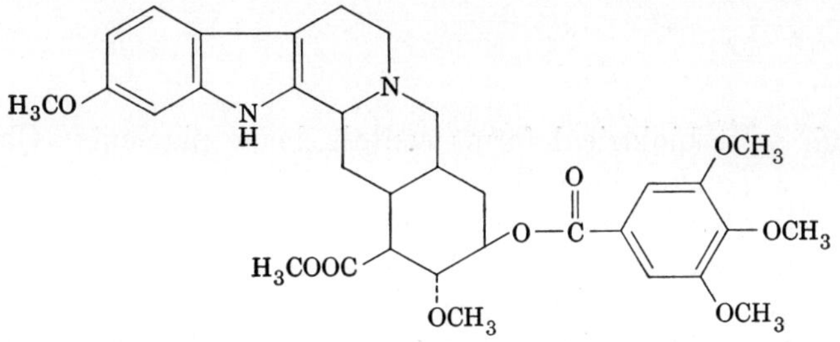

Reserpine

Among these alkaloids is reserpine, whose total synthesis has been effected by Woodward et al.[50] The administration of reserpine (and of related benzoquinolizine derivatives) to experimental animals causes the release of 5-hydroxytryptamine from various tissues (brain, intestine, blood platelets).[51]

[49] E. Shaw and D. W. Woolley, *Science,* **124,** 121 (1956).
[50] R. B. Woodward et al., *J. Am. Chem. Soc.,* **78,** 2023 (1956).
[51] A. Pletscher, *Science,* **126,** 507 (1957).

34 ·

Metabolism
of Porphyrins

Although most biological forms contain heme pigments (Chapter 6), only a few organisms have been found to require an exogenous source of porphyrins. It has long been known that the vast majority of animals, plants, and microorganisms can synthesize the requisite porphyrins from constituents of the diet, but decisive data on the metabolic pathways in this biosynthesis were not available until the isotope technique had been applied to the problem. Of special importance was the work of Shemin and Rittenberg,[1] who administered N^{15}-glycine to human subjects and to rats, and found that the isotopic nitrogen is incorporated to an appreciable extent in the pyrrole rings of the hemin (p. 178) isolated from the hemoglobin. The role of glycine as the specific precursor of the heme nitrogen was indicated by the relatively low isotope content of the hemin isolated after administration of other labeled nitrogen compounds (ammonium citrate, glutamic acid, proline, leucine, histidine). Subsequent experiments with glycine-1-C^{14} and glycine-2-C^{14} showed that, although the methylene carbon of glycine is extensively incorporated into the hemin, the carboxyl carbon is not. In addition to glycine, acetate is utilized by the rat for the synthesis of porphyrins; both the carboxyl carbon and methyl carbon of acetate are found in the porphyrin molecule, the methyl carbon being incorporated to a greater extent than the carboxyl carbon.[2] However, the incorporation of glycine carbon into hemin does not involve the intermediate formation of acetate. It may be added that carbon supplied as CO_2 or formate is not incorporated into protoporphyrin to an appreciable extent.

The utilization of glycine and acetate for protoporphyrin synthesis has been demonstrated not only *in vivo* but also *in vitro*, in experiments with mammalian reticulocytes (immature red cells), with duck erythrocytes, or with hemolysates of these cells.

---

[1] D. Shemin and D. Rittenberg, *J. Biol. Chem.*, **166**, 621, 627 (1946).
[2] N. S. Radin et al., *J. Biol. Chem.*, **184**, 745 (1950).

By careful degradation of the hemin formed in experiments such as those described above, it was possible to demonstrate that glycine contributes nitrogen to all 4 pyrrole rings of protoporphyrin, and that, for every 4 glycine nitrogens used for porphyrin synthesis, 8 methylene carbons of the amino acid enter the porphyrin. Four of these carbons appear in the methene bridges which link the pyrrole units, as shown in Fig. 1. The other 4 carbon atoms appear in one of the two α positions

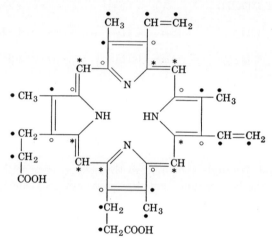

Fig. 1. Metabolic sources of atoms of protoporphyrin IX, as shown by isotope experiments (from D. Shemin and J. Wittenberg[3]). All 4 N atoms are derived from glycine; atoms marked with asterisks are derived from the methylene carbon of glycine; atoms marked with solid circles are derived from the methyl carbon of acetate; atoms marked with open circles are derived mainly from the methyl carbon of acetate and in small part from the carboxyl carbon of acetate; the unmarked carbon atoms of the COOH groups are derived solely from the carboxyl carbon of acetate.

of each of the pyrrole rings. Glycine thus donates 8 of the 34 carbon atoms of protoporphyrin; the remaining 26 are derived from acetate. Of these, the 2 carboxyl carbons are derived solely from the carboxyl carbon of acetate, which also contributes to the pyrrole carbons in the manner indicated in Fig. 1. As noted above, however, the methyl carbon of acetate makes a more important contribution to the porphyrin nucleus than does the carboxyl group. Three of the 4 pyrrole carbons are largely, or entirely, derived from the methyl carbon of acetate, as are the carbon atoms of the side-chain groups (except for the carboxyl carbon of the propionic acid group).[3]

[3] D. Shemin and J. Wittenberg, *J. Biol. Chem.*, **185**, 103 (1950); **192**, 315 (1951); H. M. Muir and A. Neuberger, *Biochem. J.*, **47**, 97 (1950).

The studies of Shemin showed that the utilization of acetate for porphyrin synthesis involves the intermediate formation of a succinyl derivative ($HOOCCH_2CH_2CO$—X) which arises by the decarboxylation of α-ketoglutaric acid, a component of the citric acid cycle. From the discussion of the fate of the carbons of labeled acetate as they pass through the intermediates of the citric acid cycle (cf. p. 515), it follows that the succinyl-X will initially be labeled as indicated in formula I

$$
\begin{array}{ccccccc}
(c) & \text{COOH} & \quad & (c) & \text{COOH} & \quad & (c) & \text{COOH} \\
& | & & & | & & & | \\
(m) & \text{CH}_2 & & (m) & \text{CH}_2 & & (m) & \text{CH}_2 \\
& | & & & | & & & | \\
& \text{CH}_2 & & (m) & \text{CH}_2 & & (m) & \text{CH}_2 \\
& | & & & | & & & | \\
& \text{CO—X} & & (m) & \text{CO—X} & & (c) & \text{CO—X} \\
& \text{(I)} & & & \text{(II)} & & & \text{(III)}
\end{array}
$$

(m denotes carbon derived from the methyl carbon of acetate, c denotes carbon derived from the carboxyl carbon of acetate). After one complete turn of the citric acid cycle, the oxaloacetate will have become labeled, and the succinyl-X formed in the second turn will be labeled as shown in formula II. In addition, the conversion of succinyl-X to free succinate appears to be reversible, and a small amount of symmetrically labeled succinyl-X (formula III) may be derived from compound I. From such considerations, Shemin has been able to account quantitatively for the relative extent of labeling of the carbons of protoporphyrin derived from acetate.[4] The available evidence points to the identity of succinyl-X with succinyl-CoA (p. 505).

It will be noted from Fig. 1 that the pattern of labeling in each of the pyrrole nuclei of protoporphyrin is the same; this important finding led to the recognition that a single pyrrole derivative is the common metabolic precursor of all 4 rings. The precursor pyrrole is derived from succinyl-X and glycine with the intermediate formation of δ-aminolevulinic (δ-aminolaevulic) acid[5] (cf. Fig. 2). When δ-aminolevulinic acid-5-C^{14} (the labeled carbon is denoted with an asterisk in Fig. 2) was tested as a metabolic precursor of protoporphyrin, it was found to be more effective than glycine-2-C^{14}; the pattern of labeling in the porphyrin was the same for the two precursors. It is assumed that in the biosynthesis of δ-aminolevulinic acid, α-amino-β-ketoadipic acid is formed as an intermediate[6] and is decarboxylated to release (as CO_2) the carbon derived from the carboxyl carbon of glycine.

[4] J. C. Wriston et al., *J. Biol. Chem.*, **215**, 603 (1955).

[5] D. Shemin et al., *J. Biol. Chem.*, **215**, 613 (1954); K. D. Gibson et al., *Biochem. J.*, **70**, 71 (1958); G. Kikuchi et al., *J. Biol. Chem.*, **233**, 1214 (1958).

[6] A. Neuberger et al., *Biochem. J.*, **64**, 137 (1956).

The α-carbon of glycine can be converted to a C_1 unit that is a precursor of the β-carbon of serine, the methyl carbon of methionine, the ureido carbon of purines, etc. (p. 774). Shemin has shown that the administration of δ-aminolevulinic acid-5-C^{14} to an animal also leads to labeling of serine, methionine, and purines, and has proposed a "succinate-

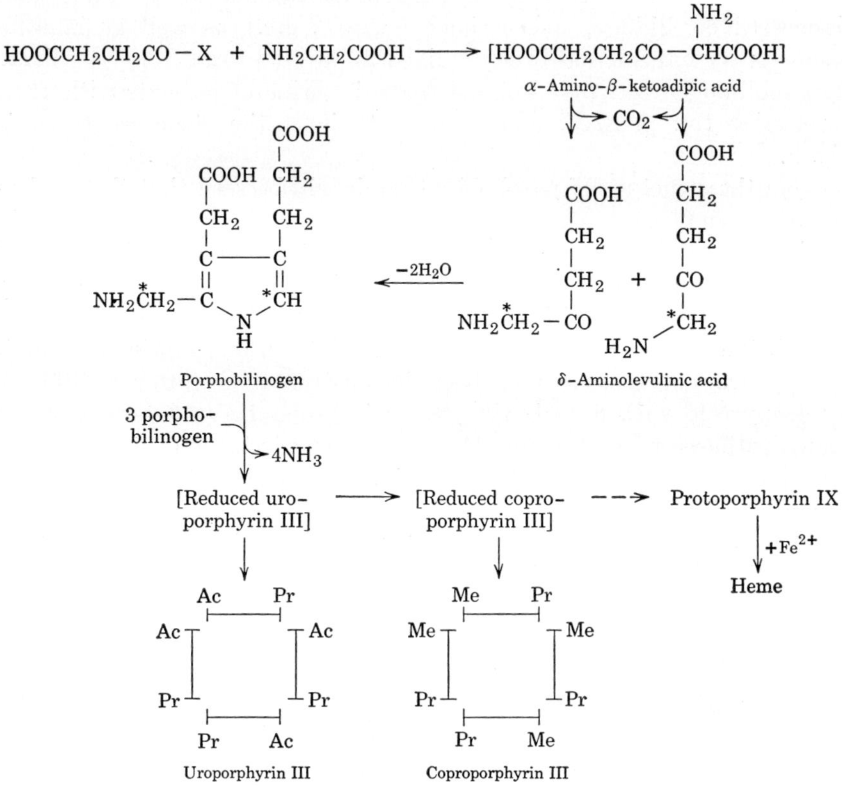

Fig. 2. Role of δ-aminolevulinic acid and of porphobilinogen in the biosynthesis of heme.

glycine" cycle as an alternative pathway of glycine metabolism.[7] It is assumed that an intermediate such as α-ketoglutaraldehyde ($HOOCCH_2$-CH_2COCHO) is formed by oxidative deamination of δ-aminolevulinic acid; the aldehyde group (derived from the α-carbon of glycine) is thought to be converted to a C_1 unit with the formation of succinate, which is reutilized in the condensation of succinyl-X with more glycine to regenerate δ-aminolevulinic acid.

The condensation of succinyl-X with glycine appears to require

[7] D. Shemin, *Harvey Lectures,* **50,** 258 (1956).

organized cell structure, and has not been demonstrated with tissue homogenates or extracts. On the other hand, the further conversion of δ-aminolevulinic acid to porphyrin is effected by extractable enzymes. The condensation of 2 molecules of δ-aminolevulinic acid gives rise to a dicarboxypyrrole named porphobilinogen. This reaction is catalyzed by an enzyme (δ-aminolevulinic dehydrase) found in several animal tissues (liver, kidney, spleen, bone marrow, etc.) as well as in some bacteria; the enzyme has been obtained in purified form from beef liver.[8] Porphobilinogen was first isolated from the urine of patients with acute porphyria[9] (cf. p. 872), and shown[10] to have the structure given in Fig. 2.

From the structure of porphobilinogen it will be seen that the condensation of 4 molecules of this substance to form a tetrapyrrole (with the elimination of the 4 amino groups) should yield a porphyrin having 4 acetic acid side chains and 4 propionic acid side chains, as in uroporphyrin III (p. 168), which is structurally related to protoporphyrin IX. Indeed, the conversion of porphobilinogen into uroporphyrin by soluble enzymes from erythrocytes has been demonstrated.[11] However, although a tetrapyrrole with 8 carboxyl groups is probably an intermediate in heme synthesis, uroporphyrin III does not appear to lie on the pathway from porphobilinogen to protoporphyrin. The possibility that the octa-carboxylic intermediate is a partially hydrogenated uroporphyrin III (methene groups reduced to methylene groups) is suggested by the finding that, if uroporphyrin III is subjected to chemical reduction with sodium amalgam, the resulting product is utilized for heme biosynthesis.[12] The enzyme system that catalyzes the conversion of porphobilinogen to uroporphyrin III has been named porphobilinogenase, and has been partially purified from erythrocytes.

In addition to uroporphyrin III, coproporphyrin III (p. 167) is also formed from porphobilinogen by erythrocyte preparations, presumably by decarboxylation of the acetic acid side chains of the intermediate with 8 carboxyl groups. Coproporphyrin III does not appear to be an intermediate in protoporphyrin formation,[13] and, like uroporphyrin III, may arise from a partially hydrogenated intermediate (Fig. 2). Although it is plausible to assume that a reduced coproporphyrin III is an intermediate in heme synthesis, the experimental evidence is indirect, and no information is available about the mechanism of the conversion of 2

[8] K. D. Gibson et al., *Biochem. J.,* **61,** 618 (1955).

[9] R. G. Westall, *Nature,* **170,** 614 (1952).

[10] G. H. Cookson and C. Rimington, *Biochem. J.,* **57,** 476 (1954).

[11] J. E. Falk et al., *Biochem. J.,* **63,** 87 (1956).

[12] R. A. Neve et al., *J. Am. Chem. Soc.,* **78,** 691 (1956).

[13] E. I. B. Dresel and J. E. Falk, *Biochem. J.,* **63,** 388 (1956).

propionic acid side chains of coproporphyrin III to the vinyl side chains of protoporphyrin IX. The mechanism for the introduction of the iron of heme is unknown, but is believed to be an enzymic reaction involving protoporphyrin IX or some closely related compound.

The condensation of porphobilinogen to a tetrapyrrole which can give rise to uroporphyrin III, coproporphyrin III, and protoporphyrin IX appears to involve a specific enzymic mechanism which effects the characteristic asymmetric arrangement of the side chains on the 4 pyrrole nuclei; the nature of this mechanism is unknown, and has been the subject of stimulating speculation.[7] It should be added that porphobilinogen can undergo nonenzymic condensation to form porphyrins; in addition to uroporphyrin III, the symmetrically substituted uroporphyrin I (p. 168) is formed.

It is clear from the foregoing that, although the role of δ-aminolevulinic acid and of porphobilinogen as metabolic intermediates in the synthesis of heme from glycine and succinate is well established, many steps in the over-all conversion still remain to be elucidated. A valuable discussion of the status of this field in 1955 may be found in the volume edited by Wolstenholme and Millar.[14]

The fact that glycine is specifically used for the synthesis of the protoporphyrin of hemoglobin has permitted a striking experiment to determine the life span of the human erythrocyte. London et al.[15] administered to a human subject N^{15}-labeled glycine for 2 days, and at intervals thereafter withdrew sufficient blood for the isolation, from the erythrocyte hemoglobin, of hemin, whose N^{15}-content was then determined. As will be seen from the solid curve in Fig. 3, there is an initial rapid rise in the isotope concentration of the isolated hemin. The high level is maintained in the normal subject for an extended period (ca. 100 days), thus indicating that the porphyrin of the adult erythrocyte does not lose N^{15}; i.e., it is not in a "dynamic" metabolic state, but remains in the erythrocyte until the cell is destroyed and the protoporphyrin is converted to bile pigments (p. 872). Since the bile pigments are end products of porphyrin metabolism, the porphyrin nitrogen is essentially removed from the metabolic pool. An examination of the solid curve in Fig. 3 shows that the cells labeled during the period of glycine administration disappear from the blood most rapidly after 120 days, which may be taken as the average life span of the normal human erythrocyte. In the pathological state known as sickle cell anemia, the shape of the isotope concentration curve for hemin is completely different (the broken line in Fig. 3); here the isotope concentration falls off

[14] G. E. W. Wolstenholme and E. C. P. Millar, *Porphyrin Biosynthesis and Metabolism*, J. and A. Churchill, London, 1955.

[15] I. M. London et al., *J. Biol. Chem.*, **179**, 463 (1949).

exponentially after an initial rise, and the newly formed cells are apparently destroyed to the same extent as the older ones.

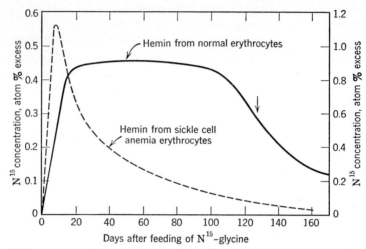

Fig. 3. N^{15} concentration in hemin after feeding N^{15}-glycine to a normal subject (ordinate on left) and to a patient with sickle cell anemia (ordinate on right). The vertical arrow denotes the time (ca. 120 days) at which the rate of destruction of labeled erythrocytes is maximal. (From I. M. London et al.[15])

Biosynthesis of Pyrrole Compounds in Microorganisms and Plants. It will be recalled that several heme proteins important in biological oxidations (cytochromes, peroxidases, catalases) are widely distributed in nature. Most organisms are able to synthesize the porphyrin portion; for example, in response to aerobic conditions of growth, yeast can make its cytochrome c from small precursors.[16] The available information indicates that the pathway of porphyrin synthesis in the formation of cytochrome is similar to that in the formation of hemoglobin, and glycine has been shown to be a specific precursor, both in yeast and in animal tissues. The specific utilization of glycine for porphyrin synthesis has also been demonstrated with *Corynebacterium diphtheriae* (cf. p. 357) and in the formation of the heme protein present in the root nodules of leguminous plants (cf. p. 164).[17]

Glycine and acetate also are utilized by green plants for the synthesis of chlorophyll,[18] and studies with the green alga *Chlorella* have shown that δ-aminolevulinic acid and porphobilinogen are intermediates in the process.[19] Artificially induced mutants of *Chlorella* that are unable to

[16] B. Ephrussi and P. P. Slonimski, *Biochim. et Biophys. Acta,* **6,** 256 (1950); M. Ycas and D. L. Drabkin, *J. Biol. Chem.,* **224,** 921 (1957).

[17] J. E. Richmond and K. Salomon, *Biochim. et Biophys. Acta,* **17,** 48 (1955).

[18] R. J. della Rosa et al., *J. Biol. Chem.,* **202,** 771 (1953).

[19] L. Bogorad and S. Granick, *Proc. Natl. Acad. Sci.,* **39,** 1176 (1953).

make chlorophyll accumulate porphyrins which may be intermediates in normal chlorophyll synthesis from porphobilinogen.[20] Thus one mutant produces a mixture of porphyrins containing between 2 and 8 carboxyl groups, and presumed to be precursors of protoporphyrin IX; among these porphyrins is hematoporphyrin IX (p. 167). Another mutant accumulates protoporphyrin IX, and in a third mutant the magnesium complex of protoporphyrin was found; the presence of the magnesium complex of the vinyl pheoporphyrin a₅ also was demonstrated. On the basis of the data available at present, it would appear that, like animals, green plants synthesize protoporphyrin IX from small fragments (glycine, acetic acid), and then convert this porphyrin to chlorophyll by a series of reactions in which the magnesium is introduced into the protoporphyrin and the resulting complex is transformed into vinyl pheoporphyrin a₅ (cf. Fig. 4). A similar pathway may be involved in the biosynthesis of bacteriochlorophyll (p. 183) by photosynthetic bacteria, such as *Rhodopseudomonas spheroides*, which can make porphyrins from δ-aminolevulinic acid.[21]

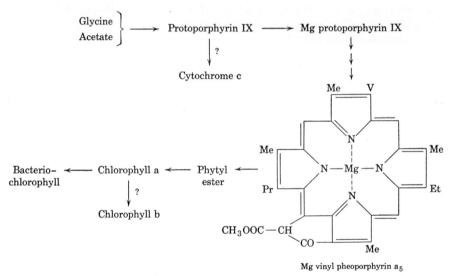

Fig. 4. Proposed pathway of biosynthesis of the chlorophylls. (From S. Granick.[22])

A few organisms require preformed porphyrins for growth; examples are the flagellated protozoan *Strigomonas* and the bacterium *Hemophilus influenzae*. Studies by Granick[22] have shown that a variety of iron

[20] S. Granick, *J. Biol. Chem.*, **183**, 713 (1950); S. Granick et al., *ibid.*, **202**, 801 (1953)

[21] J. Lascelles, *Biochem. J.*, **62**, 78 (1956).

[22] S. Granick, *Harvey Lectures*, **44**, 220 (1950).

porphyrins will support the growth of *H. influenzae;* however, if free porphyrins other than protoporphyrin are supplied, no growth ensues. This difference has been related to the presence in protoporphyrin of the vinyl groups which are thought to be essential for the metabolic introduction of the metal to form the iron-porphyrin complex. Similarly, it was found that the free carboxyl groups of the propionic acid side chains were involved in the growth-promoting process; these are believed to be important for the binding of the metalloporphyrin to the appropriate protein.

Some of the conclusions drawn from studies on the biosynthesis of tetrapyrroles from glycine and acetate also apply to the formation of the tripyrrylmethene pigment prodigiosin (p. 168) elaborated by *Serratia marcescens.* As in the synthesis of protoporphyrin in animals, the nitrogen and α-carbon of glycine, as well as both carbons of acetate, are utilized for the formation of prodigiosin.[23] A mutant strain of *S. marcescens* which cannot make the pigment elaborates an intermediate (probably a dipyrryl compound) whose structure has not been elucidated as yet.[24]

Porphyria. In the human disease known as acute intermittent porphyria, frequently characterized by nervous symptoms, large amounts of porphobilinogen are excreted in the urine.[25] After exposure to air, the urine of such patients contains porphyrins, presumably formed by nonenzymic condensation of porphobilinogen (cf. p. 869). A condition similar to acute porphyria can be produced experimentally in rabbits by the administration of drugs such as Sedormid (allyl-isopropyl-acetylurea); the tissues of treated rabbits have been found to contain higher amounts of δ-aminolevulinic dehydrase than those of untreated animals. In addition, the liver of Sedormid-treated animals accumulates relatively large amounts of green porphyrins of unknown constitution.

Another type of porphyria, known as congenital porphyria, appears to involve a dysfunction of the blood-forming organs; it is characterized by the deposition of porphyrins in the tissues, causing extreme photosensitivity, and by the excretion of relatively large quantities of uroporphyrins I and III and coproporphyrin I in the urine. When N^{15}-glycine is administered to porphyrinuric patients, the pyrrole nitrogens of the urinary porphyrins are labeled with N^{15}. The porphyrins formed in porphyria appear to be in a dynamic state, since the rates of incorporation and loss of N^{15} are extremely rapid.[26]

The Bile Pigments.[27] The metabolic breakdown of the hemoglobin released upon the disintegration of erythrocytes in the mammalian

[23] R. Hubbard and C. Rimington, *Biochem. J.,* **46,** 220 (1950).

[24] U. V. Santer and H. J. Vogel, *Biochim. et Biophys. Acta,* **19,** 578 (1956).

[25] A. Goldberg, *Biochem. Soc. Symposia,* **12,** 27 (1954).

[26] C. H. Gray et al., *Biochem. J.,* **47,** 81, 87, 542 (1950).

[27] C. H. Gray, *The Bile Pigments,* Methuen, London, 1953.

organism involves the oxidative cleavage of the porphin ring to form linear tetrapyrroles termed bile pigments; the structure of several of these is shown. The principal sites of the conversion of the heme portion

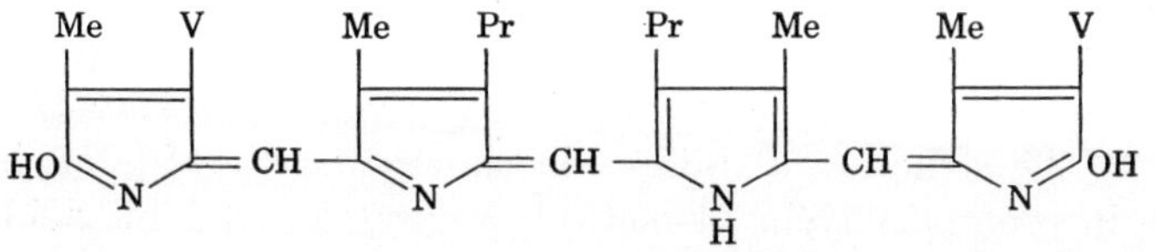

Biliverdin

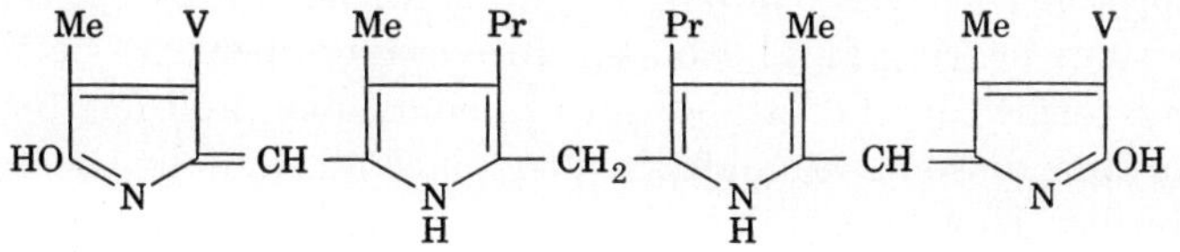

Bilirubin

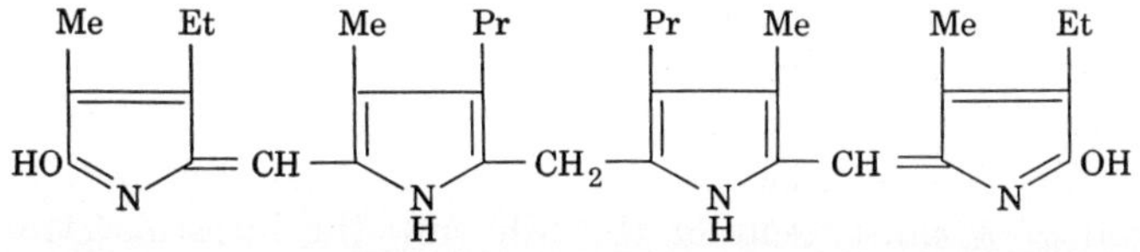

Mesobilirubin

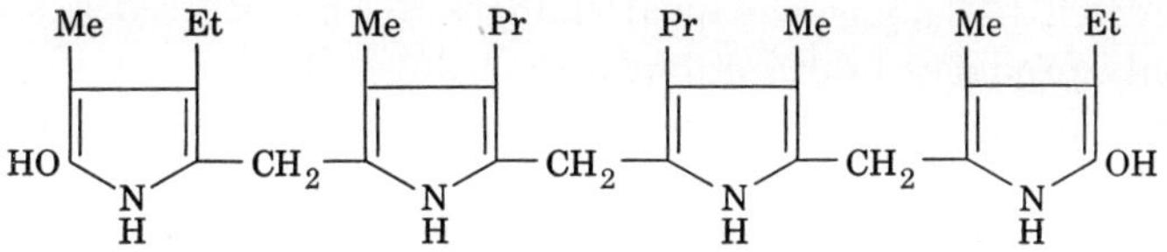

Mesobilirubinogen

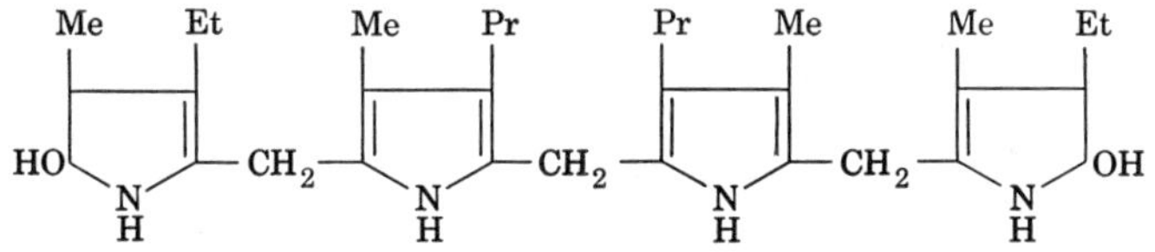

Stercobilinogen

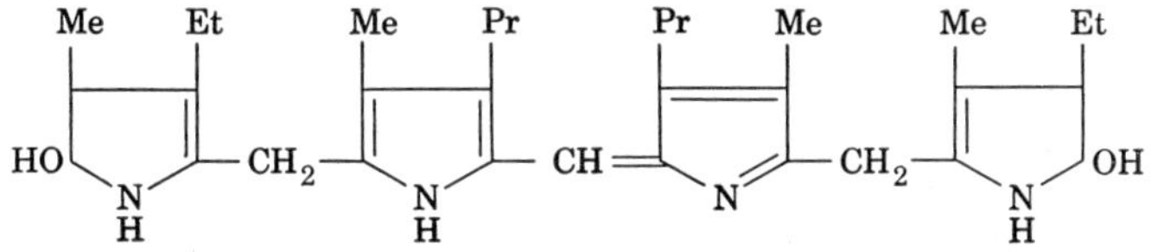

Stercobilin
(*l*-urobilin)

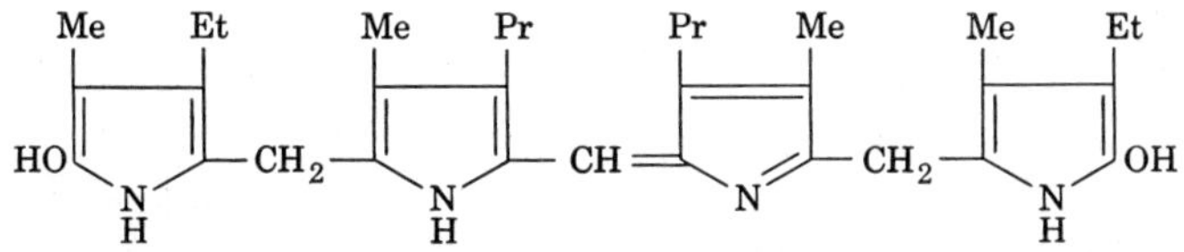

Urobilin IXα

of hemoglobin to bile pigments are believed to be the reticuloendothelial cells of the liver, the spleen, and bone marrow. The possibility exists that the oxidative cleavage of the porphin ring occurs before the proto-porphyrin is released from the globin, and Lemberg[28] has shown that

[28] R. Lemberg et al., *Biochem. J.*, **33**, 754 (1939); J. E. Kench et al., *ibid.*, **47**, 129 (1950).

hemoglobin can be oxidized by oxygen (in the presence of ascorbic acid) to a green conjugated protein (choleglobin) in which the prosthetic group is the iron complex of a bile pigment resembling biliverdin. *In vivo*, the iron released by the catabolism of hemoglobin is retained, largely in the form of ferritin (Chapter 36), and the bile pigments are excreted.

Examination of the structure of biliverdin shows that the side chains are the same as in protoporphyrin (4 methyl, 2 vinyl, 2 propionic acid), and that the porphin ring was oxidized at the methene bridge between the two pyrrole rings bearing vinyl groups. Biliverdin appears to be the first bile pigment formed in the catabolism of hemoglobin, and has been identified in the bile of some animals, in dog placenta, and in the egg shells of some birds. However, biliverdin is not found in normal human blood, where the principal bile pigment is bilirubin (ca. 1 mg per 100 ml), largely bound to serum albumin. Biliverdin is readily reduced to bilirubin, and liver contains an enzyme system which catalyzes this reduction. The bilirubin passes from the liver into the gall bladder, and thence is secreted as a constituent of the bile into the intestinal tract, where it is subjected to further chemical changes to be discussed below. The liver not only produces bilirubin but also removes it from the blood, and the ability of the liver of human subjects to remove injected bilirubin from the circulation serves as a useful clinical test of liver function ("bilirubin clearance" test). A widely used method for the determination of serum bilirubin is based on the reaction of the pigment with diazotized sulfanilic acid (van den Bergh reaction). A portion of the serum bilirubin does not react with this reagent unless ethanol is added ("indirect" van den Bergh reaction); this has been attributed to the fact that the "direct" reaction is given by the water-soluble glucuronide of bilirubin, whereas free bilirubin is sparingly soluble in water, and ethanol is required to effect the reaction with diazotized sulfanilic acid.[29] It is probable that the 2 propionic acid groups of bilirubin are involved in the conjugation with the uronic acid, and that the diglucuronide is formed in the liver by the reaction of UDP-glucuronic acid (p. 537) and the bile pigment.

Another color reaction given by bile pigments is the Gmelin reaction; treatment of a chloroform solution of bilirubin with nitric acid containing a trace of nitrous acid produces a succession of colors, changing from yellow, to green, to blue, to red, and finally to yellow again.

In various types of jaundice, the bilirubin content of human sera may rise to as much as 15 to 50 mg per 100 ml. Jaundice may result from an excessive rate of hemoglobin breakdown (hemolytic jaundice), from

[29] R. Schmid, *Science,* **124,** 76 (1956); B. H. Billing et al., *Biochem. J.,* **65,** 774 (1957); G. M. Grodsky and J. V. Carbone, *J. Biol. Chem.,* **226,** 449 (1957).

obstruction of the outflow of bile (obstructive jaundice), or as a consequence of liver damage (hepatogenous jaundice).

The bilirubin secreted into the intestine is subjected to the reductive action of enzyme systems present in the intestinal bacteria. The first product appears to be mesobilirubin, in which the vinyl groups have been hydrogenated to ethyl groups, and further successive enzymic reduction yields mesobilirubinogen and stercobilinogen.[30] Dehydrogenation of stercobilinogen by intestinal bacteria gives stercobilin, which can readily be isolated from feces. Stercobilin is strongly levorotatory ($[\alpha]_D = -3600°$).

The various intermediates in the conversion of bilirubin to stercobilin may be partly reabsorbed in the intestinal tract, and returned to the liver or excreted in the urine. In some diseases, relatively large amounts of bile pigments are found in the urine; among these are mesobilirubinogen, stercobilinogen (urobilinogen), and stercobilin (l-urobilin).

In addition to the levorotatory stercobilin, an optically inactive bile pigment (urobilin IXα, i-urobilin) has been identified in feces. It is more unstable than stercobilin; in air, urobilin IXα is dehydrogenated to form violet and red pigments. Furthermore, a dextrorotatory bile pigment (d-urobilin, $[\alpha]_D = +5000°$) has been isolated from the feces of patients whose intestinal flora had been altered by treatment with antibacterial agents (aureomycin, terramycin). The structure of d-urobilin is unknown, but is believed to be derived from mesobilirubin via a d-urobilinogen.[31] The current views about the formation of the various bile pigments discussed above are summarized in Fig. 5.

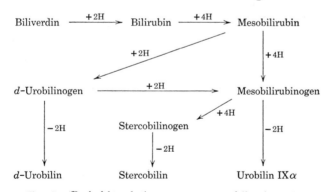

Fig. 5. Probable relations among some bile pigments.

The bile pigments in the feces represent the principal excretory end products of porphyrin metabolism in normal human subjects. When the

[30] P. T. Lowry et al., *J. Biol. Chem.*, **208**, 543 (1954).

[31] C. J. Watson and P. T. Lowry, *J. Biol. Chem.*, **218**, 633, 641 (1956); C. H. Gray and D. C. Nicholson, *Nature*, **180**, 336 (1957).

isotope content of the fecal stercobilin was examined after the administration of N[15]-glycine to a normal subject, the rapid appearance of N[15]
in the bile pigment was observed.[32]   However, as will be seen from Fig. 6,
the isotope concentration decreases rapidly, and does not rise again

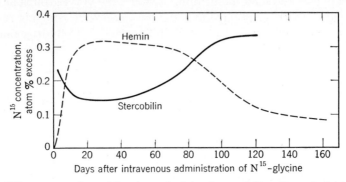

Days after intravenous administration of N[15]-glycine

Fig. 6.   N[15] concentration of hemin and of fecal stercobilin after administration of
N[15]-glycine to a normal human subject.   (From I. M. London et al.[32])

until the labeled erythrocytes begin to disintegrate.   The rapid initial
appearance of isotope in the stercobilin indicates that a portion of it
(about 10 per cent) arises from sources other than the destruction of
mature erythrocytes; possibly a portion of the newly formed protoporphyrin (or related porphyrins) is converted directly to bile pigments
instead of being incorporated into red cell hemoglobin.   In this connection, it is of interest that in congenital porphyria and in the metabolic
dysfunction known as pernicious anemia, where there is an abnormality
in the mechanisms leading to hemoglobin synthesis, an even larger part
of the fecal stercobilin is derived from sources other than the mature
circulating erythrocytes.

[32] I. M. London et al., *J. Biol. Chem.*, **184**, 351 (1950).

35 ·

Metabolism
of Nucleic Acids

It will be recalled that two types of nucleic acid are known. These are the pentose nucleic acids (PNA), also termed ribonucleic acids (RNA), and the deoxypentose nucleic acids (DNA). The chemical structure of the nucleic acids is incompletely defined, but they yield, on partial hydrolysis, nucleotides composed of a nitrogenous base (a purine or a pyrimidine), a sugar (ribose or 2-deoxyribose), and phosphoric acid. In the intact nucleic acids, the nucleotides are believed to be linked to each other largely by means of phosphoryl residues attached to the 3'-hydroxyl of one nucleoside and to the 5'-hydroxyl of another nucleoside (cf. p. 199) to form polynucleotides of considerable particle weight.

Enzymic Breakdown and Synthesis of Polynucleotides[1]

Although a large number of enzymes have been included in the broad group of "nucleases" which act at various stages of nucleic acid catabolism in higher animals, little information is available about the physiological process of degradation of nucleic acids in the mammalian digestive tract. It is assumed that, when a ribonucleic acid, such as that of yeast, enters the duodenum, it is subjected to the action of the enzyme ribonuclease, a component of the pancreatic secretion. This enzyme was discovered in 1920 by Jones, who noted its marked stability to heat treatment. Jones also showed that, during the enzymic action, the nucleic acid was degraded without the formation of inorganic phosphate. The enzyme was obtained in crystalline form by Kunitz;[2] it is a protein of relatively small particle weight (ca. 14,000) and has an isoelectric point of 7.8. Pancreatic ribonuclease is composed of a single peptide chain of 124 amino acid residues (N-terminal lysine, C-terminal valine); the

[1] G. Schmidt, in E. Chargaff and J. N. Davidson, *The Nucleic Acids,* Vol. I, Chapter 15, Academic Press, New York, 1955.

[2] M. Kunitz, *J. Gen. Physiol.,* **24,** 15 (1940); M. R. McDonald, *ibid.,* **32,** 39 (1948).

chain is believed to be cross-linked by 4 disulfide groups (cf. p. 132). The amino acid sequence of oxidized ribonuclease (disulfide groups converted to sulfonic acid groups) has been partly elucidated.[3] Treatment of ribonuclease with 8 M urea does not destroy the enzymic activity,[4] and the protein may be partially cleaved by subtilisin (p. 708) or by carboxypeptidase without loss of activity.[5]

The available evidence indicates that, in its action on yeast PNA (pH optimum, ca. 7.7), crystalline pancreatic ribonuclease is specifically adapted to the hydrolysis of bonds linking the phosphoryl group of a pyrimidine nucleoside-3'-phosphate to the 5'-hydroxyl of an adjacent purine or pyrimidine nucleoside. The enzyme acts on synthetic phosphodiesters of uridine- or cytidine-3'-phosphate with the intermediate formation of cyclic 2',3'-phosphates (cf. p. 189), which are further cleaved by the enzyme to the corresponding nucleoside-3'-phosphate.[6] As shown in the accompanying scheme, the transesterification reaction lead-

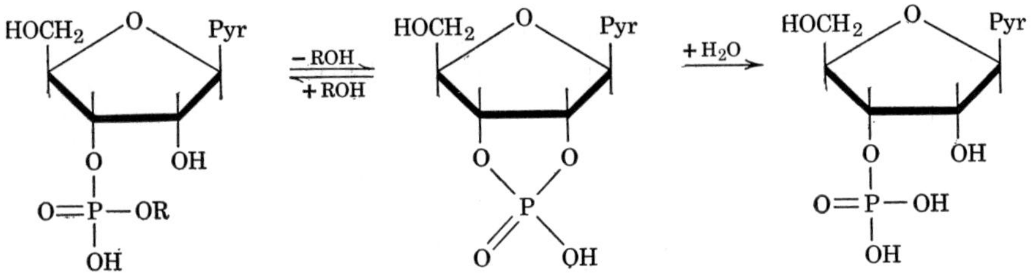

Phosphodiester of
pyrimidine nucleoside

Pyrimidine nucleoside
2',3'-phosphate

Pyrimidine nucleoside
3'-phosphate

ing to the cyclic phosphate is reversible; for example, ribonuclease catalyzes the reaction of cytidine-2',3'-phosphate with methanol to form cytidine-3'-methylphosphate, or with the 5'-hydroxyl of another molecule of itself to form oligonucleotides.[7] Hence, like other hydrolytic enzymes (glycosidases, proteinases, etc.), ribonuclease catalyzes not only hydrolysis, but also transfer or replacement reactions.

When crystalline ribonuclease acts upon yeast PNA, a portion of the nucleic acid is converted to mononucleotides (cytidine-3'-phosphate and uridine-3'-phosphate); a mixture of nondialyzable oligonucleotides pre-

[3] C. H. W. Hirs et al., *J. Biol. Chem.*, **221**, 151 (1956); R. R. Redfield and C. B. Anfinsen, *ibid.*, **221**, 385 (1956); C. B. Anfinsen, *Federation Proc.*, **16**, 783 (1957).

[4] C. B. Anfinsen et al., *Biochim. et Biophys. Acta*, **17**, 141 (1955).

[5] S. M. Kalman et al., *Biochim. et Biophys. Acta*, **16**, 297 (1955); G. Kalnitsky and W. I. Rogers, *ibid.*, **20**, 378 (1956); **23**, 525 (1957).

[6] R. Markham and J. D. Smith, *Biochem. J.*, **52**, 552 (1952); D. M. Brown et al., *J. Chem. Soc.*, **1952**, 2715.

[7] L. A. Heppel et al., *Biochem. J.*, **60**, 8 (1955); G. R. Barker et al., *J. Chem. Soc.*, **1957**, 3786.

dominantly composed of purine nucleotides is also formed.[8] In its action on PNA preparations from swine liver, ribonuclease gives products similar to those obtained with yeast PNA. However, the enzyme does not appear to hydrolyze the PNA bound in tobacco mosaic virus (the separated PNA of the virus is cleaved), nor does it attack PNA preparations obtained from pancreas, possibly because the pancreatic PNA had already been partially degraded by the ribonuclease present in the tissue extract.[9]

Ribonuclease activity has been found in many animal tissues (liver, spleen, kidney, leucocytes, etc.), in the seeds and leaves of higher plants, and in microorganisms. Except in a few instances, these enzymes have not been purified extensively, and it is probable that many of them differ in specificity from crystalline pancreatic ribonuclease. For example, although beef spleen contains a ribonuclease whose specificity resembles that of pancreatic ribonuclease,[10] this tissue also has a phosphodiesterase that can act on esters of both purine and pyrimidine nucleoside-3′-phosphates.[11] Tobacco leaves contain a ribonuclease[12] that cleaves all the internucleotide linkages in PNA preparations to form pyrimidine nucleoside-2′,3′-phosphates (which appear to be resistant to the further action of the enzyme) and purine nucleoside-2′,3′-phosphates which are hydrolyzed further to the corresponding 3′-phosphates.

Crystalline pancreatic ribonuclease does not cause the degradation of DNA preparations, such as those obtained from calf thymus. However, DNA is cleaved by another enzyme, also found in the pancreas, and named deoxyribonuclease or desoxyribonuclease (the name "dornase" has also been suggested). This enzyme, which is extremely heat-labile, was crystallized by Kunitz.[13] In contrast to ribonuclease, deoxyribonuclease requires the presence of Mg^{2+} or Mn^{2+} for activity. Studies of the action of crystalline deoxyribonuclease on calf thymus DNA have shown that, as in ribonuclease action on PNA, resistant nondialyzable oligonucleotides are formed and that the purine/pyrimidine ratio in this mixture is higher than in the original DNA preparations.[14] Ion exchange-chromatography has permitted the identification of some of the mono- and dinucleotides liberated by the action of pancreatic deoxyribonuclease

[8] R. Markham and J. D. Smith, *Biochem. J.*, **52**, 565 (1952); E. Volkin and W. E. Cohn, *J. Biol. Chem.*, **205**, 767 (1953).

[9] E. Volkin and C. E. Carter, *J. Am. Chem. Soc.*, **73**, 1516 (1951).

[10] H. S. Kaplan and L. A. Heppel, *J. Biol. Chem.*, **222**, 907 (1956).

[11] L. A. Heppel and P. R. Whitfield, *Biochem. J.*, **60**, 1 (1955)

[12] M. Holden and N. W. Pirie, *Biochem. J.*, **60**, 39 (1955); R. Markham and J. L. Strominger, *ibid.*, **64**, 46p (1956).

[13] M. Kunitz, *J. Gen. Physiol.*, **33**, 349 (1950).

[14] S. Zamenhof and E. Chargaff, *J. Biol. Chem.*, **186**, 207; **187**, 1 (1950); W. G. Overend and M. Webb, *J. Chem. Soc.*, **1950**, 2746.

on thymus DNA and wheat germ DNA; pyrimidine nucleotides appear to be liberated to a greater extent than are purine nucleotides.[15] Deoxyribonucleases have been found in various animal tissues (spleen, thymus), in plants, and in microorganisms; these enzymes seem to differ from the pancreatic enzyme in several properties, including specificity.[16]

Enzymic Dephosphorylation of Nucleotides. It was noted on p. 581 that intestinal mucosa contains phosphatases of rather broad specificity; these enzymes hydrolyze, in addition to the usual phosphate monoesters (e.g., glycerophosphate), the mononucleotides derived from the nucleic acids. The action of the intestinal phosphatases is optimal at pH values near 9 and requires the presence of Mg^{2+}. Other tissues contain phosphatases that have pH optima near 5 and do not require Mg^{2+} for their action. Both the "alkaline" and "acid" phosphatases are able to hydrolyze the 3'-phosphate bond of mononucleotides derived from PNA or DNA by the action of ribonucleases or deoxyribonucleases. They also dephosphorylate 5'-nucleotides such as adenosine-5'-phosphate. In addition to these relatively nonspecific phosphatases, nucleotidases are known that specifically hydrolyze nucleoside-3'-phosphates to nucleosides and phosphate; these enzymes (3'-nucleotidases) have been found in plants.[17] Other enzymes specifically hydrolyze the phosphate ester linkage at the 5' position of a nucleotide; they do not act on 3'-nucleotides.[18] These enzymes (5'-nucleotidases) have been found in brain, retina, prostate, and some snake venoms. A 5'-nucleotidase, found in bull semen, also dephosphorylates 5'-deoxyribonucleotides.[19]

Various phosphatases catalyze replacement reactions in which the phosphoryl group of suitable phosphate compounds is transferred to nucleosides to form nucleotides.[20]

Enzymic Synthesis of Polynucleotides. It was mentioned before that oligonucleotides can arise by the catalysis of replacement reactions by ribonuclease. A different type of replacement reaction, leading to the enzymic formation of polynucleotides, has been discovered by Ochoa;[21] it involves the conversion of nucleoside-5'-diphosphates to PNA-like products. The reaction is readily reversible, and the polynucleotides are

[15] R. L. Sinsheimer, *J. Biol. Chem.*, **208**, 445 (1954); M. E. Hodes and E. Chargaff, *Biochim. et Biophys. Acta*, **22**, 348, 361 (1956).

[16] M. Privat de Garilhe and M. Laskowski, *J. Biol. Chem.*, **215**, 269 (1955); J. F. Koerner and R. L. Sinsheimer, *ibid.*, **228**, 1039, 1049 (1957).

[17] L. Shuster and N. O. Kaplan, *J. Biol. Chem.*, **201**, 535 (1953).

[18] L. A. Heppel and R. J. Hilmoe, *J. Biol. Chem.*, **188**, 665 (1951).

[19] C. E. Carter, *J. Am. Chem. Soc.*, **73**, 1537 (1951).

[20] G. Brawerman and E. Chargaff, *Biochim. et Biophys. Acta,* **16**, 524 (1955).

[21] S. Ochoa, *Federation Proc.*, **15**, 832 (1956); M. Grunberg-Manago et al., *Biochim. et Biophys. Acta*, **20**, 269 (1956); D. O. Brummond et al., *J. Biol. Chem.*, **225**, 835 (1957); U. Z. Littauer and A. Kornberg, *ibid.*, **226**, 1077 (1957).

cleaved in the presence of inorganic phosphate to regenerate the nucleoside-5'-diphosphates; the enzyme responsible for its catalysis is named polynucleotide phosphorylase. The enzyme has been found in various bacteria, and has been partially purified from *Azotobacter vinelandii*, *Escherichia coli*, and *Micrococcus lysodeikticus;* only weak enzymic activity has been observed in yeast and higher plants. The occurrence of a polynucleotide phosphorylase in animal tissues is suggested by the finding that an enzyme preparation from rat liver nuclei causes the phosphorolysis of a polynucleotide (prepared from adenosine-5'-diphosphate by means of the *A. vinelandii* enzyme) to ADP.[22]

The reaction catalyzed by polynucleotide phosphorylase may be written as follows:

$$n[\text{X—R—P—P}] \rightleftharpoons [\text{X—R—P}]_n + n\text{P}$$

where X is a purine or pyrimidine base (adenine, guanine, hypoxanthine, uracil, or cytosine), R is ribose, and P is phosphate. When a mixture of nucleoside-5'-diphosphates is incubated with the enzyme preparation, the resulting polynucleotide material contains all the nitrogenous bases used. The polymeric products formed have average particle weights of 50,000 to 350,000; they are cleaved by alkali to give equimolar amounts of nucleoside-2'- and 3'-phosphates (cf. p. 189), and by snake venom phosphodiesterase to yield nucleoside-5'-phosphates. Pancreatic ribonuclease acts on the polymers derived from a pyrimidine nucleoside-5'-diphosphate to liberate the appropriate nucleoside-3'-phosphate (cf. p. 878). These various findings clearly indicate the presence of 3',5'-phosphodiester linkages in the polymers, as in the PNA preparations isolated from biological sources.

It will be noted that the reaction catalyzed by polynucleotide phosphorylase is similar to that effected by the polysaccharide phosphorylases, which catalyze the reversible phosphorolysis of glycogen and starch to glucose-1-phosphate (cf. p. 442). An analogous polymerization reaction is also catalyzed by the proteinase cathepsin C (cf. p. 717). The action of polynucleotide phosphorylase appears to involve the addition of mononucleotide units to a growing oligonucleotide chain, in analogy to the action of the polysaccharide phosphorylases and of cathepsin C. The discovery of polynucleotide phosphorylase raises the question whether it is involved in the intracellular biosynthesis of PNA molecules; further studies are needed before the biological role of this enzyme can be adequately assessed. It should be added, however, that the nucleoside-5'-diphosphates needed as substrates have been identified as cellular constituents, and enzymic reactions are known for their formation.

[22] R. J. Hilmoe and L. A. Heppel, *J. Am. Chem. Soc.*, **79**, 4810 (1957).

An enzyme preparation has been obtained from *Escherichia coli* which catalyzes the conversion of mixtures of deoxyribonucleoside-5′-triphosphates to polymers that resemble DNA preparations from biological sources in their stability to alkali (cf. p. 192) and cleavage by pancreatic deoxyribonuclease.[23] For the polymerization to occur, ATP and a fragment derived from *E. coli* DNA were required; the latter is thought to act as a "primer" in the reaction. The best yield of polynucleotide was obtained when a mixture of the 5′-triphosphates of four deoxyribonucleosides (thymidine, deoxyadenosine, deoxyguanosine, deoxycytidine) was employed.

Although much remains to be learned about the mechanism of action and the biological role of the bacterial enzyme systems that can form polynucleotides resembling PNA and DNA, it is clear that the important discoveries of Ochoa and of Kornberg have opened new lines of experimental study of the biosynthesis of nucleic acids (cf. p. 900).

Enzymic Interconversion of Nucleotides. Several enzymes are known to catalyze transphosphorylation reactions between a nucleoside-5′-phosphate and a nucleoside-5′-triphosphate to form nucleoside-5′-diphosphates. Thus enzyme preparations from yeast and from liver[24] effect a variety of reactions such as the following:

Adenosine-5′-P + uridine-5′-P-P-P ⇌

Adenosine-5′-P-P + uridine-5′-P-P

Uridine-5′-P + adenosine-5′-P-P-P ⇌

Uridine-5′-P-P + adenosine-5′-P-P

Uridine-5′-P + uridine-5′-P-P-P ⇌ 2 Uridine-5′-P-P

Similar transphosphorylation reactions are effected with nucleotides of guanosine and cytosine. Clearly, the presence of such enzymes makes possible the synthesis of various nucleoside-5′-diphosphates from the corresponding nucleotide in a reaction with ATP. Sheep brain and liver contain an enzyme that catalyzes the reaction:[25]

Adenosine-5′-P + inosine-5′-P-P-P ⇌

Adenosine-5′-P-P + inosine-5′-P-P

The enzymes discussed above are different from the myokinase of muscle and yeast, which is specific for the reaction AMP + ATP ⇌ 2ADP (p. 459). Mention was made previously (p. 461) of a widely distributed enzyme (nucleoside diphosphate kinase) that catalyzes reversible trans-

[23] A. Kornberg et al., *Biochim. et Biophys. Acta,* **21,** 197 (1956).

[24] I. Lieberman et al., *J. Biol. Chem.,* **215,** 429 (1955); J. L. Strominger et al., *Arch. Biochem. and Biophys.,* **52,** 488 (1954).

[25] H. A. Krebs and R. Hems, *Biochem. J.,* **61,** 435 (1955).

phosphorylation reactions such as:

Inosine-5'-P-P + adenosine-5'-P-P-P $\rightleftharpoons$

Inosine-5'-P-P-P + adenosine-5'-P-P

Uridine-5'-P-P + adenosine-5'-P-P-P $\rightleftharpoons$

Uridine-5'-P-P-P + adenosine-5'-P-P

It is probable that similar enzymic interconversions occur with the deoxyribonucleoside-5'-phosphates, and that polyphosphates can be formed by reactions of appropriate nucleotides with ATP. Since ATP is generated by oxidative phosphorylation, the energy required for the biosynthesis of polynucleotides from nucleoside di- and triphosphates is probably transferred by ATP from the respiratory chain of electron transport to the synthesis of PNA and DNA.[26]
Not only nucleotides but also nucleosides can participate in enzymic transphosphorylation reactions involving ATP. Thus yeast and mammalian tissues contain enzymes that catalyze the reaction:[27]

Adenosine + ATP $\rightarrow$ Adenosine-5'-phosphate + ADP

In addition to the enzymic transphosphorylation reactions of nucleoside-5'-diphosphates, the specific hydrolysis of inosine-5'-diphosphate, guanosine-5'-diphosphate, and uridine-5'-diphosphate is effected by an enzyme present in liver mitochondria, with the formation of the corresponding nucleoside-5'-monophosphates. The enzyme appears to be inactive toward the 5'-diphosphates of adenosine and cytidine.[28]

Cleavage and Synthesis of N-Glycosidic Bonds. It has long been known that some of the nucleosides derived from nucleic acids are readily cleaved by extracts of animal tissues to yield a purine (or pyrimidine) and the component sugar. Although it was first thought that this cleavage was a hydrolytic one, studies by Kalckar[29] demonstrated that, with inosine and guanosine as substrates, the reaction is a phosphorolysis, as shown in the scheme on page 884. The enzyme which catalyzes the reaction has been purified extensively from beef liver,[30] and acts on a variety of purine nucleosides with the formation of the purine and of α-D-ribose-1-phosphate.[31] Since the purine nucleosides derived from nucleic acids have the β-configuration about carbon 1 of the ribosyl group, the enzymic action involves an inversion of con-

[26] E. Herbert and V. R. Potter, *J. Biol. Chem.*, **222**, 453 (1956).
[27] A. Kornberg and W. E. Pricer, Jr., *J. Biol. Chem.*, **193**, 481 (1951).
[28] G. W. E. Plaut, *J. Biol. Chem.*, **217**, 235 (1955).
[29] H. M. Kalckar, *J. Biol. Chem.*, **158**, 723 (1945); **167**, 477 (1947).
[30] E. D. Korn and J. M. Buchanan, *J. Biol. Chem.*, **217**, 183 (1955).
[31] R. S. Wright and H. G. Khorana, *J. Am. Chem. Soc.*, **78**, 811 (1956).

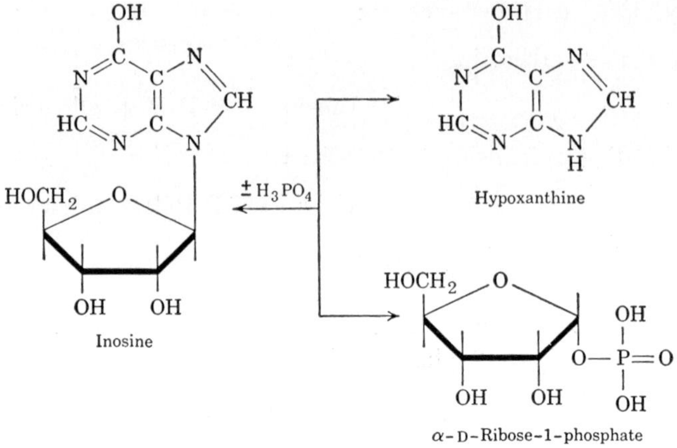

Inosine

Hypoxanthine

α-D-Ribose-1-phosphate

figuration about this carbon atom. The enzyme does not act on pyrimidine nucleosides, and has therefore been named "purine nucleoside phosphorylase." However, among its substrates appear to be the ribo-sides of 5-aminoimidazole-4-carboxamide (p. 888) and of nicotinamide (p. 308).[32] Furthermore, purine deoxyribonucleosides (e.g., hypoxanthine deoxyriboside) are also cleaved in a similar manner to form the purine and deoxyribose-1-phosphate.[33] The equilibrium in most of the reactions catalyzed by this enzyme is such as to favor the synthesis of the nucleo-side; this is analogous to the result found with crystalline muscle phos-phorylase (cf. p. 441).

A phosphorylase specific for thymidine and deoxyuridine (thymidine phosphorylase) has been prepared from horse liver,[34] and a uridine phos-phorylase has been obtained from *Escherichia coli*.[35] In addition to these purine and pyrimidine nucleoside phosphorylases, there appear to be a variety of microbial enzymes that catalyze the hydrolytic cleavage of nucleosides.[36] Bacteria also contain enzymes that catalyze the transfer of a deoxyribosyl group from deoxyribonucleosides to some purines and pyrimidines.[37]

As will be seen from the subsequent discussion (cf. p. 898), in the biosynthesis of the purines and pyrimidines of nucleic acids, an important enzymic reaction is the reversal of the cleavage, by pyrophosphate, of the glycosidic bond in a variety of nucleoside-5'-phosphates to form the

[32] J. W. Rowen and A. Kornberg, *J. Biol. Chem.*, **193**, 497 (1951).

[33] M. Friedkin and H. M. Kalckar, *J. Biol. Chem.*, **184**, 437, 449 (1950).

[34] M. Friedkin and D. Roberts, *J. Biol. Chem.*, **207**, 245, 257 (1954).

[35] L. M. Paege and F. Schlenk, *Arch. Biochem. and Biophys.*, **40**, 57 (1952)

[36] J. O. Lampen and T. P. Wang, *J. Biol. Chem.*, **198**, 385 (1952); L. A. Heppel and R. J. Hilmoe, *ibid.*, **198**, 683 (1952); A. L. Koch, *ibid.*, **223**, 535 (1956); Y. Takagi and B. L. Horecker, *ibid.*, **225**, 77 (1957).

[37] W. S. MacNutt, *Biochem. J.*, **50**, 384 (1952).

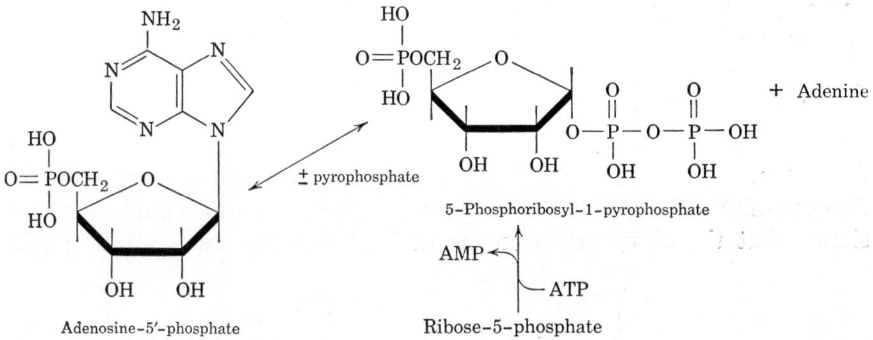

Adenosine-5'-phosphate

Ribose-5-phosphate

5-Phosphoribosyl-1-pyrophosphate

nitrogenous base and 5-phosphoribosyl-1-pyrophosphate. This reversible reaction was discovered by Kornberg et al.,[38] and the enzyme (nucleotide-1'-pyrophosphorylase) that catalyzes it has been obtained from yeast and liver. Although the configuration about carbon 1 of the sugar pyrophosphate has not been determined, it is probably α, in analogy to the nucleoside phosphorylase reaction. 5-Phosphoribosyl-1-pyrophosphate can arise by the enzyme-catalyzed transfer of a pyrophosphoryl group from ATP to ribose-5-phosphate, thus permitting the entrance of this intermediate of carbohydrate metabolism into the sequence of reactions leading to the biosynthesis of nucleic acids. Furthermore, the reversible conversion of ribose-5-phosphate to ribose-1-phosphate (p. 527) can provide the sugar phosphate needed for the action of purine nucleoside phosphorylase.

The possibility exists that the cleavage and formation of glycosidic bonds occurs not only for the nucleosides and nucleotides, as discussed above, but also for polynucleotides, since isotope studies have suggested that purines of intact nucleic acids may be replaced in transglycosidation reactions (cf. p. 901). In this connection, it is of interest that *Hemophilus influenzae* forms a capsular polysaccharide which appears to be a polyribose phosphate with 3',5'-phosphodiester bonds between the sugar units; two such polyribose phosphate chains are thought to be linked to each other by 1,1-glycosidic bonds.[39]

Deamination of Purine and Pyrimidine Derivatives. It will be recalled that the principal end product of purine metabolism in man is uric acid; in most other mammals, uric acid is converted to allantoin, and, in fishes, allantoin undergoes cleavage to glyoxylic acid and urea (p. 857). Uric acid is the product of the oxidation of hypoxanthine and of xanthine (p. 855) by xanthine oxidase. Examination of their formulae will show that hypoxanthine and xanthine are the products of the hydrolytic deamination of adenine and of guanine respectively. Although guanases,

[38] A. Kornberg et al., *J. Biol. Chem.*, **215**, 389, 403, 417 (1955).
[39] S. Zamenhof et al., *J. Biol. Chem.*, **203**, 695 (1953).

which catalyze the deamination of guanine to xanthine, have been identified in the tissues of higher animals,[40] and adenase activity has been found in microorganisms and invertebrates, enzymes for the deamination of free adenine to hypoxanthine appear to be absent from mammalian tissues. If adenine is administered to rats or dogs in large doses (ca. 500 mg per kg of body weight), appreciable amounts of 2,8-dioxyadenine are deposited in the kidney tubules. Isotope studies[41] have shown that the dioxy compound is derived directly from adenine; this

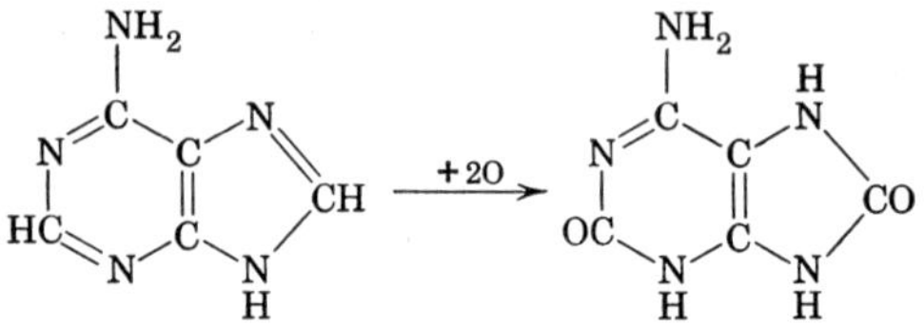

Adenine   2,8-Dioxyadenine

finding indicates the biological occurrence of an oxidation process analogous to the metabolic oxidation of hypoxanthine to uric acid by xanthine oxidase. In the formation of 2,8-dioxyadenine, however, the major intermediate is 8-oxyadenine.

Although adenine does not appear to be converted directly to hypoxanthine in mammalian tissues, they contain enzymes for the deamination of adenosine to inosine (adenosine deaminase[42]) and of adenosine-5'-phosphate to inosine-5'-phosphate (adenylic deaminase[43]). The hypoxanthine resulting from the cleavage of these products can then be oxidized to uric acid. Similar purine deaminases are present in microorganisms; for example, an enzyme preparation from *Aspergillus oryzae* can deaminate adenosine as well as a variety of adenine nucleotides.[44]

The pyrimidine cytosine is deaminated to uracil by extracts of yeast and of *Escherichia coli*,[45] and cytidine is converted to uridine by an enzyme (cytidine deaminase) found in animal tissues and in bacteria. The enzymic deamination of cytosine deoxyriboside has also been demonstrated.[46] The cleavage of these deaminated nucleosides yields uracil, whose further metabolic breakdown is discussed on p. 899.

[40] A. Roush and E. R. Norris, *Arch. Biochem.*, **29**, 124 (1950).

[41] A. Bendich et al., *J. Biol. Chem.*, **183**, 267 (1950).

[42] H. M. Kalckar, *J. Biol. Chem.*, **167**, 461 (1947).

[43] G. Nikiforuk and S. P. Colowick, *J. Biol. Chem.*, **219**, 119 (1956); Y. Lee, *ibid.*, **227**, 987, 993, 999 (1957).

[44] N. O. Kaplan et al., *J. Biol. Chem.*, **194**, 579 (1952).

[45] E. Chargaff and J. Kream, *J. Am. Chem. Soc.*, **74**, 4274, 5157 (1952).

[46] C. A. Dekker and A. R. Todd, *Nature*, **166**, 557 (1950).

Metabolism of Purines

Before the introduction of the isotope technique for the study of metabolic processes, little information was available about the biochemical pathways in the synthesis of the nitrogenous bases of the nucleic acids. It had long been known that most animals do not require an exogenous source of the constituent purines or pyrimidines, and it was clear, therefore, that these heterocyclic structures are synthesized in the animal body at a rate commensurate with the needs of the organism. From the isotope studies of Barnes and Schoenheimer,[47] it became evident that dietary ammonia nitrogen is readily utilized for the synthesis of the purines and pyrimidines of the nucleic acids in rat tissues. Subsequent experiments demonstrated that the carbon atoms of these nitrogenous bases are also derived, in animals, from simple carbon compounds (CO_2, glycine, "formate"). Some microorganisms, however, require an exogenous source of purines or pyrimidines (or derivatives of these compounds) for normal growth.

Biosynthesis of Purines.[48]   It was noted on p. 854 that uric acid is derived, in mammals and in birds, from glycine, CO_2, "formate," the nitrogen of aspartic acid, and the amide nitrogen of glutamine. Since uric acid was known to be the product of the direct oxidation of hypoxanthine, the biosynthesis of the latter was investigated. Studies with homogenates of pigeon liver (which contains little xanthine oxidase) have shown that hypoxanthine is synthesized in this tissue, and that the purine ring is derived from the simple precursors listed above for uric acid.[49] Analogous studies with mammals (e.g., rats) and microorganisms (e.g., yeast) have indicated that the compounds that provide the carbon and nitrogen atoms of uric acid and of hypoxanthine also are precursors of the purine rings of the guanine and adenine in nucleic acids.[50] The conclusion was inescapable, therefore, that the various purines have a common precursor in their biosynthesis from small fragments. It was thought for a time that hypoxanthine may be derived, more or less directly, from such a precursor, and may be converted, by amination, to adenine. However, hypoxanthine itself was found to be a poor precursor of nucleic acid purines in the rat,[51] and this made it probable

[47] F. W. Barnes, Jr., and R. Schoenheimer, *J. Biol. Chem.*, **151**, 123 (1943).

[48] P. Reichard, in E. Chargaff and J. N. Davidson, *The Nucleic Acids*, Vol. II, Chapter 23, Academic Press, New York, 1955.

[49] M. P. Schulman et al., *J. Biol. Chem.*, **196**, 499 (1952).

[50] R. Abrams et al., *J. Biol. Chem.*, **173**, 429 (1948); M. R. Heinrich and D. W. Wilson, *ibid.*, **186**, 447 (1950).

[51] H. Getler et al., *J. Biol. Chem.*, **178**, 259 (1949).

that a hypoxanthine nucleotide (e.g., inosine-5′-phosphate) is the precursor of the purine nucleotides of PNA.

In the search for intermediates in the biosynthesis of hypoxanthine, a discovery made in bacterial systems proved to be of importance. When the growth of certain strains of *Escherichia coli* is inhibited by a member of the sulfonamide group of antibiotics (e.g., sulfathiazole), there accumulates in the medium a compound identified as 5-aminoimidazole-4-carboxamide.[52] Since the production of this compound by *E. coli* was stimulated by the addition of glycine to the culture medium,[53] it was suggested that 5-aminoimidazole-4-carboxamide may be converted to hypoxanthine in biological systems. Indeed, it has been observed that the imidazole derivative can serve as a source of purines for mutant strains of several microorganisms that require for growth an exogenous source of these nitrogenous bases. For one such mutant of *E. coli*, 5-formaminoimidazole-4-carboxamide is twice as effective as the 5-amino compound.[54]

Subsequent studies showed that the imidazole derivative found in the culture fluid of sulfonamide-treated *E. coli* is probably formed by cleavage of the riboside, which has been isolated from such fluids.[55] Presumably, the extracellular riboside was derived from the corresponding ribotide (formula shown) by the action of a phosphatase. The riboside has been

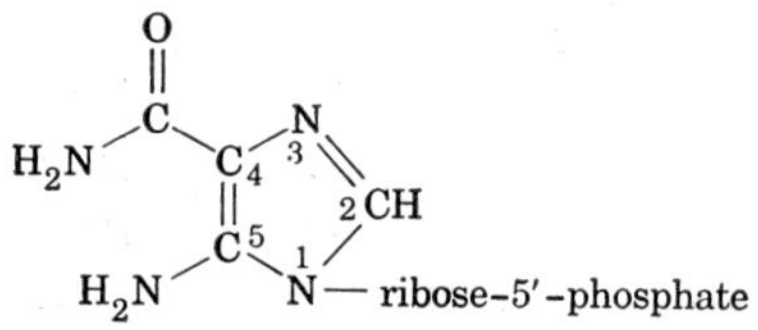

5-Aminoimidazole-4-carboxamide ribotide

converted to the ribotide by phosphorylation with ATP in the presence of a yeast extract.

Although pigeon liver homogenates can convert 5-aminoimidazole-4-carboxamide to hypoxanthine, isotope studies[56] indicated that the free imidazole compound is not a normal intermediate in the biosynthesis of purines, and that it probably is first converted to its ribotide. Furthermore, experiments with enzyme systems extracted from pigeon liver showed that inosine-5′-phosphate is the first purine compound formed, and that hypoxanthine is liberated by subsequent breakdown of the

[52] W. Shive et al., *J. Am. Chem. Soc.*, **69**, 725 (1947).

[53] J. M. Ravel et al., *J. Biol. Chem.*, **172**, 67 (1948).

[54] E. D. Bergmann et al., *J. Biol. Chem.*, **194**, 521, 531 (1952).

[55] G. R. Greenberg and E. L. Spilman, *J. Biol. Chem.*, **219**, 411, 423 (1956).

[56] C. S. Miller et al., *Science,* **112**, 654 (1950).

nucleotide[57] (Fig. 1). Such systems catalyze the transfer of a formyl group to 5-aminoimidazole-4-carboxamide ribotide, and the ring closure to yield inosine-5'-phosphate (Fig. 2). It is assumed that in this enzyme-catalyzed conversion, which is reversible, an intermediate 5-formamino-imidazole-4-carboxamide ribotide is formed. The formylation reaction

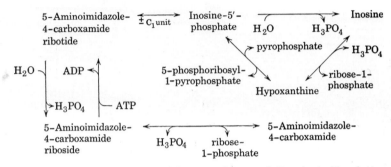

Fig. 1. Enzymic interconversion of hypoxanthine and 5-aminoimidazole-4-carboxamide.

involves the obligatory participation of a folic acid compound (denoted CoF in Fig. 2) which may be 5,6,7,8-tetrahydropteroyl-L-glutamic acid[58,59] (p. 775). The pigeon liver enzymes that catalyze the conversion of the imidazole ribotide to inosine-5'-phosphate have not been purified extensively.

The finding of the requirement for a folic acid compound as a cofactor in the formylation reaction has led to the suggestion that the accumulation of 5-aminoimidazole-4-carboxamide ribotide in sulfonamide-inhibited *E. coli* is a consequence of the inhibition of the synthesis of the *p*-aminobenzoic acid portion of the cofactor (cf. p. 260). It may also be noted that the formylation reaction leads to the introduction of carbon 2 of the purine ring; isotope studies had previously shown that this atom was derived from C_1 units related to formate.

The biosynthesis of 5-aminoimidazole-4-carboxamide ribotide by pigeon liver extracts has been elucidated in large part by Greenberg, Buchanan, and their associates. Their work has provided excellent evidence for the occurrence of most of the reactions given in Fig. 2; in general, the results of the enzymic studies have been concordant with the data on the labeling of purines by isotopic precursors.

The sequence of reactions may be said to begin with the introduction of nitrogen 9 of the purine ring; isotope experiments showed this atom

[57] G. R. Greenberg, *J. Biol. Chem.*, **190**, 611 (1951); M. P. Schulman and J. M. Buchanan, *ibid.*, **196**, 513 (1952).

[58] G. R. Greenberg, *J. Am. Chem. Soc.*, **76**, 1458 (1954).

[59] J. G. Flaks et al., *J. Biol. Chem.*, **228**, 215 (1957).

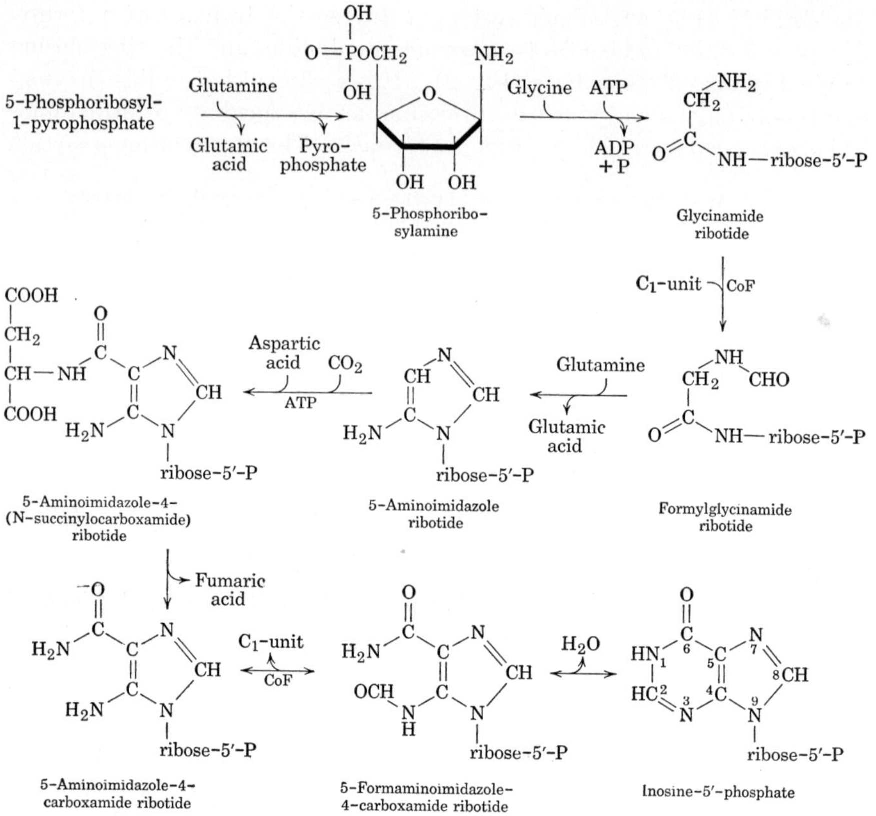

OH
|
O=POCH₂   NH₂
|
5-Phosphoribosyl-   Glutamine   OH   O   Glycine ATP   NH₂
1-pyrophosphate   CH₂
Glutamic   Pyro-   ADP   O=C
acid   phosphate   + P   NH—ribose-5′-P
OH   OH

5-Phosphoribo-   Glycinamide
sylamine   ribotide

COOH
| O
CH₂ ||
| C   C   N   Aspartic   N   C₁-unit   CoF
CH—NH   acid CO₂   CH   Glutamine   NH
| CH   CH   CH₂   CHO
COOH   H₂N   C   N   ATP   H₂N   C   N   Glutamic   O=C
| acid   NH—ribose-5′-P
ribose-5′-P   ribose-5′-P

5-Aminoimidazole-4-   5-Aminoimidazole   Formylglycinamide
(N-succinylocarboxamide)   ribotide   ribotide
ribotide

⁻O   Fumaric   O   O
|| acid || ||
H₂N   C   C   N   C₁-unit   H₂N   C   C   N   H₂O   HN   C   C   N
CH   CoF   CH   HC   C   CH
H₂N   C   N   OCH   N   C   N   HC   N   C   N
| H |
ribose-5′-P   ribose-5′-P   ribose-5′-P

5-Aminoimidazole-4-   5-Formaminoimidazole-   Inosine-5′-phosphate
carboxamide ribotide   4-carboxamide ribotide

Fig. 2. Probable pathway of purine biosynthesis in pigeon liver.

to be derived from the amide nitrogen of glutamine. Evidence has been presented for the reaction of 5-phosphoribosyl-1-pyrophosphate (PRPP) with glutamine, in the presence of enzymes of a pigeon liver extract, to yield 5-phosphoribosylamine, glutamic acid, and pyrophosphate.[60] Azaserine (p. 57), which inhibits purine biosynthesis, is a weak competitive antagonist of glutamine in this reaction. In the next step of purine synthesis, 5-phosphoribosylamine is converted to glycinamide ribotide (N-glycyl-5-phosphoribofuranosylamine) by an enzymic process in which glycine (the source of carbons 4 and 5 and nitrogen 7 of the purine ring) is added; ATP is required for this process, and is cleaved to ADP and phosphate. Glycinamide ribotide has been isolated from incubation mixtures containing pigeon liver enzymes, glycine, glutamine, ribose-5-phosphate, and ATP.[61] The formation of glycinamide ribotide

[60] D. A. Goldthwait, *J. Biol. Chem.,* **222,** 1051 (1956).

[61] D. A. Goldthwait et al., *J. Biol. Chem.,* **221,** 555, 569, 1071 (1956); S. C. Hartman et al., *ibid.,* **221,** 1057 (1956).

is followed by its formylation (cf. Fig. 2) in an enzymic reaction which involves the participation of a folic acid compound. This step, which leads to the introduction of carbon 8 of the purine ring, is thus analogous to the formylation reaction by which carbon 2 is introduced, and the same folic acid cofactor may be involved in both reactions.

Since nitrogen 3 of the purine ring has been shown by isotope data to be derived from the amide nitrogen of glutamine, it has been hypothesized that 5-aminoimidazole ribotide is formed as the next component in the biosynthetic pathway. Direct evidence for the intermediate formation of this ribotide by pigeon liver has come from the isolation of the compound from incubation mixtures, and the demonstration that it arises from formylglycinamide ribotide via formylglycinamidine ribotide.[62] In the biosynthesis of the last named compound, the $C=O$ group of formylglycinamide ribotide is converted to a $C=NH$ group, the nitrogen coming from the amide group of glutamine; azaserine and 6-diazo-5-keto-L-norleucine compete strongly with glutamine in this

$$\underset{\text{6-Diazo-5-keto-L-norleucine}}{N_2CH_2-\overset{\overset{\displaystyle O}{\|}}{C}-CH_2-CH_2-\overset{\overset{\displaystyle NH_2}{|}}{CH}-COOH}$$

reaction. 5-Aminoimidazole ribotide is converted to 5-aminoimidazole-4-carboxamide ribotide in a process that requires ATP, and involves the participation of CO_2 (known to be a source of carbon 6 of the purine ring) and of aspartic acid (which donates nitrogen 1). It is probable that, after the addition of CO_2, an intermediate 5-aminoimidazole-4-(N-succinylocarboxamide) ribotide is formed, and is cleaved by adenylosuccinase to 5-aminoimidazole-4-carboxamide ribotide and fumaric acid,[63] as shown in Fig. 2. The conversion of 5-aminoimidazole-4-carboxamide ribotide to inosine-5'-phosphate was discussed above.

It is of interest that some features of the biosynthetic scheme for the formation of the purine ring appear to apply to the biosynthesis of the isoalloxazine ring of riboflavin (cf. p. 985) and of the pteridine ring of the folic acid compounds (cf. p. 1000).

As mentioned previously, the pattern of isotopic labeling of the adenine and guanine of tissue nucleic acids was found to be the same as in uric acid (derived from hypoxanthine), indicating that inosine-5'-phosphate, or an immediate precursor such as 5-aminoimidazole-4-carboxamide ribotide,[64] is converted to adenosine-5'-phosphate and to guanosine-5'-phosphate. The enzymic conversion of inosine-5'-phosphate to adenosine-5'-phosphate is effected by extracts of E. coli in a process

[62] B. Levenberg et al., J. Biol. Chem., **224**, 1005, 1019; **225**, 163 (1957).
[63] L. N. Lukens and J. M. Buchanan, J. Am. Chem. Soc., **79**, 1511 (1957).
[64] C. E. Carter, Ann. Rev. Biochem., **25**, 123 (1956).

that involves the participation of L-aspartic acid and the intermediate formation of adenylosuccinic acid;[65] this intermediate is cleaved by the enzyme adenylosuccinase to yield adenosine-5'-phosphate and fumaric acid. It will be noted that L-aspartic acid participates in the formation of adenosine-5'-phosphate and of 5-aminoimidazole-4-carboxamide ribo-

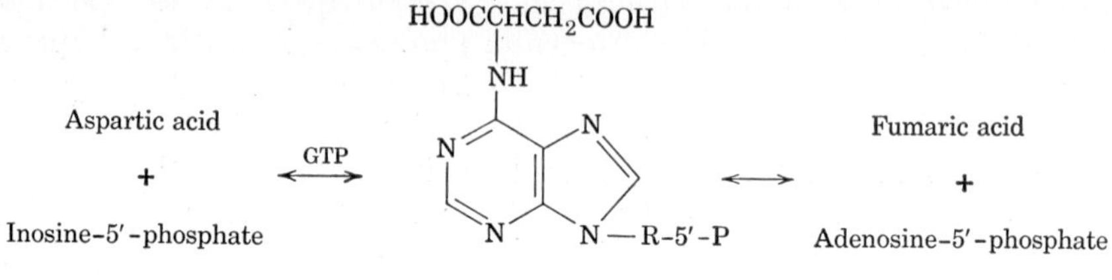

$$HOOCCHCH_2COOH$$

$$NH$$

Aspartic acid

$+$

$\xrightarrow{\text{GTP}}$

Inosine-5'-phosphate

Adenylosuccinic acid

Fumaric acid

$+$

Adenosine-5'-phosphate

tide in a manner similar to its role in the conversion of citrulline to arginine (cf. p. 851). The formation of adenylosuccinic acid from inosine-5'-phosphate requires guanosine triphosphate as a cofactor.[66]

It is probable that a similar process is operative in the formation of adenosine-5'-phosphate in animal tissues. Adenylosuccinic acid and the corresponding purine (6-succinylaminopurine) have been found in mammalian liver,[67] and enzyme preparations from rabbit bone marrow and from pigeon liver effect the amination of inosine-5'-phosphate in the presence of aspartic acid and a source of nucleotide triphosphate.[68] These tissue preparations also contain enzymes for the conversion of inosine-5'-phosphate to guanosine-5'-phosphate; inosine-5'-phosphate is

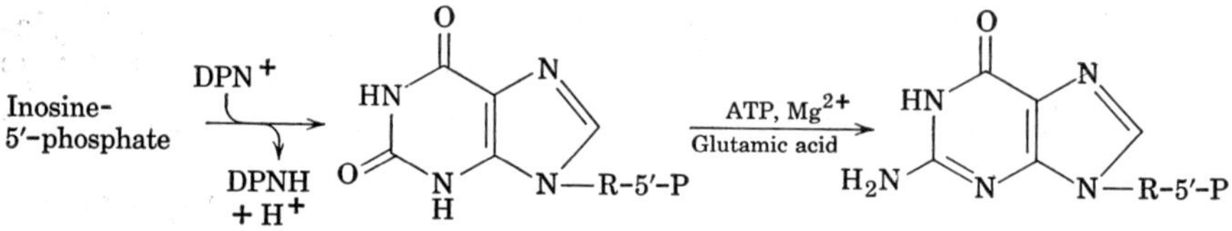

Inosine-5'-phosphate

$\xrightarrow[\text{DPNH} + H^+]{\text{DPN}^+}$

Xanthosine-5'-phosphate

$\xrightarrow[\text{Glutamic acid}]{\text{ATP, Mg}^{2+}}$

Guanosine-5'-phosphate

oxidized by DPN^+ to xanthosine-5'-phosphate, which is aminated in a reaction that requires L-glutamic acid (or L-glutamine), ATP, and Mg^{2+}. Some microorganisms (*Aerobacter aerogenes*, *E. coli*) also contain a DPN-dependent dehydrogenase which converts inosine-5'-phosphate to xanthosine-5'-phosphate,[69] and an ATP-dependent enzyme system which effects the amination reaction to form guanosine-5'-phosphate.[70] It should be added that the conversion of exogenous xanthine or guanine

[65] C. E. Carter and L. H. Cohen, *J. Biol. Chem.*, **222**, 17 (1956).

[66] I. Lieberman, *J. Biol. Chem.*, **223**, 327 (1956).

[67] W. K. Joklik, *Biochem. J.*, **66**, 333 (1957).

[68] R. Abrams and M. Bentley, *J. Am. Chem. Soc.*, **77**, 4179 (1955); U. Lagerkvist, *Acta Chem. Scand.*, **9**, 1028 (1955).

[69] B. Magasanik et al., *J. Biol. Chem.*, **226**, 339 (1957).

[70] H. S. Moyed and B. Magasanik, *J. Biol. Chem.*, **226**, 351 (1957).

to nucleic acid adenine, known to occur in these organisms, does not appear to proceed by a reversal of the above reactions.

A mutant strain of *Aerobacter aerogenes,* which requires either guanine or 2,6-diaminopurine for growth, cannot convert adenine to guanine, but can use exogenous guanine to make adenine; in this mutant, the conversion of xanthosine-5'-phosphate to guanosine-5'-phosphate is blocked, and xanthine accumulates in the culture fluid.[71] Such a metabolic block may also be present in the protozoan *Tetrahymena gelii,* which is one of the organisms that require an exogenous source of purines for growth; it grows in the presence of guanine or of guanine derivatives, but cannot use adenine as the sole source of purine. Nevertheless, the addition of adenine to a medium containing guanine spares the guanine requirements;[72] it appears, therefore, that, for the protozoan, guanine serves as a precursor of nucleic acid adenine as well as guanine. However, the reverse relationship does not hold, since the organism incorporates C^{14} supplied as adenine-8-C^{14} only into the nucleic acid adenine, but not into the guanine.[73]

Various biological forms differ in their ability to interconvert adenine and guanine. Thus, when N^{15}-labeled guanylic acid was administered to rats, the isotope appeared in the guanine of the tissue PNA, but only traces of the label were found in the adenine. On the other hand, the administration of N^{15}-labeled adenylic acid caused appreciable labeling of both the adenine and guanine of the tissue PNA.[74] Furthermore, if isotopic adenine (labeled with N^{15} in positions 1 and 3 of the purine ring) is fed to rats, the label is found in both the adenine and guanine of the tissue nucleic acids[75] (Table 1). Since the isolated guanine was labeled

Table I. Utilization of Isotopic Adenine by the Rat [75]

Compound	N^{15} Concentration, atom per cent excess	Per Cent of Compound Derived from Dietary Adenine
Dietary adenine	6.29	
Adenine isolated from tissue nucleic acids	0.857	13.7
Guanine isolated from tissue nucleic acids	0.513	8.2
Pyrimidines isolated from tissue nucleic acids	0.00	0
Adenosine triphosphate (from muscle)	0.161	2.6
Urinary allantoin	1.70	27.0
Urinary ammonia	0.02	0.32
Urinary urea	0.018	0.29

[71] M. E. Balis et al., *J. Biol. Chem.,* **219,** 917 (1956).
[72] G. W. Kidder and V. C. Dewey, *J. Biol. Chem.,* **179,** 181 (1949).
[73] M. Flavin and S. Graff, *J. Biol. Chem.,* **192,** 485 (1951).
[74] P. M. Roll and I. Weliky, *J. Biol. Chem.,* **213,** 509 (1955).
[75] G. B. Brown et al., *J. Biol. Chem.,* **172,** 469 (1948).

in the same positions (1 and 3) as the dietary adenine, it follows that a major portion of the purine ring was utilized for the synthesis of guanine from adenine. It will be noted from Table 1 that, under the conditions of this experiment, extensive degradation of the dietary adenine to allantoin had occurred, presumably via uric acid.

It is of interest that 2,6-diaminopurine is an excellent precursor of nucleic acid guanine in the rat,[76] but it is not known whether xanthosine-

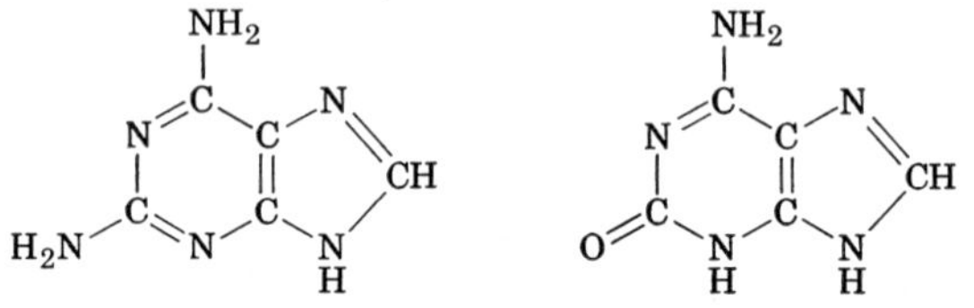

2,6–Diaminopurine   Isoguanine

5′-phosphate is an obligatory intermediate in this conversion. Another purine which might be derived from adenine is isoguanine; however, this compound is not used by the rat for guanine formation.

Metabolic Breakdown of Purines.   It was seen before that, in animals, purines are oxidized to uric acid, which may be excreted unchanged, or may be further degraded to allantoin, or to glyoxylic acid and urea (p. 857).   In some microorganisms (e.g., *Pseudomonas*) purines also appear to be broken down via allantoin to glyoxylic acid and urea; the glyoxylic acid is converted to oxalic acid, and urea is hydrolyzed to CO_2 and NH_3.[77]   With anaerobic bacteria such as *Clostridium acidi-urici* or *Clostridium cylindrosporum*, that utilize purines (uric acid, guanine, xanthine, hypoxanthine) as the sole source of carbon and nitrogen, and that derive energy from the fermentation of these purines, the products are NH_3, CO_2, HCOOH, CH_3COOH, and glycine.[78]   From studies of the fate of labeled purines and by the identification of intermediates formed in cell-free extracts, it has been shown that the pathway of purine breakdown by these *Clostridia* is probably that given in Fig. 3.[79]   In the presence of metal-binding agents, extracts of *Cl. cylindrosporum* convert xanthine to 5-ureidoimidazole-4-carboxylic acid; metal ions (Mn^{2+} or Fe^{2+}) are required for the further enzymic conversion of this product to 5-aminoimidazole-4-carboxylic acid.   Decarboxylation gives rise to 5-aminoimidazole, which is then cleaved to formiminoglycine.   In the presence of a folic acid cofactor, formimino-

[76] A. Bendich et al., *J. Biol. Chem.*, **185**, 423 (1950).

[77] W. Franke and G. E. Hahn, *Z. physiol. Chem.*, **299**, 15 (1955).

[78] H. A. Barker and J. V. Beck, *J. Bact.*, **43**, 291 (1942); N. S. Radin and H. A. Barker, *Proc. Natl. Acad. Sci.*, **39**, 1196 (1953).

[79] J. C. Rabinowitz and W. E. Pricer, Jr., *J. Biol. Chem.*, **218**, 189; **222**, 537 (1956); *J. Am. Chem. Soc.*, **78**, 1513, 4176, 5702 (1956).

glycine is converted to glycine, NH_3 and HCOOH, by a process coupled to the phosphorylation of ADP. It appears that N^{10}-formyltetrahydro-PGA (p. 775) is formed, with N^5-formiminotetrahydroPGA and $N^{5,10}$-methenyltetrahydroPGA (anhydroleucovorin) as intermediates, in a manner analogous to that found in the decomposition of formiminoglutamic acid in liver (cf. p. 822). Thus the formimino group ($NH{=}CH{-}$) of formiminoglycine is transferred to the 5 position of tetrahydroPGA

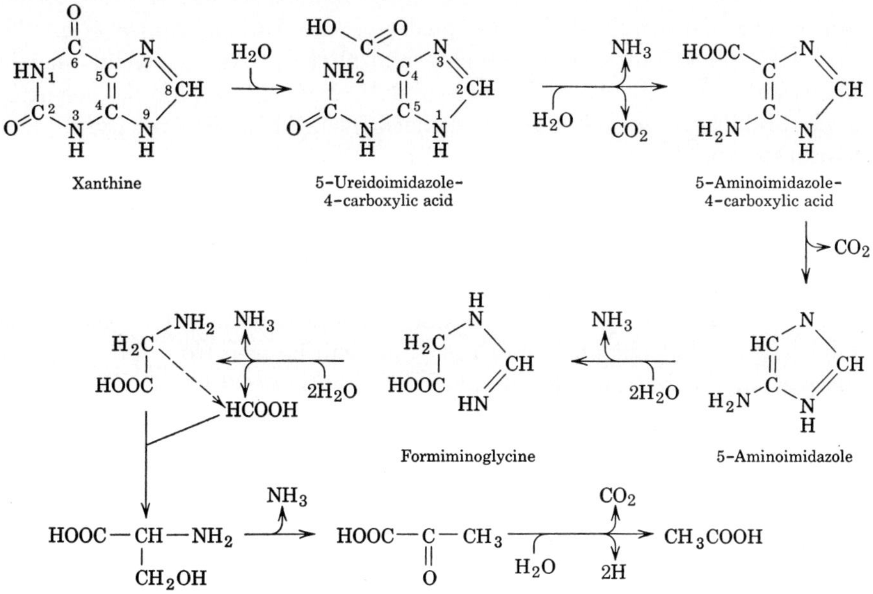

Fig. 3. Fermentation of xanthine by *Clostridium acidi-urici* and by *Clostridium cylindrosporum*.

in one enzyme-catalyzed process; another enzyme apparently effects the conversion of N^5-formiminotetrahydroPGA to anhydroleucovorin, which is readily transformed into N^{10}-formyltetrahydroPGA. The synthesis of ATP is coupled to the deformylation of the folic acid derivative, with the formation of HCOOH and the regeneration of the cofactor. The acetate that appears in purine fermentation probably arises by the intermediate formation of serine and pyruvate[80] as shown in Fig. 3.

Metabolism of Pyrimidines [48]

Biosynthesis of Pyrimidines. When N^{15}-ammonium salts are administered to rats, the isotope is incorporated into the pyrimidines of the tissue nucleic acids. However, if N^{15}-labeled uracil, cytosine, or thymine

[80] R. D. Sagers and J. V. Beck, *J. Bact.*, **72**, 199 (1956); **73**, 465 (1957).

is fed, appreciable isotope incorporation does not occur,[81] largely because the pyrimidines are rapidly broken down in the liver (p. 899). In the search for metabolic precursors of the pyrimidine nucleus, important information came from studies[82] on a number of mutant strains of *Neurospora* which require, for growth, the nucleoside uridine; several of these mutants can use, in place of uridine, oxaloacetic acid or the pyrimidine orotic acid (4-carboxyuracil) found naturally in milk. Orotic acid also is a growth factor for *Lactobacillus bulgaricus* 09; if C^{14}-labeled orotic acid is provided in the medium, the isotope appears in the uridine-5′-phosphate and cytidine-5′-phosphate of the bacterial nucleic acids, but not in the adenine or guanine.[83] Labeled carbamyl-L-aspartic acid (ureidosuccinic acid) also is utilized by *L. bulgaricus* for pyrimidine synthesis, and 4,5-dihydroorotic acid can replace orotic acid as a growth factor for this organism. The formulae of these compounds are given in Fig. 4.

Orotic acid is utilized for pyrimidine synthesis in animal tissues, since the administration of N^{15}- or C^{14}-labeled orotic acid to rats leads to the appearance of the isotope in the cytosine and uracil of the tissue nucleic acids, but not in the purines.[84] As will be seen from the following discussion, the biosynthesis of pyrimidines appears to follow a similar pathway in higher animals and in a variety of microorganisms.

The recognition of the enzymic mechanisms in the interconversion of orotic acid, dihydroorotic acid, and carbamyl-L-aspartic acid came from studies with a soil bacillus (*Zymobacterium oroticum*) that ferments orotic acid.[85] From this organism, an enzyme preparation was obtained which catalyzes the reversible reaction between orotic acid and DPNH to form L-dihydroorotic acid and DPN$^+$; this enzyme has been named dihydroorotic dehydrogenase. Dihydroorotic acid is hydrolyzed reversibly by another enzyme (dihydroorotase) to carbamyl-L-aspartic acid. These two enzymes, which link carbamyl-L-aspartic acid and orotic acid, also appear to be present in rat liver,[86] and are probably widely distributed in biological systems.

The synthesis of carbamyl-L-aspartic acid is effected by rat liver mitochondria,[87] and involves the reaction of carbamyl phosphate (p. 852) with L-aspartic acid; this reaction is catalyzed by an enzyme, "aspartate

[81] A. A. Plentl and R. Schoenheimer, *J. Biol. Chem.*, **153**, 203 (1944).

[82] H. K. Mitchell et al., *J. Biol. Chem.*, **172**, 525 (1948).

[83] L. D. Wright et al., *J. Am. Chem. Soc.*, **73**, 1898 (1951).

[84] H. Arvidson et al., *J. Biol. Chem.*, **179**, 169 (1949); R. B. Hurlbert and V. R. Potter, *ibid.*, **195**, 257 (1952).

[85] I. Lieberman and A. Kornberg, *J. Biol. Chem.*, **207**, 911 (1954).

[86] C. Cooper et al., *J. Biol. Chem.*, **216**, 37 (1955); R. Wu and D. W. Wilson, *ibid.*, **223**, 195 (1956).

[87] P. Reichard, *Acta Chem. Scand.*, **8**, 795, 1102 (1954).

carbamyl transferase," which is different from the one responsible for the synthesis of citrulline. As in the latter process, ATP, Mg^{2+}, and an acyl-L-glutamic acid are required for the formation of carbamylaspartate from L-aspartate, CO_2, and NH_3 by liver preparations; with bacterial enzyme preparations (e.g., from *Streptococcus fecalis*), no acylglutamic

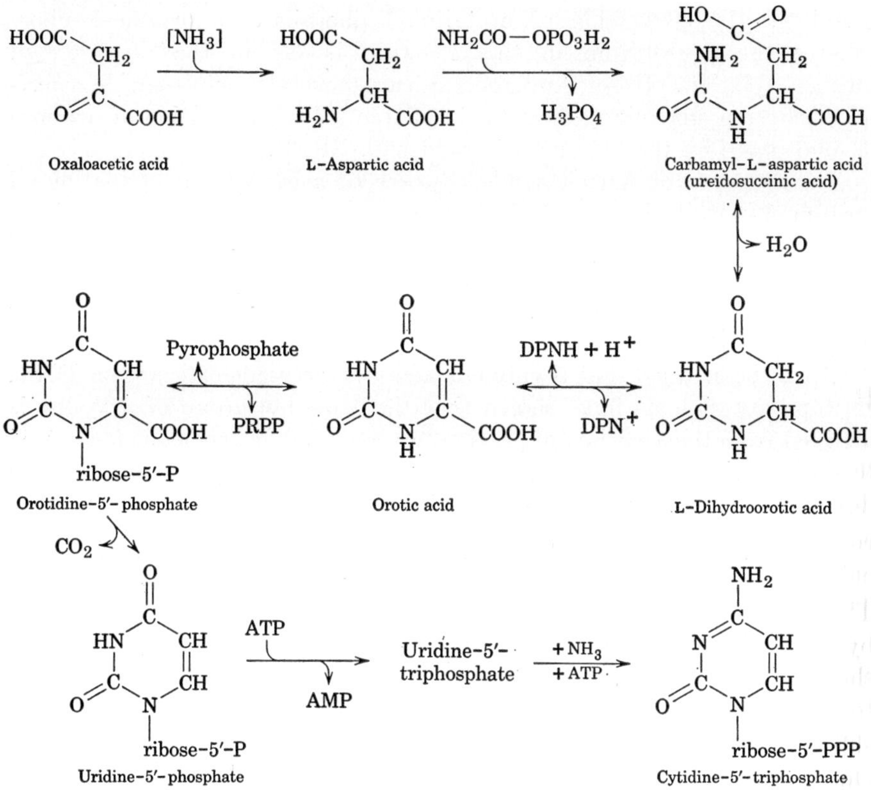

Fig. 4. Probable route of biosynthesis of uridine and cytidine nucleotides.

acid is needed.[88] It was noted above that a uridine-requiring mutant of *Neurospora* can grow on oxaloacetic acid, a component of the citric acid cycle; the conversion of this compound to L-aspartic acid by trans-amination reactions provides the mode of entry of 4 of the carbons of orotic acid, the fifth being derived from CO_2 in the reaction with carbamyl phosphate (Fig. 4).

The studies of Kornberg and his associates have shown how orotic acid can be utilized for the synthesis of the uracil and cytosine of nucleic

[88] M. E. Jones et al., *J. Am. Chem. Soc.*, **77**, 819 (1955); P. Reichard and G. Hanshoff, *Acta Chem. Scand.*, **10**, 548 (1956); J. M. Lowenstein and P. P. Cohen, *J. Biol. Chem.*, **220**, 57 (1956).

acids. In the presence of an enzyme preparation from yeast, orotic acid (but not uracil or cytosine) reacts with 5-phosphoribosyl-1-pyrophosphate (PRPP) to form the nucleotide orotidine-5'-phosphate.[89] This reaction is readily reversible, and the nucleotide is cleaved by pyrophosphate to form orotic acid, as in the comparable pyrophosphorolysis of purine nucleotides (cf. p. 885). A second enzyme, also present in yeast, catalyzes the conversion of orotidine-5'-phosphate to uridine-5'-phosphate; the equilibrium in this reaction is far in the direction of decarboxylation. In some microorganisms (several *Lactobacilli*, *Escherichia coli*) an enzymic pathway is available for the formation of uridine-5'-phosphate by the reaction of uracil with PRPP.

The cytosine of nucleic acids appears to arise by the amination of uridine-5'-triphosphate by NH_3 to form cytidine-5'-triphosphate.[90] This conversion has been demonstrated with extracts of *Escherichia coli*, and involves the participation of ATP. Although uridine-5'-phosphate is not aminated by this enzyme system, the possibility that UDP is a substrate has not been excluded (cf. p. 883).

It will be recalled that thymine is a characteristic constituent of DNA. Isotope experiments have shown that the 5-methyl group of thymine is derived from the α-carbon of glycine, the β-carbon of serine, or formate.[91] It is probable that the introduction of the methyl group of thymine involves the transfer of a C_1 unit from a folic acid compound (p. 776) to deoxyuridine (or deoxyuridylic acid), with the formation of thymidine (or thymidylic acid),[92] which is utilized for DNA synthesis. The conversion of deoxyuridine to thymidine is inhibited by a folic acid antagonist Aminopterin (p. 1001), which also inhibits nucleic acid synthesis. The metabolic origin of deoxyuridine and of deoxycytidine is indicated by isotope experiments with labeled uridine and cytidine; these have shown that the ribonucleosides may be converted by yeast and by rats to the corresponding deoxyribonucleosides without cleavage of the glycosidic bond.[93] However, the mechanism of this conversion has not been elucidated.

In the DNA of some bacteriophages, cytosine is replaced by 5-hydroxymethylcytosine (p. 196), and serves as a metabolic precursor of the latter

[89] I. Lieberman et al., *J. Biol. Chem.*, **215**, 403 (1955); I. Crawford et al., *ibid.*, **226**, 1093 (1957).

[90] I. Lieberman, *J. Biol. Chem.*, **222**, 765 (1956).

[91] D. Elwyn and D. B. Sprinson, *J. Biol. Chem.*, **207**, 467 (1954); J. R. Totter et al., *J. Am. Chem. Soc.*, **76**, 2196 (1954).

[92] M. Friedkin and D. Roberts, *J. Biol. Chem.*, **220**, 653 (1956); P. Reichard, *Acta Chem. Scand.*, **9**, 1275 (1955).

[93] E. Hammersten et al., *J. Biol. Chem.*, **183**, 105 (1950); I. A. Rose and B. S. Schweigert, *ibid.*, **202**, 635 (1953); P. M. Roll et al., *ibid.*, **220**, 455 (1956); P. Reichard, *Acta Chem. Scand.*, **11**, 11 (1957).

pyrimidine.[94]   The 5-hydroxymethyl group probably arises from a source of C_1 units, as does the methyl group of thymine, but thymine itself is not a precursor of 5-hydroxymethylcytosine.

Little is known about the metabolic origin of 5-methylcytosine, a constituent of some plant and animal DNA preparations (p. 191).

Metabolic Breakdown of Pyrimidines.   Like the purines of the nucleic acids, the pyrimidines are converted in animal tissues to end products that are removed from the organism.   The administration to rats of uracil leads to the excretion of β-alanine and of carbamyl-β-alanine (β-ureido-propionic acid), whereas the administration of thymine or dihydrothy-mine results in the appearance of urinary β-aminoisobutyric acid (Fig. 5); these products are also formed upon incubation of the pyrimidines

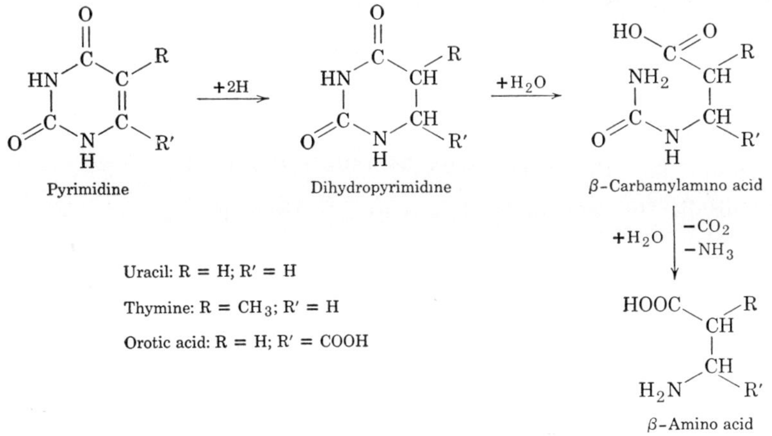

Uracil: R = H; R′ = H

Thymine: R = CH_3; R′ = H

Orotic acid: R = H; R′ = COOH

Fig. 5.   Metabolic breakdown of uracil, thymine, and orotic acid.

with liver preparations.[95]   It appears, therefore, that uracil (which may be derived directly from PNA, or by deamination of cytidine; cf. p. 886) and thymine are degraded in animals by similar pathways involving: (1) reduction of the pyrimidine ring to a dihydropyrimidine, as in the dihydroorotic dehydrogenase-catalyzed reaction; (2) opening of the ring to form β-ureidopropionic acid (from uracil) or β-ureidoisobutyric acid (from thymine), as in the dihydroorotase reaction; (3) decomposition of the ureido compound to form CO_2, NH_3, and β-alanine (from uracil) or β-aminoisobutyric acid (from thymine).   β-Alanine is extensively degraded in the rat, probably by preliminary transamination with glu-tamic acid to form formylacetic acid ($OHC\!-\!CH_2\!-\!COOH$), which is

94 S. S. Cohen and L. L. Weed, *J. Biol. Chem.,* **209,** 789 (1954); M. Green and S. S. Cohen, *ibid.,* **225,** 387 (1957).

95 K. Fink et al., *J. Biol. Chem.,* **197,** 441 (1952); **221,** 425 (1956); E. S. Canel-lakis, *ibid.,* **221,** 315 (1956); P. Fritzson and A. Pihl, *ibid.,* **226,** 223, 229 (1957).

decomposed to CO_2 and a C_2 unit.[96] In the fermentative breakdown of orotic acid by *Zymobacterium oroticum*, the pyrimidine is converted to NH_3, CO_2, and products (dicarboxylic acids, acetic acid) arising from the metabolism of L-aspartic acid.[97] The initial steps in the degradation of uracil, thymine, and orotic acid are summarized in Fig. 5.

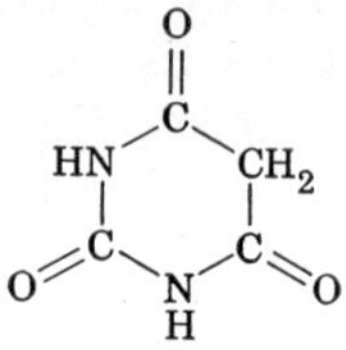

Barbituric acid 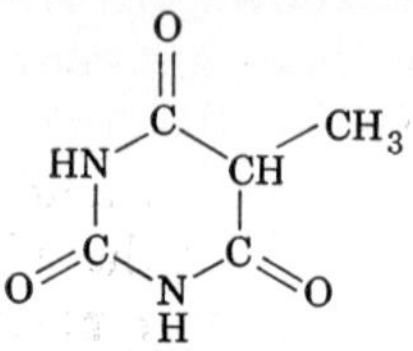   5–Methylbarbituric acid

Some microorganisms can effect the oxidation of uracil and of thymine to barbituric acid and 5-methylbarbituric acid, respectively.[98] Barbituric acid is further converted to malonic acid and urea.

Biosynthesis of Nucleic Acids

Metabolic Turnover of Nucleic Acids.[99] From the foregoing discussion of the biosynthesis of the purines and pyrimidines of PNA and DNA, it is evident that most organisms are able to make these nucleic acid constituents from simple metabolites, and that in general the synthetic pathways lead to the formation of nucleotides, which are assumed to be the metabolic precursors of the cellular polynucleotides. In animal tissues, some of the nucleic acids appear to be in a "dynamic state" (cf. p. 728), since isotope studies have shown a metabolic turnover of tissue PNA. It was mentioned before that the purine ring of adenine can be incorporated into the nucleic acids of rat tissues. Upon the administration of adenine (labeled with N^{15} in positions 1 and 3) to rats, the greatest extent of isotope incorporation was found in the adenine and guanine of the PNA fraction of the liver,[100] with a somewhat lower degree of incorporation into the PNA adenine and guanine of the intestine. In the intact rat, these two tissues appear to be the major sites of nucleic acid turnover. On the other hand, the adenine and guanine of the liver DNA were found to contain very small amounts of N^{15}, indicating that in the adult rat liver the purines of PNA are renewed at

[96] A. Pihl and P. Fritzson, *J. Biol. Chem.*, **215**, 345 (1955).

[97] I. Lieberman and A. Kornberg, *J. Biol. Chem.*, **212**, 909 (1955).

[98] O. Hayaishi and A. Kornberg, *J. Biol. Chem.*, **197**, 717 (1952).

[99] G. B. Brown and P. M. Roll; R. M. S. Smellie, in E. Chargaff and J. N. Davidson, *The Nucleic Acids,* Vol. II, Chapters 25 and 26, Academic Press, New York, 1955.

[100] S. S. Furst et al., *J. Biol. Chem.*, **183**, 251 (1950).

a much more rapid rate than the purines of DNA. A similar difference in the rate of renewal of PNA and DNA has also been observed in studies on the rate of incorporation of P^{32}, supplied as inorganic phosphate.[101]

If an appreciable portion of a rat's liver is removed surgically (partial hepatectomy), and the animal is then given isotopic adenine during the regeneration of the liver tissue, the extent of adenine incorporation into the PNA fraction is similar to that found in the normal rat. After the administration of isotopic adenine has been discontinued, the N^{15} is rapidly lost from the liver PNA. Of special interest is the finding that the DNA fraction of the regenerated rat liver shows an appreciable N^{15} content. This finding has been interpreted as evidence for the utilization of preformed adenine for the synthesis of DNA in growing tissue, and supports the view that DNA formation is a metabolic process associated with cell multiplication. Once the isotopic adenine has been incorporated into the DNA fraction of regenerated liver, the isotope is not replaced at a rapid rate; this may be taken to suggest that in a nongrowing tissue the DNA is not in a dynamic state of metabolism.

It must be stressed, however, that these conclusions apply to the metabolic relationship between administered adenine and liver nucleic acids. Rather different results have been obtained upon the administration of C^{14}-labeled purine precursors such as glycine or formate;[102] these cause a more rapid labeling of the adenine and guanine of the intestinal PNA than of liver PNA.[103] Furthermore, in contrast to the behavior of labeled adenine, these precursors are incorporated into the adenine and guanine of liver DNA,[104] and the turnover of labeled carbon in DNA is fairly rapid. The apparent contradiction between the results of studies on the incorporation of isotopic adenine on the one hand and of isotopic small fragments (glycine, formate) on the other has not yet been resolved satisfactorily. From these differences in metabolic behavior, it has been inferred that at least two types of DNA are present in rat liver cells, and that the carbons of glycine and of formate enter a "labile" DNA, whereas exogenous adenine is incorporated into a "metabolically inert" DNA. Attention was drawn previously (p. 194) to the heterogeneity of nucleic acid preparations. In addition, the possibility cannot be excluded that different mechanisms of incorporation may be involved; it has been suggested[105] that exogenous adenine may be transferred from an "active" intermediate (possibly a nucleoside or a

[101] E. Hammarsten and G. Hevesy, *Acta Physiol. Scand.*, **11**, 335 (1946); J. N. Davidson et al., *Biochem. J.*, **49**, 311 (1951).

[102] R. M. S. Smellie and J. N. Davidson, *Experientia*, **12**, 422 (1956).

[103] S. S. Furst and G. B. Brown, *J. Biol. Chem.*, **191**, 239 (1951); A. Bendich et al., *ibid.*, **203**, 305 (1953).

[104] G. A. LePage and C. Heidelberger, *J. Biol. Chem.*, **188**, 593 (1951).

[105] G. B. Brown, *Federation Proc.*, **15**, 823 (1956).

nucleotide) to a pre-existing polynucleotide by a transglycosidation ("transpurination") reaction, whereas the incorporation of the small precursors involves total synthesis of the purine nucleotides.

Although the PNA of animal tissues is in a dynamic state, as judged by isotope studies, the PNA of growing bacterial cultures does not appear to undergo intracellular degradation. For example, upon multiplication of *Escherichia coli* in the presence of P^{32}-phosphate, the isotope is retained in the cellular PNA and DNA, and there is no apparent turnover.[106] This difference in the behavior of animal tissues and of growing bacteria is analogous to that observed in studies of their protein metabolism (cf. p. 746).

Except for the enzymic studies on the synthesis of polynucleotides, discussed previously, little is known about the mode of assembly of nucleotide units in the intracellular synthesis of PNA and DNA. Isotopic methods similar to those used in the study of the pattern of labeling of proteins (cf. p. 736) have yielded data that are difficult to interpret, because of the heterogeneity of nucleic acid preparations. For example, simultaneous administration of P^{32}-phosphate, orotic acid-6-C^{14}, and glycine-2-C^{14} to rats, and determination of the pattern of labeling in the nucleotides of liver DNA preparations, showed that the phosphorus, pyrimidines, and purines had become uniformly labeled; on the other hand, the phosphorus and pyrimidines of liver PNA were found to be labeled nonuniformly.[107]

Inhibition of Nucleic Acid Synthesis. Earlier in this chapter, mention was made of several substances that inhibit nucleic acid synthesis because of their interference with individual enzymic steps in the biosynthesis of purines and pyrimidines. Thus structural analogues of pteroylglutamic acid (e.g., Aminopterin, A-methopterin; p. 1001) interfere with the formation of cofactors required for formylation reactions, and azaserine inhibits the utilization of glutamine for purine synthesis (cf. p. 891). A number of purine derivatives (e.g., 6-mercaptopurine, 8-azaguanine) have been found to interfere with the synthesis of normal nucleic acids, but the mode of their action is not clear.[108] It is known that 8-azaguanine is incorporated into the PNA of some microorganisms, and to replace partially the guanine.[109] Structural analogues of pyrimidines (e.g., 5-bromouracil) also inhibit nucleic acid synthesis, and it has been shown

---

[106] L. Siminovitch and A. F. Graham, *Canad. J. Microbiol.,* **2,** 585 (1956).

[107] K. Moldave and C. Heidelberger, *J. Am. Chem. Soc.,* **76,** 679 (1954).

[108] G. B. Elion et al., *J. Biol. Chem.,* **204,** 35 (1953); G. H. Hitchings et al., *Ann. N. Y. Acad. Sci.,* **60,** 183 (1954).

[109] J. D. Smith and R. E. F. Matthews, *Biochem. J.,* **66,** 323 (1957); H. G. Mandel, *J. Biol. Chem.,* **225,** 137 (1957).

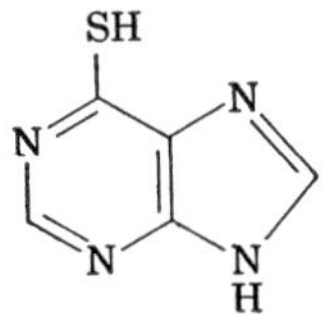

SH

6-Mercaptopurine

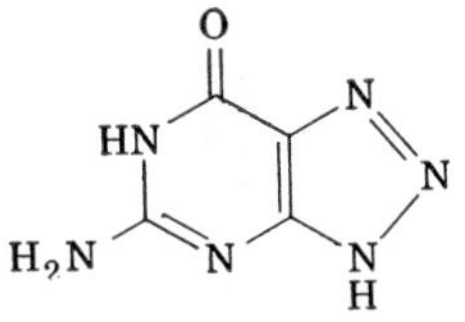

O

H₂N

8-Azaguanine

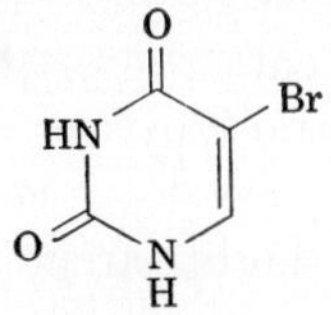

O

Br

5-Bromouracil

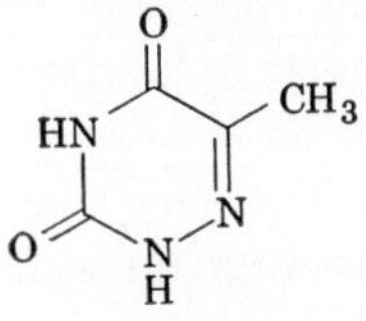

O

CH₃

"6-Azathymine"
(4-azathymine)

that they partially replace the thymine of the DNA fraction of *Escherichia coli*.[110] Another metabolic competitor of thymine is "6-azathymine" (4-azathymine according to numbering of pyrimidine ring on p. 187), which partially replaces the thymine of *Streptococcus fecalis*, and appears to be converted by the organism to the deoxyriboside azathymidine; it has been found that this nucleoside interferes with the incorporation of C^{14}-formate into DNA thymine.[111] The essential role of thymine in normal growth has been brought out in a striking manner by the studies of Cohen[112] with a thymine-requiring mutant of *E. coli*. When this mutant is incubated in the absence of thymine, but with glucose as a carbon source, rapid death of the cells ensues because DNA synthesis is blocked without inhibition of the synthesis of PNA or of protein.

A variety of purine and pyrimidine analogues, as well as their nucleosides, exert an inhibitory effect on the growth of tumor cells, and have been the objects of intensive study in the search for useful chemotherapeutic agents in the treatment of human cancer.[113] Most of the substances thus far found to inhibit tumor growth also exhibit toxicity to the host, thus limiting their clinical use.

Specific Reproduction of DNA. It will be recalled that some of the bacterial viruses (bacteriophages of *Escherichia coli*) contain DNA

[110] D. B. Dunn and J. D. Smith, *Nature*, **174**, 305 (1954); *Biochem. J.*, **67**, 494 (1957); S. Zamenhof et al., *J. Biol. Chem.*, **219**, 165 (1956).

[111] W. H. Prusoff et al., *Biochim. et Biophys. Acta*, **20**, 209 (1956); *J. Biol. Chem.*, **226**, 901 (1957).

[112] S. S. Cohen and H. D. Barner, *J. Bact.*, **69**, 59 (1955); **72**, 115 (1956).

[113] C. P. Rhoads, *Antimetabolites and Cancer*, American Association for the Advancement of Science, Washington, 1955.

(p. 194). The T_2 bacteriophage of *E. coli,* as seen under the electron microscope, is a rounded tail-bearing particle containing about 2×10^{-10} μg of DNA. Upon infection, the tail (length ca. 0.1 μ) of the phage is attached to the cell wall of the host bacterium,[114] and the DNA present in the rounded portion (diameter ca. 0.1 μ) is injected into the cell. Important studies by Hershey[115] have shown that, if T_2 phage is labeled in its DNA with P^{32} and in its protein with S^{35}, and the labeled phage is used to infect *E. coli,* only the P^{32} appears to enter the cell, and the S^{35} remains attached to the surface. The entrance of phage DNA into the host cell seems to involve an enzymic attack by the virus particle on the cell wall.[116] The entering DNA then causes a series of striking metabolic events within the cell, including the apparent cessation of the synthesis of many enzymes, and a marked increase in deoxyribonuclease activity,[117] thus leading to extensive degradation of host DNA. It is of interest that phage DNA is more resistant to the action of this enzyme than are other DNA preparations; this has been attributed to the presence of 5-hydroxymethylcytosine bound in glycosidic linkage to glucose units.[118] After a brief period following infection, phage DNA is actively synthesized, and isotope studies have shown that the constituents of the host DNA are used in this process.[119] Multiplication of the phage to several hundred or more particles is followed by disruption (lysis) of the cell, and release of the phage into the medium. For a further discussion of these phenomena, see the review by Boyd.[120]

It is evident that the entrance of the T_2 phage DNA into the *E. coli* cell leads to a marked alteration in the metabolism of the cell, and the diversion of materials from the synthesis of normal DNA to the reproduction of phage DNA. The cellular synthesis of the abnormal DNA introduced from a virulent T_2 phage thus leads to the death of the cell. Other bacterial viruses ("temperate" bacteriophages) are known which do not kill the host cell, but are reproduced together with the other cell constituents during the growth of the bacterial culture. Relatively little is known about the chemical composition of these viruses, but it is

[114] T. Anderson, *Cold Spring Harbor Symposia Quant. Biol.,* **18,** 197 (1953).

[115] A. D. Hershey and M. Chase, *J. Gen. Physiol.,* **36,** 39 (1952); A. D. Hershey, in D. E. Green, *Currents in Biochemical Research,* Interscience Publishers, New York, 1956.

[116] L. F. Barrington and L. M. Kozloff, *J. Biol. Chem.,* **223,** 615 (1956); L. M. Kozloff et al., *ibid.,* **228,** 511, 529, 537 (1957).

[117] L. M. Kozloff, *Cold Spring Harbor Symposia Quant. Biol.,* **18,** 209 (1953).

[118] S. S. Cohen, *Science,* **123,** 653 (1956).

[119] S. S. Cohen, *Bact. Revs.,* **15,** 131 (1951); M. S. H. Siddiqi et al., *J. Biol. Chem.,* **199,** 165 (1952).

[120] J. S. K. Boyd, *Biol. Revs.,* **31,** 71 (1956).

believed that they contain DNA which is reproduced during cell multiplication. Lwoff[121] has shown that, when *E. coli* cells infected with a temperate phage are irradiated with ultraviolet light or treated with chemicals known to cause mutations (cf. p. 397), they undergo lysis. During the time prior to cell lysis, the temperate phage multiplies at a rapid rate, and it appears that the biosynthesis of DNA in the cell has been diverted in the direction of phage DNA, as with the virulent phages.

Some temperate phages (e.g., of strains of *Salmonella*) are able to transfer the ability to develop one of a number of heritable characters from the cell of one strain of an organism to a cell of a different strain. This phenomenon has been termed "transduction," and is believed to involve the transfer of DNA from one cell to another.[122] The most definitive evidence for the participation of DNA in such transduction phenomena has come from studies on the "transforming principles" of pneumococci and of other microorganisms (e.g., *Hemophilus influenzae*). As mentioned previously (cf. p. 748), DNA preparations from one strain can effect heritable changes in the metabolic behavior of another strain.[123]

The specific reproduction of DNA molecules during cell multiplication, whether in viral infection or in transduction phenomena, is believed to be related to the duplication of chromosomal DNA, and the transmission of heritable characters from parent to progeny. A variety of studies have shown that the DNA content per cell nucleus, in any given species, is proportional to the chromosome number.[124] For example, the DNA content of nuclei of several types of diploid somatic cells (chromosome number, $2n$) in the fowl is about 2.4×10^{-9} mg per nucleus, whereas in the haploid sperm cells (chromosome number, n), it is about 1.25×10^{-9} mg per nucleus.[125] Furthermore, treatment of organisms with ultraviolet light, ionizing radiations (e.g., X-rays), chemical alkylating agents (e.g., N,N'-bis(2-chloroethyl)methylamine, dimethyl sulfate, β-propiolactone), or other substances (e.g., Fe^{2+}), is known to cause mutations, and it is probable that some of these agents exert an effect on chromosomal DNA. Although considerable indirect evidence has been presented for the view that the DNA of the chromosomes occupies a central role in genetic phenomena, the biochemical events in the specific replication of cellular nucleic acids are unknown. For valuable discus-

[121] A. Lwoff, *Bact. Revs.*, **17**, 269 (1953).

[122] N. D. Zinder and J. Lederberg, *J. Bact.*, **64**, 679 (1952); N. D. Zinder, *J. Cellular Comp. Physiol.*, **45**, Suppl. 2, 23 (1955); J. Lederberg, *Am. Scientist*, **44**, 264 (1956).

[123] S. Zamenhof, in S. Graff, *Essays in Biochemistry*, John Wiley and Sons, New York, 1956.

[124] R. Vendrely and C. Vendrely, *Intern. Rev. Cytol.*, **5**, 171 (1956).

[125] A. E. Mirsky and H. Ris, *Nature*, **163**, 666 (1949).

sions of this question, see the reviews by Hotchkiss and by Brachet.[126] Clearly, the elucidation of the enzymic processes whereby cells effect the specific reproduction of nucleic acids is one of the most important tasks of present-day biochemistry.[127]

[126] R. D. Hotchkiss; J. Brachet, in E. Chargaff and J. N. Davidson, *The Nucleic Acids,* Vol. II, Chapters 27 and 28, Academic Press, New York, 1955.

[127] W. D. McElroy and B. Glass, *The Chemical Basis of Heredity,* Johns Hopkins Press, Baltimore, 1957.

36 ·

Role of Inorganic Ions in Metabolism

Although the preceding chapters have dealt mainly with the metabolism of organic compounds, it will have become evident that the inorganic constituents of living matter are essential participants in biochemical processes. For example, mention has been made of the importance of iron and copper in the action of several respiratory pigments (hemoglobins, myoglobin, hemocyanins, etc.), of electron carriers (cytochromes), and of oxidative enzymes (catalases, peroxidases, cytochrome oxidase, phenol oxidases, metalloflavoproteins). The role of magnesium in chlorophyll and in various enzyme systems that act on phosphate compounds, and the relation of molybdenum to nitrogen assimilation also have been discussed, as has the importance of other inorganic cations (Zn^{2+}, Mn^{2+}, K^+, Ca^{2+}) for a variety of enzymic processes. Among the inorganic anions, phosphate occupies a pre-eminent place in intermediate metabolism, and sulfate and the halides (e.g., iodide) are required for the biosynthesis of natural products classified as organic compounds (e.g., mucopolysaccharides, thyroxine).

However, these functions of the inorganic ions in metabolism represent only one aspect of their action in biological systems. Of equal importance is their general role in preserving the physical integrity of cells and tissues. In the consideration of this facet of the biochemical action of inorganic ions, it must be recalled that water, which represents the major chemical constituent of living organisms, is the principal medium for the occurrence of metabolic processes.[1] Not only does water serve as the vehicle for the transport of ions to and from cells, but it also participates in acid-base equilibria (cf. p. 918). Water has several physical properties that are of importance in its physiological role. In addition to its mobility and solvent power, water has a high dielectric constant (cf. p. 20), a high specific heat (1 cal per gram at 37° C), a high heat of

[1] J. F. Manery, *Physiol. Revs.*, **34**, 334 (1954).

vaporization (575 cal per gram at 37° C), and a high thermal conductivity.

Metabolic Functions of Inorganic Ions [2]

It has long been known that, for normal growth and function, inorganic salts must be supplied to all biological forms. Thus Pasteur showed in 1860 that yeast will grow only when the culture medium contains inorganic compounds, in addition to ammonia and a fermentable carbon compound. The fact that higher plants require a variety of inorganic ions was clearly demonstrated in the same year by Sachs and by Knop. The importance of inorganic salts in the diet of higher animals emerged from the work of Osborne and Mendel on the nutritional requirements of the rat; in 1919 these investigators devised a salt mixture which is still widely used as a constituent of synthetic diets.

Of the metallic elements identified in biological material, fewer than half have been shown to be indispensable for the growth and normal function of animals or plants (Table 1). The indispensable elements may

Table I. Metallic Cations of Animal or Plant Tissues

Indispensable	Dispensable
"Bulk" Elements	"Nontoxic" Elements
Sodium	Caesium
Potassium	Chromium
Calcium	Nickel
Magnesium	Rubidium
	Silicon
	Strontium
	Tin
"Trace" Elements	"Toxic" Elements
Iron	Antimony
Cobalt	Arsenic
Copper	Barium
Manganese	Beryllium
Zinc	Bismuth
Aluminum	Cadmium
Boron	Lead
Molybdenum	Mercury
(Vanadium)	Selenium
	Silver
	Tellurium
	Thorium

[2] W. Stiles, *Trace Elements in Plants and Animals,* The Macmillan Co., New York, 1946; E. J. Underwood, *Trace Elements in Human and Animal Nutrition,* Academic Press, New York, 1956; A. Pirson, *Ann. Rev. Plant Physiol.,* **6,** 71 (1955).

be separated into two groups: (1) the so-called "bulk" elements, which are found in high concentrations, and (2) the "trace" elements. Not all of the elements listed in Table 1 as "indispensable" are required by every animal and plant. Thus Na^+, which is of vital importance to higher animals, is known to be a dispensable cation for many bacteria and also for most plants, with the exception of the blue-green algae.[3] On the other hand, only some higher plants have been shown to require aluminum, boron, or vanadium; molybdenum appears to be essential only to organisms that derive all their nitrogen from inorganic sources (cf. p. 674). A number of the nonessential trace elements may be considered both nonnutritive and nontoxic, but others produce toxic symptoms in living organisms. It is probable that many of the effects of metallic ions, such as Ag^+, Hg^{2+}, Pb^{2+}, are associated with the fact that they are potent inhibitors of numerous enzymes.

Most of the elements in Table 1 occur in animals and plants as cations; as noted earlier, several inorganic anions also play important metabolic roles. The inorganic anion found in the highest concentration in all living forms is phosphate, which is required by all organisms. A second bulk element found, in part, in the form of inorganic anions, is sulfur, which is required by organisms that must synthesize organic compounds (sulfur-containing amino acids, biotin, etc.) from inorganic substances (cf. p. 799). However, most organisms presumably can satisfy their sulfur requirements by the utilization of organic sulfur compounds and form sulfate by the oxidation of the sulfur amino acids. Of the halides, only chloride is a bulk anion and appears to be required by all animals and plants. Iodide is essential for higher animals (thyroxine formation); bromide and fluoride, both of which are found in animal and plant material, are generally considered nonnutritive and toxic for higher animals. It will be recalled that fluoride is an inhibitor of carbohydrate metabolism.

Although the mineral requirements of higher animals and plants have been investigated extensively, the requirements of microorganisms are less clearly established.[4] Most microbiological media are made up to contain Na^+, K^+, Mg^{2+}, Fe^{2+}, SO_4^{2-}, Cl^-, phosphate, and, sometimes, Mn^{2+} and Ca^{2+}. The study of the role of trace elements in bacterial metabolism and in the nutrition of higher forms of life is hindered by the difficulty of preparing pure samples of inorganic salts. A further complication is the fact that an apparent requirement for a specific ion may be the result of an imbalance in the proportions of the various ions supplied or of the presence of toxic ions. Moreover, ele-

[3] G. E. Fogg, *Bact. Revs.,* **20,** 148 (1956).
[4] S. G. Knight, in C. H. Werkman and P. W. Wilson, *Bacterial Physiology,* Academic Press, New York, 1951.

ments may appear to be "dispensable" for growth but are required for the production *in vivo* of individual enzymes (e.g., mammalian xanthine oxidase,[5] bacterial formic dehydrogenase[6]).

Bulk Elements. K^+ is found almost universally as the principal inorganic cation of cells, whereas Na^+ is present mainly as the cation of extracellular tissue fluids of animals. The important role of these cations and of the anion Cl^- in the osmotic regulation of body and tissue fluids will be discussed in a later section of this chapter. Although the classification of the univalent ions as bulk elements was based on the relatively large amounts required for osmotic activity, it is now recognized that K^+ and Na^+ also serve as essential activating ions for specific enzyme systems (Table 2).[7] In general, enzymes that are activated by K^+ and Na^+ also can be activated by NH_4^+ and Rb^+.

Table 2. Some Physiological Effects of Bulk Metallic Cations

Cation	Enzyme Systems Affected *in vitro*		Other Roles
	Activation	Inhibition	
Na^+	Apyrases (brain and bacteria)	ATP-pyruvic trans-phosphorylase Aceto-CoA-kinase Phosphotransacetylase	Principal cation of extracellular tissue fluids
K^+	ATP-pyruvic trans-phosphorylase Apyrase (bacteria) Fructokinase Phosphotransacetylase Aceto-CoA-kinase		Principal cation of most cells
Ca^{2+}	Actomyosin-ATPase Apyrase (potato) Phospholipase C	Enolase Some dipeptidases Flavokinase	Blood coagulation Bone formation
Mg^{2+}	Phosphatases Transphosphorylases Enolase Some peptidases Keto acid decarboxylases Phospholipase C	Actomyosin-ATPase	Bone formation Chlorophyll formation

The univalent cations, together with Ca^{2+} and Mg^{2+}, are important in the preservation of the integrity of cell membranes and in the normal activity of excitable tissues (cf. p. 925). The inclusion of Ca^{2+} and Mg^{2+} among the bulk ions of the tissues of vertebrates is primarily a reflection of their presence in bone, in the form of carbonates and

[5] E. C. DeRenzo, *Advances in Enzymol.*, **17**, 293 (1956).

[6] J. Pinsent, *Biochem. J.*, **57**, 10 (1954).

[7] W. D. McElroy and A. Nason, *Ann. Rev. Plant Physiol.*, **5**, 1 (1954).

phosphates; approximately 99 per cent of the calcium and 70 per cent of the magnesium in the mammal is found in skeletal structures.

The role of Ca^{2+} in blood coagulation has already been discussed (p. 703). In human blood, calcium is present mainly in the plasma, where ca. 50 per cent is in ionic form and the remainder is in combination, in a nondiffusible form, with serum proteins. A decrease in the Ca^{2+} content of blood, such as may result from a dietary deficiency or from an insufficiency of the parathyroid hormone (p. 945), may lead to tetany; an excess of Ca^{2+} in the blood may be followed by a calcification of several internal organs.

The absorption of dietary Ca^{2+} (and also of Mg^{2+}) from the intestinal tract may be prevented by the simultaneous ingestion of organic acids (e.g., oxalic acid, phytic acid) with which the cation forms insoluble salts. Consequently, the availability of dietary Ca^{2+} is greatly influenced by the other constituents of the diet. Both Ca^{2+} and Mg^{2+} are excreted mainly via the large intestine rather than the kidney. For this reason, the administration of calcium and magnesium salts can result in the production of an acid urine, since the accompanying anions are excreted by the kidney (cf. p. 918). For an extensive review of calcium metabolism, see Nicolaysen et al. or Irving.[8]

In contrast to the distribution of calcium in mammalian blood, more magnesium is present in red cells than in plasma. Furthermore, the Mg^{2+} content of muscle cells is relatively high. In the latter tissue, Mg^{2+} plays an important role, as an activating ion, in many of the enzymic reactions (Table 2). Indeed, nearly all transphosphorylation reactions involving ATP require the presence of Mg^{2+}. This activating effect of Mg^{2+} may, in many instances, be duplicated *in vitro* by Mn^{2+} and, in some reactions, by other divalent cations such as Co^{2+}, Ni^{2+}, Zn^{2+}, or Ca^{2+}.

The signal biochemical importance of the phosphate group will have become evident in the chapters dealing with the metabolism of carbohydrates, fats, proteins, and vitamins (cf. also McElroy and Glass[9]). The presence of phosphate in bone was noted above, and its function in the regulation of blood pH is described on p. 918. It may be added that the normal formation of bone depends on the relative amounts of dietary phosphorus and calcium, and, in addition, on the availability of vitamin D (Chapter 39). The inorganic ions of bone are in equilibrium with those of the blood and of the other tissues (cf. p. 915).

Trace Elements. It is probable that the nutritional requirements for the indispensable trace cations is related to their participation in the

---

[8] R. Nicolaysen et al., *Physiol. Revs.*, **33**, 424 (1953); J. T. Irving, *Calcium Metabolism,* Methuen, London, 1957.

[9] W. D. McElroy and B. Glass, *Phosphorus Metabolism*, Vols. I and II, Johns Hopkins Press, Baltimore, 1951–1952.

action of various enzymes. For example, the activity of the iron-containing enzymes is greatly reduced in microorganisms cultured in media deficient in iron. With the heme enzymes or the zinc-containing enzymes (carbonic anhydrase, several dehydrogenases), a specific inorganic cation is an integral part of the metalloenzyme complex. However, the catalytic action of many enzymes has been found either to require or to be stimulated by the presence of one of several bivalent inorganic cations (Mg^{2+}, Mn^{2+}, Co^{2+}, Zn^{2+}). In such metal-activated enzyme systems (e.g., transphosphorylases, phosphatases, arginase, some exopeptidases, and several keto acid decarboxylases), the activating cation may be intimately involved in the formation of enzyme-substrate complexes. Since several cations may serve as activators of a single enzyme, it is frequently difficult to establish which of these is the "natural" activator. For a discussion of the role of metal ions in enzyme systems, see Lehninger.[10]

Among the indispensable trace elements listed in Table 1, iron occupies a primary place in the metabolism of higher animals, because of its presence as a structural constituent of hemoglobin. Of the total iron in the human body (ca. 4.3 grams per 70 kg), about 70 per cent is present in hemoglobin, about 3 per cent in myoglobin, and most of the remainder is in ferritin, the storage form of iron.[11] Ferritin is found in the spleen, the liver, and (to a lesser extent) in the bone marrow; it consists of a protein (apoferritin) containing tightly bound micelles of a ferric hydroxide having the approximate composition $[Fe(OOH)_8 \cdot (FeOPO_3H_2)]$. The iron content of ferritin is variable, and may reach values as high as 23 per cent. Upon the addition of cadmium chloride, ferritin may be obtained in the form of crystals,[12] but ultracentrifugal study of such material has shown it to be inhomogeneous. Apoferritin may be prepared by reduction of the ferric ion to the ferrous form at pH 4.5, followed by dialysis to remove the metal ions. Addition of cadmium chloride to the protein solution gives crystalline apoferritin, which behaves as a homogeneous protein in the ultracentrifuge (particle weight ca. 465,000). A crystalline preparation with properties similar to those of natural ferritin has been obtained by treatment of crystalline apoferritin with an inorganic ferrous salt in the presence of oxygen, and it is believed that ferritin is formed *in vivo* by an analogous process.[13]

The pathway of iron (Fe^{3+}) from the foodstuffs to hemoglobin and to

[10] A. L. Lehninger, *Physiol. Revs.*, **30**, 393 (1950).

[11] S. Granick, *Physiol. Revs.*, **31**, 489 (1951); D. L. Drabkin, *ibid.*, **31**, 345 (1951); A. Mazur, in S. Graff, *Essays in Biochemistry*, John Wiley & Sons, New York, 1956; E. Shorr, *Harvey Lectures*, **50**, 112 (1956).

[12] V. Laufberger, *Bull. soc. chim. biol.*, **19**, 1575 (1938).

[13] H. J. Bielig and E. Bayer, *Naturwissenschaften*, **42**, 125 (1955); R. A. Fineberg and D. M. Greenberg, *J. Biol. Chem.*, **214**, 97, 107 (1955).

ferritin probably involves the following processes: (1) the Fe^{3+} of the dietary material is reduced to Fe^{2+} in the gastrointestinal tract; (2) after absorption into the cells of the intestinal mucosa, the Fe^{2+} is incorporated into ferritin as Fe^{3+}; (3) the Fe^{2+} in the mucosa is also converted to plasma Fe^{3+} (bound by the iron-binding globulin named "transferrin" or "siderophilin"); (4) the plasma Fe^{3+} is in equilibrium with the iron in the liver, spleen, and bone marrow. In these tissues, the changes shown in the accompanying scheme are believed to occur.

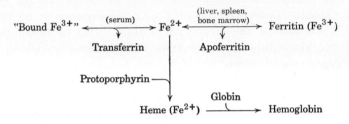

In the catabolism of hemoglobin, after the disintegration of the erythrocytes (cf. p. 869), very little of the iron is excreted, and most of it is used again for hemoglobin formation or is stored as ferritin. A normal adult animal requires and absorbs relatively little iron from dietary sources.[14] Upon the administration of Fe^{59} (as ferric salts) to rats, the isotope appears rapidly in liver ferritin; other iron-containing proteins (cytochrome b_5, catalase) are labeled more slowly.[15] If very large amounts of iron are present in the animal body, the capacity of ferritin to store iron may be exceeded, and hemosiderin (a form of ferric hydroxide) is deposited in the liver. This condition (hemosiderosis) may accompany anemias in which the level of plasma iron is markedly elevated. In the disease known as hemochromatosis, the iron content of some tissues (liver, pancreas) may be as high as 3 grams per 100 grams dry weight, instead of the 20 to 50 mg normally present.

For the utilization of iron in hemoglobin synthesis, a dietary source of copper is essential.[16] Experimental animals on diets deficient in copper develop an anemia characterized not only by a marked decrease in the total iron and heme content in the blood and tissues, but also by an increased amount of free protoporphyrin in the erythrocytes. Presumably, copper-containing enzyme systems are involved in some step in hemoglobin formation. Cobalt also appears to be essential for the normal formation of erythrocytes; this effect is probably a reflection of the presence of cobalt in vitamin B_{12} (Chapter 39), which is required

[14] C. J. Gubler, *Science*, **123**, 87 (1956).

[15] R. B. Loftfield and R. Bonnichsen, *Acta Chem. Scand.*, **10**, 1547 (1956).

[16] H. R. Marston, *Physiol. Revs.*, **32**, 66 (1952); S. H. Allen, *Biochem. J.*, **63**, 461 (1956); C. H. Gallagher et al., *Proc. Roy. Soc.*, **145B**, 134, 195 (1956).

for the formation of hemoglobin *in vivo*. It may be added that, in the nutrition of higher animals, normal copper metabolism depends on the relative proportions of copper, molybdenum, and sulfate in the diet; in some cases, an excess of dietary molybdenum can lead to the symptoms of a copper deficiency.

Practically all the copper of plasma is bound in a copper protein (ceruloplasmin; p. 181), which contains 8 atoms of copper per unit of 150,000, its probable particle weight. In the hereditary condition known as Wilson's disease (hepatolenticular degeneration) a marked decrease in ceruloplasmin is observed, possibly as a consequence of an impaired capacity to synthesize the protein; this abnormality is associated with an excessive absorption of copper from the intestinal tract, and with a marked deposition of copper in the tissues, notably in liver and brain.[17]

Much of the information about the requirements of higher plants for trace elements has come from the study of the diseases of field plants. Specific pathological conditions have been described for plants growing in soil deficient in manganese, boron, copper, or molybdenum.

Homeostasis[18]

A striking characteristic of living organisms is their ability to maintain the "constancy of the internal environment" in the face of changes in the external environment. This concept was initially developed by Claude Bernard for higher animals in which the blood (together with the lymph and extracellular tissue fluids) may be considered to be the "internal environment" (*milieu intérieur*). However, it applies also to higher plants and to lower forms of life, all of which display an ability to regulate the concentration of materials dissolved in the cellular or body fluids. Thus the osmotic activity, which is largely determined by the total concentration of Na^+, K^+, Cl^-, and HCO_3^-, is kept within the narrow limits compatible with life. The relative concentrations of the principal cations (K^+, Na^+, Ca^{2+}, Mg^{2+}) must also be maintained, since these ions determine the integrity of cell membranes and the characteristic bioelectric potentials of the tissues. In addition, the pH within the cells and tissues must be carefully regulated by the removal of excess acid or alkali arising from the metabolism of nutrients.

Ionic Equilibria.[1,19] The phenomenon of homeostasis has been studied most extensively with reference to the mammalian organism, where all the fluids of the internal environment have essentially the same inorganic

[17] J. M. Walshe, *Brit. Med. Bull.*, **13**, 132 (1957).

[18] H. Davson, *A Textbook of General Physiology*, J. and A. Churchill Ltd., London, 1951.

[19] A. B. Hastings, *Harvey Lectures*, **36**, 91 (1941).

composition; in effect, the lymph and extracellular tissue fluids represent protein-free ultrafiltrates of blood plasma (Table 3). As first suggested

Table 3. Inorganic Constituents of Human Blood Plasma

	Average Value per 100 ml	
	Milligrams	Milliequivalents
Cations		
Sodium	316	13.7
Potassium	17	0.43
Calcium	20	1.0
Magnesium	3	0.25
Total		15.4
Anions		
Chloride	365	10.3
Bicarbonate		2.7
Phosphate		0.2
Sulfate		0.1
Total		13.3†

† At the pH of human blood, approximately 1.8 milliequivalents of cations per 100 ml are neutralized by anionic groups of plasma proteins (cf. p. 100). An additional 0.3 milliequivalents of plasma cations is neutralized by organic anions (e.g., lactate).

by Starling, the relationship of blood plasma to the other fluids with respect to their diffusible constituents can be explained readily by the high content of proteins in plasma and the resultant distribution, according to the Gibbs-Donnan law (cf. p. 111), of the diffusible substances between two solutions separated by a semipermeable membrane. The filtration pressures which account for the passage of water and solutes from the arterial end of capillaries to extracellular tissue fluids and for the return of water and solutes to the blood in the venous portion of the capillaries are primarily due to the variation in the hydrostatic pressure (blood pressure) as the blood passes through the capillaries (Table 4).

Table 4. Capillary Pressures in Man

	Pressure, cm of water	
	Arterial End	Venous End
Hydrostatic pressure	44	17
Effective osmotic pressure (due to plasma proteins)	36	36
Filtration pressure	8	−19
Movement of water and diffusible solutes	Plasma → Tissue fluid	Tissue fluid → Plasma

Thus the water and electrolytes of the blood are kept at their required levels, and nutrients can be transported to the tissue cells while metabolic products are transferred from tissue cells to the blood.

The ultrafiltration of blood from the afferent arterioles in the kidney tubules during the formation of urine also may be explained by the force of the filtration pressure of the blood. However, to prevent the loss, via the urine, of essential inorganic and organic constituents of blood, there occurs a selective reabsorption of such constituents of the glomerular filtrate into the blood of the efferent arterioles. This reabsorption (and also the secretion of certain compounds into the glomerular filtrate by tubule cells) may involve the "active transport" of ions rather than a diffusion or simple exchange of ions across a semipermeable membrane (cf. p. 922).

In a model system in which a salt solution and a solution containing both salt and protein are separated by a collodion membrane, the equilibrium distribution of inorganic ions (anions and cations) across the membrane may be described by means of the Gibbs-Donnan equation. In the physiological system composed of erythrocytes and serum, the equilibrium distribution of the principal anions (i.e., Cl^- and $HCO_3{}^-$) accords with this relationship.

$$\frac{[Cl^-]_{cell}}{[Cl^-]_{fluid}} = \frac{[HCO_3{}^-]_{cell}}{[HCO_3{}^-]_{fluid}} = r$$

In the respiratory process, there is a constant influx of CO_2 into the blood circulating through the tissue blood vessels and a corresponding loss of CO_2 from the blood vessels in the lungs. As a consequence of the relatively high CO_2 pressure in the tissues, CO_2 passes rapidly into the plasma and thence to the red cells. By the action of the cellular carbonic anhydrase (cf. p. 912), much of this CO_2 is rapidly converted to carbonic acid which, by simple dissociation and by interaction with the potassium salts of oxyhemoglobin and hemoglobin, gives rise to bicarbonate.

$$CO_2 + H_2O \xrightarrow{\text{carbonic anhydrase}} H_2CO_3 \rightarrow H^+ + HCO_3{}^-$$

$$H_2CO_3 + K^+ + \left\{\begin{matrix}(HbO_2)^-\\ \text{or}\\ Hb^-\end{matrix}\right\} \longrightarrow \left\{\begin{matrix}HHbO_2\\ \text{or}\\ HHb\end{matrix}\right\} + K^+ + HCO_3{}^-$$

To compensate for the increase in cellular $HCO_3{}^-$, there occurs a transfer of $HCO_3{}^-$ from erythrocytes to plasma accompanied by the entrance of Cl^- from the plasma into the red cells in order to restore the Gibbs-Donnan equilibrium ratio involving these two anions (the so-called "chloride shift"). However, such an exchange reaction still leaves the cells with a relatively higher concentration of osmotically active ions, and, hence, some water enters the cells to restore osmotic equilibrium between erythrocytes and plasma. The passage of blood through the lungs is accompanied by the release of CO_2 from the blood to the alveolar air; the series of reactions outlined above is reversed, and the red cells lose water. Similar fluid exchange occurs in response to the transport of ions across cell membranes in tissues other than blood.[20]

Although the relative concentrations of anions in erythrocytes and plasma are in accord with the Gibbs-Donnan law, the relative concentrations of cations cannot be described by this equation. Since the red cell membrane is permeable to both K^+ and Na^+, the maintenance of the K^+ concentration within the cell and the exclusion of Na^+ from the cell must depend upon a mechanism involving the active uptake of K^+ and the active extrusion of Na^+. Thus, in any biological system in which more nondiffusible ions (e.g., proteins) are present on one side of a membrane than on the other, an unequal distribution of "freely diffusible" ions is to be expected; these ions will diffuse (be "passively transported") in accordance with the Gibbs-Donnan law. The movement of "actively transported" ions (cf. p. 922) need not conform to this relationship, and such movement can play an important role in determining the over-all distribution of ions across biological membranes.

In respect to the cations of erythrocytes, it should be added that, in different mammals, the molar ratio of K^+ to Na^+ varies greatly, although the total concentration of the two cations is nearly the same. In human erythrocytes, the K^+ concentration is ca. 150 milliequivalents per liter, and the ratio K^+/Na^+ is about 9.1. For other mammals, this ratio is as follows: guinea pig 7, rat 8.4, rabbit 6.2, cat 0.06, dog 0.08. In all these species, the K^+/Na^+ ratio of plasma is approximately the same (ca. 0.03).

It is worthy of note that the concentration of inorganic ions in the tissues of marine invertebrates (e.g., lobsters, crabs, crayfish) is relatively low. However, the intracellular concentration of amino acids is particularly high (ca. 3 grams per 100 grams of fresh muscle), and it has been assumed that free amino acids serve in place of intracellular inorganic ions in the maintenance of osmotic equilibrium between the tissues and the blood. The inorganic electrolyte concentration of the blood of marine invertebrates is nearly the same as that of sea water.

Among insects, there is a wide variation in the total concentration of inorganic ions in the blood (hemolymph); relatively large amounts of free amino acids also may be present. The K^+/Na^+ ratio varies widely, and, in plant-eating insects, the blood contains high concentrations of K^+ and of Mg^{2+}, the principal inorganic cations of plant tissues.

[20] A. Leaf, *Biochem. J.*, **62**, 241 (1956).

Acid-Base Balance and CO$_2$ Transport.[21]   The pH range of the blood compatible with mammalian life is 7.0 to 7.9; normally the blood pH is about 7.4, and the difference between arterial and venous blood is rarely more than 0.02 to 0.04 pH unit.   It must be inferred, therefore, that changes in blood pH due to the addition of large amounts of acid or alkali are prevented by the action of the blood buffers.   The buffer systems in plasma include $NaHCO_3$-H_2CO_3, Na_2HPO_4-NaH_2PO_4, and the plasma proteins, which may be represented NaPr-HPr.   In the red cells the buffer pairs include $KHCO_3$-H_2CO_3, K_2HPO_4-KH_2PO_4, and the proteins, of which hemoglobin (KHb-HHb) and oxyhemoglobin ($KHbO_2$-$HHbO_2$) are the most important.   In the physiological pH range 7.0 to 7.9, most of the buffering power of the hemoglobin may be ascribed to the ionization of the imidazolyl group of the histidine residues (cf. p. 94).

The phosphate content of blood is quite low, and the $NaHCO_3$-H_2CO_3 system is, by far, the most important buffer in the plasma.   The entrance of H^+ into the blood is immediately reflected by a rise in the H_2CO_3 (and CO_2) content which causes a stimulation of the respiration rate and the rapid loss of excess CO_2 via the lungs.

Excess acid is also excreted by the kidney, which plays an important role in the maintenance of the blood pH at its characteristic value of about 7.4.   As noted earlier, the glomerular filtrate is essentially an ultrafiltrate of plasma.   Since, at pH 7.4, $NaHCO_3/H_2CO_3$ = ca. 20 and Na_2HPO_4/NaH_2PO_4 = ca. 4, the excretion of urine having the same pH as plasma would result in a serious loss of Na^+.   However, during the passage of the glomerular filtrate down the kidney tubules there occurs an exchange of Na^+ present in the filtrate for H^+ secreted by the tubule cells; this H^+ presumably is formed within the tubule cells as a result of the reaction between CO_2 and H_2O, catalyzed by carbonic anhydrase.   Consequently, H^+ is excreted in the urine while Na^+ (reabsorbed from the glomerular filtrate) and HCO_3^- (formed within the tubule cells) are returned to the blood.   Thus, when the metabolic production of acid is in excess of the amount of cations absorbed in the diet, the urine will be much more acid than the blood.   The Na^+-H^+ exchange described above would produce an extremely acid urine were it not for the presence in urine of the phosphate buffer pair.   Normally, the pH of urine varies from 4.8 to 7.8, and is determined largely by the ratio Na_2HPO_4/NaH_2PO_4.

Another mechanism for the conservation of Na^+ involves its replacement by NH_4^+ formed within the tubule cells by the deamidation of glutamine and by the deamination of α-amino acids.   Thus, in very acid

[21] L. J. Henderson, *Blood,* Yale University Press, New Haven, 1928; F. J. W. Roughton, *Harvey Lectures,* **39,** 96 (1944); R. F. Pitts, *ibid.,* **48,** 172 (1954).

urine, the amount of ammonia will be relatively high. In addition, the kidney can reabsorb the elements of "bicarbonate-bound base" (bicarbonates of sodium or of other cations) at the expense of H^+. The formation of urine in the kidney may be seen, therefore, to involve an ultrafiltration of plasma, followed by cationic exchange reactions between the ultrafiltrate and the tubule cells (Fig. 1). Since most of the water

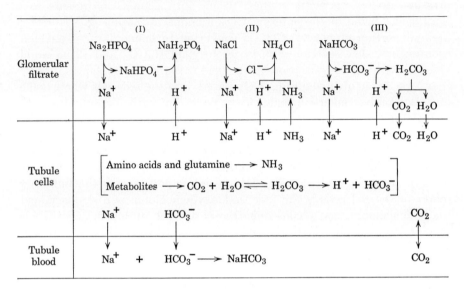

Fig. 1. Reactions associated with (I) the acidification of urine, (II) the excretion of ammonia, and (III) the reabsorption of bicarbonate-bound cations.

and inorganic ions are reabsorbed from the glomerular filtrate and returned to the blood, the kidney functions as a regulator of the electrolyte balance as well as of the pH of blood.

Carbon dioxide represents the major end product of the metabolism of organic compounds, and its transport from the tissues to the lungs is one of the most important functions of the blood. Only approximately 5 per cent of the total blood CO_2 is present as "free," i.e., dissolved, CO_2; the remainder is found as "bound" CO_2, a term used to designate HCO_3^-, carbamino-bound CO_2, and bound forms of undetermined composition. The first unequivocal evidence for the existence in blood of carbamino-bound CO_2 was presented by Henriques in 1928; the importance of this type of compound in the transport of CO_2 has been emphasized by the studies of Roughton. Carbamino compounds are formed by a spontaneous, reversible reaction between CO_2 and the free amino groups of amino acids or proteins. The plasma proteins and the red cell proteins both bind CO_2 in this manner. It is of special interest that more CO_2 can be bound by hemoglobin than by oxyhemoglobin; thus, as oxygen is released from the blood to the tissues, i.e., as $HbO_2 \to Hb + O_2$, there is a simultaneous increase in the amount of protein capable of reacting with the entering CO_2 to form carbamino-bound CO_2.

The entrance of CO_2 into the blood plasma is presumed to occur by simple diffusion of a dissolved gas from a solution having a high partial pressure of CO_2 (as in the tissues) to one with a low CO_2 pressure, i.e., the blood. Some of the entering CO_2 remains in plasma as free CO_2; a small portion of plasma CO_2 is converted to bound forms by (1) a spontaneous, slow reaction with water to yield H_2CO_3 and (2) a rapid reaction with the plasma proteins to yield carbamino compounds. More than two thirds of the entering CO_2 passes into the red cells where some of it is rapidly converted, under the influence of carbonic anhydrase, to H_2CO_3 and another portion is converted to carbamino hemoglobin; the red cells also contain some free CO_2. The newly formed H_2CO_3 and carbamino groups are partially dissociated to produce H^+ and the corresponding anions, and the H^+ is taken up by the respective buffer systems of both the cells and plasma. Of special importance in the buffering power of the red cells is the fact that oxyhemoglobin is a stronger acid than hemoglobin; as a consequence, at the pH of blood, less K^+ is required to neutralize HHb than is needed for $HHbO_2$ (Fig. 2). It will

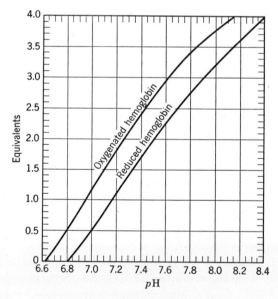

Fig. 2. Equivalents of alkali bound by oxygenated and reduced hemoglobin (per mole of hemoglobin iron) at various pH values. (From J. P. Peters and D. D. Van Slyke, *Quantitative Clinical Chemistry*, Vol. I, Williams and Wilkins Co., Baltimore, 1931.)

be clear, therefore, that the conversion of oxyhemoglobin to hemoglobin (as O_2 diffuses from the blood to the tissues) provides an additional supply of K^+ to neutralize the newly formed HCO_3^-. This phenomenon has been described as the "isohydric carriage of CO_2."

The various reactions involved in the uptake of CO_2 by the blood from the tissues are represented schematically in Fig. 3; the liberation of CO_2 from the blood to the alveolar air involves the reversal of the reactions shown in the figure.

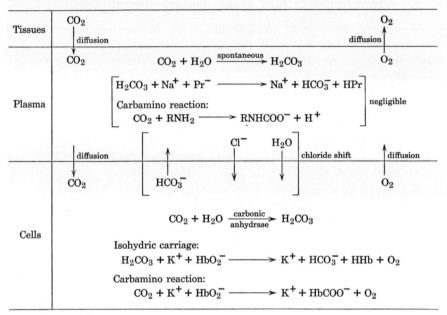

Fig. 3. Reactions associated with the uptake of CO_2 and loss of O_2 by blood.

It should be noted that tissue cells and fluids other than those of the blood and kidney contain buffer systems that make an important contribution to the neutralization of acids or bases liberated *in vivo*. Such neutralization reactions also may be accompanied by the redistribution of ions between cells and extracellular fluids, as in the formation of glandular secretions (e.g., saliva, pancreatic juice, gastric juice).[22] In addition, the regulation of the over-all balance of body electrolytes and of water in mammals is under the control of hormones elaborated by the adrenal cortex and the posterior pituitary (Chapter 38).

Intracellular pH is difficult to define because of the heterogeneity of intracellular structure, and it is probable that gradients of H^+ concentration exist between formed elements (e.g., mitochondria) and cytoplasmic fluid. The average intracellular pH of animal cells appears to

[22] J. F. Manery et al., *Canad. J. Biochem. Physiol.*, **33**, 453 (1955).

be near **7**, although under conditions such as gastric secretion of H^+ or muscle rigor (cf. p. 486) the value may be considerably lower. As noted previously, the pH of plant tissues may undergo a diurnal variation which reflects changes in the concentration of organic acids (cf. p. 517), and may vary between pH 4 and 6. For a discussion of intracellular pH, see Caldwell.[23]

Movement of Ions across Natural Membranes[24]

As applied to animal tissues, the term semipermeable membrane generally refers to a relatively thin layer (composed of protein and lipid material) which separates the bulk of the intracellular protoplasm from the extracellular fluid. In vacuolated plant cells, the cell membrane may be considered to include the relatively large amount of material lying between the cell wall (which is believed to be freely permeable to most solutes) and the vacuole containing the cell sap, in which inorganic ions are accumulated. Three types of mechanisms for the penetration of natural membranes have been proposed; these are (1) the passage of particles through the pores or holes in the membrane, which may be thought of as an organic sieve; (2) solution of particles in the membrane lipid; and (3) chemical interaction between a penetrating particle and a constituent of the membrane at the outer surface of the membrane, followed by diffusion of the newly formed compound to the inner surface and release of the particle. The third type of mechanism might involve the exchange of one ion for another of like charge, as in ion-exchange chromatography (cf. p. 122).

The movement of ions across membranes can occur by passive diffusion or by active transport; the latter process is dependent on the oxidative metabolism of cells and generally is characterized by the cellular secretion or cellular accumulation of ions against a concentration gradient. However, the distinction between passive diffusion and active transport is not always a clear one. For example, in most cases that have been investigated, it has been observed that the two sides of animal or plant membranes differ in electrical potential. Such a potential gradient, like a concentration gradient, can cause the redistribution of ions across a membrane, and this response has been described as passive diffusion. Although the mechanism by which these potential differences are established and maintained is not clear, it must involve the continuous

---

[23] P. C. Caldwell, *Intern. Rev. Cytol.*, **5**, 229 (1956).

[24] H. T. Clarke and D. Nachmansohn, *Ion Transport across Membranes*, Academic Press, New York, 1954; H. Lundegårdh, *Ann. Rev. Plant Physiol.*, **6**, 1 (1955); E. J. Harris, *Transport and Accumulation in Biological Systems*, Academic Press, New York, 1956.

expenditure of chemical energy. Thus, in effect, the membrane potential is an electrical manifestation of a biochemical reaction. Consequently, the statement that the distribution of ions between a cell and its external environment is associated with the difference in bioelectric potential across the cell membrane implies that the ionic distribution is the ultimate result of some active metabolic process.[25]

The active transport of ions has been studied in mammalian tissues, in amphibian skin, in the root tissues of higher plants, and in microorganisms. For example, the maintenance of a high K^+ and a low Na^+ concentration within cells of the nerve tissues such as brain cortex and retina has been shown to depend on the aerobic oxidation of glucose (or of lactic or pyruvic acid). Similarly, loss of K^+ from red cells occurs when intracellular energy-yielding reactions are inhibited, and the accumulation of K^+ by yeast cells ceases during "starvation" of cells devoid of carbohydrate reserves, or is inhibited in actively fermenting cells by azide or by other poisons of heavy metal catalysts. Not only inorganic ions but also organic ions (e.g., amino acids) are subject to active transport.[26] It should be noted that the distribution of inorganic and organic ions, and of water, is determined both by their passage across cell membranes and by their passage across intracellular boundaries; structural units such as mitochondria and nuclei play a role in the uptake or the extrusion of ions by intact cells.[27]

As noted earlier, the passage of both K^+ and Na^+ across the red cell membrane is believed to involve the active transport of each cation. Apparently, the two ions are transported by somewhat different mechanisms, although the active extrusion of Na^+ may be linked to the active uptake of K^+.[28] Different mechanisms for the transport of K^+ and of Na^+ also have been found in yeast cells and in marine algae.[29] Moreover, the transport of a given ionic species such as K^+ into a single cell type can occur both by active transport and by passive diffusion in accordance with the Gibbs-Donnan law.

The energy required for active transport appears to be supplied by processes involving electron transfer and the production of ATP by oxidative phosphorylation, or by other metabolic processes, but the mech-

---

[25] R. E. Davies, *Biol. Revs.*, **26**, 87 (1951); W. Bartley et al., *Proc. Roy. Soc.*, **142B**, 187 (1954); A. Leaf and A. Renshaw, *Biochem. J.*, **65**, 82, 90 (1957).

[26] L. M. Birt and F. J. R. Hird, *Biochem. J.*, **64**, 305 (1956); J. V. Taggart, *Science*, **124**, 401 (1956).

[27] A. K. Solomon and G. L. Gold, *J. Gen. Physiol.*, **38**, 371, 389 (1955); A. B. Hope and R. N. Robertson, *Nature*, **177**, 43 (1956).

[28] I. M. Glynn, *J. Physiol.*, **134**, 278 (1956); R. L. Post and P. C. Jolly, *Biochim. et Biophys. Acta*, **25**, 118 (1957).

[29] E. J. Conway et al., *Biochem. J.*, **58**, 158 (1954); G. T. Scott and H. R. Hayward, *J. Gen. Physiol.*, **37**, 601 (1954).

anisms that link active transport to known metabolic reactions have not been elucidated. Although it is probable that the "ion carriers" (the substances with which the penetrating ions react in the transport process) are organic compounds present in the membranes, their chemical nature is unknown at present.

One of the biological systems in which extensive studies have been made of ion transport is gastric mucosa.[30] The secretion of HCl into the stomach is associated with the "oxyntic" or "parietal" cells in the gastric mucosa, and the secretory activity of these cells depends on their respiratory activity. Although the oxyntic cells derive their electrolytes from the blood, the acid solution liberated by the cells has a pH of 1 to 2, and contains an amount of HCl that is approximately isotonic with the total electrolyte content of plasma.

It has long been known that the release of HCl into the stomach is accompanied by a transient increase in blood bicarbonate (the so-called "alkaline tide"). Experiments *in vitro* have indicated that the secretion of HCl is balanced by the uptake, from the nutrient solution bathing the nonsecretory side of isolated gastric mucosa, of CO_2 and the release of HCO_3^-. The rapid production of HCO_3^- from CO_2 is probably effected by the enzyme carbonic anhydrase. This enzyme is involved in the transport of CO_2 from the tissues to the expired air (cf. p. 921), and is believed to play a role in the transport of ions in tissues such as kidney (cf. p. 918), pancreas, eye, and brain.[31] The activity of carbonic anhydrase is inhibited by sulfonamides;[32] one of the most effective of these is 2-acetylamino-1,3,4-thiadiazole-5-sulfonamide ("Diamox" or acetazoleamide). Such inhibitors of carbonic anhydrase, when administered to animals, alter the ability of the above tissues to secrete ions.

$$\text{CH}_3\text{CONH}-\overset{\overset{\displaystyle N----N}{\|\qquad\|}}{\text{C}\qquad\text{C}}-\text{SO}_2\text{NH}_2$$
$$\diagdown\;\diagup$$
$$\text{S}$$

Diamox (acetazoleamide)

Antagonism of Ions[33]

The preceding section on the transport of ions has dealt mainly with the response of cells to single ions or single salts. However, under

[30] E. Heinz and K. J. Öbrink, *Physiol. Revs.,* **34,** 643 (1954).

[31] H. Gibian, *Angew. Chem.,* **66,** 249 (1954); R. W. Berliner and J. Orloff, *Pharmacol. Revs.,* **8,** 137 (1956).

[32] D. Keilin and T. Mann, *Nature,* **146,** 164 (1940); W. H. Miller et al., *J. Am. Chem. Soc.,* **72,** 4893 (1950).

[33] R. Höber, *Physical Chemistry of Cells and Tissues,* The Blakiston Co., Philadelphia, 1945.

physiological conditions, cells and tissues are in contact with media containing a variety of ions, and the normal behavior of living matter depends on a proper balance among the inorganic anions to which it is exposed.

This was first observed by Ringer in a study of the beat of isolated frog heart. Ringer found in 1882 that, in order to maintain normal contractility, it was necessary to perfuse the heart with a medium containing Na^+, K^+, and Ca^{2+} in approximately the same proportions found in sea water. It is now recognized that Na^+ is required for the sustained contractility of all animal muscle and that K^+ has a paralyzing effect which is antagonized by Ca^{2+} or by some other divalent cations such as Mg^{2+} or Sr^{2+}. The electrolyte solution initially devised by Ringer has since been used as the basis for media employed in biochemical or physiological studies on isolated animal tissues. A widely used modification of this solution was developed by Krebs ("Krebs-Ringer phosphate solution").[34] It is prepared by mixing the following solutions: (1) 100 parts (by volume) of 0.154 M NaCl; (2) 4 parts of 0.154 M KCl; (3) 3 parts of 0.11 M $CaCl_2$; (4) 1 part of 0.154 M $MgSO_4$; and (5) 21 parts of 0.16 M phosphate buffer (pH 7.4). Since the solution is supersaturated with respect to calcium phosphate, turbidity develops; this may be avoided by the use of one half of the above amount of $CaCl_2$. Other modifications of Ringer's solution are described by Umbreit et al.[35]

Although the effects of cations on contractile tissues cannot, as yet, be explained satisfactorily in terms of their biochemical action, it has been reported that the molecular shape and adenosine triphosphatase activity (p. 488) of isolated muscle proteins are dependent on the proper balance among the uni- and bivalent ions. Since carbohydrate metabolism is of vital importance to muscle function, it is of special interest that glycolysis (by preparations of muscle, brain, and microorganisms) has been reported to be inhibited by Na^+ and stimulated by K^+. These cations influence enzymic reactions involving ATP (cf. p. 910),[36] and it has been suggested that such effects may be related to differences in the molecular configuration of the monopotassium and the monosodium salts of ATP.[37]

The antagonisms among uni- and bivalent cations first observed by Ringer with frog heart apply to many other living tissues of both animals and plants. For example, Loeb noted in 1903 that the inhibitory effect of high concentrations of NaCl on the development of fertilized eggs

[34] H. A. Krebs, Z. physiol. Chem., **217**, 191 (1933).

[35] W. W. Umbreit et al., Manometric Techniques and Tissue Metabolism, 2nd Ed., Burgess Publishing Co., Minneapolis, 1949.

[36] J. A. Clark and R. A. MacLeod, J. Biol. Chem., **211**, 531, 541 (1954).

[37] N. C. Melchior, J. Biol. Chem., **208**, 615 (1954).

of the fish *Fundulus* was counteracted by the addition to the medium of bivalent cations such as Ca^{2+} or Mg^{2+}. In 1906 Osterhout observed that certain marine plants soon died if placed in a NaCl solution isotonic with sea water, although they would live for some time in distilled water. The toxic action of the NaCl solution was markedly reduced by the addition of small amounts of $CaCl_2$ and KCl; the inclusion of $MgCl_2$ to give an electrolyte solution containing Na^+, K^+, Ca^{2+}, and Mg^{2+} in the proportions in which they are found in sea water provided a synthetic mixture equal to sea water in its ability to sustain life. The hypothesis was then proposed that one ionic species may overcome the toxic action of another by hindering the entrance of the toxic ion into the cell. Subsequent experimental work has provided evidence that the apparent permeability of cell membranes is determined by the electrolytes present in the external fluid. This aspect of ion antagonism has been discussed by Osterhout,[38] by Stiles,[39] and by Davson.[18]

It was noted earlier that many natural membranes exhibit characteristic bioelectric potentials. When ions traverse these membranes, as in the secretion of HCl by the gastric mucosa, marked changes occur in the so-called "resting" potential. Similarly, nerve and muscle fibers have been shown to exhibit both resting and "action" potentials, and it has been well established that the apparent permeability of the tissue membranes changes when an impulse passes along a fiber.[40] In the resting state, the membrane appears to be moderately permeable to both K^+ and Cl^- but almost impermeable to Na^+. Under these conditions Na^+ must be subject to active outward transport in order to maintain the Na^+ concentration within the fiber at its normal low value. However, the electric activity associated with the passage of an impulse is accompanied by a large, but transient, increase in the permeability to Na^+. At this time, Na^+ rapidly enters the cell, and its uptake is approximately balanced by the outward movement of K^+. For a return to the resting state, prior to the passage of a second impulse, the initial ion distribution must be restored. Such extrusion of Na^+ and uptake of K^+ by nerve tissue appears to be associated with the rapid intracellular hydrolysis of acetylcholine (p. 577). It is of interest that the inhibition of the acetylcholine esterase in isolated muscle preparations also inhibits the extrusion of Na^+ by this tissue.[41]

Bacteria also exhibit physiological responses that may be associated with the antagonistic action of inorganic ions. As with higher forms of

[38] W. J. V. Osterhout, *J. Gen. Physiol.*, **39**, 963 (1956).
[39] W. Stiles, *An Introduction to the Principles of Plant Physiology*, 2nd Ed., Methuen and Co., London, 1950.
[40] A. L. Hodgkin, *Biol. Revs.*, **26**, 339 (1951).
[41] W. G. Van der Kloot, *Nature*, **178**, 366 (1956).

life, the unicellular organisms require for growth and normal function a medium of suitable osmotic pressure and ionic composition. For example, the antagonism between K^+ and Na^+, already well known in excitable tissues such as muscle and nerve, has been found to apply to the growth of lactic acid bacteria.[42] For these organisms, K^+ is an essential growth factor, and is required in greatly increased amounts when the culture medium contains Na^+ or NH_4^+. Studies with cell-free preparations have shown that the antagonism between K^+ and Na^+ is related to their effects on glycolysis, whereas the antagonism between K^+ and NH_4^+ appears to be caused by the inhibitory effect of NH_4^+ on the uptake of K^+ by intact cells.[36]

[42] R. A. MacLeod and E. E. Snell, *J. Biol. Chem.*, **176**, 39 (1948).

37 ·

Heat Changes in Metabolism

It was noted previously that the combustion of an organic substance (e.g., glucose) to CO_2 and water is accompanied by the liberation of energy (cf. p. 226). If the combustion of glucose is conducted at constant temperature and pressure under conditions where no useful work is done, the energy that is liberated appears in the form of heat, whose quantity may be measured in a calorimeter. It will be recalled that the heat energy liberated at constant temperature and pressure is denoted by the symbol ΔH and is termed the change in "enthalpy" or "heat content." This quantity is, in general, different from the maximum useful energy ΔF that may be derived from the chemical reaction. The equation $\Delta F = \Delta H - T\,\Delta S$ takes account of the quantity of energy ($T\,\Delta S$) not measured in the usual enthalpy determinations; hence the change in free energy is more meaningful than is ΔH in considering the capacity of a chemical reaction to do useful work (p. 229).

Since the classical studies of Lavoisier and Laplace in 1780 (cf. p. 285), it has been recognized that a relation exists between the heat produced in the combustion of organic substances and the "animal heat" released when such substances are subjected to metabolic oxidation in the animal body. The term "energy metabolism" has frequently been applied to the heat changes observed during the metabolic transformation of body constituents and of foodstuffs. In particular, clinical studies on the factors in health and disease that influence heat production by human subjects have tended to equate such heat changes with the energy changes in metabolic reactions. It must be remembered, however, that the human, and all other biological systems, cannot be considered merely as a kind of furnace in which organic substances are burned in the presence of oxygen with the liberation of heat, which is then utilized (as in the steam engine) for useful work. The discussion in the preceding chapters of this book has attempted to emphasize the fact that biological systems are extremely complex chemical assemblies in which endergonic reactions are driven by specific coupling with exergonic processes. Any heat energy that is evolved in the course of this metabolic activity is unavailable for useful work at constant temperature. For example, the formation of ADP from ATP (at pH 7.5 and 20° C) in the enzymic transphosphorylation reaction by which creatine is converted to creatine phosphate (p. 379) is accompanied by a relatively small change in ΔH (ca. -1 kcal per mole). On the other hand, the ΔH_{293} for the formation of ADP and inorganic phosphate by the reaction of ATP with water (in the presence of ATP-ase) is much larger (ca. -5 kcal per mole). Clearly, the heat liberated during the conversion of ATP to ADP in a calorimeter is unavailable for chemical work, and, therefore, the hydrolytic process may be said to be more "wasteful" than the transphosphorylation reaction. In large measure, the production of heat by biological systems may be considered a consequence of the "inefficiency" of the chemical and physical processes in such systems. In the example cited above, the hydrolysis of ATP contributes to metabolic inefficiency and leads to a dissipation of useful energy. However, if, as believed by some investigators, the hydrolysis of ATP can be coupled in mammalian muscle to mechanical work (p. 488), the chemical hydrolysis is not entirely "wasteful" in this tissue, although it may be "wasteful" in another biological system.

It must be re-emphasized that a biological system does not operate in the same manner as a bomb calorimeter, and that all dissipated energy does not necessarily appear as heat. As pointed out by Clark:[1]

The energy changes in the body are manifold. It is only when these manifold energy-changes between body-states A and B have been such that the second state B is the same as the previous state A, and when all additional forms of energy-change have been degraded to heat, that a measurement of the heat produced is meaningful.

Many studies have been performed on the production of heat by animals, plants, and microorganisms. In numerous instances these studies involved the direct calorimetric measurement (with apparatus of widely varying precision) of the heat output. Furthermore, assumptions were made to permit a calculation of the extent of heat production without an actual calorimetric measurement (indirect calorimetry; p. 931). Such direct and indirect measurements of heat changes in biological systems have considerable practical value, and, when applied to human subjects, provide empirical data of considerable importance in clinical practice. For the student of biochemistry, however, it is important to remember that such heat changes are related in an extremely complex manner to chemical reactions in metabolism, and that the production of heat in

[1] W. M. Clark, *Topics in Physical Chemistry*, 2nd Ed., Williams and Wilkins Co., Baltimore, 1952.

biological systems is related to the thermodynamic inefficiency of physiological processes. Except for conditions where new cellular material is formed, most of the energy released on oxidation of nutrients appears as heat. When there is no change in body state, the quantity of energy required to maintain the constancy of the internal environment usually represents a small fraction of the energy potentially available from the degradation of food materials.

From a physiological point of view, the apparent inefficiency of biological processes is of importance in the adaptation of many living forms to changes in the external environment. By physiological regulation of the rate of heat production and of heat loss, such organisms (homoiothermic organisms) are able to maintain their bodies at constant temperature.[2] Other biological forms (poikilothermic organisms) are unable to regulate their body temperature, but have evolved metabolic mechanisms that permit them to survive under conditions of heat or cold deleterious to the homoiothermic forms.

Direct Calorimetry in Biological Systems. In their studies on "animal heat," Lavoisier and Laplace placed a guinea pig in a chamber containing a known weight of ice and, from the amount of ice melted, they calculated the heat production. Another method employed by these investigators was to surround the animal chamber with a known volume of water and to measure the rise in temperature of the water. The latter procedure is, in principle, the basis for more modern methods of direct calorimetry, such as those described by Rubner in 1894. These methods were brought to a high point in 1897, when Atwater and Rosa described a calorimeter for use with human subjects. This apparatus was subsequently improved by Benedict; a detailed description of its construction and operation is given by Lusk.[3]

Direct measurements of heat production also have been made with plants. For example, during the germination of seeds or the opening of flowers, appreciable heat may be evolved, and the temperature of the plant tissue may be raised considerably above that of the environment.[4,5] An indication of the magnitude of the heat production is provided by the observation that germinating seeds of the pea (*Pisum sativum*) evolve approximately 4.9 kcal per day per gram.

Studies with microorganisms have indicated appreciable heat production in the course of their metabolic activity. For example, *Escherichia*

[2] J. D. Hardy, *Harvey Lectures,* **49,** 242 (1955).

[3] G. Lusk, *Elements of the Science of Nutrition,* 4th Ed., Saunders and Co., Philadelphia, 1928.

[4] M. Thomas, *Plant Physiology,* 3rd Ed., J. and A. Churchill Ltd., London, 1947.

[5] W. Stiles, *Introduction to Principles of Plant Physiology,* 2nd Ed., Methuen and Co., London, 1950.

coli produces, during the first hour of its growth cycle, approximately 6×10^{-12} cal per cell.[6] Clearly, the heat production of a growing microbial culture is a measure of the energy not utilized for the chemosynthesis required for cell multiplication. This may be illustrated by data on *Nitrobacter*, which derives its energy exclusively from the oxidation of nitrite to nitrate (cf. p. 679). At the concentration of nitrite (3.03 M) found to be optimal for the growth of this organism, the free-energy change in the oxidation of nitrite to nitrate is $\Delta F_{298} = -17.5$ kcal.[7] Under conditions favorable for growth, the conversion of 1 mole of CO_2 into organic matter (assumed to have the same energy content as glucose) requires the concomitant oxidation of approximately 90 moles of nitrite to nitrate. Since the free-energy change in the conversion of CO_2 to glucose is approximately 115 kcal per mole of CO_2, the thermodynamic efficiency of *Nitrobacter* may be estimated to be

$$\frac{115}{90 \times 17.5} \times 100 = 7.3 \text{ per cent}$$

Experimental determination of the heat production by *Nitrobacter* has shown that approximately 95 per cent of the energy available from the oxidation of nitrite to nitrate appears as heat energy which may be measured in a calorimeter.[8]

Other microorganisms exhibit considerably higher "machine efficiency" in their synthetic activity. Thus the synthesis, by *Chilomonas*, of the hexose units of starch from acetate is accomplished with an efficiency of about 27 per cent. For a discussion of efforts to determine the thermodynamic efficiency of assimilative processes, see Hutchens.[9]

Indirect Calorimetry. The measurement, by direct calorimetry, of the heat output of animals requires expensive apparatus, and an indirect method is frequently employed for this purpose. Indirect calorimetry is based on the assumption that the over-all reaction for the degradation of a metabolite (or body constituent) is the same in the animal body as in a bomb calorimeter. This is approximately true for the metabolic oxidation of carbohydrates and fats in normal animals; however, the oxidation of proteins in animal metabolism is less complete than in a bomb calorimeter, and correction factors must be applied.

As will be seen, it is possible to calculate, by the "indirect method," the heat production of animals from data for oxygen consumption, CO_2 production, and the quantity of urinary nitrogen. Of special importance is the measurement of the respiratory exchange; several experimental

[6] S. Bayne-Jones and H. S. Rhees, *J. Bact.*, **17**, 123 (1929).

[7] L. G. M. Baas-Becking and G. S. Parks, *Physiol. Revs.*, **7**, 85 (1927).

[8] O. Meyerhof, *Pflüg. Arch.*, **164**, 353 (1916).

[9] J. O. Hutchens, *Federation Proc.*, **10**, 622 (1951).

assemblies have been described for this purpose. They are, in general, of two types: (1) closed-circuit type (first developed by Regnault and Reiset in 1849), which involves recirculation of the same air after removal of CO_2 by a suitable absorbent (e.g., soda lime) and replacement of the consumed oxygen by an equal quantity of fresh oxygen; and (2) open-circuit type (invented by Pettenkofer and Voit in 1862), which involves the continuous passage of outside air through the system. A convenient modification of the latter type is the apparatus devised by Haldane in 1892; for details of the procedure, and further modifications of the open-circuit method, see Brody.[10] In the determination of the respiratory exchange in human subjects, the gas analysis apparatus invented by Haldane in 1897 is generally employed.[11]

It will be recalled that the oxidation of glucose to CO_2 and water is given by the equation

$$C_6H_{12}O_6 + 6O_2 \rightarrow 6CO_2 + 6H_2O$$

and is attended by a ΔH_{293} of -673 kcal per mole of glucose, or -3.74 kcal per gram (673/180). The value of ΔH_{293} for the combustion of sucrose is -3.94 kcal per gram, and that of starch -4.18 kcal per gram. Since polysaccharides constitute the bulk of the carbohydrates in the diet of animals, the "caloric value" of the mixed carbohydrates ingested in the food is assumed to be approximately 4.1 to 4.2 kcal per gram.

Under conditions where carbohydrates are the principal organic substances subjected to oxidation in metabolism, the degradation of 1 mole of a glucose unit of starch would require the uptake of 6×22.4 liters of O_2 (at standard temperature and pressure); this corresponds to an uptake of 829 ml of O_2 per gram of starch. Since in the oxidation of carbohydrate the respiratory quotient (p. 285) is 1.0, 829 ml of CO_2 are produced per gram of starch oxidized.

In a similar manner, the metabolic oxidation of fats (triglycerides) is assumed to be complete, and the average value of -9.46 kcal per gram is taken to denote the magnitude of ΔH_{293}. However, in the oxidation of triglycerides (e.g., triolein), the R.Q. is near 0.7.

$$C_{57}H_{104}O_6 + 80O_2 \rightarrow 57CO_2 + 52H_2O \qquad (R.Q. = 0.713)$$

By convention, the value of the R.Q. for mixed fats is assumed to be 0.707; the O_2 uptake is 2019 ml per gram, and the CO_2 output is 1427 ml per gram.

Thus, under conditions where only carbohydrate and fat are converted

---

[10] S. Brody, *Bioenergetics and Growth,* Reinhold Publishing Corp., New York, 1945.

[11] J. P. Peters and D. D. Van Slyke, *Quantitative Clinical Chemistry,* Vol. II, Williams and Wilkins Co., Baltimore, 1932.

to CO_2 and water, a determination of the R.Q. will provide a measure of the relative proportion of the two types of foodstuffs that are undergoing oxidation. A condensed list of these relations is given in Table 1 (for an extended table, see Lusk[3]).

Table I. Oxidation of Mixtures of Carbohydrate and Fat

R.Q.	Per Cent of Total O_2 Consumed Carbohydrate (1)	Fat (2)	Kcal Produced per Liter of O_2 (3)
0.707	0	100	4.686
0.75	14.7	85.3	4.739
0.80	31.7	68.3	4.801
0.85	48.8	51.2	4.862
0.90	65.9	34.1	4.924
0.95	82.9	17.1	4.985
1.00	100	0	5.047

$$(1) \quad \frac{R.Q. - 0.707}{1 - 0.707} \times 100$$

$$(2) \quad \frac{1 - R.Q.}{1 - 0.707} \times 100$$

$$(3) \quad 4.686 + \frac{R.Q. - 0.707}{1 - 0.707} \times (5.047 - 4.686)$$

The values given in Table 1 refer to the situation when no protein is oxidized, i.e., the "nonprotein R.Q." It is known that the over-all process of oxidation of proteins in the animal body cannot be assumed to be the same as that in a bomb calorimeter since the end products of protein metabolism (e.g., urea) are further oxidized in the calorimeter. For this reason, the average caloric value of protein is taken to be 4.3 kcal per gram, although its combustion in a bomb calorimeter yields ca. 5.7 kcal per gram. If it is assumed that the animal is in a state of nitrogen equilibrium (p. 723), a measure of the R.Q. for the oxidation of protein may be obtained by subtracting from the grams of carbon, hydrogen, and oxygen fed as protein the amounts excreted in the urine and feces (see Lusk[3]). Of the remaining hydrogen, 2 atoms may be considered to be combined with each oxygen atom to form "intramolecular" water. After the quantity of hydrogen so combined with all the available oxygen atoms has been deducted, the oxidation of the residual carbon and hydrogen is characterized by an R.Q. of approximately 0.80. If the average nitrogen content of proteins is assumed to be 16 per cent (p. 27), and correction is made for the loss of nitrogen in the feces, it may be calculated that, on the average, 5.94 liters of O_2 are taken up and 4.76 liters of CO_2 are produced per gram of urinary nitrogen excreted.

The uptake of 1 liter of O_2 for the oxidation of protein corresponds to a production of 4.463 kcal; consequently, the excretion of 1 gram of urinary nitrogen corresponds to the liberation of 26.5 kcal from protein oxidation.

The calculation of heat production by indirect calorimetry may be illustrated by the following example. Assume that a human subject consumed (per hour) 17 liters of oxygen and, during the same time, eliminated 14 liters of CO_2 and 0.5 gram of urinary nitrogen. The oxidation of the protein represented by the urinary nitrogen may be calculated as follows:

$$0.5 \times 5.94 = 2.97 \text{ liters of oxygen consumed}$$

$$0.5 \times 4.76 = 2.38 \text{ liters of } CO_2 \text{ exhaled}$$

If these values are subtracted from the volumes of gas measured in the gas analysis apparatus, it follows that 14 liters of oxygen were consumed for the oxidation of carbohydrate and fat and 11.6 liters of CO_2 were derived from the oxidation of these metabolites. The ratio $11.6/14 = 0.83$ gives the nonprotein R.Q. From Table 1 (expanded form) it may be noted that this R.Q. corresponds to the production of 4.838 kcal per liter of O_2 consumed. Hence $4.838 \times 14 = 67.73$ kcal were derived from the oxidation of carbohydrate and fat, and $0.5 \times 26.5 = 13.25$ kcal were derived from the oxidation of protein. Thus the heat production by the subject may be calculated to be about 81 kcal per hour, or 1944 kcal per day.

It must be added that, under a variety of metabolic circumstances, the nonprotein R.Q. may have a value outside the range 0.7 to 1.0. An example is the situation when appreciable quantities of carbohydrate are converted to fat. In this conversion chemical energy liberated by the oxidation of a portion of the carbohydrate is utilized for the synthesis of long-chain fatty acids from C_2 units (cf. Chapter 25) which are not oxidized to CO_2 and water. R.Q. values of 1.2 to 1.5 are frequently observed under these conditions since carbohydrate may be considered to provide "endogenous" oxygen for the oxidation of fats, whose oxygen content is appreciably lower than that of carbohydrates.

The general principles of indirect calorimetry have been applied not only to the study of man and experimental animals but to plants and microorganisms as well. However, calculation of heat production from the magnitude of the respiratory exchange is subject to considerable uncertainty in these systems. In some plants, for example, little CO_2 is released at night, although much oxygen is taken up; this is associated with the accumulation of organic acids. With germinating seeds, R.Q. values of 0.6 to 3 have been reported.[12]

[12] W. Stiles and W. Leach, *Proc. Roy. Soc.,* **113B,** 405 (1933).

Basal Metabolism. The heat production of homoiothermic animals is influenced by a variety of factors, such as the external temperature, the nature of the diet, the extent of muscular activity, and emotional stress. To determine the effect of these and other factors on the respiratory exchange and heat production, it is necessary to define a "basal state." The metabolism (basal metabolism) at this state may be considered to be the totality of the processes required to maintain the *status quo* of the organism. For human subjects, the basal state is defined as that at which the individual is supine, motionless, and calm; has not eaten for 12 to 14 hr ("postabsorptive" state), and is in a room maintained at 20° C. The heat production per unit time under these conditions is termed the "basal metabolic rate" (BMR), and is expressed in kilogram calories per square meter of surface area per hour. Empirical studies have shown that the heat output of human subjects per unit of surface area is independent of variations in height, weight, or shape. Since the routine determination of the surface area of the human body is a tedious operation, use is made of DuBois' formula:

$$\log A = 0.425 \log W + 0.725 \log H + 1.8564$$

where A is the surface area (in square centimeters), W is the weight (in kilograms) and H is the height (in centimeters).

Many studies have been made of the basal heat production of adult animals of widely varying size. The data of Benedict[13] support the view that a proportionality exists between the logarithm of the heat production and the logarithm of the body weight. The results given in Fig. 1 are

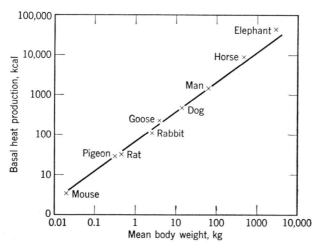

Fig. 1. Logarithmic plot of basal heat production against mean body weight for several species. (From F. G. Benedict.[13])

[13] F. G. Benedict, *Vital Energetics,* Carnegie Institution, Washington, 1938.

best fitted by the formula

$$\log \text{ heat production} = \log k + 0.73 \log \text{ body weight}$$

For a further discussion of this relationship see Brody.[10]

Attempts to relate the basal metabolic rate of various animals to the rate of oxygen uptake (Q_{O_2}; p. 288) of isolated tissues taken from these animals have been inconclusive. In this connection, the discussion presented by Krebs[14] is of importance. An examination of the Q_{O_2} values given in Table 2 shows that there is a similarity in general trend

Table 2. Respiratory Quotient of Animal Tissues in Relation to Basal Heat Production

Animal	Average Body Weight, kg	Heat Production per kg (24 hr), kcal	$-Q_{O_2}$ of Tissue Slices				
			Brain cortex	Kidney cortex	Liver	Spleen	Lung
Mouse	0.02	158	32.9	46.1	23.1	16.9	12.0
Rat	0.21	100	26.3	38.2	17.2	12.7	8.6
Guinea pig	0.51	82	27.3	31.8	13.0	11.6	8.5
Rabbit	1.05	60	28.2	34.5	11.6	14.2	8.0
Cat	2.75	50	26.9	22.7	13.2	8.4	3.9
Dog	15.9	34	21.2	27.0	11.7	6.6	4.9
Sheep	49	25	19.7	27.5	8.5	6.9	5.4
Cattle	420	20	17.2	23.5	8.2	4.4	4.3
Horse	725	17	15.7	21.5	5.4	4.2	4.4

in the basal heat production and the rate of respiration of the tissues mentioned, but that no definite correlation can be established. Although an inverse relation between liver cytochrome oxidase activity (p. 359) and body weight has been reported for the mouse, rat, and dog, no such correlation was found in a comparison of the cytochrome oxidase activity of brain and kidney in these three animals.[15] It will be noted that muscle tissue is omitted from the list in Table 2; since this tissue makes the largest contribution to the total heat production of the animal body, and since the heat output of muscle is highly variable, a clear-cut relationship between the oxygen uptake of excised tissues and the heat production of intact animals is not to be expected.[16]

The basal metabolic rate of human subjects varies greatly with age and sex. For 6-year-old boys the standard BMR is 52.7 kcal per sq

[14] H. A. Krebs, *Biochim. et Biophys. Acta,* **4,** 249 (1950).

[15] H. O. Kunkel and J. E. Campbell, Jr., *J. Biol. Chem.,* **198,** 229 (1952).

[16] J. Field et al., *J. Cellular Comp. Physiol.,* **14,** 143 (1939).

meter per hr; for girls of the same age the value is 50.7. The BMR decreases rapidly with age, and at 19 the value for males is 42.1 and for females is 37.2. The change in BMR is less marked after the age of 21, but decreases in parallel for both men and women, and at 60 the values are 36.0 and 33.8, respectively.

The basal metabolic rate is lowered by malnutrition (e.g., a deficiency of dietary protein), starvation, and in some diseases (thyroid insufficiency; cf. p. 944). The BMR is markedly increased above the standard value in hyperthyroidism.

Standard Metabolic Rate of Poikilothermic Animals. In general, the heat production of cold-blooded animals at rest is a function of the environmental temperature and the area of body surface. For example, at 20° C, the standard heat production of the rattlesnake is ca. 17 kcal per sq meter of body surface, whereas at 36° the value is ca. 88 kcal; similar values have been obtained for snakes of widely different weight (pythons, gopher snakes). Since the heat production of the poikilothermic animals varies widely with the environmental temperature, the term "basal metabolism," as employed previously, does not apply; for this reason, reference is made to the standard heat production at a given temperature.

Specific Dynamic Action of Foodstuffs. After the ingestion of food, the extent of heat production is greater than can be accounted for merely on the basis of the "caloric value" of the diet. This effect (specific dynamic action, SDA) is greatest with a protein diet and least with a fat diet. There has been considerable controversy concerning the biochemical basis for the increased heat production, and the question remains unsettled.[17] It appears that the specific dynamic action of several amino acids (e.g., phenylalanine, tyrosine, leucine) is especially marked, and it has been suggested that their metabolic oxidation is relatively "inefficient," much of the energy released being dissipated as heat.

Heat Production in Work. It has long been known that the heat produced by animals doing muscular work is greater than that produced in the resting state. The heat production of isolated muscle has been the subject of much study, especially by Hill.[18] Although the biochemical processes responsible for this heat liberation have not been identified, it is believed by some physiologists that the breakdown of ATP is involved. Efforts have been made to calculate, for the intact animal, the efficiency of muscular work on the assumption that the oxygen uptake during work is an index of the energy potentially available. The studies of Brody[10] have shown that, for men as well as for horses, the performance of 25 kcal of mechanical work requires the expenditure of at least

[17] C. M. Wilhelmj, *Physiol. Revs.*, **15**, 202 (1935).
[18] A. V. Hill, *Proc. Roy. Soc.*, **137B**, 40 (1950).

100 kcal of energy (as measured by the extent of oxygen consumption). The maximal "gross efficiency" is thus said to be 25 per cent.

Since the heat production of human subjects varies considerably with age, sex, and activity, the level of food intake required to balance this output must be adjusted accordingly. Thus an adult individual, engaged in a sedentary occupation, requires a daily diet whose "caloric value" is approximately 2000 to 2500 kcal, and which contains optimal proportions of protein, fat, and carbohydrate. On the other hand, men engaged in heavy manual labor may require a food intake corresponding to 4000 to 6000 kcal per day. Clearly, these figures apply to the caloric requirements for the maintenance of body form and function (the basal metabolism) plus the requirements for muscular work. When new tissue is formed, as in the growth of children, the food intake must be increased. For further discussion of these and related topics, see Sherman.[19]

[19] H. C. Sherman, *Chemistry of Food and Nutrition,* 7th Ed., The Macmillan Co., New York, 1946.

38 ·

The Hormonal Control of Metabolism

A remarkable feature of the physiological activity of animal organisms is the regulation of the myriad biochemical processes so as to result in a relative constancy in the concentration of many important metabolites in the tissue fluids. Mention was made on p. 497 of the regulation, in normal human subjects, of the blood sugar level; clearly, there must be physiological mechanisms by which a balance is maintained among the processes that cause the breakdown of glucose in the tissues (glycolysis), the conversion of glucose to glycogen (glycogenesis), the conversion of liver glycogen to blood glucose (glycogenolysis), and the formation of glucose from noncarbohydrate precursors (gluconeogenesis). This maintenance of the blood sugar level is another striking example of "homeostasis" (p. 914); in such physiological regulation of complex metabolic processes, a variety of chemical substances, termed "hormones," occupy a central role.

In the mammalian organism, the hormones are secreted into the blood by specialized ductless organs ("organs of internal secretion"), and are carried by the circulation to other tissues, where the action of the hormones is exerted. The available knowledge indicates that hormones do not, in themselves, initiate biochemical processes, but rather that these "chemical messengers" effect, in extremely small concentrations, the acceleration or inhibition of metabolic processes in the "target" tissues. Although it is widely assumed that the hormones control the rates of metabolic processes by influencing the activity of specific enzymes, the experimental evidence for this view is largely indirect.

In the present chapter, primary emphasis will be placed on the hormonal regulation, in higher animals, of the metabolism of carbohydrates, lipids, and proteins, and of the electrolyte balance. It must be added, however, that the hormones exert physiological effects whose biochemical attributes are not clearly understood at present; among these effects are (1) the hormonal control of the development of specialized organs (e.g., the gonads) and (2) the interaction of hormonal and neural processes in the determination of animal behavior. The latter aspect of the physiology of hormones points to the fact that these substances must be considered as components in a complex and highly integrated mechanism which also involves the nervous system. Of the many stimulating discussions of this integration, the classic monograph of Cannon[1] is especially recommended.

The term "hormone" (Greek *hormon,* arousing, exciting) was introduced into the scientific literature by Bayliss and Starling, who in 1904 described the stimulation of the secretion of pancreatic juice by a chemical substance (secretin) which is liberated by intestinal cells into the blood and carried to the pancreas. The history of research on hormones may be traced, however, to observations made in the nineteenth century that many of the physiological effects of the surgical removal of one of a number of organs (testis, pancreas, etc.) could be counteracted by implantation into the animal of the appropriate glandular tissue or by the injection of a suitably prepared extract of that tissue. These findings led to the study of the hormones elaborated by these "endocrine" organs (Greek *endon,* within; *krinein,* to separate), and this area of biochemistry is now designated "endocrinology." Much of the research in this field has been concerned with the purification and chemical characterization of individual hormones, and the availability of well-defined preparations of the hormones has permitted the closer study of their role and interrelationships in metabolism. A valuable treatise dealing with the extensive literature on endocrinology has been edited by Pincus and Thimann.[2]

The regulation of metabolism by substances elaborated in one part of an organism· and transported to the site of hormonal action, is not limited to higher animals; in the latter part of this chapter, some of the hormones of invertebrates and of higher plants will be considered.

Mammalian Endocrine Organs

Pancreas. The demonstration of the endocrine function of the pancreas stems from the discovery made by von Mering and Minkowski in 1889 that the surgical removal of this organ (pancreatectomy) from dogs was followed by symptoms akin to those long known to be associated with diabetes mellitus. This disease of man is characterized by a marked loss of weight, a pronounced increase in the blood sugar level

---

[1] W. B. Cannon, *The Wisdom of the Body,* 2nd Ed., W. W. Norton Co., New York, 1939.

[2] G. Pincus and K. V. Thimann, *The Hormones,* Vols. I–III, Academic Press, New York, 1948, 1950, 1955.

(hyperglycemia), the appearance of sugar in the urine (glycosuria), an increase in the concentration of ketone bodies in the blood (ketonemia) and in the urine (ketonuria), and the excretion of a large volume of urine (polyuria). These clinical symptoms, as well as the effects of pancreatectomy in dogs, can be corrected by the parenteral administration of a pancreatic extract first prepared by Banting and his associates in 1921. The active agent present in the extract was termed "insulin";[3] this name derives from the demonstration that the hormone is elaborated by the islets of Langerhans, which are distinctive tissue elements of the pancreas and are sharply differentiated from the "acinar tissue," the source of the digestive enzymes. The islet tissue is largely composed of two types of cells (α and β); the β cells are considered to be the source of insulin. This view is supported by the demonstration that experimental diabetes may be induced by the administration of alloxan, which causes the selective destruction of the β cells of the islet tissue.[4]

Alloxan

The crystallization of insulin was achieved in 1926 by Abel, who demonstrated the protein nature of the purified hormone. The intravenous administration of purified insulin (from swine, beef, or sheep pancreas) into guinea pigs elicits the formation of antibodies, showing that the hormone can act as an antigen.[5] It will be recalled that the minimum molecular weight of insulin is about 6000, and that the amino acid sequence of insulins from several animal species has been elucidated (p. 146). Insulin loses its physiological activity upon treatment with sulfhydryl compounds, which cause the reduction of the disulfide linkages in the protein; the hormonal action is also destroyed after treatment with alkali (ca. pH 10) or with proteinases such as chymotrypsin. Thus far no synthetic peptide or cleavage product of insulin has been shown to have physiological activity. It would appear, therefore, that this activity depends on the structural integrity of the entire protein molecule. The potency of insulin preparations is given in terms of an international unit, defined as the hormonal activity of 0.125 mg of an international standard preparation. A widely used method of assay involves the subcutaneous injection of the hormone into fasting rabbits

[3] H. F. Jensen, *Insulin*, The Commonwealth Fund, New York, 1938.
[4] F. D. W. Lukens, *Physiol. Revs.*, **28**, 304 (1948).
[5] P. J. Moloney and M. Coval, *Biochem. J.*, **59**, 179 (1955).

and the determination of the rate and extent of the lowering of the blood sugar level.

In the intact animal, circulating insulin is destroyed relatively rapidly, probably by proteinases ("insulinase") present in tissues such as the liver.[6] The relation of insulinase to the known cathepsins (p. 700) has not been established. A variety of chemical substances, upon administration to a suitable animal, cause a fall in blood sugar; among these "hypoglycemic" agents are several indolyl compounds, which may exert their effect by an inhibition of insulinase action. A group of drugs extensively tested as possible therapeutic agents in human diabetes are arylsulfonylurea derivatives such as N-toluenesulfonyl-N'-n-butylurea (Orinase, Tolbutamide); although the oral administration of these compounds exerts a hypoglycemic effect in some diabetics and in experimental animals (but not in alloxan-diabetic rats), the mode of their action has not been elucidated.[7]

In 1923, Kimball and Murlin found in pancreas a substance that causes a rise in blood sugar upon intravenous injection into experimental animals. This hyperglycemic factor (glucagon, HG-factor) appears to be elaborated by the α-cells of the islet tissue, and is frequently present in insulin preparations as an impurity; the administration of such impure insulin preparations may lead to an initial rise in blood sugar, followed by the hypoglycemia characteristic of insulin action. Glucagon has been obtained in crystalline form,[8] and found to be a polypeptide having the following amino acid sequence:[9]

His-Ser-Glu(NH$_2$)-Gly-Thr-Phe-Thr-Ser-Asp-Tyr-Ser-

Lys-Tyr-Leu-Asp-Ser-Arg-Arg-Ala-Glu(NH$_2$)-Asp-Phe-

Val-Glu(NH$_2$)-Try-Leu-Met-Asp(NH$_2$)-Thr

The secretion of insulin from the pancreas is stimulated by many factors (cf. p. 959), including hyperglycemia caused by the administration of glucose,[10] or by the action of glucagon.[11] In turn, glucagon secretion appears to be stimulated by hypoglycemia induced by insulin.

Thyroid Gland. This organ of internal secretion, located in most species in the form of two lobes on either side of the trachea, was named the thyroid by Wharton (1656) because of its resemblance to a shield (Greek *thyreoides*, shield-shaped). The recognition of its endocrine

[6] M. Vaughan, *Biochim. et Biophys. Acta,* **15**, 432 (1954); I. A. Mirsky et al., *J. Biol. Chem.,* **214**, 397 (1955); **228**, 77 (1957).

[7] I. A. Mirsky et al., *Endocrinology,* **59**, 715 (1956); C. v. Holt et al., *Science,* **125**, 736 (1956).

[8] A. Staub et al., *J. Biol. Chem.,* **214**, 619 (1955).

[9] W. W. Bromer et al., *J. Am. Chem. Soc.,* **79**, 2807 (1957).

[10] E. M. Brown Jr., et al., *Endocrinology,* **50**, 644 (1952).

[11] P. P. Foà et al., *Am. J. Physiol.,* **171**, 32 (1952).

nature came, during the nineteenth century, from the clinical studies by Gull and others on the human disease myxedema, characterized by a swelling of the skin on the face and extremities, muscular weakness, and progressive diminution in mental alertness. Subsequent investigations showed that partial or complete extirpation of the thyroid led to symptoms similar to those observed in myxedema, and that the symptoms could be ameliorated by the administration of extracts of the gland. In 1895 Baumann demonstrated the presence of unusually large amounts of iodine in the thyroid, and later work showed this iodine to be largely bound to a protein (thyroglobulin) whose particle weight is about 650,000. Upon hydrolysis with alkali, thyroglobulin is cleaved to yield the amino acid thyroxine, first isolated by Kendall (1916), and whose structure was shown by Harington[12] (1926) to be 3,5,3',5'-tetraiodo-L-thyronine (p. 69). Since the administration of thyroxine causes the physiological effects observed with thyroid extracts, this amino acid was long considered to be the sole active principle elaborated by the gland. Subsequent work showed that 3,5,3'- and 3,3',5'-triiodothyronine, as well as 3,3'-diiodothyronine, are constituents of thyroglobulin[13] and are active as hormones; 3,5,3'-triiodothyronine exhibits greater hormonal activity than does thyroxine. It appears, however, that the principal circulating hormone is thyroxine (or small peptides of thyroxine) liberated by the proteolysis, in the thyroid, of thyroglobulin. This protein represents the storage form of the hormone in the endocrine organ.[14] The blood thyroxine appears to be bound to plasma protein (probably an α-globulin[15]). In normal human subjects the level of serum iodine is 4 to 8 μg per 100 ml. In myxedema and other hypothyroid states the serum iodine may drop to 1 μg per 100 ml; in hyperthyroidism (e.g., in Graves' or Basedow's disease) the level may reach 15 to 20 μg per 100 ml. Thyroxine is excreted as a glucuronide,[16] probably formed by an enzymic reaction with UDP-glucuronic acid (p. 537).

Thyroxine and the other iodothyronines are made by the iodination of tyrosine (p. 831) in the thyroid gland, which traps iodide ion supplied by the circulation.[17] Presumably, I^- is oxidized to I_2, which is thought to combine rapidly with tyrosine residues of thyroid protein.[18] The process whereby the gland removes iodide from the circulation is inde-

[12] C. R. Harington, *The Thyroid Gland,* Oxford University Press, London, 1933; *Proc. Roy. Soc.,* **132B,** 223 (1944).

[13] J. Roche et al., *Biochim. et Biophys. Acta,* **19,** 308 (1956).

[14] W. Tong et al., *J. Biol. Chem.,* **191,** 665 (1951).

[15] J. Robbins et al., *J. Biol. Chem.,* **212,** 403 (1955).

[16] A. Taurog et al., *J. Biol. Chem.,* **194,** 655 (1952); J. Roche et al., *Biochim. et Biophys. Acta,* **13,** 471 (1954).

[17] C. P. Leblond and J. Gross, *Endocrinology,* **43,** 306 (1948).

[18] A. Taurog et al., *J. Biol. Chem.,* **161,** 537 (1945); **213,** 119 (1955).

pendent of the iodination reactions, since the administration of "antithyroid" substances (sulfonamides, substituted thioureas, thiouracil and its derivatives) only inhibits the formation of the hormone. These drugs cause a clinical condition known as goiter, characterized by the enlargement of the thyroid gland, and are believed to interfere with the enzymic synthesis of thyroxine.[19] The most frequent cause of goiter is an inadequate intake or utilization of iodide. Thiocyanate ion also inhibits the formation of thyroid hormone, and induces goiter; this effect probably is caused by an inhibition of iodide absorption by the thyroid, and can be counteracted by the administration of large amounts of iodide.

The principal effect of a thyroid insufficiency is a marked decrease in the basal metabolic rate (p. 935); this was discovered by Magnus-Levy in 1896. In young individuals hypothyroidism is accompanied by an inhibition of growth and normal development. The human disorder known as cretinism is a consequence of hypothyroidism in infancy; the disease is characterized by dwarfism and retarded mental capacities.

Studies on muscle tissue excised from thyroidectomized mice showed that the rate of oxygen uptake is much less than for muscle from normal mice. Similar results with other tissues suggest that a major biochemical role of thyroxine is to accelerate the rate of oxygen uptake. This view is concordant with the finding that the tissues of thyroidectomized rats contain less than one half the amount of cytochrome c (cf. p. 358) found in normal animals; if thyroxine is injected, the normal level of this important electron carrier is restored.[20] Furthermore, the level of TPNH-cytochrome c reductase (p. 341) activity is reduced in the liver of thyroidectomized rats, and can be partly restored by the administration of thyroxine.[21]

It was mentioned previously that thyroxine "uncouples" oxidative phosphorylation by rat liver mitochondria (p. 385). This effect, which is also exerted by other iodothyronines, does not appear to be a direct one, but is related to the action of the hormone in promoting the swelling of liver mitochondria.[22] The possibility exists, therefore, that the hormone influences oxidative phosphorylation by altering the permeability of the mitochondrial membrane. It is of interest that mitochondria from some tissues (spleen, brain, testis) do not exhibit appreciable swelling upon incubation in the presence of thyroxine; when slices of these tissues are prepared from animals treated with thyroxine, their oxygen consumption does not differ markedly from that of tissue slices from untreated animals.

[19] E. B. Astwood, *Ann. N. Y. Acad. Sci.,* **50,** 419 (1949).

[20] D. L. Drabkin, *J. Biol. Chem.,* **182,** 335 (1950).

[21] A. H. Phillips and R. G. Langdon, *Biochim. et Biophys. Acta,* **19,** 380 (1956).

[22] D. F. Tapley and C. Cooper, *J. Biol. Chem.,* **222,** 341 (1956); *Nature,* **178,** 1119 (1956); F. Dickens and D. Salmony, *Biochem. J.,* **64,** 645 (1956).

The action of the iodothyronines in promoting oxygen uptake and in inhibiting oxidative phosphorylation is also exhibited by the corresponding iodothyroacetic acid derivatives (the alanine group of thyronine is replaced by $-CH_2COOH$). 3,5,3'-Triiodothyroacetic acid is active as a hormone, and has been identified in rat kidney after injection of 3,5,3'-triiodothyronine.[23]

One of the most striking effects of thyroid hormones is the acceleration of metamorphosis in amphibia (e.g., frog, salamander).[24] This phenomenon (discovered by Gudernatsch in 1912) is so sensitive a test that the tadpole has been widely used for the assay of the potency of thyroid hormone preparations.

Parathyroid Glands. These endocrine organs usually are found as two pairs of glands in close proximity to the thyroid. In early studies of the effect of thyroidectomy on dogs and cats, the parathyroids also were removed, and the resulting nervous irritability, followed by tetany, convulsions, and ultimately death, were attributed to thyroid insufficiency. The discovery of the parathyroids (Sandstrom, 1880; Gley, 1891) led to the demonstration that the nervous symptoms were caused by the absence of the hormonal secretion of these glands. The parathyroid hormone appears to be protein in nature, but only partially purified preparations have been described.[25]

The effects of parathyroid insufficiency on the nervous system are closely associated with a marked decrease in the level of calcium ion in the circulating fluids, and the symptoms may be relieved by the administration of Ca^{2+} salts. The decrease in serum calcium, observed in hypoparathyroidism, is accompanied by an appreciable increase in the inorganic phosphate of the serum. The administration of preparations of the parathyroid hormone causes a rapid increase in the rate of urinary excretion of phosphate, with a concomitant drop in the level of serum phosphate. This effect has been attributed to the action of the hormone on the reabsorption of phosphate by the kidney tubules. The parathyroid hormone exerts a direct influence on the metabolism of bone, leading to an increased release of bone Ca^{2+} and citrate into the blood. However, the manner in which the hormone acts on the kidney and on bone is unknown, nor has it been established whether the effects on phosphate reabsorption and on the release of calcium and citrate are caused by the same component of the hormone preparations used.[26]

---

[23] J. Roche et al., *Endocrinology,* **59,** 425 (1956).

[24] T. C. Bruice et al., *J. Biol. Chem.,* **210,** 1 (1954).

[25] W. F. Ross and T. R. Wood, *J. Biol. Chem.,* **146,** 49 (1942); M. V. L'Heureux et al., *ibid.,* **168,** 167 (1947).

[26] R. O. Greep and A. D. Kenney, in G. Pincus and K. V. Thimann, *The Hormones,* Vol. III, Chapter 4, Academic Press, New York, 1955.

Adrenal Glands. These paired rounded organs, also termed supra-renal glands, lie near the kidneys, and are composed of two types of tissue which differ histologically and functionally. The central portion (the medulla) of each mammalian adrenal is sharply differentiated from the outer portion (the cortex), which is the more essential for life.

The adrenal medulla secretes epinephrine (adrenalin; p. 828) and the closely related norepinephrine (noradrenalin, *l*-arterenol; p. 828). On intravenous injection, epinephrine causes an immediate and pronounced elevation in blood pressure. This action is due to two factors: (1) a con-striction of arterioles in all tissues except the heart and muscles, and (2) a specific stimulation of the rate and force of contraction of the heart. In addition, epinephrine causes an increase in the rate of glyco-genolysis in the liver and muscle (p. 960).

The adrenal cortex is the source of a number of steroids that possess hormonal activity in the regulation of carbohydrate metabolism and of electrolyte balance. Although approximately thirty crystalline steroids have been isolated from adrenal cortical extracts, the compounds of special interest are 17-hydroxy-11-dehydrocorticosterone (cortisone, com-pound E), 17-hydroxycorticosterone (cortisol, hydrocortisone, compound F), corticosterone (compound B), 11-dehydrocorticosterone (compound A), 17-hydroxy-11-deoxycorticosterone (11-deoxycortisol, compound S), 11-deoxycorticosterone (cortexone, DOC), and aldosterone; the formu-lae of these seven compounds are shown on p. 639. The adrenal corti-cal hormones present in the venous blood leaving the gland are principally cortisol, corticosterone, and aldosterone; in most animals, cortisol is the major component with lesser amounts of the other two. Cortisol does not appear to be secreted by the rat adrenal, and corticosterone appears to be absent from the adrenal secretion in the monkey. The biosynthesis and the metabolic breakdown of the adrenal steroids have been discussed in Chapter 26.

The essential role of the adrenal cortex in the maintenance of life was first indicated in the clinical studies of Addison, who in 1855 drew attention to the fatal disease (now termed Addison's disease) charac-terized by a variety of symptoms, which include general apathy, gastro-intestinal disturbances, muscular weakness, and discoloration of the skin; on autopsy, degeneration of both adrenal cortices is observed. During the period 1920 to 1930, reliable surgical methods were devel-oped for the removal of the adrenals (adrenalectomy) of experimental animals. In most animals adrenalectomy is fatal; dogs may survive for 5 to 15 days after the operation, and rats survive longer. Adrenalec-tomized animals exhibit loss of appetite (anorexia), muscular weakness, hemoconcentration, hypoglycemia, and extreme susceptibility to all types of stress (cold, heat, injury, infections, toxic chemicals, etc.). These symptoms may be counteracted and the life of the animals maintained by the injection of an extract of adrenal cortex in a lipid solvent. The important role of the adrenal cortex in the maintenance of the electrolyte balance is shown by the fact that the administration of sodium chloride (in the drinking water) to an adrenalectomized animal is sufficient to prolong life. However, other physiological consequences of adrenal insufficiency are not corrected by the administration of salt; this question will be considered later in this chapter.

Because of the variety of physiological effects observed upon the injection of adrenal cortical steroids into adrenalectomized animals, the choice of the method of biological assay is a matter of considerable importance.[27] Among the criteria that have been employed for such assays are: (1) decrease in the urinary ratio of Na^+/K^+ in adrenalectomized rats or mice, (2) promotion of the survival and growth of young adrenalectomized rats, (3) prolongation of the survival time of adrenalectomized dogs, (4) improvement in the muscle-work performance of adrenalectomized rats, (5) increase in the liver glycogen of fasted rats or mice. A comparison of the activity of the seven steroids in such tests is given in Table 1. Although all the steroids tested show biological

Table I. Approximate Relative Activity of Adrenal Cortical Steroids in Adrenalectomized Animals

Steroid	Urinary Na^+/K^+ (Rats)	Growth and Survival (Rats)	Survival (Dogs)	Muscle-Work Test (Rats)	Glycogen Deposition (Rats)
Cortisone	0.6	2.5	0.5	10	10
Cortisol	0.8	0.5		19	16
Corticosterone	1.4	1.7			5
11-Dehydrocorticosterone		1.0		5	5
11-Deoxycortisol	0.8			0.2	
Cortexone (DOC)	10	10	10	0.2	0.1
Aldosterone	1000		250		3

activity in promoting the growth and survival of young rats, the compounds that are oxygenated at carbon 11 of the steroid nucleus are more active in promoting glycogenesis and in improving the muscle-work performance. It will be noted that aldosterone is the most effective steroid in promoting survival, and that cortexone (DOC) is also more effective in this respect than are the other 11-oxygenated steroids. Since aldosterone and DOC are especially active in the regulation of the electrolyte balance (as shown by the effect on the Na^+/K^+ ratio), the prolongation of life is directly related to the action of these two hormones in promoting the retention of Na^+ and the excretion of K^+.

[27] R. I. Dorfman, *Physiol. Revs.*, **34**, 138 (1954).

Several synthetic steroids have been found to exhibit a greater effect on carbohydrate metabolism than any of the 11-oxygenated steroids isolated from adrenal extracts. Among these are 9α-fluorocortisol, 1-dehydrocortisone, 1-dehydro-9α-fluorocortisone, and 2-methyl-9α-fluorocortisone.[28]

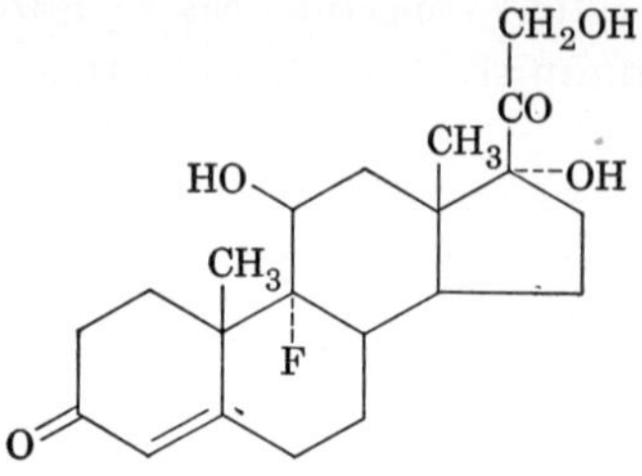

9α-Fluorocortisol

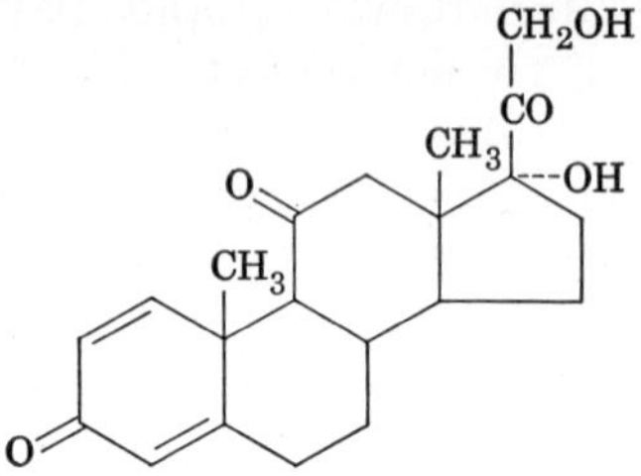

1-Dehydrocortisone

Sex Organs (Gonads). It will be recalled that the ovary secretes a steroid hormone (estradiol-17β) which induces estrus (p. 640) when administered to sexually immature females. The rate of liberation of this hormone is under the control of the follicle-stimulating hormone (FSH) of the pituitary (p. 952); an increased secretion of estradiol-17β leads to the development of the follicular tissue which surrounds the ovum. When the follicle has matured, it ruptures, liberating the ovum, and, under the influence of another pituitary hormone (luteinizing hormone, LH; p. 952), the ruptured follicle is converted to a "corpus luteum," which secretes the steroid hormone progesterone (p. 638). If fertilization occurs, the secretion of progesterone continues and is essential for the implantation of the fertilized ovum and for the development of the mammary glands. Because of its structural similarity to DOC, progesterone resembles this adrenal steroid in its effect on the maintenance of the electrolyte balance. Progesterone has also been isolated from adrenal cortical extracts.

The testis secretes the steroid hormone testosterone (p. 641), which induces the development of the male reproductive organs and of the secondary sex characteristics. Androsterone (p. 641), isolated from urine, is a metabolic transformation product of testosterone. The endocrine nature of the testis was clearly demonstrated by numerous investigators.[29] For example, the injection of an extract of bull testicles into capons caused a striking development of the secondary sex characters; the most conspicuous of these was the growth of the cockscomb.

[28] J. Fried et al., *J. Am. Chem. Soc.*, **77**, 1068, 4181 (1955); H. L. Herzog et al., *Science*, **121**, 176 (1955); R. F. Hirschmann et al., *J. Am. Chem. Soc.*, **77**, 3166 (1955); J. A. Hogg et al., *ibid.*, **77**, 6401 (1955).

[29] F. C. Koch, *Physiol. Revs.*, **17**, 153 (1937).

Examination of the formula of androsterone shows that it bears a keto group at position 17 of the steroid nucleus, and that it may be termed a "17-ketosteroid." In alkaline solution such compounds give a characteristic violet color with m-dinitrobenzene, and this reaction is employed for the determination of 17-ketosteroids in urine and blood. Increased excretion of these androgenic steroids is noted upon sexual development in males and a decrease is observed upon failure of sexual function. It must be added that the urinary excretion of 17-ketosteroids is an index not only of gonadal function but of adrenal cortical function as well. Androgens have been isolated from adrenal cortical extracts, and hyperactivity of the adrenal cortex leads to increases in the concentration of 17-ketosteroids in blood and in urine.

Pituitary Gland (Hypophysis). Of the various mammalian endocrine organs the pituitary is perhaps the most important because it elaborates hormones which regulate the secretory activity of other endocrine tissues (the thyroid gland, the adrenal cortex, and the gonads). In addition, other pituitary hormones exert direct effects on the metabolic activity of nonendocrine tissues.

The pituitary is a small gland located under the brain and is composed of two anatomically distinct regions, the adenohypophysis, a portion of which comprises the anterior lobe of the pituitary, and the neurohypophysis, a portion of which is part of the posterior lobe of the gland. The remainder of the neurohypophysis is termed the hypophysial stalk, which joins the pituitary to the hypothalamus (a region of the brain below the cerebral cortex). Studies of the endocrine functions of the pituitary were hampered for many years by the surgical difficulties involved in operations so close to the brain, but in 1910 Aschner devised a technique for the hypophysectomy of dogs, and an operation was devised for the rat by P. E. Smith in 1926. When the anterior pituitary is removed surgically, a variety of physiological effects are observed: (1) partial atrophy of the thyroid gland and the consequences of thyroid deficiency; (2) partial atrophy of the adrenal cortex and the consequences of adrenal cortical insufficiency; (3) atrophy of the gonads and accessory sex organs in the adult animal and failure of the gonads to mature in young animals; (4) failure of lactation; (5) loss of tissue in the adult animal and, in the young animal, retardation and ultimate cessation of growth; (6) marked alterations in the metabolism of carbohydrates, associated with increased sensitivity to the hypoglycemic action of insulin, and in the metabolism of lipids and proteins. In contrast to the far-reaching physiological consequences of removal of the anterior pituitary, or of complete hypophysectomy, a deficiency in the secretion of the posterior pituitary alone is, in general, accompanied only by an increased output of urine (polyuria). This condition is observed in the human disease diabetes insipidus, which is characterized by an abnormally large exchange of water (a daily intake and output of as much as 20 liters, instead of ca. 1.5 liters), and which is due to damage to the posterior pituitary.

The variety of physiological effects caused by total hypophysectomy, or by the clinical condition (Simmonds' disease) in which there is impairment of the anterior pituitary, is a consequence of the multiple nature of the hormonal secretion of this gland. At least six well-defined hormones have been isolated from the anterior pituitary (Table 2).[30]

Table 2. Hormones Elaborated by the Anterior Pituitary

Hormone	Target Organ	Physiological Effects
Corticotrophin (adrenocorticotrophic hormone, ACTH)	Adrenal cortex	Secretion of adrenal cortical steroids
Thyrotrophin (thyrotrophic hormone, thyroid-stimulating hormone, TSH)	Thyroid	Elaboration of thyroxine
Follicle-stimulating hormone (FSH)	Ovary	Development of follicular tissue
	Testis	Spermatogenesis; development of seminiferous tubules
Luteinizing hormone (LH, interstitial cell-stimulating hormone, ICSH)	Ovary	Development of corpus luteum; secretion of progesterone
	Testis	Development of interstitial tissue; secretion of male sex hormone
Prolactin (lactogenic hormone)	Mammary gland	Secretion of milk
Growth hormone (somatotrophin)	General effect on tissues	Retention of protein; growth of muscle and bone; metabolism of carbohydrate and fat

Four of the pituitary hormones listed in Table 2 (ACTH, TSH, FSH, and LH) are "trophic" hormones (Greek *trophikos*, nursing); this designation derives from the effect of these hormones in "nourishing," or counteracting the degeneration of the appropriate target endocrine organ. The administration, to normal animals, of one of the trophic hormones leads to hyperfunction of the target gland. The trophic hormones are frequently denoted "tropic" hormones (e.g., thyrotropic hormone) to indicate that the target organ responds to the stimulus of the hormone (Greek, -*tropos*, turning).

Studies on the metabolic effects of the hormones listed in Table 2 have

[30] A. White, *Physiol. Revs.*, **26**, 574 (1946).

been greatly facilitated by the isolation of these principles from extracts of anterior pituitary glands. Because of the central role of the adrenal cortex in the maintenance of life, much attention has been devoted to the purification of corticotrophin (ACTH). Although preparations of this hormone were obtained from sheep and swine pituitaries in the form of apparently homogeneous proteins (approximate particle size 20,000; isoelectric point ca. pH 4.7),[31] subsequent studies have shown that the biological activity is also exhibited by peptides obtained by treatment of the ACTH protein with acid or with pepsin.[32] The use of chromatographic and countercurrent distribution methods has given several closely related active peptides (sheep α-corticotrophin, swine β-corticotrophin, swine corticotrophin A, swine corticotrophin B). By means of methods similar to those used in studies with insulin (cf. p. 145), β-corticotrophin was found to be a single-chain peptide of 39 amino acids arranged in the following sequence:[33]

Ser-Tyr-Ser-Met-Glu-His-Phe-Arg-Try-Gly-Lys-Pro-Val-Gly-

Lys-Lys-Arg-Arg-Pro-Val-Lys-Val-Tyr-Pro-Asp-Gly-Ala-Glu-

Asp-Glu(NH$_2$)-Leu-Ala-Glu-Ala-Phe-Pro-Leu-Glu-Phe

The other corticotrophic peptides mentioned above have amino acid sequences similar to that of β-corticotrophin.[34] It appears that the hormonal activity depends on the integrity of the N-terminal amino acid sequence, since brief treatment with kidney aminopeptidase (p. 144) causes extensive inactivation of swine corticotrophin A.[35]

In the assay of the biological potency of ACTH preparations, advantage is taken of the fact that, after hypophysectomy, the adrenal glands decrease in size; the administration of ACTH leads to an increase in the weight of the adrenals. Also, when the pituitary hormone is injected into hypophysectomized rats, a marked decrease in the level of adrenal ascorbic acid is observed.[36] The drop in ascorbic acid is accompanied by a decrease in the adrenal cholesterol. The biochemical significance of these changes is not clear (cf. p. 643); however, the effect on the adrenal ascorbic acid level in the hypophysectomized rat is extremely specific and has not been induced by any known agent other than the pituitary hormone.

[31] C. H. Li and H. M. Evans, *Vitamins and Hormones,* **5,** 198 (1947).

[32] R. W. Payne et al., *J. Biol. Chem.,* **187,** 719 (1950); C. H. Li, *Advances in Protein Chem.,* **11,** 101 (1956).

[33] R. G. Shepherd et al., *J. Am. Chem. Soc.,* **78,** 5051, 5059, 5067 (1956).

[34] W. F. White and W. A. Landman, *J. Am. Chem. Soc.,* **77,** 771, 1711 (1955); C. H. Li et al., *Nature,* **176,** 687 (1955).

[35] W. F. White, *J. Am. Chem. Soc.,* **77,** 4691 (1955).

[36] M. A. Sayers et al., *Endocrinology,* **42,** 379 (1948).

In this connection it may be added that similar reduction in the adrenal ascorbic acid and cholesterol is observed when normal animals are subjected to a variety of stress (injury, cold, heat, drugs, toxins, lack of oxygen, etc.). Hypophysectomized animals do not show a drop in the adrenal ascorbic acid or cholesterol under these conditions. As noted earlier, the adrenal cortex is indispensable in enabling an animal to resist many unfavorable changes in its environment; since the secretory action of this tissue is under the control of the anterior pituitary, it is clear that the pituitary-adrenal relationship represents one of the most important homeostatic mechanisms in animals.[37] The mechanism whereby the secretion of ACTH is increased in response to stress has not been elucidated.[38] Among the factors that influence ACTH secretion are: (1) changes in the concentration of cortical steroids in the blood,[39] (2) stimulation by increased concentrations of circulating epinephrine liberated from the adrenal medulla under conditions of stress,[40] (3) control by hitherto unidentified chemical agents liberated by the activity of nerve fibers in the hypothalamus.[41] Such neurohumoral control by the hypothalamus appears to be the most important factor in the response of the pituitary to stress, and may apply to the secretion not only of ACTH but of other pituitary hormones as well. The possibility exists that the action of epinephrine on the pituitary may be exerted via the hypothalamus. The importance of an uninterrupted secretion of ACTH becomes clearer from the fact that the adrenal cortex, although continuously elaborating steroid hormones, does not appear to store appreciable quantities of biologically active material.[42]

Two of the other trophic hormones elaborated by the anterior pituitary, the gonadotrophins (FSH and LH), have been prepared in the form of reportedly homogeneous proteins.[43] FSH (from sheep pituitaries) has been obtained as a glycoprotein (containing mannose and hexosamine units) of approximate particle size 70,000; its isoelectric point is near pH 4.5. However, more active FSH preparations that are heterogeneous have been obtained from swine pituitaries.[44] The LH preparation from sheep pituitaries appears to have a particle weight of 40,000 and an isoelectric point at pH 4.6; the LH obtained from swine pituitaries is a larger protein (particle weight ca. 100,000) with its isoelectric point at pH 7.45. The thyrotrophic hormone (TSH) of the beef pituitary is a

[37] G. Sayers, *Physiol. Revs.*, **30**, 241 (1950).

[38] C. N. H. Long, *Ann. Rev. Physiol.*, **18**, 409 (1956).

[39] J. R. Hodges, *J. Endocrinol.*, **9**, 343 (1953); **10**, 173 (1954).

[40] C. N. H. Long, *Recent Progr. Hormone Research*, **7**, 75 (1952).

[41] G. W. Harris, *Neural Control of the Pituitary Gland*, Arnold, London, 1955.

[42] M. Vogt, *J. Physiol.*, **113**, 129 (1951).

[43] C. H. Li, *Vitamins and Hormones*, **7**, 223 (1949).

[44] S. L. Steelman et al., *Endocrinology*, **56**, 216 (1955).

protein of low particle weight, and has been partially purified by chromatography.[45]

Purified prolactin (from beef or sheep pituitaries) has an apparent particle weight of about 32,000 and an isoelectric point near pH 6.[46] As noted in Table 2, prolactin, in association with estrogens, promotes lactation in the mammary gland. The hormone also stimulates the growth of the crop sac of hypophysectomized birds.

Highly purified preparations of the growth hormone have been obtained from beef pituitaries,[47] and from the pituitaries of other animals (monkeys, humans, etc.). Whereas beef growth hormone has a particle weight of about 46,000 and an isoelectric point at pH 6.85, the hormone from human (and monkey) pituitaries has a particle weight of about 27,000 and an isoelectric point at pH 5.5.[48] In this connection, it is of interest that the purified beef growth hormone is ineffective when administered to human subjects. For an extensive discussion of the chemical properties and the physiological role of the growth hormone, see Smith et al.[49]

The name assigned to the growth hormone requires comment, since the concept of "growth" is largely a matter of definition. As used in connection with this pituitary hormone, growth is defined as an increase in body weight without appreciable change in tissue composition. The administration of growth hormone to adult animals leads to a net increase in the protein, salts, and water of the tissues. When given to young animals the growth hormone accelerates the growth of bones as well as tissues, and causes proportionate enlargement of most anatomical features. With adult animals, however, where the epiphyses of the long bones are closed, bone growth leads to asymmetrical deformation; in man oversecretion of the hormone induces the clinical conditions known as acromegaly and gigantism. As mentioned earlier, hypophysectomy of young animals leads to retardation and ultimate cessation of growth.

It will be recalled that the posterior pituitary (neurohypophysis) is concerned in the regulation of water excretion by the animal organism. Extracts of this gland are effective in counteracting the diuresis that follows hypophysectomy. The antidiuretic activity accompanies the hormone named vasopressin, which in mammals effects a rise in blood

[45] I. G. Fels et al., *J. Biol. Chem.*, **213**, 311 (1955); J. G. Pierce and J. F. Nyc, *ibid.*, **222**, 777 (1956); P. G. Condliffe and R. W. Bates, *ibid.*, **223**, 843 (1956).

[46] A. White, *Vitamins and Hormones*, **7**, 253 (1949); R. D. Cole and C. H. Li, *J. Biol. Chem.*, **213**, 197 (1955).

[47] A. E. Wilhelmi et al., *J. Biol. Chem.*, **176**, 735 (1948); C. H. Li, *ibid.*, **211**, 555 (1954); *Federation Proc.*, **16**, 775 (1957).

[48] C. H. Li and H. Papkoff, *Science*, **124**, 1293 (1956).

[49] R. W. Smith et al., *The Hypophyseal Growth Hormone*, McGraw-Hill Book Co., New York, 1955.

pressure by contraction of peripheral blood vessels. In addition to vasopressin, posterior pituitary extracts contain a hormone that stimulates the contraction of uterine muscle, and is therefore named oxytocin (or ocytocin; Greek *ocy,* quick; *tokos,* birth). Oxytocin also has a pronounced effect in stimulating the ejection of milk, and lowers the blood pressure in the fowl. As mentioned on p. 140, vasopressin and oxytocin are peptides whose structure has been established by degradation and by synthesis. The examination of the biological activity of highly purified preparations of the isolated hormones, and of synthetic materials, has shown that no sharp line of demarcation can be drawn between oxytocin and vasopressin. Thus oxytocin exhibits a slight antidiuretic effect, and vasopressin has appreciable activity in stimulating uterine contraction, milk ejection, and vasodepression in the fowl.[50] It is probable that the hormonal secretion of the neurohypophysis is under the control of the hypothalamus.

In addition to the pituitary hormones discussed above, an additional active substance (or group of substances) is elaborated by the region of the adenohypophysis adjacent to the neurohypophysis. This "intermediate lobe" contains a hormone (intermedin) which, on administration to amphibia, fish, or reptiles, causes a dispersion of the pigment granules in the melanocytes (chromatophores) of the skin, with consequent darkening of the body color. For this reason, the hormone is also termed "melanocyte stimulating hormone" (MSH). Two peptides (α-MSH and β-MSH) have been isolated from extracts of swine pituitaries, and their amino acid sequence has been determined.[51] In α-MSH the sequence appears to be that of the first thirteen amino acids of β-corticotrophin (starting at the N-terminal serine residue; cf. p. 951). The N-terminal serine in α-MSH is substituted by a non-amino acid unit of unknown structure, and the terminal COOH group (of valine) is present as the amide. β-MSH has been reported to have the sequence:

Asp-Glu-Gly-Pro-Tyr-Lys-Met-Glu-His-

Phe-Arg-Try-Gly-Ser-Pro-Pro-Lys-Asp

The heptapeptide sequence Met-Glu-His-Phe-Arg-Try-Gly also occurs in the ACTH peptides. These structural similarities between the MSH and ACTH peptides are of interest in relation to the observation that highly purified ACTH preparations exhibit MSH activity.[33,52]

[50] H. B. van Dyke, *Recent Progr. Hormone Research,* **11,** 1 (1954).

[51] T. H. Lee and A. B. Lerner, *J. Biol. Chem.,* **221,** 943 (1956); J. I. Harris and P. Roos, *Nature,* **178,** 90 (1956); I. Geschwind et al., *J. Am. Chem. Soc.,* **79,** 615, 620 (1957); J. I. Harris and A. B. Lerner, *Nature,* **179,** 1346 (1957).

[52] H. B. F. Dixon, *Biochim. et Biophys. Acta,* **19,** 392 (1956).

Placenta. During pregnancy, the placenta secretes into the maternal blood hormones whose physiological effect is similar to the action of one or both of the pituitary gonadotrophins. Two such "chorionic gonado-trophins" have been isolated: pregnant mare serum gonadotrophin (PMSG), and human chorionic gonadotrophin (HCG), the latter from human pregnancy urine. Both hormones have been obtained in the form of partially purified glycoproteins. Although PMSG has an action analogous to the combined effect of the two pituitary gonadotrophins (FSH and LH), HCG only exerts an action on the corpus luteum or on interstitial cells of the testis.

Gastrointestinal Tract.[53] It was noted at the beginning of this chapter that the term "hormone" was first applied to secretin, which is elaborated by the small intestine and stimulates the flow of pancreatic juice. Secretin also stimulates the secretion of bile by the liver. As noted on p. 140, this hormone is a peptide (molecular weight ca. 5000).

In addition to secretin, three other hormonal principles have been shown to be secreted by the intestinal mucosa; they are named pancre-ozymin, cholecystokinin, and enterogastrone. None of these hormones has been purified extensively, and their chemical nature is not established. Pancreozymin co-operates with secretin to increase the enzyme content of the pancreatic juice.[54] Cholecystokinin exerts a specific action in stimulating the contraction of the gall bladder. Enterogastrone is appar-ently elaborated in response to exposure of the duodenal mucosa to fat, and inhibits gastric mobility.

Hormonal Regulation of Carbohydrate Metabolism in Vertebrates [55]

Insulin. Since insulin deficiency is characterized by a hyperglycemia, which is corrected by the administration of the hormone, it follows that insulin affects one or more processes involved in the metabolism of glucose. Experiments with excised rat diaphragm muscle have shown that extremely small amounts of insulin (ca. 10^{-4} unit per milliliter) cause an increase in the uptake of glucose by this tissue, accompanied by an increased rate of glycogen formation. Furthermore, diaphragms from alloxan-diabetic rats take up less glucose from the medium than does muscle from normal animals, and the extent of glycogenesis and of oxidation of glucose to CO_2 also are decreased; upon addition of insulin to the medium, the glucose utilization of muscle from diabetic rats is comparable to that of muscle from normal rats, and the rates of

[53] A. C. Ivy, *Physiol. Revs.*, **10**, 282 (1930); *Gastroenterology*, **3**, 443 (1944).
[54] L. E. Hokin and M. R. Hokin, *J. Physiol.*, **132**, 442 (1956).
[55] A. E. Renold et al., *Vitamins and Hormones*, **14**, 139 (1956).

glycogenesis and of glucose oxidation are partially restored.[56] These actions of insulin appear to be related to the binding of the hormone by muscle cells, and the magnitude of the effect on glycogenesis is roughly proportional to the amount of insulin bound.[57] It should be added that insulin combines with other animal cells, notably leucocytes.

The mechanism whereby insulin exerts its effect on the utilization of glucose by muscle has not been elucidated.[58] Evidence has been presented in favor of the view that the hormone increases the rate of entry of blood glucose into muscle cells, presumably by an effect (as yet undefined) on the cell membrane.[59] An alternative hypothesis is that insulin increases the rate of the glucokinase reaction (p. 493) by counteracting the inhibitory effect of a pituitary factor.[60]

The carbohydrate metabolism of the liver is also markedly altered in the diabetic state.[61] Liver slices from fed alloxan-diabetic rats exhibit a decreased rate of glucose uptake, of glucose phosphorylation, and of glycogenesis. Of special interest is the marked increase in glucose production by gluconeogenesis (e.g., from pyruvate) and by glycogenolysis; this increased glucose production is associated with a striking increase in the glucose-6-phosphatase activity of the liver (p. 497). Upon the administration of insulin to diabetic rats, these changes in carbohydrate metabolism are counteracted. However, in contrast to the prompt action of insulin on the glucose uptake of muscle, the liver of diabetic animals given insulin responds more slowly. It has been suggested, therefore, that the hormone may not exert a direct action on the liver, and that the changes in the carbohydrate metabolism of the liver in insulin-treated diabetic animals may be a consequence of a metabolic adaptation to altered blood levels of metabolites (e.g., lactic acid) derived from nonhepatic tissues.

The increased glucose-6-phosphatase level of the liver in the diabetic state is of interest in relation to the role of glucose-6-phosphate in glycolysis (p. 490) and in the pentose phosphate cycle (p. 531). Since glucose-6-phosphate dehydrogenase catalyzes the reduction of TPN^+, a decrease in the steady-state level of glucose-6-phosphate because of increased glucose-6-phosphatase action may be expected to lead to

[56] C. A. Villee et al., *J. Biol. Chem.*, **195**, 287 (1952).

[57] W. C. Stadie et al., *J. Biol. Chem.*, **199**, 729 (1952); **200**, 745 (1953); N. Haugaard et al., *ibid.*, **211**, 289 (1954).

[58] W. C. Stadie, *Physiol. Revs.*, **34**, 52 (1954).

[59] R. Levine and M. S. Goldstein, *Recent Progr. Hormone Research,* **11**, 343 (1955); C. R. Park et al., *Am. J. Physiol.*, **182**, 12, 17 (1955); **191**, 13 (1957).

[60] S. P. Colowick et al., *J. Biol. Chem.*, **168**, 583 (1947); M. E. Krahl and J. Bornstein, *Nature,* **173**, 949 (1954).

[61] A. E. Renold et al., *J. Biol. Chem.*, **204**, 533 (1953); **213**, 135 (1955); J. Ashmore et al., *ibid.*, **224**, 225 (1957).

marked changes in the steady-state ratio of $TPN^+/TPNH$ in favor of the oxidized form.[62]

It was mentioned previously (p. 494) that, in the liver, a separate fructokinase catalyzes the formation of fructose-1-phosphate, which may be converted to fructose-6-phosphate. Since fructose is readily utilized by diabetic animals, these reactions do not appear to be impaired in the diabetic state.[63] Furthermore, the enzymic steps leading from fructose-6-phosphate to pyruvate or to glycogen do not appear to be inhibited in diabetic animals. Since, in the sequence of glycolytic reactions, all the steps are the same for the intermediate metabolism of glucose-6-phosphate and of fructose-6-phosphate, it follows that, in diabetic livers, the conversion of extracellular glucose to intracellular glucose-6-phosphate is blocked either by decreased transport of glucose or by inhibition of the glucokinase reaction.

From the foregoing it is clear that the muscles and liver of diabetic animals exhibit a decreased utilization of extracellular glucose for oxidation to CO_2, and that insulin counteracts this deficiency. For example, when glucose is administered to fasted normal dogs, the R.Q. (0.76) is promptly increased to 0.88, denoting an increased oxidation of carbohydrate (cf. p. 933); however, with fasted diabetic dogs, the R.Q. does not rise above the initial value of 0.68.[64] Furthermore, experiments in which C^{14}-labeled glucose was administered to depancreatized dogs or to alloxan-diabetic rats showed the animals to have a lowered capacity to convert glucose to CO_2; when insulin was given to totally depancreatized dogs, the rate of glucose oxidation returned to the value observed for the normal animal.[65] It should be noted that, although the rate of utilization of glucose is markedly diminished in the diabetic animal, the rate of glucose formation (principally by gluconeogenesis) is not impaired, thus leading to hyperglycemia; if the hyperglycemia is severe, glycosuria results.

In addition to the effects of insulin in accelerating glycogenesis and glucose oxidation, the hormone also promotes lipogenesis, i.e., the formation of fat (principally long-chain fatty acids) from carbohydrate. This has been demonstrated, with the isotope technique, by the comparison of fat synthesis by liver slices from normal, insulin-treated normal, alloxan-diabetic, and insulin-treated diabetic rats.[66] The hepatic synthesis of higher fatty acids from acetate *in vitro* is also accelerated by

[62] G. E. Glock et al., *Biochem. J.*, **63**, 520 (1956).

[63] S. S. Chernick et al., *J. Biol. Chem.*, **193**, 793 (1951); I. L. Chaikoff, *Harvey Lectures*, **47**, 99 (1953); A. E. Renold et al., *J. Biol. Chem.*, **209**, 687 (1954).

[64] H. P. Marks and F. G. Young, *J. Endocrinol.*, **1**, 470 (1939).

[65] D. D. Feller et al., *J. Biol. Chem.*, **188**, 865 (1951); D. Stetten, Jr., et al., *ibid.*, **192**, 817 (1951).

[66] S. S. Chernick et al., *J. Biol. Chem.*, **186**, 527, 535 (1950).

insulin.[67]   Although the mode of the action of insulin in promoting lipogenesis from glucose is not clear, it should be recognized that the oxidation of carbohydrate is a major source of energy for endergonic reactions in metabolism.   The process of fat formation from C_2 units requires much energy, and must be coupled to energy-yielding reactions. It appears likely that any appreciable decrease in the normal rate of glucose utilization will lead to a concomitant decrease in the energy available for lipogenesis.   This view is supported by the observation that the feeding of fructose to a diabetic rat promotes fat formation from C_2 units.   Furthermore, TPNH appears to be required in fatty acid synthesis in the liver[68] (cf. p. 612), and its steady-state concentration in this organ probably depends on the rate of the oxidation of glucose-6-phosphate.   In the diabetic liver, less of this metabolite may be available for oxidation because of the increased activity of glucose-6-phosphatase.

Because of the impaired oxidation of glucose and synthesis of fatty acids, the tissues of the diabetic animal largely oxidize fatty acids; the R.Q. drops to about 0.7, and the formation of acetoacetic acid (and other ketone bodies) is increased. If the resulting ketonemia is excessive, ketonuria and acidosis (p. 848) are observed.

A further consequence of the decreased utilization of carbohydrate by the diabetic animal is an accelerated rate of breakdown of tissue proteins.   In the fasted state, such an animal excretes increased amounts of nonprotein nitrogen and goes into negative nitrogen balance (p. 723). It is likely that, as in lipogenesis, protein formation is favored by insulin through the action of the hormone on the mobilization, and ultimate oxidation, of glucose, thus providing energy for protein synthesis. Since the fasted diabetic animal continues to excrete glucose, it is clear that gluconeogenesis still proceeds in the absence of insulin; the principal sources of glucose are probably the glucogenic amino acids (p. 764) of the proteins that are catabolized. Consequently, in the diabetic state, with its characteristic disturbance in the normal rate of glucose oxidation, the animal body loses protein as well as fat; these metabolic consequences are analogous to the effects of prolonged starvation.

It should be added that, although untreated pancreatic diabetes in man, and in several carnivorous or omnivorous animals (dogs, cats, owls), is rapidly fatal, herbivorous animals (rabbits, sheep, goats) and many birds survive for much longer periods of time. When food is given to the herbivores the blood sugar is elevated, but in the fasting state the glucose level is normal.

In the intact animal the rate of secretion of insulin appears to be

[67] R. O. Brady and S. Gurin, *J. Biol. Chem.*, **187**, 589 (1950).

[68] R. G. Langdon, *J. Biol. Chem.*, **226**, 615 (1957); W. N. Shaw et al., *ibid.*, **226**, 417 (1957).

regulated, at least in part, by the glucose concentration of the blood. If large amounts of glucose are administered, as by force-feeding of carbohydrate, the islets of Langerhans undergo enlargement and the β-cells degenerate, leading to a pancreatic diabetes. However, in addition to an increased level of blood glucose, other factors to be mentioned later (e.g., growth hormone, thyroxine) also stimulate insulin production.

Adrenal Cortical Hormones. As mentioned before, the administration to normal fasting rats of one of the 11-oxygenated adrenal steroids leads to an increased deposition of liver glycogen (p. 947). Liver slices from cortisone-treated rats show an increase in glucose production from pyruvate and no decrease in glucose utilization. In the intact animal, the increased gluconeogenesis is accompanied by an increase in nitrogen excretion, suggesting that the new liver glycogen arises, in large part, from the products of protein breakdown (p. 963). The hypothesis that adrenal steroids promote gluconeogenesis from amino acids is in accord with the fact that the administration of cortical extracts to a partially diabetic animal accentuates the diabetic state, and that adrenalectomy effects an amelioration of pancreatic diabetes.[69]

Anterior Pituitary Hormones. A striking improvement in the diabetes of depancreatized animals is effected by hypophysectomy. This phenomenon was discovered in 1929 by Houssay,[70] and such depancreatized-hypophysectomized animals are termed "Houssay animals." Although the blood sugar level of such animals may on occasion be normal, and they exhibit little glycosuria or ketonuria, it would be incorrect to consider the resulting metabolic state a normal one. Hypophysectomized animals are extremely sensitive to the administration of small amounts of insulin, to marked changes in diet, and to alterations in the environmental conditions. Depending on the nature of the stimulus, the blood sugar may fluctuate between wide limits, since an important part of the normal physiological mechanism of regulation is absent.

The phenomenon discovered by Houssay directs attention to the presence, in the pituitary secretion, of a "diabetogenic" factor to which insulin is antagonistic. Of the known pituitary hormones, ACTH and growth hormone deserve special mention as antagonists of insulin; the administration of either markedly reduces the sensitivity to insulin shown by hypophysectomized animals. The fact that cortical steroids promote gluconeogenesis supports the view that ACTH exerts its diabetogenic action via the adrenal cortex. Since adrenalectomy results in an improvement of the diabetic state, the Houssay phenomenon may be a consequence, in part, of the atrophy of the adrenal cortex after hypophysectomy (p. 949).

[69] C. N. H. Long and F. D. W. Lukens, *J. Exptl. Med.*, **63**, 465 (1936).
[70] B. A. Houssay, *Endocrinology*, **30**, 884 (1942).

The administration of growth hormone to intact dogs and cats induces hyperglycemia, glycosuria, and ketonuria. In other animals (e.g., the rat), this diabetogenic action is not observed unless a moderate diabetes has been induced by partial pancreatectomy, by treatment with alloxan, or by force-feeding of glucose; under these circumstances, the administration of growth hormone accentuates the diabetic state.[71] The growth hormone also exerts, in fasted hypophysectomized rats, a "glycostatic" action which favors the retention of muscle glycogen at normal levels. Since this effect is not observed in fasted diabetic rats, it has been concluded that a greater part of the glycostatic action of the growth hormone may be due to its effect in stimulating insulin secretion[72] (p. 965). In respect to the glycostatic action of growth hormone, it is of interest that, upon administration to fasted rats, the hormone induces the attainment of even higher levels of cardiac glycogen than the high levels caused by fasting alone[73] (cf. p. 497).

It has been reported that a lipoprotein fraction from beef pituitaries and the β_1-lipoproteins from the serum of diabetic rats inhibit the uptake of glucose by diaphragm muscle, and that this inhibition is counteracted by the addition of insulin to the incubation medium. Although this effect was interpreted to indicate an antagonism between a pituitary lipoprotein and insulin in their action on muscle hexokinase, the validity of this conclusion is uncertain in view of the finding that other enzymes also are inhibited by the lipoprotein fraction.[74]

Epinephrine and Glucagon. In the normal animal, epinephrine is perhaps the most important of the various physiological factors that counteract the hypoglycemic action of insulin. A low level of blood glucose stimulates the secretion of epinephrine from the adrenal medulla, and the hormone induces an immediate elevation of blood sugar as a consequence of an increased rate of glycogenolysis in the liver and the muscles. Epinephrine secretion is stimulated by emotional excitement, by injury, or by some drugs employed as anaesthetics (ether, morphine); all these factors induce glycogenolysis.[75]

Epinephrine accelerates the conversion of glycogen to hexose phosphates by promoting the conversion of inactive phosphorylase to the active enzyme[76] (cf. p. 440). The administration of epinephrine to rats causes

[71] J. A. Russell, *Endocrinology,* **48,** 462 (1951).

[72] B. A. Illingworth and J. A. Russell, *Endocrinology,* **48,** 423 (1951).

[73] G. A. Adrouny and J. A. Russell, *Endocrinology,* **59,** 241 (1956).

[74] J. Bornstein, *J. Biol. Chem.,* **205,** 513 (1953); *Biochim. et Biophys. Acta,* **20,** 522 (1956).

[75] C. F. Cori, *Physiol. Revs.,* **11,** 143 (1931).

[76] E. W. Sutherland and C. F. Cori, *J. Biol. Chem.,* **188,** 531 (1951); E. W. Sutherland and W. D. Wosilait, *ibid.,* **218,** 459, 469, 483 (1956); T. W. Rall et al., *ibid.,* **224,** 463 (1957).

a marked rise in the phosphorylase a content of muscle, prevents the disappearance of phosphorylase a in fatigued muscle, and accelerates the resynthesis of the enzyme during recovery after fatigue.[77]

The conversion of inactive liver phosphorylase to the active enzyme is promoted not only by epinephrine, but also by glucagon (p. 942). This effect of glucagon in accelerating glycogenolysis helps to explain its hyperglycemic action. Glucagon does not appear to affect the muscle phosphorylase system, and, although its action on liver phosphorylase is similar to that of epinephrine, further studies may show differences in the mechanism whereby the two hormones exert their effect.

It will be obvious that much remains to be learned about the role of the several hormones that influence carbohydrate metabolism. Studies in whole animals have led to the formulation of biochemical problems that have been attacked in experiments with excised tissues, tissue slices, tissue homogenates, or purified enzymes. Such studies in isolated systems are made difficult, however, by the fact that in many instances the biochemical effect of a hormone on a given tissue is only demonstrable after the injection of the hormone into the intact animal; frequently incubation of the excised tissue with the hormone gives a negative result. Even where positive results are obtained with isolated tissues or enzyme systems, it is important to remember that the hormones, like the enzymes, cannot be considered to act independently of each other in a whole animal. Whereas the organization of enzyme activity is at the level of the single cell, the coordination of hormonal activity is at the level of the entire multicellular complex which constitutes the intact animal. In addition, it should be noted that, although the mechanisms involved in the physiological integration of the rate of hormone secretion are not understood, there are many indications that the central nervous system plays a decisive role in the over-all process.

Furthermore, any process that favors the synthesis of new protein, or any metabolic deficiency that prevents normal protein synthesis, may promote or retard the formation of enzymes important in the metabolism of carbohydrates, and of fats and proteins as well. There is evidence that some hormones may increase the rate of synthesis of enzymes. Clearly, not only the synthesis of enzymic proteins but also the synthesis and release of protein hormones may be controlled in this manner; consequently, a further regulatory factor is introduced into the complex array of hormonal interrelationships. For example, the rate of production of insulin by the pancreas appears to be under the control of the thyroid.[78] Thus the administration of thyroid hormone (or of thyro-

[77] G. T. Cori and B. Illingworth, *Biochim. et Biophys. Acta,* **21,** 105 (1956).

[78] B. A. Houssay, *Vitamins and Hormones,* **4,** 188 (1946).

trophic hormone; p. 950) to partially depancreatized dogs results in a diabetes which has been associated with a marked stimulation of insulin production and eventual degeneration of the β-cells of the islet tissue. If most of the pancreas (ca. 95 per cent) of a rat is removed surgically, the onset of diabetes may be markedly delayed by thyroidectomy. Once diabetes has appeared, however, thyroidectomy does not ameliorate the diabetic state.

Another example is the action of growth hormone in promoting the release of insulin by the β-cells in the cat, dog, and perhaps man.[79] In the cat, the administration of growth hormone also increases the secretion of glucagon by the α-cells, thus partly explaining the temporary hyperglycemia which ensues.

Hormonal Effects on the Metabolism of Lipids

It will be recalled that in the diabetic animal the impairment in the metabolic utilization of glucose is accompanied by a decreased net synthesis of fatty acids and an increased production of ketone bodies. Although it is not known whether insulin intervenes directly at some stage of fatty acid synthesis from C_2 units, the effect of the hormone is to favor this process (p. 957). It is of interest, however, that the utilization, by liver slices from diabetic rats, of isotopic acetate for cholesterol synthesis is greater than by liver slices from normal animals.[80] The reason for this differential effect of insulin deficiency on the synthesis of fatty acids and of cholesterol is obscure, but it may be related to a specific requirement for TPNH in fatty acid formation (cf. p. 612). It has also been suggested that the energetic requirements for sterol synthesis may be adequately met by the oxidation of fatty acids and do not require the oxidation of glucose at the normal rate. In the diabetic animal the oxidation of fatty acids proceeds at an accelerated rate, and insulin decreases the rate of breakdown of long-chain fatty acids.[81]

Although liver slices from diabetic animals convert isotopic acetate or glucose to fat at a diminished rate, in the intact diabetic animal the fat content of the liver is increased, presumably by transport from extrahepatic tissues (cf. p. 587). Apparently this increased mobilization of fat in the tissues is stimulated by pituitary hormones (possibly growth hormone, or ACTH, or both). It has been found, for example, that the administration of purified growth hormone preparations to fasted normal mice leads to a marked increase in the fat content of the liver.[82]

[79] F. G. Young, *Recent Progr. Hormone Research,* **8,** 471 (1953).
[80] S. Hotta and I. L. Chaikoff, *J. Biol. Chem.,* **198,** 895 (1952).
[81] W. J. Lossow et al., *J. Biol. Chem.,* **220,** 839 (1956).
[82] C. M. Szego and A. White, *Endocrinology,* **44,** 150 (1949).

Purified preparations of ACTH also exhibit this property, and the administration, to fasted rats, of preparations of growth hormone or of ACTH causes increased ketosis.[83] It appears that these two hormones (or pituitary factors associated with them in hormone preparations) promote the catabolism of fatty acids.[84] However, the manner in which the enzymic systems for the oxidation of fatty acids are affected is not known at present.

In adrenalectomized rats, the conversion of carbohydrate to fat (as judged by the rate of incorporation, into fatty acids, of deuterium from D_2O in the body water) is markedly increased; this suggests that the adrenal steroids inhibit fat synthesis. This conclusion is supported by studies with liver slices taken from cortisone-treated animals. A similar inhibition of fat formation has been noted in normal rats given ACTH or growth hormone, and with liver slices from animals treated with growth hormone. The findings discussed above indicate that the growth hormone and ACTH (via the adrenal steroids) act in antagonism to insulin, not only in carbohydrate metabolism, but in fat metabolism as well. That the effect of the growth hormone is not mediated by its action on the pancreas is shown by the ability of liver slices from Houssay animals to utilize acetate for fatty acid synthesis at a normal rate; the administration of growth hormone to such animals leads to a decreased capacity for hepatic lipogenesis.[85]

Glucagon and epinephrine appear to play a role in the hepatic metabolism of fatty acids; with liver slices, the presence of either hormone in the incubation medium causes an increase in ketone body formation and decreased lipogenesis.[86] It is probable that these effects are related to variations in the supply of carbohydrate, which is necessary for lipogenesis. Thus factors that lead to a decrease in the available carbohydrate (starvation, diabetes, glycogenolysis) also diminish lipogenesis.

Hormonal Effects on Nitrogen Metabolism [87]

Earlier in this chapter, it was mentioned that the increased deposition of liver glycogen observed on administration of adrenal cortical steroids is accompanied by an increased excretion of urinary nitrogen[88] (Table 3). These findings were interpreted as suggestive of an acceleration of protein breakdown; subsequent studies indicated that the C-11-oxygenated

[83] F. L. Engel and M. G. Engel, *Endocrinology,* **58,** 808 (1956).

[84] A. L. Greenbaum, *Biochem. J.,* **54,** 400 (1953); **63,** 159 (1956).

[85] R. O. Brady et al., *J. Biol. Chem.,* **193,** 459 (1951).

[86] E. S. Haugaard and W. C. Stadie, *J. Biol. Chem.,* **199,** 741 (1952); **200,** 753 (1953); E. S. Haugaard and N. Haugaard, *ibid.,* **206,** 641 (1954).

[87] J. A. Russell, *Federation Proc.,* **14,** 696 (1955).

[88] C. N. H. Long et al., *Endocrinology,* **26,** 309 (1940).

Table 3.   Effects of Adrenal Cortical Extract on Carbohydrate and
Nitrogen Metabolism [88]

Data are given in milligrams per 100 grams of body weight.

	Liver Glycogen	Muscle Glycogen	Glucose in Body Fluids	Nitrogen Excreted in 12 hr
Untreated fasting rats	7	253	37	54
Fasting rats treated hourly with cortical extract	79	260	54	81

steroids (e.g., cortisone) also inhibit the conversion of amino acids to body proteins and accelerate the degradation of amino acids. It would appear, therefore, that the adrenal cortical steroids can influence decisively the nitrogen balance of an animal, as reflected in a decreased rate of protein synthesis, and increased rates of the breakdown of tissue proteins and amino acids. It has not been established whether the effects of cortisone on nitrogen metabolism are a consequence of its action on only one or on more than one of the three processes mentioned above. An "anti-anabolic" effect of the adrenal steroids is suggested by the results of isotope experiments in which glycine-N^{15} was administered to fasting adrenalectomized rats.[89] The manner in which this effect is exerted is unknown, although the suggestion has been made that adrenal steroids may inhibit the rate of protein synthesis by antagonizing the action of insulin (cf. p. 959), thus decreasing the rate at which energy is supplied from the breakdown of glucose. Another possibility is that the adrenal steroids diminish the rate of protein synthesis by influencing the metabolism of nucleic acids[90] (cf. p. 746). Evidence for a "catabolic" action of the adrenal steroids has come from studies on the rate of mobilization of protein nitrogen from lymphoid tissues (thymus, spleen, mesenteric node, other lymph nodes) and from the liver;[91] the administration of adrenal cortical extracts to adrenalectomized mice (or of ACTH to hypophysectomized mice) leads to a rapid release of nitrogen from these tissues.

In respect to the acceleration, by cortical steroids, of amino acid breakdown, it has been reported that kidney homogenates from adrenalectomized rats exhibit a decreased capacity to oxidize proline; the "proline oxidase" activity may be restored, however, by prolonged treatment of the animals with cortisone, but not with deoxycorticos-

[89] H. D. Hoberman, Yale J. Biol. and Med., 22, 341 (1950).

[90] I. Clark and H. C. Stoerk, J. Biol. Chem., 222, 285 (1956).

[91] A. White and T. F. Dougherty, Endocrinology, 41, 230 (1947); S. Roberts, J. Biol. Chem., 200, 77 (1953).

terone.[92] Similarly, the tryptophan peroxidase (p. 837) activity of rat liver is decreased in adrenalectomized animals; the administration of cortisone to normal or adrenalectomized rats causes an increase in the enzyme level.[93]

Thyroxine, like the adrenal cortical steroids, favors the mobilization of protein from the tissues. In thyroidectomized rats, the rate of release of tissue protein nitrogen is decreased; the normal rate is restored upon treatment of the animals with thyroxine.[94] Although the net effect of thyroid hormone is to favor protein breakdown, an increase of some proteins (muscle hexokinase, cytochrome c) has been observed after the administration of thyroxine.

The role of insulin in promoting protein synthesis has been mentioned in relation to the endocrine control of carbohydrate metabolism. It is known that untreated diabetic individuals are in negative nitrogen balance, and that nitrogen equilibrium can be restored by the administration of insulin. It appears probable that insulin, by promoting the rate of glucose utilization, increases the rate at which energy derived from oxidative processes is made available for the synthesis of peptide bonds (cf. p. 718). In this connection, it is of interest that insulin promotes the incorporation of labeled alanine into the proteins of rat diaphragm.[95] Furthermore, the rate of synthesis of glutathione by rat liver slices from fasted diabetic rats is below normal values, which may be partially restored by the administration of insulin and of carbohydrate.[96] In addition to the possibility that hormones may regulate the rate of energy supply for peptide bond synthesis, other factors such as the rate of penetration of amino acids may also be under endocrine control.

The role of insulin in promoting protein synthesis is probably involved in the action of growth hormone on protein metabolism. The administration of this pituitary hormone to normal animals (either young or adult) leads to a diminished rate of excretion of nitrogen and a lower level of α-amino acid nitrogen in the blood.[97] As a consequence, a positive nitrogen balance may be induced. Prolonged treatment of rats with anterior pituitary extracts causes a marked increase in body weight associated with an increase in the amount of protein and of water.[98] This effect is observed even when the daily food intake of the treated animals is strictly limited to the amount consumed by untreated rats;

[92] W. W. Umbreit and N. E. Tonházy, J. Biol. Chem., 191, 249 (1951).

[93] W. E. Knox and V. H. Auerbach, J. Biol. Chem., 214, 307 (1955).

[94] P. K. Bondy, Endocrinology, 45, 605 (1949).

[95] F. M. Sinex et al., J. Biol. Chem., 198, 615 (1952).

[96] M. E. Krahl, J. Biol. Chem., 200, 99 (1953).

[97] W. D. Lotspeich, J. Biol. Chem., 185, 221 (1950).

[98] F. G. Young, Biochem. J., 39, 515 (1945).

such control of diet is necessary since the administration of pituitary extracts, for some unexplained reason, leads to increased appetite.

Further evidence for the role of growth hormone in promoting nitrogen retention is provided by experiments on the rate of urea production from amino acids administered intravenously to nephrectomized rats;[99] these studies support the view that the growth hormone acts to favor protein synthesis rather than to diminish amino acid breakdown. Additional support comes from the finding that, in hypophysectomized rats, the rate of replacement of serum albumin is diminished, but can be greatly accelerated by the administration of growth hormone preparations.[100] It should be added, however, that, although the incorporation of C^{14}-leucine into rat liver proteins and of C^{14}-orotic acid into the microsomal RNA (cf. p. 897) is decreased upon hypophysectomy, these effects are not reversed by the administration of growth hormone if the food intake is controlled.[101]

Other hormones implicated in protein metabolism are the androgens (e.g., testosterone), which appear to promote protein synthesis.[102] The mode of action of these hormones in influencing protein metabolism is obscure, although a synergistic action of testosterone and of growth hormone has been suggested.

Hormonal Regulation of Electrolyte Balance

It will be recalled that the administration of sodium chloride to an adrenalectomized animal markedly prolongs life by counteracting the profound disturbance in electrolyte balance that follows adrenal insufficiency. Characteristic features of such adrenal dysfunction (whether in experimental animals or in Addisonian patients) are: (1) a marked increase in the excretion of sodium, chloride, and bicarbonate ions in the urine and sweat; (2) abnormally high levels of potassium ions in the blood; and (3) a movement of potassium ions and of water into tissue cells (Table 4). The high concentrations of potassium ion are toxic to the organism. The increased excretion of sodium ions is accompanied by a net loss of water from the body; this is followed by the passage of water into the tissues, with a consequent decrease in blood volume, hemoconcentration, a diminished blood flow through the kidneys, and a reduced output of urine. These effects of adrenalectomy may be counteracted by the administration of either sodium chloride or an adrenal cortical extract. Of the known cortical steroids, the one most

[99] J. A. Russell, *Endocrinology,* **49,** 99 (1951).
[100] F. Ulrich et al., *J. Biol. Chem.,* **209,** 117 (1954).
[101] E. Reid et al., *Biochem. J.,* **64,** 33 (1956).
[102] C. D. Kochakian, *Vitamins and Hormones,* **4,** 256 (1946).

Table 4. Electrolyte and Water Content of Muscle of Normal and Adrenalectomized Dogs [103]

The data are per kilogram of fat-free muscle.

Constituent	Normal	Adrenalectomized
Chloride (milliequivalents)	19.5	15.1
Sodium (milliequivalents)	28.2	16.8
Potassium (milliequivalents)	83.5	87.6
Extracellular water (grams)	159	137
Intracellular water (grams)	604	641
Collagen nitrogen (grams)	4.9	6.0

active in promoting sodium retention and potassium excretion is aldosterone;[104] deoxycorticosterone (cortexone, DOC) is less effective (cf. p. 947). Aldosterone is about 25 times as effective as DOC in promoting Na^+ retention, and about 5 times as effective in promoting K^+ excretion. In contrast to DOC, aldosterone is active in the liver glycogen test, and resembles the other 11-oxygenated adrenal steroids in influencing carbohydrate, fat, and protein metabolism. Corticosterone and cortisol also exert an effect on electrolyte balance, but to a much lesser degree than aldosterone or DOC; since the secretion of corticosterone and of cortisol is under the control of ACTH, this pituitary hormone can also influence electrolyte balance. It appears that the secretion of aldosterone by the adrenal cortex is not controlled by ACTH to the same extent as the secretion of corticosterone.

It is probable that the primary action of aldosterone and of DOC is to promote the reabsorption of Na^+ and the clearance of K^+ in the kidney tubules.[105] The cortical steroids cause an increase in urinary volume, and prolonged treatment with cortical extract may lead to a state resembling diabetes insipidus (p. 950), characterized by great thirst and the intake and output of large volumes of water. Whereas cortisone and cortisol appear to exert this effect by inhibiting the secretion of the antidiuretic principle of the posterior pituitary, aldosterone and DOC are thought to inhibit the tubular reabsorption of water. The diuretic effect characteristic of aldosterone and of DOC is accompanied by a tendency toward the retention of fluid in the tissues as a consequence of the retention of Na^+; hence, if the water intake is limited, the diuresis may be overcome. In untreated adrenalectomized animals, the increase in K^+ of the muscles is accompanied by an increase in Mg^{2+}, a factor that also may contribute to the physiological effects of adrenal insufficiency.

[103] E. Muntwyler et al., *J. Biol. Chem.*, **134**, 367 (1940).

[104] S. A. Simpson and J. F. Tait, *Recent Progr. Hormone Research*, **11**, 183 (1955).

[105] R. Gaunt et al., *Physiol. Revs.*, **29**, 281 (1949).

As noted earlier, growth hormone promotes the growth of bone, a process dependent on the availability of calcium and phosphate ions. The administration of this pituitary factor to normal animals leads to a decrease in urinary phosphate and an increase in serum phosphate. In immature hypophysectomized rats, the administration of growth hormone causes a rise in the level of bone alkaline phosphatase (p. 581).[106]

Hormones in Invertebrates

Among the invertebrates, the clearest examples of the hormonal control of metabolism are found among the *Insecta* and *Crustacea*. Although it has been established that hormones play a role in certain phases of growth and development, reproduction, and physiological color change, few data are available about the biochemical processes under hormonal control or the chemical nature of the hormones involved. In general, the methods employed in the study of invertebrate endocrinology are similar to those applied to higher animals.

Insects.[107] In nearly all insects, growth after emergence from the egg is characterized by the process of metamorphosis.[108] Some insects such as *Lepidoptera* (moths, butterflies) and *Diptera* (flies) emerge from the egg as larvae that pass through a pupal stage, during which the larval form undergoes metamorphosis to the adult reproducing insect. These insects are considered to undergo "complete" metamorphosis and are termed "holometabolous"; they are distinguished from the "hemimetabolous" insects (e.g., grasshoppers, bugs, roaches) which undergo "incomplete" metamorphosis and emerge from the egg as a miniature adult (nymph) which gradually changes to the fully grown adult. In both holometabolous and hemimetabolous insects, growth and metamorphosis are characterized by the process of molting (ecdysis, from Greek *ekdysis*, a getting out). For example, in the growth of the larval form of the giant silkworm *Platysalmia cecropia* (a holometabolous insect of the order *Lepidoptera*), a series of four molts occurs, and the larva increases in size during the period between the shedding of the old cuticle and the hardening of the new exoskeleton; the stages between the larval molts are termed "instars." The insect then enters the pupal stage and surrounds itself with a cocoon, within which it undergoes metamorphosis to the adult moth. In *Cecropia* and other holometabolous insects, the pupal stage may be characterized by an extended period of dormancy (diapause).

[106] J. C. Mathies and O. H. Gaebler, *Endocrinology,* **45,** 129 (1949).

[107] C. M. Williams, *Harvey Lectures,* **47,** 126 (1953); P. Karlson, *Vitamins and Hormones,* **14,** 227 (1956).

[108] V. B. Wigglesworth, *The Physiology of Insect Metamorphosis,* Cambridge University Press, Cambridge, 1954.

These events in molting and metamorphosis are under the control of endocrine organs, among which are (1) neurosecretory cells (in the brain) linked to the corpus cardiacum, (2) the prothoracic gland (usually in the anterior thorax), and (3) the corpus allatum (usually a paired organ in the head). In the larvae of some insects, the corpus cardiacum and the corpus allatum are replaced by the ring gland. The neurosecretory cells release hormonal factors that travel to the corpus cardiacum, where they are stored and from which they are secreted into the circulation. Among these hormones is a "trophic" factor that stimulates the prothoracic gland to secrete a hormone (ecdysone) that induces molting. Ecdysone is essential for the metamorphosis of a wide variety of holometabolous and hemimetabolous insects, and also promotes adult differentiation; it has been termed "growth and development hormone," "molting hormone," "pupation hormone," and "metamorphosis hormone." In the larval molt, the action of ecdysone is accompanied by that of the secretion of the corpus allatum, which prevents metamorphosis and preserves the larval character of the insect; for this reason, the corpus allatum hormone is termed the "juvenile hormone" or the "larval hormone." In the absence of the prothoracic gland secretion, the juvenile hormone is inactive. During the last larval stage, the activity of the corpus allatum decreases, and the lowered amount of the juvenile hormone leads to the stimulation of metamorphosis by ecdysone.

Two crystalline substances with ecdysone activity (α-ecdysone and β-ecdysone) have been obtained from pupae of the silk moth *Bombyx mori*. α-Ecdysone has a probable formula of $C_{18}H_{30}O_4$ (or $C_{18}H_{32}O_4$), but its chemical structure has not been elucidated as yet.[109] The activity of ecdysone preparations may be tested with larvae of the blow-fly *Calliphora erythrocephala* which have been ligated so as to prevent the secretion of the ring gland from reaching the abdomen; the injection of ecdysone into the abdomen induces pupation. In *Lepidoptera*, ecdysone causes not only pupation but also characteristic color changes; it is essential for the development of the adult inside the pupa. Furthermore, α-ecdysone is active in promoting molting in hemimetabolous insects (e.g., the tropical bug *Rhodnius prolixus*).

The juvenile hormone elaborated by the corpus allatum appears to be soluble in organic solvents, and is present in significant amounts in the abdomen of male adult *Cecropia;* its chemical nature has not been established.[110]

The enzymic processes directly influenced by ecdysone and the juvenile hormone are unknown.[111] Although the phenomenon of pupation appears to involve the participation of tyrosinase, ecdysone does not activate this

[109] A. Butenandt and P. Karlson, *Z. Naturforsch.,* **9b,** 389 (1954).
[110] C. M. Williams, *Nature,* **178,** 212 (1956).
[111] P. Karlson et al., *Z. physiol. Chem.,* **300,** 35, 42 (1955).

enzyme *in vitro*. In the diapausing pupa of *Cecropia*, cytochrome b$_5$ (p. 356) appears to be the principal terminal respiratory catalyst, whereas in the developing pupa the cytochrome oxidase system is operative.[112] However, the manner in which ecdysone stimulates the transformation of the respiratory chain has not been elucidated.

In addition to the elaboration of the juvenile hormone, the corpus allatum appears to secrete factors that influence reproduction (e.g., egg maturation in the female), color changes, and other metabolic events. Little is known about the chemical nature of these hormones or their mode of action.

Crustacea.[113] Of the several hormonal activities in crustacean tissues, those involved in physiological color changes have been studied most intensively, but several aspects of the growth and reproductive processes also are known to be under hormonal control. Almost all the known crustacean hormones are believed to originate in neurosecretory cells in the brain and central nervous system. Many of the hormones appear to be released into the blood by the sinus glands (organs present in the eyestalks or, in species lacking eyestalks, in the head). However, the available data indicate that this gland serves mainly as a reservoir for hormonal material produced in the medulla by the "X-organ," which is composed of neurosecretory cells whose axons lead directly to the sinus gland. None of the crustacean hormones has been obtained in pure form, but the same types of hormonal control of physiological changes have been observed in many crustaceans.

Crustaceans from which the sinus glands (or the X-organs) have been removed molt much more frequently than normal animals. The specific physiological processes associated with molting (resorption of calcium from the exoskeleton, increased rate of oxygen consumption, and absorption of large volumes of water) become evident almost immediately after the surgical removal of the sinus glands. These effects have been attributed to the absence of a molt-inhibiting hormone, elaborated by the X-organ and the sinus gland. The X-organ also secretes a molt-promoting hormone, which stimulates the molting gland (Y-organ); thus, molting in crustacea appears to involve a "trophic" hormone, as in insects.

Upon removal of the eyestalks, the rate of oxygen consumption increases, the R.Q. falls, and hypoglycemia results; similar changes are observed with intact animals in the state prior to molting. Injection of eyestalk extracts produces hyperglycemia. The importance of the regulation of carbohydrate metabolism during molting is evident from the fact that chitin (p. 423), a major component of the exoskeleton, is

---

[112] A. M. Pappenheimer, Jr., and C. M. Williams, *J. Biol. Chem.*, **209**, 915 (1954); D. G. Shappirio and C. M. Williams, *Proc. Roy. Soc.*, **147B**, 218, 233 (1957).

[113] F. G. W. Knowles and D. B. Carlisle, *Biol. Revs.*, **31**, 396 (1956).

derived from tissue glycogen. Other biochemical factors important in the molting process (water balance, metabolism of calcium and of phosphate) also appear to be under endocrine control.

The pigments responsible for the body color of crustaceans are found in the small bodies termed chromatophores, which are either in or just under the hypodermis. The apparent color of the animal is determined by the relative dispersion and concentration of the various pigments within each chromatophore, and this, in turn, is controlled almost exclusively by hormones. The secretion of color-change hormones appears to depend on a diurnally rhythmic mechanism and on the stimulation of the nerves of the compound eye. Thus some crustaceans can adapt their body color almost at will to match that of their environment.

In general, the effects of the hormones that control body color have been studied with "eyestalkless" animals; the species most frequently used are *Palaemonetes* (a shrimp), *Crago* (a shrimp), and *Uca* (the fiddler crab). A variety of hormones have been associated with the chromatophoric pigment changes. Apparently, the "lightening hormones" induce the concentration of the dark pigments (red, black), thereby blanching the body color of the animal; the "darkening hormones" cause the dispersal of these pigments within the chromatophores. Extracts exhibiting each type of hormonal activity have been prepared from the appropriate tissues. None of the hormones that control the chromatophore systems of crustaceans has been identified with any known hormone of insects or vertebrates, although the *Uca*-darkening hormone appears to resemble intermedin (p. 954) in some respects.

To the effects of eyestalk removal discussed above must be added a marked increase in the size of the ovary (in females) and of the testes (in males). The ripening ovary of crustaceans produces a hormone that resembles progesterone (p. 638) in its action.

Each of the ommatidia of the compound eyes of crustaceans contains three types of pigment cells. The position of the pigment within the cells and the position of the "proximal-pigment cells" within the ommatidia depend, in large part, on the intensity of light to which the eyes are exposed. It has been shown that the relative positions of the retinal pigments are at least partially under hormonal control.

Plant Hormones

The term plant hormone, or phytohormone, is applied to any biologically active organic material of plant origin that is effective in very small amounts at a site remote from the tissue where it is formed. Although the use of the word hormone in plant physiology was originally adopted to describe specific growth-promoting substances ("auxins"), other factors ("wound hormones," "flowering hormones") have also been included in this category, and some of the B vitamins, steroids, and carotenoids have been classified as phytohormones. The discussion to follow will be concerned only with those phytohormones not treated elsewhere in this book. In Table 5 are listed the groups of plant hormones that have been studied most extensively.

Table 5. Plant Hormones

Type of Hormone	Physiological Effect	Tissue Response
Growth hormones	Stimulation of cell elongation	Longitudinal growth of shoots Tropisms of shoots Growth of leaf veins
	Induction or stimulation of cell division	New root formation Cambial growth Fruit formation and parthenocarpy Callus growth
	Inhibitory effect	Root growth Lateral bud development Abscission of petioles and fruit stalks Flower formation?
Cell division hormones	Induction or stimulation of cell division	"Wound callus"
Flowering hormones	Induction or stimulation of flower formation	

Plant Growth Hormones.[114]   The concept of plant growth hormones arose as the result of studies on the tropisms, or curvatures, of plant tissues in response to light (phototropism) or gravity (geotropism). The work of Charles and Francis Darwin in the latter part of the nineteenth century showed that such tropic responses were governed by the growing point of the tissue and that the "influence" responsible for the curvature of a grass coleoptile (leaf sheath) spreads downward from the apex or growing tip to the base of the tissue. Tropisms in plants were subsequently found to involve the preferential elongation of the cells on one side of a shoot or root; such cell elongation is stimulated by specific substances called auxins (Greek *auxein*, to increase). The term auxin is now used to describe any organic compound which, in low concentra-

[114] J. Bonner, *Harvey Lectures*, **48**, 1 (1954); K. V. Thimann and A. C. Leopold, in G. Pincus and K. V. Thimann, *The Hormones*, Vol. III, Academic Press, New York, 1955; L. J. Audus, *Plant Growth Substances*, Interscience Publishers, New York, 1953.

tions, promotes growth along the longitudinal axis of shoots; this process is the result of cell elongation, and not of cell multiplication.

The role of auxins as the controlling agent of many tropic responses has been explained by a hypothesis first proposed by Cholodny and subsequently confirmed by Went. The negative geotropism of a shoot (i.e., its curvature away from the earth) is attributed to an increased concentration of auxin in the cells on the lower side of a shoot held in a horizontal position; since the cells on the lower side elongate more rapidly than those on the upper side, the shoot curves upwards. Similarly, the accumulation of auxin on the lower side of a root held in a horizontal position is thought to inhibit cell elongation on this side and to induce the positive geotropism characteristic of roots. Presumably, the lateral distribution of auxins in an upright shoot is affected by light in such a way as to produce phototropic responses. The ability of auxins to induce the formation of new roots, a process generally studied in pieces of stem or "cuttings," appears to involve the normal downward transport of the growth hormones from the growing tip with the resultant accumulation of auxins in the basal region of the cutting and the production of root initials.

It was demonstrated by Went in 1926 to 1928 that the plant growth hormones can diffuse from excised coleoptile tips into agar blocks and that, when the agar block is applied to decapitated coleoptiles, cell elongation occurs. However, the concentration of active material in these tips was too small to permit isolation, and other natural materials were tested as possible sources of hormones. (For a description of the technique used to assay for auxin activity, see Went and Thimann.[115])

The best known auxin is indolyl-3-acetic acid (indoleacetic acid, IAA), probably derived from tryptophan via indolyl-3-pyruvic acid (p. 846), or via tryptamine. IAA is widely distributed in higher plants, and the plant tissues richest in IAA appear to be most active in effecting its formation from tryptophan. The hormone is formed in rapidly growing tissues (coleoptile tip, apical bud, young leaf, root tip, etc.). Much of the IAA in plants exists in conjugated form, such as IAA-protein compounds. IAA occurs in human urine, probably as a consequence of the ingestion of plant foods.

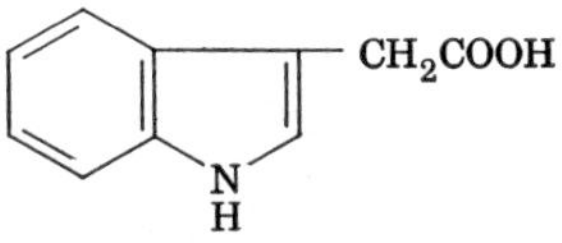

Indolyl-3-acetic acid (IAA)

[115] F. W. Went and K. V. Thimann, *Phytohormones*, The Macmillan Co., New York, 1937.

Plant tissues also contain indolyl-3-acetaldehyde, which has weak auxin activity, but is readily oxidized enzymically to IAA. In addition, indolyl-3-acetonitrile (side chain, —CH_2CN) occurs in several plants; for some coleoptiles it is a more effective auxin than is IAA.[116] Reports by Kögl on the isolation of two active cyclopentene derivatives (auxin a and auxin b) have not been confirmed, so that at present the only well-established natural auxins are indole derivatives, notably IAA.

Indoleacetic acid is inactivated in plant systems, and the steady-state concentration of IAA at its site of action is probably a resultant of the relative rates of access of the auxin and its destruction. Among the factors that are known to inactivate IAA are (1) photooxidation catalyzed by riboflavin, chlorophyll, and a variety of fluorescent dyes, and (2) an "IAA oxidase" system, which appears to involve the action of a peroxidase; some plant tissues contain an inhibitor of IAA oxidase.[117] Although indole-3-aldehyde (inactive as an auxin) may be a product of the oxidation of IAA, the mechanism of the process has not been elucidated.[118]

As noted in Table 5, natural auxins not only stimulate cell elongation in shoots, but also exert a stimulatory effect on cell division and growth in some tissues and inhibit growth or development in other tissues. A number of aromatic compounds (e.g., α-naphthalene acetic acid, 2,4-dichlorophenoxyacetic acid) are known to produce one or more of these effects in plants. However, the specific activity of these synthetic auxins relative to that of IAA may vary greatly and it depends on the physiological process under investigation. Some of the compounds act as auxin antagonists in its effect on root elongation; others promote the action of IAA. The inhibitory effect may be related to competition with IAA for an enzymic system, and the synergistic effect may be to promote auxin transport.

The biochemical basis of the action of auxin has not been elucidated. It is known that increased respiration is associated with auxin action, and involves the aerobic oxidation of carbohydrates and of organic acids. This rise in the rate of respiration is accompanied by an increase in the uptake of water, possibly by an energy-requiring process. In this connection, it is of interest that IAA also promotes the uptake of amino acids (glycine, glutamic acid) by plant cells.[119]

Cell Division Hormones. An injury to plant tissues is followed by the production of scar tissue or "wound callus" at the site of the wound.

[116] B. B. Stowe and K. V. Thimann, *Arch. Biochem. and Biophys.,* **51,** 499 (1954).

[117] W. A. Gortner and M. Kent, *J. Biol. Chem.,* **204,** 593 (1953).

[118] P. M. Ray and K. V. Thimann, *Science,* **122,** 187 (1955); *Arch. Biochem. and Biophys.,* **64,** 175 (1956).

[119] L. Reinhold and R. G. Powell, *Nature,* **177,** 658 (1956).

This is due to the induction of cell division of already fully matured plant cells and appears to be under the control of two hormonal principles. One of these probably is auxin, and the second is a "wound hormone" liberated by the injured cells. A wound hormone has been isolated from the juice of crushed bean pods and shown to be Δ^1-decene-1,10-dicarboxylic acid (traumatic acid).[120] A number of other dicarbox-

$$HOOCCH{=}CH(CH_2)_8COOH$$
Traumatic acid

ylic acids closely related in structure to traumatic acid also show wound hormone activity. In addition, a variety of other substances are known to stimulate cell division in higher plants. Among these are 1,3-diphenylurea $(C_6H_5NHCONHC_6H_5)$, present in coconut milk, and derivatives of anthocyanins[121] (p. 669), as well as 6-furfurylaminopurine (p. 207), which may be derived from DNA.[122] The biochemical mechanisms whereby traumatic acid and other cell division hormones exert their physiological effect are unknown.

Flower-Forming Hormones. Flowering depends on the exposure of a plant to alternating periods of light and darkness, and appears to be controlled by hormonal principles termed "florigens," which induce flower formation. Although attempts to prepare plant tissue extracts that have flower-forming activity have been uniformly unsuccessful, a large body of data from many laboratories supports the view that leaves are activated by photoperiodic stimuli to produce florigens which are translocated to the growing points. Furthermore, it has been reported that the "hormones" are not species-specific and that the same substances are active in long-day and in short-day plants. In the isolated instance of the pineapple, flowering is induced by synthetic auxins, but not by IAA, possibly because of the rapid destruction of IAA in pineapple leaves.

The fungus *Gibberella fujikuroi* elaborates substances (gibberellic acid, gibberellin A_1, gibberellin A_2) that exert an auxin-like action in promoting shoot growth by cell elongation and, in addition, induce flower formation. The possibility exists that these fungal substances are closely related to natural hormones of higher plants. The chemical structure of the gibberellins has not been elucidated, but gibberellic acid, the most readily accessible member of the group, appears to be a tetracyclic dihydroxy-lactonic acid of the composition $C_{19}H_{22}O_6$.[123]

[120] J. English, Jr., et al., *Proc. Natl. Acad. Sci.*, **25**, 323 (1939); *J. Am. Chem. Soc.*, **61**, 3434 (1939).

[121] E. M. Shantz and F. C. Steward, *J. Am. Chem. Soc.*, **77**, 6351 (1955); *Plant Physiol.*, **30**, Suppl. 35 (1955).

[122] C. O. Miller et al., *J. Am. Chem. Soc.*, **77**, 1392 (1955).

[123] P. W. Brian and J. F. Grove, *Endeavour*, **16**, 161 (1957).

In 1906 F. G. Hopkins suggested that the dietary requirements of animals include certain unknown "minimal qualitative factors," present in the tissues of plants and animals and similar to the "dietetic" factors then known to be involved in such diseases as scurvy and rickets. Six years later Hopkins[1] presented the first conclusive evidence that natural materials contain "accessory factors" which "secure the utilization for growth of the protein and energy contained in . . . artificial mixtures of purified proteins, fats, carbohydrates, and inorganic salts."

These accessory factors have proved to be organic compounds of relatively simple structure and are required in small amounts; consequently they are not utilized as sources of energy or of amino acid nitrogen. They are called vitamins, a name proposed by Funk in 1912 to describe the dietetic factors that prevent or cure deficiency diseases of higher animals. Originally. this term was spelled vitamines, since Funk believed the antiberiberi factor in rice polishings to be an amine essential for life (Latin *vita*, life). The term "vitamin" is usually employed to denote accessory factors for microorganisms as well as animals, although some microbial forms require "growth factors" that are not among the recognized dietary essentials for any higher animal. A valuable reference work on vitamins has been edited by Sebrell and Harris.[2]

For historical reasons, the nomenclature used in the vitamin field is often confusing. In general, these accessory factors are divided into two main groups: (1) the water-soluble vitamins, and (2) the fat-soluble vitamins (and provitamins) designated by the letters A, D, E and K. In the group of water-soluble vitamins are ascorbic acid and the ever-increasing number of compounds referred to as members of the "vitamin B complex." According to R. J. Williams, for a compound to be

[1] F. G. Hopkins, *J. Physiol.*, **44**, 425 (1912).
[2] W. H. Sebrell, Jr., and R. S. Harris, *The Vitamins*, Vols. I–III, Academic Press, New York, 1954.

classified as a member of the B group, it must act, or be presumed to act, as part of a biocatalytic system. The fact that many B vitamins have already been shown to occur as essential constituents of cofactors for a variety of enzyme systems helps to explain the vital importance of these compounds.

An examination of the early history of research on the vitamins[3] shows that the present status of this aspect of biochemistry is the outgrowth of work in many apparently unrelated fields; this is especially true with respect to the water-soluble vitamins of the B complex. For example, thiamine (vitamin B_1) was isolated in pure form as a result of an intensive search for the antiberiberi factor; riboflavin (vitamin B_2) was first shown to be a constituent of the prosthetic group of the "yellow enzyme" obtained from yeast and then was demonstrated to be an essential accessory factor for animals and for certain bacteria; pantothenic acid was initially recognized as a growth factor (a constituent of "bios") for yeast and only later shown to have activity for animals.

The study of microbial nutrition contributed much to the elucidation of the biochemical function of the water-soluble vitamins. In particular, the technique known as "competitive analogue-metabolite inhibition" has applied to growth studies with microorganisms the concepts developed earlier to explain the action of inhibitors on isolated enzyme systems (cf. p. 260). This technique is an outgrowth of the observation[4] that the bacteriostatic effect of sulfanilamide is competitively reversed by p-aminobenzoic acid, a compound not previously known to possess any biochemical function. It was suggested that the sulfonamide, a structural analogue of p-aminobenzoic acid, served as a competitive inhibitor of a bacterial enzyme system for which p-aminobenzoic was an essential cofactor. This hypothesis received support from subsequent work on the biological action of p-aminobenzoic acid. Woods' discovery of the antagonism between these two aromatic amines prompted a wide search for chemotherapeutic agents among structural analogues of compounds known to have metabolic importance.[5] The application of competitive analogue-metabolite inhibition to the study of microbial metabolism was developed by Shive and his collaborators;[6] this technique also has been used to advantage in work on mammalian metabolism.

Studies of animal nutrition have shown that the microorganisms present

[3] H. R. Rosenberg, *Chemistry and Physiology of the Vitamins,* Interscience Publishers, New York, 1942.

[4] D. D. Woods, *Brit. J. Exptl. Path.,* **21**, 74 (1940).

[5] R. O. Roblin, Jr., *Chem. Revs.,* **38**, 255 (1946); A. Albert, *Selective Toxicity,* Methuen and Co., London, 1951; D. W. Woolley, *A Study of Antimetabolites,* John Wiley & Sons, New York, 1952.

[6] R. J. Williams et al., *The Biochemistry of the B-Vitamins,* Reinhold Publishing Corp., New York, 1950.

in the intestinal tract make important contributions to the supply of vitamins available to the host animal.[7] Thus the lack of a dietary requirement by an animal for a certain vitamin may mean that sufficient quantities of the factor are made available to the organism by intestinal microorganisms. The intestinal flora also may utilize or destroy some of the dietary vitamins, thus making them unavailable to the host. Since the microbiological character of the intestinal flora is influenced by the composition of the diet, the vitamin requirements of an animal may change if the proportions of dietary carbohydrate, fat, and protein are markedly altered.

Although the vitamin requirements of higher plants have not been fully elucidated, it appears probable that microorganisms contribute vitamins to the nutrition of plant tissues. Studies with excised roots and plant embryos (under sterile conditions) have shown that an exogenous supply of several B vitamins is required by such tissues of a number of plants (e.g., tomato, pea, alfalfa, carrot).

Ascorbic Acid (Vitamin C)[8]

Scurvy, the human disease resulting from a deficiency of ascorbic acid, has been known for many centuries, and the curative action of citrus fruits has long been recognized. The discovery, made at the beginning of the present century, that the guinea pig is susceptible to scurvy, provided a test animal for the study of this metabolic disorder. In 1932 Waugh and King isolated the curative agent (vitamin C) in crystalline form from lemon juice; this crystalline material was identical with the "hexuronic acid" previously obtained by Szent-Györgyi from adrenal cortex, oranges, and cabbage juice, and was given the name ascorbic acid. The structure of ascorbic acid (L-ascorbic acid, L-xylo-ascorbic acid) was established by degradation and by synthesis in 1933.

Among higher animals, only primates and the guinea pig require a dietary supply of vitamin C, since they are not able to convert L-gulono-lactone to ascorbic acid (p. 540); other animals (e.g., rats) can synthesize the vitamin from carbohydrate. As mentioned previously (cf. p. 539), higher plants (e.g., pea seedlings) can also effect the biosynthesis of ascorbic acid. This compound is not an essential constituent of the culture media for most microorganisms, and some organisms (e.g., yeast) do not seem to contain ascorbic acid; it is catabolized, however, by some bacteria, including strains isolated from human feces.

Ascorbic acid is a strong reducing agent (cf. p. 299), and this property provides the basis for the quantitative estimation of vitamin C. A

[7] O. Mickelsen, *Vitamins and Hormones,* **14,** 1 (1956).
[8] A. P. Meiklejohn, *Vitamins and Hormones,* **11,** 61 (1953).

valuable method involves the oxidation of the vitamin to dehydroascorbic acid, which is then allowed to react with 2,4-dinitrophenylhydrazine to form the red bis-2,4-dinitrophenylhydrazone; the concentration of this product is estimated colorimetrically.[9]

$$
\begin{array}{ccc}
\text{OC}\!\!-\!\! & \text{OC}\!\!-\!\! & \text{COOH} \\
| & | & | \\
\text{HOC} & \text{OC} & \text{CO} \\
\| \quad\; \text{O} & | \quad\; \text{O} & | \\
\text{HOC} & \text{OC} & \text{CO} \\
| & | & | \\
\text{HC}\!\!-\!\! & \text{HC}\!\!-\!\! & \text{HCOH} \\
| & | & | \\
\text{HOCH} & \text{HOCH} & \text{HOCH} \\
| & | & | \\
\text{CH}_2\text{OH} & \text{CH}_2\text{OH} & \text{CH}_2\text{OH} \\
\text{L-Ascorbic acid} & \text{Dehydro-L-ascor-} & \text{Diketo-L-gulonic} \\
 & \text{bic acid} & \text{acid}
\end{array}
$$

(with $-2H$ between the first and second structures, and $+H_2O$ between the second and third)

The oxidation of ascorbic acid to the dehydro compound can be effected by a variety of mild oxidizing agents (including dyes such as 2,6-dichlorophenolindophenol; p. 302), or by molecular oxygen in the presence of traces of copper or of activated charcoal. Dehydroascorbic acid can be reduced to ascorbic acid by treatment with H_2S, glutathione, or other sulfhydryl compounds. In phosphate buffer, even at pH 7, dehydroascorbic acid is relatively unstable and undergoes hydrolysis to the more stable diketo-L-gulonic acid, which does not have vitamin C activity. On the other hand, dehydro-L-ascorbic acid, like ascorbic acid, exhibits vitamin C activity for man (and other primates) and for guinea pigs.

Although little, if any, dehydroascorbic acid or diketogulonic acid is present normally in animal tissues, these compounds are formed *in vivo* from ascorbic acid, and are excreted in the urine by man and by guinea pigs; in both species, dehydroascorbic acid can be converted to diketogulonic acid and to ascorbic acid.

The administration of L-ascorbic acid to normal human subjects is usually followed promptly by the urinary excretion of a relatively large proportion of the test dose. Only replete subjects show this response, and a delay in the excretion of ascorbic acid after the ingestion of 50 to 100 mg of the vitamin is taken as an indication of vitamin C deficiency. This test reveals a depletion of tissue ascorbic acid long before the onset of scurvy, the characteristic lesions of which are petechial hemorrhages in the skin and mucous membranes and degenerative changes in the cartilage and bone matrices. Experiments on the fate of L-ascorbic acid-1-C[14] in normal and in vitamin C-deficient guinea pigs indicate

[9] J. H. Roe and C. A. Kuether, *J. Biol. Chem.*, **147**, 399 (1943); R. R. Schaffert and G. R. Kingsley, *ibid.*, **212**, 59 (1955).

that the vitamin is rapidly taken up by the liver, spleen, adrenals, skin, cartilage, and especially the teeth.[10] It is of interest that essentially all the C^{14} in the cartilage (nasal septum) was found to be present as ascorbic acid; no isotope could be detected in the chondroitin sulfate or collagen fractions isolated from this tissue.

Studies with C^{14}-labeled ascorbic acid have shown that, in guinea pigs, the main route of its breakdown leads to the rapid production of CO_2 from all the carbon atoms of the vitamin.[11] A small amount of the isotope was found in the urine in the form of ascorbic acid, dehydro-ascorbic acid, and diketogulonic acid; in addition, labeled oxalic acid (presumably derived from carbon atoms 1 and 2 of ascorbic acid) was present. It is noteworthy that, in man, the only known metabolic products of the vitamin are dehydroascorbic acid, diketogulonic acid, and oxalic acid; ascorbic acid-1-C^{14} is not oxidized appreciably to $C^{14}O_2$.

The mechanisms whereby ascorbic acid gives rise to CO_2 and oxalic acid in animal tissues have not been elucidated, but it is assumed that the initial step is a conversion to dehydroascorbic acid. This oxidation is catalyzed by many enzyme systems, including polyphenol oxidase, peroxidase, cytochrome oxidase, and a specific ascorbic acid oxidase found in plants (p. 368).

The occurrence of several metabolic abnormalities in vitamin C-deficient animals has led to the suggestion that ascorbic acid participates in the oxidative degradation of tyrosine and in the formation of tetra-hydro derivatives of pteroylglutamic acid.[12] However, ascorbic acid does not appear to act as a specific cofactor in either process, and its role is probably that of a reducing agent. This property of ascorbic acid also may be involved in the utilization of Fe^{3+} in ferritin (cf. p. 912) for the formation of Fe^{2+}-containing enzymes.[13]

The B Vitamins [2,14]

Thiamine (Vitamin B$_1$). The first member of the B complex to be identified was thiamine, whose structure was determined by R. R. Williams and his collaborators. Thiamine is the simplest of the naturally occurring compounds with vitamin B_1 activity. All the more complex structures showing such biological activity contain a thiamine unit; thus thiamine occurs in yeast and in animal tissues mainly as thiamine pyro-

[10] J. J. Burns et al., *J. Biol. Chem.*, **191**, 501 (1951).

[11] J. J. Burns et al., *J. Biol. Chem.*, **218**, 15 (1956).

[12] K. Guggenheim et al., *Biochem. J.*, **62**, 281 (1956).

[13] Y. Takeda and M. Hara, *J. Biol. Chem.*, **214**, 657 (1955).

[14] F. A. Robinson, *The Vitamin B Complex*, John Wiley and Sons, New York, 1951.

$$
\begin{array}{c}
\underset{H_3C-\underset{N}{C^{2'}}\ \underset{3'}{\quad}\ \underset{4'}{C}-NH_2\cdot HCl}{\overset{\overset{\textstyle CH}{\underset{N_{1'}\ \overset{6'}{\diagdown}\ \underset{5'}{C}}{}}{}}-CH_2-\underset{Cl^-}{\quad}-\underset{HC^2\underset{S}{\diagup}{}_1\ \overset{5}{C}-CH_2CH_2OH}{\overset{+}{N_3}\ {}_4\overset{C-CH_3}{}}
\end{array}
$$

Thiamine chloride hydrochloride

$$
\left[\begin{array}{c}
RCH_2-N\text{------}C-CH_3 \\
OCH \qquad C-CH_2CH_2OH \\
-S
\end{array}\right]_2
\qquad\qquad
\begin{array}{c}
RCH_2-N\text{------}C-CH_3 \\
OCH \qquad C-CH_2CH_2OH \\
CH_2=CHCH_2S-S
\end{array}
$$

Disulfide form of thiamine   "Allithiamine"

phosphate (also called diphosphothiamine, cocarboxylase, or TPP), and this molecule may be bound to a protein enzyme such as yeast carboxylase (cf. p. 475). Vitamin activity is also found in higher plants, especially in cereal products, but here thiamine is generally not found in the phosphorylated form.

Not only thiamine itself but also some derivatives in which the thiazole ring has been opened exhibit biological activity for higher animals, including man; among these are the disulfide form of thiamine and "allithiamine." (In the accompanying formulae, R denotes the pyrimidine portion of the thiamine molecule.) It is of interest that "allithiamine" can be formed by extracts of garlic from the thiamine and alliin (p. 60) present as normal constituents of this plant.[15]

Thiamine is essential in the diet of all higher animals except under conditions in which the production of the vitamin by intestinal bacteria completely satisfies the requirements of the animal host. Many microorganisms synthesize thiamine *de novo;* the more exacting species exhibit several types of requirements: (1) various organisms can grow if supplied with a mixture of the thiazole and pyrimidine components of the thiamine molecule; (2) others require only one of these components and apparently are able to synthesize the other; (3) a relatively small number, including several yeasts, show an absolute requirement for thiamine. It is probable that thiamine can be synthesized in most higher plants, although some excised tissues, such as roots, have been found to require a preformed source of the thiazole or pyrimidine portions.[16]

Little is known about the sequence of synthetic reactions in the formation of the vitamin. Studies with thiamine-requiring strains of *Neurospora* suggest that this organism can synthesize thiamine by a direct coupling of the thiazole and pyrimidine units.[17] The conversion of thiamine to thiamine pyrophosphate (TPP) has been demonstrated

---

[15] A. Fujita, *Advances in Enzymol.*, **15**, 389 (1954).

[16] J. Bonner and H. Bonner, *Vitamins and Hormones*, **6**, 225 (1948).

[17] D. L. Harris, *Arch. Biochem. and Biophys.*, **57**, 240 (1955).

in many animal tissues and in microorganisms, and it involves the participation of ATP.[18] Yeast cells also convert thiamine to thiamine monophosphate and thiamine triphosphate, neither of which has co-carboxylase activity;[19] the triphosphate is hydrolyzed to TPP by apyrase (p. 489).

As mentioned previously, TPP participates not only in the reaction catalyzed by yeast carboxylase, but also in the enzymic conversion of pyruvate to acetyl-CoA (cf. p. 481) and to acetoin (cf. p. 480), in the enzymic decarboxylation of α-ketoglutarate (cf. 505) and of other keto acids, and in the reaction catalyzed by transketolase (cf. p. 529). Although all the enzymic reactions that require the participation of TPP appear to involve the initial conversion of the substrate to an "active aldehyde" that is either released as a free aldehyde (e.g., acetaldehyde) or is transferred to a suitable acceptor (as in the formation of acetoin), the chemical mechanism whereby TPP facilitates these transformations is obscure.

The first systematic study of the effects of vitamin B_1 deficiency, in pigeons, was made by Eijkman, in the 1890's. The human deficiency disease, called beriberi, appears to have been known in the Far East for over 1000 years; its prevalence in that region is due to the use of polished rice from which most of the vitamin has been lost during the milling process. In the human, thiamine deficiency generally leads first to loss of appetite (anorexia) and nausea; as the deficiency develops, there appear both neurological symptoms (leading ultimately to peripheral neuritis and degeneration of the medullary sheath) and cardiac manifestations (which may result in death due to cardiac hypertrophy). The symptoms in other mammals and in birds are similar to those in man.

Accompanying these external alterations are biochemical changes in the blood, urine, and tissues. Thus the amount of free thiamine and of TPP in the tissues falls markedly, and there is an increase in the level of pyruvic acid and lactic acid in both the blood and urine. From what has already been said of the role of TPP in the metabolic conversions of pyruvate, the increased pyruvic acid content of avitaminotic animals is readily understandable; the accumulation of lactic acid appears to be due to the fact that the action of lactic dehydrogenase is inhibited by high concentrations of pyruvic acid. Since the oxidative catabolism of lactate and pyruvate is essential for the normal activity of brain tissue, and since pyruvate is an important source of the acetyl group of acetylcholine (cf. p. 578), it follows that any interference with the oxidative decarboxylation of pyruvic acid may be expected to produce

[18] F. Leuthardt and H. Nielsen, *Helv. Chim. Acta,* **35,** 1196 (1952); E. P. Steyn-Parvé, *Biochim. et Biophys. Acta,* **8,** 310 (1952).

[19] K. H. Kiessling, *Biochim. et Biophys. Acta,* **20,** 293 (1956).

abnormalities of the nervous system. The close relation between thiamine and carbohydrate metabolism is indicated further by the observation that rats are able to survive many months without dietary thiamine if their diet contains no carbohydrate. The addition of glucose to the diet of such thiamine-deficient rats leads to loss of weight, polyneuritis, and death.

It should be noted, however, that high levels of blood pyruvate in experimental animals may be caused by factors other than a thiamine deficiency, and the administration of thiamine does not always restore the blood pyruvate to normal values. In some cases of clinical polyneuritis (usually associated with elevated blood pyruvate after the administration of glucose), the blood pyruvate does not return to normal levels when thiamine is given.

Certain foodstuffs contain substances that prevent the utilization of dietary thiamine in the normal manner. One of the most important of these is the enzyme thiaminase,[15] whose action is responsible for a disease (Chastek paralysis) in foxes.[20] This enzyme, present in the raw fish included in the fox diet, destroys thiamine by a reaction in which the thiazole unit is replaced by other bases in fish tissues. Partially purified preparations of thiaminase catalyze the reaction of thiamine with a variety of basic compounds (e.g., pyridine, aniline, quinoline); the reaction with pyridine is shown. Similar enzymes occur in some

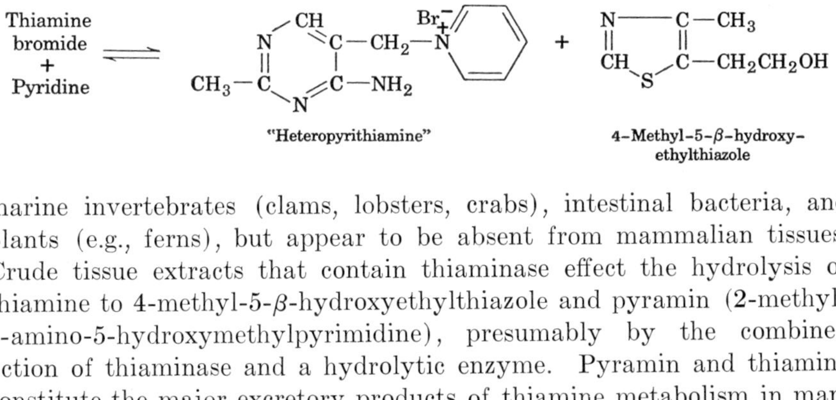

"Heteropyrithiamine"

4-Methyl-5-β-hydroxy-ethylthiazole

marine invertebrates (clams, lobsters, crabs), intestinal bacteria, and plants (e.g., ferns), but appear to be absent from mammalian tissues. Crude tissue extracts that contain thiaminase effect the hydrolysis of thiamine to 4-methyl-5-β-hydroxyethylthiazole and pyramin (2-methyl-4-amino-5-hydroxymethylpyrimidine), presumably by the combined action of thiaminase and a hydrolytic enzyme. Pyramin and thiamine constitute the major excretory products of thiamine metabolism in man, and these two substances are promptly excreted in the urine of replete individuals given large doses of the vitamin.

In addition to thiaminase, "antithiamine substances" of nonenzymic nature have been shown to be present in ferns and many higher plants; these substances appear to be flavonoids. Several synthetic compounds that are structurally related to thiamine interfere with the utilization

[20] W. H. Yudkin, *Physiol. Revs.*, **29**, 389 (1949).

of the vitamin. For example, neopyrithiamine (an analogue of thiamine in which a pyridine nucleus has been substituted for the thiazole nucleus) produces many of the symptoms of thiamine deficiency in animals and interferes with the conversion of thiamine to TPP by the "thiamine kinase" of rat liver. Oxythiamine (the 4′-hydroxy analogue of thiamine) inhibits yeast thiamine kinase, but appears to be ineffective on the mammalian enzyme system.

Various methods are available for the estimation of the thiamine content of natural materials.[2] The older biological assays with poly-neuritic pigeons or with rats have been largely supplanted by micro-

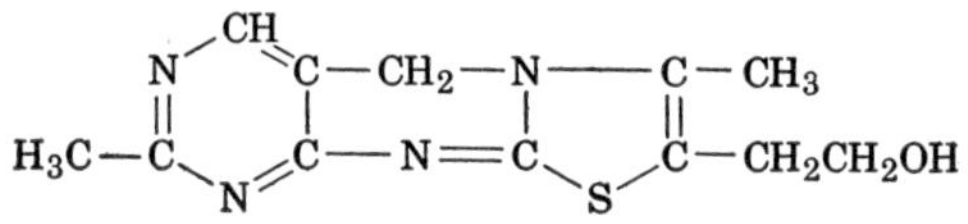

Thiochrome

biological methods; of these, a yeast fermentation method is the one most commonly used. An important chemical procedure for the deter-mination of thiamine involves its oxidation to thiochrome which has a blue fluorescence whose intensity may be measured photometrically.

Riboflavin. Riboflavin (lactoflavin) is the simplest of the naturally occurring compounds which, when included in the diets of higher animals, show vitamin B_2 activity. Clearly, any of the flavoproteins (cf. Chapter

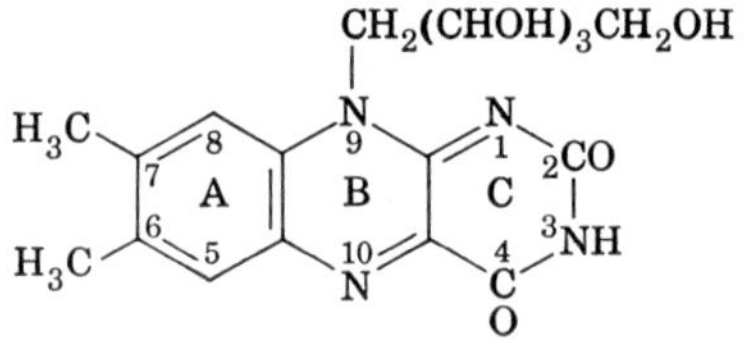

Riboflavin

13) can serve as a dietary source of this vitamin if during digestion the prosthetic group is cleaved from the conjugated protein and is made available for absorption. Several synthetic compounds also have ribo-flavin activity for rats and for some bacteria (Table 1); these compounds differ from riboflavin [6,7-dimethyl-9-(1′-D-ribityl)-isoalloxazine] in the substituents at either the 6 or 7 position of the isoalloxazine nucleus.[21] Alteration of the substituents at positions 6 or 7 may also give compounds that inhibit the utilization of riboflavin. Such antiriboflavin activity is shown by the 5,6-dimethyl analogue of riboflavin (isoriboflavin) and by flavins (e.g., D-galactoflavin) that contain sugar alcohols other than D-ribitol.

[21] J. P. Lambooy, *J. Biol. Chem.*, **188**, 459 (1951).

Table I. Biological Activity of Derivatives of 9-(1'-Ribityl)-isoalloxazine

Substituents on Ring A		Activity	
			Lactobacillus
6 Position	7 Position	Rats	*casei*
CH_3	CH_3	+	+
CH_3	H	+	+
H	CH_3	+	+
C_2H_5	CH_3	+	+
C_2H_5	C_2H_5	(−)†	+
H	H	(−)†	

† Behaves as an antagonist of riboflavin.

Riboflavin is synthesized by most higher plants and by a variety of microorganisms; the yeast *Ashbya gossypii* produces the vitamin in such large amounts that riboflavin crystals are formed in the culture medium. This organism, and the closely related *Eremothecium ashbyii*, have proved valuable in the study of the pathways of riboflavin biosynthesis. The production of the vitamin by growing cultures of *E. ashbyii* is markedly stimulated by purines,[22] and C^{14}-labeled adenine was found to be used for riboflavin formation by a process in which carbon 8 of adenine (cf. p. 187) is lost, but the remaining carbon atoms of the purine are incorporated into ring C of the vitamin.[23] *A. gossypii* and *E. ashbyii* utilize the known precursors of purines (formate, CO_2, glycine) to make ring C of riboflavin, and at least one of the nitrogen

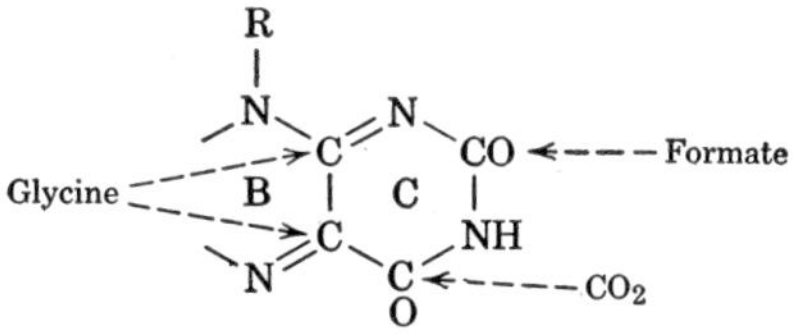

atoms of ring B (like nitrogen 7 of the purines) is derived from glycine.[24] It appears, therefore, that rings B and C of riboflavin arise from an intermediate related to the purines. The remainder of the riboflavin carbon (in the dimethylbenzene and ribityl portions) can be derived from glucose or from acetate,[25] but the mechanisms by which these precursors are used to make the vitamin have not been elucidated as yet.

The importance of the flavin nucleotides (FMN and FAD) in biological

[22] J. A. MacLaren, *J. Bact.*, **63**, 233 (1952).

[23] W. S. McNutt, Jr., *J. Biol. Chem.*, **210**, 511 (1954); **219**, 365 (1956).

[24] G. W. E. Plaut, *J. Biol. Chem.*, **208**, 513 (1954); T. W. Goodwin and O. T. G. Jones, *Biochem. J.*, **64**, 9 (1956).

[25] G. W. E. Plaut and P. L. Broberg, *J. Biol. Chem.*, **219**, 131 (1956).

oxidations, and their enzymic synthesis from riboflavin, were discussed in Chapter 13. It will be recalled that either FMN or FAD is involved in the enzymic oxidation of glucose (cf. p. 339), of fatty acids (cf. p. 597), of amino acids (cf. p. 752), and of purines (cf. p. 855). Although the biochemical action of riboflavin has been fairly well defined, it has not been possible to show how this activity is related to the syndrome of riboflavin deficiency in higher animals. In man such a deficiency is characterized by inflammation of the tongue (glossitis) and lesions at the mucocutaneous juncture of the mouth (cheilosis). Also there are changes in the eye, including marked corneal vascularization, photophobia, and other ocular symptoms. General body weakness and dermatitis may occur. However, a simple ariboflavinosis is rarely seen in man, since diets deficient in riboflavin usually are deficient in other B vitamins, especially nicotinic acid.

A considerable body of data from experiments with plant tissues and plant enzyme preparations has suggested that riboflavin and flavoproteins may play a significant role in the response of plants to light, particularly in the phototrophic curvature of various plant organs[26] (cf. p. 972). It may well be that the riboflavin molecule serves as a photoreceptor in biological systems other than those of higher plants; the well-known ocular changes in higher animals deficient in this vitamin has led to suggestions that riboflavin is involved in vision.[27]

The tissues and urine of animals fed diets deficient in riboflavin show depressed levels of riboflavin and of its nucleotides; in addition, enzymic activity ascribed to flavoproteins (e.g., D-amino acid oxidase, xanthine oxidase) appears to be diminished in the livers of avitaminotic rats.[28] Among the excretory products of riboflavin is the fluorescent substance uroflavin (aquaflavin), a degradation product of the vitamin that is found in most urine samples. Another fluorescent alloxazine derivative, lumichrome (p. 331), is also found in the urine (and milk) of ruminants. This degradation product of riboflavin can be formed from the vitamin by some soil microorganisms (e.g., *Pseudomonas riboflavina*) that cleave riboflavin to lumichrome and ribitol.[29] Presumably the intestinal bacteria of ruminants are responsible for the presence of lumichrome in urine and milk, since it has not been detected in the fluids of other higher animals. Lumichrome does not have riboflavin activity for any organism on which it has been tested; in some instances, it acts as a growth inhibitor.[30]

[26] A. W. Galston, *Science,* **111,** 619 (1950); *Botan. Rev.,* **16,** 361 (1950).
[27] M. Heiman, *Arch. Ophthalmol.,* **28,** 493 (1942).
[28] A. E. Axelrod and C. A. Elvehjem, *J. Biol. Chem.,* **140,** 725 (1941).
[29] T. Yanagita and J. W. Foster, *J. Biol. Chem.,* **221,** 593 (1956).
[30] H. K. Mitchell and M. B. Houlahan, *Am. J. Botany,* **33,** 31 (1946).

As mentioned previously (cf. p. 330), solutions of riboflavin are strongly fluorescent, and this property may be used for the photometric estimation of the vitamin. An important microbiological assay procedure involves the use of *L. casei*, for which the vitamin is an essential growth factor.

Vitamin B$_6$ (Pyridoxine, Pyridoxal, Pyridoxamine). The name vitamin B$_6$ was suggested[31] to designate a factor that prevented a rat dermatitis (called acrodynia) and which was different from riboflavin and from the pellagra-preventive factor (nicotinic acid). In 1938 a crystalline compound with B$_6$ activity was isolated independently by five different groups of investigators. The compound was subsequently shown to be 2-methyl-3-hydroxy-4,5-di(hydroxymethyl)-pyridine (pyridoxine). In the course of the development of a microbiological assay for pyridoxine using *Streptococcus fecalis* R as the test organism, Snell[32] discovered that other forms of vitamin B$_6$ exist in nature; these compounds are the

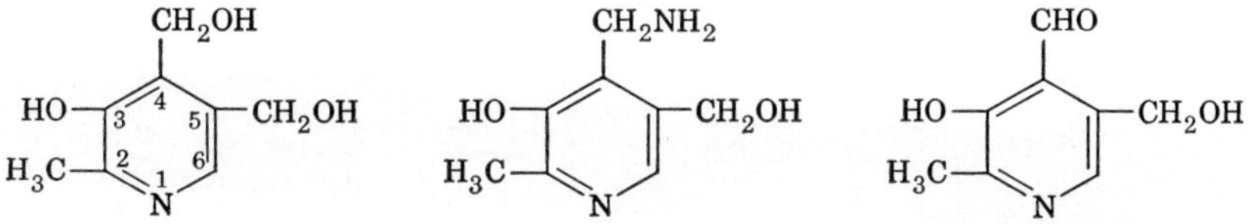

Pyridoxine   Pyridoxamine   Pyridoxal

4-aminomethyl (pyridoxamine) and 4-formyl (pyridoxal) analogues of pyridoxine.

The three members of the B$_6$ group occur in nature in combined form; pyridoxamine and pyridoxal are found as the corresponding phosphates (cf. p. 761), but the structure of the combined form of pyridoxine, which is the principal form of the vitamin in wheat and rice seeds, has not been determined. Pyridoxine, pyridoxamine, and pyridoxal are interchangeable in their biological activity for mammals and birds, but their relative activity as growth factors for microorganisms differs greatly. In general, pyridoxine is least active for bacteria, but certain yeasts and molds use pyridoxine more readily than the other two factors. Several strains of *Lactobacilli* respond only to pyridoxal phosphate or pyridoxamine phosphate; apparently, these organisms are unable to phosphorylate either pyridoxal or pyridoxamine. The fact that the B$_6$ requirement of various bacteria is dependent on the amino acid content of the culture media may be explained by the role of pyridoxal phosphate in several enzymic reactions characteristic of amino acid metabolism. This "functional form" of the vitamin is essential for transamination (cf. p. 760), decarboxylation (cf. p. 768), and racemization (cf. p. 769), as well as for steps in the metabolism of hydroxy amino acids (cf. p. 775), of sul-

[31] P. György, *Nature,* **133,** 498 (1934).
[32] E. E. Snell et al., *J. Biol. Chem.,* **143,** 519 (1942).

fur-containing amino acids (cf. pp. 756, 794), and of tryptophan (cf. p. 843).

The requirement of ruminants for vitamin B_6 is satisfied completely by the synthetic activity of the rumen bacteria. However, the pathway of biosynthesis in microorganisms and in higher plants has not been elucidated. The bacteria that require an exogenous source of pyridoxine, pyridoxamine, or pyridoxal convert these substances to pyridoxal phosphate, whose formation from pyridoxal and ATP is catalyzed by a "kinase" extracted from yeast (cf. p. 375). Similar pyridoxal kinases are present in mammalian tissues and in some bacteria.

The amount of pyridoxal phosphate in the tissues of vitamin B_6-deficient animals is below normal. In addition, apyridoxosis is characterized by a decreased urinary excretion of microbiologically active forms of the vitamin and of a biologically inactive derivative, pyridoxic acid (2-methyl-3-hydroxy-5-hydroxymethylpyridine-4-carboxylic acid). Pyr-

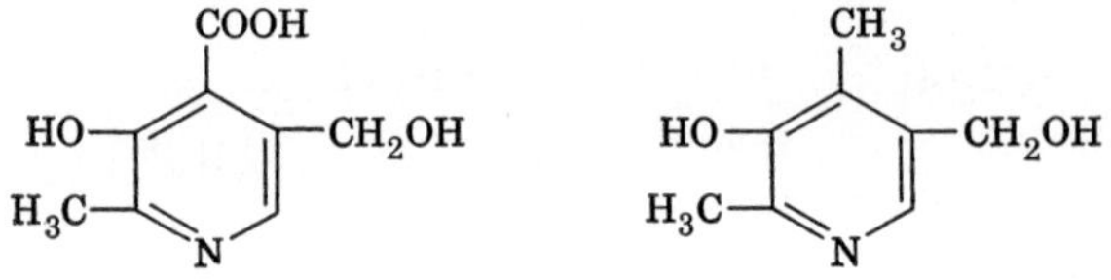

Pyridoxic acid   4-Deoxypyridoxine

idoxic acid represents the major end product of vitamin B_6 that is excreted in human urine. Apparently, this acid is formed *in vivo* by the direct oxidation of pyridoxal, since it has been found that the aldehyde oxidase of liver can convert pyridoxal to pyridoxic acid.[33]

Another typical biochemical effect of B_6 deficiency in higher animals, including man, is an abnormal tryptophan metabolism; this is reflected by the urinary excretion of decreased amounts of nicotinic acid derivatives and of kynurenine, whereas the urinary excretion of xanthurenic acid is higher than normal (cf. p. 836).

As noted earlier, the development of a dermatitis, called acrodynia, is characteristic of apyridoxosis in the rat. However, a B_6 deficiency in most laboratory animals (rat, dog, chick) is more commonly associated with anemia and nervous lesions including epileptiform seizures. In this connection, it is of interest that the conversion of glycine-2-C^{14} to labeled heme (cf. p. 864) by blood from avitaminotic ducklings is markedly depressed, but is restored to normal by the addition of pyridoxal phosphate to the blood.[34] Although a dietary supply of pyridoxine is essential for normal metabolic function in man, no typical syndrome,

[33] R. Schwartz and N. O. Kjeldgaard, *Biochem. J.,* **48,** 333 (1951).
[34] M. P. Schulman and D. A. Richert, *J. Am. Chem. Soc.,* **77,** 6402 (1955).

comparable to beriberi or pellagra, has been associated with B_6 deficiency.[35]

Among the synthetic analogues of the vitamin B_6 compounds, the substance ω-methylpyridoxal (the CH_3 group in 2 position of pyridoxal is replaced by CH_3CH_2) is of interest, since it is highly active for *Lactobacillus casei* but is not used in place of pyridoxal by yeast. The biological activity of ω-methylpyridoxal is a consequence of the ability of its 5-phosphate to replace pyridoxal phosphate as the cofactor for several bacterial enzymes.[36] On the other hand, 4-deoxypyridoxine has antivitamin B_6 activity not only for bacteria but also for higher animals; this effect has been attributed to the formation *in vivo* of the 5-phosphate, which is a competitive inhibitor of several pyridoxal phosphate-dependent enzymes. Another type of antagonism is shown by the compound 2-ethyl-3-amino-4-ethoxymethyl-5-aminomethylpyridine, which inhibits the growth of yeast and is a competitive inhibitor of yeast pyridoxal kinase.[37]

It may be noted that the normal metabolism of vitamin B_6 in higher animals is prevented by isonicotinic hydrazide (p. 309), and the toxicity of this compound appears to be related to its inhibitory action on enzyme systems for which pyridoxal phosphate is a cofactor. Although an antagonism between isonicotinic hydrazide and pyridoxal has been observed in a strain of *Mycobacterium tuberculosis*, it is not known whether this effect is directly responsible for the curative properties of the drug in tuberculosis.

Nicotinic Acid and Nicotinamide. Nicotinic acid (niacin) has been known since 1867 as a product obtained by the vigorous oxidation of the alkaloid nicotine (p. 860). It was not isolated directly from a natural source until 1912, when both Suzuki and Funk obtained it from yeast and rice polishings in the course of a search for the antiberiberi factor. However, the biological importance of this acid and its amide (nicotin-

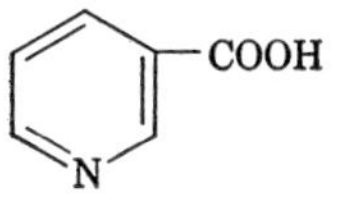

Nicotinic acid 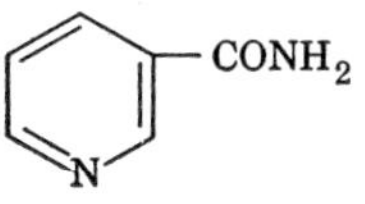   Nicotinamide

amide or niacinamide) became apparent only after the discovery of the pyridine nucleotides (DPN and TPN). This finding was rapidly followed by evidence showing that nicotinic acid and nicotinamide are growth factors for several microorganisms as well as for higher animals and

[35] R. W. Vilter et al., *Federation Proc.*, **13**, 776 (1954).

[36] J. Olivard and E. E. Snell, *J. Biol. Chem.*, **213**, 203, 215 (1955).

[37] J. Hurwitz, *J. Biol. Chem.*, **217**, 513 (1955).

that the compounds are specific curative agents for human pellagra and canine black tongue.[38]

In nature, nicotinic acid occurs mainly as the amide which is generally found in the form of DPN or TPN. These pyridine nucleotides are specific growth factors for strains of *Hemophilus;* several other bacterial species can use the nucleotides as well as free nicotinamide or free nicotinic acid. The free amide and free acid are interchangeable in the nutrition of higher animals and of some microorganisms, but some bacteria are more exacting in their growth requirements and respond to only one of the simple pyridine compounds.

The biosynthesis of nicotinic acid has already been discussed in the section dealing with tryptophan metabolism (p. 840). Tryptophan apparently is converted to the pyridine carboxylic acid by the same series of reactions in mammalian and avian tissues and in *Neurospora crassa,* but a different biosynthetic pathway appears to exist in organisms such as *Escherichia coli* and *Bacillus subtilis,* which do not form nicotinic acid from tryptophan.

Little is known about the mechanism of the formation of nicotinamide from nicotinic acid, although this reaction must be effected readily by most organisms. Washed human erythrocytes can synthesize nicotinamide mononucleotide (NMN) in the presence of nicotinamide, inorganic phosphate, and glucose; this synthesis also is effected by an erythrocyte enzyme system (NMN pyrophosphorylase) in the presence of nicotinamide and 5-phosphoribosyl-1-pyrophosphate (cf. p. 885). The NMN so formed could react with ATP to give DPN (cf. p. 310). However, in the presence of NH_4^+, erythrocytes readily convert nicotinic acid to DPN, but no NMN appears to be formed. It is possible, therefore, that free nicotinamide is not an intermediate in the incorporation of nicotinic acid into DPN, and that the amidation reaction occurs after the formation of a deamidated form of the dinucleotide.[39]

A number of derivatives of nicotinic acid and of nicotinamide have been identified as excretory products formed in higher animals. The urines of most species contain, in addition to varying amounts of the free acid and amide, N^1-methylnicotinamide (p. 805), N^1-methyl-6-pyridone-3-carboxamide, and nicotinuric acid (nicotinoylglycine); chickens excrete dinicotinoylornithine and both the α- and δ-mono-nicotinoyl derivatives of ornithine. The synthesis of nicotinuric acid by rat tissue preparations, like that of hippuric acid (cf. p. 719), re-

[38] P. J. Fouts et al., *Proc. Soc. Exptl. Biol. Med.,* **37,** 405 (1937); C. A. Elvehjem et al., *J. Am. Chem. Soc.,* **59,** 1767 (1937).

[39] I. G. Leder and P. Handler, *J. Biol. Chem.,* **189,** 889 (1951); J. Preiss and P. Handler, *ibid.,* **225,** 759 (1957); **233,** 488, 493 (1958).

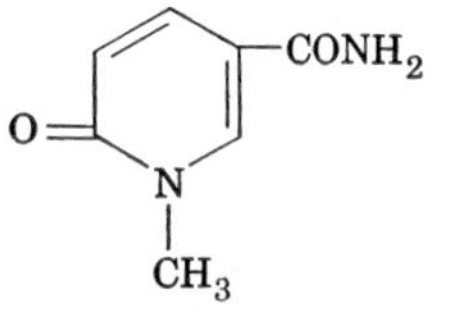

N^1-Methyl-6-pyridone-
3-carboxamide

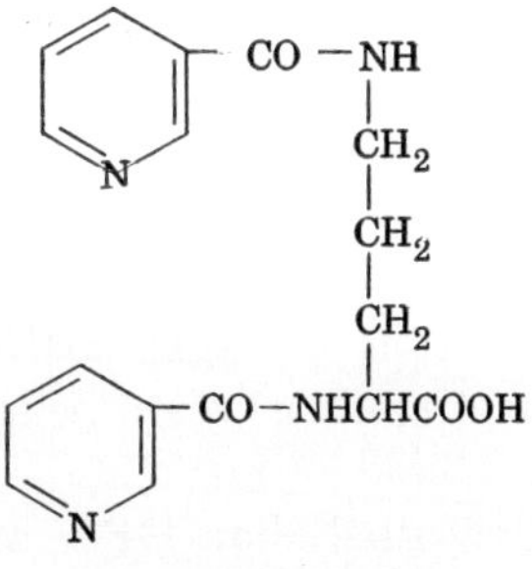

Dinicotinoylornithine

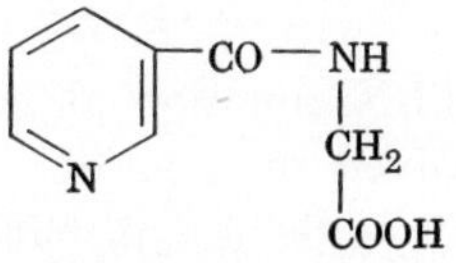

Nicotinuric acid

quires the presence of ATP.[40]   The formation of dinicotinoylornithine in birds probably is similar to that of ornithuric acid (dibenzoyl-ornithine; cf. p. 719).   The 6-pyridone derivative appears to arise by oxidation of N^1-methylnicotinamide since an enzyme system which catalyzes such an oxidation is present in rabbit liver.[41]   Thus the conversion of nicotinic acid to the 6-pyridone involves the intermediate formation first of nicotinamide and then of N^1-methylnicotinamide.[42] In addition, nicotinic acid and its amide are decarboxylated, as shown by the recovery of C^{14}O$_2$ from animals given nicotinic acid or nicotin-amide containing C^{14} in the carboxyl carbon.[43]

Many structural analogues of nicotinic acid have been tested for their biological activity in higher animals and in microorganisms.   Pyridine derivatives that have vitamin activity appear to be converted *in vivo* to

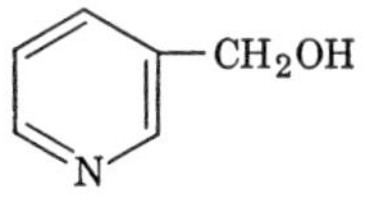

3-Hydroxymethylpyridine

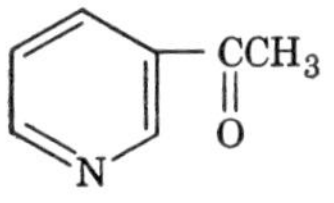

3-Acetylpyridine

nicotinic acid or its amide; these derivatives include 3-hydroxymethyl-pyridine, 3-acetylpyridine, pyridyl-3-aldehyde, and β-picoline (3-meth-ylpyridine).[44]   Although 3-acetylpyridine can serve as a precursor of the natural vitamin, it is also toxic to mice, probably because it displaces nicotinamide from DPN (cf. p. 309).   This toxicity is overcome by the

[40] K. M. Jones and W. H. Elliott, *Biochim. et Biophys. Acta,* **14,** 586 (1954).

[41] W. E. Knox and W. I. Grossman, *J. Biol. Chem.,* **166,** 391 (1946).

[42] C. J. Walters et al., *J. Biol. Chem.,* **217,** 489 (1955).

[43] E. Leifer et al., *J. Biol. Chem.,* **190,** 595 (1951).

[44] H. B. Burch et al., *J. Biol. Chem.,* **212,** 897 (1955); E. G. McDaniel et al., *J. Nutrition,* **55,** 623 (1955); R. Van Reen and F. E. Stolzenbach, *J. Biol. Chem.,* **226,** 373 (1957).

administration of nicotinamide or of DPN, but not by nicotinic acid or tryptophan; only nicotinamide counteracts the formation *in vitro* of the acetylpyridine analogue of DPN.[45] Isonicotinic hydrazide, which also displaces the nicotinamide portion of DPN, does not appear to act primarily as an antagonist of nicotinic acid, since its effect on higher animals (depletion of liver DPN and TPN, decreased excretion of N^1-methylnicotinamide) can be prevented completely by vitamin B_6 (cf. p. 989).

It will be recalled that DPN and TPN function as cofactors in the several dehydrogenation reactions involved in anaerobic breakdown of carbohydrates (cf. p. 476) and of fatty acids (cf. p. 598), in the citric acid cycle (cf. p. 508), and in the deamination of glutamic acid (cf. p. 754). Although it is known that a dietary deficiency of nicotinic acid, accompanied by a low intake of tryptophan, results in a profound disturbance of the normal metabolism of higher animals, it has not been possible as yet to relate any specific metabolic dysfunction directly to the symptoms of the deficiency disease. Pellagra, the human disease caused by nicotinic acid-deficient diets, is characterized mainly by dermatitis, diarrhea, and dementia. The last-named symptom may be a result of an impaired ability of the brain tissue to metabolize carbohydrate. However, although nervous lesions may be seen in pellagra, these are probably caused by deficiencies of other factors such as thiamine, since human diets that lead to pellagra are deficient not only in nicotinic acid but also in other members of the B complex.

Pantothenic Acid.[46]   Pantothenic acid [D-N-(α,γ-dihydroxy-β,β-dimethylbutyryl)-β-alanine] was first isolated by R. J. Williams in 1933 from concentrates of liver that possessed "bios" activity for yeast. Subsequent studies led to the recognition that pantothenic acid is identical with the factor that prevents and cures a specific dermatitis of chicks, and that it is a vitamin for rats and mice.

Essentially all of the pantothenic acid in most animal tissues and microorganisms is present as coenzyme A (p. 206), but the vitamin also occurs in other combined forms. One of these, discovered first as a growth factor for *Lactobacillus bulgaricus,* is N-(pantothenyl)-β-aminoethanethiol or pantetheine; the corresponding disulfide is pantethine. Experimental animals respond equally well to pantothenic acid, pantetheine, and coenzyme A, but microorganisms vary greatly in their ability to use the conjugated forms of pantothenic acid as growth factors.[47] For example, *Saccharomyces carlsbergensis* grows on pan-

[45] N. O. Kaplan et al., *Science,* **120,** 437 (1954).

[46] G. D. Novelli, *Physiol. Revs.,* **33,** 525 (1953).

[47] G. M. Brown et al., *J. Biol. Chem.,* **213,** 855 (1955); W. S. Pierpoint et al., *Biochem. J.,* **61,** 190 (1955).

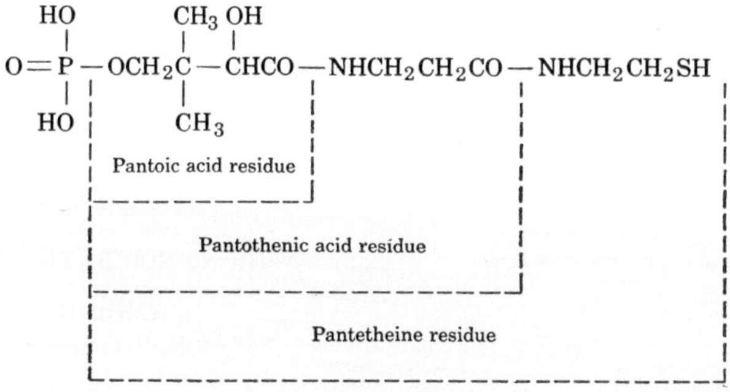

$$\begin{array}{ccc} \text{HO} & \text{CH}_3 \ \text{OH} & \\ | & | \ \ | & \\ \text{O}=\text{P}-\text{OCH}_2\text{C}-\text{CHCO}-\text{NHCH}_2\text{CH}_2\text{CO}-\text{NHCH}_2\text{CH}_2\text{SH} \\ | & | & \\ \text{HO} & \text{CH}_3 & \end{array}$$

Pantoic acid residue

Pantothenic acid residue

Pantetheine residue

4'-Phosphopantetheine

tothenic acid but not on any of its conjugates; *Lactobacillus helveticus* uses pantothenic acid, pantetheine, and (to a lesser extent) 4'-phospho-pantetheine; *Acetobacter suboxydans* grows on these three compounds, and in addition on N-pantothenylcysteine (p. 994) or coenzyme A. The failure of some of the conjugates to promote the growth of certain micro-organisms is a consequence of the inability of the compounds to penetrate the cell membrane, since they all appear to be intermediates in the biosynthesis of coenzyme A.

In addition to the pantothenic acid-requiring microorganisms, one group of organisms requires only a source of β-alanine, which they cannot make from aspartic acid (cf. p. 767) or from other precursors (cf. p. 781); another group of organisms requires only pantoic acid.

Pantoic acid is formed from α-ketoisovaleric acid (p. 780) in bacteria[48] (e.g., *Escherichia coli, Bacterium linens*), probably by the addition of a C_1 unit to give "α-ketopantoic acid" which is reduced to pantoic acid. The formation of pantothenic acid from pantoic acid and β-alanine is

$$\alpha\text{-Ketoisovaleric acid} \xrightarrow{+\ [C_1]} \text{HOCH}_2-\overset{\overset{\displaystyle \text{CH}_3}{|}}{\underset{\underset{\displaystyle \text{CH}_3}{|}}{\text{C}}}-\text{CO}-\text{COOH} \xrightarrow{+\ 2\text{H}} \text{Pantoic acid}$$

catalyzed by ATP-dependent enzyme systems (cf. p. 720) that have been extracted from *E. coli* and from *Brucella abortus*.[49] The synthesis of pantothenic acid does not occur in mammalian tissues, but the vitamin

Pantoic acid + β-alanine + ATP →

Pantothenic acid + AMP + pyrophosphate

[48] W. K. Maas and H. J. Vogel, *J. Bact.*, **65**, 388 (1953); M. Purko et al., *J. Biol. Chem.*, **207**, 51 (1954); E. N. McIntosh et al., *ibid.*, **228**, 499 (1957).

[49] W. K. Maas, *J. Biol. Chem.*, **198**, 23 (1952); H. S. Ginoza and R. A. Alternbern, *Arch. Biochem. and Biophys.*, **56**, 537 (1955).

is incorporated into coenzyme A both in animals and in microorganisms (Fig. 1).

All the reactions shown in Fig. 1 are catalyzed by enzymes extracted from mammalian and avian liver.[50] Thus pantetheine is formed from pantothenylcysteine or, in the presence of ATP, from pantothenic acid

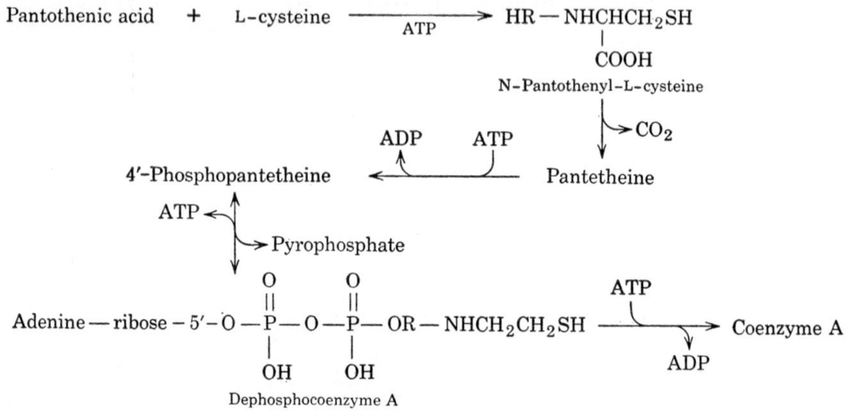

Fig. 1. Proposed pathway for the biosynthesis of coenzyme A. The group R denotes $-OCH_2C(CH_3)_2CHOHCONHCH_2CH_2CO-$.

and cysteine. Pantetheine is phosphorylated by ATP in the presence of "pantetheine kinase" to yield 4'-phosphopantetheine, which reacts with ATP in a reaction catalyzed by "dephosphoCoA pyrophosphorylase" to give dephosphocoenzyme A. The phosphorylation of the 3'-hydroxyl of ribose in dephosphoCoA is effected by ATP in the presence of "dephosphoCoA kinase." *Proteus morganii* and *Lactobacillus arabinosus* also form coenzyme A from pantothenic acid, cysteine, and ATP. Cell-free extracts of these organisms catalyze the ATP-dependent phosphorylation not only of pantetheine but also of pantothenic acid.[51]

Coenzyme A and phosphopantetheine are hydrolyzed by several phosphatases. The prostatic acid phosphatase (p. 582) and the barley 3'-nucleotidase (p. 880) convert coenzyme A to dephosphoCoA. Various pyrophosphatases (potato, snake venom, yeast, liver) hydrolyze coenzyme A to 3',5'-diphosphoadenosine and 4'-phosphopantetheine, which is dephosphorylated by the prostatic phosphatase and the intestinal alkaline phosphatase. The use of these enzymes gave valuable information in the determination of the structure of coenzyme A.

[50] L. Levintow and G. D. Novelli, *J. Biol. Chem.*, **207**, 761 (1954); M. B. Hoagland and G. D. Novelli, *ibid.*, **207**, 767 (1954).

[51] G. B. Ward et al., *J. Biol. Chem.*, **213**, 869 (1955); W. S. Pierpoint et al., *Biochem. J.*, **61**, 368 (1955).

In view of the importance of coenzyme A in the metabolism of carbohydrates, fats, and nitrogen compounds, the activity of pantothenic acid as a vitamin is readily understandable. Although no well-defined syndrome of a specific pantothenic acid deficiency has been described for man, an experimentally induced lack of the vitamin appears to cause adrenal cortical insufficiency. Specific pantothenic acid deficiencies are readily produced in experimental animals by the use of appropriate diets. Depigmentation of the hair (rats) or of the feathers (chicks) and dermatitis are common symptoms of the deficiency, and in the rat there is marked adrenal damage, accompanied by the symptoms of adrenal cortical insufficiency[52] (cf. p. 946).

Biotin.[53] This vitamin was isolated from egg yolk by Kögl in 1935 in the course of the examination of the components of the "bios" factor required by yeast. Five years later P. György and his collaborators showed that biotin was identical with the unidentified factor designated "vitamin H," which was known to protect rats (and other animals) against the toxicity of raw egg white.

$$\begin{array}{cc}
\underset{\text{Biotin}}{
\begin{array}{c}
\text{O}\\
\text{C}\\
\underset{3'}{\text{HN}}\ \ {}^{2'}\ \underset{1'}{\text{NH}}\\
\underset{4}{\text{HC}}{}^{4'}\!\!-\!\!{}^{5'}\text{CH}\\
\underset{5}{\text{H}_2\text{C}}\underset{\text{S}}{\ \ }\underset{1}{}\ {}^{2}\text{CH(CH}_2)_4\text{COOH}
\end{array}} &
\underset{\text{Oxybiotin}}{
\begin{array}{c}
\text{O}\\
\text{C}\\
\text{HN}\ \ \ \text{NH}\\
\text{HC}\ \text{---}\ \text{CH}\\
\text{H}_2\text{C}\underset{\text{O}}{\ \ }\text{CH(CH}_2)_4\text{COOH}
\end{array}}
\end{array}$$

Biotin is found in animal and plant tissues and occurs mainly in combined forms. One of these biotin complexes is biocytin (ϵ-N-biotinyl-L-lysine),[54] isolated from yeast. Another complex, whose structure has not been elucidated, is the so-called "soluble bound biotin" extracted from peptic digests of swine liver. Both of these complexes are degraded to biotin by an enzyme ("biotinidase") believed to be a peptidase.[55] At least two distinct liver protein fractions containing biotin have been described; these biotin-containing proteins have been termed "biotoproteins."[56]

Free biotin is the simplest of the naturally occurring compounds that counteract the nutritional deficiency induced in animals (including man) by the feeding of raw egg white. The toxic material in egg is a protein (avidin) with which biotin combines, in stoichiometric proportions, to

[52] E. P. Ralli and M. E. Dumm, *Vitamins and Hormones,* **11,** 133 (1953).

[53] K. Hofmann, *Advances in Enzymol.,* **3,** 289 (1943); D. B. Melville, *Vitamins and Hormones,* **2,** 29 (1944).

[54] R. L. Peck et al., *J. Am. Chem. Soc.,* **74,** 1999 (1952).

[55] R. W. Thoma and W. H. Peterson, *J. Biol. Chem.,* **210,** 569 (1954).

[56] K. Hofmann et al., *J. Biol. Chem.,* **183,** 481 (1950).

form an avidin-biotin complex. This complex is not readily dissociable except by heat treatment or acid hydrolysis; nor is it split by the enzymes of the gastrointestinal tract of higher animals. Hence the feeding of avidin can result in a biotin deficiency caused by the formation of the nondigestible complex within the intestinal tract. However, the complex can be cleaved *in vivo*, since the parenteral administration of a "synthetic" sample of the avidin-biotin compound will cure egg white injury.

Biotin deficiency is not normally encountered in man or even in laboratory animals kept on apparently biotin-free diets. This is a reflection of the ability of intestinal bacteria to synthesize sufficient biotin to meet the requirements of the host organism. Consequently, biotin deficiency is usually induced by the administration of avidin (or raw egg white), or by the elimination of intestinal bacteria which can synthesize the vitamin. The production of such a deficiency in man is followed by a characteristic dermatitis and mental symptoms; in animals the deficiency generally causes dermatitis and nervous disorders. These symptoms are cured not only by biotin but also by oxybiotin, the furane analogue of the naturally occurring thiophane compound. Oxybiotin, however, has less activity than the true vitamin.

The administration of biotin labeled with C^{14} in the carboxyl group to rats or mice gives rise to $C^{14}O_2$. Since $C^{14}O_2$ is not produced from biotin-2'-C^{14}, it appears that in animal tissues the catabolism of biotin involves oxidative degradation of the valeric acid residue but not of the imidazole nucleus.[57] Naturally occurring oxidation products of biotin are a levorotatory biotin sulfoxide, produced by *Aspergillus niger,* and a

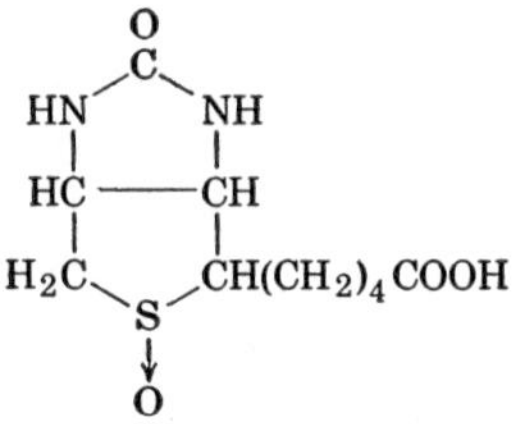

Biotin sulfoxide 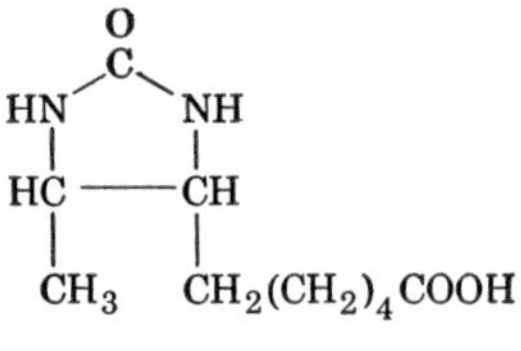   Desthiobiotin

dextrorotatory biotin sulfoxide, isolated from cows' milk;[58] the two sulfoxides differ in configuration about the asymmetric sulfur atom. Neither of the sulfoxides has vitamin activity for the rat, but both show some growth factor activity for yeast and several other microorganisms.

Oxybiotin, biocytin, and "soluble bound biotin" promote the growth

[57] R. M. Baxter and J. H. Quastel, *J. Biol. Chem.,* **201,** 751 (1953).

[58] L. D. Wright et al., *J. Am. Chem. Soc.,* **76,** 4163 (1954); D. B. Melville et al., *J. Biol. Chem.,* **208,** 495, 503 (1954).

of various microbial species. Studies on the utilization of oxybiotin by microorganisms and by the chick have led to the hypothesis that oxybiotin itself has biological activity and is not converted to biotin *in vivo*.[59] The immediate precursor of biotin appears to be the compound desthiobiotin, which can be used in place of biotin by a number of microorganisms. This imidazole derivative is believed to derive part of its molecule from pimelic acid [$HOOC(CH_2)_5COOH$], which is interchangeable with biotin for some microorganisms and stimulates biotin synthesis in others.

The isolation of biotin was followed by the demonstration that this compound was identical with coenzyme R, which had been described in 1933 as having a pronounced stimulatory effect on the respiration of nongrowing *Rhizobium*. Thus a "coenzyme" function was immediately ascribed to biotin when its activity as a vitamin was discovered. However, neither the nature of the "functional derivative" of biotin nor its exact biochemical action has yet been established.

Biotin is believed to be involved directly or indirectly in at least three phases of microbial metabolism:[60] (1) the metabolism of aspartic acid and possibly of other nitrogen-containing compounds, (2) decarboxylation reactions (substrates, oxaloacetic, oxalosuccinic, and succinic acids), and (3) oleic acid synthesis. The metabolic interrelation between the vitamin and aspartic acid was inferred from the sparing action of the amino acid on the biotin requirement of yeast and of a variety of bacteria. Biotin is essential for aspartic acid synthesis in many lactic acid bacteria; this does not appear to be the situation, however, in *Clostridium butyricum*. Early observations that both biotin and ammonium salts are required to restore to normal the respiration of biotin-deficient yeast led to the suggestion that biotin is involved in the synthesis of nitrogenous compounds in microorganisms.

A relationship between biotin and the reversible decarboxylation of oxaloacetic acid to pyruvic acid was observed in studies of the requirements of various bacteria for growth or for the reversal of growth inhibition due to inhibitory analogues of biotin. Furthermore, experiments with $C^{14}O_2$ have shown clearly that an adequate supply of biotin is essential for CO_2 fixation by both microorganisms and higher animals. A study of the activity of the malic enzyme (p. 512) in both biotin-deficient and normal cells of *Lactobacillus arabinosus* indicated that biotin is not a cofactor for this type of CO_2 fixation but may be involved in the synthesis of the specific enzymes that mediate the fixation reac-

[59] A. E. Axelrod et al., *J. Biol. Chem.*, **169**, 195 (1947); R. H. McCoy et al., *ibid.*, **176**, 1319, 1327 (1948).

[60] H. C. Lichstein, *Vitamins and Hormones*, **9**, 27 (1951); H. P. Broquist and E. E. Snell, *J. Biol. Chem.*, **188**, 431 (1951); J. M. Ravel and W. Shive, *Arch. Biochem. and Biophys.*, **54**, 341 (1955).

tion.[61] Experiments on the effect of biotin on the breakdown of glucose by *Saccharomyces cerevisiae* also suggest that the vitamin may function in the biosynthesis of enzymes; in addition, it may serve as a cofactor in reactions involved in the oxidation of carbohydrates to CO_2.[62]

In a medium containing aspartic acid, the requirement of various *Lactobacilli* for biotin is markedly reduced by some C_{18} fatty acids such as oleic acid, as well as by lactobacillic acid and dihydrosterculic acid[63] (p. 560). It is doubtful, however, whether biotin is directly involved in the microbial biosynthesis of such long-chain fatty acids.

Folic Acid Group.[64] In general, the term "folic acid vitamin" is used to denote pteroyl-L-glutamic acid (PGA) and those of its derivatives that have vitamin activity for higher animals (e.g., rat, chick) and

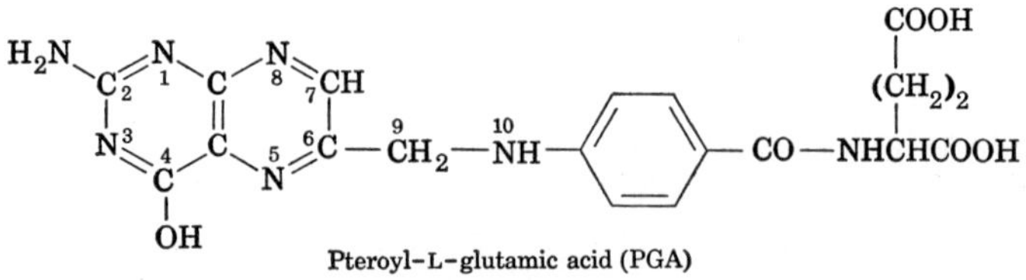

Pteroyl-L-glutamic acid (PGA)

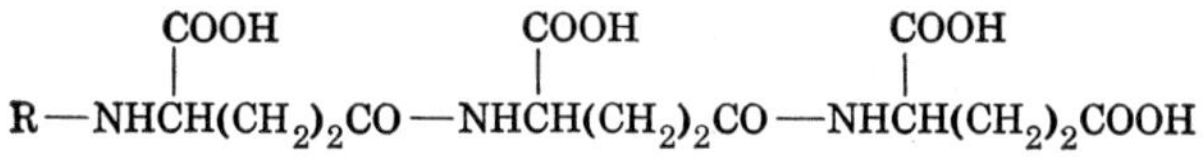

Pteroyldi-γ-glutamylglutamic acid
(R = pteroyl group)

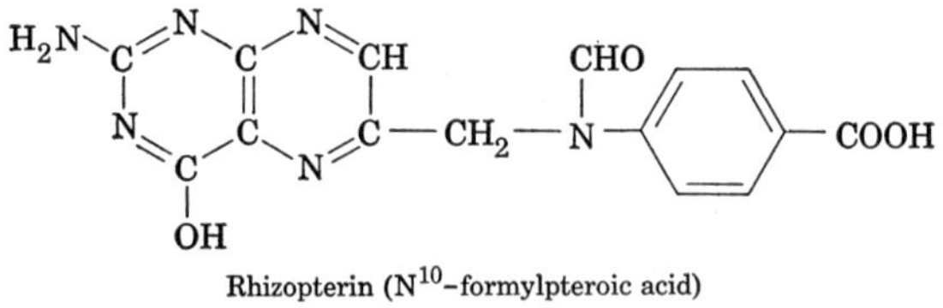

Rhizopterin (N^{10}-formylpteroic acid)

microorganisms (*Lactobacillus casei, Streptococcus fecalis*). Among the active PGA derivatives is "citrovorum factor" (CF, N^5-formyl-5,6,7,8-tetrahydroPGA; p. 775), a growth factor for *Leuconostoc citrovorum* (newer name, *Pediococcus cerevisiae*) which does not respond to PGA under the conditions of assay for activity. The general term "folinic acid" has been applied to compounds that resemble CF in its activity for microorganisms.

[61] M. L. Blanchard et al., *J. Biol. Chem.*, **187**, 875 (1950).

[62] H. C. Lichstein and R. B. Boyd, *Arch. Biochem. and Biophys.*, **55**, 307 (1955); H. C. Lichstein, *ibid.*, **71**, 276 (1957).

[63] H. P. Broquist and E. E. Snell, *Arch. Biochem. and Biophys.*, **46**, 432 (1953); K. Hofmann et al., *J. Biol. Chem.*, **210**, 687 (1954); **228**, 349 (1957).

[64] A. D. Welch and C. A. Nichol, *Ann. Rev. Biochem.*, **21**, 633 (1952); C. A. Nichol et al., *Science*, **121**, 275 (1955).

In Table 2 are listed compounds of known structure that have been isolated from natural sources and shown to exhibit folic acid activity. p-Aminobenzoic acid (PABA), a constituent of all these compounds, probably should also be included in this group. As noted previously

Table 2. Members of the Folic Acid Group

Vitamin	Other Names
Pteroyl-L-glutamic acid (PGA)	Folic acid, folacin, vitamin B_c
Pteroyldi-γ-glutamylglutamic acid	"Fermentation *L. casei* factor"
Pteroylhexa-γ-glutamylglutamic acid	Vitamin B_c conjugate
N^{10}-Formylpteroic acid	Rhizopterin, *S. lactis* R factor
N^{10}-FormylPGA	
N^{10}-FormyltetrahydroPGA†	
Citrovorum factor (CF)	N^5-FormyltetrahydroPGA, leucovorin, folinic acid-SF

† In solution, under anaerobic conditions, this substance is in equilibrium with anhydroleucovorin (cf. p. 775), whose formation is favored at acid pH values.

(p. 977), a biochemical function was initially attributed to PABA after the discovery that it reversed the bacteriostatic action of sulfanilamide. Subsequently PABA was found to be a growth factor for certain organisms, and it now seems likely that its biological activity depends on its incorporation into the pteroic acid portion of the folic acid vitamins. PABA is also found to occur as the N-acetyl derivative in the blood and urine of animals. A polyglutamic acid peptide containing, per mole, 1 PABA residue and 10 to 11 L-glutamic acid residues has been isolated from yeast;[65] this polypeptide is of special interest in view of the fact that PGA and CF also occur in conjugation with glutamic acid polypeptides.

PGA was isolated as a result of the search for the so-called vitamin B_c which had been found to cure a nutritional anemia in chicks and to serve as a specific growth factor for *Lactobacillus casei*. The pteroyltriglutamate and heptaglutamate both occur in nature and are as active as folic acid in the nutrition of higher animals; however, various microorganisms differ in their growth response to these three compounds. Rhizopterin seems to be active only for a few microorganisms (e.g., *Streptococcus fecalis* R) which can also use pteroic acid. CF, as isolated from natural sources, is one of the diastereoisomers of N^5-formyltetrahydroPGA, which has asymmetric centers at carbon 6 and at the α-carbon of L-glutamic acid; folinic acid-SF (or leucovorin) is a synthetic compound that is a mixture of two diastereoisomers and has only one half the biological activity of CF. As noted earlier (cf. p. 775), N^5-formyl-

[65] S. Ratner et al., *J. Biol. Chem.*, **164**, 691 (1946).

tetrahydroPGA is readily interconvertible with $N^{5,10}$-methenyltetra-hydroPGA (anhydroleucovorin) which also has been identified in biological systems.[66] It should be noted that most of naturally occurring substances that exhibit folic acid activity contain the tetrahydroPGA nucleus (i.e., are folinic acid derivatives); the extreme ease with which folinic acids are oxidized upon exposure to air accounts for the fact that their existence was overlooked for many years.

In addition to the compounds discussed above, there are probably other naturally occurring forms of the folic acid vitamins. Among these are the PGA derivatives of undetermined structure that participate in various aspects of the metabolism of C_1 compounds (cf. p. 776). Furthermore, it appears likely that CF (like PGA) occurs in combination with polypeptides, since there is a marked resemblance between the animal enzyme system that liberates material with folinic acid activity from tissue preparations and an enzyme from animal tissues ("folic acid conjugase") that liberates PGA from its conjugates with glutamic acid peptides.[67]

There is little information about the synthetic pathways by which folic acid is formed in nature. Since green leaves are especially rich in this vitamin, it must be synthesized readily by the tissues of higher plants. Studies with "germ-free" rats (bred and maintained so that they are completely devoid of microorganisms) suggest that folic acid also may be made in the tissues of higher animals.[68] The obvious chemical relation between PGA and the simpler natural pteridines directed attention to the latter compounds as possible precursors of PGA. Thus it was found that biopterin (p. 207) spares the PGA requirement of the protozoan *Crithidia fasciculata*,[69] and that xanthopterin (p. 207) has some folic acid activity for rats and monkeys, and under some conditions can serve as an exogenous source of the pteroic acid portion of PGA for *L. casei*. Although there is no direct evidence that either of these pteridines is a precursor of PGA, it is of interest that, in butterflies, xanthopterin and the closely related leucopterin are formed from the

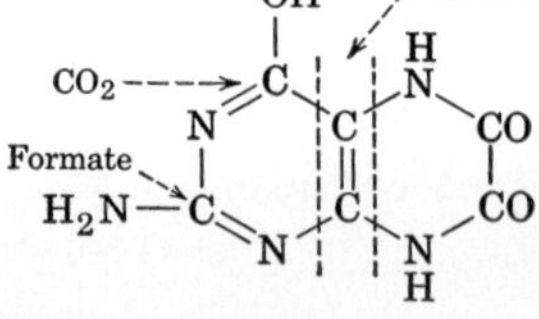

Leucopterin

[66] M. Silverman et al., *J. Biol. Chem.*, **223**, 259 (1956).
[67] C. H. Hill and M. L. Scott, *J. Biol. Chem.*, **196**, 189 (1952).
[68] T. D. Luckey et al., *J. Nutrition*, **55**, 105; **57**, 169 (1955).
[69] E. L. Patterson et al., *J. Am. Chem. Soc.*, **77**, 3167 (1955).

same simple precursors used for the biosynthesis of purines (cf. p. 887) and of riboflavin (cf. p. 985).[70]

Animal tissues and microorganisms readily convert PGA to derivatives that are cofactors in enzymic reactions; these "functional" derivatives are degraded to CF by nonenzymic reactions. In liver, CF and PGA are catabolized to compounds that do not exhibit folinic acid or folic acid activity;[71] one of the products formed is p-aminobenzoylglutamic acid.

Dietary deficiencies of folic acid are rather difficult to produce in experimental animals, since the intestinal bacteria apparently can provide the small amounts needed by the animal hosts; the feeding of succinylsulfathiazole (to inhibit the growth of intestinal bacteria) or of various

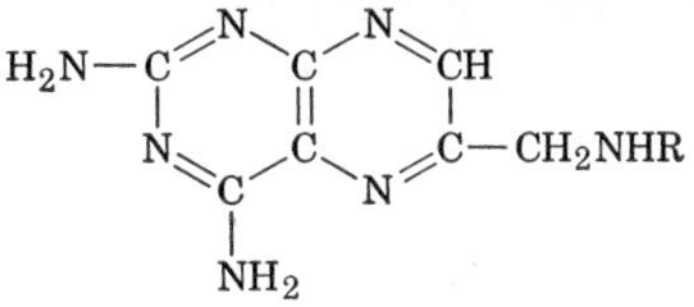

Aminopterin (4–aminoPGA) 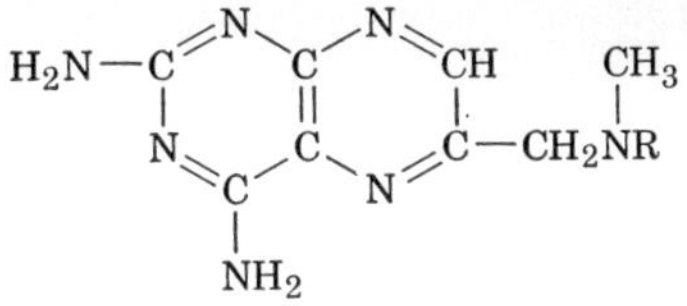   A–methopterin (4–amino–10–methylPGA)

(R = benzoylglutamic acid as in PGA)

inhibitory analogues of folic acid (e.g., Aminopterin or A-methopterin) will cause folic acid deficiencies. The 4-amino analogues of PGA inhibit the metabolic conversion of PGA to its "functional" derivatives, and consequently interfere with the biosynthesis of many tissue constituents (cf. p. 902). This antimetabolite effect of Aminopterin is believed to be responsible for its therapeutic value in the treatment of some acute leukemias.

In experimentally induced folic acid deficiencies, the development of anemia is the most obvious pathological defect. Mixtures of PGA (or CF) and vitamin B_{12} have indeed been used for the treatment of various macrocytic anemias in man. Although it is evident that derivatives of PGA play an important role in the formation of normal erythrocytes, the biochemical role of the folic acid vitamins in the prevention of anemia has not been elucidated as yet.

The Vitamin B_{12} Group.[72] The isolation from liver of red crystalline compounds which had the therapeutic activity of liver concentrates in the treatment of pernicious anemia was announced in 1948 by investigators in the United States and in England. The substance, previously known as the antipernicious anemia factor, is now called vitamin B_{12} or cyanocobalamin; the latter designation is based on the presence in

[70] F. Weygand and M. Waldschmidt, *Angew. Chem.*, **67**, 328 (1955).

[71] M. Silverman et al., *J. Biol. Chem.*, **211**, 53 (1954); S. Futterman and M. Silverman, *ibid.*, **224**, 31 (1957).

[72] R. T. Williams, *Biochem. Soc. Symposia*, No. 13 (1955).

the molecule of a cyanide ion in coordinate linkage with a cobalt atom. Cyanocobalamin is a growth factor for several microorganisms, including *Lactobacillus leishmannii, Escherichia coli* (strain 113–3), and the protozoan *Ochromonas malhamensis;* these three organisms have been used in the microbiological assay of the vitamin.[73]

The structure of cyanocobalamin has been elucidated through chemical degradation and by crystallographic studies.[74] As will be seen from the accompanying formula, cyanocobalamin contains a highly substituted

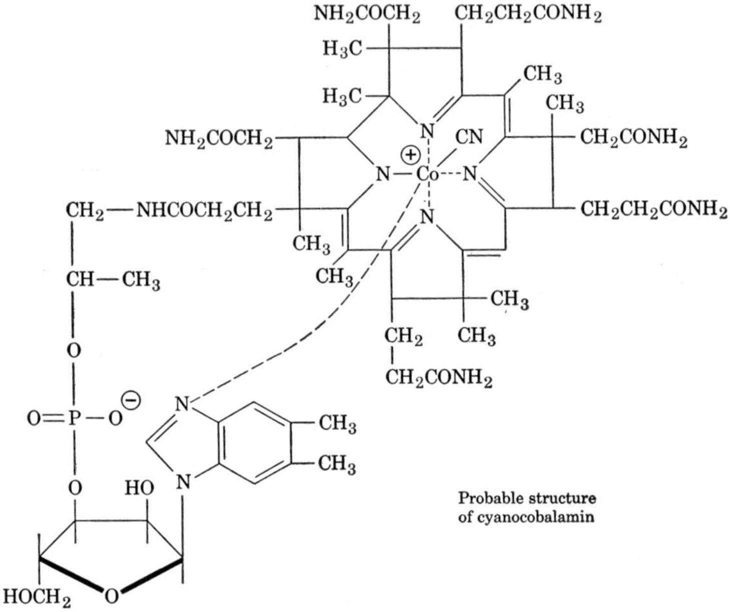

Probable structure
of cyanocobalamin

and partially hydrogenated tetrapyrrole (cf. p. 165) linked to the nucleotide 5,6-dimethyl-1-(α-D-ribofuranosyl)-benzimidazole-3'-phosphate.[75] It will be noted that the 6 coordinate valences of the cobalt atom (Co^{2+}) are satisfied by the 4 nitrogens of the reduced tetrapyrrole, a nitrogen atom of 5,6-dimethylbenzimidazole, and a cyanide ion. Of special interest is the presence of an α-glycosidic linkage in the benzimidazole nucleoside, in contrast to the β-glycosidic linkage in the nucleosides derived from PNA and DNA (cf. p. 188).

A variety of compounds with vitamin B_{12} activity have been isolated from natural sources. Some of these compounds differ from cyano-

[73] J. E. Ford and S. H. Hutner, *Vitamins and Hormones,* **13**, 101 (1955).

[74] K. Folkers and D. E. Wolf, *Vitamins and Hormones,* **12**, 1 (1954); D. C. Hodgkin et al., *Nature,* **176**, 325 (1955); **178**, 64 (1956); *Proc. Roy. Soc.,* **242A**, 228 (1957); R. Bonnett et al., *J. Chem. Soc.,* **1957**, 1158, 1168.

[75] J. B. Armitage et al., *J. Chem. Soc.,* **1953**, 3849.

cobalamin in the anion bound to the cobalt atom of the "cobalamin" unit. For example, B_{12a} (identical with the compound first designated B_{12b}) is hydroxocobalamin and may be prepared from cyanocobalamin by reduction with hydrogen (in the presence of a platinum catalyst) or with sulfite. Such cobalamins, like B_{12} itself, have been isolated from *Streptomyces griseus* fermentation liquors and can readily be converted by treatment with cyanide to the cyano compound.

Other B_{12}-like compounds differ from cyanocobalamin in respect to the basic constituents of the nucleotide portion (cf. Table 3), and are found in material that has been subjected to bacterial fermentation (e.g., rumen contents, feces, sewage, silage). Of the compounds listed in Table 3,

Table 3. Some Vitamin B_{12}-like Compounds of Natural Origin

Name	Nucleotide Base	Microbiological Activity		
		E. coli 113–3	*L. leish-mannii*	*Ochromonas malhamensis*
Cyanocobalamin (B_{12})	5,6-Dimethylbenzimidazole	+	+	+
Vitamin B_{12III} (Factor III)	5-Hydroxybenzimidazole	+	+	+
Pseudo-vitamin B_{12}	Adenine	+	+	−
Factor A (B_{12m})	2-Methyladenine	+	+	−
Factor B		+	−	−
Factor C	?	+	+	−
Factor G	Hypoxanthine	+	+	−
Factor H	2-Methylhypoxanthine	+	+	−

only cyanocobalamin and vitamin B_{12III}, which contains 5-hydroxy-benzimidazole in place of 5,6-dimethylbenzimidazole,[76] are known to exhibit vitamin B_{12} activity for higher animals (including man). Another related substance of bacterial origin is "Factor B," which represents the portion of the cyanobalamin molecule obtained upon removal of the nucleotide,[75] and which has microbiological activity only for *E. coli* strain 113–3 (a mutant that requires a source of Factor B). When this organism is grown in the presence of Factor B, it produces another (as yet uncharacterized) substance termed "Factor C," which has also been isolated from other natural sources. In the presence of both Factor B and 5,6-dimethylbenzimidazole (or the nucleotide from cyanocobalamin), *E. coli* 113–3 produces cyanocobalamin rather than Factor C. Such "directed synthesis" of B_{12}-like factors in the presence of added nitrogenous bases has been observed with several microbial strains,[77] and a large variety of B_{12} analogues (including the compounds listed in

[76] C. H. Shunk et al., *J. Am. Chem. Soc.*, **78**, 3228 (1956).

[77] J. E. Ford et al., *Biochem. J.*, **59**, 86 (1955); H. Dellweg et al., *Biochem. Z.*, **327**, 422; **328**, 81, 88, 96 (1956).

Table 3) that contain substituted benzimidazoles, purines, or other bases are formed by microorganisms. In this connection, it is of interest that either o-phenylenediamine or benzimidazole induce the formation of a B_{12} analogue that contains benzimidazole. The benzimidazole compound, as well as some of the other "unnatural" analogues of cyanocobalamin, exhibit high biological activity in man and in chicks.[78]

o–Phenylenediamine   Benzimidazole   4,5–Dimethyl-1,2–diaminobenzene

Although neither o-phenylenediamine nor benzimidazole appears to be a natural precursor of cyanocobalamin, this vitamin is produced by microorganisms in the presence of 5,6-dimethylbenzimidazole, and also when either 4,5-dimethyl-1,2-diaminobenzene or riboflavin (p. 984) is added to the culture medium. In the biosynthesis of the tetrapyrrole unit of vitamin B_{12}, δ-aminolevulinic acid is a precursor, as in the formation of porphyrins (p. 866).

Cyanocobalamin is essential for the normal growth of animals (e.g., rats, pigs, chicks) as well as for human beings. The parenteral administration of small doses (0.5 to 1 mg per day) of this vitamin controls the hematologic, neurologic, and glossal symptoms of pernicious anemia.[79] The specific effects of vitamin B_{12} are not duplicated by any folic acid vitamin such as PGA, which is used preferentially in the treatment of megaloblastic anemia in human infants and can alleviate the symptoms of nutritional megaloblastic anemias in experimental animals.

If given by mouth, vitamin B_{12} may have little if any effect on pernicious anemia unless the vitamin is fed together with normal gastric juice, which contains the "intrinsic factor" postulated by Castle to be essential for the prevention and cure of this anemia. The intrinsic factor makes orally administered vitamin B_{12} available to the anemic patient by facilitating the intestinal absorption of the vitamin. It is not certain whether this effect of the intrinsic factor is a direct consequence of its ability to combine with cyanocobalamin. The biological activity of preparations of the intrinsic factor has been tested by the oral administration of such preparations together with cyanocobalamin labeled with radioactive cobalt (Co^{60} or Co^{58}); the amount of radioactive cobalt found in the feces, blood, or urine serves as a measure of the amount of cyano-

[78] K. H. Fantes and C. H. O'Callaghan, *Biochem. J.*, **59**, 79 (1955); M. E. Coates et al., *ibid.*, **64**, 682 (1956).

[79] C. G. Ungley, *Vitamins and Hormones*, **13**, 137 (1955).

cobalamin absorbed. Several highly active preparations of the intrinsic factor have been obtained from swine stomach;[80] the activity appears to be associated with a mucoprotein of small particle weight. In respect to the binding of cyanocobalamin by the intrinsic factor, it should be added that many proteins can bind the vitamin, and thus inhibit its absorption from the intestinal tract. Such cyanocobalamin-protein complexes have been identified in sows' milk and in gastric mucosa.[81]

The biochemical activity of the vitamins of the B_{12} group has been associated with the biosynthesis of methyl groups from C_1-precursors (cf. p. 807) and with the biosynthesis of thymidine (thymine deoxyriboside) and of other deoxyribosides. In this respect the functions of the cobalamin derivatives are closely associated with those of the folic acid vitamins. Although vitamin B_{12} appears to be essential for the biosynthesis of the DNA deoxyribose in *Lactobacillus leishmannii*,[82] the mechanism of this effect has not been elucidated.

The disturbances in the metabolism of carbohydrates, fats, and proteins observed in B_{12}-deficient animals may be indirect results of the effects mentioned above or of other postulated functions of the vitamin. For example, avitaminosis B_{12} causes a marked depletion of liver cytochrome oxidase,[83] and thus could lead to an inhibition of many metabolic processes that depend on the participation of oxidative enzymes. It has also been suggested that vitamin B_{12} is involved in the metabolic reduction of dithio compounds such as homocystine or the disulfide forms of glutathione and of coenzyme A.[84] The biochemical basis of the hematopoietic effect of cyanocobalamin is unknown, and its role in promoting the normal formation of red cells may be only one aspect of a more general mode of action.

The action of vitamin B_{12} has also been shown to be responsible, at least in part, for the nutritional effect, in chicks and pigs, of the material designated as the "animal protein factor" (APF).[85] The existence of APF was initially postulated to account for the apparent nutritional deficiency of diets composed chiefly of vegetable proteins (corn, peanut, soybean) as compared to the adequacy of diets containing animal protein. Growth stimulation could be produced by the addition, to the vegetable diet, of fractions isolated from animal sources or from cultures of *Streptomyces aureofaciens*. Since vitamin B_{12} appears to be more abundant in animal than in vegetable products, it is not surprising that

[80] A. L. Latner et al., *Biochem. J.*, **63**, 501 (1956).
[81] M. E. Gregory and E. S. Holdsworth, *Biochem. J.*, **59**, 329, 335 (1955).
[82] M. Downing and B. S. Schweigert, *J. Biol. Chem.*, **220**, 521 (1956).
[83] B. L. O'Dell et al., *J. Biol. Chem.*, **217**, 625 (1955).
[84] U. D. Register, *J. Biol. Chem.*, **206**, 705 (1954).
[85] W. H. Ott et al., *J. Biol. Chem.*, **174**, 1047 (1948).

the effect of APF is in part due to the presence of this vitamin. The stimulation of growth by preparations from *S. aureofaciens* appears to be due both to the vitamin B_{12} and to antibiotics present in this source of APF. Such growth-promoting activity has been reported for aureomycin, streptomycin, terramycin, and penicillin; however, the effect of each antibiotic apparently depends on the basal diet used in the test. Presumably, the antibiotics alter the character of the intestinal flora of the animal host, but it has not been determined how this results in the better utilization, for animal growth, of proteins of vegetable origin.

Lipoic Acid. One of the microbial growth factors found in yeast and in liver is the substance named lipoic acid or thioctic acid [d-5(dithiolane-3)-pentanoic acid; p. 306],[86] which is soluble in organic solvents. Lipoic acid is reduced by DPNH in the presence of "dihydrolipoic dehydrogenase" (found in animal tissues and in microorganisms) to l-dihydrolipoic acid, which can react with acetyl-CoA to form d-6-S-acetyldihydrolipoic acid (p. 481); the latter reaction is catalyzed by "dihydrolipoic transacetylase," present in *Escherichia coli*.[87]

Much of the lipoic acid in natural materials is tightly bound to protein, and the cleavage of such lipoic acid-protein complexes is effected by enzyme preparations ("lipoic acid-splitting enzyme") obtained from pigeon liver extracts and from the protozoan *Tetrahymena pyriformis*.[88]

Although it is uncertain whether lipoic acid is required in the diet of higher animals, its role as a growth factor for microorganisms is well established. Lipoic acid is identical with "protogen" (obtained from various natural materials), which is essential for the growth of *Tetrahymena*, and with the *Lactobacillus casei* acetate factor, which replaces acetate in the promotion of the growth of *L. casei* and of other lactobacilli. Lipoic acid also serves as the "pyruvate oxidation factor," so named because of its essential role in the oxidative decarboxylation of pyruvate by *Streptococcus fecalis*. It should be added that some bacteria (*Lactobacillus delbruckii, Proteus vulgaris*) do not require lipoic acid for the oxidative decarboxylation of α-keto acids (cf. p. 483).

Carnitine (Vitamin B_T). This water-soluble vitamin, discovered by Fraenkel in a study of the nutritional requirements of the mealworm *Tenebrio molitor*, is identical with l-carnitine,[89] the betaine of β-hydroxy-γ-aminobutyric acid. In the absence of a dietary source of carnitine, larvae of *Tenebrio* and of several other insects die before metamorphosis. It is probable that vertebrates can synthesize carnitine, which has long been known to be a constituent of muscle.

[86] L. J. Reed et al., *J. Am. Chem. Soc.*, **75**, 1267 (1953); E. Walton et al., *ibid.*, **76**, 4748 (1954).

[87] I. C. Gunsalus et al., *J. Am. Chem. Soc.*, **78**, 1763 (1956).

[88] G. R. Seaman and N. D. Naschke, *J. Biol. Chem.*, **213**, 705 (1955).

[89] H. E. Carter et al., *Arch. Biochem. and Biophys.*, **35**, 241 (1952).

The metabolic function of carnitine is obscure, but it is noteworthy that O-acetylcarnitine transfers its acetyl group to coenzyme A in the presence of enzyme preparations from sheep liver or pigeon liver;[90] this finding suggests the possibility that carnitine may be involved in transacetylation reactions *in vivo*.

$$O—COCH_3$$

$$(CH_3)_3 \overset{+}{N} CH_2 \overset{|}{C} HCH_2COO^- + \text{coenzyme A} \; \rightleftharpoons$$

O-Acetylcarnitine

$$OH$$

$$(CH_3)_3 \overset{+}{N} CH_2 \overset{|}{C} HCH_2COO^- + \text{Acetyl-CoA}$$

Carnitine

B Vitamins of Doubtful Status. The compounds *myo*-inositol (p. 412) and choline (p. 800) have often been classified as vitamins belonging to the B complex. The inclusion of *myo*-inositol in this group depends mainly on work with rats and mice, in which various external manifestations of a deficiency state have been observed. Although it appears that *myo*-inositol can be synthesized in the tissues of higher animals (rat, chick),[91] when human cells (e.g., bone marrow, liver) are grown in tissue culture, this compound is an essential constituent of the medium.[92] It is also a growth factor for *Saccharomyces cerevisiae* and several other yeasts and for some fungi.

Choline is widely distributed in nature and is present in the natural materials usually employed as nutritional sources of the B complex. As noted previously (cf. p. 802), choline is readily formed *in vivo*. Although a characteristic syndrome has been associated with choline deficiency, the symptoms are actually a reflection of a deficiency in the dietary source either of labile methyl groups or of the B vitamins essential for the biosynthesis of methyl groups from other constituents of the diet.

Choline and inositol are present in animal tissues (in the phospholipids) in amounts much greater than those usually associated with the true vitamins. Furthermore, no cofactor essential for enzymic reactions has been shown to include either of these compounds as a structural unit. It is appropriate therefore to exclude choline and inositol from the list of B vitamins.

Nutritional studies have led to the discovery of other dietary factors whose present status is uncertain or which do not appear to be true B vitamins. Among these is vitamin B_{13}, which promotes the growth of rats and of chicks.[93] Although its nature has not been elucidated, it

[90] S. Friedman and G. Fraenkel, *Arch. Biochem. and Biophys.*, **59**, 491 (1955).

[91] W. H. Daughaday et al., *J. Biol. Chem.*, **212**, 869 (1955); J. W. Halliday and L. Anderson, *ibid.*, **217**, 797 (1955).

[92] H. Eagle et al., *J. Biol. Chem.*, **226**, 191 (1957).

[93] A. F. Novak and S. M. Hauge, *J. Biol. Chem.*, **174**, 647 (1948); L. Mann and S. M. Hauge, *ibid.*, **202**, 91 (1953).

is of interest that concentrates of vitamin B_{13} contain the δ-lactone of mevalonic acid (p. 629), an intermediate in the biosynthesis of sterols from acetate; this compound serves as an acetate-replacing factor for *Lactobacillus acidophilus*. Another dietary factor (the liver residue factor or LRF) found to be essential for the maintenance of the xanthine oxidase level in rats has been shown to be molybdenum (cf. p. 339).

Other Growth Factors for Microorganisms. As noted previously, strains of *Hemophilus parainfluenzae* require, for growth, a source of DPN or TPN (cf. p. 308) and of putrescine or a related diamine (cf. p. 815). Some strains of *Hemophilus* also need hemin for growth under aerobic conditions; at least one class of insects and some protozoa exhibit a similar requirement for an exogenous source of hemin. Thus hemin must be classified as a growth factor for a variety of organisms, and, because of its distribution in nature and its biochemical role as a part of the catalytic heme proteins, it may be included among the members of the B complex.

Various constituents of nucleic acids have been found to serve as growth factors for microorganisms. For example, thymidine is required by some lactobacilli when they are cultured in media devoid of PGA or CF (cf. p. 898). Furthermore, a strain of *Lactobacillus gayonii* requires for optimal growth a source of any one of the nucleotides derived from yeast PNA; the corresponding nucleosides do not appear to be effective.

The growth-promoting ability of peptides has been mentioned previously (p. 745); among these growth factors, the material termed "strepogenin" is of special interest. In this connection it may be added that the protozoan *Glaucoma scintillans* requires for growth an exogenous source of peptides or of proteins (e.g., casein) as well as free amino acids; however, preparations of strepogenin are ineffective in meeting this peptide requirement.[94]

Another type of growth factor is required by a strain of *Lactobacillus bifidus* isolated from the intestinal flora of human infants. This organism requires an exogenous source of a complex oligosaccharide present in human milk, but not in cows' milk. Simpler compounds such as N-acetylneuraminic acid (p. 426) or the β-methylglycoside of N-acetyl-D-glucosamine can partly replace this growth factor for *L. bifidus*.[95]

The Fat-Soluble Vitamins[2]

As noted earlier, the vitamins classified under the letters A, D, E, and K are fat-soluble factors essential for the normal growth or main-

[94] G. W. Kidder et al., *Proc. Soc. Exptl. Biol. Med.*, **86**, 685 (1954).

[95] F. Zilliken et al., *J. Biol. Chem.*, **208**, 299 (1954); *Arch. Biochem. and Biophys.*, **54**, 564 (1955).

tenance of some higher animals. Most of the fat-soluble compounds to be discussed in this section are found in large amounts only in plants; with the possible exception of the carotenoids (the provitamins A), little is known of their biochemical function in the plant kingdom. Nor is much information available about their actual metabolic roles in animal tissues, although certain deficiency diseases of animals have been associated with each vitamin group. With the demonstration that many members of the vitamin B complex are essential to enzymic reactions, it was postulated that a similar biochemical function would be found for the fat-soluble vitamins. This hypothesis has yet to be supported by unequivocal experimental data for vitamins D, E, and K; and the demonstrated role of vitamin A in the visual process (cf. p. 660) does not fully explain the nutritional requirement for this substance.

In addition to vitamins A, D, E, and K, the "essential fatty acids" (p. 560) are occasionally classified as fat-soluble vitamins; these acids had been designated "vitamin F," but this term is now obsolete.

The Vitamin A Group.[96] During the period 1913 to 1915, the work of McCollum and Davis and of Osborne and Mendel demonstrated the existence of two types of "accessory factors"; these were at first termed "fat-soluble A" and "water-soluble B." In 1922 McCollum and his collaborators showed that the fat-soluble material present in butter fat or cod liver oil contained at least two distinct vitamins: one (vitamin A) with antixerophthalmic activity, the second (vitamin D) with antirachitic activity. Subsequently it became clear that a number of natural products possess vitamin A activity for higher animals; these include the isoprenoid alcohols vitamins A_1 and A_2 (p. 656), found in animal tissues, and a variety of "provitamins," which are plant carotenoids converted in the animal body to vitamin A_1.

Vitamin A_1 was isolated as a result of the search for the antixerophthalmic factor which is also essential for the growth of higher animals, whereas vitamin A_2 was detected initially by spectroscopic examination of the oils from fresh water fish. Pure vitamin A_2 is biologically active; in the rat this compound shows about 40 per cent of the activity found for vitamin A_1, and is not converted in $vivo$ to the A_1 molecule.[97] It is of interest that the administration of vitamin A_2 to rats leads to the replacement of retinal retinene$_1$ by retinene$_2$ (cf. p. 660).

The provitamins include α-, β-, and γ-carotene, and cryptoxanthin, found in higher plants, and also myxoxanthin, isolated from a blue-green alga. Each of these carotenoids is composed of 8 isoprene units, and each contains at least one unsubstituted β-ionone ring, which appears to

[96] S. H. Rubin and E. DeRitter, *Vitamins and Hormones,* **12,** 101 (1954); J. S. Lowe and R. A. Morton, *ibid.,* **14,** 97 (1956); T. Moore, *Vitamin A,* Elsevier Publishing Co., Amsterdam, 1957.

[97] E. M. Shantz and J. H. Brinkman, *J. Biol. Chem.,* **183,** 467 (1950).

be essential for the provitamin activity. β-Carotene shows vitamin A_1 activity only when it is fed by mouth. Thus the parenteral administration of β-carotene does not alleviate the symptoms of a vitamin A deficiency, although it does lead to the deposition of the carotene in the liver. The main site of the conversion of the provitamins into vitamins is the wall of the small intestine; the formation of the vitamin alcohol from retinene$_1$, the corresponding aldehyde, also has been found to take place in this tissue. The liver, which is the chief storage depot for carotenoids and for vitamin A, apparently cannot convert the provitamins into the vitamin.[98]

Since β-carotene, which is the most potent of the provitamins, is only one half as active (on a weight basis) as vitamin A_1 in animal assays, this symmetrical carotene molecule apparently is degraded *in vivo* with the ultimate formation of only 1 molecule of vitamin per molecule of β-carotene. Presumably the other provitamins can be metabolized by a similar pathway. The mechanism by which the carotenoids are cleaved is not known; it has been suggested, however, that the degradation is not effected by an oxidative cleavage of the central ethylenic bond (between carbons 15 and 15' of β-carotene; cf. p. 653) to yield a C_{20} compound, but by an initial oxidation at one of the "terminal" double bonds to yield an aldehyde with 27 or 30 carbon atoms (a "carotenal"). Such aldehydes have vitamin A activity when tested with vitamin-deficient rats. Stepwise oxidation of the long-chain aldehydes would be expected to yield vitamin A_1 aldehyde (retinene$_1$), which is readily reduced to vitamin A_1 (cf. p. 659).

In view of the relation of the vitamins A to the visual process in animals, it is obvious why the onset of a vitamin A deficiency can most readily be detected by tests for dark adaptation, i.e., for the visual response of the retinal rods. Indeed, "night blindness" is the most common symptom of this avitaminosis in the human. It should be added, however, that vitamin A has been implicated as a key substance not only in the visual response in dim light but also in color vision, which depends on the visual pigments of the retinal cones (cf. p. 660).

Xerophthalmia, the syndrome of acute vitamin deficiency in the rat, is very rarely encountered in man, and is probably a secondary manifestation of the general change in epithelial tissues that characterizes the deficiency in higher animals. In the rat, avitaminosis A is also characterized by loss of weight, skeletal abnormalities, and disturbances of normal sexual processes. The biochemical role of vitamin A in this aspect of metabolism has not been elucidated, but is believed to be distinct from the role of the vitamin as a precursor of the visual pigments.

[98] S. M. Patel et al., *Arch. Biochem. and Biophys.*, **30**, 103 (1951).

Vitamin A is toxic to animals when it is taken in large doses over a long period of time.[99]

The Vitamin D Group.[100] The term vitamin D was proposed originally to designate the antirachitic principle in preparations of the "fat-soluble A" factor. However, before the actual isolation by Brockmann and other investigators of the active compound (now called vitamin D_3 or cholecalciferol) from fish liver oils, it was shown that an antirachitic compound (vitamin D_2, calciferol, or ergocalciferol) could be produced in the laboratory by the irradiation of the plant sterol ergosterol (p. 623). The term vitamin D_1 has been discarded since the material to which it was first applied has been found to be a mixture of calciferol and several sterols.

The observations of Steenbock, of Hess, and of Rosenheim that vitamin D activity could be produced by the irradiation (preferably by ultraviolet light) of plants or of certain sterols had, in fact, been foreshadowed by the demonstration that sunlight had a pronounced curative action on rachitic children or laboratory animals. Clearly this effect is due to the formation *in vivo* of vitamins from provitamins. The latter term, as applied to vitamin D, implies a sterol which can be converted by irradiation into a D vitamin. Thus 7-dehydrocholesterol yields vitamin D_3, and 22-dihydroergosterol yields vitamin D_4. Several other provitamins have been reported to be present in natural materials, and all the provitamins appear to be sterols in which carbon atom 3 bears an hydroxyl group and ring B contains the $\Delta^{5,7}$-dienic group.

During the activation of the provitamins, ring B is cleaved between carbon atoms 9 and 10 (cf. p. 620). The sequence of reactions that occurs during the photochemical activation of the sterols *in vitro* has not been elucidated, nor has the mechanism by which the provitamins are activated *in vivo* been determined. Indeed, it is still not clear where this process takes place. It has been suggested that in higher animals the ultraviolet radiations of the sun (or of an artificial light source) act on the provitamins in the skin and that the resultant vitamins are then absorbed into the blood and transported to other tissues. However, this hypothesis does not explain how the vitamins are formed in animals whose skin is seldom exposed to radiations of sufficient strength to activate the provitamins (e.g., heavily furred land animals, fish that live far below the surface of the ocean).

Although no marked qualitative difference has been observed in the biological activity of the various forms of vitamin D or of provitamin D, quantitative differences in the potency of these compounds do exist; this is especially true when a comparison is made of the relative activity of

[99] C. Nieman and H. J. Klein Obbink, *Vitamins and Hormones,* **12,** 69 (1954).
[100] R. Nicolaysen and N. Eeg-Larsen, *Vitamins and Hormones,* **11,** 29 (1953).

the various compounds for different animal species. Since the ingestion of a specific form of vitamin D is followed by the appearance of that compound in the milk of mammals or the eggs of birds, each D vitamin appears to be metabolized independently of the others.

In higher animals, vitamin D deficiency causes abnormalities in calcium and phosphate metabolism and results in structural changes in the bones and teeth; the syndrome characteristic of a severe deficiency in children is called rickets; that in adults, osteomalacia. The ingestion of excessive amounts of vitamin D also produces toxic symptoms; initially there is a rise in the blood calcium level followed by metastatic calcification of various internal organs and, ultimately, by decalcification of skeletal structures.

The D vitamins stimulate the absorption of Ca^{2+} from the intestinal tract, but do not appear to exert a direct effect on the absorption of phosphate; the lowered accumulation of bone salts in avitaminotic animals is chiefly a result of an impaired ability to absorb calcium. In addition, vitamin D appears to function in the internal tissues. For example, the amount of citrate present in the bones and internal organs (kidney, heart) of vitamin D-deficient rats rises rapidly when the vitamin is given. Although it is generally agreed that the D vitamins play an important role in the process of growth and especially in the formation and maintenance of bones, the biochemical functions of this group of vitamins remain obscure.[101]

The Vitamin E Group. It was mentioned previously (p. 667) that the vitamin E group consists of a series of chroman derivatives termed tocopherols. The characteristic symptoms of experimentally induced avitaminosis E vary with the animal species. In the mature female rat reproductive failure occurs as the result of the resorption of the developing fetus; in the mature male rat sterility is due to degeneration of the germinal tissues. The deficiency in rabbits and guinea pigs is characterized mainly by the development of an acute muscular dystrophy resembling the progressive muscular dystrophy in man. Muscular dystrophy is also seen in rats, but here the condition is acute only in very young animals. In the chick, vitamin E deficiency leads to specific abnormalities in the vascular system; in monkeys, an anemia accompanies the muscular weakness. No well-defined syndrome of vitamin E deficiency has been described in man, and the administration of tocopherols to patients with progressive muscular dystrophy does not prevent the further development of this fatal disease.

The specific biochemical function of vitamin E in metabolism has

---

[101] G. E. Wolstenholme and C. M. O'Connor, *Bone Structure and Metabolism*, Little, Brown and Co., Boston, 1956; G. H. Bourne, *The Biochemistry and Physiology of Bone*, Academic Press, New York, 1956.

not been determined. In the muscular dystrophies, the level of creatine in the muscles is markedly decreased, and there is a pronounced creatinuria. The muscles of vitamin E-deficient rabbits contain abnormally large amounts of free amino acids other than glycine.[102] Furthermore, avitaminotic rabbits and monkeys excrete large amounts of allantoin (p. 856), possibly as a result of an increased rate of nucleic acid turnover in liver and skeletal muscle.[103] One of the most obvious characteristics of dystrophic tissues is their abnormally high oxygen consumption, and avitaminosis E apparently results in a stimulation of respiratory processes.

The biological activity of the tocopherols has been attributed to their action as antioxidants. It is known that α-tocopherol (p. 667) can undergo the series of interconversions shown in the accompanying scheme,[104] and that the tocopherols can protect various compounds

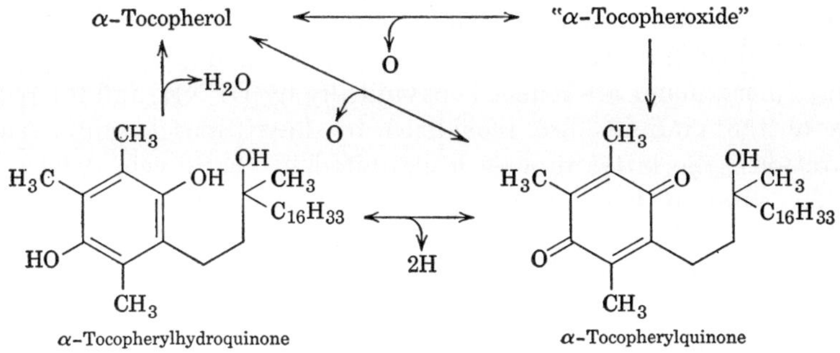

against oxidation in air; for example, the addition of any tocopherol to solutions of vitamin A in oil inhibits the oxidation of vitamin A and consequent loss of vitamin activity. This antioxidant action is of importance in animal nutrition, where the feeding of vitamin E improves the utilization of dietary vitamin A. However, this effect is nonspecific, since other antioxidants such as methylene blue also improve the utilization of vitamin A.[105] According to Dam, many of the manifestations of tocopherol deficiency in higher animals may be ascribed to the lack of these antioxidants in tissues and the resultant destruction of cellular metabolites by abnormal oxidation reactions. In this connection, it is of interest that several of the tocopherols can activate preparations of muscle cytochrome c reductase (p. 356) from which the natural lipid

[102] H. H. Tallan, *Proc. Soc. Exptl. Biol. Med.,* **89,** 553 (1955).

[103] J. S. Dinning, *J. Biol. Chem.,* **212,** 735 (1955).

[104] W. H. Harrison et al., *Biochim. et Biophys. Acta,* **21,** 150 (1956); C. Martius and H. Eilingsfeld, *Biochem. Z.,* **328,** 507 (1957).

[105] H. Dam et al., *Acta Physiol. Scand.,* **18,** 161 (1949); S. M. C. Miles et al., *Proc. Soc. Exptl. Biol. Med.,* **70,** 162 (1949).

components have been removed.[106]   Although the lipid material extracted from the muscle preparations contains some vitamin E (presumably as a tocopheryl quinone), it is not known whether the vitamin is directly involved in the activity of cytochrome c reductase.

The possible biochemical role of the oxidation products derived from the tocopherols is uncertain.   Such derivatives of α-tocopherol have been reported to prevent or to cure the nutritional muscular dystrophy in rabbits maintained on vitamin E-deficient diets, but only "α-tocopheroxide" shows any activity in the prevention of fetal resorption in rats.

The Group of K Vitamins.   The chemistry and metabolism of the natural compounds that exhibit vitamin K activity has been discussed before (p. 668), as has the "antivitamin K" activity of dicumarol (p. 704).   Vitamin K_1 has been considered as a possible electron carrier in biological oxidations, and the suggestion has been offered that the anticoagulant action of dicumarol may be related to its ability to "uncouple" oxidative phosphorylation (cf. p. 385), an effect that is reversed by vitamin K_1.[107]   Both vitamin K_1 and the synthetic vitamin K_3 (menadione) are reduced enzymically by DPNH, and the reduced forms of the vitamins are reoxidized by heart muscle mitochondrial preparations; the latter process is inhibited by Antimycin A.[108]

Unlike vitamin K_1, menadione appears to inhibit oxidative phosphorylation.   This difference between the effects of menadione and of vitamin K_1 is of interest in relation to the observation that large doses of menadione (but not of the natural vitamin K_1) are highly toxic to experimental animals.

Liver and heart mitochondria, yeasts, and bacteria contain representatives of a group of quinones (variously named ubiquinone, mitoquinone, coenzyme Q) that are structurally related to the K vitamins.[109]   They are derivatives of 2,3-dimethoxy-5-methyl-1,4-benzoquinone, with an isoprenoid chain (6 to 10 isoprene units) similar to that of vitamin K_2 (p. 668) at position 6 of the benzene ring.   These substances undergo reversible oxidation-reduction, and restore the succinoxidase activity of heart muscle preparations from which lipids had been extracted with organic solvents (cf. p. 356).

[106] A. Nason and I. R. Lehman, *Science,* **122,** 19 (1955); K. O. Donaldson and A. Nason, *Proc. Natl. Acad. Sci.,* **43,** 364 (1957).

[107] C. Martius and D. Nitz-Litzow, *Biochem. Z.,* **327,** 1 (1955).

[108] J. P. Colpa-Boonstra and E. C. Slater, *Biochim. et Biophys. Acta,* **23,** 222 (1957).

[109] R. L. Lester et al., *J. Am. Chem. Soc.,* **80,** 4751 (1958); R. A. Morton et al., *Helv. Chim. Acta,* **41,** 2343 (1958).

Index

Abietic acid, 663
Absolute specificity, 273, 276
Absorbance, 72
Absorbancy index, 72
Absorption coefficient, 72
Acetaldehyde, activated, 475, 480–481
  conversion, to acetate, 481
    to acetyl-CoA, 483
    to acetyl phosphate, 326
    to deoxyribose-5-phosphate, 534–535
    to ethanol, 316, 475–476
    to fatty acids, 611
  formation, from ethanol, 316, 475
    from glucose, 467
    from pyruvate, 474–476, 480
    from threonine, 792
Acetaldehyde dehydrogenase, 328, 481
Acetaldehyde-TPP compound, 475, 480–481
Acetal phosphatide, 569
Acetal phospholipids, 568–569
Acetamide, 711
Acetate-activating enzyme, 484
Acetazoleamide, 924
Acetic acid, activation, 484, 596, 720
  conversion, to acetyl-CoA, 484, 596
    to acetyl phosphate, 483–484
    to cholesterol, 626–631
    to citrate, 506, 518–520
    to fatty acids, 612–614
    to glycogen, 513–515
    to pyruvate, 513–515
    to squalene, 628, 629–631
    to steroid hormones, 642, 644
  dissociation, 85–88
  formation, from acetone, 605–606
    from acetylcholine, 577
    from butyrate, 608
    from glucose, 478

Acetic acid, formation, from glutamate, 818
    from glycine, 757–758, 777–778
    from 17α-hydroxyprogesterone, 644
    from propionate, 602
    from purines, 894–895
    from pyruvate, 480–483
    from threonine, 792
  free energy of formation, 237
  in β-carotene formation, 665
  in eburicoic acid formation, 665–666
  in glyoxylate cycle, 519–520
  in lysine formation, 810
  in methane fermentation, 609
  in porphyrin formation, 864–872
  in sphingosine formation, 618
Acetic anhydride, 50
Acetoacetate-activating enzyme, 596, 605
Acetoacetic acid, activation, 596–597
  conversion to β-hydroxybutyrate, 316, 599, 605–607
  formation, from acetoacetyl-CoA, 605
    from acetyl-CoA, 600
    from fatty acids, 590–605, 607
    from leucine, 788
    from tyrosine, 827–828
  in cholesterol synthesis, 627, 630–631
  metabolism, 603–608
Acetoacetyl-CoA, conversion, to acetoacetate, 605
    to β-hydroxybutyryl-CoA, 316, 598–599
  formation, from acetoacetate, 596–597
    from acetyl-CoA, 600
  in cholesterol formation, 630–631
Acetoacetyl-CoA deacylase, 605, 608
Aceto-CoA kinase, 596, 602, 910
  in fatty acid formation, 612
Acetoin, 479–480

Acetokinase, 484, 578, 596
α-Acetolactic acid, 480, 783
Acetone, conversion to carbohydrate, 606
  dielectric constant, 21
  formation, 549, 590, 605
  in C_1 unit metabolism, 774
  in protein precipitation, 20
Acetone bodies, definition, 590
  formation, 590–602, 787–788
  metabolism, 603–608
Acetylacetone, 413
N-Acetyl-p-aminobenzoic acid, 999
Acetyl-AMP, 484, 720
O-Acetylcarnitine, 1007
Acetyl chloride, 49–50
Acetylcholine, formula, 275
  metabolism, 275, 281, 577–578
  physiological role, 377, 577
Acetylcholine esterase, active center, 272,
    281–282
  catalytic action, 275, 281, 577–578
  physiological role, 577, 926
Acetyl-chymotrypsin, 694
Acetyl-CoA, conversion, to acetoacetate,
    600
  to acetyl phosphate, 483
  energy-rich bond, 377–379
  formation, from acetaldehyde, 483
    from acetate, 376, 483–484, 596
    from O-acetylcarnitine, 1007
    from β-ketoacyl-CoA compounds,
      599–600, 604–605, 833–834
    from ketogenic amino acids, 784–
      785, 788
    from pyruvate, 481–483, 506–507
  formula, 482
  in acetylation of amines, 465, 719
  in acetylcholine formation, 578
  in cholesterol formation, 630–631
  in citrate formation, 506–508, 518
  in fatty acid metabolism, 595–601, 608,
    611–613
  in glucose oxidation, 600
Acetyl-CoA thiophorase, 596, 608
Acetyl-coenzyme A, see Acetyl-CoA
Acetyldihydrolipoic acid, 481
Acetylgalactosamine, 413, 424–428
  UDP-, 466
Acetylglucosamine, metabolism, 437, 464–
    466
  occurrence, 423–428, 749
  test for, 413
  UDP-, 464–466
Acetylglucosamine-1-phosphate, 465–466
Acetylglucosamine-6-phosphate, 465–466
Acetylglutamic acid, 814–815, 852

Acetylglutamic-γ-semialdehyde, 814–
    815
S-Acetylglutathione, 379
Acetylglycine, 92
Acetylhistidine, 824
Acetylhyalobiuronic acid, 424, 437
Acetylimidazole, 67, 379
N-Acetyllysine, 808
Acetylmethylcarbinol, 479–480
Acetylneuraminic acid, 426, 1008
O-Acetyl-p-nitrophenol, 694
Acetylornithine, 814
Acetylphenylcarbinol, 480
Acetyl phosphate, energy-rich bond,
    378
  enzymic hydrolysis, 328, 483
  formation, 328, 482–484, 531
  formula, 326
  in citrate formation, 506
  in fatty acid metabolism, 483–484, 595,
    608
  in Stickland reaction, 757
Acetyl phosphate phosphatase, 483
Acetyl pool, 601
3-Acetylpyridine, 309, 991–992
Ac-globulin, 703–704
Acid-base balance, 918–922
Acid hematin, 178
Acidosis, 100, 848
Acids, 85–88, 228, 238
Aconitase, 503–504, 510, 514
cis-Aconitic acid, 503–504, 516, 520
Acriflavine, 358
Acrodynia, 987, 988
Acroleylaminofumaric acid, 841
Acrylic acid, 779
Acrylyl-CoA, 602
ACTH, see Adrenocorticotrophic hor-
    mone
Actin, 488, 733
Actinomycin, 53, 138
Action potential, 926
Active transport, 922–924, 926–927
Activity coefficient, 86, 232
Actomyosin, 487–488
Actomyosin ATP-ase, 487–488, 910
Acylamino acids, 49–50
Acyl-AMP compounds, 484, 720, 735
Acylases, 710, 838
Acylating agents, 67, 133–136, 142–144
Acyl-CoA dehydrogenases, chemistry,
    338, 344–345
  catalytic action, 344–345, 597, 612
  in fatty acid metabolism, 600, 612
Acyl dehydrogenases, see Acyl-CoA de-
    hydrogenases

Acyl-enzymes, formation, in glyceralde-
    hyde-3-phosphate   dehydrogenase
    action, 325
  in hydrolysis, 281–282, 694, 715
  in thiolysis, 604
  in transamidation, 694, 715, 718
Acylimidazoles, 379
Acyl migration, 56, 562
Acyloins, 480
Acyl-oxygen fission, 281
Adaptive enzymes, 746, 838
Addison's disease, 946, 966
Adenase, 886
Adenine, breakdown, 894
  chemistry, 187, 196
  deamination, 886
  formation, 887, 891–893
  formula, 187
  in nucleic acid formation, 900–902
  in riboflavin formation, 985
  occurrence, in nucleic acids, 187, 191,
    197–198
  in nucleotides, 203–206
  in pseudo-vitamin B_{12}, 1003
Adenosine, 187–188
  metabolism, 805, 883, 886
Adenosine deaminase, 886
Adenosine-2′,5′-diphosphate, 310
Adenosine-3′,5′-diphosphate, 994
Adenosine-5′-diphosphate, chemistry,
    203–204, 376–378, 487
  effect on respiration, 383–384
  formation from ATP, by alcoholic fer-
    mentation, 470–471, 476
  by ATP-ase, 489
  by glycolysis, 488–492
  by nucleotide transphosphorylases,
    459, 882–883
  oxidative phosphorylation, respiratory
    chain, 381–385, 509, 521–524
  substrate linked, 380, 505–506, 521
  phosphorylation, 374–377, 380–385
  by acetyl phosphate, 484
  by carbamyl phosphate, 852, 854
  by creatine phosphate, 486–487
  by diphosphoglycerate, 373, 376
  by hexose phosphates, 459–461
  by inorganic phosphate, 505–506, 518,
    721
  by nucleotides, 376, 459, 512
  by phosphoenolpyruvate, 473
  in alcoholic fermentation, 470–471,
    473, 490–491
  in citric acid cycle, 521–524
  in glycolysis, 489–492, 521
  in nitrate reduction, 680

Adenosine-5′-diphosphate, phosphoryla-
    tion, in photosynthesis, 554–555
  in purine breakdown, 895
  in Stickland reaction, 757–758
  see also Adenosine-5′-triphosphate
Adenosine monophosphate, see Adeno-
    sine-5′-phosphate
Adenosine-2′-phosphate, 189–190
Adenosine-2′,3′-phosphate, 189–190
Adenosine-3′-phosphate, 189–190
Adenosine-5′-phosphate, conversion, to
    ADP, 376, 459, 882
  to ATP, 484, 595, 851
  deamination, 886
  formation, 489, 882–883, 891–893
  formula, 189
  hydrolysis, 880
  in histidine formation, 821
  in phosphorylase activation, 440
  occurrence, 190, 203–205
  pyrophosphorolysis, 885
Adenosine-3′-phosphate-5′-phosphosul-
    fate, 647, 795–796
Adenosine-5′-phosphoryl carbonate, 788
Adenosine-5′-pyrophosphate, see Adeno-
    sine-5′-diphosphate
Adenosine-5′-tetraphosphate, 204
Adenosine triphosphatase, 473–474, 488–
    489
Adenosine-5′-triphosphate, chemistry, 203–
    204, 487, 925
  energy-rich bonds, 377–380
  hydrolysis, 228, 374, 378
  enzymic hydrolysis, 283, 473–474, 487–
    489
  inhibition by fluoride, 381
  formation, from ADP, see Adenosine-
    5′-diphosphate,   oxidative   phos-
    phorylation and phosphorylation
    from AMP, 484, 595, 851
  formula, 204
  in alcoholic fermentation, 470–471, 473,
    490–491
  in amide bond formation, 635, 718–721,
    734, 819
  in amino acid formation, 790–791, 851–
    853
  in bioluminescence, 346
  in carbon dioxide fixation, 512, 788
  in citric acid cycle, 505–506, 521–524
  in coenzyme A formation, 721, 993–994
  in fatty acid activation, 376, 484, 720
  in fatty acid cycle, 594–595, 602, 612
  in flavin nucleotide formation, 335, 336
  in glycolysis, 489–492, 494
  in hexose metabolism, 459–462, 526, 536

Adenosine-5′-triphosphate, in metaphosphate formation, 584
  in muscular contraction, 487–492
  in nucleic acid formation, 882, 890–892, 897
  in nitrate reduction, 680
  in pentose metabolism, 527–528, 885
  in phosphagen metabolism, 376, 486–487
  in phospholipid formation, 615–617
  in phosphoprotein metabolism, 742
  in phosphorylase activation, 440–441
  in photosynthesis, 551–552, 554–555
  in protein formation, 720, 734, 747
  in pyridine nucleotide formation, 310
  in pyridoxal phosphate formation, 375, 988
  in sulfate activation, 795
  in thiamine pyrophosphate formation, 475, 982
  in transmethylation, 804
  in triose metabolism, 376, 513
  in urea formation, 851–853
  occurrence, 203, 491
  transfer of energy, 374–375, 377
S-Adenosylhomocysteine, 804
S-Adenosylmethionine, 804–805, 815, 829–831
Adenylacetate, 484, 720
Adenylate kinase, see Myokinase
Adenylic acid, 186–190
  cyclic dianhydrodi-, 204, 441
  see also Adenosine-5′-phosphate
Adenylic acid a, 189–190
Adenylic acid b, 189–190
Adenylic deaminase, 886
Adenylosuccinase, 891, 892
Adenylosuccinic acid, 892
Adenylpyrophosphatase, 489, 910, 982
Adenylpyrophosphate, see Adenosine-5′-triphosphate
ADH, see Alcohol dehydrogenase
ADP, see Adenosine-5′-diphosphate
Adrenalectomy, 946–947, 964–965
Adrenalin, chemistry, 299
  formula, 828
  in ACTH secretion, 952
  in carbohydrate metabolism, 441, 960–961
  in lipid metabolism, 963
  in phosphorylase action, 441, 960–961
  metabolism, 828–830
  occurrence, 768, 946, 960
  pressor action, 946
Adrenochrome, 384, 829–830

Adrenocortical hormones, chemistry, 638–639, 947
  in ACTH secretion, 952
  in carbohydrate metabolism, 947, 959
  in electrolyte balance, 947, 966–967
  in lipid metabolism, 963
  in protein metabolism, 963–965
  metabolism, 641–644, 646–650
  secretion, 946, 950
Adrenocorticotrophic hormone, chemistry, 951, 954
  in adrenal cortex activity, 950, 951–952, 967
  in ascorbic acid metabolism, 951–952
  in carbohydrate metabolism, 959
  in cholesterol metabolism, 643, 951–952
  in lipid metabolism, 962–963
  in protein metabolism, 964
  melanocyte-stimulating action, 954
  secretion, 952
Adrenosterone, 645, 648, 649
Aesculin, 664
Agene, 61
Aglucone, 432
Agmatine, 767, 815, 823
Alanine, chemistry, 54, 118
  formula, 54
  metabolism, 778–779
D-Alanine, configuration, 78
  metabolism, 762, 769, 779
  occurrence, 749
L-Alanine, chemistry, 78, 79–80, 237
  conversion, to acetate, 757–758, 778–779
    to pyruvate, 752, 754, 760
  formation, 767, 778, 816
  glucogenic action, 765, 778
  occurrence, 125
β-Alanine, breakdown, 899–900
  formation, 767, 779, 781, 899
  formula, 54
  in pantothenic acid formation, 720–721, 993
  occurrence, 54, 137
L-Alanine dehydrogenase, 754, 765, 778
Alanine racemase, 769–770, 779
Alanine-serine transaminase, 789
Albumins, 16, 17, 20
  in lipase activation, 575
Albumoses, 130
Alcaptonuria, 398, 826–828
Alcohol dehydrogenase, catalytic action, 317–323
  crystallization, 218
  hydrogen transfer, 319
  in coenzyme-linked reactions, 327–328
  in fermentation, 475–478

Alcohol dehydrogenase, in vision, 659
  liver, 218, 316, 319–323
  specificity, 316
  yeast, 218, 316–319
  zinc in, 319–321
Alcoholic fermentation, definition, 456
  early studies, 212–214, 456–457
  Embden-Meyerhof scheme, 476–477
  enzymic reactions, 457–464, 467–475
  free-energy changes, 491
  inhibition, by fluoride, 467–468, 472, 476
    by iodoacetate, 476
    by sulfite, 467, 478
  Neuberg's first form, 478
  Neuberg's second form, 478
  relation to glycolysis, 489–491
Alcohols, enzymic oxidation, 317–321
Aldehyde dehydrogenase, 316, 326, 483
Aldehyde mutase, 328
Aldehyde oxidase, catalytic action, 339,
    823, 988
  prosthetic group, 338
Aldehydes, enzymic oxidation, 323–327,
    339
  enzymic reduction, 317–321
  reactions with amino acids, 51, 91
Aldohexoses, 403–405
Aldolase, catalytic action, 216, 468
  in alcoholic fermentation, 468–470, 476
  in glycolysis, 468–470
  liver, 469, 493–494
  muscle, catalytic action, 468–470
    crystallization, 218, 469
    in myogen A, 217
    metabolism, 737
    particle weight, 469
    terminal amino acids, 143
  occurrence, 469
  specificity, 469
Aldosterone, formation, 642–644
  formula, 639
  in carbohydrate metabolism, 947
  in electrolyte balance, 947, 967
  secretion, 638, 946, 967
Alginic acid, 423
Alkaline tide, 924
Alkaloids, 859–863
Alkalosis, 100, 848
Allantoic acid, 857
Allantoicase, 857
Allantoin, 856–857, 1013
Allantoinase, 857
Alliin, 60, 981
Allithiamine, 981
Allohydroxyproline, 82, 138
D-Alloisoleucine, 138, 781

L-Alloisoleucine, 82, 781–782
Allopregnane, 638
Allopregnane-3,20-dione, 647
Allopregnan-3-ol-20-one, 647
Allose, 404
D-Allothreonine, 82
L-Allothreonine, 82
Alloxan, 299, 941
Alloxan diabetes, 941
Alloxanic acid, 857
S-Allylcysteine sulfoxide, 60, 981
Allylisopropylacetylurea, 872
Altrose, 404
Aluminum, 768, 908, 909
Aluminum hydroxide, 24
Aluminum silicate, 24
Amberlite resins, 122, 126
A-methopterin, 902, 1001
Amidases, activation by metal ions, 262–
    263, 697
  catalytic action, 274, 710–711, 763
  type reactions, 216
ω-Amidases, 763
Amide bond, 52, 710–711
  see also Peptide bond
Amidophosphate, 485, 582
Amino acid-activating enzymes, 720
Amino acid amides, 52, 62–63
Amino acid composition of proteins, 122–
    125
Amino acid deaminases, 745, 755
Amino acid decarboxylases, 745, 766–770
L-Amino acid dehydrogenase, 757
Amino acid esters, 52
Amino acid oxidases, 335–338, 751–755
  in ammonia excretion, 848
D-Amino acid oxidases, catalytic action,
    335–336, 751–754, 755
  flavin nucleotides in, 336–338, 751, 755
  fluorescence, 337
  inhibition by atebrin, 337
  Michaelis constant, 337
  occurrence, 751–752, 755
  specificity, 277, 337, 752, 755
  turnover number, 752
L-Amino acid oxidases, catalytic action,
    751–754, 808
  flavin nucleotides in, 337, 338, 752
  inhibitors, 751
  occurrence, 751–752
  specificity, 277, 752, 808
  turnover number, 752
Amino acids, absolute configuration, 78
  activation, 720, 736
  active transport, 744–745, 923, 974
  as electrolytes, 90–97

Amino acids, chemistry, 52–84, 90–97
  acid lability, 47
  acylation, 49–50, 132–136
  alkali lability, 47
  amino group reactions, 48–52, 91
  carboxyl group reactions, 52, 769–770
  chelation, 108
  color reactions, 51–52, 58, 65–66, 68–69
  solubility, 94–97
  chromatography, 115–126
  classification, 46
  configuration, 78–80, 97
  conversion to urinary ammonia, 848
  dipole moment, 92
  dispensable, 724–726, 731–732, 764–765
  dissociation, 92–97
  enzymic deamination, 750–759
  enzymic decarboxylation, 766–770
  estimation, chemical, 113–116, 120–125, 126–129
    enzymic, 754, 766
  excretion, 847, 858
  formation, from ketoacids, 754–766
    from oximes, 678
    from proteins, 694, 695–698, 700
    in plants, 681
    photosynthesis in, 553
    transamination in, 764–766
  formol titration, 91
  free energy of formation, 237
  glycogenic, 763–764
  heat of combustion, 226–227
  in blood, 739, 858
  incorporation into proteins, 729–738, 744–745
  indispensable, 673–674, 724–728, 735, 759
  in homeostasis, 917–918
  in proteins, 125
  intestinal absorption, 700
  isoionic point, 94
  isolation, 46–48, 58, 68
    as salts, 62–66, 69–72, 96–97, 114
    by column chromatography, 126
  ketogenic, 763–764
  melting points, 92
  metabolism, 771–859
    see also individual amino acids
  occurrence in nucleotides, 748–749
  optical activity, 78–83, 97
  pK values, 713
  R_F values, 118
  racemic, enzymic resolution, 84, 710, 714, 754
  racemization, 47, 769–770
  relation to plant alkaloids, 859–862

Amino acids, release from proteins, 736
  salting in, 95–96
  salting out, 96–97
  solubility, 94–97
  titration, 91–92
  transport, 732–733, 739, 744–745
  X-ray analysis, 157
D-Amino acids, enzymic deamination, 335–336, 751–754, 755
  occurrence, 80–81, 137–139
Amino acid sequence in proteins, 142–143, 145–148
Amino acid transaminases, 750, 759–763, 765–766
Aminoacrylic acid, 844
Aminoacyl-AMP, 720, 735
α-Aminoadipic acid, 808–809, 810
α-Aminoadipic-ε-semialdehyde, 809, 810
Amino alcohols, 52
o-Aminobenzoic acid, 834, 841, 842–843
p-Aminobenzoic acid, formula, 260
  metabolism, 719, 778, 834
  occurrence, 207, 999
  vitamin activity, 999
α-Aminobutyric acid, 54, 779, 794
γ-Aminobutyric acid, formula, 54
  metabolism, 762, 767–768, 817
3-Amino-3-deoxyribose, 413
2-Amino-4,6-dioxypteridine, 207
Aminoethanol, conversion, to choline, 802
  to glycine, 771, 777
  formation from phospholipids, 580
  formula, 568, 772, 777
  in phospholipid formation, 615, 616–617
  occurrence, 56, 137, 568–569
Aminoethanolphosphorylserine, 55, 56
p-Aminohippuric acid, 719
α-Amino-γ-hydroxybutyric acid, 757, 790–791, 794, 812
γ-Amino-α-hydroxybutyric acid, 767
5-Aminoimidazole, 894–895
5-Aminoimidazole-4-carboxamide, 888–889
5-Aminoimidazole-4-carboxamide riboside, 884, 888, 889
5-Aminoimidazole-4-carboxamide ribotide, in histidine formation, 821
  in purine formation, 888–891
5-Aminoimidazole-4-carboxylic acid, 894–895
5-Aminoimidazole ribotide, 890–891
5-Aminoimidazole-4-(N-succinylocarbox-amide) ribotide, 890–891
β-Aminoisobutyric acid, 899
4-Amino-3-isoxazolidone, 57

α-Amino-β-ketoadipic acid, 866–868
δ-Aminolaevulic acid, *see* δ-Aminolevulinic acid
δ-Aminolevulinic acid, conversion to porphyrins, 868–869, 870–872
  formation, 866–868
  formula, 867
  in C_1 unit metabolism, 774, 867
  in glycine breakdown, 776
  in vitamin B_{12} formation, 1004
δ-Aminolevulinic dehydrase, 868, 872
4-Amino-10-methylPGA, 902, 1001
α-Amino-γ-methylthiobutyric acid, 792
Aminopeptidases, action, on corticotrophin A, 951
  on papain, 220, 705
  activation by metal ions, 697
  catalytic action, 696–698
  in end group analysis of proteins, 144
  occurrence, 685, 696, 701–702
  specificity, 274, 696–697
4-AminoPGA, 898, 902, 1001
α-Amino-γ-phenylbutyric acid, 778
Aminopterin, 898, 902, 1001
Amino sugars, 412–413, 423–426, 428
δ-Aminovaleric acid, 758
Ammonium ions and ammonia, activation of enzymes, 910
  antagonism to potassium, 927
  as dietary nitrogen source, 725–726
  conversion to carbamyl phosphate, 852–853
  detoxication, 817, 853
  dissociation, 89–90
  excretion, 847–849, 918–919
  formation, by nitrogen fixation, 674–677
    from amino acids, 750–759, 764–766, 853–854
    from nitrate, 681, 682
    from purines, 894–895
    from pyrimidines, 899–900
    from urea, 849
  in amino acid formation, 721, 754–758, 765–766, 819
  in ketone body metabolism, 607
  in nicotinamide formation, 990
  in nitrogen fixation, 674–676
  in protein formation, 673–674, 681, 742–743
  in purine formation, 854–855
  in pyrimidine formation, 895, 897–898
  in urea formation, 818, 848–853
  oxidation to nitrate, 679
  toxicity, 817, 853
  urinary, 848–849, 918–919

Ammonium sulfate, 19–21
Ammonotelic organisms, 847
AMP, *see* Adenosine-5′-phosphate
Ampholyte, 92
AMP-luciferin, 346
Amygdalin, 210, 416, 432
Amylases, 433–437
α-Amylases, activation by chloride, 434
  catalytic action, 434
  crystallization, 218, 434
  effect of pH, 271
  metabolism, 734–735
β-Amylases, catalytic action, 434, 444–445
  crystallization, 218, 434
Amylo-1,6-glucosidase, 436, 444–446
Amylomaltase, 453
Amylopectin, activation of phosphorylase, 442
  enzymic hydrolysis, 434–436
  iodine reaction, 417
  particle weight, 420
  structure, 419–420
Amylose, enzymic hydrolysis, 433–437
  iodine reaction, 417, 437
  particle weight, 417
  structure, 418–420, 437
Amylosucrase, 452
Anabasine, 860
Anabolism, 387
Androgens, breakdown, 647, 649–650, 651
  formation, 643, 644–645
  occurrence, 641, 644
  physiological effects, 948–949, 966
  secretion, 948–949, 950
  structure, 638, 641, 645
Androstane, 638
5α-Androstane, 638
5β-Androstane, 638
Androstane-3α,17β-diol, 649, 651
Androstane-3,17-dione, 649, 651
Androstan-3α-ol-17-one, 649
Androstan-17β-ol-3-one, 649
Δ⁴-Androstene-3,17-dione, 645–646, 649
Δ⁴-Androstene-3,11,17-trione, 645, 648, 649
Δ⁴-Androsten-11β-ol-3,17-dione, 645, 648, 649
Δ⁴-Androsten-19-ol-3,17-dione, 646
Androsterone, 641, 649, 948–949
Anemias, 876, 1001, 1004–1005, 1012
  see also Sickle cell anemia
Anemonin, 637
Angiostomy technique, 397–398
Angiotonin, 140–141
Angstrom unit, 73
Anhydroleucovorin, chemistry, 773
  formula, 775

Anhydroleucovorin, metabolism, 822, 895
  occurrence, 999–1000
Animal heat, 929–937
Animal protein factor, 1005–1006
Anion-exchange resins, 122
Anorexia, 946
Anserine, 137, 805, 824
Anthocyanidins, 669–670, 672
Anthocyanins, 669
Anthranilic acid, breakdown, 834, 841
  formula, 840, 843
  in tryptophan metabolism, 841–843
Anthrone, 408
Anthrone reaction, 407, 421
Antibiotics, D-amino acid content, 80–81,
    137–138
  APF activity, 1006
  competitive inhibition, 260
Antibodies, chemistry, 740
  formation, 739–741
  to enzymes, 221
  to polysaccharides, 427, 429
Antifibrinolysin, 703
Antigens, 427, 429, 739–740
Antihemorrhagic factor, 668
Antimetabolites, 977
Antimony, 980
Antimony trichloride test, 656
Antimycin A, 356, 359–361, 1014
Antioxidants, 564, 1013
Antiplasmin, 703–704
Antisterility factor, 666–667, 1012
Antithrombin, 703–704
Antithromboplastin, 703–704
APF, 1005–1006
Apigenin, 671
Apoenzyme, 220, 321
Apoferritin, 912–913
Apyrases, 489, 910, 982
Aquaflavin, 986
Arabans, 423
Arabinose, excretion, 529
  occurrence, 423, 570
  UDP-, 528
D-Arabinose, formula, 404
  metabolism 528, 538
  occurrence, 206
L-Arabinose, formula, 538
  metabolism, 447, 538
  occurrence, 410, 416, 423
  optical rotation, 406
Arabonic acid, 538
Arabono-γ-lactone, 538
Arabulose, 447
Arachain, 707
Arachidic acid, 559

Arachidonic acid, formula, 559
  metabolism, 560–561, 609, 614
  occurrence, 559, 573
Arachin, 53
Arginase, 271, 849–850, 853
Arginine, alkaline lability, 47, 65
  conversion, to glutamate, 812–815
    to proline, 812–814
  deamination, 752, 812
  dissociation, 93–94
  estimation, 65
  formation, 731, 811–815, 850–853
  formula, 64, 851
  glucogenic action, 764
  in creatine formation, 803–804
  indispensable nature, 725, 728, 811
  in urea formation, 811, 849–853
  isolation, 64, 114
  microbial breakdown, 853–854
  occurrence, 64–66, 125, 201
  optical rotation, 79
  phosphorylation, 487
  R_F values, 118
  transamidination, 811–812
Arginine decarboxylase, 767
Arginine desimidase, 854
Arginine kinase, 487
Arginine phosphate, 65, 378–379, 485
Arginine phosphokinase, 487
Argininosuccinic acid, 851–853
Arrhenius equation, 263, 265–266
Arsenate, 326, 439
Arsenic, 806, 908
Arsenite, 504
Arsenocholine, 800, 801
Arsenolysis, 326, 439
l-Arterenol, 828–829, 946
Ascorbic acid, adrenal metabolism, 951–
    952
  antioxidant action, 564
  breakdown, 979
  deficiency, 978–979
  estimation, 978–979
  excretion, 979
  formation, 539–540, 978
  formula, 306, 540, 979
  in iron metabolism, 980
  in nitrite reduction, 682
  in PGA metabolism, 980
  in phenylalanine and tyrosine metabo-
    lism, 825, 828, 980
  in photosynthetic phosphorylation, 554
  occurrence, 978
  oxidation, 362–363, 368, 382–383, 539
  oxidation-reduction system, 299, 305–
    306

Ascorbic acid, vitamin activity, 978
Ascorbic acid oxidase, 368
Asparaginase, 710
Asparagine, chemistry, 51, 62–63, 71
  enzymic hydrolysis, 710
  formation, 819
  formula, 62
  occurrence, 62, 131, 819
  optical rotation, 79
  plant metabolism, 742–743, 819
  transamidation, 718
  transamination, 762–763, 819
Aspartase, 240, 755, 765
Aspartate carbamyl transferase, 896–897
Aspartic acid, formula, 62, 240
  free energy of formation, 237
  R_F values, 118
  titration curve, 93
D-Aspartic acid, 338, 755
L-Aspartic acid, amidation, 819
  breakdown, 767, 818–819
  conversion to fumarate, 240, 851–852, 891–892
  formation, 240, 710, 731
  glucogenic action, 764, 818
  in citric acid cycle, 502
  in isoleucine formation, 818
  in lysine formation, 810, 818
  in methionine formation, 818
  in nitrogen fixation, 675, 678
  in photosynthesis, 553
  in protein metabolism, 765
  in purine formation, 855, 891–892
  in pyrimidine formation, 895–896
  in threonine formation, 790–791, 818
  in urea formation, 851–852
  occurrence, 62, 125
  optical rotation, 79
  oxidative deamination, 752, 755, 760
  phosphorylation, 790–791
  relation to biotin, 997
  transamination, 759–763
L-Aspartic acid decarboxylases, 767
D-Aspartic acid oxidase, 338, 755
Aspartic-β-semialdehyde, 790
Aspartic semialdehyde dehydrogenase, 791
β-Aspartokinase, 790–791
β-Aspartyl phosphate, 790–791
Astacin, 655
Astaxanthin, 655
Asymmetric carbon atom, 78
Atebrin, 337
Atmungsferment, see Cytochrome oxidase

Atom per cent excess, 391
ATP, *see* Adenosine-5′-triphosphate
ATP-AMP transphosphorylase, 376, 459
ATP-arginine transphosphorylase, 487
ATP-ases, 473–474, 488–489
ATP-creatine transphosphorylase, 376, 486–488
ATP-1,3-diphosphoglyceric transphosphorylase, *see* ATP-phosphoglycerate transphosphorylase
ATP-hexose transphosphorylase, *see* Hexokinase
ATP-phosphoglycerate transphosphorylase, catalytic action, 373–374, 470–471
  crystallization, 218, 470
  in alcoholic fermentation, 470–471, 476
  in glycolysis, 476
ATP-phosphopyruvic transphosphorylase, catalytic action, 473
  effect of metal ions, 473, 910
  crystallization, 218
  in alcoholic fermentation, 473, 476
  in glycolysis, 490
Atropine, 578, 860
Aureomycin, 875, 1006
Aureusidin, 671
Aurone, 670
Aurones, 671
Autocatalytic reaction, 262, 688
Autolysis, 700–703
Autotrophic organisms, 285
Autoxidation, 305
Auxin, 846, 972–974
Auxotroph, 126, 397
Avidin, 202, 995–996
Avidin-biotin complex, 996
Avogadro's number, 149
Azaguanine, 902
Azaserine, 57, 890–891, 902
Azathymine, 903
Azelaic acid, 611
Azetidine-2-carboxylic acid, 71
Azide, 385
Azoproteins, 740

Bacitracins, 138
Bacteriochlorophyll, 183, 549, 871
Bacteriophages, 185, 904–905
  nucleic acid in, 194, 196, 198
Baikain, 71
BAL, 355–356
Barbituric acid, 900
Barium, 22, 908
Basal metabolic rate, 931–936
Basal metabolism, 935–937

Base, 85
Basedow's disease, 943
Batyl alcohol, 566
Beer's law, 72
Behenic acid, 559
Bence-Jones protein, 741
Benedict's solution, 407
Benzalacetophenone, 670
Benzalcoumaran-3-one, 670
Benzaldehyde, 210, 432
Benzimidazole, 1002–1004
Benzoic acid, free energy of formation, 238
    metabolism, 590, 719, 832–834
Benzoylglycine, *see* Hippuric acid
Benzyloxycarbonyl chloride, 49–50, 133–135
Beriberi, 982–983
Beryllium, 908
Betaine, formula, 54, 800
    lipotropic action, 588
    metabolism, 776, 801–802, 807–808
    occurrence, 54, 801
Betaine aldehyde, 802
Betaine aldehyde dehydrogenase, 802
Betaine-homocysteine transmethylase, 802
Betaines, 824, 858–859, 1006–1007
Bicarbonate-bound base, 919
Bile acids, 632–635, 651
Bile pigments, 167–168, 869, 872–876
Bile salts, formation, 633, 635
    in lipid metabolism, 575, 584
    use in cytochrome preparation, 354–355
Bilirubin, 385, 873–875
Bilirubin clearance test, 874
Biliverdin, 873, 874
Biochemical genetics, 398–399
Biocytin, 995–997
Biological half-life, 396
Bioluminescence, 345–346, 570
Biopterin, 207–208, 1000
Bios, 977, 992, 995
Biotin, 995–998
Biotinidase, 995
Biotin sulfoxide, 996
N-Biotinyllysine, 995
Biotoproteins, 995
γ-Bisabolene, 662, 663
Bismuth, 908
Biuret, 130
Biuret reaction, 130
Bixin, 654
Blackman reaction, 548–549
Black tongue, 308, 990

Blood, coagulation, 702–704
    glucose, 497–498
    inorganic constituents, 914–916
    pH regulation, 916–921
    proteins, *see* Hemoglobin, Plasma proteins
Blood-brain barrier, 733
Blood-group substances, 427–428
Bond energy, 380
Bone, 581, 953, 968, 1012
Boric acid, 414–415
Borneol, 432, 662
Boron, 908, 909, 914
Bound carbon dioxide, 919
Bragg equation, 157
Branched-chain amino acid transaminase, 782–783
Branching enzymes, 443–444, 454, 492
Brassicasterol, 624
Brodie solution, 287
Bromcresol green, 89
Bromcresol purple, 89
Bromelin, 705
Bromide ions, 909
Bromoacetic acid, 144
Bromobenzene, 59
β-Bromolactic acid, 80
p-Bromophenylmercapturic acid, 59
5-Bromouracil, 902–903
Bromphenol blue, 89
Brucine, 81
Buffers, 87–88
Bufotenine, 846
Bufotenine-N-oxide, 846
Bulk elements, 909–911
Buna rubber, 480
Bushy stunt virus, 23, 42, 197, 202
Butadiene, 480
2,3-Butanediol, 480
Butein, 671
Butyric acid, formation, from glutamate, 818
    from threonine, 818
    occurrence, 559
    oxidation, 597, 608
Butyryl-CoA, 597

C^{13}, 389
C^{14}, 392
Cadaverine, 767, 823, 862
Cadinene, 662, 663
Cadmium, 908
Caesium, 908
Caffeic acid, 672
Caffeine, 206
Calciferol, 622, 1011–1012

Calcium, activation of enzymes, 488, 575, 707, 910
  effect on oxidative phosphorylation, 385
  excretion, 911
  in blood, 108, 945, 1012
  in blood coagulation, 703–704
  in bone metabolism, 581, 945, 968, 1012
  indispensability, 910–911, 926
  inhibition of enzymes, 473, 910
  intestinal absorption, 911, 1012
  in trypsin formation, 690–691
Caloric value of foodstuffs, 932–933, 937–938
Calorie, 225–226
Calorimetry, for chemical reactions, 225, 226, 228
  for living organisms, 930–934
Camphor, 662
Canaline, 66, 812
Canavanine, 66, 812, 852
Cannizzaro reaction, 328
Canthaxanthin, 655
Capric acid, 559
Caproic acid, 559, 603–604
Caprylic acid, formula, 559
  interaction with proteins, 109
  oxidation, 592–594, 603–604
Carbamic acid, 849, 852
Carbamino acids, 51
Carbamino-bound carbon dioxide, 919–920
Carbamyl-β-alanine, 899
Carbamylaspartic acid, 854, 896–897
Carbamylglutamic acid, 852
Carbamyl phosphate, 852–854, 896–897
Carbobenzoxy chloride, 49–50, 133–135
Carbobenzoxy method, 133–135
Carbohydrases, 430–438
Carbohydrate metabolism, alcoholic fermentation, 457–464, 467–475
  ascorbic acid formation, 539–540
  citric acid cycle, 500–510, 515–517
  digestion of carbohydrates, 436
  disaccharide metabolism, 451–455
  energy relations, 520–524
  formation of carbohydrates, 492, 493–495
  in photosynthesis, 520–553
  glycogenesis, 492–495
  glycogenolysis, 497
  glycolysis, 484–485, 489–491, 499–500, 521–524
  glyoxylate cycle, 519–520
  heptose metabolism, 541–542

Carbohydrate metabolism, hexose metabolism, 457–467, 535–539, 543–544
  hormonal control, 955–962, 974
  in diabetes mellitus, 956–957, 959
  in thiamine deficiency, 983
  link to lipid metabolism, 520–521, 611–613
  link to protein metabolism, via alanine, 778
    via arginine, 813
    via aspartate, 818
    via glutamate, 813, 817–818
    via glycine, 772–773, 777
    via histidine, 821
    via hydroxyproline, 816
    via α-ketoacids, 759, 763–765
    via α-ketoglutarate, 754, 810, 818
    via leucine, 786
    via methionine, 794
    via phenylalanine, 827, 834
    via prephenic acid, 834
    via proline, 813, 816
    via pyruvate, 754, 781, 810
    via ribose, 821, 842–843
    via serine, 777, 790
    via threonine, 790, 792
    via tryptophan, 842–843, 844
    via tyrosine, 827, 834
    via valine, 780, 781
  pentose metabolism, 540–541, 543
  pentose phosphate pathway, 525–534
  polysaccharide breakdown and formation, 430–450
  respiratory quotient, 502, 932
  role, of ACTH, 959
    of adrenalin, 960–961
    of adrenocortical hormones, 947, 959
    of auxin, 974
    of biotin, 977–998
    of glucagon, 961
    of growth hormone, 959–960
    of insulin, 955–959
  tetrose metabolism, 541
Carbohydrates, antiketogenic action, 607
  caloric value, 932
  chemistry, monosaccharides, 402–414
    oligosaccharides, 414–417
    polysaccharides, 417–429
  occurrence in lipids, 570–572
  optical activity, 406
    mutarotation, 406
  protein-sparing action, 765
  stereochemistry, 403–406
  tests, 407–408
  see also individual carbohydrates

Carboligase, 480
Carbon cycle in nature, 545
Carbon dioxide, activation, 787–788
  carbamino-bound, 919–920
  conversion, to carbonic acid, 916–917
    to formate, 316, 483
  effect on oxyhemoglobin, 175–177
  formation, by amino acid decarboxyla-
    tion, 766–770
    by carbohydrate fermentation, 476,
      478, 520
    by carbohydrate oxidation, 508, 531–
      532, 550–551
    by fatty acid oxidation, 606–607
    by purine breakdown, 894–895
    by pyrimidine breakdown, 899–900
    from formate, 483
    from pyruvate, 479–480, 508
    from urea, 849
  free energy of formation, 237
  in carbon cycle, 545
  incorporation, into carbamyl phosphate,
    852–853, 897
    into pteridines, 1000
    into purines, 854–855, 891
    into pyrimidines, 897
    into riboflavin, 985
    into urea, 848, 851–853
  isohydric carriage, 920–921
  transport in blood, 916–921
Carbon dioxide fixation, biotin in, 997
  in glycogen formation, 515
  in photosynthesis, 546–547, 549–553,
    555–556
  into β-hydroxy-β-methylglutarate, 631,
    787–788
  into isocitrate, 504
  into malate, 512–513
  into methylmalonate, 602
  into oxaloacetate, 510–512, 553
  into 3-phosphoglycerate, 527–528, 551–
    552
  into succinate, 601–602
Carbon disulfide, 50, 144
Carbonic acid, free energy of formation,
    237
  metabolism, 916–917, 920, 924
Carbonic anhydrase, 912, 916–917, 920,
    924
  crystallization, 218
Carbon monoxide, 176–177, 348–349, 363
Carbon monoxide hemoglobin, 172, 176–
    177, 348
Carbon tetrachloride, 587
N-Carboxyanhydrides, 50, 135–136
4-Carboxy-2-azetidinone, 71

2-Carboxy-2,3-dihydro-5,6-dihydroxyin-
    dole, 831
2-Carboxy-2,3-dihydroindole-5,6-quinone,
    831
3-O-Carboxyethyl-N-acetylglucosamine,
    749
Carboxyhemoglobin, 172, 176–177, 348
Carboxylase, 475–476, 480, 529
γ-Carboxymethyl-Δ$^\alpha$-butenolide, 831
β-Carboxymuconic acid, 831
Carboxypeptidase, activation, 696, 702,
    706
  amino acid composition, 125
  crystallization, 218, 696
  effect on ribonuclease, 878
  enzyme-substrate compounds, 277–278
  esterase action, 696
  formation from procarboxypeptidase,
    696
  frictional ratio, 150
  inhibition, 258
  occurrence, 685, 702
  particle weight, 696
  pH optimum, 271, 702
  proteolytic action, 696, 701, 710
  specificity, 274, 276–277, 699
Carboxypeptidase method, 144
Carcinogens, 626
Cardiac glycosides, 637
Δ^3-Carene, 662
Carnitine, 1006–1007
Carnosine, 137, 824
Carolic acid, 539
Carotenal, 1010
α-Carotene, 653–655, 1009
β-Carotene, 653–655, 1009–1010
γ-Carotene, 653–655, 1009
ζ-Carotene, 653
Carotenes, 652–656
Carotenoids, biological action, 547–548,
    654, 657–658
  metabolism, 655–656, 657–661, 665–666
  occurrence, 652–657, 669
Carr-Price reaction, 656
Carvone, 661–662
Casein, chemistry, 17, 56
  coagulation, 689
  iodination, 831
  metabolism, 582, 737, 741–742
Catabolism, 387
Catalases, catalytic action, 179, 216, 365–
    366
  chemistry, 164, 365
  crystallization, 218
  enzyme-substrate compounds, 365–366
  heat inactivation, 270

Catalases, heat of activation, 268
  metabolism, 728, 913
  occurrence, 164, 218, 365
  particle weight, 42, 164, 365
Catalysis, 8, 210–211
Catalysts, nonenzymic, 273, 279–281
Catechol, 306, 367, 832–834
Catechol oxidase, 833
Cathepsin A, 700–701
Cathepsin B, 700–701, 706, 715
Cathepsin C, 700–701; 713, 715–717
Cathepsins, activation, 701, 706
  hydrolytic action, 700–701
  peptide bond synthesis, 713
  pH optima, 701, 715
  specificity, 700–702
  transamidation, 715–717
Cation-exchange resins, 122
CDP, 205, 616–618, 882
CDP-choline, 616–618
CDP-glycerol, 205
CDP-ribitol, 205
Cell division hormones, 972, 974–975
Cell membranes, 922–923, 926
Cellobiose, 406, 415, 432, 437
Cellulase, 437
Cellulose, 422, 437
Cephalins, chemistry, 566, 568, 573
  metabolism, 577–580, 615–617
Ceramide, 618
Cerebrocuprein, 181
Cerebron, 572
Cerebronic acid, 572
Cerebrosides, 572–573, 618
Cerebroside sulfuric acid, 572
Cerotic acid, 559
Ceruloplasmin, 181, 914
Cetyl sulfonate, 584
CF, 998–1001
  see also N⁵-FormyltetrahydroPGA
Chalcone, 670
Chalcones, 671
Chalinasterol, 624
Chastek paralysis, 983
Chaulmoogric acid, 560
Cheilosis, 986
Chelation, 108, 279–280
Chemical potential, 231–232
Chemiluminescence, 345
Chenodeoxycholic acid, 632–635
Chimyl alcohol, 566
Chitin, 423, 437, 465, 970–971
Chitinase, 437
Chloride ions, 434, 909, 916–917
Chloride shift, 916
Chlorine-starch-iodide test, 130

Chlorocruorins, 164, 166, 178
p-Chloromercuribenzoate, 59, 325
p-Chlorophenylalanine, 745
Chlorophyllase, 182
Chlorophyll esterase, 182
Chlorophylls, absorption spectra, 548
  chemistry, 181–183
  formation, 870–871
  formula, 182
  in auxin metabolism, 974
  in photosynthesis, 546–550, 553–556
  occurrence, 182–183, 669
Chloroplast reaction, 550
Chlorphenol red, 89
Cholanic acid, 632
Cholecalciferol, 623, 1011–1012
Cholecystokinin, 955
Choleglobin, 179, 874
Δ⁵,²⁴-Cholestadien-3β-ol, 628–629
5β-Cholestane, 621
Cholestanol, 619–622, 624–626
Cholestanone, 625, 626
Δ⁵-Cholestene, 621
Δ⁷-Cholestenol, 623, 625
Δ⁴-Cholestenone, 625–626, 651
Cholesterol, conversion, to bile acids, 633–635
    to 7-dehydrocholesterol, 625
    to steroid hormones, 641–645
  excretory products, 625–626
  formation, 626–632, 788, 962
  formula, 620
  in adrenal gland, 641–644, 951–952
  in blood, 110, 573, 621–622
  in fatty liver formation, 587
  intestinal absorption, 624–625, 633
  microbial degradation, 625–626, 651
  occurrence, 619, 621–622, 624, 641
  stereochemistry, 619–621
  turnover, 632
Cholesterol esterase, 576
Cholesterol esters, 573, 576, 621–622
Cholic acid, 632–635
Choline, acetylation, 578
  formation, 577–578, 580, 802, 807
  formula, 577, 800
  in phospholipid formation, 615–618
  in transmethylation, 801–802
  lipotropic action, 587–589
  occurrence, 566–567, 571, 755, 801
  oxidation, 802, 807–808
  phosphorylation, 616
  vitamin activity, 1007
Choline acetylase, 578
Choline esterase, 577
Choline oxidase, 802

Choline phosphokinase, 616
Cholyl-CoA, 635
Chondrillasterol, 624
Chondroitin, 424
Chondroitin sulfates, 424–425, 796
Chondrosamine, 412–413, 428
Chondrosine, 424
Chorionic gonadotropins, 955
Chromatography, column, 24–25, 115–116, 120–126, 652
    gas-liquid, 564–565
    ion-exchange, 122–126
    of amino acids, 115–126
    of carbohydrates, 413–414
    of carotenoids, 652
    of fatty acids, 563–564
    of nucleic acid derivatives, 142, 189, 195
    of peptides, 147
    of proteins, 24–25
    of steroids, 622–623
    paper, 116–120
Chromium, 908
Chromoproteins, 17
Chromosomal nucleoproteins, 202, 905–906
Chrysanthemum monocarboxylic acid, 662
Chrysin, 671
Chylomicrons, 575–576, 585–586
Chymopapain, 218, 704
α-Chymotrypsin, action, on proteins, 692, 695
    on synthetic substrates, 274–275, 281–282, 693–694
    active center, 261–262, 694
    acyl-enzyme formation, 281–282, 694
    crystallization, 218, 693
    denaturation, 221
    effect of DFP, 261, 694
    esterase action, 693–694
    formation, 260–262, 692–693, 734
    in digestion, 694
    in plastein formation, 721
    isoelectric point, 102, 693
    occurrence, 685, 689
    particle weight, 43, 693
    peptide bond synthesis, 711–713
    specificity, 274–275, 693–694, 698–699
    transamidation, 715
β-Chymotrypsin, 692–693
γ-Chymotrypsin, 692–693
δ-Chymotrypsin, 692
π-Chymotrypsin, 692
Chymotrypsin B, 693

Chymotrypsinogen, conversion to chymotrypsin, 260–262, 692–693
    denaturation, 269
    formation, 735
    properties, 26, 101–102, 692
Citral, 661
Citric acid, asymmetric metabolism, 511–512, 514–515
    cleavage to oxaloacetate, 518
    conversion, to cis-aconitate, 503–504
        to isocitrate, 503–504
    formation, 506–507, 518–520, 595
    in CO_2 fixation, 511–512
    occurrence, 5, 516, 518, 1012
    oxidation, 503–510, 514–515, 519
Citric acid cycle, fate of acetate carbon, 514–515
    enzymic reactions, 501–512
    in amino acid metabolism, 517, 520–521, 853
    in fatty acid oxidation, 600–601
    in oxidative phosphorylation, 521–524
    in photosynthesis, 550
    in porphyrin formation, 866
    occurrence, 500, 509, 516–517
Citritase, 518
Citrovorum factor, 998–1001
    see also N^5-FormyltetrahydroPGA
Citrulline, 65, 850–854
Clearing factor, 576
Clionasterol, 624
Clupein, 64, 201
cn+ gene, 839
Co^{60}, 392
CoA, see Coenzyme A
CoA transferase, 597, 605
CoA transphorase, 596, 608
Cobalamin, 1003
Cobalt, activation of enzymes, 461, 696, 850, 911
    metabolism, 913, 1002–1005
Cobalto-histidine complex, 108
Cocarboxylase, see Thiamine pyrophosphate
Codehydrogenase I, see Diphosphopyridine nucleotide
Codehydrogenase II, see Triphosphopyridine nucleotide
Coenzyme, 200, 307, 321
Coenzyme I, see Diphosphopyridine nucleotide
Coenzyme II, see Triphosphopyridine nucleotide
Coenzyme A, acylation, 376–377, 484, 505–506, 595–597, 1007

Coenzyme A, formation and degradation, 583, 994, 1005
 formula, 206
 in amide bond formation, 635, 719, 815
 in citrate formation, 506–507, 518
 in ester bond formation, 578, 616
 in fatty acid formation, 611–612, 630–631
 in fatty acid oxidation, 595–605, 779–781, 787–788, 833
 in α-keto acid decarboxylation, 481–483, 505–506, 757
 occurrence, 205, 482, 992–993
Coenzyme-linked dismutation, 328
Coenzyme R, 997
CoF, 889–890
Collagen, metabolism, 707, 733, 737
 structure, 64, 125, 131
Collagenase, 707
Colligative properties, 29–30
Colloids, 29
Color vision, 660–661
Column chromatography, 120–126
Competitive analogue-metabolite inhibition, 977
Competitive inhibition, 256–259, 977
Compound A, 946
Compound B, 946
Compound E, 639, 946
Compound F, 639, 946
Compound S, 639, 946
Conarachin, 53
Condensing enzyme, 506–508
Congenital porphyria, 872
Coniferyl alcohol, 422
Coniine, 860
Conjugated proteins, 17, 162, 303, 321
Continuing metabolism, 730
Conway method, 63
Copper, chelation by acids, 108, 279–280
 in enzymes, 338, 345, 366–368
 metabolism, 181, 913–914
Copper diglycinate, 108
Copper phthalocyanine, 169–170
Copper porphyrins, 167
Copper proteins, 181
Coproporphyrin I, 167–169, 872
Coproporphyrin III, 167, 868–869
Coprostane, 621
Coprostanic acids, 635
Coprostanol, 620–622, 624–625
Coprosterol, 620
Cord factor, 561
Cori cycle, 492
Cori ester, see α-D-Glucose-1-phosphate
Corpuscular proteins, 148
Cortexone, 946

Corticosteroids, see Adrenocortical hormones
Corticosterone, formula, 639
 metabolism, 642–644, 946
 physiological effects, 947, 967
Corticotrophin, 950–951
α-Corticotrophin, 951
β-Corticotrophin, 951
Corticotrophin A, 951
Corticotrophin B, 951
Corticotropin, 950
Cortisol, formula, 639
 metabolism, 638, 642–644, 647–648, 946
 physiological effects, 947, 967
Cortisone, formula, 639
 metabolism, 638, 644, 647–648, 946
 physiological effects, 947, 959, 963–964
Cortol, 648
Cortolone, 648
p-Coumaric acid, 672
Countercurrent distribution, 139
Cozymase, see Diphosphopyridine nucleotide
Creatine, excretion, 804, 857
 formula, 53, 804
 metabolism, 376, 486–487, 803–805, 807
 occurrence, 53, 485, 804–805
Creatine kinase, 486–487
Creatine phosphate, dephosphorylation, 486–487, 581–582
 energy-rich bond, 376–380, 485
 formation, 376, 491
 formula, 379
 in muscular contraction, 485–487, 491
Creatinine, excretion, 847, 849, 857–858
 formula, 53
 metabolism, 804, 857
p-Cresol, 833
Cresol red, 89
Cretinism, 944
Crocetin, 654
Crotonase, 218, 597–598, 631
Crotonic acid, 559
Crotonyl-CoA, 597–598
Cryptosterol, 624
Cryptoxanthin, 655, 1009
C-terminal amino acid, 141–142, 144
CTP, 204, 616, 898
Cucumber mosaic virus, 197
C_1 units, conversion, to C-methyl groups, 629, 666, 898
 to N- and S-methyl groups, 806–807, 860, 1005
 formation, 605–606, 773–776, 807, 867
 in purine formation, 889, 891
Curie, 393

Cyanide ions, activation of proteinases, 705–706
  as respiratory poison, 341, 347
  metabolism, 796, 1002
  reaction, with DPN, 313
    with heme proteins, 172, 177–178, 363
Cyanidin, 670
Cyanocobalamin, 1001–1005
Cyanopsin, 660
Cyclol structure, 862
Cycloserine, 57
Cystathionine, 793–795
Cysteic acid, 58, 767, 797
Cysteine, activation of enzymes, 262–263, 324, 461, 701, 705–708
  chemistry, 47, 51, 57–60, 93–94
  formula, 57, 793
L-Cysteine, breakdown, 756, 796–798
  formation, 792–795, 797, 799
  free energy of formation, 237
  heat of combustion, 226–227
  in coenzyme A formation, 994
  in glutathione formation, 721
  in penicillin formation, 798–799
  interconversion with cystine, 792, 798
  occurrence, 57–60, 132, 351–352
  optical rotation, 79
Cysteine desulfhydrase, 756, 770, 799
Cysteine sulfenic acid, 58
Cysteine sulfinic acid, 58, 767, 796–798
Cysteinylglycine, 718
Cystine, chemistry, 47, 57–60, 237
  formula, 57
  R_F values, 118
L-Cystine, deamination, 752
  formula, 83
  glucogenic action, 764
  metabolism, 728, 792–799
  occurrence, 58, 125, 798
  optical rotation, 79
  solubility, 94–96
meso-Cystine, 32
Cystinuria, 798, 858
Cytidine, 187, 898–899
Cytidine-5′-diphosphate, 205, 617–618, 882
Cytidine diphosphate choline, 616–618
Cytidine diphosphate glycerol, 205
Cytidine diphosphate ribitol, 205
Cytidine-2′-phosphate, 189–190
Cytidine-3′-phosphate, 189–190, 878
Cytidine-5′-phosphate, 617, 896, 898
Cytidine-5′-triphosphate, 204, 616, 898
Cytidylic acid, 186–190
Cytochrome a, absorption maxima, 349–350
  chemistry, 354–355

Cytochrome a, in electron transport, 354, 359–362, 372
  in oxidative phosphorylation, 382–384
  oxidation-reduction potential, 299, 354
Cytochrome a_1, 355
Cytochrome a_2, 355
Cytochrome a_3, absorption maxima, 350
  carbon monoxide compound, 348
  chemistry, 354–355
  in ascorbic acid oxidation, 980
  in electron transport, 354, 359–362
Cytochrome b, absorption maxima, 349–350
  action on succinate, 355
  chemistry, 355
  in electron transport, 359–362, 372
  in oxidative phosphorylation, 382–384
Cytochrome b_1, 357
Cytochrome b_2, 357
Cytochrome b_3, 357
Cytochrome b_4, 357
Cytochrome b_5, 356–357, 913, 970
Cytochrome b_6, 357
Cytochrome c, absorption maxima, 349–351
  frictional ratio, 150
  in electron transport, 341–344, 354, 356–362, 372
  in oxidative phosphorylation, 382–384
  isoelectric point, 102, 351
  metabolism, 870, 944
  molecular weight, 42, 164, 351
  oxidation-reduction potential, 299, 304, 353, 363
  prosthetic group, 352
  structure, 164, 179, 350–353
Cytochrome c_1, 353
Cytochrome c_2, 353
Cytochrome c_3, 353
Cytochrome c_4, 353
Cytochrome c_5, 353
Cytochrome c reductases, 342–344, 1013–1014
Cytochrome e, 353
Cytochrome f, 353, 554
Cytochrome h, 357–358
Cytochrome m, 356–357, 913, 970
Cytochrome oxidase, 347–349, 354, 970, 1005
  see also Cytochrome a_3
Cytochromes, absorption maxima, 348–351, 355–357
  bacterial, 353, 355, 357
  chemistry, 164, 349–358
  in electron transport, 354, 356–357, 359–362, 372

Cytochromes, in nitrite oxidation, 679
  in oxidative phosphorylation, 382–384
  in succinoxidase, 359
  reaction, with CO, 353–356
    with cyanide, 353, 356
    with oxygen, 353–356
Cytoflave, 330
Cytosine, formula, 187
  metabolism, 886, 895–896, 898
  occurrence, 187, 191, 197–198
  pK, 196
Cytosine deoxyriboside, 886

Darkening hormones, 971
Dark reaction, 549–550
Deacylases, 505, 600, 780
Debranching glucosidases, 436
Debye-Hückel equation, 86
Decanoic acid, 559
Decarboxylation, 216
Dehydration, 216
Dehydroascorbic acid, 305–306, 368, 979–
  980
Dehydroascorbic reductase, 368
Dehydrobufotenine, 846
7-Dehydrocholesterol, 623, 625, 629, 1011
11-Dehydrocorticosterone, 638–639, 644,
  946–947
1-Dehydrocortisol, 650, 948
Dehydroepiandrosterone, 644–645
1-Dehydro-9-fluorocortisone, 948
Dehydrogenases, definition, 216, 314
  hydrogen transfer, 319–320
  pyridine nucleotide dependent, cata-
    lytic action, 319–327
    kinetics of reactions, 317–319, 321–322
    pyridine nucleotide specificity, 315–
      316
    substrate specificity, 315
Δ^1-Dehydropipecolic acid, 809
Δ^4-Dehydropipecolic acid, 71
Dehydroquinase, 542
Dehydroquinic acid, 541–542
Dehydroshikimic acid, 541–542, 834
Dehydroshikimic reductase, 541
Delactonizing enzyme, 831
Delphinidin, 671
Demethylase, 776–777
Denaturation of proteins, 153–154, 160,
  233–234
Denitrification, 680, 682–683
D enzyme, 454
Deoxyadenosine, 191
Deoxyadenylic acid, 191
1-Deoxy-1-(N-amino acid)-2-ketohexo-
  ses, 735

Deoxycholic acid, 632, 634–635
Deoxycorticosterone, formula, 639
  metabolism, 642–644, 650
  physiological effects, 947, 967
  secretion, 638, 946
Deoxycortisol, see 17-Hydroxydeoxycor-
  ticosterone
Deoxycytidine, 898
Deoxycytidine-3′,5′-diphosphate, 192
Deoxycytidylic acid, 191
6-Deoxyglucose, 410–411
Deoxyguanosine, 191
Deoxyguanylic acid, 191
Deoxypentose nucleic acids, as bacterial
    transforming factors, 200, 748, 905
  chemistry, 191–192
  chromosomal, 748, 905–906
  determination, 192–193
  digestion, 879
  formation, 748, 904–905, 1005
  from viruses, 194
  hydrolysis, by acid, 197
    by deoxyribonuclease, 879–880
  in protein synthesis, 747–748
  linkages in, 199–201
  metabolic turnover, 900–902
  nucleotide composition, 198
  occurrence, 192–194
4-Deoxypyridoxine, 762, 989
Deoxyribonuclease, 218, 747, 879–880,
  904–905
Deoxyribonucleic acids, see Deoxypen-
    tose nucleic acids
Deoxyribonucleosides, 191–192, 880, 884,
  898
Deoxyribonucleoside-5′-triphosphates,
  882–883
Deoxyribonucleotides, 191–192, 880, 883
Deoxyribose, 191–192, 410, 1005
Deoxyribose-1-phosphate, 884
Deoxyribose-5-phosphate, 534–535
Deoxyuridine, 884, 898
DephosphoCoA, 994
DephosphoCoA kinase, 994
DephosphoCoA pyrophosphorylase, 994
Depot fat, 586–587, 589
Desmosterol, 628–629
Desoxyribonuclease, see Deoxyribo-
    nuclease
Desthiobiotin, 996–997
Desulfhydration, 216
Detoxication, mercapturic acid forma-
    tion, 59
  of ammonium ions, 817, 853
  of aromatic acids, 53, 537, 719
  of cyanide ions, 796

Detoxication, of hydrogen peroxide, 365
  of indole, 844
  of phenols, 537–538
  role of hydroperoxidases, 364–365
Deuterium, 389
Dextrans, 429, 451–452
Dextran sucrase, 451–452
Dextrins, 433, 437, 453
DFP, formula, 261
  inhibition, of esterases, 578, 691
    of proteinases, 261, 691–692, 694, 702
Diabetes insipidus, 950, 967
Diabetes mellitus, 940–942
  effect, on carbohydrate metabolism,
    498, 956–957, 959
    on lipid metabolism, 590, 607, 613,
      957–958
    on protein metabolism, 763–764, 958–
      959
Diabetogenic factor, pituitary, 959–960
Diacetyl, 480
Diacetylmethylcarbinol, 480
Dialysis, 29
Diamagnetism, 170
Diamine oxidase, 823, 860
α,γ-Diaminobutyric acid, 138
Diaminopimelic acid, 83, 766, 810–811
Diaminopimelic decarboxylase, 766–767
Diaminopimelic racemase, 810
2,6-Diaminopurine, 893–894
Diamox, 924
Dianhydrodiadenylic acid, 204, 441
Diapause, 968
Diaphorase, 338, 343
Diastase, 210
Diastereoisomers, 81
O-Diazoacetylserine, 57
Diazobenzenesulfonic acid, 66
6-Diazo-5-ketonorleucine, 891
Dibenzoylornithine, 719
Dibromotyrosine, 68–69
Dicarboxylic acid cycle, 518–519
3,4-Dichlorobenzenesulfonic acid, 66
2,6-Dichlorophenolindophenol, 302–303
2,4-Dichlorophenoxyacetic acid, 974
Dicumarol, 385, 704
Dicyclohexylcarbodiimide, 134–135
Dicyclohexylurea, 135
Dielectric constant, 20, 92
Dielectric increment, 92
Diethylchlorophosphite, 134
Difference spectrum, 360–361
Diffusion coefficient, 41, 149, 151
Diffusion constant, 41, 149, 151
Digestion, early studies, 209–210
  hormonal control, 955

Digestion, of carbohydrates, 436
  of lipids, 574–575, 577–580, 584–586
  of nucleic acids, 877, 879
  of proteins, 684–685, 694–696, 698–700
Digitogenin, 636
Digitonin, 621, 636
Digitoxigenin, 636–637
Diglycerides, 574, 579, 616–617
Dihydrocholesterol, 619–622, 624–626
Dihydrocortisol, 648
Dihydrocortisone, 648
22-Dihydroergosterol, 1011
Dihydrolipoic acid, formula 306, 448
  in α-keto acid decarboxylation, 481–
    482, 505
  in photosynthesis, 553–554
  interconversion with lipoic acid, 328,
    482, 1006
Dihydrolipoic dehydrogenase, 328, 482,
  1006
Dihydrolipoic transacetylase, 1006
Dihydroorotase, 896
Dihydroorotic acid, 896–897
Dihydroorotic dehydrogenase, 896
Dihydrosphinogosine, 571
Dihydrosterculic acid, 998
Dihydrothymine, 899
Dihydroxyacetone, 313, 468, 616
Dihydroxyacetone phosphate, formation,
  468–470, 494, 616
  formula, 318, 468
  in pentose phosphate pathway, 531–532
  isomerization, 469–470
  reduction to glycerophosphate, 318,
    477–478
Dihydroxy acid dehydrase, 782–784
3,7-Dihydroxycoprostane, 634
α,β-Dihydroxy-β-ethylbutyric acid, 782–
  783
5,6-Dihydroxyindole, 831
α,β-Dihydroxy-β-methylbutyric acid, 782–
  783
α,β-Dihydroxy-β-methylvaleric acid, 782–
  783
β,δ-Dihydroxy-β-methylvaleric acid, 629–
  631, 1008
2,5-Dihydroxyphenylacetic acid, 826–828,
  832
3,4-Dihydroxyphenylacetic acid, 830–831
3,4-Dihydroxyphenylalanine, enzymic oxidation, 367, 382
  formula, 68, 367, 831
  metabolism, 766–767, 828–831, 839
  oxidation-reduction potential, 299
3,4-Dihydroxy-β-phenylethylamine, 767,
  828–829

2,5-Dihydroxyphenylpyruvic acid, 826
4,8-Dihydroxyquinoline, 838
4,8-Dihydroxyquinoline-2-carboxylic acid, 836–837, 840
9,10-Dihydroxystearic acid, 562
Diimide, 676
3,3'-Diiodothyronine, 831–832, 943–944
3,5-Diiodotyrosine, 68–69, 79
Diisopropylfluorophosphate, *see* DFP
2,5-Diketogluconic acid, 536
Diketogulonic acid, 979–980
Dilatometric method, 709
2,3-Dimercaptopropanol, 324, 355–356
Dimethylacrylic acid, 629–631, 665
Dimethylacrylyl-CoA, 630–631, 788
Dimethyladipic acid, 594
6,7-Dimethylalloxazine, 331
p-Dimethylaminobenzaldehyde test, 413, 426
Dimethylaminoethanol, 802, 807
6-Dimethylaminopurine, 207
5,6-Dimethylbenzimidazole, 1002, 1004
4,4'-Dimethylcholestadienol, 628
β,β'-Dimethylcysteine, 60
4,5-Dimethyl-1,2-diaminobenzene, 1004
Dimethylglycine, 776
Dimethyl-*p*-phenylenediamine, 354
Dimethylpropiothetin, 800, 801, 803, 807
5,6-Dimethyl-1-ribosyl-benzimidazole-3'-phosphate, 1002
Dimethylselenide, 805–806
2,2-Dimethylstearic acid, 594
Dimethyl sulfate, 418
Dimethylsulfide, 798
Dimelthyltelluride, 805–806
Dimethylthetin, 800, 801, 803, 807
N,N-Dimethyltryptamine, 846
N,N-Dimethyltryptamine-N-oxide, 846
Dinicotinoylornithine, 900–901
2,4-Dinitrofluorobenzene method, 142–143
2,4-Dinitro-1-naphthol-7-sulfonic acid, 64
2,4-Dinitrophenol, 385, 524, 734, 736
2,4-Dinitrophenyl amino acids, 50
2,8-Dioxyadenine, 886
Dipeptidases, 685, 697, 699, 702, 708
Diphenylamine, 192–193
Diphenylphosphate, 583
1,3-Diphenylurea, 975
2',5'-Diphosphoadenosine, 310
3',5'-Diphosphoadenosine, 994
1,3-Diphosphoglyceric acid, action of triose phosphate dehydrogenase, 316, 324–325, 470
  energy-rich bond, 377–378
  formula, 324, 471
  in alcoholic fermentation, 470, 476

1,3-Diphosphoglyceric acid, in glycolysis, 490
  interconversion, with 2,3-diphosphoglycerate, 472
    with 3-phosphoglycerate, 373–374, 376, 470
2,3-Diphosphoglyceric acid, 472
Diphosphoinositide, 570, 583
Diphosphoinositol, 570
Diphosphopyridine nucleotidase, 309
Diphosphopyridine nucleotide, absorption spectrum, 311, 315, 317
  acetylpyridine analogue, 309, 991–992
  addition reactions, 313
  as microbial growth factor, 308
  binding, by alcohol dehydrogenases, 320–323
    by triose phosphate dehydrogenase, 324, 325
  chemistry, 307–309
  cleavage, 309–310
  discovery, 307
  formation, 309–310, 990
  formula, 309
  in acetaldehyde dehydrogenase action, 483
  in alcoholic fermentation, 475–476
  in amino acid metabolism, 754
  in betaine aldehyde oxidation, 802
  in citric acid cycle, 508
  in dehydrogenase action, 314–329
  in dihydroorotic dehydrogenase action, 896
  in fatty acid oxidation, 598–599, 780, 785
  in glycerol formation, 477–478
  in glycolysis, 479, 490
  in histidine formation, 820
  in inositol oxidation, 544
  in isocitric dehydrogenase action, 504
  in α-keto acid decarboxylation, 481–482, 505
  in lipoic acid metabolism, 481
  in mannitol-1-phosphate oxidation, 543
  in PGA metabolism, 775
  in purine metabolism, 892
  in quinic acid metabolism, 541
  in steroid hormone metabolism, 643, 646, 649, 651
  in Stickland reaction, 757–758
  in UDP-galactose epimerization, 464
  in UDP-glucose oxidation, 467
  in vision, 659–660
  in xylitol oxidation, 540
  occurrence, 308
  oxidation-reduction potential, 299, 322

Diphosphopyridine nucleotide, photore-
    duction, 555
  reduced, action of flavoproteins, 342–
    343
    aerobic oxidation, 359–352, 371–372
    binding by alcohol dehydrogenase,
      320–323
    chemistry, 312–313
    formula, 312
    in fatty acid formation, 612
    in homoserine formation, 790
    in hydroxylamine reduction, 681
    in menadione reduction, 1014
    in nitrite reduction, 682
    in nitrogen equilibrium, 765
    in oxidative phosphorylation, 382–
      384, 521
    in proline formation, 813–814
    in steroid metabolism, 647, 651
    oxidation, 311, 339, 521
  stereospecific reduction, 319–320
Dipolar ion, 92
Dipole moment, 92
Direct calorimetry, 930–931
Disaccharides, chemistry, 406, 414–416,
    418
  formation, 446–451
  phosphorolysis, 446–449
  see also individual sugars
Dismutation reactions, coenzyme linked,
    328
Dissociation constant, acid, 87–88
Dissymmetry constant, 149–151
Diterpenes, 661, 663
Djenkolic acid, 60
DNA, see Deoxypentose nucleic acids
DNFB, 142–143
DNP method, 142–143
DOC, see Deoxycorticosterone
Dodecanoic acid, 559, 586, 603
Dodecyl aldehyde, 346
Dodecyl sulfate, 109, 153
Dopa, see 3,4-Dihydroxyphenylalanine
Dopa decarboxylase, 768, 829
Dopa oxidase, 367
Dopa quinone, 839
Dornase, 879
Double refraction of flow, 152
Dowex resins, 122, 147
DPN, see Diphosphopyridine nucleotide
DPNase, 309
DPNH, see Diphosphopyridine nucleo-
    tide, reduced
DPNH-cytochrome c reductase, 338, 343
DPNH oxidase, 359–362
DPN pyrophosphorylase, 310

Dynamic equilibrium, 730

Eadie equation, 253–254
Eburicoic acid, 663, 664, 665–666
Ecdysone, 969–970
Echinenone, 655
Edestin, 35, 42, 62, 125
Edman method, 143–144
Egg albumin, antigenicity, 740
  cleavage by subtilisin, 708
  composition, 17, 28, 125
  crystallization, 22
  electrophoresis, 104
  formation, 737–738
  frictional ratio, 150
  interaction with ions, 108–109
  ionizable groups, 98
  isoelectric point, 102
  particle weight, 33, 42
  solubility, 101–102
  terminal amino acids, 143
Eicosanoic acid, 559
Einstein's law of photochemical equiva-
    lence, 547
Einstein unit, 547
Elaidic acid, 560
Elastase, 689
Elastin, 53, 689
Electrocortin, see Aldosterone
Electrode potentials, 293–295, 327
Electrolyte balance, 915–917, 919
  hormonal control, 947, 966–968
Electron carrier systems, biological, 304–
    306
Electron microscopy of proteins, 35
Electron transfer in biological systems,
    303–306, 321
  action, of copper-containing oxidases,
    367–368
    of cytochromes, 359–362
    of flavoproteins, 334–335, 340–342
    of pyridine nucleotides, 329, 340–342
  effect of antimycin A, 356
  effect of BAL, 355–356
  in oxidative phosphorylation, 381–385
  pathways, 362, 368–369, 371–372
Electron-transferring flavoprotein, 345
Electron-volt, 392
Electrophoresis, 37–39, 102–107
  paper, 120
Electrophoresis-convection, 107
Electrophoretic mobility, 104–105
Electrostriction, 695, 709
Eleostearic acid, 559
Embden-Meyerhof pathway, for alco-
    holic fermentation, 476–477

Embden-Meyerhof pathway, for anaerobic glycolysis, 489–491
  relation to pentose phosphate pathway, 533–534
Emulsin, 210, 432, 454
Enantiomorph, 77
Endergonic reactions, 230–232
  linked to exergonic reactions, 372–377, 713–714
    by pyridine nucleotides, 327–328, 374–375
    by substrates, 239–241, 372–374
  sources of energy for, 284, 372–377
End-group analysis, for peptides and proteins, 141–144
  for polysaccharides, 418–419
Endocrine organs, 940
Endopeptidases, 687
  see also Proteinases
Endothermic reaction, 226
Energy, 225–226, 380
  of activation, 265–266
Energy metabolism, 928
Energy-poor bond, 377–378
Energy-rich bond, 377–380
  formation in oxidative phosphorylation, 384–385, 521–522
Energy transfer, 284, 372–377, 384–385
Enolase, activation, 472, 910
  catalytic action, 472–473, 476, 490
  crystallization, 218, 472
  inhibition, 472, 910
Enoylhydrases, 597–598, 600
Enteramine, 768, 844–846, 863
Enterogastrone, 955
Enterokinase, 262, 691
Enthalpy, 226
  of activation, 266–269
  of formation, 236
Enthalpy change, 226–228
  of chemical reactions, 224–228, 266–269
  of combustion, 226–227
  of ionization, 228
  of protein denaturation, 233–234
  relation, to equilibrium constant, 227–228
    to free-energy change, 229–230
Entner-Doudoroff fermentation, 535
Entropy, 229
  of activation, 266–269
Entropy change, 229–230, 234, 236
  of protein denaturation, 234
Enzyme induction, 746
Enzymes, activation, 262–263, 269–271, 910

Enzymes, active center, 260–263, 271, 278, 281–282
  acyl derivatives, 281–282, 325–326
  adaptive, 746, 838
  antigenic nature, 221
  assay, 246–247
  classification, 215–216, 273–274
  crystallization, 217–220
  history, 212–214
  homogeneity, 217, 219, 247
  inactivation, by heat, 153, 233–234, 269–271
    by pH change, 221, 272
    by proteolysis, 220
  induced, 746, 838
  inhibition, 221, 256–260, 261, 263
  nomenclature, 214–215, 220, 315, 318, 455
  physical properties, 220–221
  protein nature, 217–221
  specific activity, 246–247
  specificity, 83–84, 274–278, 319–320
  sulfhydryl groups in, 325–326, 705–706
  turnover number, 211, 255
Enzyme-substrate compounds, 250–256, 266–268, 277–282
  in acetylcholine hydrolysis, 281
  in aconitase reaction, 503, 514
  in aldolase reaction, 469
  in catalase reaction, 365–366
  in dehydrogenase reactions, 320, 325–326
  in fatty acid activation, 484
  in peroxidase reaction, 364
  in proteolytic reactions, 282, 697–699, 715
  polyaffinity relations in, 277–278
  three-point attachment, 511, 514
Enzymic reactions, acyl-enzyme formation, 281–282, 325–326
  coupled, 240, 370–374
  effect, of pH, 271–272
    of substrate concentration, 249–256
    of temperature, 266–271
  energy of activation, 266–268
  energy relations, 234–243, 268–269
  inhibition, 256–260
  kinetics, 245–256, 322–323
  mechanisms, 279–282
  oxidation-reduction, 303–306, 313–329, 334–335
  product inhibition, 257
  reversibility, 215, 273
  transition states in, 266–270
  types, 273

Ephedrine, 480, 861
Epicholestanol, 621
Epinephrine, see Adrenalin
12,13-Epoxyoleic acid, 562
Equilenin, 640–641
Equilibrium, thermodynamic, 241–242
Equilibrium constant, apparent, 232
  determination, 235–236, 241–242, 322–323
  effect of pH, 236
  in reversible reactions, 224
  relation, to enthalpy change, 227–228
    to free-energy change, 233, 235–236
    to Michaelis constant, 256
    to oxidation-reduction potential, 300–301
    to rate constants, 322–323
  thermodynamic, 232
Equilibrium dialysis method, 109–110
Equilin, 640–641
Ergocalciferol, 623, 1011–1012
Ergocornine, 862
Ergokryptine, 862
Ergometrine, 862
Ergosterol, 622, 624, 629, 1011
Ergot alkaloids, 138, 862
Ergotamine, 862
Ergothioneine, 67, 824
Ergotoxines, 862
Eriodictyol, 671
Erythrocruorins, 163–164, 174
Erythrocytes, 427, 869–870, 916–917
Erythrose, 404
Erythrose-4-phosphate, 531–532, 541
Erythrulose, 529
Eserine, 578, 861
Essential amino acids, 724–728
Essential fatty acids, 561, 587, 614
Esterases, catalytic action, 216, 576–578, 624–625
  mechanism of action, 281–282
  occurrence, 576–577
  specificity, 275, 277, 576–578
Esteratic site, 281
Estradiol, see Estradiol-17β
Estradiol-17α, 646
Estradiol-17β, formula, 640
  metabolism, 646, 650
  occurrence, 640, 948
Estradiol-17β dehydrogenase, 646
Estrane, 638
Estriol, 640, 646
Estrogens, metabolism, 643, 645–646, 651
  occurrence, 640–641, 645, 948
  physiological effects, 953
  structure, 638, 640–641
Estrone, 640, 645–646

Ethanol, conversion to fatty acids, 611
  dielectric constant, 21
  formation, from acetaldehyde, 316, 475–476
    in alcoholic fermentation, 476
    in heterolactic fermentation, 535–536
    in phosphoroclastic reaction, 483
  free energy of formation, 237
  in protein precipitation, 20–22
  oxidation to acetaldehyde, 316, 365–366, 475–476
Ethanol-acetaldehyde system, oxidation-reduction potential, 327
Ethanolamine, see Aminoethanol
Ethereal sulfates, 795–796
Ethylchlorocarbonate, 134
Ethyldichlorophosphite, 134
Ethylenediaminetetraacetate, 324
Ethylene reductase, 597
N-Ethylmaleimide, 59
Etiocholane, 638
Etiocholane-3,17-dione, 649–650
Etiocholanolone, 649–650
Etioporphyrin, 166
Euglobulins, 17, 20–21
Excelsin, 42
Exergonic reactions, 230–232, 301, 303
  linked to endergonic reactions, 372–377, 713–714
    by pyridine nucleotides, 327–328, 374–375
    by substrates, 239–241, 372–374
Exopeptidases, 867
  see also Peptidases
Exoskeleton, crustacean, 970–971
  insect, 968
Exothermic reaction, 226
Extinction coefficient, 72

FAD, see Flavin adenine dinucleotide
FAD pyrophosphorylase, 336
Faraday, 293, 301
Farnesenic acid, 631
Farnesol, 662, 663, 664
Fastigiatin, 141
Fats, compound, 566–573
  digestion, 574–576, 578, 580
  intestinal absorption, 584–586, 624–625
  metabolism, see Fatty acids, Lipid metabolism
  neutral, 557–566
  rancidity, 564
  simple, 557–566
  unsaponifiable, 619
  see also Sterols, Lipids, Phospholipids, Sphingolipids

Fatty acid activating enzymes, 484, 595–596
  in fatty acid cycle, 600–601
  in phospholipid formation, 616
  in triglyceride formation, 616
  mechanism of action, 484, 720
Fatty acid cycle, enzymic reactions, 595–601
  in fatty acid formation, 609, 612–613
  in fatty acid oxidation, 599–601, 785
  scheme, 600
Fatty acid dehydrogenase, 587
Fatty acid peroxidase, 609
Fatty acids, activation, 484, 595–596, 720
  branched-chain, 558–560
  chemistry, 558–564, 594
  chromatography, 563–564
  essential, 561, 587, 614
  formation, 586–587, 609–614
    effect of insulin, 957–958, 962
    fatty acid cycle in, 609, 612–613
    from carbohydrates, 611–612
    from ethanol, 611
    from protein, 611
  incorporation into triglycerides and phospholipids, 585, 614–618
  inhibition of lipases, 575
  intestinal absorption, 584–586
  metabolism, 585–587, 590–618
  occurrence, 558–562, 565–567, 571–572
  oxidation, 586–587, 590–609
    citric acid cycle in, 600–601
    fatty acid cycle in, 595–607
    hormonal control, 963
    in animals, 586–587, 590–609
    in diabetes, 613
    in microbes, 608
    in plants, 602, 609
    relation to glucose oxidation, 606–607
    respiratory quotient, 590, 932
    theories of, 592–594
    to acetoacetate, 590–605, 607
    to acetyl-CoA, 595–601
    to CO_2, 590, 600–601, 604, 606–607
  release from triglycerides and phospholipids, 574–577
  transport in blood, 585–586
  turnover in vivo, 614
  unsaturated, chemistry, 559–560, 564–565
    metabolism, 586–587, 610–611, 614
    occurrence, 558–562, 569, 975
Fatty livers, 587–588
Fe[59], 392
Fehling's solution, 407
Felinine, 60

Fermentation, 456
Fermentation Lactobacillus casei factor, 999
Ferments, 209, 213–214
Ferric hydroxide, 24
Ferric ions, see Iron
Ferriheme, 178
Ferrihemoglobin, see Methemoglobin
Ferritin, 181, 830, 912–913, 980
Ferrous ions, see Iron
Feulgen reaction, 192, 568
Fibrin, 57, 702–704
Fibrinogen, isolation, 22
  metabolism, 702–704, 738
  physical properties, 21, 42, 150
  tyrosine-O-sulfate from, 69
Fibrinolysin, 703
Ficin, 705, 713, 715
First-order reactions, 244–245, 248–249
Flavanones, 670
Flavianic acid, 64
Flavin adenine dinucleotide, chemistry, 336–337
  formation, 336
  formula, 336
  in flavoproteins, 336–340, 751–753, 755, 802
Flavin mononucleotide, absorption spectrum, 334
  formation, 335–336
  formula, 332
  in bioluminescence, 345–346
  in flavoproteins, 332–335, 337–340, 752–753
  oxidation-reduction potential, 333
Flavin nucleotides, autoxidation, 305
  chemistry, 332–333, 336–337
  in electron transport, 340–344, 372
  in flavoproteins, 332–340
  oxidation-reduction potential, 304, 333
Flavins, 330–332, 345–346, 372
  see also Riboflavin
Flavokinase, 335, 910
Flavone, 670
Flavones, 670, 672
Flavonol, 670
Flavonols, 670, 672
Flavoproteins, antibiotic action, 339
  autoxidation, 335, 337, 340–343
  catalytic, 335–340, 345
  flavin nucleotide specificity, 337–338
  fluorescence, 333, 337
  in amino acid oxidation, 751–753, 755
  in cellular respiration, 340–344
  in fatty acid oxidation, 597, 600
  in oxidative phosphorylation, 383–384

Flavoproteins, in photosynthetic phosphorylation, 554
  in succinoxidase, 359–362
  interaction, with cytochrome c, 341–344
    with pyridine nucleotides, 341–344
  metal-containing, 338–340, 343–345, 357
  protein-flavin nucleotide bonds, 337
  turnover numbers, 340
  vitamin activity, 984
Florigens, 975
Flow birefringence, 152
Flowering hormones, 972, 975
Fluorescence polarization, 152
Fluoride ions, 381, 467–468, 472, 909
Fluoroacetic acid, 510
Fluoroacetyl-CoA, 510
Fluorocitric acid, 510
9α-Fluorocortisol, 948
1-Fluoro-2,4-dinitrobenzene, 50
FMN, see Flavin mononucleotide
Folacin, 999
Folic acid, 207, 998–999
  see also Pteroylglutamic acid
Folic acid conjugase, 1000
Folic acid vitamins, 998–1000
Folin-Ciocalteu reagent, 709
Folinic acid, 998–1000
Folinic acid-SF, 999
Follicle-stimulating hormone, 948, 950, 952
Follicular hormones, see Estrogens
Formaldehyde, in serine metabolism, 774–775
  interconversion with labile methyl groups, 774, 776, 806–808
  oxidation to formate, 326, 776
  reaction, with amino acids, 51, 59, 67, 91
    with tetrahydroPGA, 775
Formaldehyde dehydrogenase, 316, 326, 776
Formamide, 822
Formamidinoglutaric acid, 821–823
Formamidoglutamic acid, 821–823
5-Formaminoimidazole-4-carboxamide, 888
5-Formaminoimidazole-4-carboxamide ribotide, 889
Formic acid, formation, from acetone, 605–606
  from glycine, 772, 775–776, 778
  from glyoxylate, 338
  from oxalate, 520
  from pyruvate, 483
  hydrogen bonding of, 155
  in histidine metabolism, 819, 821–822
  in nucleic acid formation, 901–902

Formic acid, in pteridine formation, 1000
  in purine metabolism, 854–855, 889, 891, 894–895
  in riboflavin formation, 985
  in serine metabolism, 773–775
  interconversion with labile methyl groups, 774, 776, 806–807
  oxidation, 316, 483
  reduction, 316, 326
Formic acid-carbon dioxide system, 299
Formic dehydrogenase, 316
Formiminoglutamic acid, 821–823
Formiminoglycine, 894–895
Formimino group transfer, 822, 895
N^5-FormiminotetrahydroPGA, 822, 895
Formol titration, 91, 98–99
Formylacetic acid, 899–900
Formylase, 838
Formylglutamic acid, 822
S-Formylglutathione, 326
Formylglycinamide ribotide, 890–891
Formylglycinamidine ribotide, 891
Formylkynurenine, 837–838
N^{10}-FormylPGA, 775, 999
N^{10}-Formylpteroic acid, 998, 999
N^5-FormyltetrahydroPGA, 773, 775, 998–1001
N^{10}-FormyltetrahydroPGA, 773, 775, 895, 999
Free energy, 229
  of activation, 266–269
  of formation, 236–240
Free energy change, 229
  determination, 232–242, 375
    for coupled reactions, 373–374
    from equilibrium constant, 232–236
    from oxidation-reduction potentials, 301
    from thermal data, 236–240
  effect of pH, 236
  in chemical reactions, 228–233
  in biochemical reactions, 233–243, 268–269
  in coupled oxidation-reduction reactions, 372
  in DPN-linked reactions, 327–328
  in endergonic reactions, 230
  in exergonic reactions, 230
  in oxidation-reduction reactions, 300–301
  in protein denaturation, 233–234
  in substrate-linked reactions, 373–374
  relation, to chemical potential, 231–232
    to energy metabolism, 928–929, 931
    to enthalpy change, 229–230

Free energy change, relation, to entropy
    change, 229–230
  to equilibrium constant, 231–233, 235–
    236
  to oxidation-reduction potential, 301
  to reaction velocity, 230
  standard, 232
Freezing point depression, 30–32
Frictional ratio, 149–151
Fructokinase, 460, 492–494, 910
Fructose, amino acid derivatives, 735
  chemistry, 409–410
  conversion to glycogen, 493–494
  formation, from glucose, 500
    from sorbitol, 495, 500
    from sucrose, 433, 451–452
  formula, 410
  in sucrose formation, 446–447, 450
  metabolism in diabetes, 957
  occurrence, 409, 500
    in oligosaccharides, 409, 415–416
    in polysaccharides, 409, 421, 429
  optical rotation, 406
  phosphorylation, 460, 493–494
  tests, 409
Fructose-amino acids, 735
Fructose-1,6-diphosphatase, 461, 494, 582
Fructose-1,6-diphosphate, conversion, to
    fructose-6-phosphate, 460–461, 494,
    582
  to triose phosphates, 468–470, 494
  formation, from fructose-1-phosphate,
    493–494
    from fructose-6-phosphate, 460–461,
    494
    from triose phosphates, 468–470, 494
  formula, 458, 468
  in alcoholic fermentation, 460–461, 468–
    470
  in pentose phosphate pathway, 531
Fructose-1-phosphate, 469, 493–494
Fructose-6-phosphate, action, of transal-
    dolase, 530
  of transketolase, 530, 532
  conversion, to fructose diphosphate,
    460–461
  to glucose-6-phosphate, 460, 494
  to glycogen, 494
  to mannitol-1-phosphate, 543
  to mannose-6-phosphate, 463
  to sucrose phosphate, 450
  formation, from fructose, 460
    from fructose diphosphate, 461, 494
    from glucosamine-6-phosphate, 465
    from glucose-6-phosphate, 460
  formula, 458, 530

Fructose-6-phosphate, phosphorolysis, 531
Fructose-1-phosphate aldolase, 469
β-Fructosidases, 433
    see also Invertase
Fructosides, 409, 433
FSH, 948, 950, 952
Fuchsin sulfurous acid reaction, 193,
    568
Fucose, formula, 411
  occurrence, 410, 414, 426, 428
  optical rotation, 406
Fucosyllactose, 414
Fumarase, catalytic action, 235, 272
  coupling with aspartase, 239–240
  crystallization, 218
  in citric acid cycle, 502, 508
Fumaric acid, formation from fumaryl-
    acetoacetate, 827–828
  formula, 234, 240
  free energy of formation, 237
  in adenylosuccinate metabolism, 891–
    892
  in argininosuccinate metabolism, 851–
    852
  in citric acid cycle, 502, 508
  interconversion, with aspartate, 240,
    851–852, 891–892
    with malate, 235, 239–240, 502
    with succinate, 289–290, 344, 502
Fumaric hydrogenase, 344
Fumarylacetoacetic acid, 827–828
Fumarylacetoacetic hydrolase, 828
Furanose ring, 408
Furanosides, 408–409
Furfural, 187, 407
6-Furfurylaminopurine, 207, 975

Galactans, 423
Galactoflavin, 984
Galactokinase, 463
Galactolipins, 572–573, 618
Galactonic acid, 536
Galactonolactone, 536, 539–540
Galactopyranose, 405
Galactopyranosylglycerol, 570
Galactosamine, 412–413, 428
Galactose, chemistry, 405, 408
  conversion to ascorbic acid, 539–540
  formula, 404
  heat of combustion, 227
  in disaccharide formation, 452, 465
  occurrence, in lipids, 570–572
    in oligosaccharides, 414, 416
    in polysaccharides, 423, 426, 428
  optical rotation, 406
  oxidation, 536

Galactose, phosphorylation, 463
Galactosemia, 465, 858
Galactose-1-phosphate, 463–464
β-Galactosidase, 432, 454, 746–747
Galactowaldenase, 464
Galacturonic acid, 411, 423, 438, 538–539
Gamabufotalin, 637
Gangliosides, 571–572
Gas constant, 227, 232, 293
Gastrophilus respiratory pigment, 163–164, 174
Gaucher's disease, 572
GDP, 505–506, 735, 882–883
Geiger-Müller tube, 392–393
Gelatin, 125, 707–708
Gentianose, 416–417
Gentiobiose, 415–416
Geotropism, 972–973
Geraniol, 661–662, 664
Gibberellins, 975
Gibbs-Donnan effect, 111–112, 915–917
Gibbs' phase rule, 25–26
Gitogenin, 636
Gitonin, 636
Glass electrode, 19
Gliadin, 70, 130, 727
Globin, 163
  see also Hemoglobin
Globin hemochromogen, 172–173
Globular proteins, 148, 160
Globulins, 16–17
  in seeds, 17, 742
  in serum, 19, 22, 573, 741
α-Globulins, 106, 425, 738, 943
β-Globulins, 106, 573, 738
γ-Globulins, 106, 150, 740
  formation, 739–741
  in multiple myeloma, 741
  relation to antibodies, 740
Glossitis, 986
Glucagon, 441, 942, 961–963
Glucokinase, 460, 492–494, 500, 956–957
Gluconeogenesis, 493, 495–496
  hormonal control, 956–957, 959
Gluconic acid, 314, 411, 526, 536
Gluconokinase, 526
Gluconolactone, 314, 339
α-D-Glucopyranose, 403, 405
β-D-Glucopyranose, 403, 406–407
Glucosamine, 412–413, 425–428, 460
Glucosamine-1-phosphate, 466
Glucosamine-6-phosphate, 460, 465
Glucosazone, 408
Glucose, blood levels, 497–498
  breakdown, by fermentation, 476–478
    by glycolysis, 490, 494

Glucose, breakdown, by pentose phosphate pathway, 531
  chemistry, 402–409
  conversion, to ascorbic acid, 539–540
    to fatty acids, 611–612
    to fructose, 494–495
    to gluconic acid, 314, 339, 526
    to glucose-6-phosphate, 375, 459–460, 492–494
    to glucosone, 537
    to glucuronic acid, 537
    to glycogen, 492–495
    to inositol, 543–544
    to kojic acid, 542–543
    to quinic acid, 541–542
    to shikimic acid, 541–542
    to sorbitol, 495, 500
    to tetronic acids, 538–539
  formation, from maltose, 431, 453
    from pyruvate, 474
    from sorbitol, 543
    from sucrose, 433, 451–452
    via pentose phosphate pathway, 531–532, 552
  formula, 404
  free energy of formation, 237
  heat of combustion, 226–227
  inhibition of phosphorylase, 441
  intestinal absorption, 492–493
  link to amino acid metabolism, *see* Protein metabolism, link to carbohydrate metabolism
  mutarotation, 406
  occurrence, 402
    in bacteriophage DNA, 196, 904
    in oligosaccharides, 414–416
    in polysaccharides, 417, 421–422, 428–429
    in sphingolipids, 572
  optical rotation, 406
  oxidation, citric acid cycle in, 501–510
    effect of insulin, 955–957
    energy relations, 520–524
    pentose phosphate pathway in, 525–534
    to hexonic acids, 526, 535–536
  tests, 407–408
  tolerance curve, 498–499
  transport, 956
  UDP-, *see* UDP-glucose
Glucose-1-arsenate, 439
Glucose dehydrogenase, 314–316, 320
Glucose-1,6-diphosphate, 461–462, 466
Glucose oxidase, 338–339, 407, 526
Glucose-6-phosphatase, 446, 497, 956

α-D-Glucose-1-phosphate, conversion, to disaccharides, 446–447, 450–451
  to glucose-6-phosphate, 461–462, 470
  to polysaccharides, 441–445
  dissociation, 441
  formation, from disaccharides, 446–448
  from galactose-1-phosphate, 463–464
  from polysaccharides, 438–439, 441–445
  formula, 439
  hydrolysis, 450
β-D-Glucose-1-phosphate, 447
Glucose-6-phosphate, conversion, to fructose-6-phosphate, 460, 476
  to glucose-1-phosphate, 461–462, 490
  to 6-phosphogluconic acid, 310–311, 313–314, 330–335, 525–526
  to polysaccharides, 463
  to trehalose phosphate, 465
  formation, from glucose, 375, 459–460, 492–494
  from glucose-1-phosphate, 461–462
  formula, 458
  hydrolysis, 497, 581
Glucose-6-phosphate dehydrogenase, 313–314, 316, 526
Glucose-1-phosphate kinase, 462–463
Glucose-1-phosphate transphosphorylase, 462
α-Glucosidases, 431, 433, 436
β-Glucosidases, 276–277, 431–432
Glucosides, 408–409, 451–454
Glucosone, 537
Glucuronic acid, conversion to xylose, 538
  formation, from glucose, 537
  from inositol, 544
  formula, 411
  occurrence, 423–425, 428
  UDP-, see UDP-glucuronic acid
Glucuronidase, 432, 437, 647
Glucuronide, benzoyl-, 537
  bilirubin, 874
  indole, 844
  phenyl-, 537
  thyroxine, 832, 943
Glucuronides, formation, 537–538, 646
  excretion, 537
  hydrolysis, 432
  transglycosidation reactions, 454
Glucuronolactone, 539–540
Glutamic acid, chemistry, 62–63, 93, 95, 118
  formula, 62
D-Glutamic acid, metabolism, 762, 769
  occurrence, 81, 138, 749

L-Glutamic acid, breakdown, 817–818
  conversion to glutamine, 721
  deamination, 316, 752, 754, 759–760
  decarboxylation, 768
  fermentation, 817–818
  formation, 731
  from γ-aminobutyrate, 817
  from glutamine, 710
  from histidine, 821–822
  from lysine, 808–809
  free energy of formation, 237
  glucogenic action, 764
  in glutathione formation, 721
  in nitrogen fixation, 675
  in protein metabolism, 765–766
  interconversion with arginine, 812–815
  interconversion with proline, 812–814
  isolation, 62, 114
  metabolism, 812–818
  occurrence, 62–63, 125, 207, 817
  in peptides, 136, 141, 999–1000
  optical rotation, 79
  relation to citric acid cycle, 502
  transamination reactions, 759–760, 762–763, 765–766
  transport, 744–745, 817
Glutamic-alanine transaminase, 760–762, 778
Glutamic-aspartic transaminase, 760–763
Glutamic decarboxylase, 271, 767–768
Glutamic dehydrogenase, 218, 316, 754, 760, 765–766
Glutamic-leucine transaminase, 782–783
Glutamic-oxaloacetic transaminase, 760–763
Glutamic-pyruvic transaminase, 760–762, 778
Glutamic semialdehyde, 762, 813
Glutaminase, 710, 918
Glutamine, as source of urinary ammonia, 848, 918
  chemistry, 62–63
  conjugation, 719, 825, 846
  conversion, to α-ketoglutarate, 763
  to γ-glutamyl peptides, 717–718
  formation, 718, 721
  formula, 62
  hydrolysis, 710, 718
  in electrolyte balance, 918
  in histidine formation, 821
  in nitrogen fixation, 675
  in purine formation, 855, 890–891
  metabolism, 752, 816–817
  occurrence, 62–63, 131, 141
  optical rotation, 79
  transamidation reactions, 717–718

Glutamine, transamination reactions, 762–763

Glutamylaminopropionitrile, 63

γ-Glutamyl peptides, 138–139, 717–718

Glutaric acid, 808–809

Glutathione, activation of proteinases, 701, 705–706
  antioxidant action, 564
  formation, 718, 721, 965
  formula, 136
  hydrolysis, 710–711, 718
  in dehydroascorbic reductase reaction, 368
  in formaldeyhde dehydrogenase reaction, 326
  in glyceraldehyde-3-phosphate dehydrogenase reaction, 325
  in glyoxylase reaction, 479
  in oxidative phosphorylation, 385
  occurrence, 136
  oxidation, 316
  oxidation-reduction system, 305
  reduction of oxidized form, 314–315, 1005
  transamidation reactions, 718
  turnover, 721

Glutathione reductase, 314–316, 368

Glutelins, 16–17, 742

D-Glyceraldehyde, action, of alcohol dehydrogenase, 494
  of aldolase, 469
  of glycerokinase, 616
  of transketolase, 529
  configuration, 80
  formation, 494
  formula, 80, 404
  phosphorylation, 494

L-Glyceraldehyde, 79–80

Glyceraldehyde-3-phosphate, action, of aldolase, 468–469, 494
  of glyceraldehyde-3-phosphate dehydrogenase, 324–326, 372–374, 470–471
  of transaldolase, 530
  of transketolase, 529–530, 532
  of triose phosphate isomerase, 469–470
  formation, from fructose diphosphate, 468–470
    from glycerol, 616
  formula, 324, 468, 530
  in deoxypentose formation, 534–535
  in fermentations, 470–471, 476, 535–536
  in glycolysis, 490, 494
  in pentose phosphate pathway, 531–532
  in photosynthesis, 551–552
  oxidation-reduction system, 327

Glyceraldehyde-3-phosphate dehydrogenase, action, 316, 320, 323–327
  crystallization, 218, 323–324
  formation, 737
  in coupled reactions, 327–328, 373–374
  in fermentation, 470–471, 476
  in glycolysis, 490
  in photosynthesis, 551

Glyceric acid, 536

Glyceric dehydrogenase, 536

Glycerokinase, 616

Glycerol, formation from glucose, 467, 477–478
  heat of combustion, 227
  incorporation, into phospholipids, 615–617
    into triglycerides, 615–616
  intestinal absorption, 577
  occurrence, 205, 557, 565–570
  phosphorylation, 616

Glycerophosphatase, 579–580, 910

L-α-Glycerophosphate, action of phosphatases, 478, 580
  enzymic oxidation, 316, 318
  formation, from dihydroxyacetone phosphate, 477–478
    from glycerol, 616
    from phospholipids, 580
  formula, 318, 478
  occurrence, 567
  oxidation-reduction system, 327

β-Glycerophosphate, 264, 581

Glycerophosphate dehydrogenase, 217, 316, 318–319, 477

Glycerylphosphorylaminoethanol, 568–569, 580

Glycerylphosphorylcholine, 568, 579–580

Glycerylphosphorylcholine diesterase, 580, 583

Glycerylphosphorylserine, 580

Glycinamide, 92, 711–712

Glycinamide ribotide, 890

Glycine, as dietary nitrogen source, 726
  breakdown, 771–772
  chemistry, 51, 53–54, 108, 118
  conjugation, 635, 719, 729, 990–991
  conversion, to acetate, 777–778
    to creatine, 803–804
    to serine, 773–776
  deamination, 752–753, 757–758
  dissociation, 90–92, 94, 228
  fermentation, 777–778
  formation, 731–732, 771–777, 792
    from betaine, 766
    from choline, 802
    from purines, 894–895

Glycine, formation, from sarcosine, 805
  from serine, 772–775
  from threonine, 791–792
  free energy of formation, 236–237
  glucogenic action, 764, 777
  heat of combustion, 227
  indispensable nature, 726
  in glutathione formation, 721
  in porphyrin formation, 864–872, 876
  in pteridine formation, 1000
  in purine formation, 854–855, 890, 901–
    902
  in riboflavin formation, 985
  metabolism, 771–778
    PGA in, 773–775
    pyridoxal phosphate in, 775
    succinate-glycine cycle in, 867
  occurrence, 53, 125, 633
  titration curve, 90–91
  transamidination reactions, 803, 812
Glycine-ethanolamine cycle, 777
Glycine oxidase, 337–338, 752–753
Glycine reductase, 758
Glycocholic acid, 633, 635
Glycocyamine, 487, 803, 811–812
Glycocyamine phosphate, 486–487
Glycogen, chemical properties, 421–422
  conversion, to glucose-1-phosphate,
    441–445, 490
    to lactate, see Glycolysis
  formation, 492–497, 513–515, 523
    hormonal control, 947, 955–957, 960
  hydrolysis, 433, 436
  mobilization, 497
  phosphorolysis, 438–439, 441–445
  structure, 421, 445
  turnover, 495–497
Glycogenesis, 493
  see also Glycogen, formation
Glycogenolysis, 493, 497
  hormonal control, 956, 960
Glycogen storage disease, 446
Glycolaldehyde, 529, 771–772
Glycolic acid, conversion to glycine, 771–
    772
  formation from glyoxylate, 316, 318
  formula, 318, 520, 772
  oxidation to glyoxylate, 338, 520
Glycolic oxidase, 338, 609
N-Glycolylneuraminic acid, 426
Glycolysis, 457, 493
  aerobic, 516
  anaerobic, ATP formation in, 490, 521–
    522
    Embden-Meyerhof pathway, 489–491
    energy relations, 491, 521–524

Glycolysis, anaerobic, formation of lac-
    tate, 489–492
  in animal tissues, 489–491, 499–500
  in fatty acid formation, 613
  in photosynthesis, 551
  relation to pentose phosphate path-
    way, 533–534
Glyconeogenesis, 493, 495–496
  hormonal control, 956–957, 959
Glycoproteins, 17
  see also Mucoproteins
Glycosidases, 216, 430–438, 454
Glycosides, cardiac, 637
  chemistry, 408–409
  cleavage, by glycosidases, 430–438
    by phosphorylases, 438–450
    by transglycosidases, 451–455
  oligosaccharides as, 414
  plant pigment, 669–671
  polysaccharides as, 418–419, 421–424
  steroid, 635–637
  triterpene, 664
Glycosidic bond, 409
Glycostatic action, 960
Glycosuria, 498, 941
Glycylglycinamide, 274
Glyoxalases, 479
Glyoxylic acid, conversion, to formate, 772
  to glycine, 771–772
  to glycolate, 316, 318
  to oxalate, 520
  formation, from allantoin, 857
    from glycine, 753
    from glycolate, 338
    from hydroxyamino acids, 56–57
  formula, 56, 318, 772
  in isocitritase reaction, 518
  in malate synthetase reaction, 519
Glyoxylic acid cycle, 519–520, 778
Glyoxylic reductase, 316, 318–319, 338
Gmelin reaction, 874
Goiter, 944
Gonadotrophins, 952, 954–955
Gout, 856
Gradient elution method, 122–123
Gramicidins, 81, 137, 385
Gram stain, 193
Grana, 548
Graves' disease, 943
Ground substance, 424
Growth and development hormone, 969
Growth factor, 976
Growth hormone, in bone formation, 953,
    968
  in carbohydrate metabolism, 959–960,
    962

Growth hormone, in lipid metabolism, 962–963
  in protein metabolism, 965–966
  properties, 950, 953
GTP, 204, 467, 735, 892
Guanase, 885–886
Guanidine, 153, 155, 812
Guanidinoacetate methylpherase, 804
Guanidinoacetic acid, 487, 803, 811–812
Guanidinoethanol, 486
Guanidino group, 93–94
Guanine, formula, 187
  incorporation into DNA and PNA, 900–901
  metabolism, 886–887, 891–894
  occurrence, 187, 191, 197–198
Guanosine, 187, 883–884
Guanosine-5'-diphosphate, 505–506, 735, 882–883
Guanosine diphosphate mannose, 205, 467
Guanosine-2'-phosphate, 189–190
Guanosine-3'-phosphate, 189–190
Guanosine-5'-phosphate, 882, 891–893
Guanosine-5'-triphosphate, 204, 467, 735, 892
Guanylic acids, 186, 188–190
Gulonic acid, 539–540
Gulonolactone, 539–540, 978
Guluronic acid, 423
Gynaminic acid, 426

Hagedorn-Jensen method, 407
Half-life of metabolites, 733
Half-time of chemical reactions, 244, 248
Hapten, 740
Harden-Young ester, see Fructose-1,6-diphosphate
Harman, 861
HCG, 955
H disease, 846
Heat capacity, 225
Heat content, 226
Heat of activation, 263–270
Heat of combustion, 226
Heat of formation, 236
Heat production in biological systems, 928–938
Helical structure, 159–160, 200–201, 436–437
Helicorubin, 358
α-Helix, 159–160
Hemagglutination, 426–427
Hematin, 178
Hematoporphyrin, 166, 352
Heme, absorption spectra, 169
  electronic structure, 171–172

Heme, formation, 864–869, 988
  formula, 170
  in metalloflavoproteins, 357
  reaction with bases, 169–170, 172
Heme proteins, 162–165, 169, 179–180
  see also Cytochromes, Hemoglobin, Hydroperoxidases, Myoglobin
Hemerythrins, 180–181
Hemicelluloses, 423
Hemimetabolous insects, 968–969
Hemin, 178, 1008
Hemochromatosis, 913
Hemochromes, 169
Hemochromogens, 169–172, 179, 353
Hemocuprein, 181
Hemocyanin, 42–43, 180–181
Hemoglobin, amino acid composition, 125
  antigenic nature, 739
  as blood buffer, 100, 918–921
  chemistry, 162–165, 172–173, 178
  combination with oxygen, 173–177
  conversion to bile pigments, 869, 872–876
  electronic structure, 172
  formation, 736–737, 864, 869–870, 912–914
  in CO_2 transport, 916–921
  in mammalian erythrocyte, 163
  iron content, 28
  isoelectric point, 102, 163, 173
  occurrence, 162–164
  oxidation-reduction potential, 299, 363
  particle weight, 33, 42–43, 163
  shape, 150
  solubility, 21
  terminal amino acids, 143
  X-ray analysis, 160
Hemoglobin A, 163
Hemoglobin F, 163
Hemoglobin S, 163
Hemosiderin, 913
Hemosiderosis, 913
Henderson-Hasselbalch equation, 87–88
Heparin, 425, 576, 703–704
Hepatectomy, 397, 728, 901
Hepatocuprein, 181
Heptoses, 409–410, 530–531, 551–552
Heterolactic fermentation, 535–536
Heterolipids, 566
Heteropyrithiamine, 983
Heterotrophic organisms, 285
Hexadecanoic acid, see Palmitic acid
Hexanoic acid, 559, 603–604
trans-Hex-3-enoyl-CoA, 598
Hexokinase, action, 375, 459, 476
  crystallization, 218

Hexokinase, in absorption of sugars, 492–493
  occurrence, 460
  properties, 42, 459–460
  relation to Pasteur effect, 523
Hexonic acids, 526, 531, 535–537
Hexosamines, chemistry, 412–413
  metabolism, 460, 465–466
  occurrence, 205, 423–426, 428, 749
Hexose monophosphate shunt, 525–535, 541, 551–553
Hexose phosphates, chemistry, 413, 458
  in fermentation, 476
  in glycolysis, 490
  in pentose phosphate pathway, 531
  in photosynthesis, 552
  interconversion, 463–467
  see also individual hexose phosphates
Hexoses, chemistry, 402–409, 411–414
  conversion to inositols, 543–544
  enzymic phosphorylation, 457–464, 492, 500
  fermentation, 457–478
  formation from pentoses, 529–533, 543
  intestinal absorption, 492–493
  see also individual hexoses
HG-factor, 441, 942, 961–963
Hill reaction, 550, 553–555
Hill's equation, 175
Hippuric acid, enzymic hydrolysis, 710
  excretion, 590
  formation, 719, 729
  formula, 53
  free energy of formation, 237–238
Hippuricase, 710
Hirudin, 703
Histaminase, 823
Histamine, 66–68, 767, 823–824
Histidase, 755, 821
Histidinal, 820
Histidine, chemistry, 66–67, 108, 118, 142
  dissociation, 93–95
  formula, 66
D-Histidine, 752, 819
L-Histidine, deamination, 752, 755
  glucogenic action, 764
  indispensable nature, 725, 728, 819
  in enzyme action, 282
  isolation, 114
  metabolism, 774, 819–824
  occurrence, 66–67, 100, 125, 201
  optical rotation, 79, 97
Histidine-α-deaminase, 755, 821
Histidine decarboxylase, 767–768
Histidinol, 820
Histidinol dehydrogenase, 820

Histidinol phosphate, 820
Histohematin, 349
Histones, 17, 64, 201
Histozyme, 710
Holoenzyme, 220, 321
Holometabolous insects, 968–969
Homeostasis, 509, 914–922
  hormonal regulation, 939–940, 952, 954
Homocysteine, breakdown, 757, 793–794
  chemistry, 61–62
  conversion to methionine, 800–803, 806–807
  formation from methionine, 793–795, 804
  formula, 61, 793
Homocysteine thiolactone, 61
Homocystine, 61–62, 793, 1005
Homogentisic acid, 826–828, 832
Homogentisic oxidase, 827–828
Homoiothermic organisms, 930, 935–937
Homolipids, 557
Homoprotocatechuic acid, 830–831
Homoserine, 757, 790–791, 794, 812
Homoserine dehydrogenase, 791
Homovanillic acid, 830–831
Hopkins-Cole reaction, 69–70
Hordenine, 860–861
Hormones, adrenocortical, see Adrenocortical hormones
  anterior pituitary, 950–953, 959–960
  corpus luteum, see Progesterone
  crustacean, 970–971
  definition, 939–940
  gastrointestinal, 955
  hypothalamic, 952, 954
  insect, 968–970
  of adrenal medulla, 946, 960–961
  ovarian, see Estrogens
  pancreatic, see Glucagon, Insulin
  parathyroid, 945
  peptide, 140–141
  pituitary, 949–954
  placental, 955
  plant, 971–975
  posterior pituitary, 140, 953–954
  steroid, see Steroid hormones
  testicular, see Androgens
  thyroid, see Thyroxine
Houssay animal, 959
Hüfner's equation, 174
Human chorionic gonadotrophin, 955
Humin, 47
Hyalobiuronic acid, 424
Hyaluronic acid, 424, 437
Hyaluronidase, 437–438, 455
Hydantoic acids, 50

Hydantoins, 50
Hydrases, 216
Hydration of proteins, 149–151
Hydrazine, 135, 144, 676
Hydrindantin, 51
Hydrochloric acid, gastric secretion of, 924
Hydrocortisone, see Cortisol
Hydrogen, action of hydrogenase, 676
   formation from formate, 483
   in amino acid deamination, 758
   in nitrogen fixation, 676–677
   in photosynthesis, 546–547, 549, 676–677
Hydrogenase, 338, 340, 676–677, 758
Hydrogen bonds, definition, 155
   in DNA, 201
   in proteins, 148, 154–155, 159–160
Hydrogen electrode, 291–292, 296, 299
Hydrogen ion, activity, 18
   excretion, 918–919
   free energy of formation, 237
Hydrogenlyase, 483
Hydrogen peroxide, action, of catalase, 365
   of peroxidase, 363–364
   formation, 305, 338–339, 753–754
   free energy of formation, 237
   in bioluminescence, 346
   in fatty acid oxidation, 609
   in tryptophan peroxidase-oxidase reaction, 837
Hydrogen peroxide-oxygen system, 299
Hydrogen sulfide, activation of proteinases, 705–706
   as reductant in photosynthesis, 549
   formation, from cysteine, 756, 797
      from cystine, 58
   microbial oxidation, 799
Hydrogen transfer, 319–320
Hydrolases, 216, 273–274
Hydroperoxidases, 362–366
Hydrophilic substances, 557
Hydrophobic substances, 557
Hydroquinone, 289–290, 297, 299
Hydrosulfite, 311–312
Hydroxamic acids, 484, 715, 717, 720
Hydroxocobalamin, 1003
β-Hydroxyacyl-CoA dehydrase, 600
β-Hydroxyacyl-CoA dehydrogenase, 316, 598–599
Hydroxyanthranilic acid, 840–842
p-Hydroxyazobenzenesulfonic acid, 65
p-Hydroxybenzaldehyde, 422
Hydroxybenzimidazole, 1003
p-Hydroxybenzoic acid, 832–835

β-Hydroxybutyric-acetoacetic system, 299
D-β-Hydroxybutyric acid, conversion to acetoacetate, 316, 382, 599, 605–607
   formation from fatty acids, 590
   stereochemistry, 598
β-Hydroxybutyric dehydrogenase, 316, 599, 605
D-β-Hydroxybutyryl-CoA, 316, 599
L-β-Hydroxybutyryl-CoA, 316, 597–599
β-Hydroxybutyryl-CoA dehydrogenase, 316, 599
7α-Hydroxycholesterol, 634
6-Hydroxychroman, 667
p-Hydroxycinnamic acid, 258, 682–683
17-Hydroxycorticosterone, see Cortisol
β-Hydroxydecanoic acid, 570
17-Hydroxy-11-dehydrocorticosterone, see Cortisone
17-Hydroxydeoxycorticosterone, formula, 639
   metabolism, 642–644, 650
   physiological effects, 947
   secretion, 638, 946
Hydroxyeleostearic acid, 562
β-Hydroxyglutamic acid, 63
γ-Hydroxyglutamic acid, 767
γ-Hydroxyglutamic semialdehyde, 816
5-Hydroxyindolylacetic acid, 846
β-Hydroxyisobutyric acid, 780–781
β-Hydroxyisobutyryl-CoA, 780–781
α-Hydroxyisocaproic acid, 786–787
β-Hydroxyisovaleric acid, 630, 665
β-Hydroxyisovaleryl-CoA, 630–631, 787–788
Hydroxykynurenamine, 838
Hydroxykynurenine, 837–841
Hydroxylamine, inactivation of papain, 706
   metabolism, 677–682
   reaction, with acyl groups, 484, 715, 717–718, 720
      with aldehydes, 659
Hydroxylamine reductase, 681
11β-Hydroxylase, 643–644
17-Hydroxylase, 643–644
21-Hydroxylase, 643–644
Hydroxylysine, chemistry, 64, 79, 81–82
   formula, 64, 810
   metabolism, 764, 809
   occurrence, 64, 125
p-Hydroxymandelic acid, 682–683
Hydroxymethylcytosine, 196, 898–899, 904
Hydroxymethyldeoxycytidylic acid, 198
Hydroxymethylfurfural, 407

β-Hydroxy-β-methylglutaric acid, 630, 665
β-Hydroxy-β-methylglutaryl-CoA, 630–631, 787–788
Hydroxymethylhomocysteine, 807
Hydroxymethylpyridine, 991
HydroxymethyltetrahydroPGA, 775–776, 807
9-Hydroxyoctadec-12-enoic acid, 652
p-Hydroxyphenylacetic acid, 832
p-Hydroxyphenylethanol, 832
p-Hydroxyphenylethanolamine, 829
p-Hydroxyphenyllactic acid, 835
p-Hydroxyphenylpyruvic acid, 826–828, 832, 835
p-Hydroxyphenylpyruvic oxidase, 826
5-Hydroxypipecolic acid, 71, 809
5-Hydroxypiperidine-2-carboxylic acid, 71, 809
17α-Hydroxyprogesterone, 642–645
Hydroxyproline, chemistry, 49, 71–72, 79, 81–82
  formula, 48
  glucogenic action, 764
  metabolism, 815–816
  occurrence, 71, 125
β-Hydroxypropionic acid, 602
β-Hydroxypropionyl-CoA, 602
2-Hydroxypyridine, 280, 406
Hydroxypyruvic acid, 529, 536, 789
4-Hydroxyquinoline-2-carboxylic acid, 836–838, 840
α-Hydroxysteroid dehydrogenase, 647–648, 651
β-Hydroxysteroid dehydrogenase, 320, 643, 647, 651
5-Hydroxytryptamine, 767–768, 844–846, 863
5-Hydroxytryptophan, 845–846
5-Hydroxytryptophan decarboxylase, 767–768
Hydroxytyramine, 828–829
Hygrine, 860–861
Hyocholic acid, 632
Hyperglycemia, 498, 940–941, 955
Hyperglycemic factor, 441, 942, 961–963
Hypertensin, 140–141
Hyperthyroidism, 943
Hypoglycemia, 498, 942
Hyponitrous acid, 676, 679, 681–682
Hypophysectomy, 949–951, 959
Hypotaurine, 767, 797
Hypothyroidism, 943–944
Hypoxanthine, fermentation, 894
  formation, 887–890
    from adenine, 886

Hypoxanthine, formation, from inosine, 884
  formula, 203, 855, 884
  in sulfite oxidation, 797
  occurrence, 203, 206, 1003
  oxidation to uric acid, 339, 855
Hypoxanthine deoxyriboside, 884
Hypoxanthine riboside, 206

I[131], 392
IAA, 846, 973–974
IAA oxidase, 974
Iceland spar, 74
ICSH, 950, 952
Idose, 404
IDP, 461, 505–506, 512, 882–883
Iduronic acid, 425
Imidazolone propionic acid, 822
Imidazolylacetaldehyde, 823
Imidazolylacetic acid, 823
Imidazolylacetol phosphate, 820
Imidazolylglycerol phosphate, 820–821
Imidazolyl group, 93–94, 173
Imidazolylpyruvic acid, 819, 823
Imino acids, 48, 335–336, 753
Immune reactions, 739–740
IMP, 203, 886, 888–892
Inborn errors of metabolism, 398
  alcaptonuria, 398, 826
  congenital porphyria, 872
  galactosemia, 465
  glycogen storage disease, 446
  phenylketonuria, 825
Inclusion bodies, 194
Indican, 844
Indicators, pH, 88–89
Indicator yellow, 659
Indigo, 844
Indirect calorimetry, 931–934
Indispensable amino acids, 724–728
Indole, 842–844
Indoleacetic acid, 846, 973–974
Indoleacetic acid oxidase, 974
Indolealdehyde, 974
Indole alkaloids, 861–862
Indole-5,6-quinone, 830–831
Indolyl-3-acetaldehyde, 974
Indolyl-3-acetic acid, 846, 973–974
Indolyl-3-acetonitrile, 974
Indolylacetylglutamine, 846
Indolylglycerol phosphate, 842–843
Indolyl-3-pyruvic acid, 835–836, 846
Indophenol oxidase, 354
Indoxylglucuronic acid, 844
Indoxylsulfuric acid, 844
Induced enzymes, 746, 838

Inhibition of enzyme action, 256–260
Inorganic ions, activation of enzymes, 262–263, 910–912
  antagonism, 924–927
  binding by chelating agents, 108, 324
  dispensable, 908–909
  electrolyte balance, 914–921
  hormonal regulation, 945, 947, 966–968
  indispensable, 908–909
  in enzymes, 338–340, 366–368
  in nitrogen fixation, 674
  interaction with proteins, 22, 108–110
  occurrence, 10, 908–909, 917
  physiological role, 907, 909–914
  toxicity, 908–909
  transport, 915–919, 922–924, 926–927
  see also individual elements
Inosine, 206, 883–884, 886, 889
Inosine-5'-diphosphate, 461, 505–506, 512, 882–883
Inosine-5'-phosphate, 203, 886, 888–892
Inosine-5'-triphosphate, 461, 512, 882–883
Inosinic acid, 203, 886, 888–892
Inositides, 470
meso-Inositol, see *myo*-Inositol
myo-Inositol, formula, 412
  metabolism, 543–544, 618, 1007
  occurrence, 412, 570, 573
  vitamin activity, 1007
Inositol monophosphate, 570, 583
Inositols, 412
Insulin, absorbance, 74
  A-chain, 145
  amino acid composition, 125
  amino acid sequence, 145–146
  antigenic nature, 941
  B-chain, 145–146
  binding by cells, 956
  crystallization, 941
  cystine in, 58, 131
  effect, on blood glucose, 498
    on carbohydrate metabolism, 955–959
    on lipid metabolism, 957–958, 962
    on protein metabolism, 958, 964–965
  formula, 146
  frictional ratio, 150
  metabolism, 737–738, 942, 961–962
  molecular weight, 43, 142
  particle weight, 43
  pituitary antagonists, 959–960
  secretion, 941–942, 958–960, 962
  structure, 145–146
    species differences, 146
  terminal amino acids, 143
  titration curves, 99

Insulin, unit, 941–942
Insulinase, 942
Intermediate metabolism, 388
Intermedin, 954, 971
Interstitial cell-stimulating hormone, 950, 952
Intrinsic factor, 1004–1005
Intrinsic viscosity, 151
Inulin, 421
Invertase, catalytic action, 433, 454
  inhibition by glucose, 257
  kinetics, 250, 252–253, 255
  occurrence, 210, 432
Iodine, in thyroid hormones, 69, 831, 943–944
  physiological role, 909
Iodine number, 564
Iodine test, 417, 421
Iodoacetate, effect on muscle, 486–487
  inhibition, of glyceraldehyde-3-phosphate dehydrogenase, 324, 476, 490
    of proteinases, 706
Iodogorgoic acid, 68–69
p-Iodophenylsulfonyl chloride, 128, 143
Iodopsin, 660
3-Iodotyrosine, 69, 831–832
Ion carriers, 924
Ion-exchange resins, 122–126, 147
Ionic strength, 20–21, 94–97, 101
α-Ionone, 654
β-Ionone, 653–654
Ionophoresis, 106–107
Ion product constant of water, 18
Ion transport, 915–919, 922–924, 926–927
Iron, electronic states, 170–171
  excretion, 913
  ferric, activation of histidine decarboxylase, 768
  ferrous, activation, of aconitase, 503
    of catechol oxidase, 833
    of homogentisate oxidase, 827
    of hydroxyanthranilate cleavage, 841
    of peptidases, 708
    of phenylalanine hydroxylase, 825
  ferrous-ferric oxidation-reduction system, 291–293, 299
  incorporation, into ferritin, 913
    into hemoglobin, 869, 912–913
  in flavoprotein enzymes, 338, 343–345
  intestinal absorption, 913
  in tryptophan peroxidase-oxidase reaction, 837–838
  metabolism, 912–914, 980
  storage, 913
Iron-containing proteins, *see* Ferritin, Heme proteins, Hemerythrins

Isoagglutinins, 427
Isoalloxazine, 330
Isoamylamine, 767, 787
Isobutyl alcohol, 780
Isobutylamine, 767, 780
Isobutyric acid, 780
Isobutyryl-CoA, 780–781
Isocaproic acid, 643
Isocitric acid, action, of aconitase, 503–504
    of isocitric dehydrogenase, 316, 504
    of isocitritase, 518
    conversion to α-ketoglutarate, 504
    formula, 503
    in citric acid cycle, 508
    occurrence, 516
Isocitric dehydrogenase, 316, 504, 508, 613
Isocitritase, 518, 520
Isoelectric point, 94, 100–102, 112
Isoelectric precipitation, 19, 101–102
Isoguanine, 207, 894
Isohydric carriage of CO_2, 920–921
Isoionic point, 94, 100–101
Isoleucine, chemistry, 55, 81–82, 118
    formula, 55
L-Isoleucine, breakdown, 784–785
    configuration, 82
    deamination, 752, 757
    formation, 781–784
    glucogenic action, 764, 784
    indispensable nature, 724–725, 728, 781–782, 784
    ketogenic action, 764, 784
    metabolism, 781–785
    occurrence, 125
    optical rotation, 79
Isomaltose, 429, 436, 451–452
Isonicotinic hydrazide, 309, 989, 992
Isoprene, 653
Isoprene rule, 629, 631, 664–665
Isoprenoid compounds, 663–664
Isopropanol, 549
Isoriboflavin, 984
Isotope-competition technique, 786
Isotope dilution method, 127–129
Isotope effect, 394
Isotope-exchange reaction, 283
Isotopes, 388–396
    in amino acid analysis, 127–129
    in study of enzyme mechanisms, 281–283
    radioactive, 391–393
    stable, 389–391
Isovaleric acid, in cholesterol formation, 627, 631

Isovaleric acid, metabolism, 630, 787–788
    occurrence, 558, 631
Isovaleryl chloride, 134
Isovaleryl-CoA, 631, 788
Itaconic acid, 520
ITP, 461, 512, 882–883

Jaundice, 874–875
Joule, 226
Juvenile hormone, 969–970

K_m, 252
Kaempferol, 671
Kaolin, 24
Kerasin, 572
Keratein, 131, 695
Keratin, 58, 131, 686, 694–695
α-Keratin, 159–160
β-Keratin, 157–159
α-Keto acids, conversion to amino acids, 754–766
    decarboxylation, 273, 475, 504–505, 910
    formation from amino acids, 336, 750–758
β-Keto acids, activation, 595–597, 833
    decarboxylation, 279–280, 512
α-Ketoadipic acid, 809–810
β-Ketoadipic acid, 832–834
β-Ketoadipyl-CoA, 831
α-Keto-ε-aminocaproic acid, 809
α-Ketobutyric acid, 756–757, 783, 791, 794
2-Keto-3-deoxygalactonic acid, 536
2-Keto-3-deoxy-7-phosphoglucoheptonic acid, 541
2-Keto-3-deoxy-6-phosphogluconic acid, 535
2-Ketogluconic acid, 536
5-Ketogluconic acid, 536
Ketoglutaraldehyde, 867
Ketoglutaramic acid, 762–763
α-Ketoglutaric acid, conversion to glutamate, 316, 754, 759–763, 765–766
    decarboxylation, 504–506, 508, 521–522
    formation, from arabinose, 538
        from 2,5-diketogluconate, 536
        from glutamine, 763
        from glutarate, 809
        from isocitrate, 504
        from oxalosuccinate, 504, 508
    in citric acid cycle, 502, 508
    in lysine formation, 810
    in ornithine formation, 814
α-Ketoglutaric dehydrogenase, 505, 509
2-Keto-myo-inositol, 544
α-Ketoisocaproic acid, 783, 785–788

α-Ketoisovaleric acid, 780–784, 786, 993
Ketol group, 529, 638
α-Keto-γ-methylthiobutyric acid, 795
α-Keto-β-methylvaleric acid, 781–784
Ketone bodies, definition, 590
   formation, 590–602, 787–788
   metabolism, 603–608, 848, 941
Ketonemia, 848, 941
Ketonuria, 941
Ketopantoic acid, 993
2-Keto-6-phosphogluconic acid, 536
3-Keto-6-phosphogluconic acid, 526
β-Ketoreductase, 598
Ketosis, 607, 848, 941
17-Ketosteroid, 949
Ketosuccinamic acid, 762–763, 819
β-Ketothiolase, 599–600, 604–605
Kinases, 262, 459
Kinetics of enzymic reactions, effect, of
   pH, 271–272
   of inhibitors, 256–259
   of substrate concentration, 249–256
   of temperature, 265–271
   order of reaction, 245–249
Kinetin, 207, 975
Kjeldahl method, 28
Kojic acid, 542–543
Krebs cycle, see Citric acid cycle
Krebs ornithine cycle, 850, 853
Krebs-Ringer solution, 925
Kynurenic acid, 836–838, 840
Kynureninase, 841
Kynurenine, 836–842
Kynurenine formamidase, 838

Lactaminic acid, 426
Lactase, 432, 746
Lactic acid, 227, 289–290
D-Lactic acid, configuration, 80
   formation, from glucose, 479, 535–536
      from methylglyoxal, 479
DL-Lactic acid, 479
L-Lactic acid, conversion, to glycogen,
      492, 495–496
   to pyruvate, 316, 318, 490
   formation by glycolysis, 485, 489–491,
      516
   in thiamine deficiency, 982–983
Lactic dehydrogenase, animal tissues, ac-
      tion, 316, 318–319
   crystallization, 219
   in glycolysis, 490
   inhibition by pyruvate, 982
   zinc in, 319
   bacterial, 479
   yeast, 357, 479

Lactic-pyruvic oxidation-reduction sys-
      tem, 299, 327
Lactobacillic acid, 560, 998
Lactochrome, 330
Lactoflavin, 984
Lactogenic hormone, 950, 953
β-Lactoglobulin, amino acid composition,
      125
   denaturation, 153
   electrophoresis, 105
   elementary analysis, 45
   enzymic hydrolysis, 695
   formation, 737
   frictional ratio, 150
   homogeneity, 25
   interaction with ions, 109
   isoelectric point, 102
   particle weight, 42, 45
   terminal amino acids, 143
   titration curves, 98–99
Lactonase, 314
Lactonizing enzyme, 831
Lactoperoxidase, 164, 363
Lactose, formula, 415
   hydrolysis, 432
   induction of β-galactosidase, 746
   metabolism, 465
   occurrence, 414–415
   optical rotation, 406
S-Lactylglutathione, 479
Lanosterol, 624, 628, 664
Lanthionine, 60, 83
Larval hormone, 969
Lathosterol, 623
Lathyrism, 63
Lauric acid, 559
Lead, 908, 909
Lead phosphate, 24
α-Lecithin, 567, 569, 615–618
Lecithinase A, 578–580
Lecithinase B, 579
Lecithinase D, 579–580, 910
Lecithins, 566–567, 577–580
Leucine, chemistry, 54–55, 118
   formula, 55
D-Leucine, metabolism, 752, 785–786
   occurrence, 81, 137–138
L-Leucine, breakdown, 787–788
   deamination, 752, 757
   decarboxylation, 766–767
   formation, 782–786
   free energy of formation, 237
   heat of combustion, 227
   indispensable nature, 724–725, 728, 784–
      786
   isolation, 65

L-Leucine, ketogenic action, 764, 787–788
   metabolism, 782–783, 785–788
   occurrence, 55, 125, 862
   optical rotation, 79, 97
Leucine aminopeptidase, 696–699, 701, 707
Leuco-2,6-dichlorophenolindophenol, 302
Leucomethylene blue, 302–303
Leucopterin, 1000–1001
Leucovorin, 773, 775, 998–1001
Leucrose, 452
Leukemia, 1001
Levans, 429, 452
Levan sucrase, 452
Levulinic acid, 407
LH, 948, 950, 952
Liebermann-Burchard reaction, 622
Lightening hormones, 971
Light scattering, 33–35
Lignin, chemistry, 422
   formation, 774, 805, 807, 835
   occurrence, 422
Lignoceric acid, 559, 571–572
Limit dextrins, 434, 445
Limonene, 661–662
Lineweaver-Burk equations, 252–254, 257–259
Linoleic acid, formula, 559
   metabolism, 560–561, 587, 614
   occurrence, 559, 569, 573
   oxidation by lipoxidase, 609
Linolenic acid, 559–560, 609, 614
γ-Linolenic acid, 559–561
Lipases, 574–577, 616, 735
Lipemia, 576
Lipid metabolism, formation of lipids,
      see Lipogenesis
   hormonal regulation, 957–958, 962–963
   in diabetes, 957–958, 962
   link to protein metabolism, see Protein
      metabolism, link to lipid metabolism
   see also Fatty acids, metabolism
Lipids, analysis, 562–565, 568, 573
   caloric value, 932
   classification, 557, 568, 571
   compound, 566–573
   deposition in tissues, 585–589
   fatty acids from, 558–562
   protein-sparing action, 765
   simple, chemistry, 557–566
      enzymic hydrolysis, 574–577
      intestinal absorption, 584–586
   see also Phospholipids, Sphingolipids
Lipins, 566
Lipogenesis, 609–617
   definition, 613

Lipogenesis, hormonal regulation, 957–958, 963
Lipoic acid, formula, 306, 481, 554
   in keto acid decarboxylation, 481–482, 505
   in photosynthesis, 553–554
   in sulfite oxidation, 797
   occurrence, 1006
   oxidation-reduction system, 306
   vitamin activity, 1006
Lipoprotein lipase, 575–576
Lipoproteins, in plasma, 150, 573, 622
   metabolism, 575–576
   occurrence, 573
   physiological role, 573, 960
Lipotropic agents, 588
Lipovitellin, 573
Lipoxidase, 564, 609
Liquid-junction potential, 292
Liquiritigenin, 671
Lithium aluminum hydride, 52
Lithium borohydride, 52, 131, 144
Lithocholic acid, 632, 634–635
Liver residue factor, 1008
Lombricine, 486
Lombricine phosphate, 486
LRF, 1008
Luciferase, 345–346
Luciferin, 345–346
Lumichrome, 331, 986
Lumiflavin, 331
Lumi-rhodopsin, 658–659
Lutein, 655
Luteinizing hormone, 948, 950, 952
Luteolin, 671
Lycomarasmin, 138
Lycopene, 652–655, 664, 666
Lycophyll, 655
Lycoxanthin, 655
Lycoxanthophyll, 655
Lymph, 584–586, 915
Lyochromes, 330
Lyophilization, 24
Lysergic acid, 862
Lysergic acid diethylamide, 862–863
Lysine, chemistry, 63–64, 118, 142
   dissociation, 93–95
   formula, 64
D-Lysine, 808
L-Lysine, breakdown, 752, 808–809
   conversion to hydroxylysine, 809
   formation, 766–767, 808, 810–811
   in alkaloid formation, 859–860
   indispensable nature, 724–725, 728, 731–732, 808
   isolation, 114

L-Lysine, linkage in proteins, 131
    metabolism, 764, 808–811
    occurrence, 64, 125, 201
    optical rotation, 79
    urinary excretion, 798
Lysine decarboxylase, 767
Lysine peptides, 202
Lysolecithin, 578–579
Lysolecithinase, 579
Lysozyme, 25, 143, 438
Lyxose, 404

Magnesium, activation, of carboxylase,
        475
    of citritase, 518
    of creatine kinase, 487
    of deoxyribonuclease, 879
    of enzymes, 910
    of isocitritase, 518
    of α-ketoglutarate dehydrogenase,
        504–505
    of methionine-activating enzyme, 804
    of peptidases, 696, 698
    of phosphatases, 489, 581, 880, 910
    of phosphoglucomutase, 461
    of phosphogluconic dehydrogenase,
        526
    of phospholipase C, 910
    of thiokinases, 595
    of transketolase, 529
    of transphosphorylases, 460, 470, 472–
        473, 910
    complexes with ATP and ADP, 487
    hormonal regulation, 967
    in acyloin formation, 480
    in chlorophylls, 182
    in fatty acid oxidation, 594
    inhibition of ATP-ase, 488
    in oxidative phosphorylation, 385
    physiological role, 910–911, 917, 926
Magnetic moment, 170–171
Magnetic susceptibility, 170–171
Malate synthetase, 519
Maleylacetoacetic acid, 827–828
Maleylacetoacetic isomerase, 828
Malic acid, conversion, to fumarate, 234–
        235, 502, 508
    to oxaloacetate, 316, 318, 508
    formation, 234–235, 512–513, 518–519
    formula, 234, 318, 502
    free energy of formation, 237
    in citric acid cycle, 502
    in CO₂ fixation, 512–513
    occurrence, 516
Malic dehydrogenase, 316, 318–319, 502,
        513

Malic enzyme, 512–513, 555
Malic-oxaloacetic oxidation-reduction
        system, 299, 327
Malonate, effect, on citric acid cycle, 507–
        510
    on fatty acid oxidation, 606
    formation from barbituric acid, 900
    inhibition of succinic dehydrogenase,
        260, 502
Maltase, 431–432
Maltose, chemistry, 414–415
    enzymic cleavage, 431–432, 436, 451–
        453
    formation, 434–436, 447
    formula, 414
    heat of combustion, 227
    optical rotation, 406
Maltose phosphorylase, 447–449
Maltotriose, 434
Malvidin, 671
Mandelic nitrile, 432
Manganese, activation, of arginase, 850
    of decarboxylases, 504, 512
    of deoxyribonuclease, 879
    of enolase, 472
    of enzymes, 911
    of malic enzyme, 512
    of peptidases, 696, 698, 707
    chelation by amino acids, 108
    occurrence, 908
    physiological role, 914
Mannan, 422–423, 433
Mannitol, 411–412, 543, 748
Mannitol-1-phosphate, 543
Mannoheptulose, 409, 530
Mannose, chemistry, 405, 408
    formula, 404, 405
    GDP-, 205, 467
    occurrence, 205, 422, 426
    optical rotation, 406
    phosphorylation, 460
Mannose-1-phosphate, 467
Mannose-6-phosphate, 460, 463
Mannuronic acid, 411, 423
Maritimetin, 671
Mass law, 223
Mass spectrometer, 389–390
Megaloblastic anemia, 1004
Melanin, 367, 830, 839
Melanocyte stimulating hormone, 954
Melanoma, 830
Melanuria, 830
Melibiase, 432
Melibiose, 406, 415–416, 432
Membrane potentials, 922–923, 926
Menadione, 299, 554, 668, 1014

Menthol, 661–662
6-Mercaptopurine, 902–903
Mercaptopyruvic acid, 796–797
Mercapturic acids, 59
Mercury, 66, 70, 257, 908–909
Meromyosins, 488
Mesaconic acid, 818
Mesobilirubin, 873, 875
Mesobilirubinogen, 873, 875
Meso compounds, 83
*Meso*cystine, 83
Mesoporphyrin, 166
Metabolic pool, 732, 737
Metabolism, definition, 10, 387–388
    inborn errors of, 398
    methods of study, 388–401
Metabolite antagonists, 399, 902, 977
Metalloflavoproteins, 338–340, 343–345, 357
Metalloporphyrin proteins, *see* Catalases, Cytochromes, Hemoglobin, Myoglobin, Peroxidase
Metamorphosis hormone, 969
Metamorphosis of insects, 968–971
Metaphosphatase, 581, 583–584
Metaphosphates, 584
Meta-rhodopsin, 659
Methane fermentation, 609
Methanol, 21
Methemoglobin, 172, 178–179, 363
Methemoglobinemia, 178
N⁵,¹⁰-MethenyltetrahydroPGA, *see* Anhydroleucovorin
Methionine, chemistry, 60–62, 118
    formula, 61, 793
D-Methionine, 752, 792
L-Methionine, conversion, to S-adenosylmethionine, 804
    to methyl mercaptan, 798
    to sulfate, 798
    deamination, 752, 795
    formation, from homocysteine, 793–795, 799–803, 805–807
    from D-methionine, 792
    in adrenalin formation, 829–831
    in anserine formation, 824
    in creatine formation, 803–804
    in cysteine formation, 792–795, 801–802, 806–807
    indispensable nature, 724–725, 735, 792–794, 800
    in lignin formation, 835
    in nicotine formation, 860
    in spermidine formation, 815
    lipotropic action, 588
    metabolism, 764, 792–797, 800–808

L-Methionine, methyl group, formation, 806–807
    oxidation, 807–808
    transmethylation, 800–805
    occurrence, 125
    optical rotation, 79
Methionine-activating enzyme, 804
Methionine methyl sulfonium salt, 61, 800–801, 803
Methionine sulfone, 61
Methionine sulfoxide, 61, 795
Methionine sulfoximine, 61
2-Methoxy-6-aminopurine, 206
Methoxyestrone, 650
3-Methoxy-4-hydroxymandelic acid, 830
p-Methoxyphenylalanine, 207
α-Methylacetoacetyl-CoA, 785
Methylacrylyl-CoA, 780–781
2-Methyladenine, 1003
Methylamine, 85, 88–89, 753
6-Methylaminopurine, 196
Methylation of carbohydrates, 418–419
Methylbarbituric acid, 900
β-Methylbutyl alcohol, 787
α-Methylbutyryl-CoA, 785
β-Methylcrotonic acid, 629–631, 665
S-Methylcysteine, 795
S-Methylcysteine sulfoxide, 60, 795
5-Methylcytosine, 191, 196, 198, 899
6-Methyldeoxyadenylic acid, 198
5-Methyldeoxycytidine, 191
5-Methyldeoxycytidylic acid, 191
11-Methyldodecanoic acid, 558
Methyl donors, 801
α-Methylene-γ-aminobutyric acid, 767
Methylene blue, enzymic reduction, 314, 331, 343, 359
    formula, 302
    oxidation-reduction system, 299, 302–303
γ-Methyleneglutamic acid, 63, 767–768, 817
γ-Methyleneglutamine, 63
Methylethylthetin, 801
2-Methyl-9α-fluorocortisone, 948
Methylfructofuranoside, 409
2-Methylfumaric acid, 818
Methylglucofuranoside, 408–409
N-Methyl-L-glucosamine, 413
α-Methylglucoside, 408–409, 431
β-Methylglucoside, 408, 431
γ-Methylglutamic acid, 817
N-Methylglycine, *see* Sarcosine
Methylglyoxal, 479
Methyl groups, 801, 806–808
Methylguanidinoacetic acid, *see* Creatine
3-Methylhistamine, 823–824

1-Methylhistidine, 67
3-Methylhistidine, 67
α-Methyl-β-hydroxybutyryl-CoA, 785
4-Methyl-5-hydroxyethylthiazole, 983
N-Methyl-5-hydroxytryptamine, 845
2-Methylhypoxanthine, 1003
1-Methylimidazolylacetic acid, 823–824
3-Methylimidazolylacetic acid, 823–824
N-Methyllysine, 808
Methylmalonic acid, 602
Methylmalonic semialdehyde, 780–781
Methylmalonyl-CoA, 602
Methylmercaptan, 795, 798, 805
S-Methylmethionine, 61, 800–801, 803
2-Methyl-1,4-naphthoquinone, 299, 668
N-Methylnicotinamide, 805, 990–991
Methyl orange, 89, 108–110
Methylpentoses, 410–411
3-Methylpyridine, 991
N-Methyl-6-pyridone-3-carboxamide,
    990–991
Methylpyridoxal, 989
Methyl red, 89
13-Methyltetradecanoic acid, 558
Methyltetronic acid, 539
5'-Methylthioadenosine, 206, 805
Methyl-β-thiogalactoside, 746
S-Methylthioglycolic acid, 803
5-Methylthioribose, 206
O-Methyltyrosine, 207
N-Methylvaline, 138
Mevalonic acid, 629–631, 1008
Michaelis constant, 252–255, 267–268, 278,
    321–323
Michaelis-Menten   equations,   252–255,
    257–259
Microbiological assay of amino acids,
    126–127
Microsomes, 9
Midpoint potential, 299, 302–303
Millon reaction, 68, 72
Minimal molecular weight, 28–29
Mitochondria, 9, 371
Molar absorbance, 72–73
Molecular weight of proteins, 28–44
Molisch test, 407
Molting, 968–969, 970–971
Molting hormone, 969
Molt-inhibiting hormone, 970
Molt-promoting hormone, 970
Molybdenum, in copper metabolism, 914
    in flavoprotein enzymes, 338–340
    in nitrate reduction, 680
    in nitrogen fixation, 674, 677
    physiological role, 908–909, 914, 1008
Monoamine oxidase, 829, 846

Monoethylcholine, 801
Monoglycerides, 574, 577
Monolayers, 155–156, 561–562
Monomethylaminoethanol, 802
Monosaccharides, chemistry, 402–414
    optical rotation, 406
    tests for, 407–408
    see also individual sugars
Monoterpenes, 661–662
MSH, 954
Mucins, see Mucoproteins
Mucoitin sulfate, 424
cis,cis-Muconic acid, 832–834
Mucopolysaccharides,   424–428,   437–438,
    455
α1-Mucoprotein, 425
Mucoproteins, blood-group substances as,
    427–428
    inhibition, of hemagglutination, 426–
        427
    of trypsin, 691
    in plasma, 425
    intrinsic factor activity, 1005
    mucopolysaccharides in, 425–428
    occurrence, 425–428, 952, 955
    urinary excretion, 425
Multiple-alternate-oxidation theory, 592–
    593
Multiple myeloma, 741
Murexine, 755
Muscle adenylic acid, see Adenosine-5'-
    phosphate
Muscular contraction, 486–492, 501
Muscular dystrophy, 1012–1013
Mutarotase, 406
Mutarotation, 280, 406, 414
Mutation, 397, 748, 905
Mycolic acid, 561
Mycomycin, 561
Myeloperoxidase, 164, 363
Myogen A, 217, 219
Myoglobin, combination with oxygen,
    173
    isoelectric point, 164
    oxidation-reduction potential, 299, 363
    particle weight, 42, 164
    properties, 164
    terminal amino acids, 143
Myohematin, 349
Myokinase, 270, 376, 459, 882
Myosin, ATP-ase activity, 487–489
    metabolic turnover, 733
    physical and chemical properties, 143,
        152, 488–489
Myrcene, 661–662
Myricyl alcohol, 565

Myristic acid, 559, 609, 613
Myxedema, 943
Myxoxanthin, 1009

N^{15}, 389
Naphthalene acetic acid, 974
Naphthalenesulfonic acid, 65
Naphthol test, 407
Naphthoquinone, 52
Naringenine, 671
Nebularine, 206
Negative nitrogen balance, 723
Negatrons, 391
Neopyrithiamine, 984
Nervon, 572
Nervonic acid, 572
Nessler reagent, 28
Neuberg ester, 458
Neuraminic acid, 426, 572
Neurohormones, 845, 952, 954
Neurosporene, 653
New yellow enzyme, 337–338, 340–341
Niacin, see Nicotinic acid
Niacinamide, see Nicotinamide
Nickel, 908, 911
Nicol prism, 74–75
Nicotinamide, antimetabolites, 991–992
  breakdown, 990–991
  deficiency, 992
  formation, 309, 990
  formula, 308, 989
  methylation, 311, 805
  occurrence, 308–310, 990
  vitamin activity, 989–990
Nicotinamide methylpherase, 805
Nicotinamide mononucleotide, 308–310, 990
Nicotinamide riboside, 884
Nicotine, 774, 805, 807, 860
Nicotinic acid, breakdown, 990–991
  formation, 840–842
  formula, 840
  in nicotine formation, 860
  occurrence, 990
  vitamin activity, 308, 989–990
Nicotinoylglycine, 990
Nicotinoylornithine, 990
Nicotinuric acid, 990
Nigerose, 420
Night blindness, 1010
Ninhydrin, 51–52, 117–118
Nitramide, 676, 679, 682
Nitrate, as terminal electron acceptor, 680
  effect on nitrogen fixation, 675
  enzymic reduction, 339, 680–682
  in protein formation, 674, 680–681

Nitrate, in sulfur oxidation, 800
  metabolism, 674, 679–683
Nitrate reductase, 338–340, 680
Nitric oxide, 682
Nitrification, 679, 683
Nitrite, 674–675, 679–683
Nitrite reductase, 681
Nitrogen, 674–680, 682
Nitrogenase, 676
Nitrogen balance, definition, 723–724, 743
  effect of diet, 765
  hormonal regulation, 964–966
  indispensable amino acids for, 724–728
  sources of urinary nitrogen in, 729–730
Nitrogen equilibrium, see Nitrogen balance
Nitrogen fixation, 674–678, 683
Nitrogen trichloride, 61
Nitrophenylphosphate, 581
Nitroprusside test, 58, 72
Nitrous acid method, 49, 52, 71
Nitrous oxide, 676, 680, 682
Nitroxyl, 681–682
NMN, 308–310, 990
NMN phosphorylase, 990
Noncompetitive inhibition, 257, 259–260
Nonprotein nitrogen, 709
Nonprotein R.Q., 933
Noradrenalin, 828–829, 946
Norepinephrine, 828–829, 946
Norleucine, 55
Normal oxidation-reduction potential, 296
Nornicotine, 860
Notatin, 338–339, 407, 526
N-terminal residue, 141–144
Nucleases, 877
Nucleic acids, absorbance, 74, 193
  asymmetry, 185
  digestion, 877, 879
  estimation, 192–193
  hydrolysis, 186–190, 192, 877–880
  inhomogeneity, 186, 193–194, 200
  in protein formation, 735, 746–749
  interaction with proteins, 202
  linkages in, 198–201
  metabolism, breakdown, 877–886
    formation, 883, 900–903
    hormonal control, 966
    pentose phosphates in, 534–535
    turnover in, 900–902
    vitamin E in, 1013
  occurrence, 184–186, 192–194
  particle weight, 185–186
  preparation, 185–186
  structure, 194–201

Nuclein, 184
Nucleoproteins, 17, 184–185, 201–203, 735
Nucleosidase, 450, 883–884
Nucleoside diphosphates, 880–883
Nucleoside diphosphokinases, 461, 882–883
Nucleoside-2'-phosphates, 189–190
Nucleoside-2',3'-phosphates, 189–190, 878
Nucleoside-3'-phosphates, 189–190, 581–582, 880
Nucleoside-5'-phosphates, 190, 581, 880, 882, 884–885
Nucleoside phosphorylase, 450, 883–884
Nucleoside pyrophosphatases, 883
Nucleosides, 187–188, 206–207
  cleavage, 450, 883–885
Nucleoside triphosphates, 203–204, 882–883
3'-Nucleotidase, 581–582, 880, 994
5'-Nucleotidase, 581, 880
Nucleotide pyrophosphatase, 309–310, 336
Nucleotide pyrophosphorylase, 885
Nucleotides, 186–192
  conversion to nucleosides, 581–582, 880
  dissociation, 197
  growth factor activity, 1008
  in nucleic acids, 188–191, 197–200
  occurrence, 203–206, 748–749, 1002–1003
  pyrophosphorolysis, 884–885, 898
  transglycosidation reactions, 885
  transphosphorylation reactions, 882–883

O^{18}, 389
Octadecanoic acid, see Stearic acid
Octadecatetraenoic acid, 559
Octanoic acid, 559, 592–594, 603–604
Octopine, 66
Oils, 557–558
Okanin, 671
Old yellow enzyme, see Yellow enzyme, old
Oleanolic acid, 664
Oleic acid, formation, 610–611, 997–998
  formula, 560
  heat of combustion, 227
  occurrence, 558–559, 573, 604
Oligo-1,6-glucosidase, 436
Oligonucleotides, 200, 583, 878
Oligosaccharides, 402, 407, 414–417
  as activators of phosphorylases, 444
  transglycosidation reactions, 453–454
Omega oxidation, 594–595
Ophidine, 137
Ophthalmic acid, 136
Opsin, 658–661

Optical activity, 74–83
  of amino acids, 78–83, 97
  of diastereoisomers, 81–83
  of proteins, 83, 160
  of sugars, 406
  polarimetric measurement, 75–76
Optical density, 72
Orcinol test, 407
Orinase, 942
Ornithine, chemistry, 65
  conversion, to arginine, 811–812, 814
    to citrulline, 852–853
    to dibenzoylornithine, 719
    to dinicotinoylornithine, 991
    to glutamate, 812–814
    to proline, 812–814
    to putrescine, 815
  deamination, 752, 812
  formation, 812–815
    from arginine, 65, 812, 849–850
    from α-ketoglutarate, 814
  formula, 65, 803, 814
  in alkaloid formation, 859–860
  in urea formation, 850–853
  occurrence, 65, 137
  transamidination reactions, 812
  transamination reactions, 762
Ornithine carbamyl transferase, 852
Ornithine cycle, 850, 853
Ornithine decarboxylase, 767
Orotic acid, 896–898, 900, 902
Orotidine-5'-phosphate, 897–898
Osazones, 408
Osmotic pressure of proteins, 29–33, 112
Osteomalacia, 1012
Ostreasterol, 624
Ovalbumin, see Egg albumin
Ovomucoid, 424–426, 691
Oxalic acid, conversion to formate, 520
  formation, from ascorbic acid, 539, 980
    from glyoxylate, 520
    from purines, 894
  occurrence, 516
Oxaloacetic acid, conversion, to aspartate, 759–760, 762–763
    to citrate, 506–508, 518
    to fluorocitrate, 510
    to glyoxylate, 520
    to malate, 316, 318, 502, 508
    to pyruvate, 511–513
    to threonine, 790–791
  formation, from asparagine, 763
    from aspartate, 755, 759–760
    from phosphoenolpyruvate, 512
  in citric acid cycle, 502
  in glycogen formation, 495

Oxaloacetic acid, in glyoxylate cycle, 520
    in nitrogen fixation, 678
    in photosynthesis, 553
    in pyrimidine formation, 896–897
Oxaloacetic decarboxylase, 511–513
Oxalosuccinic acid, 316, 504, 508
Oxalosuccinic decarboxylase, 508
Oxamycin, 57
Oxazolidone diones, 50
Oxazolines, 56
Oxazolones, 135–136
Oxidases, 216, 286, 368–369
    copper-containing, 366–368
    iron-porphyrin, 347–366
Oxidation, 285–286, 288–289
β-Oxidation-condensation theory, 592–593
Oxidation potential, 293
Oxidation-reduction potential, definition, 294
    determination, 291–293, 327
    effect of pH, 296–299
    in electron transport, 371–372
    of biological systems, 299–300, 305–306
    of conjugated proteins, 303, 322
    relation, to equilibrium constant, 300–301
        to free energy change, 301
Oxidation-reduction reactions, 289–291, 300–301
    biological, 303–306, 313–329, 334–335, 358–362
    coupled, 371–372
    free-energy changes, 300–301
    kinetics, 256
    semiquinone formation, 290–291, 295, 332
Oxidation-reduction systems, 289–290, 300–301
    biological, 299–300, 304, 327, 360, 363
    conjugated proteins as, 303
    electrode equation, 293, 296–298, 300
    organic dyes as, 302–303
β-Oxidation theory, 591–593
Oxidative phosphorylation, by mito-chondria, 381–385
    effect of polynucleotides, 384
    effect of thyroxine, 385, 944–945
    in active transport, 923
    in phospholipid formation, 616
    in photosynthesis, 554–555
    in protein formation, 734, 736, 747
    in urea formation, 853
    relation to citric acid cycle, 521–524
    uncoupling, 385, 1014
Oximes, 678–679, 681

Oximinoglutaric acid, 681
Oximinosuccinic acid, 677–678, 681
β-Oxyacyl dehydrogenase, 598
8-Oxyadenine, 886
Oxybiotin, 995–997
Oxygen, combination, with hemoglobins, 173–177
    with myoglobins, 173–174
    formation in photosynthesis, 546, 549–550, 554, 556
    in catechol oxidase reaction, 833
    in homogentistic oxidase reaction, 827
    in hydroxyanthranilate cleavage, 841
    in hydroxyphenylpyruvate oxidation, 826
    in kynurenine hydroxylation, 838
    in phenylalanine hydroxylation, 825
    in steroid hydroxylation, 643–644, 650
    in symbiotic nitrogen fixation, 678
    in tryptophan peroxidase-oxidase reaction, 837
    transport in blood, 175, 920–921
Oxygen electrode, 299
Oxyhemoglobin, 23, 172–177, 916–921
Oxymyoglobin, 173–177
Oxynervon, 572
Oxynervonic acid, 472
Oxythiamine, 984
Oxytocin, 141, 954

P^{32}, 392
PABA, see p-Aminobenzoic acid
Palmitaldehyde, 346, 569–570
Palmitic acid, formula, 559
    free energy of formation, 237
    heat of combustion, 226–227
    metabolism, 586–587, 610
    occurrence, 558–559, 573
    oxidation, 590, 604, 609
Palmitoleic acid, 559, 573, 610
Palmityl dehydrogenase, 597
Pancreatectomy, 587, 940
Pancreatin, 689
Pancreozymin, 955
Panose, 454
Pantetheine, 992–994
Pantetheine kinase, 994
Pantoic acid, 720–721, 993
Pantothenic acid, conversion to CoA, 994
    deficiency, 992, 995
    formation, 720–721, 993
    in CoA, 205, 482
    occurrence, 992
    phosphorylation, 994
    vitamin activity, 977, 992–993
Pantothenylaminoethane thiol, 992–994

Pantothenylcysteine, 994
Pantoyl-AMP, 721
Papain, action on fibrinogen, 702
  activation, 705–706
  amino acid composition, 125
  crystallization, 219, 704
  effect of aminopeptidase, 200, 261, 705
  in plastein formation, 721
  mercury derivative, 705
  peptide bond synthesis, 713
  *p*H dependence, 715
  physical properties, 705
  specificity, 705
  terminal amino acids, 143
  transamidation reactions, 715–716
Papainases, 705–706
Paper chromatography, 116–120
Paramagnetism, 170
Parathyroid hormone, 945
Partial specific volume, 37, 41
Particle weight of proteins, 29–44, 112
Passive transport, 922–923
Pasteur effect, 523–524
Pauly reaction, 66, 72
PC-cytidyl transferase, 617
Pectic acid, 423
Pectic enzymes, 438
Pectin, 411, 423, 538
Pectinase, 438
Pelargonic acid, 611
Pelargonidin, 671
Pellagra, 308, 990, 992
Penicillamine, 60, 81, 138
Penicillin, action of penicillinase, 711
  chemistry, 60, 81, 157
  effect on bacteria, 749
  formation, 780, 798–799
  nutritional effect, 1006
  occurrence, 138
Penicillinase, 219, 711
Penicillin G, 60
Pentachlorophenol, 385
Pentosamines, 413
Pentose nucleic acids, chemistry, 186–190
  determination, 192–193
  digestion, 877
  formation, 748, 900–902
  from viruses, 194, 197
  hydrolysis, by alkali, 188–189, 197
    by ribonuclease, 199, 877–879
  in protein synthesis, 735, 746–748
  interaction with proteins, 201–202
  linkages in, 199–200
  metabolic turnover, 900–902
  nucleotide composition, 195–197
  occurrence, 192–194

Pentose phosphate pathway, 525–535, 541, 551–553
Pentoses, chemistry, 404, 406, 410
  conversion to hexoses, 529–533
  formation from hexuronic acids, 538
  in urine, 529
  metabolism, 527–535, 543
  tests, 407
Pentosuria, 541–542
P enzyme, 505–506
Peonidin, 671
Pepsin, action, on ACTH, 951
  on cytochrome c, 352
  on pepsinogen, 688
  on proteins, 686–689
  on synthetic substrates, 686–687
  autodigestion, 220, 688–689
  crystallization, 23, 219, 686
  denaturation, 272
  discovery, 210, 685
  formation, 688–689
  in digestion, 694
  inhibition, 689
  in plastein formation, 721
  ionizable groups, 98
  isoelectric point, 102, 686
  occurrence, 685
  particle weight, 686
  *p*H dependence, 271, 686
  specificity, 686–688, 698–699
Pepsinogen, 688–689
Peptidases, action, 216, 274, 698–699
  activation, 262–263, 707–708, 910
  esterase action, 696
  in animal tissues, 685, 701–702
  in digestion, 695–696, 698–700
  in microbes, 707–708, 745
  in plants, 707
  specificity, 274–275, 698–699
Peptide bond, definition, 52
  enzymic cleavage, analytical methods, 709
    by proteolytic enzymes, 282, 685–708
    energy changes, 378, 711–713
    in digestion, 684–685, 694–696, 698–700
  enzymic synthesis, 713–718
    role of ATP, 718–721
  in proteins, 129–131, 141
Peptide linkage, *see* Peptide bond
Peptides, amino acid sequence, 141–147
  as antibiotics, 137–138
  as growth factors, 745, 1008
  as hormones, 140–141
  chemistry, 129–130, 132–136, 155
  chromatography, 147

Peptides, enzymic cleavage, 685–708
  enzymic synthesis, 716–717
  helical structure, 160
  hydrogen bonds in, 155
  in digestion, 694–696, 698–700
  in plasma, 739
  in protein hydrolysates, 130, 145
  in protein synthesis, 737–738, 745
  ionization, 713
  isolation, 139–140
  occurrence, 136–141, 779, 862
  synthesis, 132–136
  UDP-derivatives, 749
  X-ray analysis, 157–158
Peptone, 130, 708
Peracetic acid, 58
Performic acid, 145
Perfusion of organs, 399
Periodate oxidation, 56–57, 64, 420
Periodicity hypothesis, 147–148
Periplogenin, 637
Pernicious anemia, 876, 1004–1005
Peroxidase, catalytic action, 216, 363–365,
    980
  crystallization, 219, 363
  enzyme-substrate compounds, 251,
    364
  occurrence, 164, 363
  physiological role, 364
  properties, 164, 179, 363
PGA, see Pteroylglutamic acid
pH, 18, 86–88, 236
  determination, 19, 296
  effect on optical rotation, 79–80, 97
  indicators, 88–89
  in enzymic reactions, 271–272
  intracellular, 921–922
  of blood, 100, 916–921
Phalloidine, 138
Phase rule, 25–26
Phenaceturic acid, 590
Phenazine methosulfate, 344
Phenol, 537–538, 795–796, 832–835
Phenol oxidase, 366–367, 980
Phenolphthalein, 89, 91–92
Phenol red, 89
Phenolsulfuric acid, 795–796
Phenylacetic acid, excretion, 719, 825
  inhibition of carboxypeptidase, 258
  metabolism, 590, 825, 832
Phenylacetylglutamine, 719, 825
Phenylalanine, absorption spectrum, 73–
    74
  chemistry, 67–68, 118
  formula, 68
D-Phenylalanine, 137, 258, 752

L-Phenylalanine, breakdown, in mam-
    mals, 824–828
  in microbes, 832, 834
  conversion, to adrenalin, 828–829
    to lignin, 835
    to tyrosine, 824–825, 832, 834
  deamination, 752
  decarboxylation, 766–767
  formation, 834–835
  in alkaloid formation, 859–861
  indispensable nature, 724–725, 728, 825
  ketogenic action, 764
  metabolism, 824–835
  occurrence, 67–68, 125, 207, 862
  optical rotation, 79
Phenylalanine hydroxylase, 825
Phenylalanine-3,4-quinone, 831, 839
2-Phenyl-1,4-benzopyrone, 670
Phenylbutyric acid, 590
o-Phenylenediamine, 1004
p-Phenylenediamine, 359
β-Phenylethylamine, 767
Phenylhydrazine, 408–409
Phenylisocyanate, 50
Phenylisothiocyanate, 50, 143–144
Phenylketonuria, 825
Phenyllactic acid, 825
Phenylpropionic acid, 590, 694
Phenylpyruvic acid, 825, 832, 835
Phenylpyruvic oligophrenia, 825
Phenylthiocarbamyl method, 143–144
Phenylthiohydantoic acid, 50
Phenylthiohydantoin, 50, 144
Phenylvaleric acid, 590
Pheophorbide a, 182–183
Pheophytin a, 182
Pheoporphyrin a$_5$, 182
Phlorizin, 441, 490, 763
Phosgene, 50
Phosphagens, 485–487
Phosphatases, action, 450, 580–584, 880,
    994
  activation, 262–263, 581, 910
  classification, 580–581
  energy of activation, 264
  in bone, 581, 968
  inhibition by phosphate, 581
  occurrence, 493, 581–583
  transphosphorylase action, 582–583
Phosphate, in alcoholic fermentation,
    457–459, 470, 473–474
  in anaerobic glycolysis, 488–490
  in blood, 100, 918
    hormonal control, 945, 968
  incorporation, into nucleic acids, 901–
    902

Phosphate, incorporation, into phospholipids, 615–618
 into phosphoproteins, 741
 indispensable nature, 911
 in fatty acid oxidation, 608
 in glyceraldehyde-3-phosphate dehydrogenase action, 324–326
 in phosphorylase reaction, 439
 in Stickland reaction, 757–758
 interaction with proteins, 108
 in urine, 918
 occurrence, 911
Phosphate esters, energy changes, 377–379
 hydrolysis by phosphatases, 580–584
Phosphatidalaminoethanol, 569
Phosphatidalcholine, 569
Phosphatidalserine, 569
Phosphatidase C, 580
Phosphatides, 566–570
 see also Cephalins, Lecithins
Phosphatidic acids, 567, 615–617
Phosphatidylaminoethanol, 568, 578–580, 615–617
Phosphatidylcholine, 567, 579, 615–618
Phosphatidylinositol, 570
Phosphatidylserine, 568, 578–580
Phosphoamides, 378–380, 485, 581–582
Phosphoarginine, 65, 378–379, 485
Phosphocreatine, *see* Creatine phosphate
Phosphodiesterases, 190, 581, 583, 879
Phosphoenolpyruvic acid, action of ATP-phosphopyruvic transphosphorylase, 473, 476, 490
 action of enolase, 378, 471–473, 476, 490
 conversion to glycogen, 495
 fixation of CO_2, 512
 formation, from oxaloacetate, 512
 from 3-phosphoglycerate, 471–473
 from pyruvate, 513
 hydrolysis, energy change, 378, 472
 enzymic, 581
 in shikimic acid formation, 541
Phosphofructokinase, 461
Phosphoglucoisomerase, 460, 476, 490
Phosphoglucomutase, 461–462, 492
Phosphogluconic acid, 311, 313–314, 526, 535
Phosphogluconic dehydrogenase, 526
Phosphogluconolactone, 310–311, 313–314, 526
Phosphoglyceracetals, 568
Phosphoglycerate kinase, *see* ATP-phosphoglycerate transphosphorylase

2-Phosphoglyceric acid, 378, 471–473, 476, 490
3-Phosphoglyceric acid, conversion, to phosphoenolpyruvate, 471–473
 to 2-phosphoglycerate, 471, 476, 490
 to serine, 789
 formation from diphosphoglycerate, 376, 470–471, 476
 formula, 471, 528
 in alcoholic fermentation, 468, 471–472, 476
 in photosynthesis, 527–528, 550–553
Phosphoglycerides, 568
Phosphoglyceroisomerase, 469–470, 494
Phosphoglyceromutase, 471–472, 476, 490
Phosphohexoisomerase, 460, 476, 490
Phosphohexokinase, 461, 476, 490
Phosphohydroxypyruvic acid, 789
Phosphoinositides, 570
Phosphoketopentoepimerase, 527
Phospholipase A, 578–580
Phospholipase B, 579
Phospholipase C, 579–580, 910
Phospholipase D, 580
Phospholipids, chemistry, 566–571, 573
 classification, 568, 571
 digestion, 578–580, 585
 enzymic hydrolysis, 578–580
 formation, 585, 615–618
 in succinoxidase, 359
 intestinal absorption, 585
 metabolic turnover, 588
 occurrence, 566, 573, 622
 physiological role, 580
Phosphomannose isomerase, 463
Phosphomolybdotungstic acid, 709
Phosphomonoesterases, 580–582, 686, 880
Phosphopantetheine, 993–994
Phosphoprotein phosphatase, 582, 742
Phosphoproteins, 17, 56, 108, 741–742
Phosphoribomutase, 527
Phosphoribosylamine, 890
Phosphoribosylpyrophosphate, formation, 885
 formula, 843, 885
 in histidine formation, 821
 in indole formation, 842–843
 in nicotinamide nucleotide formation, 990
 in nucleotide pyrophosphorylase reaction, 884–885
 in purine formation, 890
 in pyrimidine formation, 898
Phosphoribulokinase, 527
Phosphoric acid, 88, 237, 441
Phosphoroclastic reaction, 483

Phosphorolysis, 216, 326, 430
Phosphorylase, liver, 440–441, 494, 961
  potato, 443–444, 449
Phosphorylase a, action, 441–445, 449
  crystallization, 23, 219, 439
  formation, 737
  in glycogen formation, 492
  inhibition, 441
  kinetics, 441–442
  particle weight, 439
  pyridoxal phosphate in, 440
Phosphorylase b, 440, 960–961
Phosphorylase-rupturing enzyme, 440
Phosphorylases, 283, 438–450
Phosphorylating enzyme, 505–506
Phosphorylcholine, 579–580, 582, 616–618
3-Phosphoryl-D-glyceric acid, see 3-Phos-
  phoglyceric acid
Phosphoserine, enzymic hydrolysis, 582
  formula, 55
  metabolism, 742, 789
  occurrence, 56, 462, 686
Phosphotransacetylase, 483, 910
  in acetyl-CoA formation, 483, 596
  in citrate formation, 506
  in fatty acid oxidation, 608
Phosphotungstic acid, 113
Phosvitin, 56, 582
Photodissociation of CO-heme proteins,
  177, 348–349, 363
Photolysis of water, 549–550
Photon, 391, 547
Photoreduction, 546, 553–555
Photosynthesis, 545–556
  alternative pathways, 552
  aspartic acid in, 553
  ATP formation, 554–555
  biological importance, 285, 545
  carbohydrate formation, 550–553
  chlorophyll in, 553–556
  CO_2 fixation, 546–547, 549–553, 555–556
  efficiency, 547, 555–556
  energy relations, 555–556
  Hill reaction, 553–555
  hydrogen formation, 676–677
  lipoic acid in, 553–554
  nitrate reduction in, 680
  oxaloacetate in, 553
  pentose phosphate pathway, 551–553
  photochemical reaction, 546, 549–550,
    553–556
Phototropism, 658, 972–973, 986
Phrenosin, 572
Phthalic anhydride, 50
Phthalocyanine, 157, 169–170
Phthaloylamino acids, 135

Phthienoic acid, 558
Phthiocol, 299, 668
Phycobilins, 168, 548
Phycocyanins, 168
Phycoerythrins, 168
Phylloquinone, 668, 1014
Physostigmine, 861
Phytoene, 654
Phytofluene, 654
Phytohormones, 971–975
Phytol, 182, 657, 663
Phytomonic acid, 560
Phytosphingosine, 571
pI, 94, 100–101
β-Picoline, 991
Picolinic acid, 841
Picric acid, 64, 108
l-Pimaric acid, 663
Pimelic acid, 997
α-Pinene, 662, 665
Pipecolic acid, 71, 808–809
Piperidine-2-carboxylic acid, 71, 808–809
Δ^1-Piperidine-2-carboxylic acid, 809
Δ^6-Piperidine-2-carboxylic acid, 809
Pipsylamino acids, 128–129
pK, 87, 228
Plakalbumin, 708
Planck's constant, 266, 547
Plant growth hormones, 972–974
Plasma cells, 740
Plasmalogens, 568
Plasmal reaction, 568
Plasmapheresis, 738
Plasma proteins, abnormal metabolism,
    741
  as blood buffers, 100, 918–921
  binding of CO_2, 919–921
  electrophoresis, 105–106
  formation, 734, 738–741
  fractionation, 16, 19, 22
  glycoproteins, 425
  interaction with ions, 22, 108
  lipoproteins, 573
  physiological functions, 739
  see also Fibrinogen, Serum albumin,
    Serum globulins
Plasmin, 703–704
Plasminogen, 703–704
Plastein, 721–722
Platelet substances, 703–704
Pleated sheet structure, 158–159
PMSG, 955
PNA, see Pentose nucleic acids
Pneumococcal polysaccharides, 428–429
Pneumococci, transformation of types,
    200

Poikilothermic organisms, 930, 937
Polarimeter, 75–76
Polyaffinity theory, 277–278, 698–699
Polyglycine, 160
Polylysine, 202
Polymyxins, 81, 138
Polyneuritis, 983
Polynucleotide phosphorylase, 881
Polynucleotides, enzymic cleavage, 878–881
  enzymic synthesis, 880–882
  nucleic acids as, 198–199
Polypeptides, see Peptides
Polyphenol oxidase, 366–367, 980
  see also Tyrosinase
Polyphosphates, 584
Polysaccharidases, 431, 433–438
Polysaccharides, as antigens, 427–429
  bacterial, 428–429, 885
  chemistry, 417–429
  definition, 402
  enzymic cleavage, 433–439
  enzymic synthesis, 441–445, 451–455, 463
  in hexokinase, 459–460
  in phosphorylase reaction, 442
  nutrient, 417
  occurrence, 417, 421–424, 426–427
  structural, 417
  tests, 407, 417, 421
  see also Mucopolysaccharides, Mucoproteins
Polystyrene, sulfonated, 47, 122
Polyuria, 949, 953
P/O ratio, 381–383, 521–522
Porphin, 165–166
Porphobilinogen, 868–872
Porphobilinogenase, 868
Porphyria, 167, 868, 872, 876
Porphyrins, absorption spectra, 168–169
  chemistry, 165–167
  growth factor activity, 871–872
  in porphyria, 872
  iron complexes, 165, 169–172
  metabolism, 864–872
  metal complexes, 169–172
  occurrence, 165–167, 181–182
  urinary excretion, 167, 872
Porphyropsin, 660
Positive nitrogen balance, 723–724
Potassium, effect on enzymes, 473, 910, 925
  hormonal regulation, 947, 966–967
  physiological role, 909–910, 917
  transport, 817, 917, 923, 926–927
Potentiometric titration, 294–296

Precipitin reaction, 739–740
Pregnane, 638
5α-Pregnane, 638
5β-Pregnane, 638
Pregnanediol, 639–642, 648–649
Pregnane-3,20-dione, 648
Pregnant mare serum gonadotrophin, 955
Pregnenolone, 643, 648
Δ^4-Pregnen-20α-ol-3-one, 649
PR enzyme, 440
Prephenic acid, 834–835
Primeverose, 416
Procarboxypeptidase, 696
Prodigiosin, 168, 872
Profibrinolysin, 703
Progesterone, formula, 640
  metabolism, 642–643, 647–650
  occurrence, 638–639
  physiological effects, 638, 948
  secretion, 948, 950
Prolactin, 950, 953
Prolamines, 16–17, 62, 742
Prolidase, 685, 698, 702
Proline, chemistry, 48–49, 70–71, 118
  formula, 70
L-Proline, conversion, to δ-aminovalerate, 758
    to glutamate, 812–814, 816
    to hydroxyproline, 815–816
  deamination, 752
  dehydrogenation, 813
  formation, 812–814
  glucogenic action, 764
  metabolism, 812–814, 815–816
  occurrence, 70, 125, 862
  optical rotation, 79
Proline oxidase, 813, 964–965
Proline reductase, 758
Propanediamine, 815
Propanediol, 606
Propionamide, 711
Propionic acid, activation, 601–602
  conversion, to β-alanine, 779
    to higher fatty acids, 612
  formation, from fatty acids, 601
    from glycerol, 510
    from methionine, 794
    from serine, 778–779, 791
    from threonine, 791
    in fermentations, 510, 778–779, 791
  oxidation, 601–602
Propionylcholine, 577
Propionyl-CoA, 601, 781, 784–785
Prosthetic group, 17, 162, 321
Prostigmine, 578
Protaminase, 689

Protamines, action of proteolytic enzymes, 686, 689–690
chemistry, 64, 66, 201
occurrence, 17, 184, 201
Proteases, *see* Proteolytic enzymes
Proteinases, action, 216, 267, 684–695
activation, 705–706, 707
esterase action, 690, 693–694, 701, 705
in blood coagulation, 702–703
inhibition, 705, 706
in peptide bond formation, 713–717
intracellular, 700–702
microbial, 707–708
plant, 704–707
specificity, 274–275, 698–700, 713–716
transamidation reactions, 714–717
Protein metabolism, amino acid incorporation, 729–738, 744–745
digestibility of proteins, 695, 727
digestion of proteins, 684–685, 694–696, 698–700
dynamic state, 728–734
effect of antibiotics, 1006
endogenous, 729, 734
end products, 729, 847–848
exogenous, 729
formation of proteins, 673–674, 727, 729–741
hormonal regulation, 964–966
in bacteria, 744–746
in plants, 742–744
nucleic acids in, 746–749
theories, 737–738
hormonal control, 958–959, 961–966
in diabetes, 958, 959, 965
intracellular breakdown, 736, 742
link to carbohydrate metabolism, via alanine, 754, 778
via arginine, 813
via aspartic acid, 818
via glutamic acid, 754, 813, 817–818
via glycine, 777
via histidine, 821
via isoleucine, 783
via α-keto acids, 759, 763–766
via leucine, 786
via lysine, 808, 810
via methionine, 794
via prephenic acid, 834
via proline, 813, 816
via serine, 777, 789–790
via threonine, 790, 792
via transamination, 763–766
via tryptophan, 842–844
via tyrosine, 827, 835
via valine, 780–781, 783

Protein metabolism, link to lipid metabolism, 611, 763–765
via isoleucine, 784
via leucine, 787–788
via lysine, 810
via threonine, 792
via tyrosine, 827
nitrogen balance, 723–728
turnover of proteins, in animal tissues, 727–736
in bacteria, 746
in plants, 743–744
of plasma, 738–739, 741
vitamin B_{12} in, 1005–1006
Protein minimum, 724
Proteins, absorbance, 37–38, 40, 74, 97
adsorption, 22, 24
amino acid composition, 113–116, 120–129
amino acid sequence, 142–143, 145–148
amino acids in, 45–46, 81–83
antigenic nature, 221, 739–740
association, 21, 43, 110
asymmetry, 83, 278
biological value, 727
biuret reaction, 130
buffering properties, 100
caloric value, 932–933, 937
carbamino derivatives, 51, 919
chromatography, 24–25, 126
classification, 16–17
colloidal behavior, 29
color tests, 72, 130
conjugated proteins, 17, 220, 303, 321
crystallization, 22–25, 217–219
C-terminal residues, 143
denaturation, 18–19, 24, 153–155
chemical changes, 148, 160, 234, 695
energy changes, 233–234
kinetics, 269–270
dielectric constant, 20, 152
diffusion, 41, 149–151
dissociation, 43
electron microscopy, 35
electrophoresis, 102–107
elementary composition, 27–29, 45
end-group analysis, 141–144
flow birefringence, 152
formol titration, 98–99
fractionation, 17–24
frictional ratio, 149–151
Gibbs-Donnan effect, 111–112
helical structure, 159–160
history, 14–15
homogeneity, 24–27, 40, 105–106, 247
hydration, 149–151

Proteins, hydrogen bonds in, 154–155, 159–160
  hydrolysis, by acid, 46–47, 113
    by alkali, 47–48, 60, 65
    by enzymes, 69–70, 154, 686–690, 695
  ionization, 98–112, 153–154
  interaction with ions, 20–22, 96–97, 108–110
  isoelectric point, 100–102, 112
  isoionic point, 100–101
  isolation, 16–24, 101–102, 105–107
  light scattering, 33–35
  linkages in, 130–132, 154–156, 686, 690
  minimal molecular weight, 28–29
  molecular weight, 43–44, 160–161
  nitrogen content, 27–28
  N-terminal residues, 143
  optical activity, 83, 153–154, 160
  osmotic pressure, 29–33
  partial specific volume, 37, 41
  particle weight, 29–44
  peptide nature, 130–132, 141, 148, 686
  plasma, see Plasma proteins
  precipitation, 20–22, 108, 709
  salting in, 21–22, 96–97
  salting out, 19–21, 96–97
  sedimentation, 35–43
  shape, 29, 148–152, 154
  solubility, 16–21
    as criterion of purity, 25–27
    effect of denaturation, 153
    effect of dielectric constant, 20
    effect of ionic strength, 19, 21, 96–97
    effect of pH, 19, 101–102
    effect of temperature, 18
  specific dynamic action, 937
  structure, 113–161
  sulfur content, 28, 61
  surface films, 155–156
  urinary, 425, 741
  viscosity, 151
  X-ray analysis, 157–160
Proteinuria, 425, 741
Proteolytic enzymes, 684–708
  in autolysis, 700–702
  in digestion, 684–685, 694–696, 698–700
  occurrence, 685, 700–708
  specificity, 698–701, 705, 708, 713–716
Proteose, 130
Prothrombin, 668, 703–704
Protoanemonin, 637
Protocatechuic acid, 832–834
Protocatechuic oxidase, 831
Protogen, 1006
Protoheme, 165
Protoplast, 747

Protoporphyrin, absorption spectrum, 169
  as growth factor, 871–872
  conversion to bile pigments, 873–874
  formation, 864–869
  formula, 165
  in chlorophyll formation, 871
  in heme proteins, 165, 351–352, 363, 365
  metal complexes, 169
Provitamins, 655, 1009–1012
PRPP, see Phosphoribosylpyrophosphate
Pseudocholine esterase, 578
Pseudoglobulin, 17, 21
Pseudomonomolecular reaction, 247–248
Pseudo-vitamin B_{12}, 1003
Pterins, 207–208, 1000–1001
Pteroic acid, 207
Pteroyldiglutamylglutamic acid, 998–999
Pteroylglutamic acid, antimetabolites, 1001
  chemistry, 773
  deficiency, 1001
  formation, 1000
  formula, 207, 998
  formyl derivatives, 773–775
  glutamic acid conjugates, 999–1000
  hydroxymethyl derivatives, 775–776
  in glycine metabolism, 773–775
  in histidine metabolism, 821–822
  in methionine formation, 807
  in methyl group oxidation, 808
  in purine metabolism, 889, 891, 894–895
  in serine metabolism, 773–775
  in thymine formation, 898
  metabolism, 980, 1000–1001
  occurrence, 207, 998–1000
  vitamin activity, 998–1000
Pteroylhexaglutamylglutamic acid, 999
Purine nucleoside phosphorylase, 883–884
Purines, absorbance, 193
  as growth factors, 893
  breakdown, 856–857, 894–895
  deamination, 885–886
  formation, 774, 887–894
  incorporation into nucleic acids, 900–901
  in nucleic acids, 187–188, 191, 195
  in riboflavin formation, 985
  interconversion, 891–894
  occurrence, 203–207, 1003–1004
  tests, 195
Puromycin, 206–207, 413
Putrescine, 767, 815, 823, 862
Pyocyanine, 299
Pyramin, 983
Pyranose, 403
Pyranoside, 408

Pyrethrin, 662–663
Pyrethrolone, 662
Pyridine-2-carboxylic acid, 841
Pyridine-3-carboxylic acid, see Nicotinic acid
Pyridine-2,6-dicarboxylic acid, 811
Pyridine ferroprotoporphyrin, 170
Pyridine nucleotides, absorption spectra, 311, 313, 315, 317
 addition reactions, 313, 320
 as growth factors, 308, 990
 chemistry, 307–313
 in dehydrogenase action, 313–329
 in linked dismutations, 327–328
 oxidation-reduction potential, 304, 312
 oxidation-reduction reactions, 310–313
 reduced, 312
  in oxidative phosphorylation, 383–384
  oxidation by cytochromes, 341–344, 355–357
  reaction with flavoproteins, 334–335, 341–344
 see also Diphosphopyridine nucleotide, Triphosphopyridine nucleotide
Pyridine nucleotide transhydrogenases, 328
Pyridoxal, 375, 760–762, 987–988
Pyridoxal kinase, 988–989
Pyridoxal phosphate, action, 769–770
 formation, 375, 988
 formula, 375, 761
 in alanine racemase action, 769
 in amino acid decarboxylases, 768–770
 in amino acid metabolism, 769–770
 in cystathionine metabolism, 794
 in desulfhydrase action, 756–757
 in diamine oxidase action, 823
 in glycine metabolism, 775
 in hydroxyamino acid dehydrases, 756
 in kynureninase action, 841
 in phosphorylase, 440
 in serine metabolism, 775
 in threonine formation, 791
 in transaminases, 760–762
 in tryptophanase reaction, 844
 in tryptophan desmolase reaction, 843
Pyridoxamine, 987
Pyridoxamine phosphate, 761–762
Pyridoxic acid, 988
Pyridoxine, 768–769, 987
Pyridoxine phosphate, 762
Pyridyl-3-aldehyde, 991
Pyrimidines, absorbance, 193
 breakdown, 899–900
 deamination, 886
 formation, 895–899

Pyrimidines, incorporation into nucleic acids, 900–902
 in nucleic acids, 187–188, 191, 195
Pyrocatechase, 833
γ-Pyrones, 543
Pyrophosphatase, 219, 489, 581, 583, 994
Pyrophosphate, formation, 484, 616, 720, 885
 hydrolysis, 378, 489
 incorporation into ATP, 720
Pyrrolidone carboxylic acid, 63
Pyrroline carboxylic acid, 813
Pyruvate kinase, see ATP-phosphopyruvic transphosphorylase
Pyruvic acid, CO_2 fixation by, 510–513, 515
 conversion, to acetaldehyde, 474–476
  to acetoin, 479–480
  to acetyl phosphate, 482–483
  to alanine, 754, 760, 778
  to cysteine, 797
  to ethanol, 483
  to glucose, 474
  to glycogen, 495–496, 514–515
  to isoleucine, 783
  to lactic acid, 316, 318, 490
  to leucine, 786
  to malate, 508, 512–513
  to oxaloacetate, 508, 511–512
  to phosphoenolpyruvate, 473
  to serine, 789
  to succinate, 508, 519
  to valine, 783
 formation, by glycolysis, 478
  from acetate, 513–515
  from alanine, 757
  from cystathionine, 795
  from cysteine, 756, 797–798
  from cystine, 58
  from glucose, 478, 535
  from ketohexonic acids, 535–536
  from mercaptopyruvate, 796
  from mesaconate, 818
  from phosphoenolpyruvate, 473
  from serine, 56, 756
  from tryptophan, 844
 in citric acid cycle, 502, 508
 in fermentation, 474–476
 in glycolysis, 490
 in lysine formation, 810
 in prephenic acid formation, 835
 metabolism, 474–476, 478–483, 500–510, 516–517
 oxidation, energy relations in, 521–524
  in muscle, 500–510, 523
  in liver, 510–512

Pyruvic acid, oxidation, in thiamine deficiency, 982–983
  phosphoroclastic cleavage, 483
  phosphorylation, 474, 513
  reduction, 289–290
Pyruvic decarboxylase, 475
Pyruvic oxidation factor, 1006
Pythocholic acid, 632

Q_{10}, 263
Q_{CO_2}, 288
Q_{O_2}, 288, 359, 936
Q enzyme, 444
Quantum value, 547
Quercetin, 671
Quinacrine, 337
Quinaldic acid, 836
Quinic acid, 541–542
Quinine, 81
Quinoline carboxylic acid, 836
Quinolinic acid, 840–841
Quinone, 289–290, 306, 367

R_F, 118
Racemic acid, 77, 84
Racemic compound, 77, 81, 84
Racemization, 80
Radioactivity, 392–393
Radioautography, 550
Raffinose, enzymic cleavage, 433, 452
  formula, 416
  occurrence, 417
  optical rotation, 406
Raoult's equation, 30
Rate constant, enzymic reactions, 250–256, 278
  first-order, 244
  relation to equilibrium constant, 322–323
  reversible reaction, 248–249
  second-order, 248
  temperature dependence, 263–270
  zero-order, 245
Rauwolfia alkaloids, 863
Receptor destroying enzyme, 427
Reduction, 288–289
Reduction potential, 293–294
Reductive pentose phosphate pathway, 551–552
Reichert-Meissel number, 563
Reineckate, 71–72
Relative specificity, 276
Relaxation time, 151
Rennin, 219, 685, 689
R enzyme, 436
Replacement agent, 714

Replacement reactions, 216, 273
Reserpine, 863
Resolution, 81, 84
Resonance hybrid, 166, 291
Resorcinol, 407
Respiration, cellular, CO_2 formation, 500, 502
  cytochromes in, 359–362
  effect of carbon monoxide, 348–349
  effect of cyanide, 341, 347
  effect of vitamin E, 1013
  electron transport, 355–357
  flavoproteins in, 340–344
  in carbon cycle, 545
  in plants, 367–368
  iron-porphyrins in, 347–362
  phosphorylation in, 381–385
  history, 6, 285–286
  measurement, 288, 931–932
Respiratory chain phosphorylation, 381
Respiratory enzyme, see Cytochrome oxidase
Respiratory pigments, 163–164, 180–181, 348–349
Respiratory quotient, 284, 932–933
Resting potential, 926
Retinine$_1$, 658–661, 1010
Retinine$_2$, 660–661
Retinine isomerase, 660
Retinine reductase, 659
Reversible boundary-spreading test, 106
Rhamnose, formula, 411
  occurrence, 410, 416, 428, 570
Rhamnulose, 450
Rhizopterin, 998–999
Rhodanese, 796
Rhodanilate, 70–71
Rhodopsin, 658–660
Ribitol, 330, 412, 986
Riboflavin, antimetabolites, 984–985
  auxin inactivation, 974
  chemistry, 330–332
  conversion to flavin nucleotides, 335–336
  deficiency, 986
  estimation, 987
  fluorescence, 331
  formula, 330, 984
  metabolism, 985–986
  occurrence, 330
  oxidation-reduction potential, 299, 331
  relation to vitamin B_{12}, 1004
  vitamin activity, 984, 986
Riboflavin phosphate, see Flavin mononucleotide
Ribofuranoside, 409

Ribokinase, 528
Ribonuclease, action on PNA, 190, 196, 199
 amino acid composition, 124, 147
 chromatography, 25
 crystallization, 219, 877
 effect of proteolytic enzymzes, 220, 708, 878
 effect of urea, 878
 formation, 735, 737–738
 frictional ratio, 150
 heat stability, 153, 877
 homogeneity, 25
 inhibition of amino acid incorporation, 747
 isoelectric point, 102, 877
 molecular weight, 42, 124, 877
 occurrence, 879
 pH optimum, 878
 specificity, 190, 583, 878–879
 terminal amino acids, 143
 transferase action, 878
Ribonucleic acid, see Pentose nucleic acids
Ribose, chemistry, 410
 formula, 188, 404
 in glycine formation, 772
 in nucleotide formation, 885
 occurrence, 188, 206–207, 885, 1002
 optical rotation, 406
 phosphorylation, 528
Ribose-1,5-diphosphate, 527
Ribose nucleic acid, see Pentose nucleic acids
Ribose-1-phosphate, 527, 883–884
Ribose-5-phosphate, conversion to PRPP, 885
 formation, from ribose, 528
  from ribulose-5-phosphate, 527
 formula, 527
 in histidine formation, 821
 in indole formation, 843
 in phosphoribomutase reaction, 527
 in transaldolase reaction, 531
 in transketolase reaction, 529–530
Ribose-5-phosphate isomerase, 527
Ribosylimidazolylacetic acid, 823
Ribulokinase, 528
Ribulose, 410, 528
Ribulose-1,5-diphosphate, 527–528, 551–552
Ribulose diphosphate carboxylase, 527–528
Ribulose diphosphate dismutase, 527–528
Ribulose-5-phosphate, 526–528, 551–552
Ricinoleic acid, 562

Rickets, 1012
Ringer's solution, 925
RNA, see Pentose nucleic acids
Robison ester, see Glucose-6-phosphate
Rotary diffusion, 151
R.Q., 285, 932–933
Rubber, 664–665
Rubidium, 908, 910
Rubixanthin, 655
Rutinose, 416

S^{35}, 392
Saccharase, see Invertase
Sakaguchi reaction, 65, 72
Salmine, 125, 201
Salting in, 95–96
Salting out, 19–21, 96–97, 130
Salting out constant, 21
Santalbic acid, 561
Sapietic acid, 663
Sapogenins, 636
Saponification, 557–558
Saponification number, 563
Saponins, 635–636, 664
Sarcosine, chemistry, 53
 metabolism, 776–777, 805
 occurrence, 53, 138
 oxidation, 753, 807
Sarcosomes, 359
Sarmentogenin, 637
Schardinger dextrin, 437
Schiff bases, formation, 51
 in transamination, 761
 in tryptophan desmolase reaction, 843
 of pyridoxal phosphate, 770, 775
Schiff's reagent, 568
Schlieren method, 37–39, 104
Schmidt-Thannhauser method, 192
Schneider method, 192–193
Scleroproteins, 16, 53, 148
Scurvy, 828, 978–979
Scyllitol, 412
Second-order reaction, 247–248, 256
Secretin, 140, 940, 955
Sedimentation constant, 40–41
Sedimentation equilibrium method, 36–37
Sedimentation velocity method, 37
Sedoheptulose, 409–410, 530
Sedoheptulose phosphate, 530, 551–552
Sedormid, 872
Selachyl alcohol, 566
Selenium, 806, 908
Semiquinones, 290–291, 295, 332
Senecioic acid, see Dimethylacrylic acid
Sequential induction, 832

Sericin, 55
Serine, chemistry, 51, 55–57, 118
  formula, 55
L-Serine, conversion, to aminoethanol,
    777
    to cystathionine, 794
    to glycine, 772–775
    to hydroxypyruvate, 529
    to S-methylcysteine, 795
  deamination, 752, 755–756
  fermentation, 779, 790–791
  formation, 772–776, 789
  glucogenic action, 764, 790
  isolation, 65
  metabolism, 772–775, 789–790
    methyl group formation, 806–807
    role of PGA, 773–775
    role of pyridoxal phosphate, 775
  occurrence, 55–57, 125, 486, 568–569
  optical rotation, 79
  role, in glycine metabolism, 777
    in sphingosine formation, 618
    in tryptophan formation, 843
    in uric acid formation, 854
Serine aldolase, 775
Serine dehydrase, 756, 770, 790
Serine hydroxymethylase, 775
Serotonin, 767–768, 844–846, 863
Serum albumin, absorbance, 74
  amino acid composition, 120, 122
  binding, of bilirubin, 874
    of ions, 109
    of steroids, 110
  cleavage by pepsin, 686
  electrophoresis, 106
  in blood, 163
  isoelectric point, 102
  isoionic point, 100
  isolation, 19, 22
  metabolism, 738–739
  osmotic pressure, 33
  particle weight, 42
  shape, 151–152
  solubility, 21
  terminal amino acids, 143
Serum globulins, in blood, 163
  isolation, 19
  metabolism, 738–739
  see also α-, β-, and γ-Globulins
Serylarginine, 692
Sesquiterpenes, 661–663
Shikimic acid, 541–542, 834–835, 842
Shikimic acid-5-phosphate, 835
Sialic acid, 426
Sickle cell anemia, 163, 869–870
Siderophilin, 913

Silicon, 908
Silk fibroin, 53–55, 148, 159
Silver, 113, 257, 908–909
Simmonds' disease, 950
Simultaneous adaptation, 832
β-Sitosterol, 622
γ-Sitosterol, 622, 624
Skatole, 844
Snell's law, 74
Soaps, 558, 575
Sodium, effect on enzymes, 473, 910
  hormonal regulation, 947, 966–967
  physiological role, 910, 917–919
  transport, 917, 923, 926–927
Solanain, 707
Solubility product method, 114
Soluble bound biotin, 995–997
Somatotrophin, 950
  see also Growth hormone
Somogyi method, 407
Sorbitol, conversion to fructose, 495, 500
  formation from glucose, 495
  formula, 412
  occurrence, 411
  oxidation, 543
Sorbitol dehydrogenase, 495
Sorbose, formation, 543
  formula, 410
  in disaccharides, 447, 448, 450
Soret band, 168
Specific absorbance, 72
Specific activity of enzymes, 246–247
Specific dynamic action, 937
Specific radioactivity, 393
Specific rotation, 76
Spectrophotometry, 72–74
Spermidine, 66, 815
Spermine, 66, 815
Sphingolipids, 571–573
Sphingomyelin, formation, 618
  formula, 571
  hydrolysis, 579
  occurrence, 573
Sphingosine, 571–572, 618
Spinasterol, 622
Spirographis respiratory pigment, 163,
    166, 178
Spongosine, 206
Spongothymidine, 206
Spongouridine, 206
Spreading factor, 438
Squalene, formation, 627–631
  formula, 627
  in cholesterol formation, 628–629
  in eburicoic acid formation, 666
  in ergosterol formation, 629

Squalene, occurrence, 628
  structure, 664
Stachydrine, 859
Standard state, 233
Starch, chemistry, 417–420
  formation, 551
  hydrolysis, 433–437
  occurrence, 418, 516
  phosphorolysis, 439
  see also Amylopectin, Amylose
Starch chromatography, 120, 122
Steady state, 241–243, 360–362, 383–384
Stearic acid, formation, 610, 613
  formula, 559
  heat of combustion, 227
  occurrence, 559, 573
  oxidation, 609
  oxygenated derivatives, 562
Stearic aldehyde, 569
Stercobilin, 873, 875–876
Stercobilinogen, 873, 875
Sterculic acid, 560
Stereochemistry, 78–83
Steroid, 619
Δ^1-Steroid dehydrogenase, 651
Steroid glucuronides, 646
Steroid glycosides, 635–637
Steroid hormones, chemistry, 638–641,
    642, 645
  classification, 638–641
  excretion, 646, 648–650
  hydroxylation, 643–645, 647–651
  metabolism, 641–651
  occurrence, 638–641, 644, 646
  physiological role, 946–949, 959, 967
Steroid isomerase, 651
Steroids, see Bile acids, Steroid glyco-
    sides, Steroid hormones, Sterols
Steroid sulfatase, 647
Steroid sulfates, 646–647, 796
Sterol dehydrogenase, 625
Sterols, chemistry, 619–624
  intestinal absorption, 624–625
  metabolism, 624–635, 641–651
  nomenclature, 621
  occurrence, 619, 620, 621–624
Stickland reaction, 757–758
Stigmasterol, 622
Stokes' law, 149
Strepogenin, 745, 1008
Streptococcus lactis R factor, 999
Streptokinase, 703
Streptomycin, 413, 1006
Strontium, 908
Strophanthidin, 636–637
Sturin, 66, 201

Suberic acid, 637
Suberylarginine, 637
Substrate, 211
Substrate-linked phosphorylation, 380
Subtilin, 60, 83
Subtilisin, 692, 708, 878
Succinate-fumarate system, 299, 301–303
Succinate-glycine cycle, 776, 867
Succinic acid, activation, 597
  conversion, to δ-aminolevulinic acid,
    866–868
    to isocitrate, 518
    to succinyl-CoA, 505
  enzymic oxidation, 344, 355, 358–362
  formation, from acetate, 519
    from glycerol, 510
    from α-ketoglutarate, 504–506
    from propionate, 601–602
    from pyruvate, 510–512, 519
    from succinyl-CoA, 505, 508
  free energy of formation, 237
  in citric acid cycle, 502, 508, 514–515
  in β-ketoadipate metabolism, 833
  in oxidative phosphorylation, 383, 521–
    522
  in porphyrin formation, 866–868
  oxidation, 289–290, 296–297, 302–303
Succinic dehydrogenase, in citric acid
    cycle, 502, 508
  inhibition by malonate, 260, 507
  in succinoxidase system, 359
  properties, 338, 344
Succinic semialdehyde, 505, 762
Succinoxidase, 358–362, 580
Succinylaminopurine, 892
Succinyl-CoA, conversion to succinate,
    505
  formation, from β-ketoadipic acid, 833
    from α-ketoglutarate, 505, 508
    from propionate, 602
    from succinate, 377
  formula, 505
  hydrolysis, 505, 508
  in succinyl-CoA thiophorase reaction,
    596–597
Succinyl-CoA deacylase, 505
Succinyl-CoA thiophorase, 596–597, 605
Sucrase, 433
Sucrose, action of dextran sucrase, 451–
    452
  chemistry, 415, 418
  formation, 446–448, 450–451, 551
  formula, 415, 418
  free energy of formation, 237
  heat of combustion, 227
  hydrolysis, 250, 433

Sucrose, optical rotation, 406
Sucrose phosphate, 450–451
Sucrose phosphorylase, 446–449
Sugar tolerance curve, 498–499
Sulfanilamide, 260, 719
Sulfatases, 796
Sulfate, active, 795
  formation, 795–800
  in copper metabolism, 914
  in mucopolysaccharides, 424
  microbial utilization, 799
Sulfates, ethereal, 795–796
  organic, 646–647, 795–796
Sulfhydryl compounds, activation, of
    aconitase, 503
  of enzymes, 262–263, 535
  of proteolytic enzymes, 701, 705–706,
    708
  reduction of keratin, 132, 695
Sulfhydryl group, dissociation, 93–94
  in dehydrogenases, 324–326
  in proteins, 153
  reagents, 58–59
Sulfide, 799
Sulfinylpyruvic acid, 796–799
Sulfite, effect on carbohydrate metabo-
    lism, 467, 478
  metabolism, 796–799
Sulfite oxidase, 797
Sulfonamides, 260, 719, 888–889, 924, 944
Sulfonic acids, aliphatic, 108–109
  aromatic, 64–66, 114
Sulfonium compounds, 380, 801, 804
Sulfosalicylic acid, 108
Sulfur, 58, 799–800, 909
Sulfuretin, 671
Svedberg unit, 41
Symbiotic nitrogen fixation, 677–678
Syringaldehyde, 422

Tabtoxinine, 83
Talose, 404
Tanacetone, 662
Tartaric acid, occurrence, 5, 516
  optical activity, 75, 77
  resolution, 84
Taurine, formation, 767, 797
  formula, 58, 797
  in bile salts, 633, 635
  occurrence, 58, 487, 633
Taurocholic acid, 633–635
Taurocyamine, 487
Taurocyamine phosphate, 486–487
Taurodeoxycholic acid, 634
TDH, see Glyceraldehyde-3-phosphate
    dehydrogenase

Tellurium, 806, 908
Template theory, 737–738, 748
Terpenes, formation, 664–666
  structure, 661–664
Terramycin, 875, 1006
Testosterone, breakdown, 647, 649–650
  conversion to estrone, 645–646
  formation, 644–645
  formula, 641
  occurrence, 641
Tetracosanoic acid, 559
Tetradecanoic acid, 559
Tetraethylpyrophosphite, 134
Tetrahydrocortisol, 647–648
Tetrahydrocortisone, 647–648
Tetrahydroharman, 861
Tetrahydrolycopene, 653
TetrahydroPGA, formula, 775
  in histidine metabolism, 822
  in purine metabolism, 889, 891, 895
  in serine metabolism, 773–775
3,5,3',5'-Tetraiodothyronine, 831
Tetranucleotide theory, 194
Tetraphenyl-p-phenylene diamine, 290
Tetraterpenes, 661, 665
Tetroses, 404, 530–532, 552
Theobromine, 206
Thermodynamics, biochemical reactions,
    233–243
  biological systems, 230, 240–243
  chemical reactions, 224–233
  first law, 224–225
  second law, 228
Thetin-homocysteine transmethylase, 802
Thiaminase, 983
Thiamine, antimetabolites, 983–984
  conversion to allithiamine, 981
  deficiency, 982–983
  estimation, 984
  formula, 981
  metabolism, 981, 983
  occurrence, 980–981
  phosphorylation, 475, 981–982, 984
  vitamin activity, 977, 980–981
Thiamine kinase, 981–982, 984
Thiamine monophosphate, 982
Thiamine pyrophosphate, formation, 475,
    981–982, 984
  formula, 475
  in acetoin formation, 480
  in α-ketoglutarate decarboxylation,
    504–505
  in pentose metabolism, 529, 531
  in pyruvate decarboxylation, 475, 481,
    483
  in Stickland reaction, 757

Thiamine pyrophosphate, in transketo-
lase reaction, 529
occurrence, 980–981
Thiamine triphosphate, 982
Thiazolidine carboxylic acid, 59
Thiocarbamate method, 144
Thiochrome, 984
Thioctic acid, *see* Lipoic acid
Thiocyanate, 108, 796, 944
Thioglycolic acid, 131
Thiokinases, in fatty acid oxidation, 595–
596, 600
in phospholipid formation, 616
in triglyceride formation, 616
occurrence, 596, 605
specificity, 596
Thiolase, 599–600, 604–605
Thiol esterases, 216, 505, 600
Thiol esters, chemistry, 59, 379–380
Thiolysis, 599
Thiophorases, 596–597, 605
Thiosulfate, 796, 798–800
Thiothiazolidones, 50, 135, 144
Thiotransacetylase, 482
Thiouracil, 944
Thiourea, 944
Thorium, 908
Threonine, chemistry, 47, 57, 118
formula, 57
stereoisomers, 81–82
D-Threonine, 82, 791
L-Threonine, configuration, 82
conversion, to glycine, 791–792
to isoleucine, 783
deamination, 752, 756, 791
fermentation, 779, 791
glucogenic action, 764, 792
indispensable nature, 724–725, 728, 791
metabolism, 790–792
occurrence, 125
optical rotation, 79
Threonine aldolase, 792
Threonine dehydrase, 756, 791
Threonine racemase, 791
Threose, 404
Thrombin, 702–704
Thrombokinase, 703
Thromboplastin, 703–704
β-Thujone, 662
Thunberg method, 314
Thunberg-Wieland cycle, 518–519
Thymidine, chemistry, 191
formation, 898, 1005
growth factor activity, 1008
phosphorolysis, 884
Thymidine-3′,5′-diphosphate, 192

Thymidine phosphorylase, 884
Thymidylic acid, 191, 898
Thymine, breakdown, 899
dissociation, 196
formation, 774, 895–896, 898
formula, 191
growth factor activity, 903
occurrence, 191, 198, 206
Thymine deoxyriboside, *see* Thymidine
Thymol blue, 89
Thymus nucleic acid, 191–192, 194
see also Deoxypentose nucleic acids
Thyroglobulin, 69, 943
Thyroidectomy, 943–944
Thyroid hormones, 69, 831–832, 943–945
Thyroid-stimulating hormone, 950, 952–
953
Thyronine, 69, 831–832
Thyrotrophic hormone, 950, 952–953, 961–
962
Thyrotrophin, 950, 952–953
Thyroxine, breakdown, 832
excretion, 943
formation, 831–832, 943–944
formula, 69
in insulin formation, 961–962
in oxidative phosphorylation, 385, 944
in protein metabolism, 965
occurrence, 69, 831, 943–944
secretion, 950
transport, 943
Tiglyl-CoA, 785
Tigogenin, 636
Tigonin, 636
Tin, 908
Tiselius apparatus, 102–104
Tissue, culture, 397, 728
homogenates, 400
slices, 399–400
Titration curves, acids, 87–89
amino acids, 90–94
proteins, 98–100
Tobacco mosaic virus, *see* Virus, tobacco
mosaic
Tocol, 667
Tocopherols, formulae, 667
metabolism, 1013–1014
occurrence, 666
vitamin activity, 1012, 1014
Tocopheroxide, 1013
Tocopherylhydroquinone, 1013
Tocopherylquinone, 1013
Tolbutamide, 942
Toluenesulfonyl chloride, 135
Tomato bushy stunt virus, 23, 42, 197,
202

Tomato-wilt factor, 138
Torularhodin, 654
TPN, *see* Triphosphopyridine nucleotide
TPNH, *see* Triphosphopyridine nucleotide, reduced
TPNH-cytochrome c reductase, 338, 342–343, 944
TPNH-nitrate reductase, 338–340, 680
TPP, *see* Thiamine pyrophosphate
Trace elements, 908–912
Transacetylase, *see* Phosphotransacetylase
Transaldolase, 530–531, 533
Transamidation, 714–718
Transamidinase, 812
Transamidination, 803, 811–812
Transaminase, alanine-serine, 789
  branched-chain amino acid, 782–783
  catalytic action, 759–763, 770
  glutamic-leucine, 782
  in amino acid formation, 769
  in protein metabolism, 765–766
  kynurenine, 838
  occurrence, 759–762
  specificity, 762–763
Transamination, 759–766
  in glycine metabolism, 771–772
  in histidine metabolism, 820
  in isoleucine formation, 782–783
  in kynurenic acid formation, 838
  in leucine formation, 782–783
  in ornithine formation, 813–814
  in phenylalanine formation, 835
  in serine formation, 789
  in tyrosine metabolism, 826, 835
  in valine metabolism, 780, 782–783
  in xanthurenic acid formation, 838
  mechanism, 761
  nonenzymic, 759, 761, 769–770
Transduction, 905
Transesterification, 273, 576–577
Transfer reactions, 216
Transferrin, 913
Transforming factors, 200, 747–748, 905
Transglycosidases, 216, 433, 451–455
Transglycosidation, in nucleic acid metabolism, 902
  in polysaccharide metabolism, 437, 443–444
  mechanism, 433, 448–449
Transglycosylation, 433
Transhydrogenases, 328
Transition state, 265–270
Transketolase, catalytic action, 529–530
  crystallization, 219, 529
  in glycine formation, 772

Translational diffusion, 149–151
Transmethylation, 800–805
Transpeptidation, 714–718
Transphosphorylation, 216, 374–376
  activation by magnesium, 910–911
  by phosphatases, 582–583
Transpurination, 902
Traumatic acid, 975
Trehalose, 406, 415, 561
Trehalose phosphate, 465
Tricarboxylic acid cycle, *see* Citric acid cycle
Tricarboxymethyltrimethylenetriamine, 51
Trichloroacetic acid, 108, 709
Triethylenetetramine, 366
Triglycerides, analysis, 562–565
  chemistry, 557–565
  digestion, 574–575, 577
  formation, 577, 585, 615–617
  hydrolysis, 574–577
  intestinal absorption, 584–586
  occurrence, 575
Trigonelline, 859
Trihydroxycoprostane, 634
Trihydroxycoprostanic acid, 635
Trihydroxyflavylium hydroxide, 669
Triiodothyroacetic acid, 945
3,5,3′-Triiodothyronine, 69, 831–832, 943–944
3,3′,5-Triiodothyronine, 831–832, 943–944
Triketohydrindene hydrate, 51
Trimetaphosphatase, 583
Trimetaphosphate, 583
Trimethylamine, 858
Trimethylamine oxide, 858
Trimethylarsine, 805–806
Trimethylglycine, *see* Betaine
Trimethylisoalloxazine, 331
Trinitrophenol, 64
Triose phosphate dehydrogenase, *see* Glyceraldehyde-3-phosphate dehydrogenase
Triose phosphate isomerase, 469–470, 494
Trioses, 404
Tripeptidase, 685, 697–699, 701–702
Triphosphopyridine nucleotide, absorption spectra, 311, 315, 317
  chemistry, 307, 310
  cleavage, 310
  formation, 310
  in amino acid metabolism, 754
  in citric acid cycle, 504, 508
  in dehydrogenase action, 313–329
  in glucose-6-phosphate oxidation, 525
  in kynurenine metabolism, 838

Triphosphopyridine nucleotide, in malic enzyme action, 512
  in pentose phosphate pathway, 533
  in 6-phosphogluconic acid metabolism, 526
  in shikimic acid metabolism, 541
  in xylitol oxidation, 541
  occurrence, 310, 533
  reduced, action of flavoproteins, 334–335, 342–343
    action of peroxidase, 364
    chemistry, 312–313
    in fatty acid formation, 775
    in homoserine formation, 790
    in nitrate reduction, 680
    in nitrite reduction, 681
    in phenylalanine metabolism, 825
    in photosynthesis, 551–555
    in steroid metabolism, 643–644, 647
    oxidation, 311, 368, 521
  structure, 310
Trisaccharides, 417–418, 454
Triterpenes, 661, 663–666
Tritium, 392
Trophic hormone, 950
Tropic hormone, 950
Tropine, 860–861
Tropomyosin, 488
Trypsin, action, on chymotrypsinogen, 260–262, 692–693
    on cytochrome c, 352
    on β-lactoglobulin, 695
    on phosphorylase a, 440
    on procarboxypeptidase, 696
    on proteins, 689–690
    on prothrombin, 703
    on synthetic substrates, 690
    on trypsinogen, 262, 690–691
  active center, 261
  amidase action, 710
  blood coagulation by, 692, 702–703
  crystallization, 219
  denaturation, 153, 233–234
  discovery, 210, 214, 689
  effect of DFP, 691–692
  esterase action, 690
  formation, 262, 690–691
  in digestion, 694
  inhibition, 258, 691–692, 695
  occurrence, 685, 689–690
  pH optimum, 689
  physical properties, 689
  specificity, 274–275, 689–690
  terminal amino acids, 143, 691
  transamidation reactions, 715–716
Trypsinogen, amino acid sequence, 691

Trypsinogen, conversion to trypsin, 262, 690–691
  formation, 735
  physical properties, 691
Tryptamine, 861
Tryptophan, absorption spectrum, 73–74
  chemistry, 47, 49, 69–70, 118
  formula, 70
D-Tryptophan, 835–836
L-Tryptophan, breakdown, 834, 836–842, 844–846
  conversion, to alkaloids, 859, 861
    to anthranilic acid, 841–842
    to 5-hydroxytryptamine, 845
    to indole, 842, 844
    to indoleacetic acid, 846
    to insect pigments, 839
    to kynurenic acid, 836–838, 840
    to nicotinic acid, 840–842
    to xanthurenic acid, 836–838, 840
  deamination, 752
  estimation, 113
  formation, 835–836, 842–843
  indispensable nature, 724–725, 728, 835–836
  isolation, 48
  metabolism, 764, 774, 835–846
  occurrence, 125
  optical rotation, 79
Tryptophanase, 844
Tryptophan cycle, 842
Tryptophan desmolase, 843
Tryptophan peroxidase-oxidase, 837–838, 965
Tryptophan synthetase, 843
TSH, 950, 952–953
Tuberculostearic acid, 558
Turacin, 167
Turnip yellow mosaic virus, 197
Turnover number, 211, 255
Turnover rate, 396, 733
Tyndall effect, 33
Tyramine, 767, 862
Tyrocidine, 137–138
Tyrosinase, in adrenalin formation, 829
  in melanin formation, 830
  in pupation, 969
  in xanthommatin formation, 839
  see also Polyphenol oxidase
Tyrosine, absorption spectrum, 73–74, 97
  chemistry, 68–69, 142
  color tests, 68, 709
  dissociation, 93–94
L-Tyrosine, breakdown, in mammals, 825–828, 830–831
  in microbes, 832, 834

L-Tyrosine, breakdown, role of ascorbic
acid, 980
conversion, to adrenalin, 828–829
to melanins, 830
to thyroid hormones, 831–832
deamination, 752, 755
decarboxylation, 766
formation, in mammals, 731, 824–825
in microbes, 832, 834–835
free energy of formation, 237
glucogenic action, 764
heat of combustion, 227
indispensable nature, 728
iodination, 831
ketogenic action, 764
metabolism, 824–835
occurrence, 68–69, 125, 829
optical rotation, 79
oxidation, 367
solubility, 68, 95–96
transport, 744
Tyrosine decarboxylase, 766–767
Tyrosine-O-sulfate, 69
Tyrosol, 832

UDP, see Uridine-5'-diphosphate
UDP-acetylgalactosamine, 466
UDP-acetylglucosamine, 464–466
UDP-arabinose, 528
UDPG, see UDP-glucose
UDP-galactose, 464, 466
UDP-galactose epimerase, 464
UDP-galacturonic acid, 538
UDP-glucosamine, 466
UDP-glucose, formation, 451, 464, 617
formula, 205, 464
hydrolysis, 583
in sucrose formation, 450–451
in trehalose formation, 465
oxidation, 467, 537
reactions, 464, 466
UDP-glucuronic acid, formation, 357, 467
formula, 464
in glucuronide formation, 537–538
reaction, with bilirubin, 874
with steroids, 646
with thyroxine, 943
UDP-xylose, 528
Ultracentrifuge, 35–36
UMP, 205, 882, 896–898
Uncompetitive inhibition, 259
Uncoupling of oxidative phosphorylation,
385
Unit cell, 160–161
Uracil, dissociation, 196
formation from cytosine, 886

Uracil, formula, 187
metabolism, 895–900
occurrence, 187, 197, 206
Urea, as dietary nitrogen source, 726, 849
effect on ribonuclease, 878
enzymic hydrolysis, 246–247, 849
excretion, 847–849
formation, 811, 848–853
effect of growth hormone, 966
from ammonia, 818
from arginine, 65, 849–850
from aspartic acid, 818
from barbituric acid, 900
from creatine, 805
from uric acid, 856–857
free energy of formation, 237
heat of combustion, 227
history, 1, 849
in nitrogen fixation, 675
in protein denaturation, 153–155
Urease, catalytic action, 246–247, 849
activation energy, 268
specificity, 276
crystallization, 217, 219
occurrence, 849, 853
Ureidoimidazole carboxylic acid, 894–895
β-Ureidoisobutyric acid, 899
β-Ureidopropionic acid, 899
Ureidosuccinic acid, 854, 896–897
Ureotelic organisms, 847
Uric acid, breakdown, 856–857
conversion to allantoin, 856–857
excretion, 847–849, 856
fermentation, 894
formation, 854–856
formula, 203, 856
in gout, 856
occurrence, 203, 207
Uric acid riboside, 206
Uricase, 368, 856–857
Uricotelic organisms, 847
Uridine, 187, 898
Uridine-5'-diphosphate, dephosphorylation, 882–883
derivatives, 205, 749
see also UDP-compounds
formula, 205
phosphorylation, 451, 461, 882–883
Uridine monophosphate, 205, 882, 896–898
Uridine-2'-phosphate, 189–190
Uridine-3'-phosphate, 189–190, 878
Uridine-5'-phosphate, 205, 882, 896–898
Uridine phosphorylase, 884
Uridine-5'-pyrophosphate, see Uridine-5'-diphosphate

Uridine-5'-triphosphate, amination, 898
  conversion to UDP-glucose, 451, 617
  occurrence, 204
  transphosphorylation, 461, 882
Uridylic acid, 186–190
Uridyl transferase, 464–466
Urine, acidification, 918–919
  formation, 916, 918–919
  nitrogenous constituents, 849
Urobilin IXα, 875
d-Urobilin, 875
i-Urobilin, 875
l-Urobilin, 873, 875–876
Urobilinogen, 875
Urocanase, 821–822
Urocanic acid, 755, 821–822
Urocanylcholine, 755
Uroflavin, 986
Uronic acids, 411, 423–425, 428
Uroporphyrin I, 167–168, 872
Uroporphyrin III, 167–168, 868–869, 872
UTP, see Uridine-5'-triphosphate

cis-Vaccenic acid, 558–559
trans-Vaccenic acid, 560
Valeric acid, 592
Valine, formula, 54
D-Valine, 137–138, 780
L-Valine, chemistry, 54, 79, 118
  deamination, 752, 757
  decarboxylation, 766–767
  glucogenic action, 764, 780–781
  indispensable nature, 724–725, 728, 779, 784
  in ergot alkaloids, 862
  in penicillin formation, 798–799
  metabolism, 779–781, 782–784
  occurrence, 125
Vanadium, 674, 908–909
Van den Bergh reaction, 874
Vanillin, 422
Van Slyke ninhydrin method, 51
Van Slyke nitrous acid method, 49, 52
van't Hoff equation, for enthalpy change, 227
  for osmotic pressure, 31–32
Vasopressin, 141, 953–954
Velocity constant, see Rate constant
Verdoperoxidase, 164, 363
Vernolic acid, 561–562
v+ gene, 839
Vicianose, 416
Vinylacetyl-CoA, 598
Vinyl pheoporphyrin a5, 871
Violacein, 845

Violaxanthin, 655
Violet receptor, 661
Virus, bushy stunt, 23, 42, 197, 202
  cucumber mosaic, 197
  tobacco mosaic, chemistry, 143, 158, 197
    metabolism, 744, 747
    nucleic acid, 186, 200
  turnip yellow mosaic, 197
Viruses, 185
  nucleic acids from, 194, 197
  nucleoprotein nature, 202–203
Viscosity, 151
Vision, 658–661, 986
Visual cycle, 659–661
Visual pigments, 658, 660–661
Visual purple, 658
Vitamin, 976
Vitamin A, chemistry, 655–657, 663
  deficiency, 1010
  in vision, 658–661
  metabolism, 655–656, 1009–1011
Vitamin A1, activity, 1009–1010
  chemistry, 655–657
  enzymic oxidation, 659
  formation, 1010
  formula, 656, 657
Vitamin A2, activity, 1009
  formula, 656
  occurrence, 655–656
Vitamin A1 aldehyde, 658
Vitamin A2 aldehyde, 660
Vitamin B1, see Thiamine
Vitamin B2, see Riboflavin
Vitamin B6, antimetabolites, 989
  biological activity, 987–988
  deficiency, 760, 768, 987–988
  in D-alanine formation, 779
  in isoleucine metabolism, 782
  in leucine metabolism, 786
  in tryptophan metabolism, 836, 840
  occurrence, 987
  see also Pyridoxal, Pyridoxal phosphate, Pyridoxamine, Pyridoxamine phosphate, Pyridoxine
Vitamin B12, chemistry, 1001–1003
  deficiency, 1005
  formula, 1002
  function, 1005
  in methionine formation, 807
  lipotropic action, 588
  metabolism, 1003–1005
  occurrence, 1001–1006
  related factors, 1003
  X-ray analysis, 157, 1002
Vitamin B13, 1007–1008
Vitamin Bc, see Pteroylglutamic acid

Vitamin B$_c$ conjugate, 999
Vitamin B$_T$, 1006–1007
Vitamin B complex, 976–977
Vitamin C, see Ascorbic acid
Vitamin D, 1011–1012
Vitamin D$_1$, 1011
Vitamin D$_2$, 622, 1011–1012
Vitamin D$_3$, 623, 1011–1012
Vitamin D$_4$, 1011
Vitamin E, antioxidant effect, 564
  biochemical role, 356, 1012–1014
  chemistry, 667
  deficiency, 1012–1013
  metabolism, 667
  occurrence, 666–667
  see also Tocopherols
Vitamin H, 995
Vitamin K, chemistry, 667–668
  in photosynthesis, 554
  in prothrombin formation, 704
  metabolism, 668–669
  occurrence, 668
  physiological role, 668, 1014
Vitamin K$_1$, 668, 1014
Vitamin K$_2$, 668
Vitamin K$_3$, 554, 668, 1014
Vitamins, classification, 976–977
  intestinal synthesis, 977–978, 996
  see also individual vitamins
Vitellin, 17, 56
Volt-faraday, 226
von Gierke's disease, 497

Walden inversion, 80, 283
Warburg apparatus, 286–287
Warburg-Dickens pathway, 525
Water, activity, 235
  dielectric constant, 20
  free energy of formation, 237
  in photosynthesis, 546, 549–550, 554
  ion product, 18
  metabolism, adrenocortical steroids in, 966–967
    pituitary hormones in, 949–950, 953
    urine formation, 919
  physiological role, 907–908
Waxes, 565–566
Werner complexes, 70–72
Willstätter-Schudel method, 407
Wilson's disease, 858, 914
Wood-Werkman reaction, 510–511
Work, 229
Wound hormones, 972, 975

Xanthine, derivatives, 206
  enzymic oxidation, 339, 855

Xanthine, fermentation, 894–995
  formation from guanine, 885–886
  formula, 203
Xanthine oxidase, 338–339, 823
  in uric acid formation, 855
  metabolism, 728, 1008
Xanthommatin, 839
Xanthophylls, 654, 655
Xanthoproteic reaction, 68, 72
Xanthopterin, 207, 1000–1001
Xanthosine-5'-phosphate, 892
Xanthurenic acid, 836–837, 840
Xanthydrol reaction, 70
Xerophthalmia, 1009, 1010
Ximenynic acid, 561
X-ray analysis, 156–161
Xylan, 423, 538
Xylitol, 540–541
Xyloascorbic acid, 978
Xylose, conversion, to arabinose, 528
    to disaccharides, 448, 452
    to xylulose, 528
  enzymic oxidation, 315
  formation from glucuronic acid, 538
  formula, 404, 410
  in disaccharides, 416
  in polysaccharides, 423
  in urine, 529
  optical rotation, 406
  UDP-, 528
D-Xylulose, 410
  conversion, to disaccharides, 447, 450
    to xylitol, 540–541
  formation from xylose, 528
  phosphorylation, 528, 541
L-Xylulose, 540–541
Xylulose-5-phosphate, 527–532, 536, 541
Xylulose-5-phosphate isomerase, 527

Yeast adenylic acid, see Adenosine-3'-phosphate
Yeast nucleic acid, 186–190, 195–196
  see also Pentose nucleic acids
Yellow enzyme, new, 337–338, 340–341
  old, absorption spectrum, 334
    catalytic action, 334–335, 340–341
    crystallization, 219, 332
    dissociation, 332–334
    occurrence, 331
    oxidation-reduction potential, 299, 333
    prosthetic group, 332, 338

Zeaxanthin, 655
Zein, 63, 70
Zeo-Karb 216, 122

Zero-order reaction, 245
Zinc, activation of enzymes, 472, 696, 912
  binding by histidine, 108
  in carboxypeptidase, 696
  in dehydrogenases, 319–321, 754
  in protein precipitation, 22
Zone electrophoresis, 106–107, 122
Zwischenferment, 313

Zwitterion, 92
Zymase, 307
Zymogens, 260, 262
  see also Chymotrypsinogen, Pepsinogen, Procarboxypeptidase, Trypsinogen
Zymohexase, 470
Zymosterol, 622–623, 628–629